"For us, the low season is the high season"

C000004033

CC 2013
10th edition

CampingCard ACSI
Ten years your off-season discount card

€12 €14 €16

2504 campsites

INSPECTED CAMPINGS

Maximum 3 children free at 527 cam...

CampingCard ACSI
€12 €14 €16 CC
2013 Your off-season discount card
DISCOUNT CARD

Price: € 14,95

Discount camping in the low season

- Up to 50% discount at more than 2500 campsites in Europe
- Camping for € 12, € 14 or € 16
- Campsites are inspected by ACSI once a year
- Start saving money after just a few nights

Order in a few easy steps via: **www.WEBSHOP.ACSI.eu/facile**

ACSI

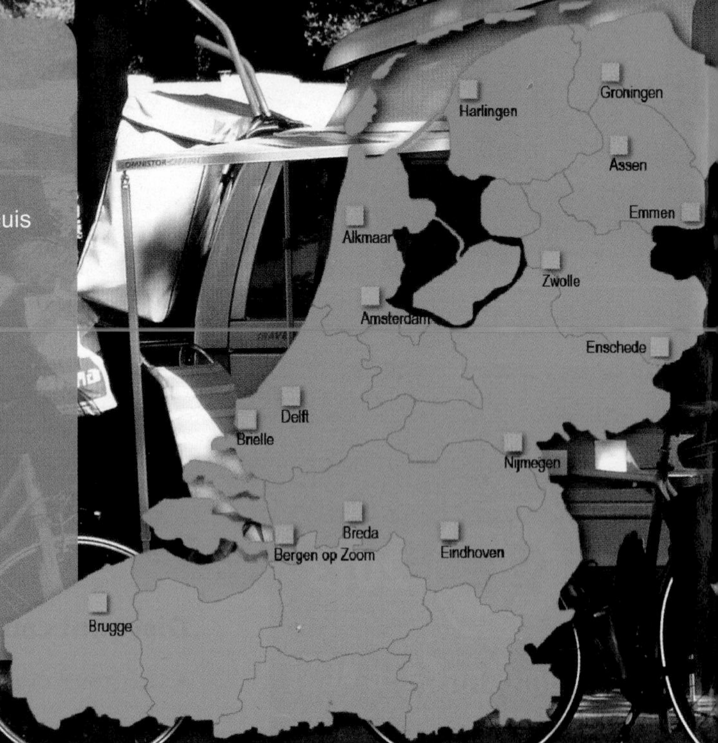

COLOPHON

A publication of:

Facile Media, Berghem
Hoessenboslaan 40
5351 PD Berghem
Postbus 555
5340 AN Oss
tel: 0412 65 68 85
fax: 0412 65 68 86

Chief editor
Anne van den Dobbelsteen

The draft of this version is saved
in October 2012

Comments or suggestions can
be sent to the publisher:

Facile Media
Postbus 555, NL-5340 AN Oss
Tel.: +31 (0)412 65 68 85
Fax: +31 (0)412 65 68 86
E-mail: info@camperstop.com
Internet: www.camperstop.com

ISBN 978-90-76080-31-4

Copyright 2012 Facile Media

Preface

Since 1996, Facile Media has been publisher of European
motorhome guides. As of 2005, the information about
motorhome stopovers in Europe is available in a multilingual
version. Due to the great interest of the English motorhome
enthusiasts, we have decided to also release a full English
version of the guide. It is with pride that we present you the new
Camperstop Europe 2013. The guide contains indispensable
information about motorhome stopovers, service facilities and
tourist information in the main European motorhome countries.

Reliable information
Every summer, 50 teams of Facile Media drive all across Europe
to inspect the motorhome stopovers. The inspections take
place according to predefined guidelines. The inspections by
these specially trained motorhome enthusiasts have made it
possible to make the information in the guide as up-to-date as
possible. Almost 7500 motorhome stopovers and more than 5000
illustrative photos are the result.

Unique way to find the motorhome sites
The motorhome stopovers can be easily located on the 40 maps.
Next to each map, you'll find a location name index with map
referral and a page number where the location can be found
in the guide. In addition, the type of motorhome stopover is
indicated. In a glance, you'll be able to see whether it is the type of
stopover you had in mind. In order to provide you with additional
information, the location is described extensively on the relevant
page, usually with a picture.

GPS-data sets on your navigation system
In addition to this guide, you can order datasets online, which you
can download. The sets can be uploaded to the most common
navigation systems. This allows you to drive to the motorhome
stopovers listed in this guide without any effort. More information
about this is available on page 8.

Traveling with "Camperstop Europe" will be a pleasant experience
and a relaxed vacation in your motor home. We therefore wish
you happy motorhome season, with many
pleasant and surprising travels.

Anne van den Dobbelsteen
Chief editor

Table of contents

Table of contents

How to use the guide

Searching in a region

In the table of contents, at the beginning of the guide, one can search a region in preferred country. On the page of the region a map indicates the different departments/provinces with a reference to the pages.

Maps

On pages 10-11 the countries are divided into sections. The number in each box is the number of the map. On the map the red dots indicate the location of the town. Next to each map an index is published with the places on maps. The index shows the name, type of stopover, map code and page number of each location. This way the description of the motorhome stopover can be found quickly and easy.

Searching for a town

Places identified in this guide can be found under the name of the local town in the alphabetical index at the back. Use the index like a dictionary to look for specific towns, the facilities offered, map references and relevant page numbers.

Country specific rules

When travelling you have to take into account that each country has its own rules and regulations. These rules are written on the first page of each countries section.

Advise

It is recommended not to wait to long to look for an overnight stop. It could be that chosen motorhome stopover is already full and you have to go looking for an alternative.

How to use the guide

Description motorhome stopover

The information per motorhome stopover always begins with a colored block containing the type of stopover, town name and reference to the map. Directly below the name, address, GPS coordinates mostly followed by a picture. Beneath the picture you find the following information: number of pitches, rate, facilities and opening period. After that, if known, distances to city centre, shop, restaurant etc. Specific information of the motorhome stopover and a brief route description.

Motorhome facilities

 MOTORHOME PARK
This symbol indicates a motorhome park, a park designed for motorhomes with a range of facilities.

 OFFICIAL MOTORHOME STOPOVER
This symbol indicates an area suitable for overnight parking

 OVERNIGHT PARKING TOLERATED
In some countries tolerated places are mentioned. This means that it is officially prohibited but is being tolerated by local authorities. Therefore the local or national situation may change at any time. Nevertheless these places are listed because they were frequently being used by motorhomes at the time of writing.

 OVERNIGHT STAY AT FARM/VINEYARD
Farms and vineyards that welcome motorhomes, you may be encouraged to sample and buy their fare.

 OVERNIGHT STAY AT RESTAURANT
Motorhomes are allowed to stopover on the car park of a hotel, restaurant or bar. You should expect to dine or drink in the bar. Some restaurants insist on you having dinner. Sometimes a nominal charge is asked for the overnight stay

 OVERNIGHT STAY AT SPA
A growing number of spas and thermal baths offer stopovers to motorhomes.

 OVERNIGHT STAY AT ZOO/MUSEUM/ AMUSEMENT PARK
Motorhomes are allowed to stopover on the car park of a zoo, museum or amusement park. Entrance is not always obligated.

 OVERNIGHT STAY AT COMPANY/ ENTERPRISE
Overnight stay, mostly inside the gates, at companies/ enterprises.

 OVERNIGHT STAY OUTSIDE THE CAMPSITE
Motorhomes are allowed to stopover on the parking place outside the gate of a campsite.

 CAMPSITE
Overnight stay on a campsite.

 CAR-PARK
Motorhome parking bays, suitable for daytime use only. Often in large cities and/or tourist towns, charges may apply.

Other symbols

꿈 Motorhome stopover, number of pitches and rate
⬆ Signposted on the spot
➡ Signposted in town
✖ No signs to indicate the motorhome stopover

Payment
🅥 Collector parking fee
🅟 Parking meter
💳 Payment only with a credit/debit card
💳 Payment with cash and credit/debit card

S Service facilities
This symbol indicates that there are service facilities available.

🚰 drinking water
grey water dump
Ch chemical toilet disposal point
🔋 charging battery
⚡ electricity available
WC toilets
🚿 showers
🔲 washing machine/ dryer on the spot
📶 wifi access point

GPS - convenience

Downloading GPS-coordinates

Downloads of the gps-coordinates for the motorhome stopovers listed in this guide are available from www.camperstop.com. The files are suitable for most navigation systems. The data that appears on the screen gives the town name and page number in this guide so you can look up the details of the facilities very easily.

The downloadable files list the stopovers and most of the other facilities mentioned in the guide. Therefore it could be a stopover with or without service facilities, a place with service facilities only, but also a tourist information office or a campsite.

You can easily check for your nearest stopover, the navigation system will list the stopovers by distance. Use the guide to see what facilities are available. Once a choice has been made you can navigate to there without a problem.

The costs for downloading are € 3.00 per country/dataset. The Netherlands/Belgium/Luxembourg are sold as one country, also Austria/Switzerland and Spain/Portugal are treated the same.

Full downloading instructions are found on at www.camperstop.com. There are different downloads of several navigation systems.

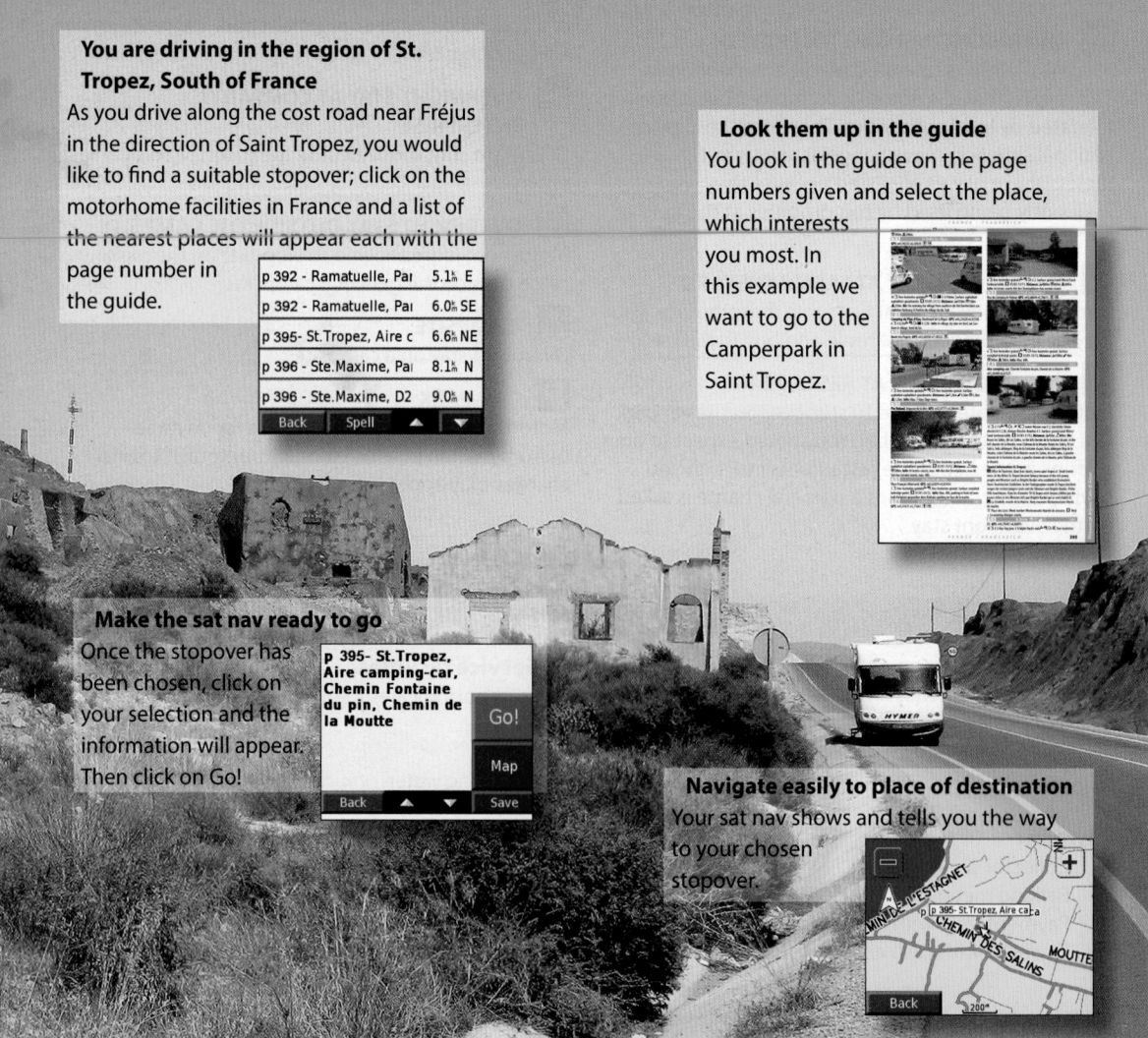

You are driving in the region of St. Tropez, South of France
As you drive along the cost road near Fréjus in the direction of Saint Tropez, you would like to find a suitable stopover; click on the motorhome facilities in France and a list of the nearest places will appear each with the page number in the guide.

p 392 - Ramatuelle, Par	5.1½ E
p 392 - Ramatuelle, Par	6.0½ SE
p 395- St.Tropez, Aire c	6.6½ NE
p 396 - Ste.Maxime, Par	8.1½ N
p 396 - Ste.Maxime, D2	9.0½ N

Back Spell ▲ ▼

Look them up in the guide
You look in the guide on the page numbers given and select the place, which interests you most. In this example we want to go to the Camperpark in Saint Tropez.

Make the sat nav ready to go
Once the stopover has been chosen, click on your selection and the information will appear. Then click on Go!

p 395- St.Tropez, Aire camping-car, Chemin Fontaine du pin, Chemin de la Moutte
Go!
Map
Back ▲ ▼ Save

Navigate easily to place of destination
Your sat nav shows and tells you the way to your chosen stopover.

8

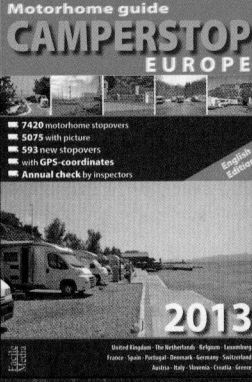

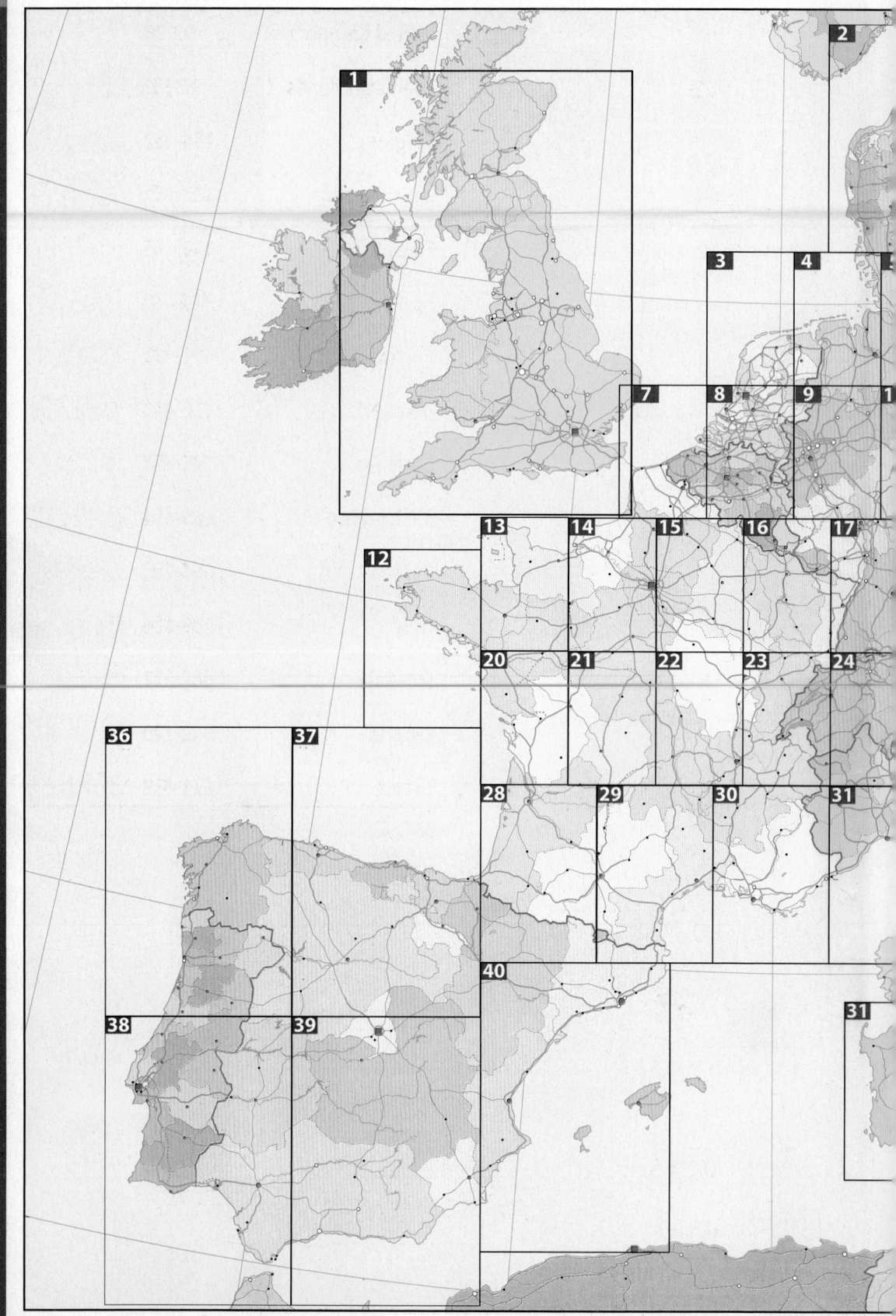

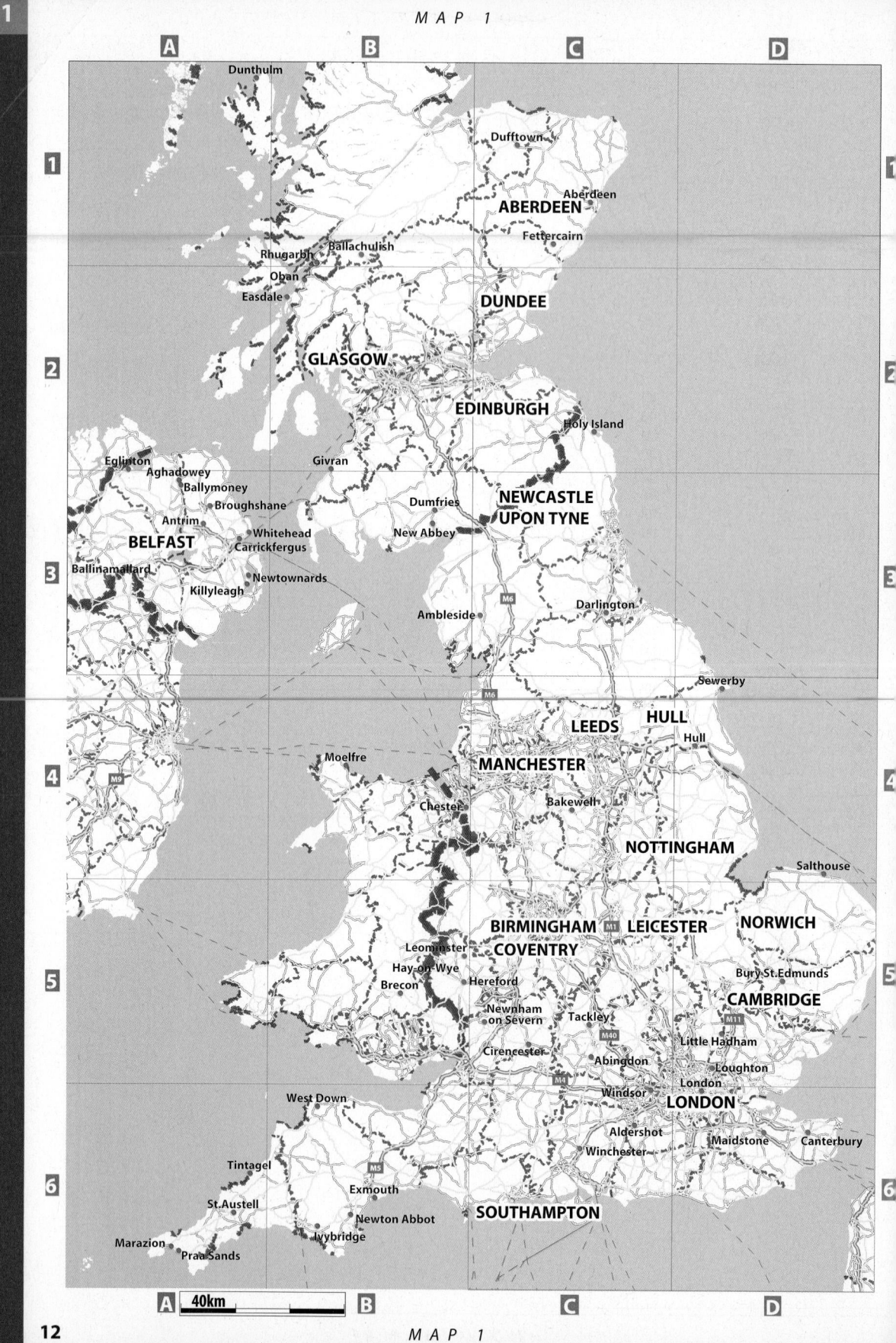

A B C D

1

2

GÖTEBORG

Skagen
Aalbæk
Hirtshals
Strandby
Sindal Kvissel
Tårs (Hjørring) Frederikshavn

Løkken
Saltum Flauenskjold
Pandrup Voerså
Hjallerup Aså

Jutland
Hanstholm Fjerritslev Aalborg
Veslos Hals
Thisted Logstør Nibe AALBORG
Storvorde

Hadsund

Vesterfig Nykøbing Mors Roslev
Hurup Skals Mariager Havndal
Harboøre Hobro
Lemvig Spøttrup Højslev Glesborg Bonnerup Strand
Struer Vinderup Randers Allingåbro Grenaa
Langå
Karup Fårvang Århus
Ulfborg Ebeltoft Vejby
Tim Jutland Sunds
Ringkøbing Ikast Silkeborg Hundested
Engesvan Ry Malling Nykøbing
Hvide Sande Østbirk Odder AARHUS
Skjern Brædstrup KØBENHAVN
Tarm Horsens Hørve Copenhagen
Hemmet Hoven Føllenslev Vipperød Taastrup
Nørre Nebel Sdr. Omme Jyderup Vallensbæk
VEJLE Juelsminde Seeland
Vejers Strand Varde Martofte Ringsted
Hvidbjerg Egtved Frederikcia Otterup Strøby
Esbjerg Holsted Kolding Asperup Rødvig
Fanø Brørup Bjert Middelfart Odense Nyborg Korsør Boeslunde
ESBJERG Rødding Sjølund Nr. Åby ODENSE Karrebæksminde Fakse
Ribe Hejls Funen Rude
Gram Assens Hesselager Tranekær
Røma Haderslev Haarby Stenstrup Skårup Stege
Skærbæk Toftlund Ebberup Fåborg Svendborg Møn
Jutland Rødekro Nordborg Rudkøbing Farø
Bredebro Åbenrå Søby, ærø Torrig Guldborg Horbelev
Bylderup-Bov Augustenborg Tårs (Harpelunde) Lolland

20km

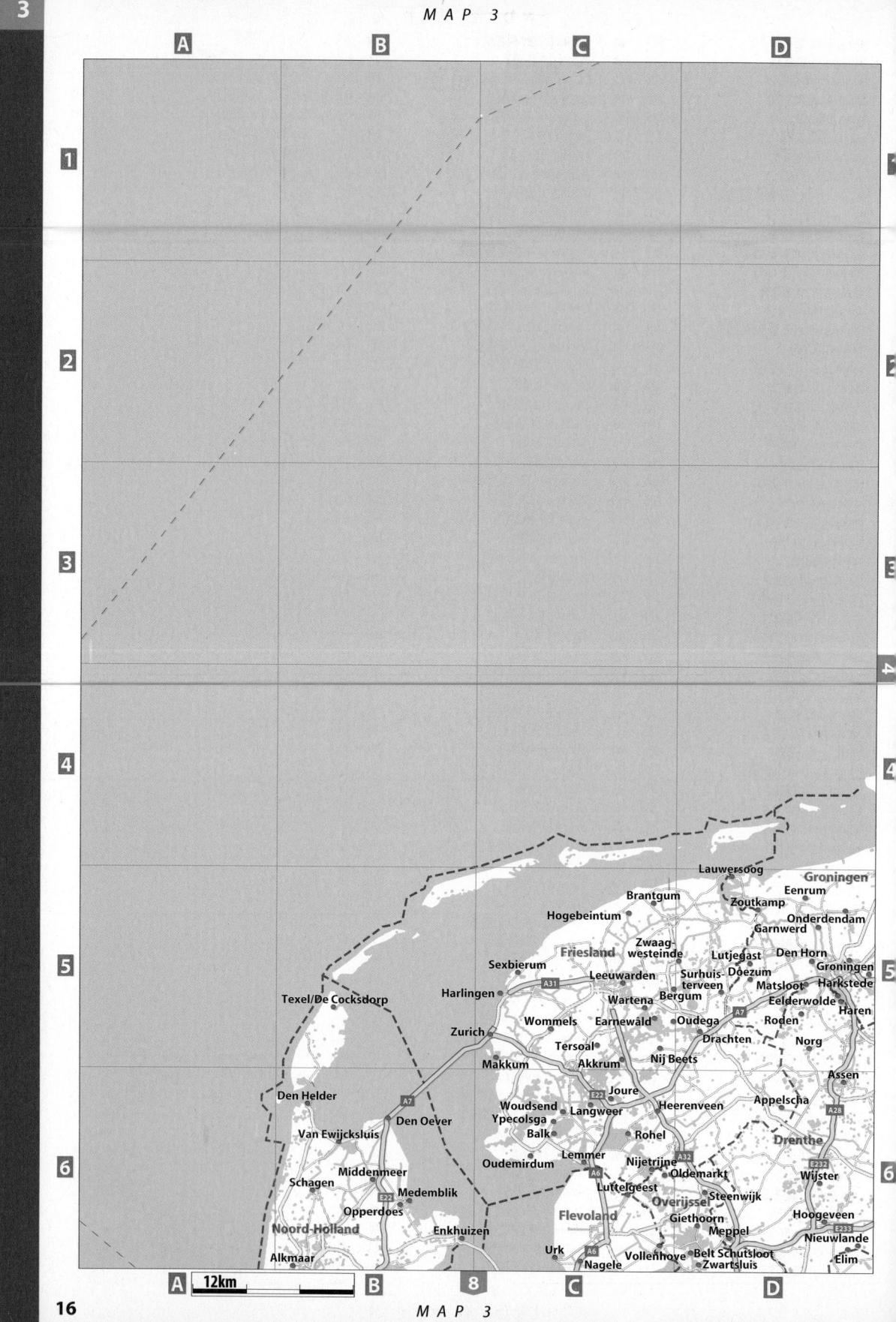

A   B   C   D

1

2

3

4

4

5

6

Lauwersoog
Groningen
Brantgum   Zoutkamp   Eenrum
Hogebeintum   Onderdendam
Friesland   Zwaag-   Garnwerd
Sexbierum   westeinde   Lutjegast   Den Horn
            Leeuwarden   Surhuis- Doezum   Groningen
Harlingen   A31   Wartena   terveen   Matsloot   Harkstede
Texel/De Cocksdorp   Bergum   Eelderwolde   Haren
            Wommels   Earnewald   Oudega   A7   Roden
Zurich   Drachten   Norg
            Tersoal   Nij Beets
Makkum   Akkrum   Assen
            E22   Joure   Appelscha
Den Helder   A7   Woudsend   Langweer   Heerenveen   A28
Van Ewijcksluis   Den Oever   Ypecolsga   Rohel   Drenthe
            Balk   Lemmer   Wijster
            Oudemirdum   Nijetrijne   Oldemarkt
Schagen   Middenmeer   A6   Luttelgeest   A32   Steenwijk
Opperdoes   E22 Medemblik   Flevoland   Overijssel   Giethoorn   Hoogeveen
Noord-Holland   Enkhuizen   Meppel   E233   Nieuwlande
            Urk   A6   Vollenhove   Belt Schutsloot   Elim
Alkmaar   Nagele   Zwartsluis

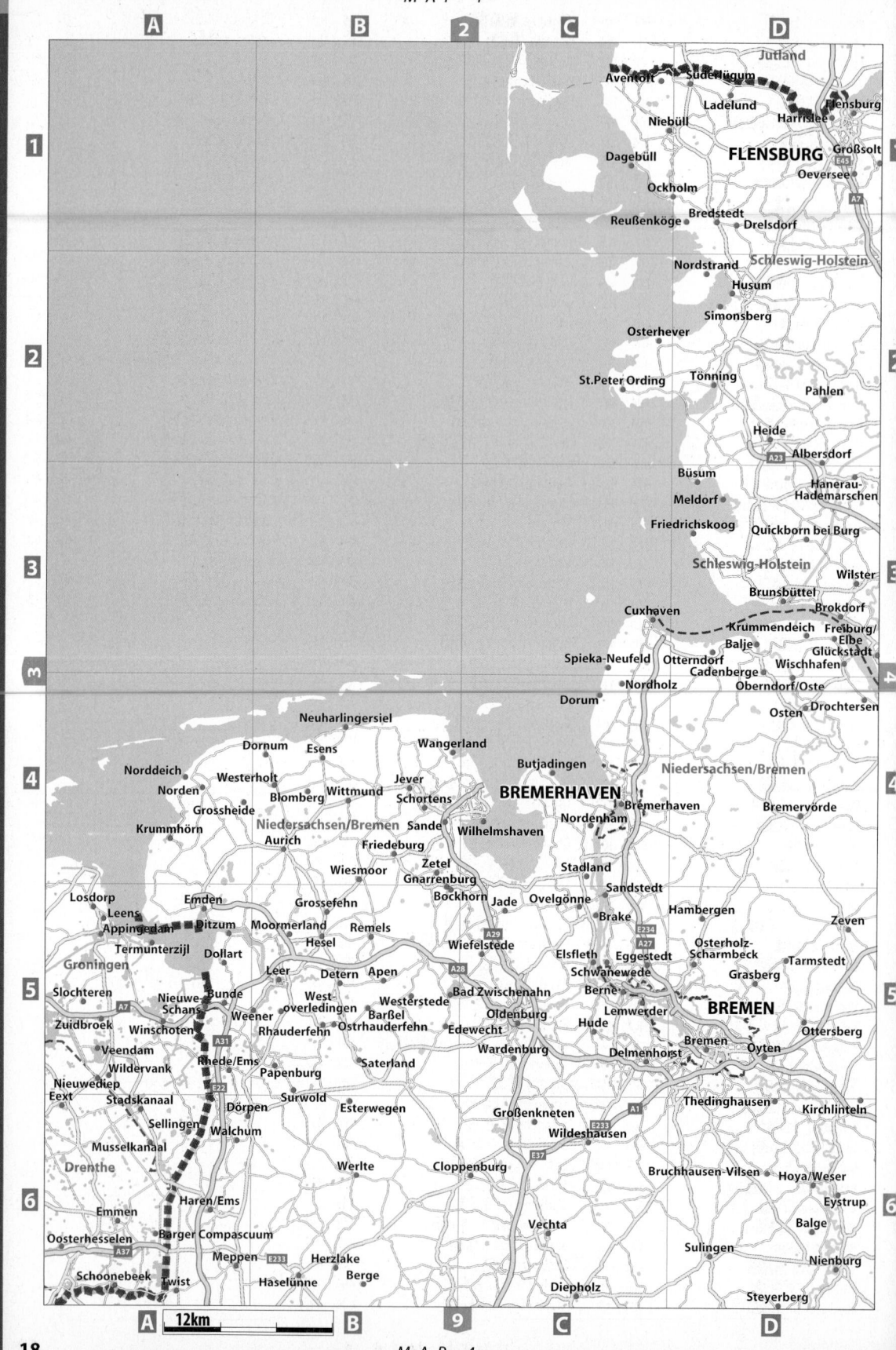

A B C D

1

Putgarten
Dranske/Bakenberg
Lohme

2

Zingst
Ahrenshoop
Barth
Neuendorf Dabitz
Ostseebad
Wustrow
Graal-Müritz

Bergen/Rügen Binz
Sehlen
Ostseebad Sellin/Rügen
Lauterbach
E251

Stralsund Poseritz
STRALSUND
E22

D

Greifswald
GREIFSWALD
Lütow Ückeritz Bansin
Neuhof Heringsdorf
Ahlbeck
E65
A20 E22
Mecklenburg-Vorpommern
Gützkow

3

Dalwitz
Anklam Karnin
Usedom
Kamminke
Mönkebude
Sommersdorf
Ueckermünde Altwarp
Güstrow
Malchin

5

NEUBRANDENBURG
Neubrandenburg
SZCZECIN
E65
A19 Nossentin Waren
Alt Schwerin Malchow Kargow
Lenz Petersdorf Sembzin
über Malchow
Röbel
E251

4

Neustrelitz Carpin
Buchholz
Wesenberg
Priepert Lychen
Fürstenberg (Havel)
Templin
D
Schwedt-Oder
E28
Angermünde
A11
Stolzenhagen
Brandenburg

5

Baumgarten
A24
E55
E251

Nackel
E26
Dreetz
Tiefensee
Kienitz

6

Berlin
BERLIN
Alt-Zeschdorf
BRANDENBURG
AN DER HAVEL
Schmergow
E55
FRANKFURT
(ODER)
Sachsen-Anhalt
Brandenburg Potsdam
E51
POTSDAM
A12 E30
A10

A 12km B 11 C D

A **B** **C** **D**

1

2

Ouddorp

3

Kamperland

Wolphaartsdijk

Oostkapelle

Middelburg

Zeeland Hansweert

Groede

Knokke-Heist **NL** Terneuzen Vogel-
waarde

St.Laureins Zaamslag Hengst-
dijk

Bredene Maldegem Sas van Gent Axel

4 Oudenburg Brugge Eeklo Westdorpe

Westende Beernem Oost Vlaanderen

Nieuwpoort Gistel Aalter Lokeren

DUNKERQUE Veurne West Vlaanderen GENT

CALAIS Oye-plage Kortemark Gentbrugge

Calais Gravelines Roeselare Zulte Berlare

Wissant Bergues Hondschoote **B** Gavere

Tardinghen **F** Geraardsbergen

Ambleteuse Poperinge Geluveld Kortrijk Harelbeke

5 Boulogne-sur-Mer Cassel Wallonie Oudenaarde Lessines

Le Portel Arquès Bailleul Mesen Mouscron Dottignies

Equihen-Plage Comines Lahamaide Wallonie

Hardelot Longfossé Nord-Pas-de-Calais LILLE Tournai/Doornik Leuze-en-Hainaut Brugelette

Le Touquet-Paris Plage Richebourg Antoing Aubechies Beloeil **B**

Stella-plage Embry Basècles Quevaucamps

Merlimont Bernissart Blaton Nimy

6 Berck-sur-Mer Quaregnon

Fort Mahon Plage **F** Hornu Mons/Bergen

Quend Roisin

Quend-plage-les-Pins Nunq-Hautecôte Arras

Le Crotoy Picardie Bavay

A **14** **B** 12km **C** **15** **D**

MAP 8

MAP 8

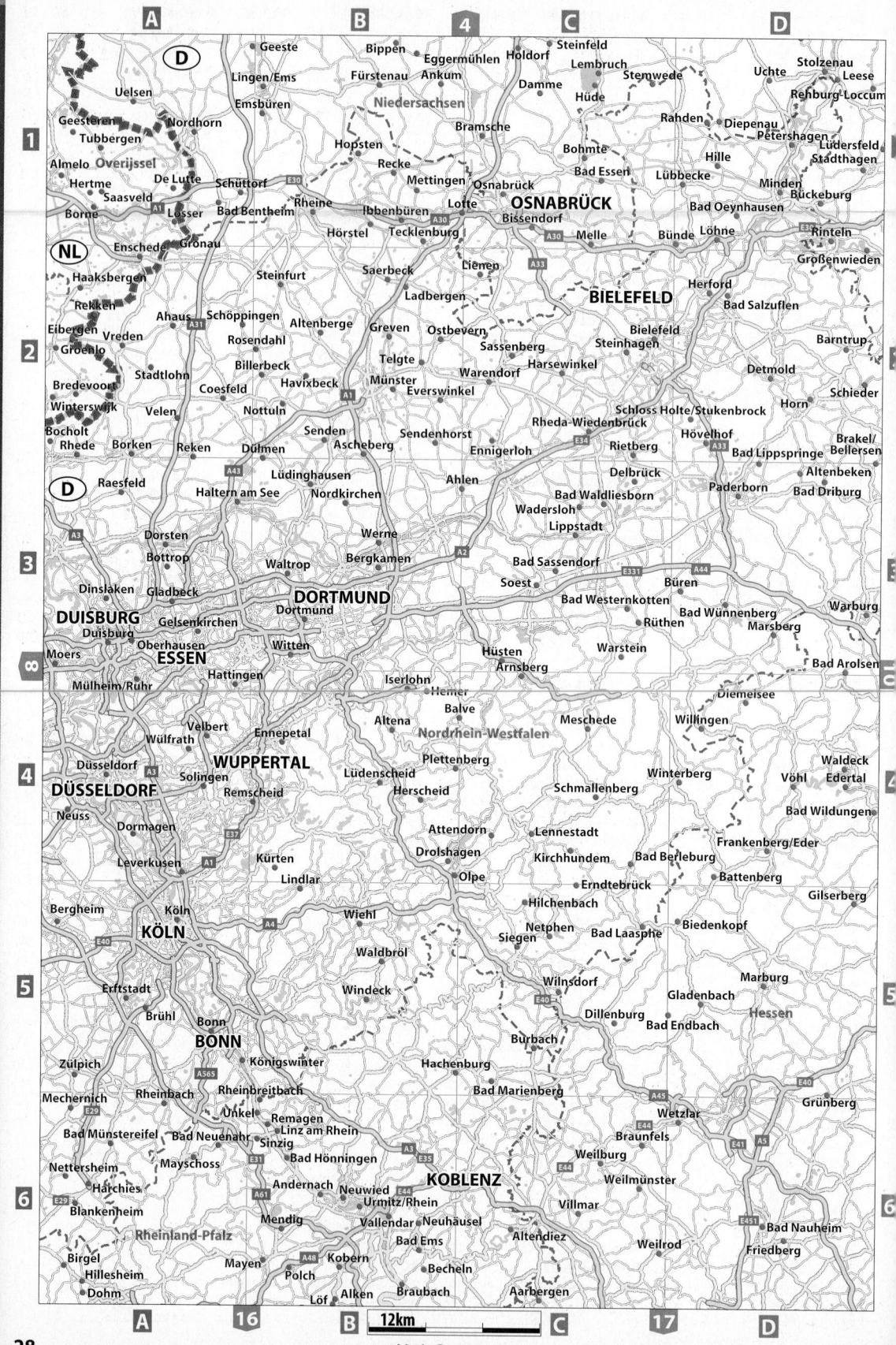

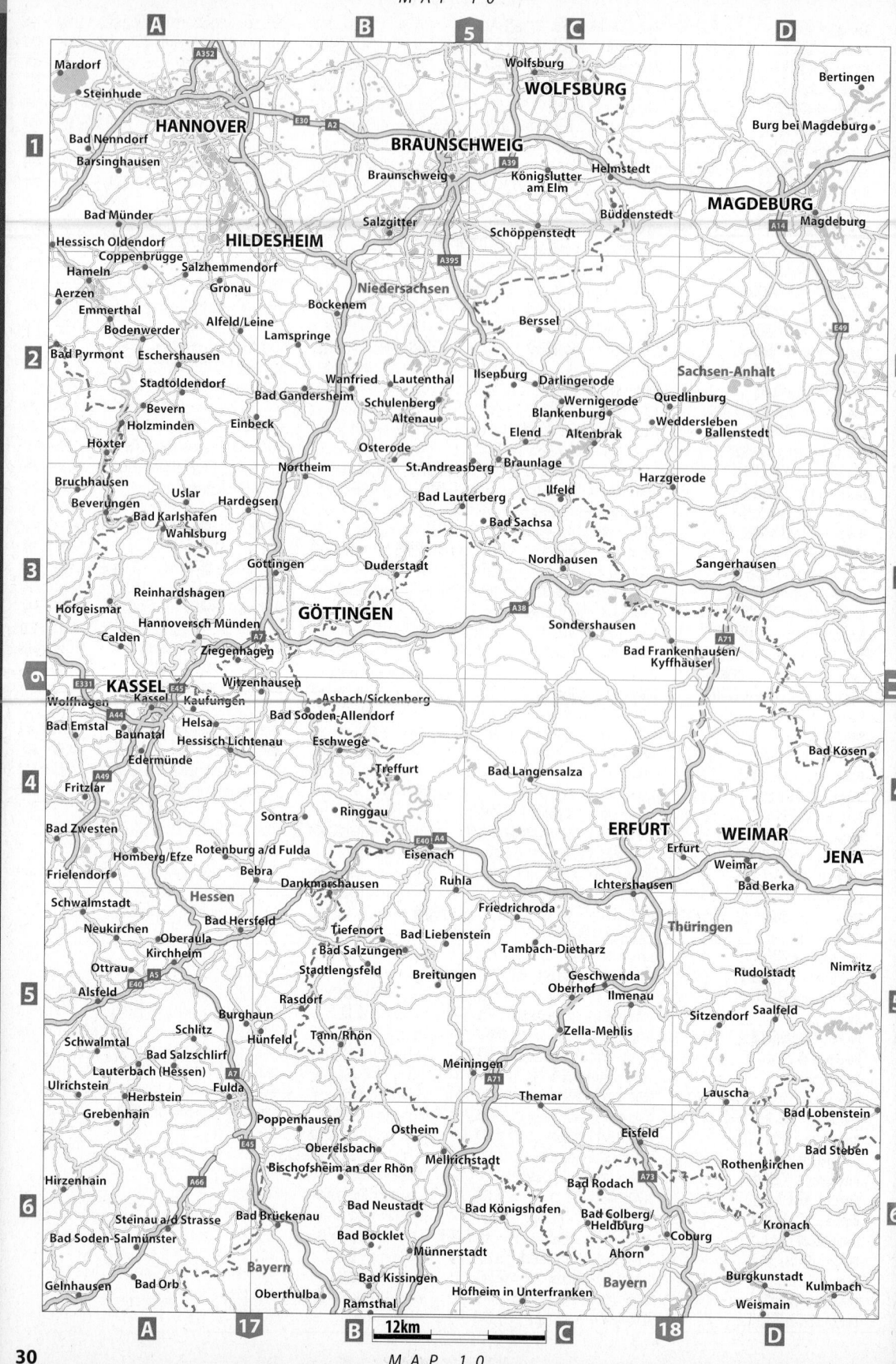

MAP 10

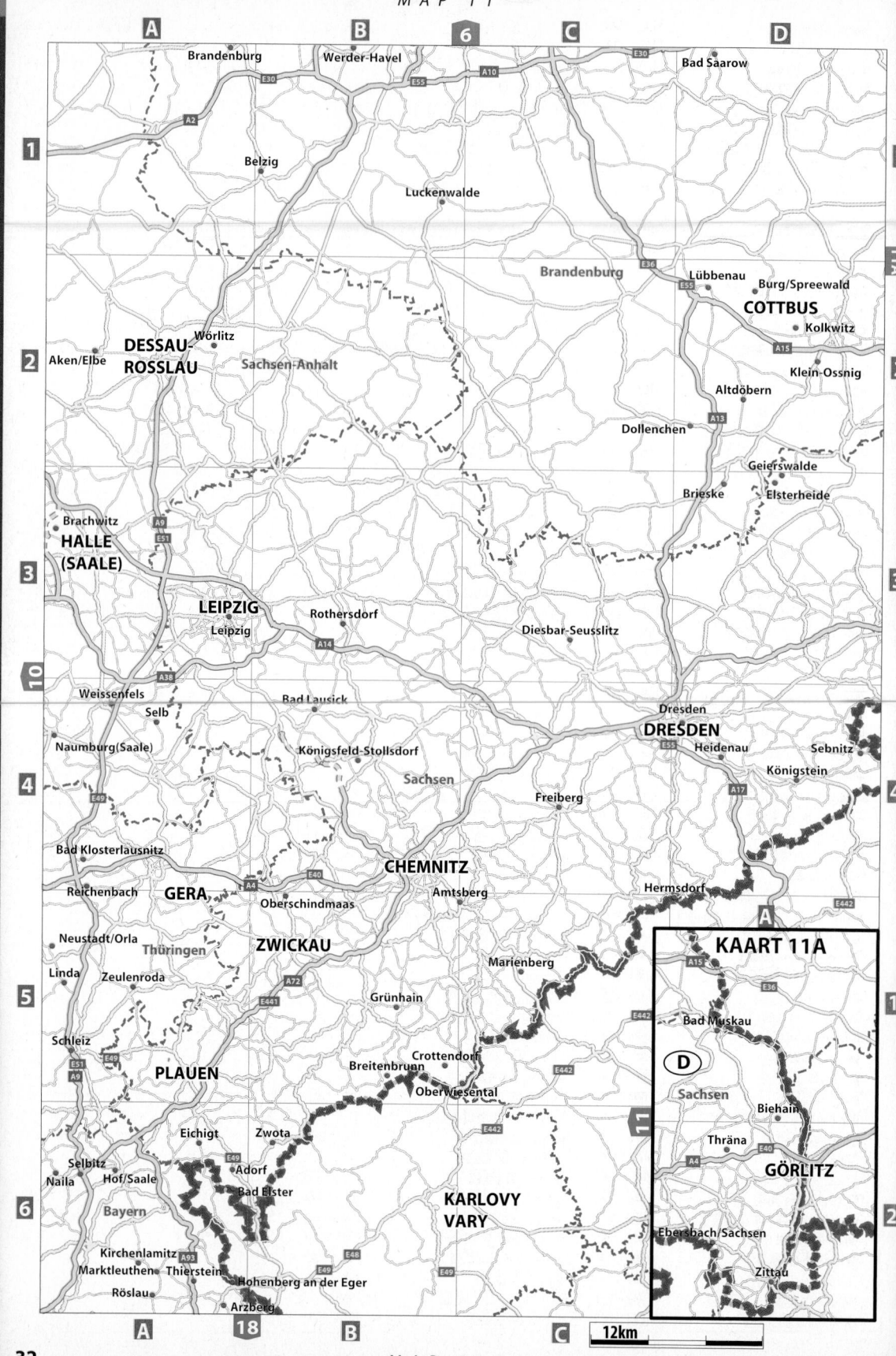

Brandenburg
Werder-Havel
Bad Saarow

1

Belzig

Luckenwalde

Brandenburg

Lübbenau
Burg/Spreewald
COTTBUS
Kolkwitz

2
Aken/Elbe
**DESSAU-
ROSSLAU**
Wörlitz

Sachsen-Anhalt

Klein-Ossnig
Altdöbern
Dollenchen

Geierswalde
Brieske
Elsterheide

Brachwitz
**HALLE
(SAALE)**

3

LEIPZIG
Leipzig
Rothersdorf
Diesbar-Seusslitz

10

Weissenfels
Selb
Bad Lausick
Dresden
DRESDEN
Heidenau
Sebnitz
Königstein

Naumburg(Saale)
Königsfeld-Stollsdorf
Sachsen
Freiberg

4
Bad Klosterlausnitz

CHEMNITZ
Amtsberg
Hermsdorf

Reichenbach
GERA
Oberschindmaas

A

Neustadt/Orla
Thüringen
ZWICKAU
Marienberg

Linda
Zeulenroda

5
Schleiz
Grünhain

PLAUEN
Crottendorf
Breitenbrunn
Oberwiesental

Eichigt
Zwota

Selbitz
Adorf
Naila
Hof/Saale
Bad Elster
**KARLOVY
VARY**

6
Bayern

Kirchenlamitz
Marktleuthen
Thierstein
Hohenberg an der Eger
Röslau
Arzberg

KAART 11A

Bad Muskau

D

Sachsen
Biehain

Thräna

GÖRLITZ

Ebersbach/Sachsen

Zittau

12km

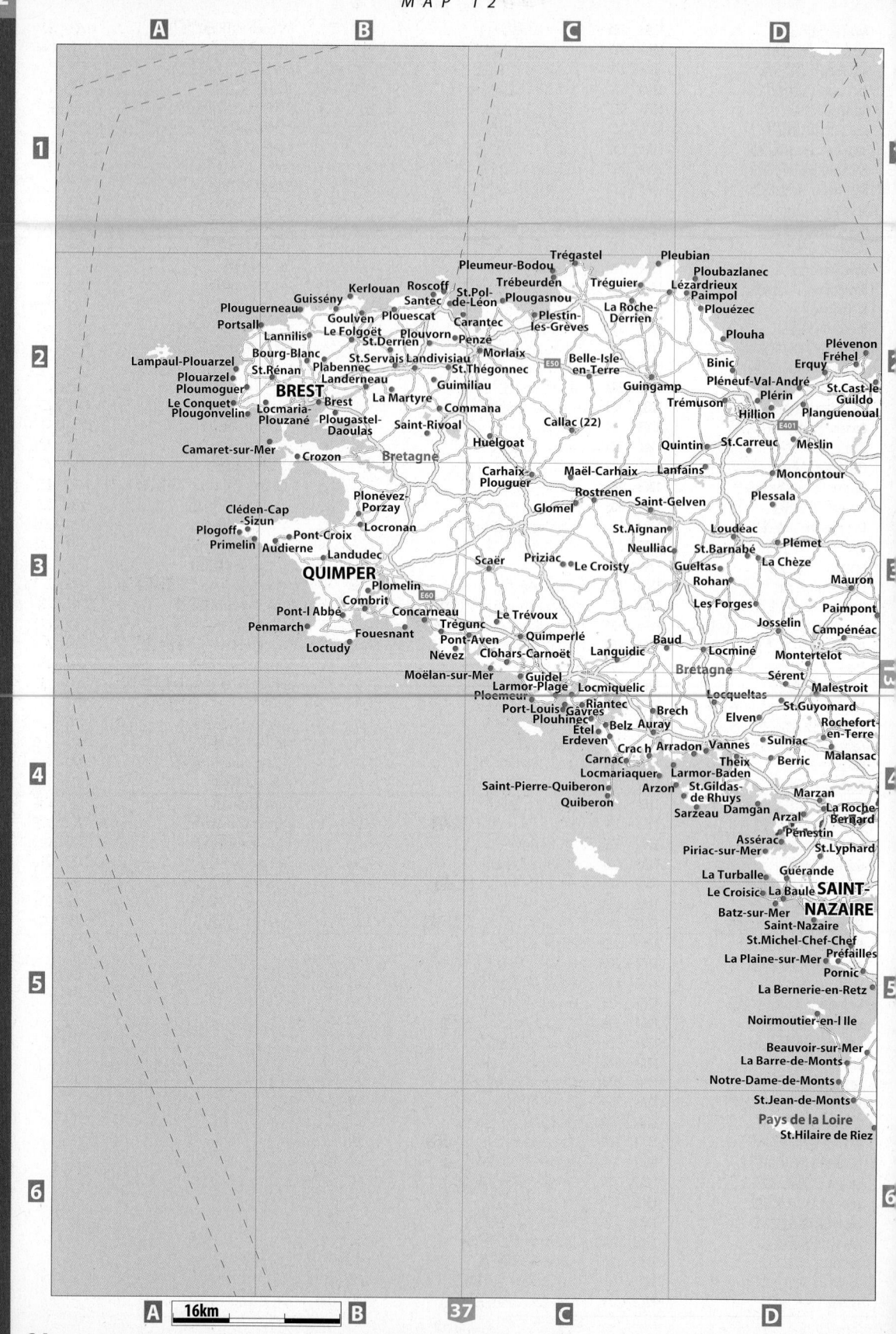

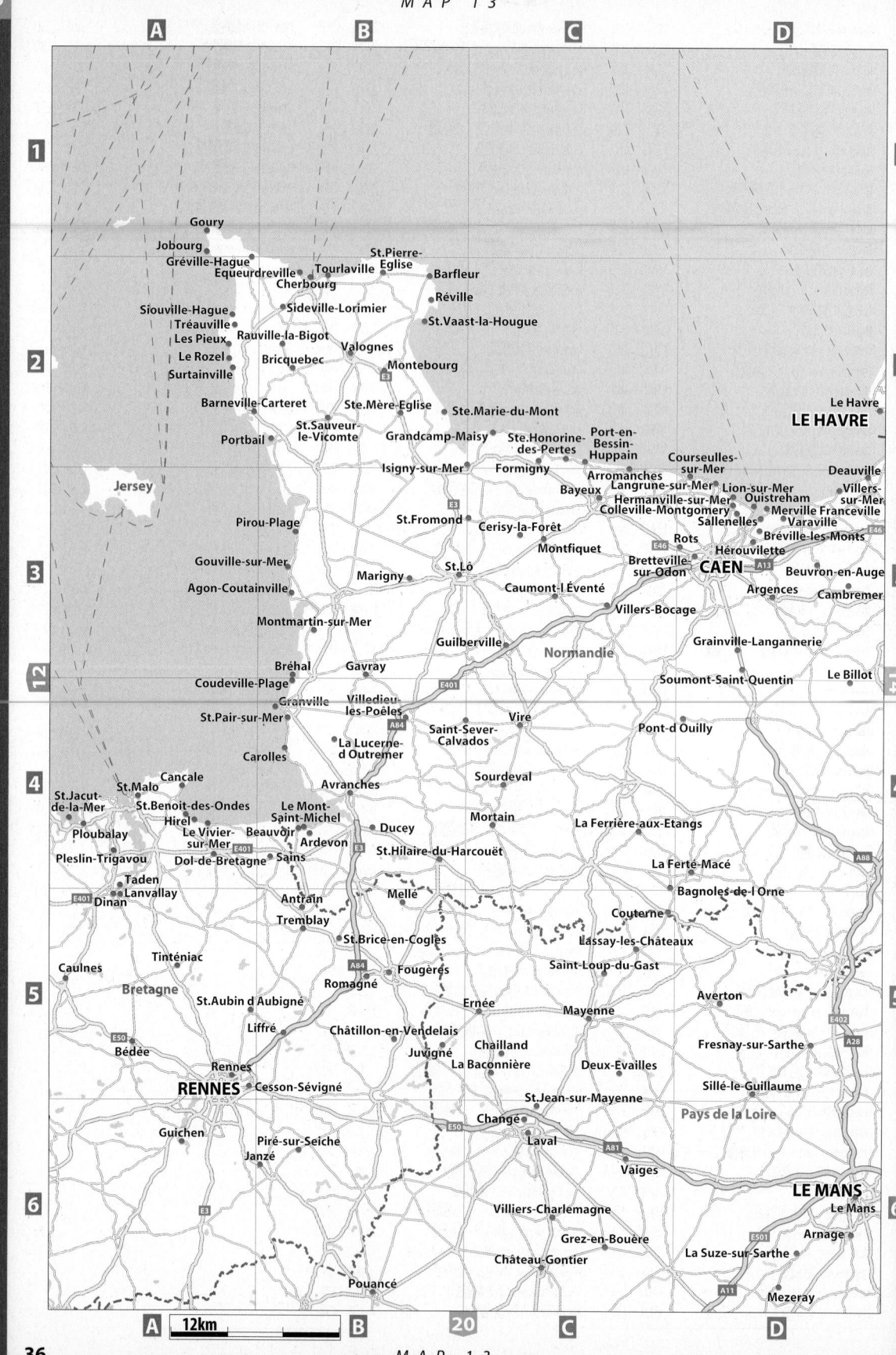

Jersey

Goury
Jobourg
Gréville-Hague
Equeurdreville
Cherbourg
Tourlaville
St.Pierre-Eglise
Barfleur
Réville
Siouville-Hague
Sideville-Lorimier
St.Vaast-la-Hougue
Tréauville
Les Pieux
Rauville-la-Bigot
Valognes
Le Rozel
Bricquebec
Surtainville
Montebourg
Barneville-Carteret
Ste.Mère-Eglise
Ste.Marie-du-Mont
St.Sauveur-le-Vicomte
Portbail
Grandcamp-Maisy
Ste.Honorine-des-Pertes
Port-en-Bessin-Huppain
Isigny-sur-Mer
Formigny
Courseulles-sur-Mer
Le Havre
LE HAVRE
Deauville
Arromanches
Langrune-sur-Mer
Lion-sur-Mer
Ouistreham
Villers-sur-Mer
Bayeux
Hermanville-sur-Mer
Merville Franceville
Pirou-Plage
St.Fromond
Colleville-Montgomery
Sallenelles
Varaville
Cerisy-la-Forêt
Rots
Bréville-les-Monts
Gouville-sur-Mer
Montfiquet
Bretteville-sur-Odon
Hérouvilette
Marigny
St.Lô
CAEN
Beuvron-en-Auge
Agon-Coutainville
Caumont-l Événté
Argences
Cambremer
Montmartin-sur-Mer
Villers-Bocage
Guilberville
Grainville-Langannerie
Normandie
Bréhal
Gavray
Soumont-Saint-Quentin
Le Billot
Coudeville-Plage
Granville
Villedieu-les-Poêles
St.Pair-sur-Mer
Vire
Pont-d Ouilly
Saint-Sever-Calvados
Carolles
La Lucerne-d Outremer
Avranches
Sourdeval
Cancale
St.Malo
St.Jacut-de-la-Mer
St.Benoit-des-Ondes
Hirel
Le Mont-Saint-Michel
Mortain
La Ferrière-aux-Etangs
Ploubalay
Le Vivier-sur-Mer
Beauvoir
Ducey
Ardevon
St.Hilaire-du-Harcouët
La Ferté-Macé
Pleslin-Trigavou
Dol-de-Bretagne
Sains
Taden
Mellé
Bagnoles-de-l Orne
Lanvallay
Dinan
Antrain
Couterne
Tremblay
Lassay-les-Châteaux
St.Brice-en-Cogles
Saint-Loup-du-Gast
Tinténiac
Caulnes
Fougères
Averton
Bretagne
Romagné
St.Aubin d Aubigné
Ernée
Mayenne
Liffré
Châtillon-en-Vendelais
Chailland
Fresnay-sur-Sarthe
Bédée
Juvigné
La Baconnière
Deux-Evailles
Sillé-le-Guillaume
Rennes
Cesson-Sévigné
St.Jean-sur-Mayenne
Pays de la Loire
RENNES
Guichen
Changé
Piré-sur-Seiche
Laval
LE MANS
Janzé
Vaiges
Le Mans
Villiers-Charlemagne
Arnage
Grez-en-Bouère
La Suze-sur-Sarthe
Château-Gontier
Pouancé
Mezeray

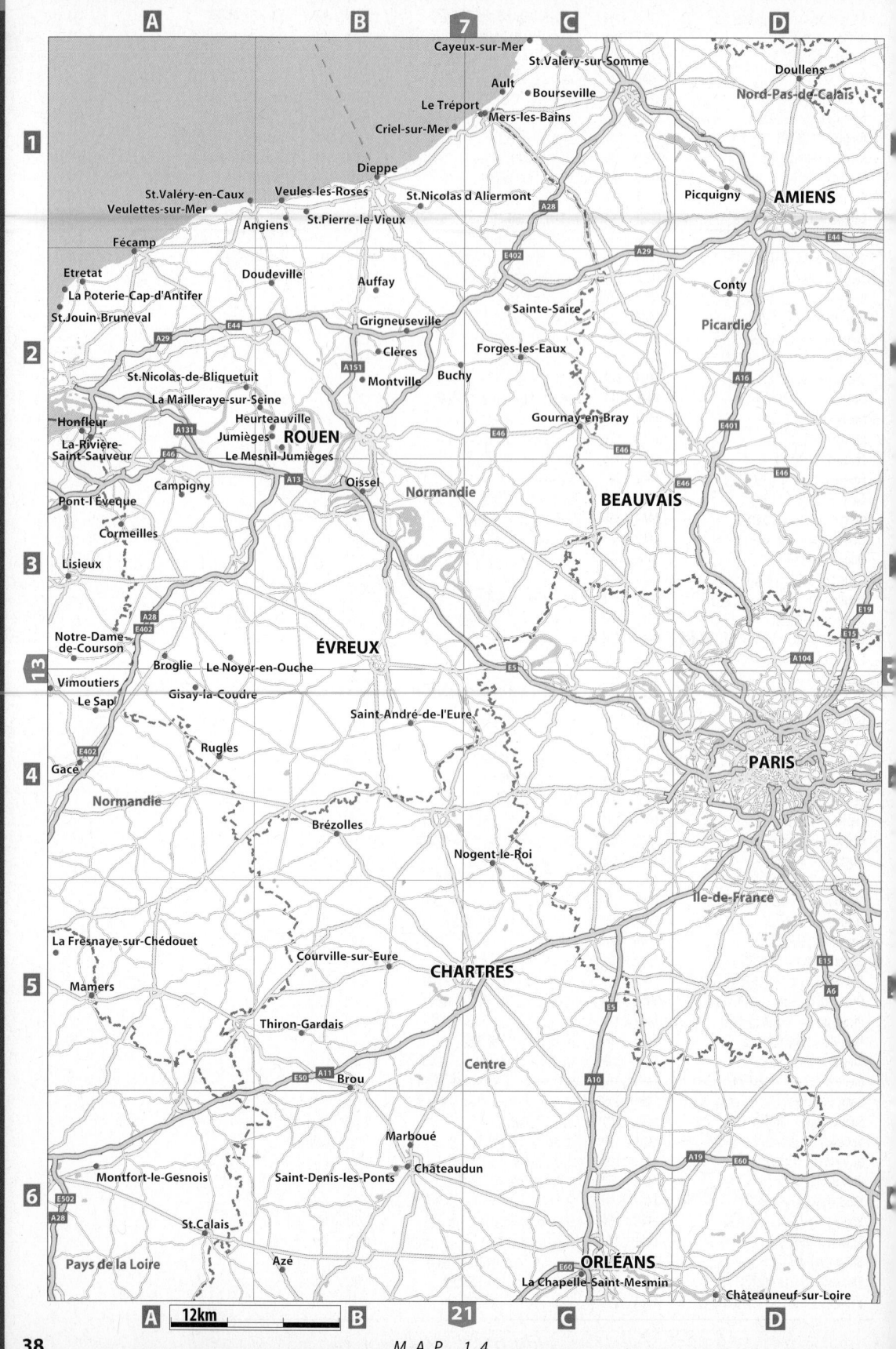

A   **B**   **7**   **C**   **D**

Cayeux-sur-Mer
St.Valéry-sur-Somme
Doullens
Ault   Bourseville
Nord-Pas-de-Calais
Le Tréport
Criel-sur-Mer   Mers-les-Bains

1

Dieppe
St.Nicolas d'Aliermont
Picquigny   **AMIENS**
St.Valéry-en-Caux   Veules-les-Roses
Veulettes-sur-Mer
Angiens   St.Pierre-le-Vieux
A28

Fécamp
Conty
Etretat   Doudeville
Auffay
La Poterie-Cap-d'Antifer
Sainte-Saire
St.Jouin-Bruneval
Grigneuseville   **Picardie**
A29   E44
Forges-les-Eaux

2

Clères
St.Nicolas-de-Bliquetuit   A151
La Mailleraye-sur-Seine   Montville   Buchy
A16
Heurteauville
Gournay-en-Bray
Honfleur
Jumièges   **ROUEN**
A131
La Rivière-   Le Mesnil-Jumièges
Saint-Sauveur   E46
E401
Campigny   A13   Oissel
Pont-l'Eveque   **Normandie**   E46
E46

Cormeilles   **BEAUVAIS**
E46

3

Lisieux
Notre-Dame-   A28
de-Courson   E402
ÉVREUX
13   Broglie   Le Noyer-en-Ouche
E19
Vimoutiers
Le Sap   Gisay-la-Coudre   E15
E5
Saint-André-de-l'Eure   A104
Rugles

4

Gace   E402
Normandie   **PARIS**
Brézolles
Nogent-le-Roi
Ile-de-France

La Frèsnaye-sur-Chédouet   E15
Courville-sur-Eure
A6

5

Mamers   **CHARTRES**
E5
Thiron-Gardais
A10
Centre
E50   A11   Brou
Marboué
A19   E60
Montfort-le-Gesnois   Saint-Denis-les-Ponts   Châteaudun

6

E502
A28
St.Calais
ORLÉANS
Azé
Pays de la Loire   E60
La Chapelle-Saint-Mesmin
Châteauneuf-sur-Loire

A   12km   **B**   **21**   **C**   **D**

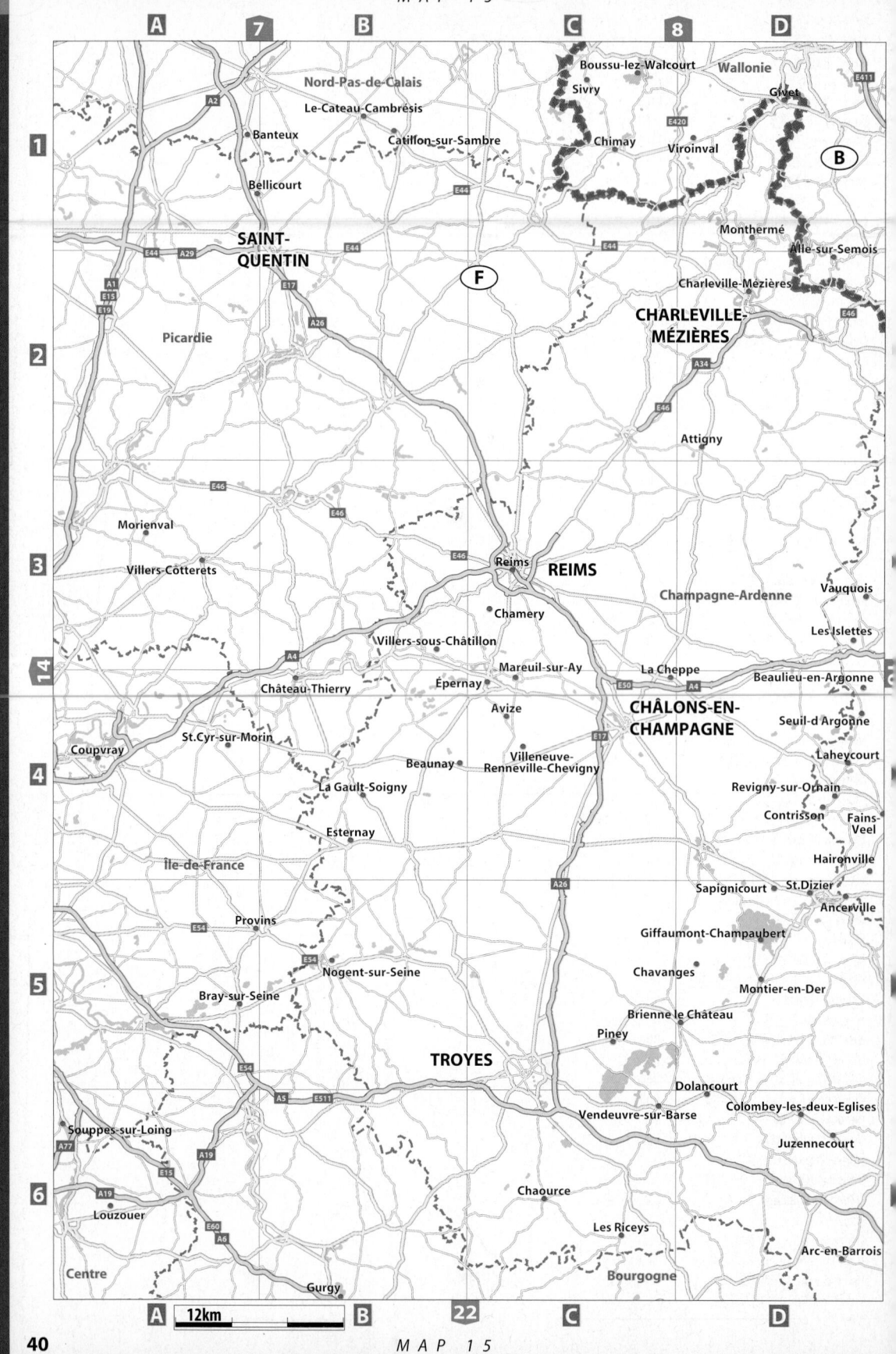

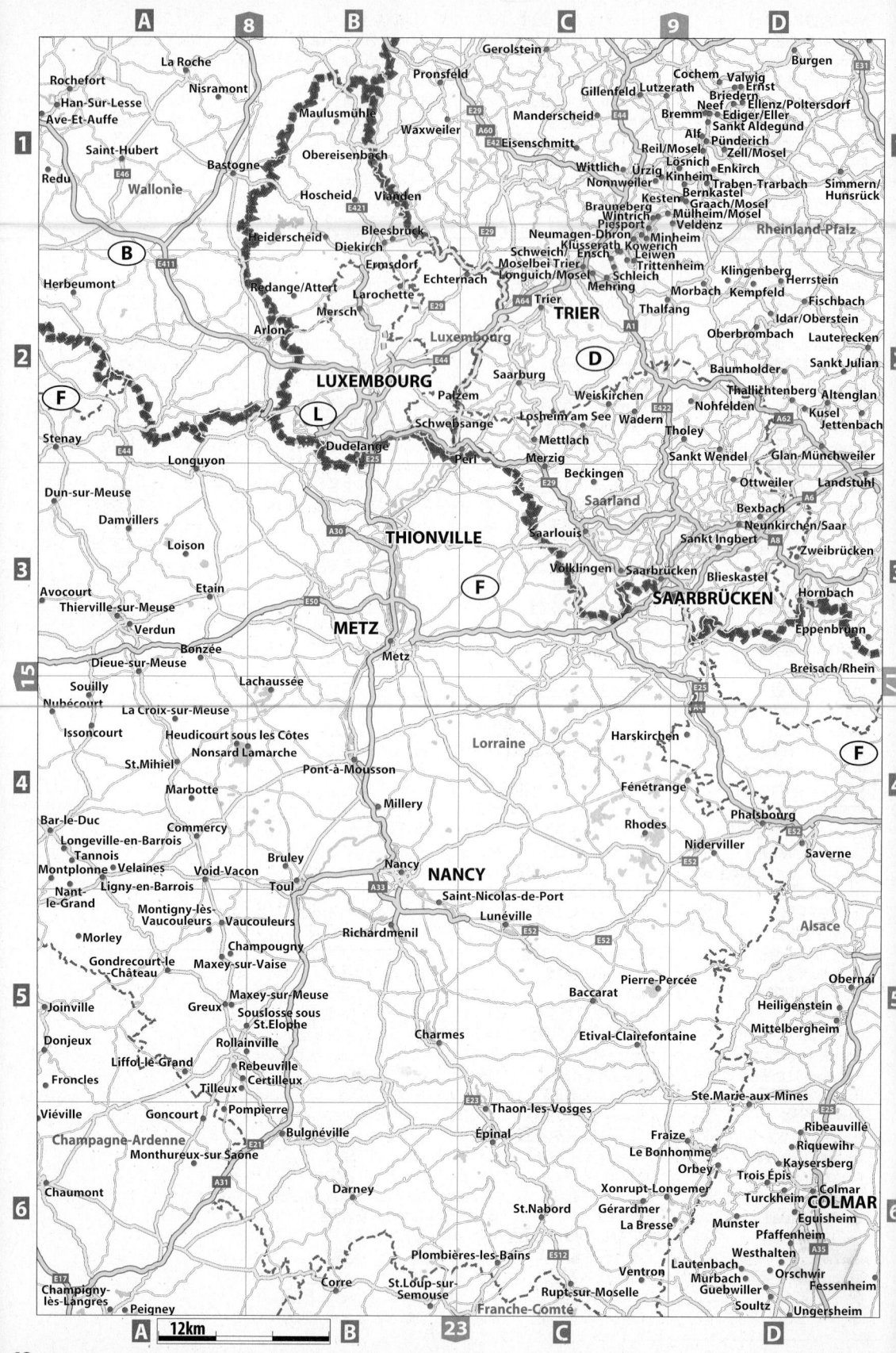

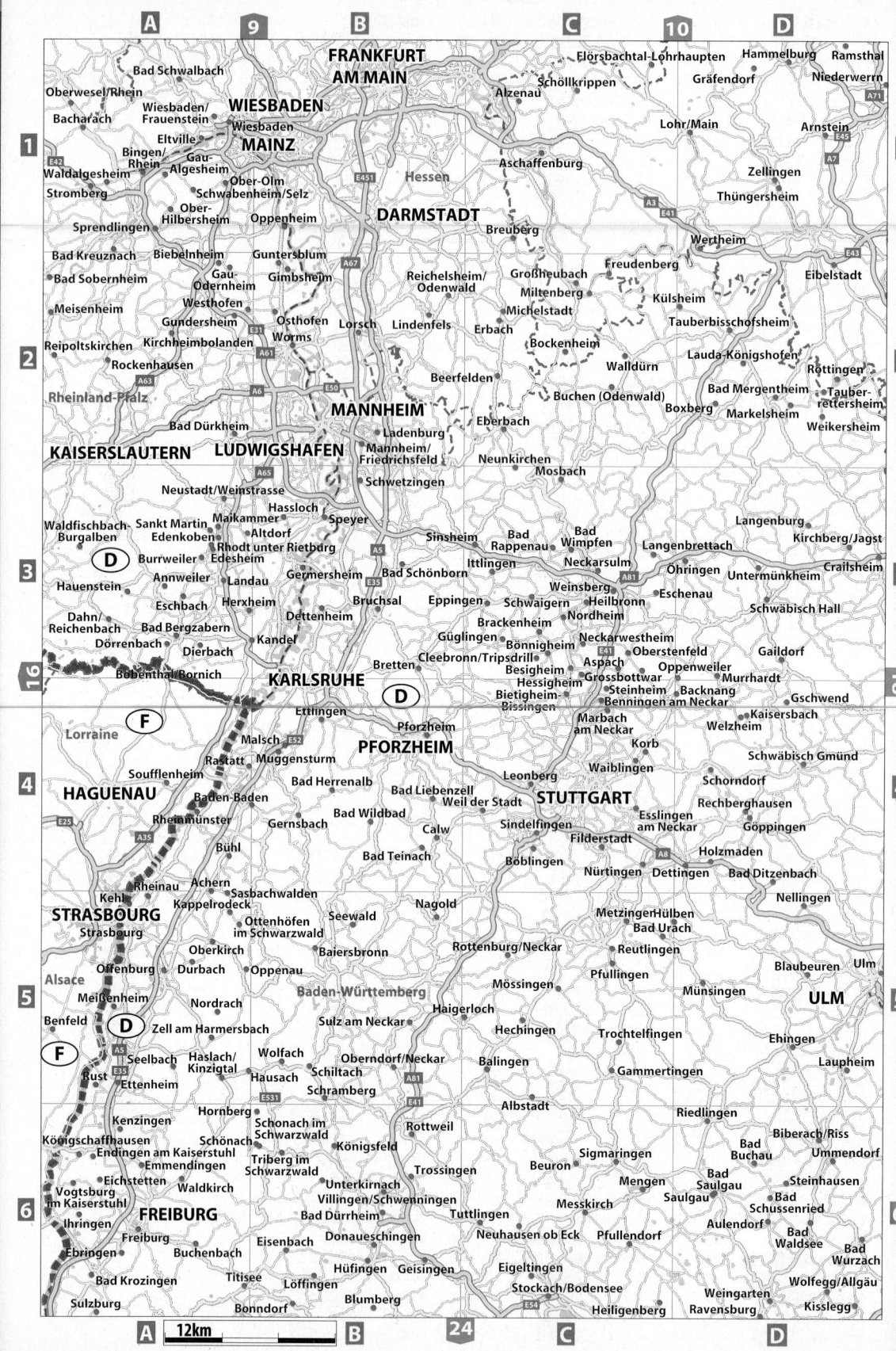

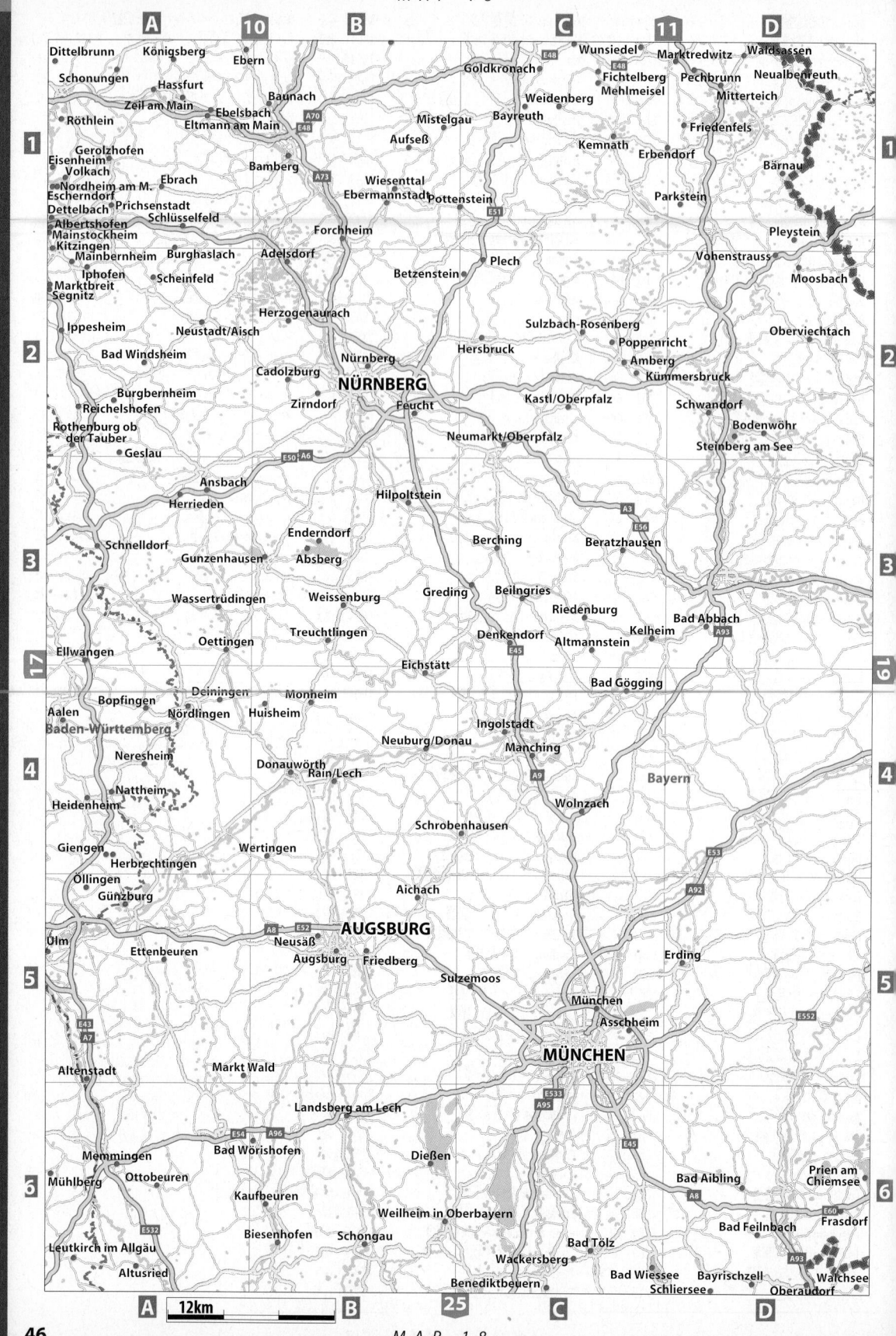

A · **10** · **B** · **C** · **11** · **D**

Dittelbrunn · Königsberg · Ebern · Goldkronach · Wunsiedel · Marktredwitz · Waldsassen

Schonungen · Hassfurt · Baunach · Fichtelberg · Pechbrunn · Neualbenreuth

Zeil am Main · Weidenberg · Mehlmeisel · Mitterteich

Röthlein · Ebelsbach · Mistelgau · Bayreuth · Friedenfels

Eltmann am Main · A70 · Aufseß · Kemnath · Erbendorf

A48

Gerolzhofen · Bamberg · Wiesenttal · Bärnau

Eisenheim · Volkach · Ebrach · Ebermannstadt · Parkstein

Nordheim am M. · Pottenstein

Escherndorf · A73 · E51

Dettelbach · Prichsenstadt · Forchheim · Plech · Pleystein

Albertshofen · Schlüsselfeld

Mainstockheim · Vohenstrauss

Kitzingen · Betzenstein

Mainbernheim · Burghaslach · Adelsdorf · Moosbach

Iphofen · Scheinfeld

Marktbreit · Herzogenaurach

Segnitz · Sulzbach-Rosenberg · Oberviechtach

Ippesheim · Neustadt/Aisch · Hersbruck · Poppenricht

Bad Windsheim · Cadolzburg · NÜRNBERG · Amger

Kümmersbruck

Burgbernheim · Zirndorf · Feucht · Kastl/Oberpfalz · Schwandorf

Reichelshofen · Bodenwöhr

Rothenburg ob · Neumarkt/Oberpfalz · Steinberg am See

der Tauber

Geslau · E50 · A6

Ansbach · Hilpoltstein · A3 · E56

Herrieden · Beratzhausen

Schnelldorf · Enderndorf · Berching

Gunzenhausen · Absberg

Wassertrüdingen · Weissenburg · Greding · Beilngries · Riedenburg · Bad Abbach

Ellwangen · Oettingen · Treuchtlingen · Denkendorf · Altmannstein · Kelheim · A93

Eichstätt · E45

17 · Bad Gögging · 19

Deiningen · Monheim

Bopfingen · Huisheim · Ingolstadt

Aalen · Nördlingen

Baden-Württemberg · Neuburg/Donau · Manching · Bayern

Neresheim · Donauwörth · A9

Heidenheim · Rain/Lech · Wolnzach · E53

Giengen · Wertingen · Schrobenhausen · A92

Herbrechtingen

Öllingen · Aichach

Günzburg

Ulm · A8 · E52 · AUGSBURG · Erding

Ettenbeuren · Neusäß · E552

Augsburg · Friedberg

Altenstadt · Sulzemoos

E43 · München

A7 · Asschheim

Markt Wald · MÜNCHEN

Landsberg am Lech · E533

E54 · A96 · A95

Memmingen · Bad Wörishofen · Dießen · Bad Aibling · Prien am Chiemsee

Mühlberg · Ottobeuren · A8

Kaufbeuren · E60 · Frasdorf

E532 · Bad Feilnbach

Leutkirch im Allgäu · Biesenhofen · Weilheim in Oberbayern · A93 · Walchsee

Altusried · Schongau · Bad Tölz · Bayrischzell

Wackersberg · Bad Wiessee · Oberaudorf

Benediktbeuern · Schliersee

A B C D

1

PLZEN

2

Chammünster
Bad Kötzting
Arnbruck
Bodenmais
Viechtach

CESKE
BUDEJOVICE

3

Steinach/Straubing
Bernried
Bogen
Deggendorf
Lalling
Grafenau
Freyung
Plattling
Eging am See
Waldkirchen
Bad Großpertholz
Langschlag Mitterschlag
Hastach

18

Landau/Isar
Dingolfing
Vilshofen
Passau
Kefermarkt
Königswiesen

4

Bayern
Neuhaus/Inn
Bad Birnbach
Suben
Bayerbach
Bad Griesbach
Kirchham
Bad Füssing
Eferding
LINZ
Gallneukirchen
Steyregg
Naarn
Massing
Eggenfelden
Altötting
Ranshofen
Marchtrenk
Aschbach Markt
Burghausen
Burgkirchen
Geboltskirchen
WELS
Kremsmünster
Weistrach
STEYR

5

Gmunden Scharnstein
St.Pankraz
Hollenstein/Ybbs
Wonneberg
Petting
Mondsee
Nußdorf am Attersee
Traunstein
Freilassing
Unterach am Attersee
Ebensee
Übersee/Chiemsee
Siegsdorf
Inzell
SALZBURG
St.Wolfgang
Bergen/Chiemgau
Bad Reichenhall
Ruhpolding
Berchtesgaden
Reit im Winkl
Kössen
Bischofswiesen
Gosau
Liezen

6

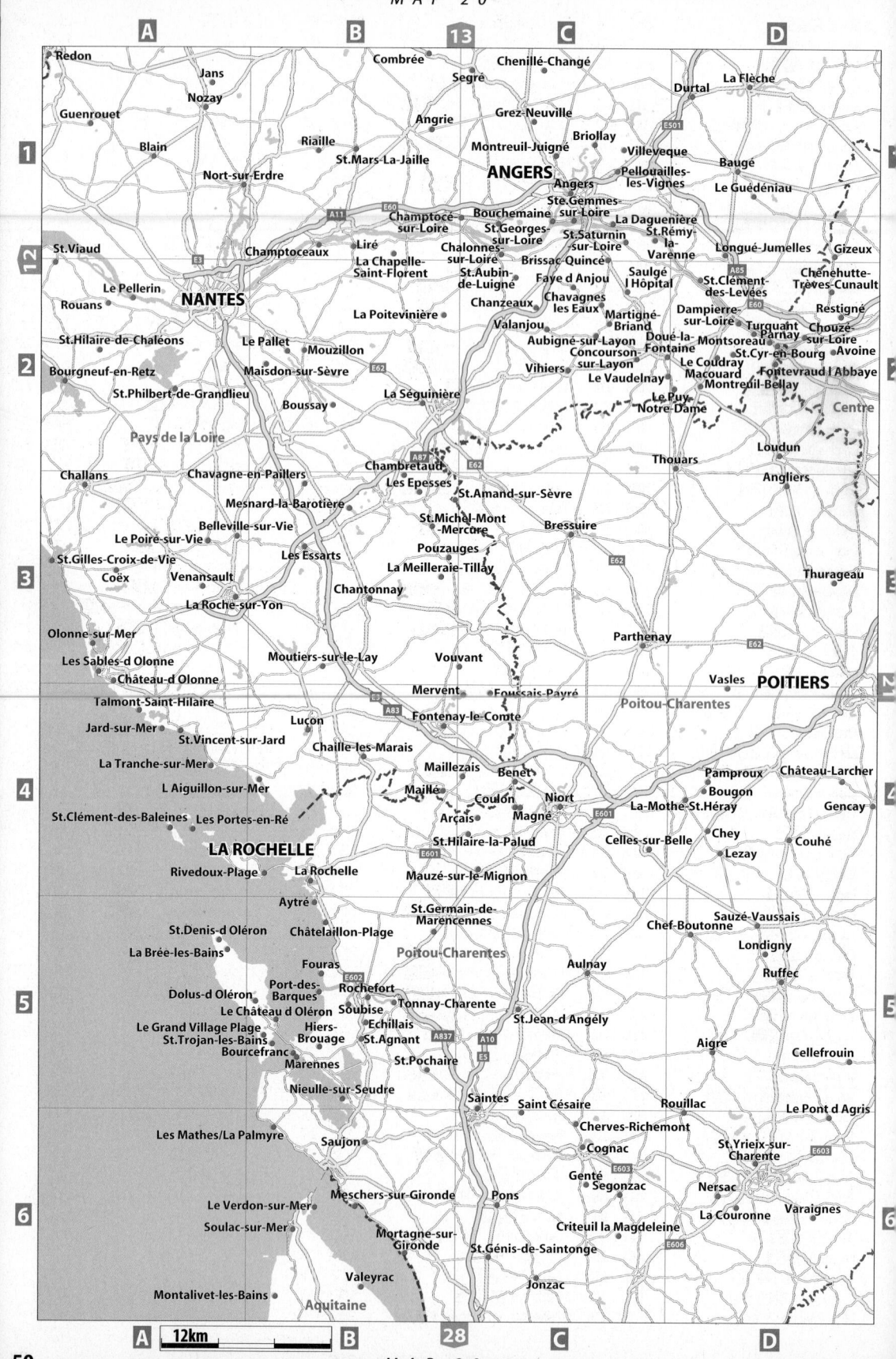

A   B   13   C   D

Redon
Jans
Nozay
Guenrouet
Blain
Nort-sur-Erdre
St.Viaud
Le Pellerin
Rouans
St.Hilaire-de-Chaléons
Bourgneuf-en-Retz
St.Philbert-de-Grandlieu

Combrée
Segré
Angrie
Riaille
St.Mars-La-Jaille
Champtocé-sur-Loire
Liré
Champtoceaux
La Chapelle-Saint-Florent
NANTES
Le Pallet   Mouzillon
Maisdon-sur-Sèvre
Boussay
La Poitevinière
La Séguinière

Chenillé-Changé
Grez-Neuville
Montreuil-Juigné
Briollay
ANGERS
Angers
Ste.Gemmes-sur-Loire
Bouchemaine
St.Georges-sur-Loire
Chalonnes-sur-Loire
St.Aubin-de-Luigné
Brissac-Quincé
Faye d'Anjou
Chanzeaux
Chavagnes les Eaux
Valanjou
Aubigné-sur-Layon
Concourson-sur-Layon
Vihiers
Le Vaudelnay
La Daguenière
St.Saturnin-sur-Loire
St.Rémy-la-Varenne
Saulgé l'Hôpital
Martigné-Briand
Doué-la-Fontaine
Le Coudray Macouard
Le Puy-Notre-Dame

Durtal   La Flèche
Villeveque
Pellouailles-les-Vignes
Baugé
Le Guédéniau
Longué-Jumelles   Gizeux
Chênehutte-Trèves-Cunault
St.Clément-des-Levées
Restigné
Dampierre-sur-Loire
Turquant   Chouzé-sur-Loire
Parnay
Montsoreau   St.Cyr-en-Bourg   Avoine
Fontevraud l'Abbaye
Montreuil-Bellay
Centre

St.Viaud
Pays de la Loire
Challans
Chavagne-en-Paillers
Mesnard-la-Barotière
Belleville-sur-Vie
Le Poiré-sur-Vie
St.Gilles-Croix-de-Vie
Coëx
Venansault
La Roche-sur-Yon
Les Essarts
Chantonnay
Chambretaud
Les Epesses
St.Amand-sur-Sèvre
St.Michel-Mont-Mercure
Pouzauges
La Meilleraie-Tillay
Bressuire
Thouars
Loudun
Angliers
Thurageau

Olonne-sur-Mer
Les Sables-d Olonne
Château-d Olonne
Talmont-Saint-Hilaire
Jard-sur-Mer
St.Vincent-sur-Jard
La Tranche-sur-Mer
L Aiguillon-sur-Mer
St.Clément-des-Baleines
Les Portes-en-Ré
Moutiers-sur-le-Lay
Vouvant
Mervent
Foussais-Payré
Fontenay-le-Comte
Luçon
Chaille-les-Marais
Maillezais
Maillé
Benet
Coulon
Arçais   Magné   Niort
Parthenay
Vasles   POITIERS
Poitou-Charentes
Pamproux   Château-Larcher
Bougon
La-Mothe-St.Héray
Gencay
Celles-sur-Belle   Chey   Couhé
Lezay

LA ROCHELLE
Rivedoux-Plage
La Rochelle
Aytré
St.Denis-d Oléron
La Brée-les-Bains
Dolus-d Oléron
Le Grand Village Plage
St.Trojan-les-Bains
Bourcefranc
Marennes
Nieulle-sur-Seudre
Châtelaillon-Plage
Fouras
Port-des-Barques
Rochefort
Soubise   Tonnay-Charente
Echillais
St.Agnant
St.Pochaire
Mauzé-sur-le-Mignon
St.Hilaire-la-Palud
St.Germain-de-Marencennes
Poitou-Charentes
Aulnay
St.Jean-d Angély
Le Château d Oléron
Hiers-Brouage
Chef-Boutonne
Sauzé-Vaussais
Londigny
Ruffec
Aigre
Cellefrouin

Les Mathes/La Palmyre
Saujon
Le Verdon-sur-Mer
Soulac-sur-Mer
Meschers-sur-Gironde
Mortagne-sur-Gironde
St.Génis-de-Saintonge
Montalivet-les-Bains
Valeyrac
Aquitaine
Jonzac
Pons
Saintes
Saint Césaire
Cherves-Richemont
Cognac
Genté   Segonzac
Criteuil la Magdeleine
Rouillac
St.Yrieix-sur-Charente
Nersac
La Couronne
Varaignes
Le Pont d Agris

A   12km   B   28   C   D

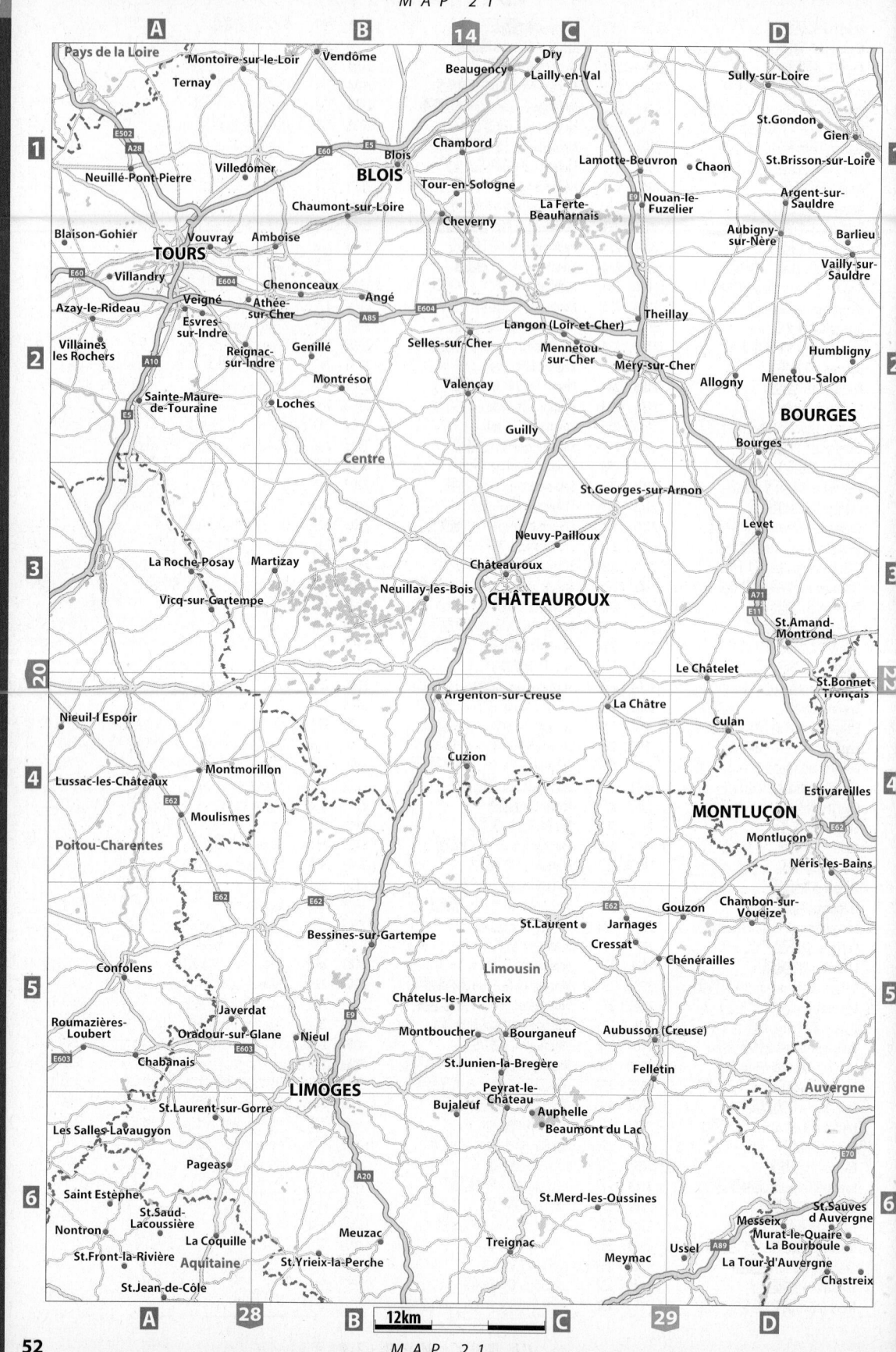

Pays de la Loire
Montoire-sur-le-Loir
Vendôme
Beaugency
Dry
Lailly-en-Val
Sully-sur-Loire
Ternay
St.Gondon
Gien
St.Brisson-sur-Loire
E502
A28
Chambord
Lamotte-Beuvron
Chaon
Villedômer
Blois
BLOIS
Tour-en-Sologne
La Ferte-Beauharnais
Nouan-le-Fuzelier
Argent-sur-Sauldre
Neuillé-Pont-Pierre
Chaumont-sur-Loire
Cheverny
E9
Aubigny-sur-Nère
Barlieu
Blaison-Gohier
Vouvray
Amboise
TOURS
Villandry
Chenonceaux
Angé
Vailly-sur-Sauldre
E60
E604
Athée-sur-Cher
E604
Theillay
Humbligny
Azay-le-Rideau
Veigné
Langon (Loir-et-Cher)
Mennetou-sur-Cher
Menetou-Salon
Esvres-sur-Indre
Selles-sur-Cher
Méry-sur-Cher
Allogny
Villaines-les-Rochers
A10
Reignac-sur-Indre
Genillé
Valençay
BOURGES
Sainte-Maure-de-Touraine
Montrésor
Loches
Bourges
E5
Guilly
Centre
St.Georges-sur-Arnon
Levet
Neuvy-Pailloux
La Roche-Posay
Martizay
Châteauroux
A71
Vicq-sur-Gartempe
Neuillay-les-Bois
CHÂTEAUROUX
E11
St.Amand-Montrond
20
Le Châtelet
St.Bonnet-Tronçais
22
Argenton-sur-Creuse
La Châtre
Culan
Nieuil-l'Espoir
Cuzion
Montmorillon
Estivareilles
Lussac-les-Châteaux
E62
MONTLUÇON
Moulismes
Montluçon
E62
Poitou-Charentes
Néris-les-Bains
E62
E62
Gouzon
Chambon-sur-Voueize
St.Laurent
Jarnages
Bessines-sur-Gartempe
Cressat
Chénérailles
Confolens
Limousin
Roumazières-Loubert
Châtelus-le-Marcheix
Javerdat
E9
Oradour-sur-Glane
Nieul
Montboucher
Bourganeuf
Aubusson (Creuse)
E603
Chabanais
E603
St.Junien-la-Bregère
Felletin
LIMOGES
Peyrat-le-Château
Auvergne
St.Laurent-sur-Gorre
Bujaleuf
Auphelle
Les Salles-Lavaugyon
Beaumont du Lac
Pageas
E70
A20
Saint Estèphe
St.Merd-les-Oussines
St.Sauves d'Auvergne
St.Saud-Lacoussière
Messeix
Murat-le-Quaire
Nontron
Meuzac
La Bourboule
La Coquille
Treignac
Ussel
A89
St.Front-la-Rivière
Meymac
La Tour-d'Auvergne
Aquitaine
St.Yrieix-la-Perche
Chastreix
St.Jean-de-Côle

28
12km
29

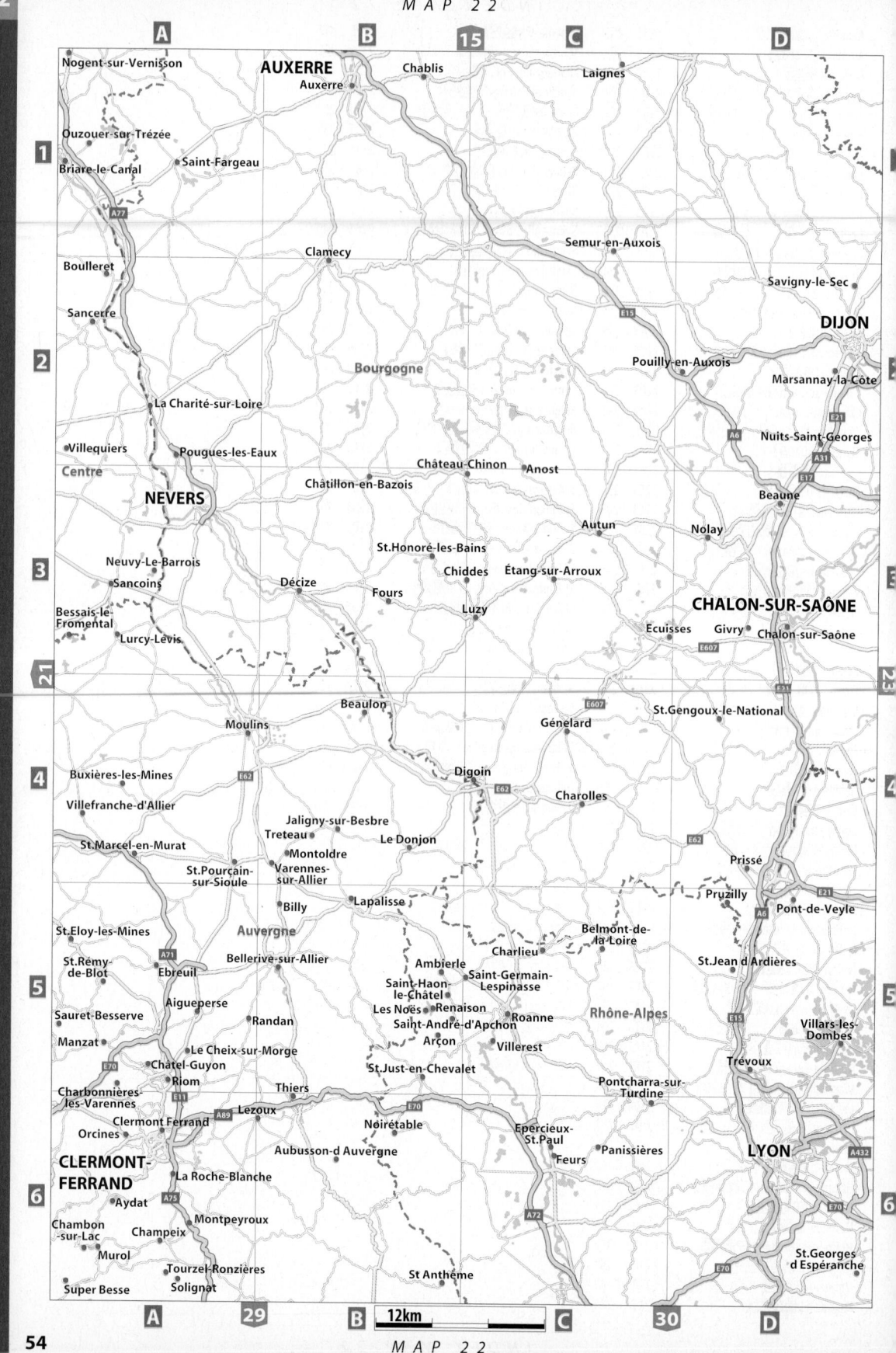

A   B   **15**   C   D

Nogent-sur-Vernisson

AUXERRE
Auxerre
Chablis
Laignes

1
Ouzouer-sur-Trézée
Saint-Fargeau
Briare-le-Canal
A77

Boulleret
Semur-en-Auxois
Savigny-le-Sec

Sancerre
E15
DIJON

Clamecy
Pouilly-en-Auxois
Marsannay-la-Côte

2
Bourgogne
A6
Nuits-Saint-Georges
A31

La Charité-sur-Loire
E17

Villequiers
Château-Chinon
Anost
Beaune

Centre
Pougues-les-Eaux
Châtillon-en-Bazois

NEVERS
Autun
Nolay

St.Honoré-les-Bains
Étang-sur-Arroux
CHALON-SUR-SAÔNE

3
Neuvy-Le-Barrois
Chiddes

Sancoins
Décize
Fours
Luzy
Écuisses   Givry   Chalon-sur-Saône

Bessais-le-Fromental
E607

Lurcy-Lévis

21
23

Beaulon
E607
St.Gengoux-le-National

Moulins
Génelard

4
Buxières-les-Mines
E62
Digoin
Charolles

Villefranche-d'Allier
E62

St.Marcel-en-Murat
Jaligny-sur-Besbre
E62
Prissé

Treteau
Le Donjon

St.Pourçain-sur-Sioule
Montoldre
Pruzilly
E21

Varennes-sur-Allier
Pont-de-Veyle

Billy
Lapalisse
A6

St.Eloy-les-Mines
Belmont-de-la-Loire

A71
Charlieu
St.Jean d'Ardières

5
St.Rémy-de-Blot
Bellerive-sur-Allier
Ambierle
Rhône-Alpes
E15

Ebreuil
Saint-Germain-Lespinasse

Sauret-Besserve
Aigueperse
Randan
Saint-Haon-le-Châtel
Villars-les-Dombes

Manzat
Les Noës   Renaison
Roanne

Le Cheix-sur-Morge
Saint-André-d'Apchon
Trévoux

E70
Chatel-Guyon
Arçon
Villerest

Charbonnières-les-Varennes
Riom
St.Just-en-Chevalet

E11
Lezoux
Pontcharra-sur-Turdine

Orcines
A89
Thiers
E70

Clermont Ferrand
Noirétable
LYON

CLERMONT-FERRAND
A432

6
Aydat
A75
Épercieux-St.Paul
Panissières
E70

Chambon-sur-Lac
La Roche-Blanche
Aubusson-d'Auvergne
Feurs

Champeix
Montpeyroux
A72

Murol
St.Georges d'Espéranche

Super Besse
Solignat
St Anthème
E70

A   **29**   B   12km   C   **30**   D

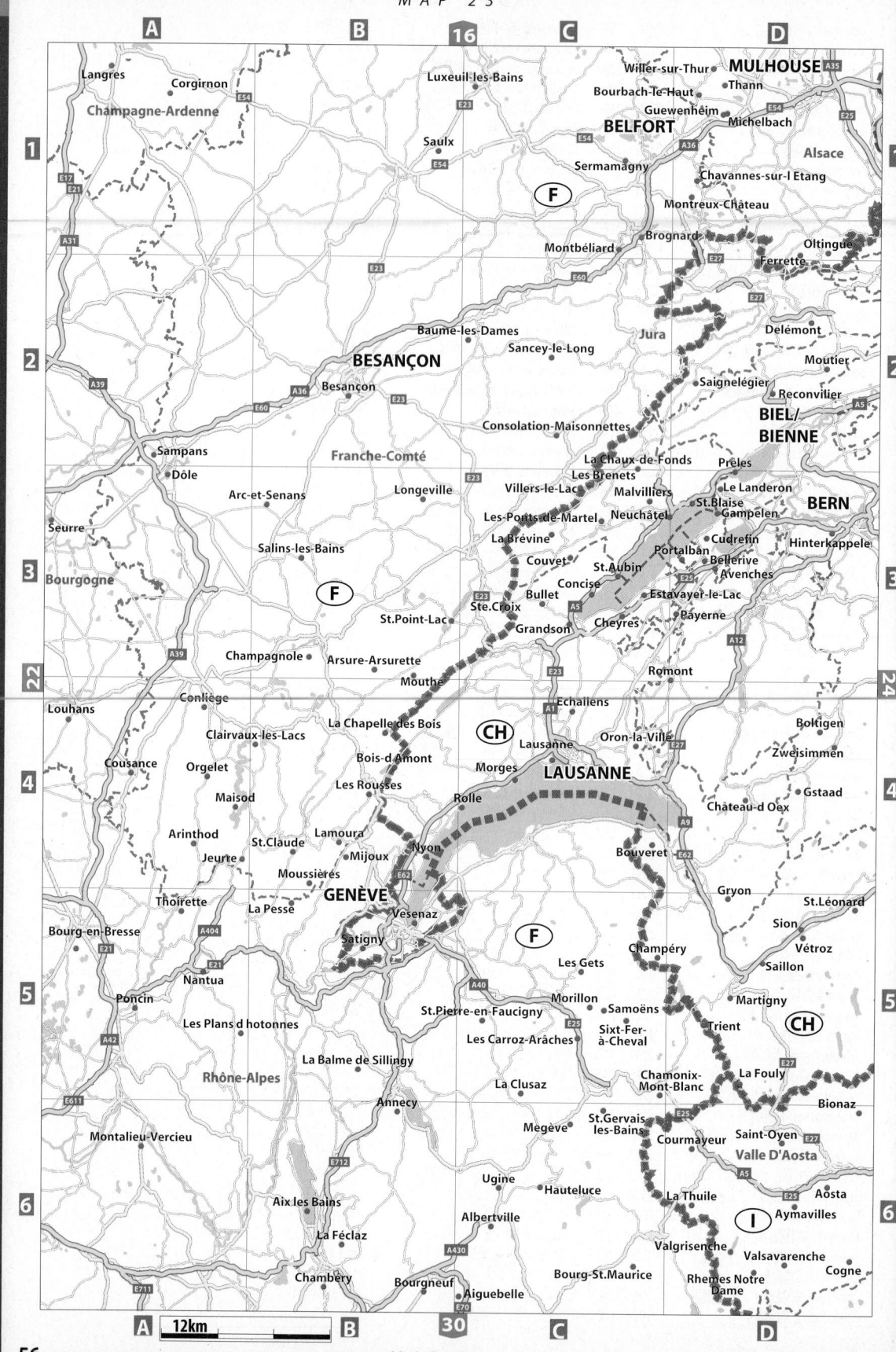

Langres
Corgirnon
Champagne-Ardenne
E54

Luxeuil-les-Bains

Willer-sur-Thur
Bourbach-Te-Haut
Guewenhéim
MULHOUSE A35
Thann
Michelbach

BELFORT
E54

E23

Saulx
E54

Sermamagny

F

Chavannes-sur-l Etang
Montreux-Château

Alsace
E25

E17
E21

E23

E60

Brognard

Montbéliard

Jura

Oltingue
Ferrette
E27

Delémont

Moutier

Baume-les-Dames
Sancey-le-Long

BESANÇON

A39

Besançon
E23
A36
E60

Saignelégier

Reconvilier
A5

**BIEL/
BIENNE**

Consolation-Maisonnettes

Prêles

Franche-Comté

La Chaux-de-Fonds
Les Brenets

Le Landeron
St.Blaise
Gampelen

BERN

Sampans
Dôle

Arc-et-Senans

Longeville
E23

Villers-le-Lac
Les-Ponts-de-Martel
Malvilliers
Neuchâtel

Cudrefin
Portalban
Bellerive
Avenches

Hinterkappele

Seurre
A31

Bourgogne

Salins-les-Bains

La Brévine
Couvet
St.Aubin
Concise
E25

Estavayer-le-Lac
Payerne

A39

Champagnole
Arsure-Arsurette

St.Point-Lac

F

Ste.Croix
Bullet

Grandson

Cheyres

A12

Romont

22

Conliège

Mouthe

E23

Echallens

24

Louhans

Clairvaux-les-Lacs

La Chapelle des Bois

A1

Lausanne

Oron-la-Ville
E27

Boltigen

Zweisimmen

Orgelet
Maisod

Bois-d Amont

Morges

LAUSANNE

Rolle

Château-d Oex

Gstaad

Cousance

Les Rousses

A9

Arinthod
Jeurte

St.Claude

Lamoura
Mijoux

Moussières

CH

Nyon

Bouveret
E62

Gryon

St.Léonard

Sion
Vétroz
Saillon

Thoirette

La Pesse
A404

GENÈVE
Vesenaz
E62

F

Champéry

Martigny

CH

Bourg-en-Bresse
E21

Satigny

Les Gets

La Fouly
E27

Nantua
E21

Poncin

Les Plans d hotonnes

A40

St-Pierre-en-Faucigny
Morillon
Les Carroz-Arâches
E25

Samoëns
Sixt-Fer-
à-Cheval

Trient

Bionaz

A42

La Balme de Sillingy

La Clusaz

Chamonix-
Mont-Blanc

Valle D'Aosta

Montalieu-Vercieu

Rhône-Alpes

Annecy

Megève

St.Gervais
les-Bains
E25

Courmayeur

Saint-Oyen
E27

Aosta

E611

Ugine
Hauteluce

La Thuile
A5

I

Aymavilles

E712

Aix les Bains

La Féclaz

Albertville

A430

Bourgneuf

Aiguebelle
E70

Bourg-St-Maurice

Valgrisenche

La Thuile

Rhemes Notre
Dame

Valsavarenche

Cogne

E711

Chambéry

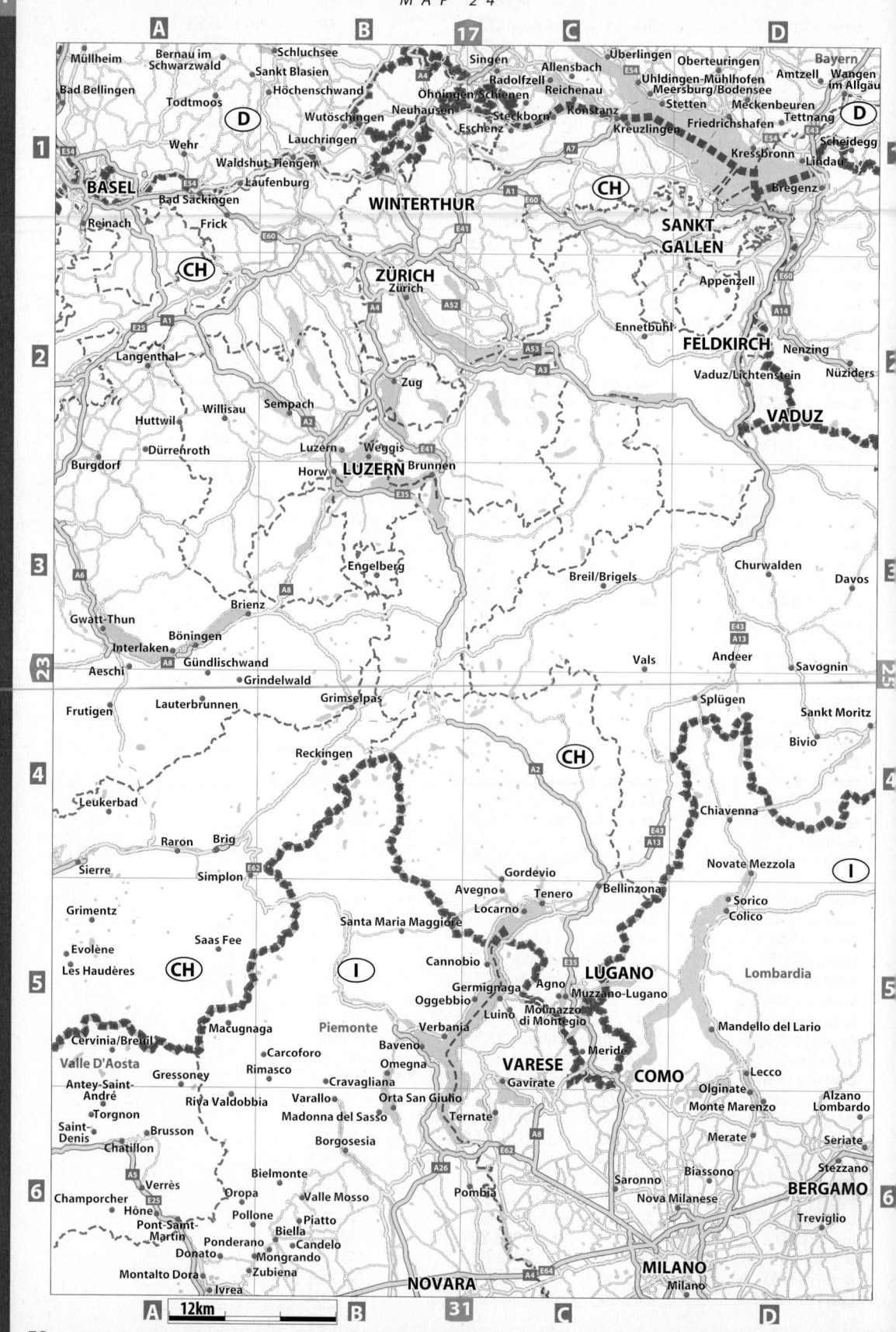

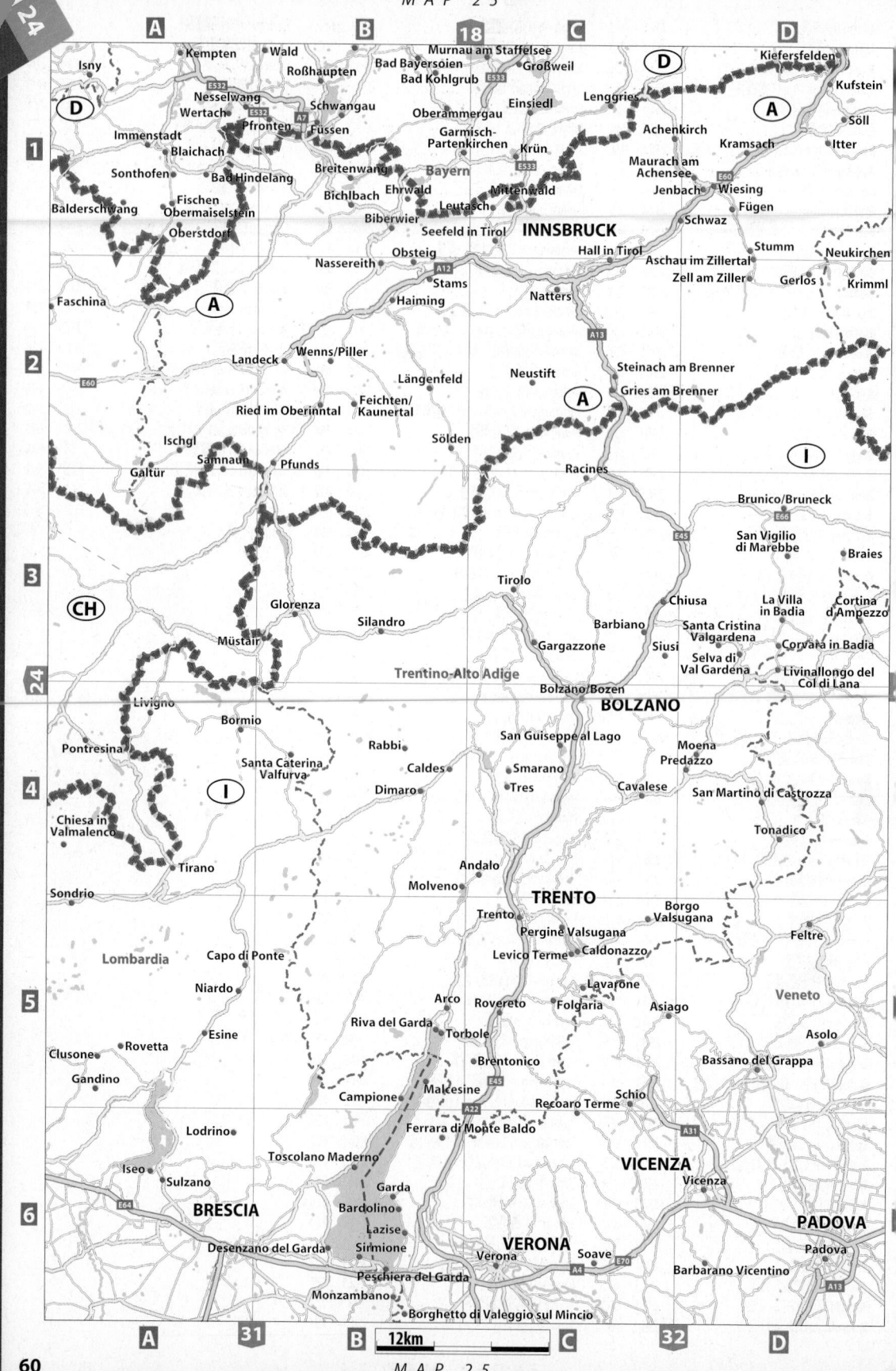

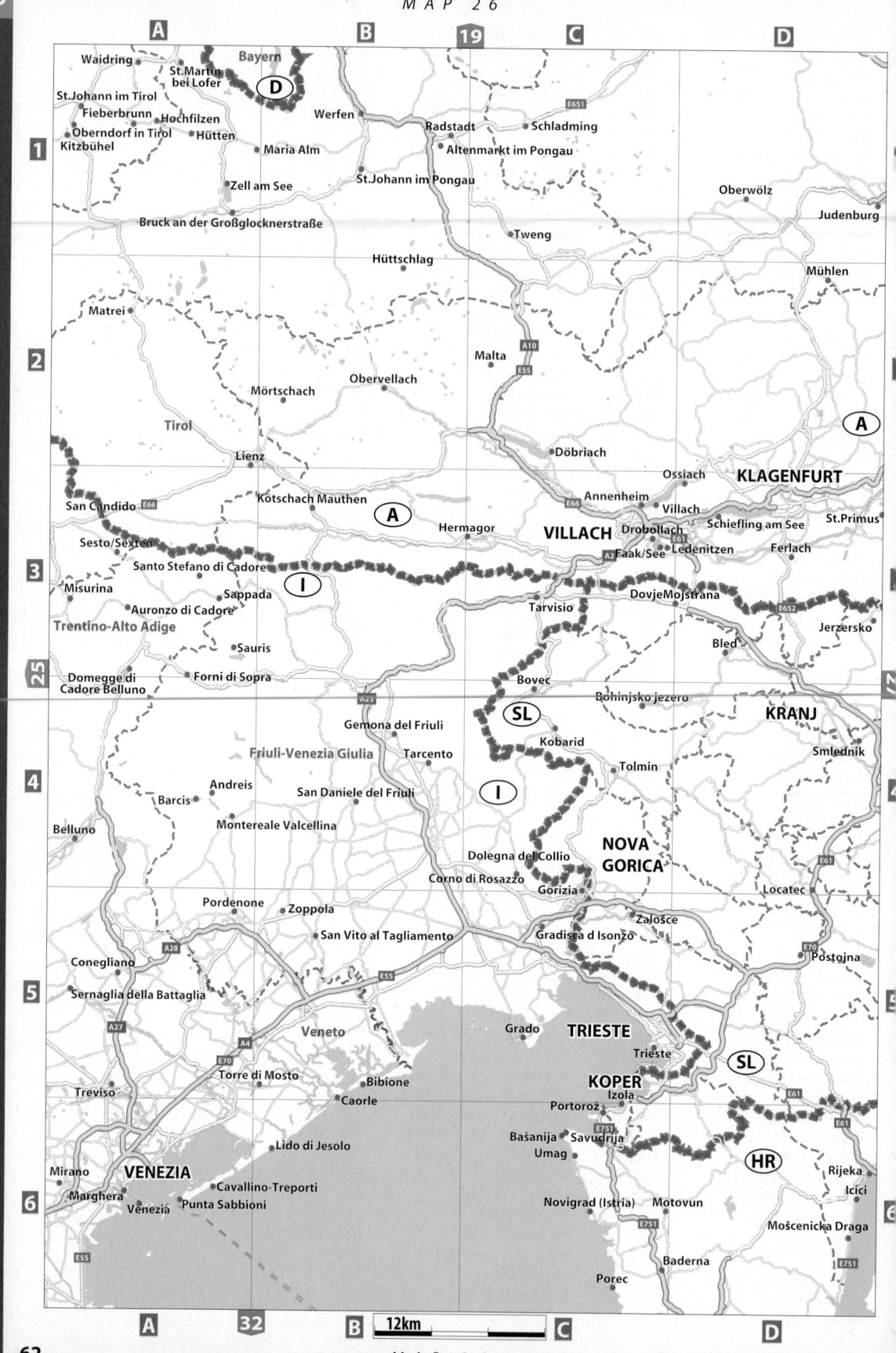

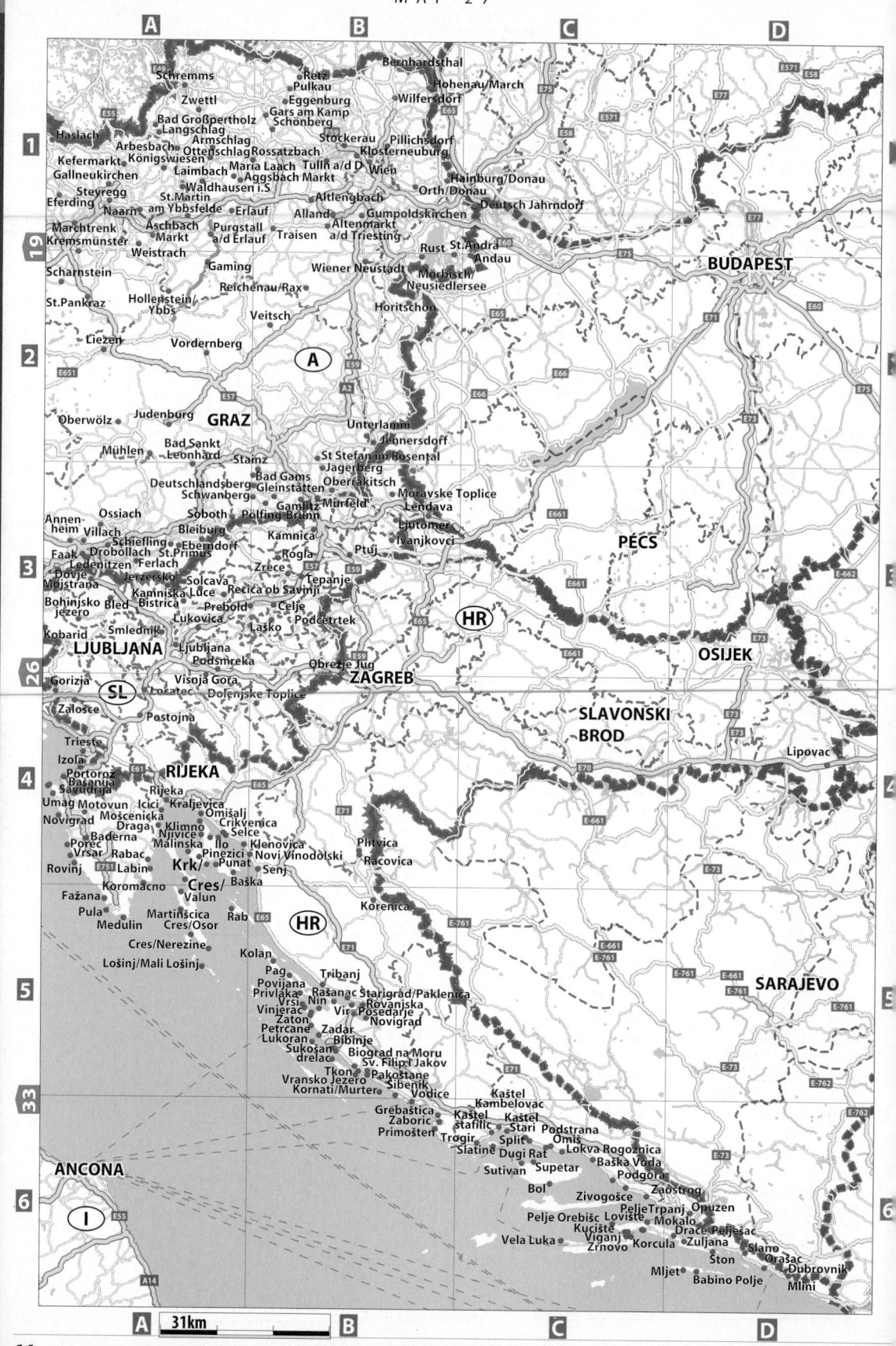

Place	Ref
Aggsbach Markt (AT)	27A1 700
Alland (AT)	27B1 700
Altenmarkt/ T(AT)	27B1 700
Altlengbach (AT)	27B1 700
Ancona (IT)	27A6 773
Andau (AT)	27C2 704
Annenheim (AT)	27A3 704
Arbesbach (AT)	27A1 700
Armschlag (AT)	27A1 700
Aschbach Markt (AT)	27A1 700
Babino Polje (HR)	27D6 816
Bad Gams (AT)	27B3 704
Bad Großpertholz (AT)	27A1 700
Bad Sankt Leonhard (AT)	27A3 704
Baderna (HR)	27A4 813
Bašanija (HR)	27A4 813
Baška Voda (HR)	27C6 816
Bernhardsthal (AT)	27B1 700
Bibinje (HR)	27B5 816
Biograd na Moru (HR)	27B5 816
Bled (SL)	27A3 808
Bleiburg (AT)	27A3 704
Bol (HR)	27C6 816
Castelfidardo (IT)	27A6 774
Celje (SL)	27B3 809
Cres/Cres (HR)	27A4 813
Cres/Martinščica (HR)	27A5 813
Cres/Nerezine (HR)	27A5 813
Cres/Osor (HR)	27A5 813
Cres/Valun (HR)	27A5 813
Crikvenica (HR)	27A4 813
Deutsch Jahrndorf (AT)	27C1 700
Deutschlandsberg (AT)	27B3 705
Dolenjske Toplice (SL)	27B4 809
Drace-Pelješac (HR)	27D6 816
Dubrovnik (HR)	27D6 816
Dugi Rat (HR)	27C6 816
Eberndorf (AT)	27A3 705
Eferding (AT)	27A1 700
Eggenburg (AT)	27B1 700
Erlauf (AT)	27A1 701
Faak/See (AT)	27A3 705
Fažana (HR)	27A5 813
Ferlach (AT)	27A3 705
Gallneukirchen (AT)	27A1 701
Gaming (AT)	27A2 701
Gamlitz (AT)	27B3 705
Gars am Kamp (AT)	27B1 701
Gleinstätten (AT)	27B3 705
Gorizia (IT)	27A4 743
Grebaštica (HR)	27B6 816
Gumpoldskirchen (AT)	27B1 701
Hainburg/Donau (AT)	27B1 701
Haslach (AT)	27A1 701
Hohenau/March (AT)	27B1 701
Hollenstein/Ybbs (AT)	27A2 701
Horitschon (AT)	27B2 705
Ičići (HR)	27A4 813
Ivanjkovci (SL)	27B3 809
Izola (SL)	27A4 808
Jagerberg (AT)	27B3 705
Jennersdorf (AT)	27B2 705
Jerzersko (SL)	27A3 808
Judenburg (AT)	27A2 705
Kamnica (SL)	27B3 809
Kamniška Bistrica (SL)	27A3 808
Kaštel Kambelovac (HR)	27C6 816
Kaštel Štafilic (HR)	27C6 816
Kaštel Stari (HR)	27C6 816
Kefermarkt (AT)	27A1 701
Klenovica (HR)	27A4 813
Klosterneuburg (AT)	27B1 701
Kobarid (SL)	27A3 808
Kolan (HR)	27B5 816
Königswiesen (AT)	27A1 701
Korčula (HR)	27C6 816
Korenica (HR)	27B5 816
Kornati/Murter (HR)	27B5 816
Koromačno (HR)	27A4 813
Kraljevica (HR)	27A4 813
Kremsmünster (AT)	27A1 701
Krk/Baška (HR)	27A4 813
Krk/Klimno (HR)	27A4 813
Krk/Krk (HR)	27A4 813
Krk/Malinska (HR)	27A4 813
Krk/Njivice (HR)	27A4 813
Krk/Omišalj (HR)	27A4 813
Krk/Pinezici (HR)	27A5 813
Krk/Punat (HR)	27A4 813
Krk/Šilo (HR)	27A4 813
Kucište (HR)	27C6 816
Labin (HR)	27A4 813
Laimbach am O (AT)	27A1 701
Langschlag-M (AT)	27A1 701
Laško (SL)	27B3 809
Lendava (SL)	27B3 810
Liezen (AT)	27A2 706
Lipovac (HR)	27D4 819
Ljubljana (SL)	27A3 808
Ljutomer (SL)	27B3 810
Locatec (SL)	27A4 808
Lokva Rogoznica (HR)	27C6 817
Loreto (IT)	27A6 777
Lošinj/Mali Lošinj (HR)	27A5 813
Lovište (HR)	27C6 817
Luče (SL)	27A3 809
Lukoran (HR)	27B5 817
Lukovica (SL)	27A3 809
Marchtrenk (AT)	27A1 701
Maria Laach (AT)	27A1 701
Marina di M (IT)	27A6 777
Medulin (HR)	27A5 814
Mlini (HR)	27D6 817
Mljet (HR)	27D6 817
Mokalo (HR)	27C6 817
Moravske Toplice (SL)	27B3 810
Mörbisch/N (AT)	27B2 706
Moščenička Draga (HR)	27A4 814
Motovun (HR)	27A4 822
Mühlen (AT)	27A2 706
Murfeld (AT)	27B3 706
Naarn (AT)	27A1 702
Nin (HR)	27B5 817
Novi Vinodolski (HR)	27B4 814
Novigrad (Dalmatia) (HR)	27B5 817
Oberrakitsch (AT)	27B3 706
Oberwölz (AT)	27A2 706
Obrežje Jug (SL)	27B3 810
Omiš (HR)	27C6 817
Opuzen (HR)	27D6 817
Orašac (HR)	27D6 817
Orth/Donau (AT)	27B1 702
Ottenschlag (AT)	27A1 702
Pag (HR)	27B5 817
Pakoštane (HR)	27B5 817
Pelješac/Orebić (HR)	27C6 817
Pelješac/Trpanj (HR)	27C6 817
Petrcane (HR)	27B5 817
Pillichsdorf (AT)	27B1 702
Plitvička (HR)	27B4 819
Podčetrtek (SL)	27B3 810
Podgora (HR)	27C6 817
Podmreka (SL)	27A3 810
Podstrana (HR)	27C6 817
Pölfing-Brunn (AT)	27B3 707
Poreč (HR)	27A4 814
Porto Recanati (IT)	27A6 780
Portorož (SL)	27A4 809
Posedarje (HR)	27B5 817
Postojna (SL)	27A4 809
Potenza Picena (IT)	27A6 780
Povijana (HR)	27B5 817
Prebold (SL)	27B3 810
Primošten (HR)	27B6 817
Privlaka (HR)	27B5 817
Ptuj (SL)	27B3 810
Pula (HR)	27A5 814
Pulkau (AT)	27B1 702
Purgstall an der Erlauf (AT)	27A1 702
Rab (HR)	27A5 815
Rabac (HR)	27A4 815
Racovica (HR)	27B4 820
Ražanac (HR)	27B5 817
Recanati (IT)	27A6 780
Rečica ob Savinji (SL)	27A3 810
Reichenau/Rax (AT)	27B2 702
Rijeka (HR)	27A4 815
Retz (AT)	27B1 703
Rogla (SL)	27B3 810
Rossatzbach (AT)	27A1 703
Rovanjska (HR)	27B5 818
Rovinj (HR)	27A4 815
Rust (DE)	27B2 635
Savudrija (HR)	27A4 815
Scharnstein (AT)	27A2 703
Schiefling am See (AT)	27A3 707
Schönberg (AT)	27B1 703
Schremms (AT)	27A1 703
Schwanberg (AT)	27B3 707
Selce (HR)	27A4 815
Senj (HR)	27B4 818
Šibenik (HR)	27B5 818
Slano (HR)	27D6 818
Slatine (HR)	27C6 818
Smlednik (SL)	27A3 809
Soboth (AT)	27A3 707
Solcava (SL)	27A3 810
Split (HR)	27C6 818
St Stefan im R (AT)	27B2 707
St.Andrä (AT)	27B2 707
St.Martin am Y (AT)	27A1 703
St.Pankraz (AT)	27A2 703
St.Primus (AT)	27A3 707
Stainz (AT)	27B3 707
Starigrad/P (HR)	27B5 818
Steyregg (AT)	27A1 703
Stockerau (AT)	27B1 703
Ston (HR)	27D6 818
Sukošan (HR)	27B5 818
Supetar (HR)	27C6 818
Sutivan (HR)	27C6 819
Sv. Filip I Jakov (HR)	27B5 819
Tepanje (SL)	27B3 810
Tkon (HR)	27B5 819
Traisen (AT)	27B1 703
Tribanj (HR)	27B5 819
Trieste (IT)	27A4 744
Trogir (HR)	27C6 819
Tulln an der Donau (AT)	27B1 703
Umag (HR)	27A4 815
Unterlamm (AT)	27B2 707
Veitsch (AT)	27B2 707
Vela Luka (HR)	27C6 819
Viganj (HR)	27C6 819
Villach (AT)	27A3 707
Vinjerac (HR)	27B5 819
Vir (HR)	27B5 819
Visnja Gora (SL)	27A4 818
Vodice (HR)	27B6 819
Vordernberg (AT)	27A2 707
Vransko Jezero (HR)	27B5 819
Vrsar (HR)	27A4 815
Vrsi (HR)	27B5 819
Waldhausen im S (AT)	27A1 703
Weistrach (AT)	27A1 703
Wien (Vienna) (AT)	27B1 703
Wiener Neustadt (AT)	27B2 704
Wilfersdorf (AT)	27B1 704
Zaboric (HR)	27B6 819
Zadar (HR)	27B5 819
Zalošce (SL)	27A4 809
Zaostrog (HR)	27C6 819
Zaton (HR)	27B5 819
Ždrelac (HR)	27B5 819
Živogošce (HR)	27C6 819
Zrece (SL)	27B3 811
Žrnovo (HR)	27C6 819
Žuljana (HR)	27D6 819
Zwettl (AT)	27A1 704

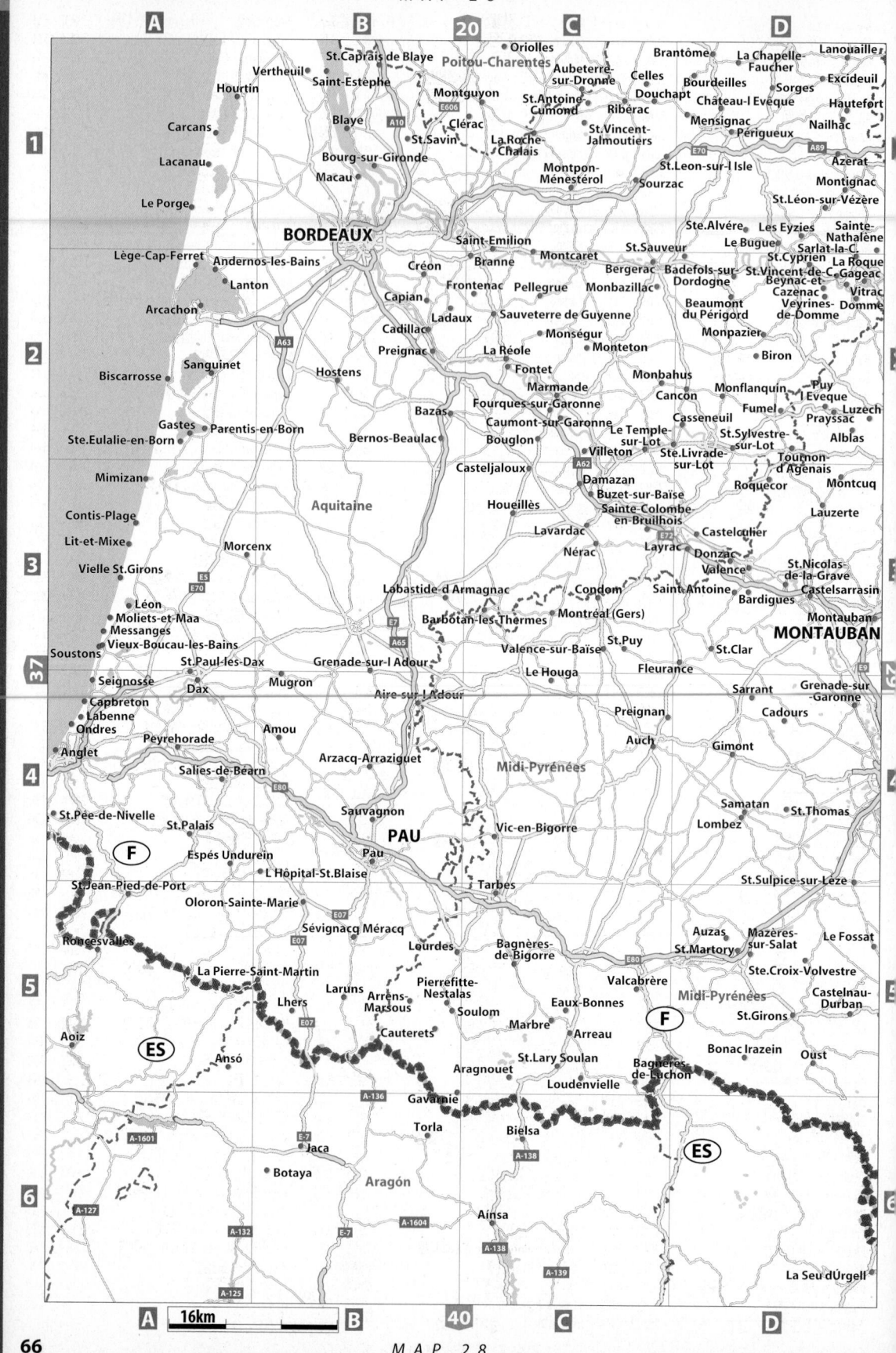

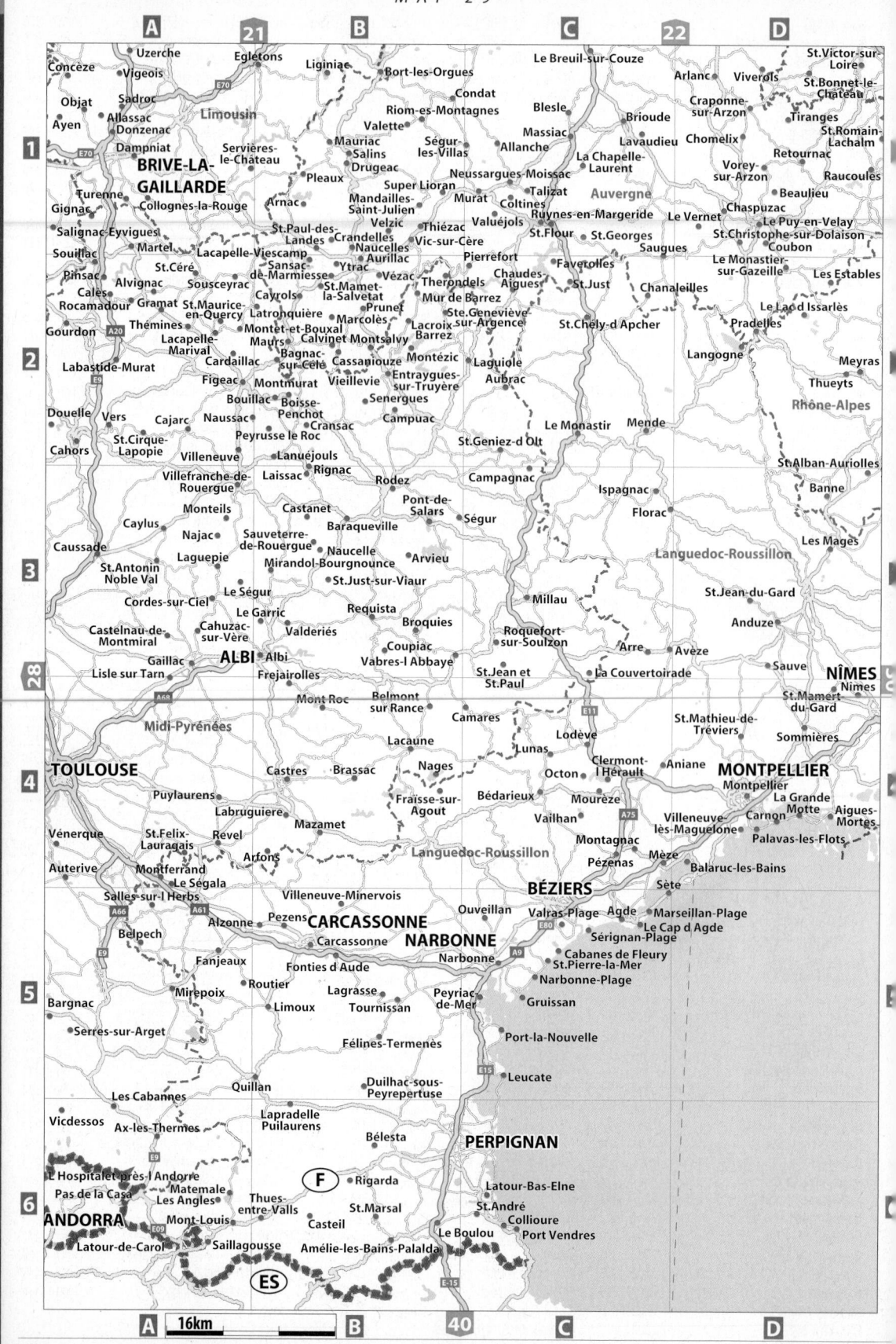

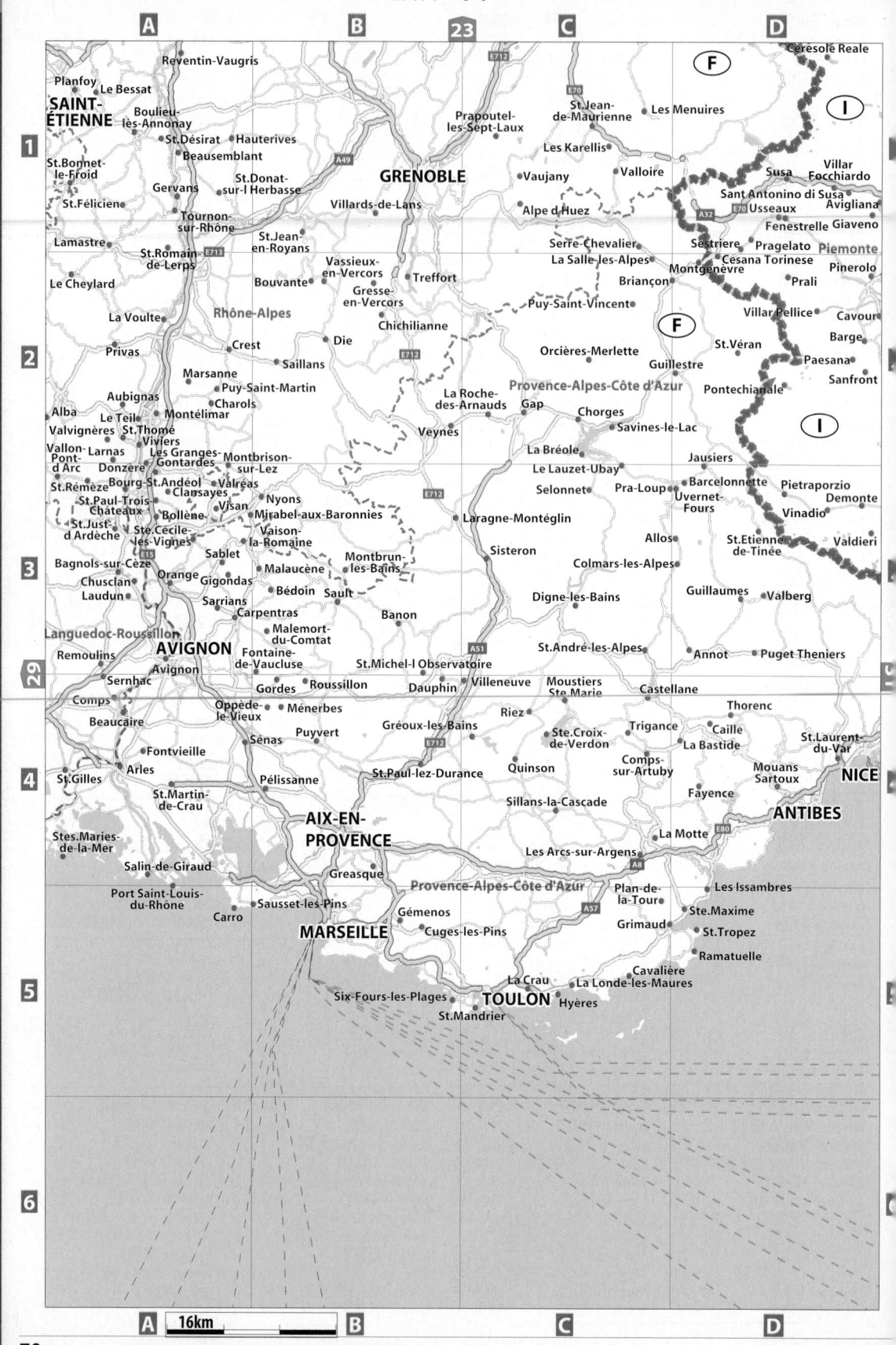

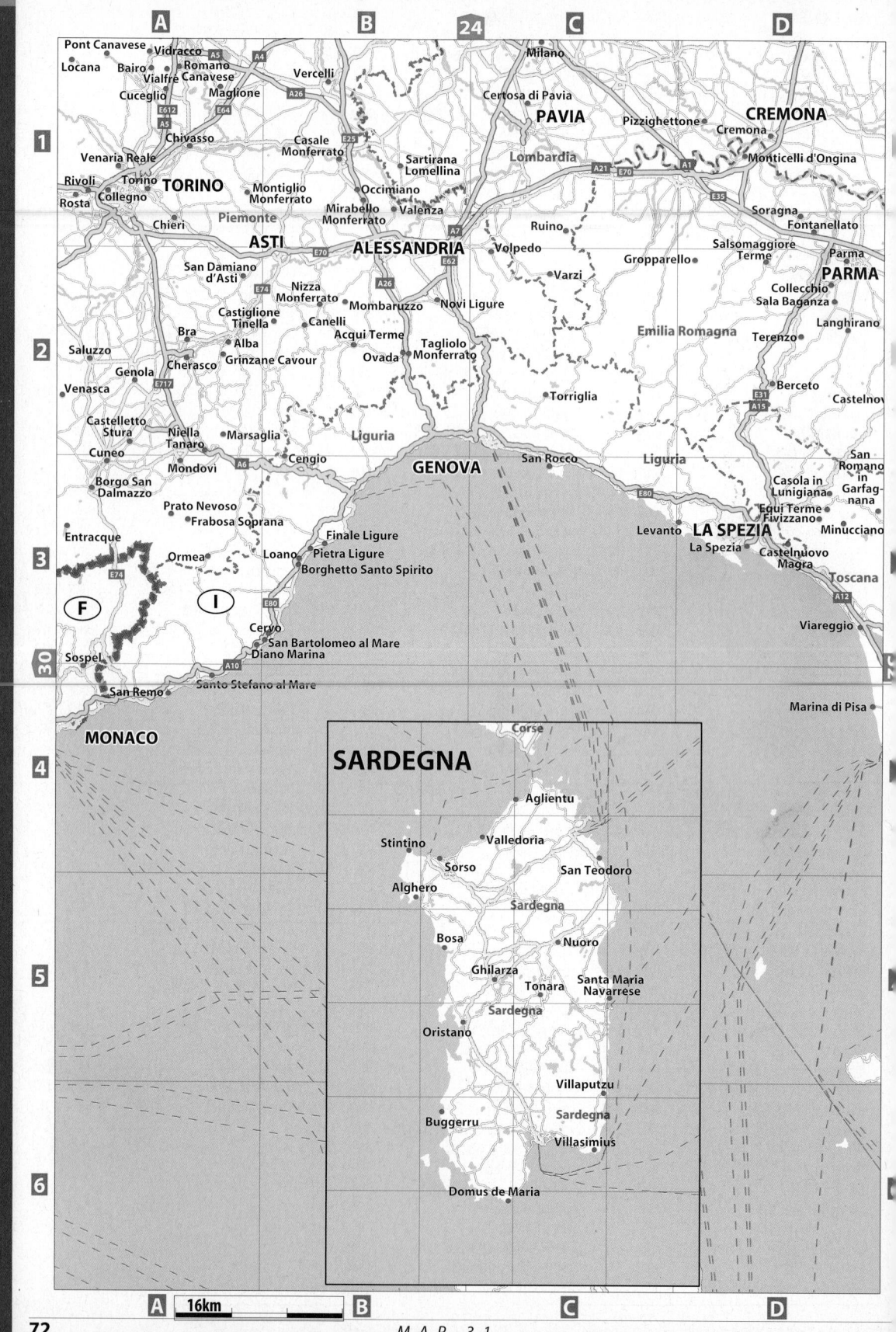

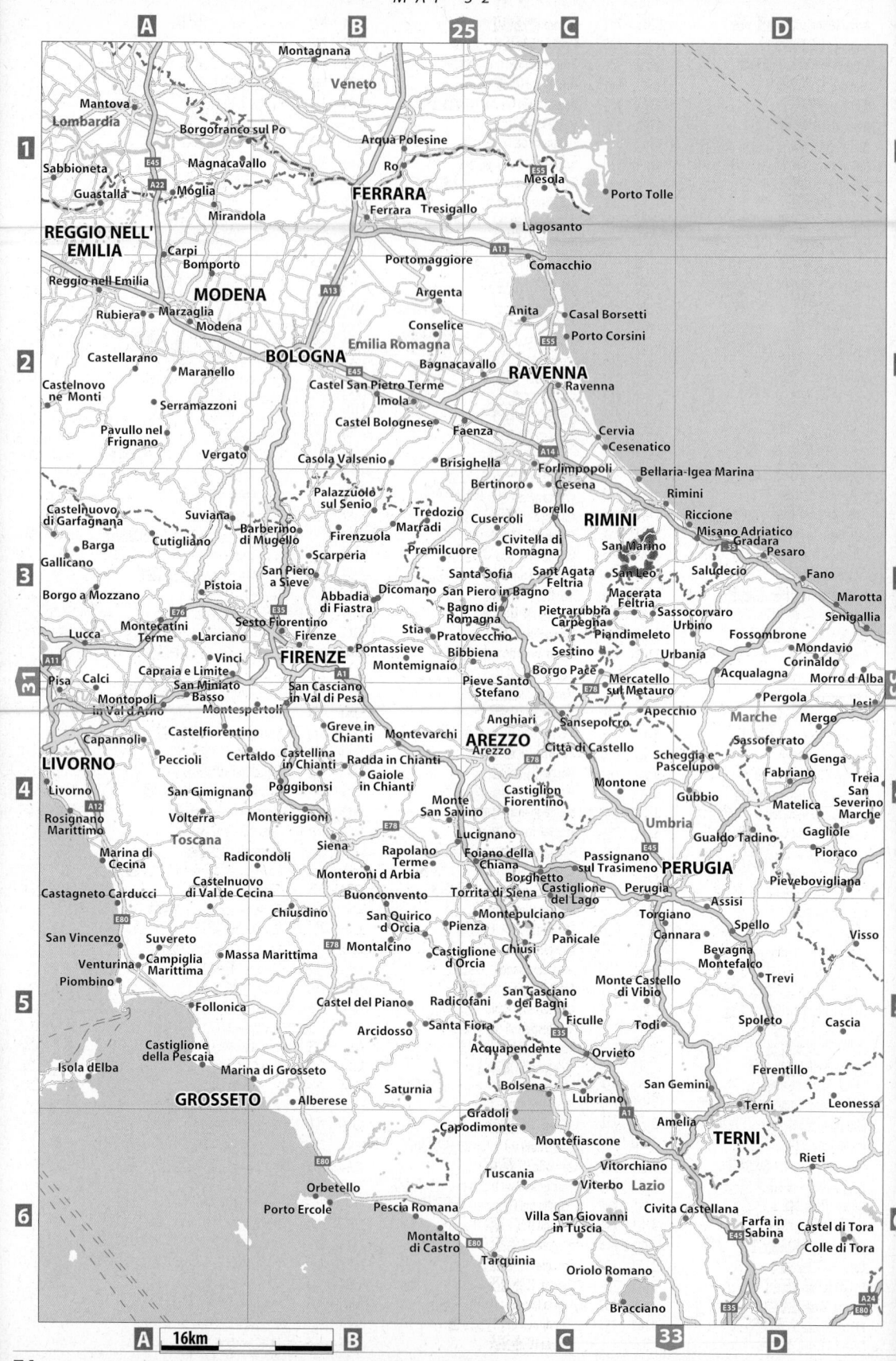

A   B   25   C   D

Montagnana

Veneto

Mantova
Lombardia
Borgofranco sul Po
Arquà Polesine
Sabbioneta
Magnacavallo
Ro
Mesola
Porto Tolle
Guastalla
Mòglia
Mirandola
Ferrara
Tresigallo
Lagosanto
FERRARA

REGGIO NELL'
EMILIA
Carpi
Bomporto
Portomaggiore
Comacchio
Reggio nell Emilia
MODENA
Argenta
Conselice
Anita
Casal Borsetti
Rubiera
Marzaglia
Modena
Emilia Romagna
Porto Corsini
Castellarano
Maranello
BOLOGNA
Bagnacavallo
RAVENNA
Castelnovo ne Monti
Serramazzoni
Castel San Pietro Terme
Ravenna
Imola
Pavullo nel Frignano
Castel Bolognese
Faenza
Cervia
Cesenatico
Vergato
Casola Valsenio
Brisighella
Forlimpopoli
Bellaria-Igea Marina
Castelnuovo di Garfagnana
Palazzuolo sul Senio
Bertinoro
Cesena
Rimini
Suviana
Tredozio
Cusercoli
Borello
RIMINI
Riccione
Barga
Cutigliano
Barberino di Mugello
Marradi
Misano Adriatico
Gradara
Gallicano
Firenzuola
Premilcuore
Civitella di Romagna
San Marino
Saludecio
Pesaro
Borgo a Mozzano
Scarperia
Santa Sofia
Sant'Agata Feltria
San Leo
Fano
Pistoia
San Piero a Sieve
San Piero in Bagno
Macerata Feltria
Marotta
Abbadia di Fiastra
Dicomano
Bagno di Romagna
Pietrarubbia
Sassocorvaro
Senigallia
Lucca
Montecatini Terme
Sesto Fiorentino
Stia
Pratovecchio
Carpegna
Piandimeleto
Urbino
Fossombrone
Larciano
Firenze
Pontassieve
Bibbiena
Sestino
Urbania
Mondavio
Corinaldo
Pisa
Calci
Vinci
FIRENZE
Montemignaio
Borgo Pace
Acqualagna
Morro d'Alba
Montopoli in Val d'Arno
Capraia e Limite
San Miniato Basso
San Casciano in Val di Pesa
Pieve Santo Stefano
Mercatello sul Metauro
Pergola
Jesi
Montespertoli
Anghiari
Sansepolcro
Apecchio
Marche
Mergo
Capannoli
Castelfiorentino
Greve in Chianti
Montevarchi
AREZZO
Città di Castello
Sassoferrato
LIVORNO
Peccioli
Certaldo
Castellina in Chianti
Radda in Chianti
Arezzo
Scheggia e Pascelupo
Genga
Livorno
San Gimignano
Poggibonsi
Gaiole in Chianti
Montone
Gubbio
Fabriano
Treia
San Severino Marche
Rosignano Marittimo
Volterra
Monteriggioni
Castiglion Fiorentino
Matelica
Gagliole
Toscana
Radicondoli
Siena
Monte San Savino
Umbria
Gualdo Tadino
Pioraco
Castagneto Carducci
Castelnuovo di Val de Cecina
Monteroni d'Arbia
Rapolano Terme
Lucignano
Foiano della Chiana
Passignano sul Trasimeno
PERUGIA
Pievebovigliana
Marina di Cecina
Chiusdino
Buonconvento
Borghetto
Castiglione del Lago
Perugia
Assisi
Visso
San Vincenzo
Suvereto
San Quirico d'Orcia
Pienza
Torrita di Siena
Montepulciano
Torgiano
Spello
Venturina
Campiglia Marittima
Massa Marittima
Montalcino
Chiusi
Panicale
Cannara
Bevagna
Montefalco
Trevi
Piombino
Castiglione d'Orcia
Monte Castello di Vibio
Follonica
Castel del Piano
Radicofani
San Casciano dei Bagni
Ficulle
Todi
Spoleto
Cascia
Arcidosso
Santa Fiora
Acquapendente
Orvieto
Castiglione della Pescaia
Isola d'Elba
Marina di Grosseto
Saturnia
Bolsena
San Gemini
Ferentillo
GROSSETO
Alberese
Gradoli
Capodimonte
Lubriano
Terni
Amelia
TERNI
Leonessa
Montefiascone
Rieti
Orbetello
Vitorchiano
Viterbo
Lazio
Porto Ercole
Pescia Romana
Tuscania
Civita Castellana
Farfa in Sabina
Castel di Tora
Montalto di Castro
Villa San Giovanni in Tuscia
Oriolo Romano
Colle di Tora
Tarquinia
Bracciano

A   16km   B   C   33   D

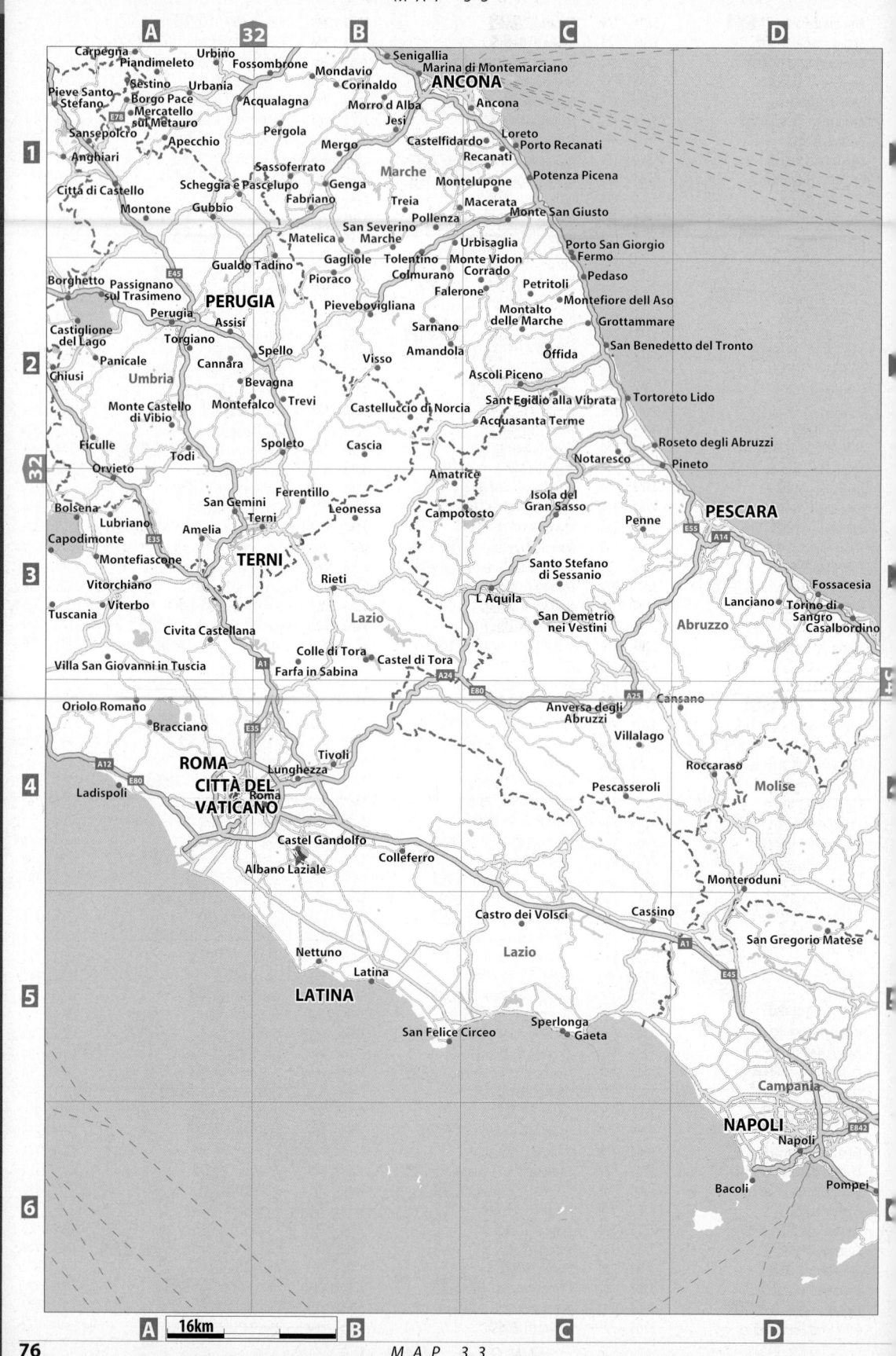

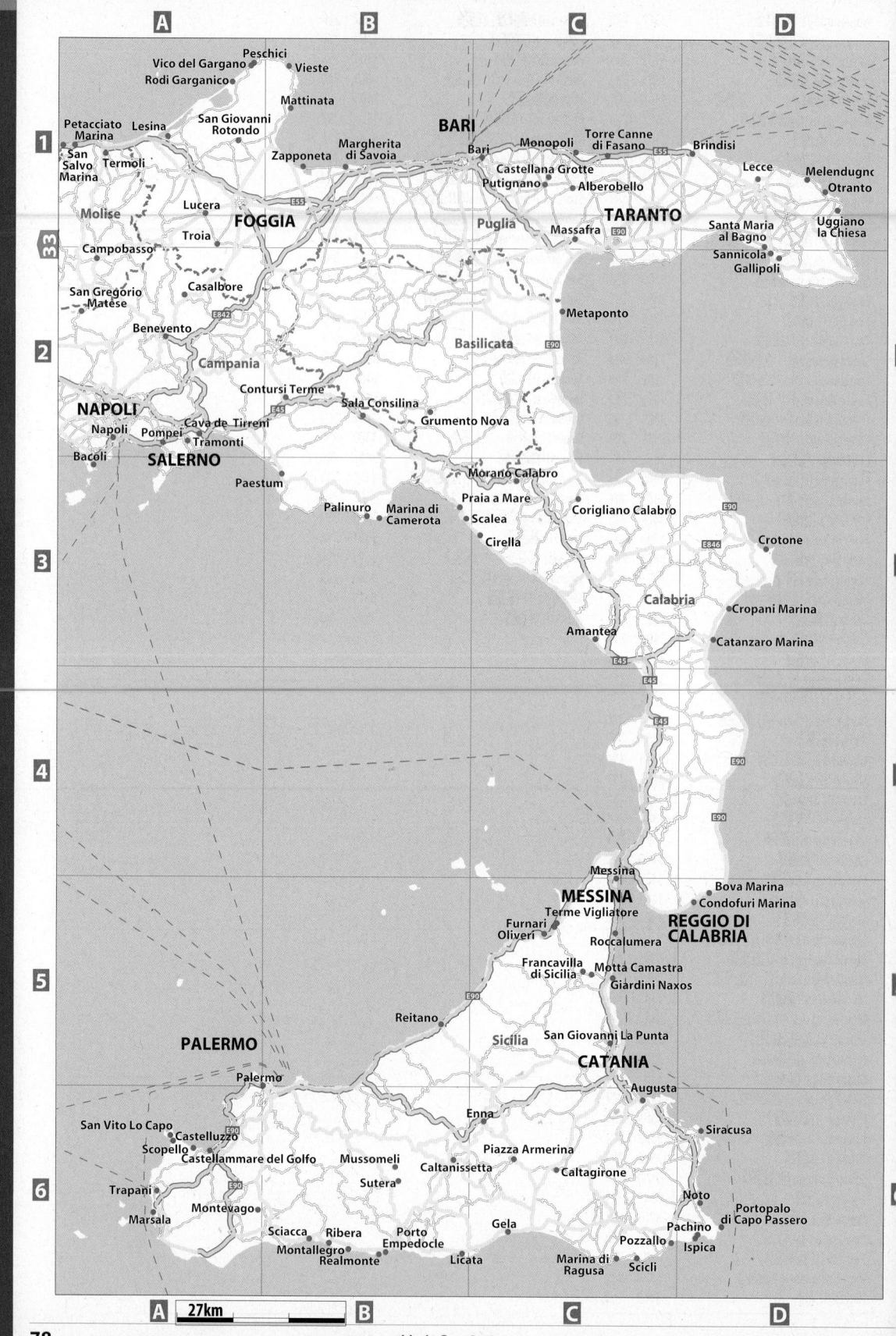

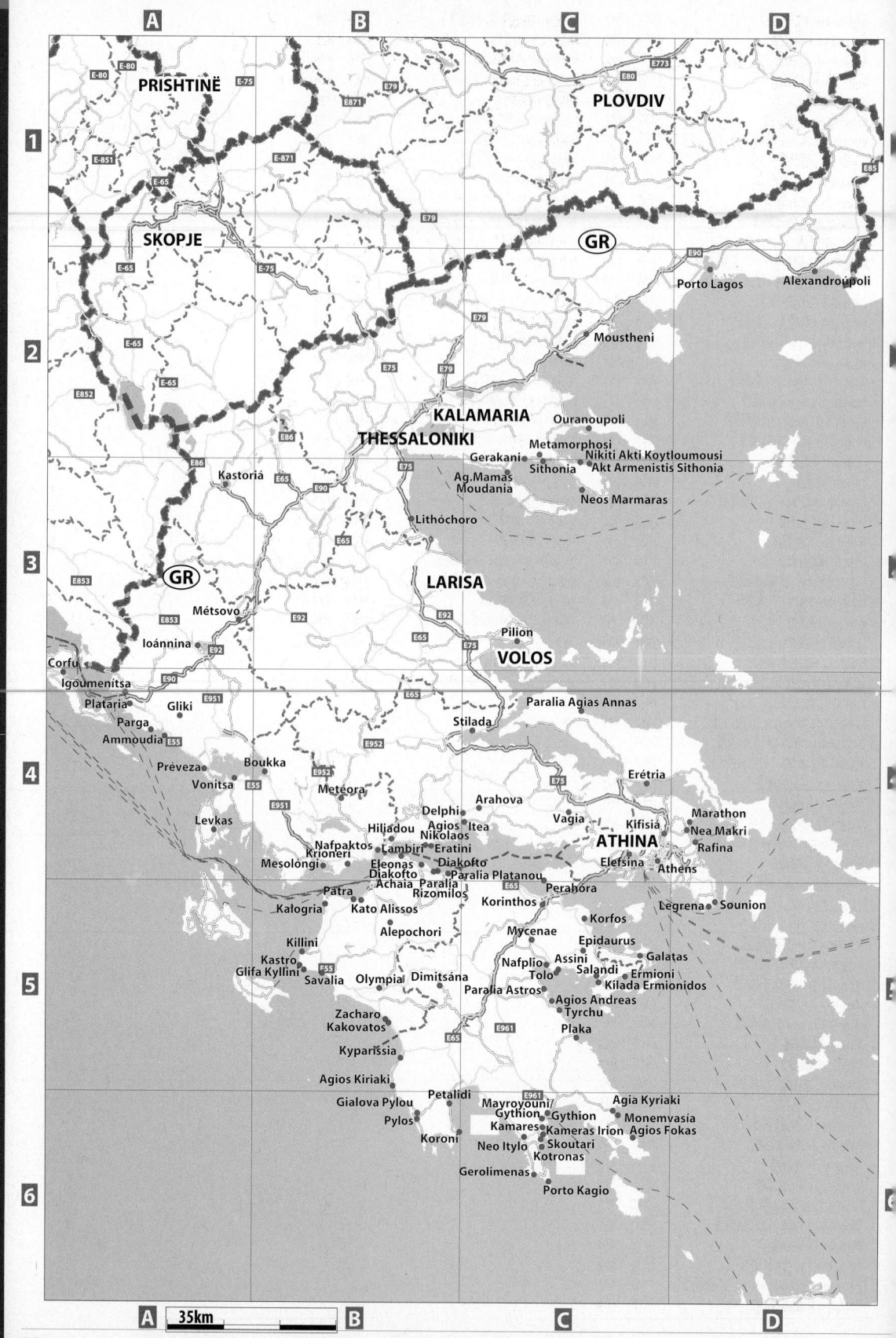

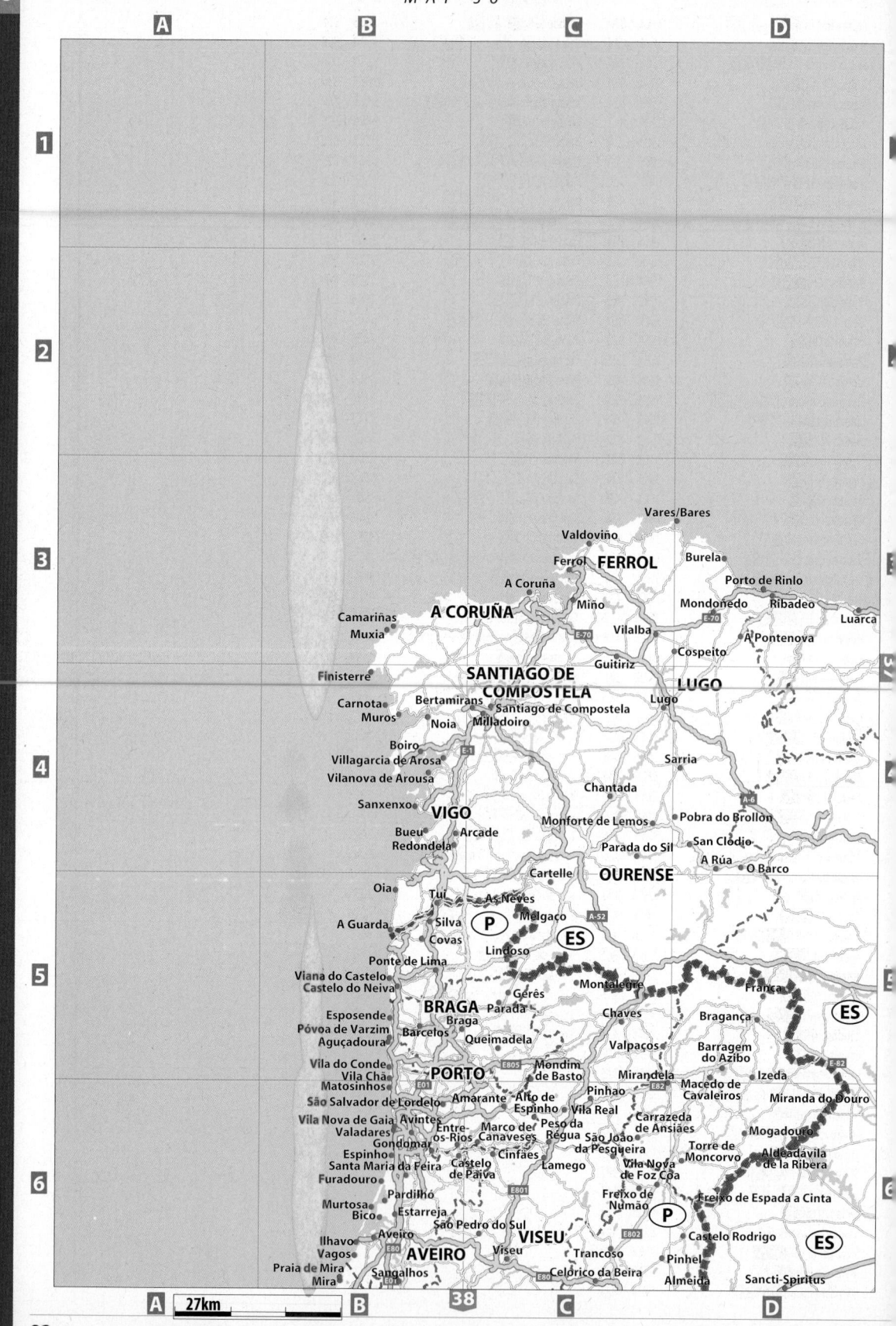

A   B   C   D

1

2

3

Vares/Bares

Valdoviño

Ferrol   FERROL   Burela

A Coruña   Porto de Rinlo

Camariñas   Miño   Mondoñedo   Ribadeo

Muxia   Vilalba   A Pontenova   Luarca

Cospeito

Guitiriz

Finisterre

SANTIAGO DE   LUGO

COMPOSTELA   Lugo

Carnota   Bertamirans   Santiago de Compostela

Muros   Noia   Milladoiro

Boiro   Sarria

Villagarcia de Arosa

Vilanova de Arousa   Chantada

4

Sanxenxo   Monforte de Lemos   Pobra do Brollon

VIGO   Parada do Sil   San Clodio

Bueu   Arcade   A Rúa   O Barco

Redondela

Cartelle   OURENSE

Oia   Tui   As Neves

Silva   Melgaço   (P)

A Guarda   Covas   (ES)

Lindoso

Ponte de Lima

Viana do Castelo   Gérês   Montalegre   Franca

Castelo do Neiva   Parada

5   Esposende   BRAGA   Chaves   Bragança   (ES)

Póvoa de Varzim   Braga   Valpaços   Barragem

Aguçadoura   Barcelos   Queimadela   do Azibo

Vila do Conde   Mirandela   Izeda   E-82

Vila Chã   PORTO   E805   Mondim   Macedo de   Miranda do Douro

Matosinhos   E01   de Basto   Pinhao   Cavaleiros

São Salvador de Lordelo   Amarante   Alto de   Vila Real

Vila Nova de Gaia   Avintes   Espinho   Carrazeda   Mogadouro

Valadares   Entre-   Marco de   Peso da   de Ansiães

Gondomar   os-Rios   Canaveses   Régua   São João   Torre de   Aldeadávila

Espinho   Cinfães   da Pesqueira   Moncorvo   de la Ribera

Santa Maria da Feira   Castelo   Lamego   Vila Nova

Furadouro   de Paiva   de Foz Côa   Freixo de Espada a Cinta

6   Murtosa   Pardilhó   E801   Freixo de

Bico   Estarreja   Numão   (P)

Ilhavo   Aveiro   São Pedro do Sul   (ES)

Vagos   E80   VISEU   Castelo Rodrigo

Praia de Mira   Viseu   Trancoso   Pinhel

Mira   AVEIRO   Sangalhos   E80   Celorico da Beira   Almeida   Sancti-Spiritus

A   27km   B   38   C   D

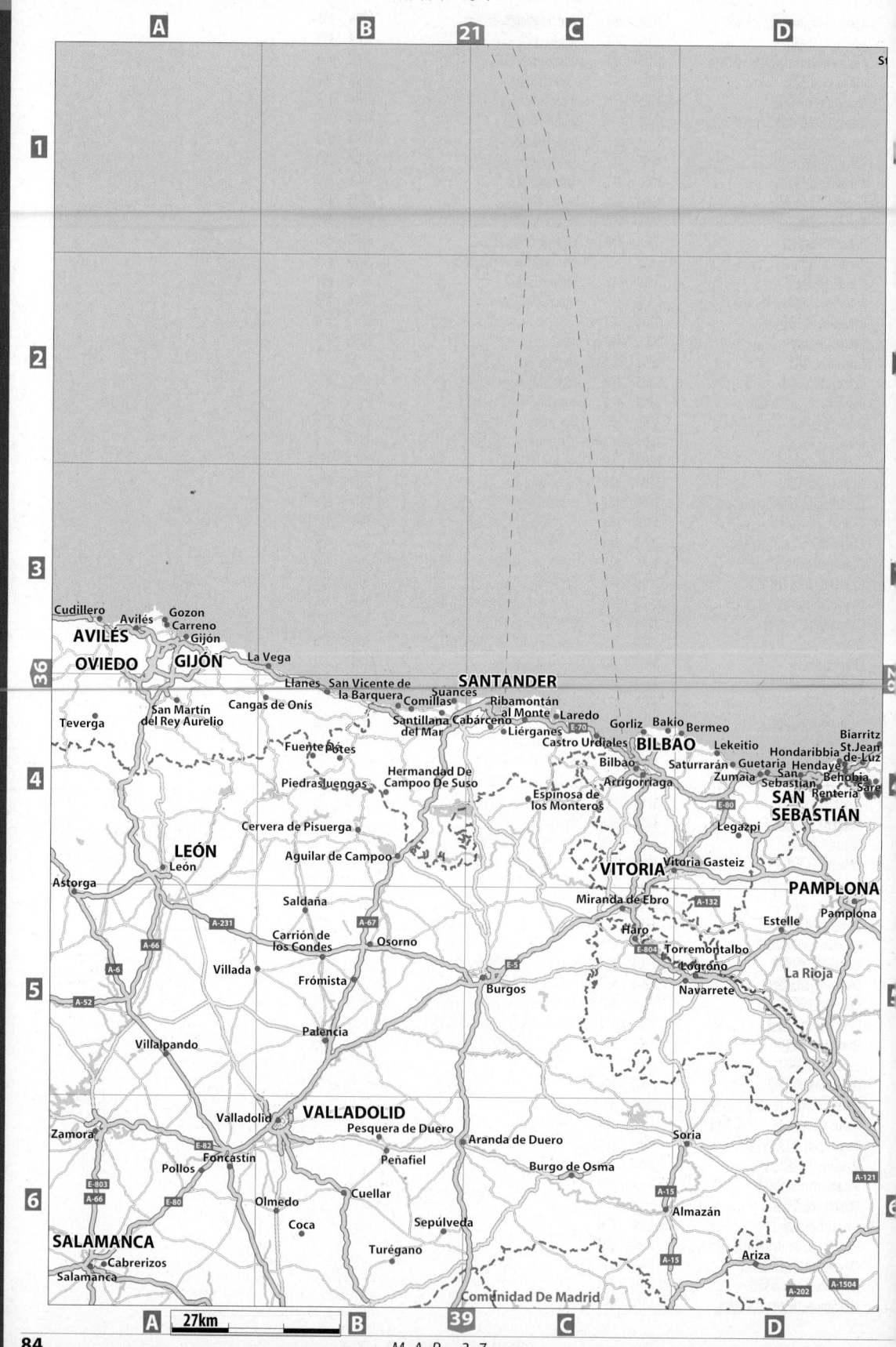

A   B   21   C   D

1

2

3

36

Cudillero
Gozon
Avilés   Carreno
AVILÉS   Gijón
OVIEDO   GIJÓN   La Vega
Llanes   San Vicente de
la Barquera   Suances
Teverga   San Martín   Cangas de Onís   Comillas   Ribamontán
del Rey Aurelio   Santillana   al Monte   Laredo
del Mar   Cabárceno   Gorliz   Bakio   Bermeo
Fuente   Potes   Liérganes   Castro Urdiales   BILBAO   Lekeitio   Biarritz
Piedrasluengas   Bilbao   Saturrarán   Guetaria   Hondaribbia   St.Jean
Hermandad De   Espinosa de   Arrigorriaga   Zumaia   San   Hendaye   de-Luz
Campoo De Suso   los Monteros   E-80   Sebastian   Renteria   Behobia
Cervera de Pisuerga   SAN   Sare
Aguilar de Campoo   VITORIA   SEBASTIÁN
LEÓN   Vitoria Gasteiz   Legazpi
León   PAMPLONA
Astorga   Saldaña   Miranda de Ebro   A-132
A-231   A-67   Haro   Estelle   Pamplona
A-66   Carrión de   Osorno   E-804   Torremontalbo
los Condes   Logroño   La Rioja
A-6   Villada   E-5   Navarrete
A-52   Frómista   Burgos

SANTANDER

4

5   Palencia

Villalpando

VALLADOLID
Valladolid
Zamora   Pesquera de Duero   Soria
E-82   Aranda de Duero
Fontastin   Peñafiel   A-121
Pollos   Burgo de Osma
E-803   Cuellar   A-15
6   A-66   E-80   Olmedo   Almazán
Coca   Sepúlveda
SALAMANCA   Turégano   Ariza
Cabrerizos   A-15
Salamanca   A-202   A-1504
Comunidad De Madrid

A   27km   B   39   C   D

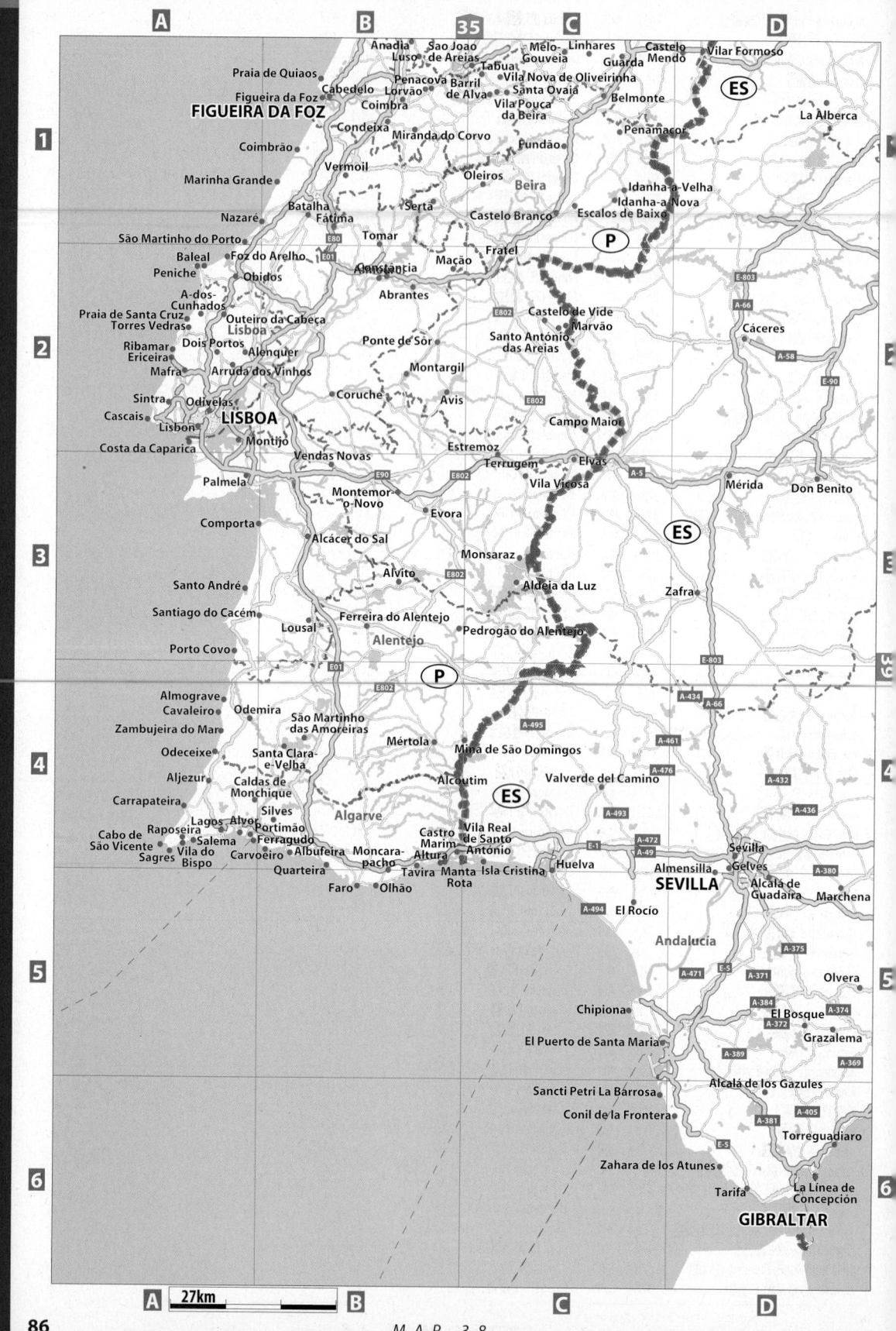

	A	B	37	C	D

E-803

A-50

Palazuelos de Eresma

Avila

A-211

1

A-23

A-1511

MADRID

A-1512

Lagartera

Toledo

2

Logrosán

Consuegra

E-901

A-3

A-31

A-43

Jalance

3

A-422

A-423

38 E-5

Yelca

El Pinós

CÓRDOBA

Córdoba

A-431

A-306

A-44 A-316

MURCIA

4

Mula

Murcia

Santaella

A-316

A-315

A-351

Alcaudete

A-317

Vélez-Rubio

Cabra

Priego de Córdoba

Alicún de las Torres

Cartagena

A-45 Rute

A-339

E-902

Cullar

Ramonete

Cañada
de Callego

Cuevas de
San Marcos

A-308

E-15 Calnegre

Villanueva
de Algaidas

GRANADA

A-334

San Juan de los Terreros

A-384

Granada

Andalucía

A-349

5

Archidona

Güejar Sierra

A-402 A-338

Sierra Nevada

A-356

A-348

E-15

Agua Amarga

MÁLAGA

Orgiva

A-397 A-355

Alhaurín del la Torr

Motril

Castillo de Baños

La Garrofa

La Isleta

Marbella

Carchuna

Castell de Ferro

Cabo de Gata

6

A	27km	B		C		D

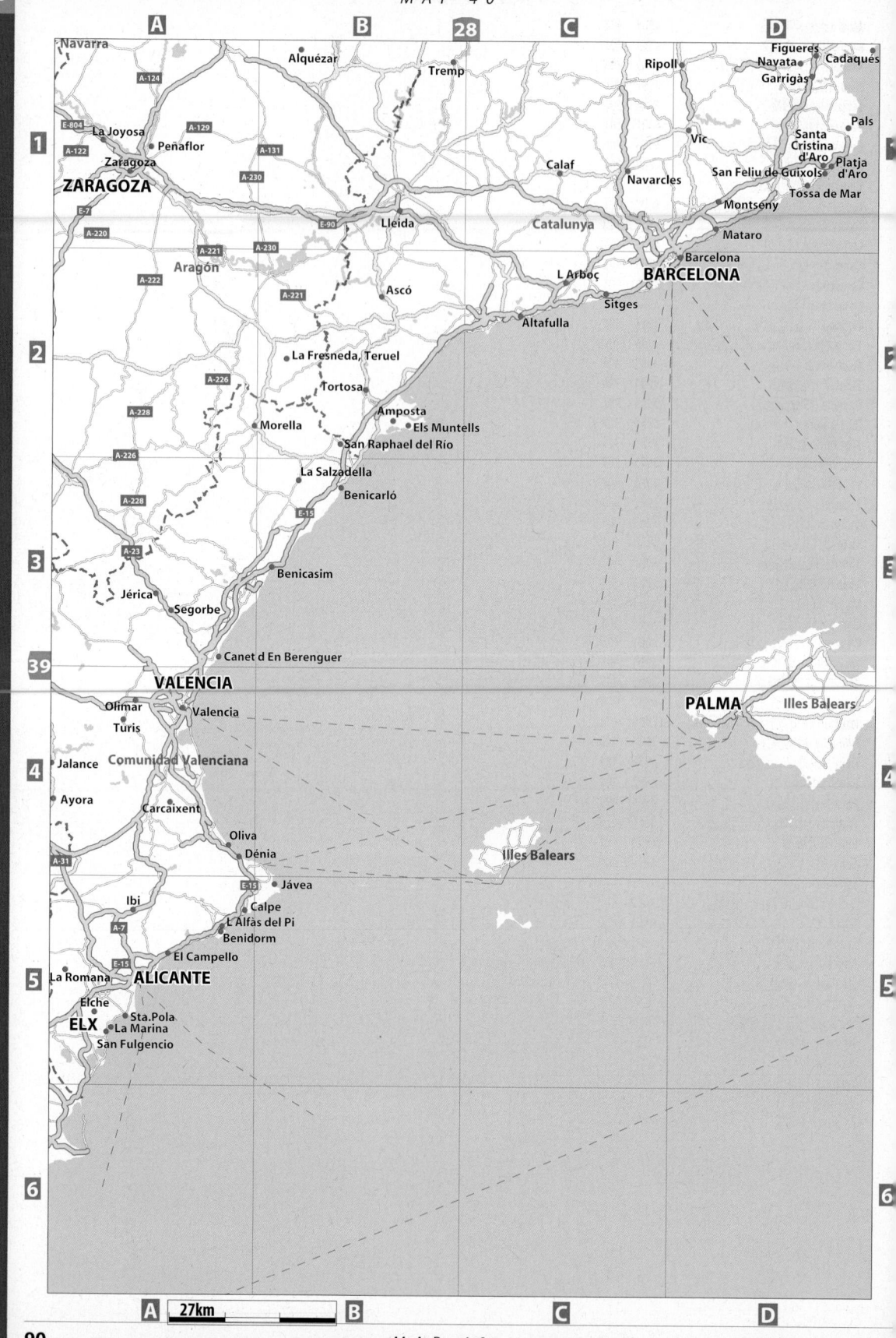

UNITED KINGDOM

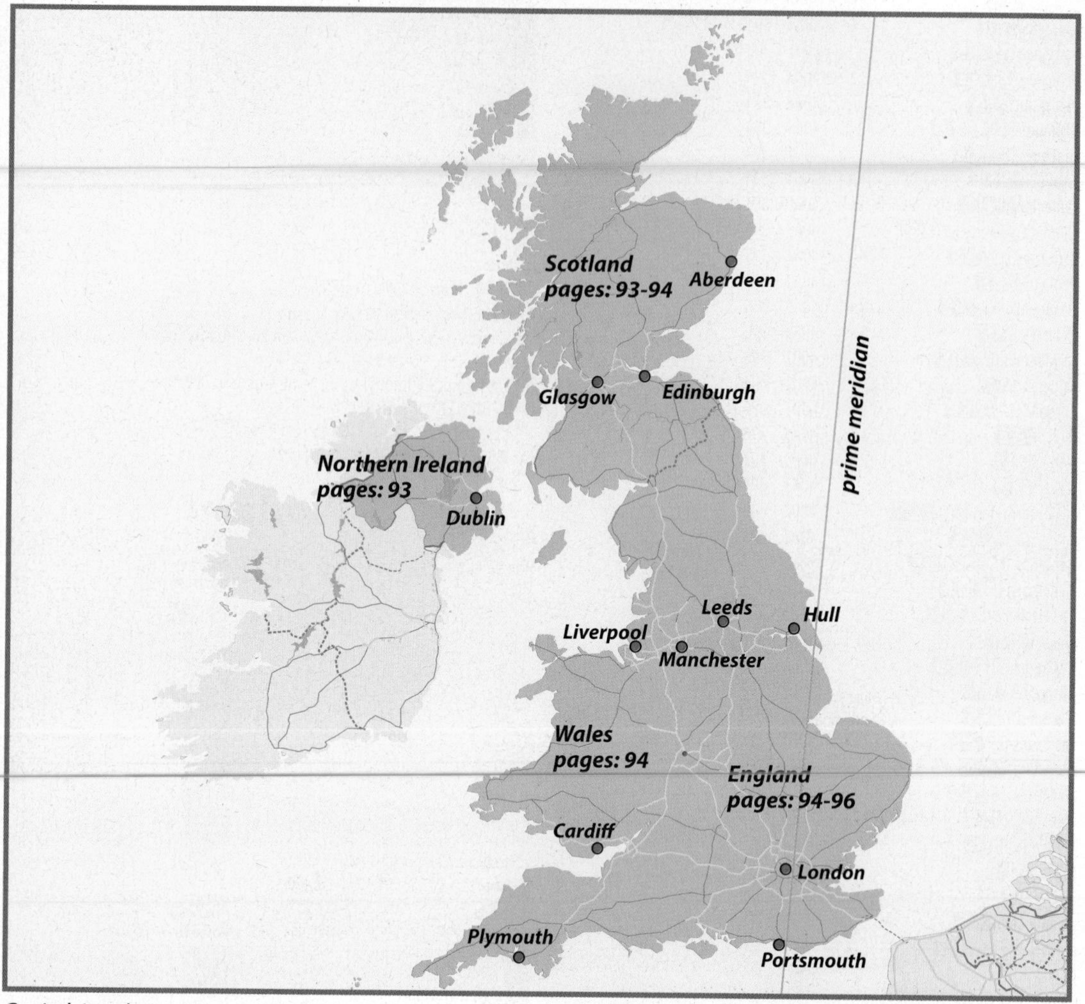

Scotland
pages: 93-94

Aberdeen

Glasgow   Edinburgh

Northern Ireland
pages: 93

Dublin

prime meridian

Leeds   Hull

Liverpool

Manchester

Wales
pages: 94

England
pages: 94-96

Cardiff

London

Plymouth

Portsmouth

Capital: London
Government: Constitutional monarchy
Official Language: English
Population: 61,200,000 (2010)
Area: 244,820 km².

General information
Dialling code: 0044
Currency: Pound sterling (GBP),
£ 1 = € 1,16, € 1 = £ 0.86 (January 2011)

Regulations for overnight stays
Wild camping is forbidden in the UK. Motorway
service stations allow overnight parking.

Opening hours
Shops: Monday-Saturday 9am-5.30pm, Sunday 10am-
4pm (or 11am-5pm).
Banks: Monday-Friday 9.30am-4.30pm
Pubs: Generally Monday-Saturday 11am-11pm,
Sunday 11am-10.30pm, many
close in the afternoon and stay open later in the
evening.

Great Britain

Northern Ireland

Aghadowey 1A3
Golf Car Park, Brown Trout Golf and Country Inn, 209 Agivey Road, A54. **GPS:** n55,02413 w6,59985.
free.
Remarks: Max. 2 nights.

Antrim 1A3
The Ramble Inn, 236 Lisnevenagh Road. **GPS:** n54,77412 w6,24533.
free.
Distance: Antrim 7km.

Ballinamallard 1A3
Ballinamallard Football Club, Ferney Park. **GPS:** n54,41340 w7,6006.

free.
Distance: 1,5km.
Tourist information Ballinamallard:
Ballinamallard River, Kilgortnaleague Bridge, A35 Enniskillen > Irvinestown. Wild Salmon and Trout River.

Ballymoney 1A3
Anglers' Rest, 139 Vow Road. **GPS:** n54,99597 w6,56997.
free.
Tourist information Ballymoney:
Tourist Information Office, Ballymoney Townhall, 1 Townhead Street.
Leslie Hill Open Farm, 9, Macfin Road. Living history on the farm, picnic area, playground, Tea-room etc. Easter-31/05: Su-Bank Holidays 14-18h, 01/06-30/06: Sa-Su 14-18h, 01/07-31/08: Mo-Sa 11-18h, Su 14-18h.
Old Bushmills Distillery, Main Street, Bushmills. World's oldest licensed whiskey distillery. Mo-Sa 9.30-17h, Su 12-17h Good Friday, 12/07, 25-26/12, 31/12-01/01.

Broughshane 1A3
Houston Mills, Buckna road. **GPS:** n54,89307 w6,20107.

free. 1 Ch.

Carrickfergus 1A3
Carrickfergus Harbour Car Park, Rodgers Quay. **GPS:** n54,71177 w5,8119.
Ch.

Eglinton 1A2
Decks Bar & Restaurant, McLean Road, Campsie Industrial Estate. **GPS:** n55,04060 w7,2006.
free.

Killyleagh 1A3
Ringdufferin Country Club, Ringdufferin Road. **GPS:** n54,43210 w5,6528.
free.
Distance: Killyleagh 4km.
Tourist information Killyleagh:
Castle Ward, Strangford, Downpatrick. 18th-century mansion. 01/01-31/12.
Sea Treks of Strangford, 11 Shore Road. Water taxi service on Strangford

Lough. 01/01-31/12. £ 10/h.

Newtownards 1A3
Daft Eddys, Sketrick Island. **GPS:** n54,48812 w5,64807.

free.
Distance: Newtownards 17km.
Tourist information Newtownards:
Somme Heritage Centre, 233 Bangor Road, Conlig, A21. The centre examines Ireland's role in the 1st World War.
Castle Espie Wildfowl And Wetlands Centre, 78 Ballydrain Road, Comber. 01/01-31/12. 23-25/12.

Whitehead 1A3
Car Park. GPS: n54,76391 w5,71238.
Ch.

Scotland

Aberdeen 1C1
Hazelhead Park, Hazeldene Road. **GPS:** n57,13987 w2,17956.

free. **Surface:** asphalted.
Distance: 200m 400m 400m.

Ballachulish 1B1
Glencoe, A82 Ballachulish > Achallader. **GPS:** n56,63295 w4,82744.

free.
Remarks: Parking ski-lifts.

Dufftown 1C1
Castle Road. **GPS:** n57,45325 w3,12912.

UK

+20 🗑️free. **Surface:** asphalted.
Distance: 🚶400m ⊗400m 🍴400m.

| 📷 | **Dumfries** | 1B3 |

P Long Stay, White Sands. **GPS:** n55,06722 w3,6125.

10 🗑️free. **Surface:** asphalted. ⬛ 01/01-31/12
Distance: 🚶100m 🛒on the spot ⊗on the spot 🍴100m.

| 📷 S | **Dunthulm** 🌿♨️🏕️ | 1A1 |

Isle of Skye. **GPS:** n57,65020 w6,40459.
12 🗑️£ 12 ⛽Ch WC. **Surface:** metalled.
Remarks: Neaby Dunthulm Castle.

| 📷 S | **Easdale** 🌿♨️🏕️ | 1B2 |

Souvenir shop, Ellenabeich, Isle of Seil. **GPS:** n56,29540 w5,6462.

10 🗑️£ 10 ⛽Ch WC. **Surface:** metalled.
Distance: 🚶on the spot ☀️on the spot ⊗on the spot 🚰on the spot.

| 📷 | **Fettercairn** | 1C1 |

Car Park Bowling Club, Fettercairn, Laurencekirk. **GPS:** n56,84971 w2,57306.
🗑️.

Tourist information Fettercairn:
👁️ Fettercairn Distillery Visitor Centre Information, Distillery Road.One of
Scotland's oldest malt whiskey distilleries. ⬛ 01/05-30/09, Mon-Sa 10-14.30h.
🚰 free.

| 📷 | **Givran** | 1B2 |

Harbour street- Henriettastreet. **GPS:** n55,24324 w4,85869.

50 🗑️free. **Surface:** asphalted. ⬛ 01/01-31/12
Distance: 🚶100m ⛱️sandy beach 50m ⊗50m.

| 📷 | **New Abbey** 🌿♨️ | 1B3 |

Parking Sweetheart Abbey, A710, Main Street. **GPS:** n54,98070 w3,61966.

6 🗑️free. **Surface:** metalled.

| 📷 | **Oban** ⚓ | 1B2 |

Longsdale Car park, Longsdale Road. **GPS:** n56,41997 w5,46846.
± 10 🗑️free. **Location:** Central.
Surface: asphalted. ⬛ 01/01-31/12
Distance: 🚶400m ☀️300m 🏊50m 🍴400m.

| 📷 | **Rhugarbh** 🏕️ | 1B1 |

Parking Scottish Sea Life Sanctuary, A828 Rhugharb - Barcaldine. **GPS:**
n56,51731 w5,34679.

10 🗑️free. **Surface:** metalled.

Wales

| 🗑️ | **Brecon** | 1B5 |

Car Park, Watton. **GPS:** n51,94412 w3,38305.
🗑️free. **Surface:** asphalted. ⬛ 18-8h
Remarks: Max. 1 night.

| 🗑️ | **Hay-on-Wye** | 1B5 |

Car Park, Oxford Road. **GPS:** n52,07316 w3,12592.
🗑️free. **Surface:** asphalted. ⬛ 18-8h
Remarks: Max. 1 night.

| 🗑️ | **Moelfre** | 1B4 |

Lligwy Bay. **GPS:** n53,35910 w4,26132.
🗑️£ 10/night.
Remarks: Beach parking.

England

| 🗑️ S | **Abingdon** | 1C5 |

Rye Farm Pay & Display car park. **GPS:** n51,66593 w1,27799.
8 🗑️£ 7/24h WC.
Distance: 🚶500m ⊗500m.
Remarks: A415 going south, on the left hand side just across the bridge.

Tourist information Abingdon:
ℹ️ Tourist Information Centre, 25 Bridge Street.

| 🗑️ | **Aldershot** | 1C6 |

Parsons Barracks Car park, Ordnance Road. **GPS:** n51,24979 w0,75731.
🗑️£ 1. **Surface:** asphalted. ⬛ 01/01-31/12

| 🗑️ S | **Ambleside** 🌿🍃 | 1C3 |

Miller Field Motorhome Camping, Rothay Rd. **GPS:** n54,42898 w2,96586. ⬆️.
50 🗑️£ 10 ⛽🍴Ch. 🚻
Location: Rural, comfortable, quit. **Surface:** grassy.
Distance: 🚶200m 🛶Lake Windmere 800m 🚲on the spot 🚶on the spot.
Remarks: At Lake District National Park.

| 🗑️ | **Bakewell** 🎪 | 1C4 |

Car Park, Asford Lane, Monsal Head. **GPS:** n53,24015 w1,72325.
🗑️£ 10.

Tourist information Bakewell:
ℹ️ Bakewell tourist information office, Old Market Hall, Bridge Street, www.
visitpeakdistrict.com.

UK

Bury St.Edmunds 1D5
Ram Meadow Carpark, Cotton Lane. **GPS:** n52,24775 e0,71893.

5 🛒£1.20/day WC. 🅾 01/01-31/12

Canterbury 1D6
Kingsmead coach park, Kingsmead Road. **GPS:** n51,28554 e1,08492.
🛒£ 10/12h 🔧🍳Ch ✂ included.
Distance: 🚶650m ⊗650m.

Canterbury 1D6
Park&Ride, New Dover Road. **GPS:** n51,26249 e1,10239. .
24 🛒£ 2/day £ 4/night 🔧🍳Ch ✂ WC included.
Distance: ⊗Vintage Inn.

Tourist information Canterbury:
ℹ️ Canterbury Tourist Information Centre, The Buttermarket, 34 St Margret's Street, www.canterbury.co.uk.

Chester 1B4
Car Park, Little Roodee, Castle Road. **GPS:** n53,18447 w2,89245.
🛒£ 5/18-09h, gates closed 22.30-7.00h 🍳 WC.
Distance: 🚲3,5km.
Remarks: A483 Grosvenor Road > Castle Road, by river Dee.

Tourist information Chester:
ℹ️ Tourist Information Centre, Town Hall, Northgate Street, www.chestertourism.com.Tourist town with historical centre.

Cirencester 1C5
Old Cricklade Road. **GPS:** n51,70760 w1,955.
🛒£ 6,20. **Surface:** metalled.
Distance: ⊗100m 🍺50m.
Remarks: Near McDonalds.

Cirencester 1C5
The Crown Inn, High Street, Cerny Wick. **GPS:** n51,66264 w1,88933.
5 🛒🔧🍳Ch.

Darlington 1C3
Car Park, Chesnut Street. **GPS:** n54,52993 w1,54758.
🛒£ 4/day £ 4/night. **Surface:** metalled.
Distance: 🚶700m 🚲4,7km.

Exmouth 1B6
GPS: n50,61191 w3,40775.
🛒£ 5.
Remarks: Max. 24h. End of the seafront > Orcombe Point.

Hereford 1B5
GPS: n52,06247 w2,71487.
🛒£ 1/day, night free. **Surface:** asphalted.
Remarks: Next to football ground.

Holy Island 1C2
Lindisfarne Causeway. **GPS:** n55,67815 w1,87552.
5 🛒. **Surface:** metalled.

Hull 1D4
Priory Park, Priory way. **GPS:** n53,72150 w0,41784.
🛒£ 10 🔧🍳Ch ✂ WC ⬛. **Surface:** asphalted. 🅾 01/01-31/12
Distance: 🍺150m 🚐on the spot.
Remarks: Caution key € 2.

Ivybridge 1B6
Lee Mill Services, A38. **GPS:** n50,38493 w3,97041.⬆➡
🛒£ 8/night. 🅾 01/01-31/12

Leominster 1B5
Car Park, Broad Street. **GPS:** n52,22981 w2,7388.
🛒free WC.

Little Hadham 1D5
Stone House Farm, Mr&Mrs Mardell, Stortford Road. **GPS:** n51,88280 e0,09950.

5 🛒£ 6/night 🔧🍳Ch. 🅾 01/01-31/12
Distance: 🚉London/Cambridge 50km.

London 1D6
Tower Bridge Road.
GPS: n51,50399 w0,07723.
🛒£ 20/24h.
Remarks: Monitored truck parking, along river nearby Tower Bridge.

Loughton 1D5
Willow Farm, Mrs Teresa Mhatré, Lippits Hill, High Beach. **GPS:** n51,65597 e0,02000.

5 🛒£ 5-10 🔧🍳Ch WC.
🅾 01/01-31/12
Distance: 🚉on the spot 🚲7km 🚐3km 🍺100m 🚲3km 🚌1,5km 🐾100m.

Maidstone 1D6
Maidstone Services, M20. **GPS:** n51,26568 e0,61588.
8 🛒£ 8 WC ⬛.
Distance: 🚲200m ⊗on the spot 🍺on the spot.

Tourist information Maidstone:
ℹ️ Maidstone Tourist Information Centre, The Gatehouse, Palace Gardens, Mill Street.
Ⓜ Museum of Kent Life, Lock Lane, Sandling.History and traditions of Kent. 🅾 14/02-05/11, 10-17h.

Marazion 1A6
Car Park, Kings Road. **GPS:** n50,12415 w5,47587.
🛒£ 4.
Remarks: Parking at sea, nearby Saint Michael's Mount, not suitable for big motorhomes. Follow Marazion Car Parkings.

Marazion 1A6
Wheal Rodney, Gwallon. **GPS:** n50,12563 w5,46373.
🛒£ 8-13, 2 pers.incl 🔧🍳Ch ✂ WC ⬛against payment. 🅾 01/01-31/12

Tourist information Marazion:
ℹ️ Tourist Information Centre, Station Road, Penzance.
👁🗡 Saint Michael's Mount.Rocky island with medieval castle and church. 🅾 01/04-31/10.

Newnham on Severn 1C5
Elton Farm, Littledean Road. **GPS:** n51,82355 w2,44753.
5 🛒🔧🍳Ch. **Surface:** unpaved.
Distance: 🚐on the spot.

Newton Abbot 1B6
Sunnyside, Yvonne Bassett, Totnes Road, A381, Ipplepen. **GPS:** n50,48552 w3,63509.

UK

Almer road coach park, Almerroad. **GPS:** n51,48389 w0,61456.
against payment. **Surface:** asphalted.
Distance: 800m.
Remarks: Free from 18-09h, nearby Windsor Castle.

5 £ 6/night WC. 01/01-31/12

Praa Sands   1A6

Car Park, Castle Drive. **GPS:** n50,10375 w5,38888.
against payment.

Salthouse   1D4

GPS: n52,95525 e1,10136.
free.
Remarks: Beach parking.

Sewerby   1D4

The Ship Inn, Cliff Road. **GPS:** n54,10167 w0,16411.
5 Ch. **Surface:** unpaved.

St.Austell   1A6

Edgemoor, Christopher Thorne, St.Dennis. **GPS:** n50,39853 w4,8698.

5 £ 4/night Ch WC. 01/01-31/12

Distance: St.Austell 14,5km.
Remarks: Between Roche and St.Dennis, nearby Gothers Road.

Tackley   1C5

Sturdys Castle Pub, Banbury Road, A4260. **GPS:** n51,87041 w1,32883.
5 £ 5/night.
Distance: Woodstock 3km.
Remarks: Parking behind the pub.

Tintagel   1A6

King Arthur's Car Park, Fore Street. **GPS:** n50,66356 w4,75129.
£ 3.50. 16-10h
Distance: on the spot.
Remarks: Opposite Tintagel Old Post Office.

Tourist information Tintagel:
Tourist Information Centre, Bossiney Road, www.visitboscastleandtintagel.
com.
Tintagel Old Post Office, Fore Street.600 year-old traditional Cornish
Longhouse.
King Arthur's Castle, Castle Road. 10-17/18h 24-26/12, 01/01.

West Down   1B5

Pipcott Fields, West Down Post Office Stores, West Down, Ilfracombe. **GPS:**
n51,15250 w4,12417.
5 £ 5 Ch WC. 01/04-30/09
Remarks: Behind villages shop.

Tourist information West Down:
Tourist Information Centre, The Landmark Theatre, The Seafront, Ilfracombe,
www.ilfracombe-tourism.co.uk.

Winchester   1C6

Car Park, Worthy Lane, B3044. **GPS:** n51,06890 w1,31669.
£ 4.
Remarks: Max. 24h.

Tourist information Winchester:
Tourist Information Centre, Winchester Guildhall, High Street, www.
visitwinchester.co.uk.

THE NETHERLANDS

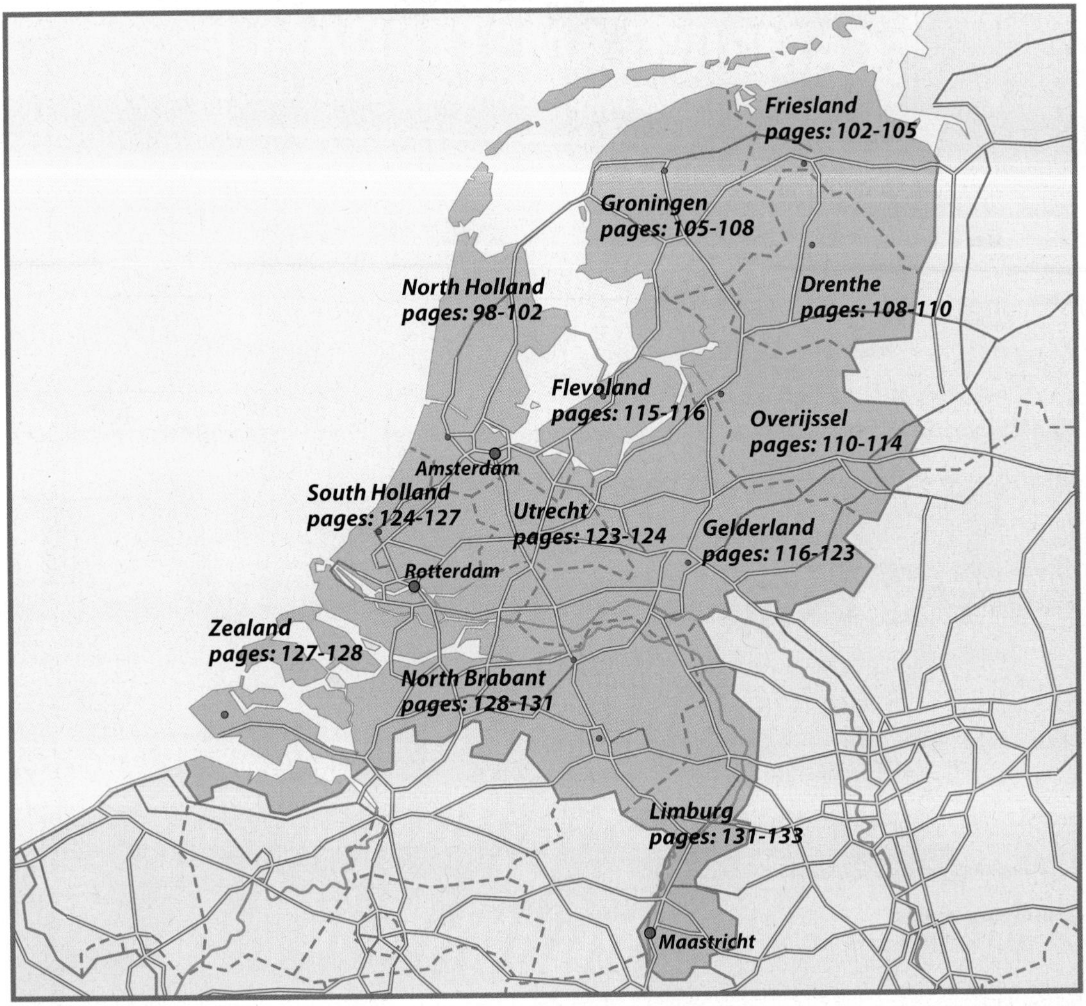

Friesland
pages: 102-105

Groningen
pages: 105-108

North Holland
pages: 98-102

Drenthe
pages: 108-110

Flevoland
pages: 115-116

Overijssel
pages: 110-114

Amsterdam

South Holland
pages: 124-127

Utrecht
pages: 123-124

Gelderland
pages: 116-123

Rotterdam

Zealand
pages: 127-128

North Brabant
pages: 128-131

Limburg
pages: 131-133

Maastricht

The Netherlands
Capital: Amsterdam
Government: Constitutional monarchy
Official Language: Dutch
Population: 16,669,000 (July 2011)
Area: 41, 526 km².

General information
Dialling code: 0031.
Currency: Euro
Credit cards are not accepted everywhere.

Regulations for overnight stays
Wild camping is forbidden in the Netherlands. A few
motorhome-friendly municipalities have regulated
facilities where overnight parking is allowed.

Opening hours
Shops: Monday-Friday 9am-6pm, Saturday 9am 5pm.
Supermarkets in bigger cities: Monday-Friday till 8pm
and sometimes later.
Banks: Monday-Friday 9am-4pm.
Post Office: Monday-Friday 9am-6pm, Saturday
9/10am-1.30pm.

NL

North Holland

Abbenes 8A2
Hoeve 't Groene Hart, Kaagweg 50. **GPS:** n52,22630 e4,61911.

15 € 10, 2 pers.incl Ch included € 2 **Location:** Rural, comfortable, quit. **Surface:** grasstiles/metalled. 15/03-01/11
Distance: 4km 900m 1,5km 1,5km 4km.

Alkmaar 3B6
Citycamp Alkmaar, Bergerweg 201. **GPS:** n52,64231 e4,72362.

56 € 20 € 0,50 Ch WC included € 0,50 € 5 € 5.
Surface: grasstiles/metalled.
01/01-31/12
Distance: 2km 6km on the spot on the spot on the spot 10m.
Remarks: Tel: +31 (0)72-5116924. Alkmaar, beltway West, exit Bergen, follow signs.

Tourist information Alkmaar:
VVV, Waagplein 2 - 3, www.vvvalkmaar.nl.Dutch cheese town, 400 monuments.
Het Hollands Kaasmuseum, Waagplein.Cheese museum. 01/04-31/10 Mo-Sa 10-16h.
Kaasmarkt. 02/04-03/09 10-12.30h.

Amsterdam 8B1
Amsterdam City Camp, Papaverweg 55. **GPS:** n52,39847 e4,90010.

60 € 20 € 2/100liter Ch (30x)€ 3, 10Amp WC included.
Location: Urban, comfortable.
Surface: metalled. 15/04-01/10
Distance: 2km 20m 100m 1km 1,5km 500m.

Amsterdam 8B1
Citycamp Zeeburg, Zuider IJdijk 20. **GPS:** n52,36569 e4,95818.
100 € 28 2 pers incl € 0,50 Ch WC included € 0,80 against payment. **Surface:** metalled. 01/01-31/12
Distance: 5km on the spot on the spot.
Remarks: Tel:+31(0)20- 6944430.

Amsterdam 8B1
Het Amsterdamse Bos, Kleine Noorddijk 1, Amsterdam-zuid. **GPS:** n52,29271 e4,82171.

100 Ch WC 01/01-01/12
Distance: 500m on the spot 500m on the spot 50m.
Remarks: A9 exit 6, N231 dir Aalsmeer, after 500m turn right: Bosrandweg, campsite on the left after 2 km.

Amsterdam 8B1
Fam. Ackermann, Lutkemeerweg 149, Amsterdam-Osdorp. **GPS:** n52,36358 e4,77240.

16 € 10 2 pers.incl, >7m: +€ 1 m € 2,50 Ch € 4,50/day.
Surface: metalled.
01/01-31/12
Distance: 10km city centre 2km 1km.
Remarks: Via Osdorperweg, special license.

Tourist information Amsterdam:
VVV, Stationsplein 10 en Leidseplein 1, www.visitamsterdam.nl.Amsterdam Pass: Card gives entrance to museums, public transport, boattrip on the canals etc., 24h/ € 39, 48h/€ 49, 72h/€ 59, available at VVV.
Canalbus.Boat trip on the canals. € 13.
Joods Historisch Museum, Jonas Daniel Meijerplein 2/4.Jewish historical museum. 11-17h.
Nemo, Oosterdok 2.Science and technology. Tue-Su 10-17h, holidays Mo-Su. € 11.
Stelling van Amsterdam.Forts built to protect Amsterdam.
Albert Cuyp, Albert Cuyp.Arts and antiques market. daily Su.
Antiek, Noordermarkt. 01/05-30/09 last Sa of the month.
Artis.City-zoo. 9-17/18h.
Villa Arena, Naast Arena.Furniture mall, 80 shops. Tue-Sa 10-18h, Mo 13-18h.

De Rijp 8B1
Bloembolbedrijf Stoop, Zuiddijk 34. **GPS:** n52,54813 e4,83416.

€ 7 € 1. **Surface:** concrete. 01/01-31/12
Remarks: Between Alkmaar and Purmerend, exit De Rijp.

Den Helder 3B6
Willemsoord, Willemsoord 47. **GPS:** n52,96134 e4,76856.

15 € 10 € 0,50/80liter Ch € 0,50 € 3.

NL

Surface: metalled.
🅾 01/01-31/12
Distance: 400m.
Remarks: Max. 48h, ferry boat to Texel 500m,
caution sanitary € 15.

Tourist information Den Helder:
ℹ VVV, Bernhardplein 18, www.vvvkopvannoordholland.nl.Naval basis.
⚓ Toeristische juttersmarkt. 🅾 summer Tue 10-17h.

| | | Den Oever | | 3B6 |

Haventerrein Oostkade, Oostkade 3. **GPS:** n52,93395 e5,03974.⬆

15 € 11 € 0,50/100liter € 0,50 Ch WC included. **Surface:**
metalled. 🅾 01/01-31/12
Distance: 500m 1,4km 200m offshore fishing 500m 500m
on the spot.
Remarks: Max. 3 days, Sa-morning fishmarket. At old harbour.

| | | Enkhuizen | | 3B6 |

Dirck Chinaplein. **GPS:** n52,69806 e5,29005.

6 € 10/12-12h WC.
Surface: asphalted.
Distance: on the spot.
Remarks: Max. 48h.

Tourist information Enkhuizen:
Ⓜ Zuiderzeemuseum.Historical little town.
🅾 Apr-autums holiday 10-17/18h.

| | | Hoorn | | 8B1 |

Jachthaven Hoorn, Visserseiland 221. **GPS:** n52,63467 e5,05676.⬆

15 € 12,50 Ch WC € 0,50. **Surface:** metalled.
🅾 01/04-31/10
Distance: 500m 2,8km 50m 100m on the spot.
Remarks: Check in at harbourmaster.

| | | Huizen | 8B1 |

Recreatieterrein Wolskamer, IJsselmeerstraat. **GPS:** n52,30860 e5,24046.

8 free. **Surface:** grassy.
Distance: on the spot.
Remarks: Max. 48h.

Tourist information Huizen:
⚓ Weekmarkt. 🅾 Sa.

| | | Katwoude | 8B1 |

De Simonehoeve, Wagenweg 2. **GPS:** n52,48620 e5,03196.

10 free. 🅾 18(20)-8h
Remarks: Cheese farm, nearby Hotel Volendam. Nearby hotel Volendam.

| | | Laren (NH) | 8B1 |

Sportcomplex De Biezem, Schapendrift 64. **GPS:** n52,25717 e5,23884.

2 free Ch WC. **Surface:** metalled.
Distance: 1km.
Remarks: Max. 1 night. Nearby sports complex 'De Biezem'.

| | | Medemblik | | 3B6 |

Haven Medemblik, Pekelharinghaven 50. **GPS:** n52,77139 e5,11361.

3 € 8 + € 0,70/pp tourist tax Ch € 1,75. **Surface:** metalled.
Distance: 1km 1km 1km.
Remarks: Max. 48h.

Tourist information Medemblik:
Ⓜ Museum Stoomtram.Steam tram museum: Hoorn-Medemblik.
🏰 Kasteel Radbout.Medieval citadel. 🅾 Easter-Oct Mo-Sa 10-17, Su 12-17h,
winter Su.

⌗S Middenmeer 3B6
Jachthaven Middenmeer, Havenstraat. **GPS**: n52,81236 e4,99112. ⬆.

6 ⌗€ 5 + €1/pp tourist tax ⛽🚰 Ch ⚡€ 1 WC🚿€ 0,50 📷📶. **Surface:** metalled. ☐ 01/01-31/12
Distance: 🛒500m 🏊1,7km ⊗500m.
Remarks: Max 48h, check in at harbourmaster.

⌗S Monnickendam 🌿🏖 8B1
Jachthaven Waterland, Galgeriet 5a. **GPS**: n52,45920 e5,04059.

5 ⌗€ 18,50 ⛽€ 0,50/100liter 🚰Ch ⚡€ 0,50/2kWh WC🚿. ☐ 30/04-15/10
Distance: 🛒500-800m ⊗on the spot.
Remarks: Check in at harbourmaster.

⌗ Naarden 🌿🏖 8B1
Parking De Abri, Kapitein G. A. Meijerweg. **GPS**: n52,29162 e5,16756.

3 ⌗free. **Surface:** metalled.
Distance: 🛒Naarden-Vesting 450m 🚰350m.
Remarks: Max. 48h. Parking just outside centre.

Tourist information Naarden:
ℹ Fortified city with city walls.
Ⓜ Vestingmuseum.Fortress museum. ☐ 01/03-31/10 Tue-Fri 10.30-17h, weekend 12-17h, summer Mo-Fri, 01/11-28/02 Su 12-17h.

⌗ Oosthuizen 8B1
Recreatieknooppunt Oosthuizen, Hoornse Jaagweg. **GPS**: n52,57609 e4,99719. ⬆.

2 ⌗free. **Location:** Quit. ☐ 01/01-31/12

Distance: ⊗200m 🚰500m 🚽100m > Volendam 🚲on the spot 🚶on the spot.
Remarks: Max. 48h.

⌗S Opperdoes 3B6
Imkerij de Bijenstal, Zwarte pad. **GPS**: n52,76367 e5,08253.

3 ⌗€ 10,50, 2 pers.incl ⛽€ 1/100liter 🚰⚡€ 2. **Surface:** gravel.
Remarks: Boat rental.

Tourist information Opperdoes:
Ⓜ Museum stoomtram, Medemblik.Steam tram museum: Hoorn-Medemblik. .

⌗ Oudendijk 8B1
Bruin Eetcafé Les Deux Ponts, Slimdijk 2. **GPS**: n52,60462 e4,95983.
⌗.
Remarks: Between Hoorn and Purmerend, exit Averhorn.

⌗ Purmerend 8B1
Neckerstraat/West. **GPS**: n52,50972 e4,93944.

5 ⌗free. **Surface:** metalled. ☐ 01/01-31/12
Distance: 🛒450m ⊗400m.
Remarks: Max. 72h.

Tourist information Purmerend:
🎪 Centrum. ☐ Tue.

⌗S Schagen 🌿⛵🍴 3B6
Jachthaven, Lagedijkerweg 2B. **GPS**: n52,79088 e4,78746. ⬆.

15 ⌗€ 5,10 + € 0,80/pp tourist tax ⛽€ 0,50/100liter 🚰Ch ⚡€ 1,50 WC🚿€ 0,50 📷 washing machine/dryer € 4 📶€ 2. **Surface:** metalled. ☐ 01/01-31/12
Distance: 🛒500m 🚲on the spot ⊗400m 🚰500m.
Remarks: Check in at harbourmaster, caution key sanitary building € 15.

Tourist information Schagen:
ℹ VVV, Loet 10.
🎪 West Friese Folkloremarkt.Folkore market. ☐ Jun-Jul-Aug: Thu.

🍴 Stompetoren 8B1
Het Schermer Wapen, Oterlekerweg 3. **GPS**: n52,61420 e4,82115.
4 ⌗.

⌗ Texel/De Cocksdorp 3B5
De Krim, Roggeslootweg 6. **GPS**: n53,15110 e4,85996.
8 ⌗€ 15-€ 25. **Surface:** metalled. ☐ 01/01-31/12

Van Ewijcksluis 🚐 S | 3B6

Jachthaven Amsteldiep, Amsteldiepweg 1. **GPS**: n52,88633 e4,87562.
3 🚐 € 5, 2 pers.incl ⊞ 📶 Ch ⚓ WC ⊟ included. 🅾 01/05-01/09
Distance: 🚶 on the spot ⚓ on the spot.

Volendam 🌿🚿⛺🚐 | 8B1

Marinapark Volendam, De Pieterman 1. **GPS**: n52,48944 e5,05972. ⬆.

36 🚐 € 6 10-17h, € 14 17-10h ⊞📶 Ch ⚓ included ⊡.
Surface: grasstiles/metalled.
🅾 01/01-31/12
Distance: 🚶1,5km 🏊50m ⚓50m 🛒300m 🍴300m 🛒300m.

Tourist information Volendam:
ℹ VVV, Zeestraat 37, www.vvv-volendam.nl.Old fishermen's village.
Ⓜ Volendams Museum, Zeestraat 41.Life and Work in Volendam, 1800-1900.
🅾 Easter-autums holiday 10-17h.

Friesland

Akkrum 🚐 S | 3C5

Tusken de Marren, Ulbe Twijnstrawei 31. **GPS**: n53,04853 e5,82577.

20 🚐 € 10 ⊞ € 0,50/100liter 📶 Ch ⚓ € 1 WC ⊟ € 0,50. **Surface:** grassy/
metalled. 🅾 15/03-01/11
Distance: 🚶200m 🏊on the spot ⚓on the spot 🍴700m 🚌500m.
Remarks: Information at harbourmaster, boat rental.

Appelscha 🚐 S | 3D6

De Compagnonshoeve, Vaart Noordzijde 104. **GPS**: n52,95222 e6,36278.

10 🚐 € 7 ⊞📶 Ch ⚓ € 1. **Surface:** grassy. 🅾 01/01-31/12
Distance: 🚶on the spot 🏊3km ⚓on the spot 🛒200m 🍴400m ⊡400m
🚌50m.

Tourist information Appelscha:
😊 Speelpark Duinenzathe, Noorder Es 1.Playground. 🅾 01/04-30/09 +
autums holiday + weekend Oct 9.30-17h. 🎫 >3: € 11.

Appingedam 🌿🚿⛺🚐 S | 4A5

Busstation-Qbuzz, Farmsumerweg 21. **GPS**: n53,32062 e6,86689. ⬆.

10 🚐 free ⊞📶 free ⚓ € 1. **Surface:** metalled. 🅾 01/01-31/12
Distance: 🚶on the spot ⚓Damsterdiep ⚓500m 🍴500m.

Balk 🚐 S | 3C6

Jachthaven Lutsmond, Sleatemar 1a. **GPS**: n52,90389 e5,59694.

10 🚐 € 10 excl. tourist tax ⊞📶 Ch ⚓ € 2 WC ⊟. **Surface:** grassy. 🅾
01/01-31/12
Distance: 🚶1km 🏊on the spot ⚓on the spot 🛒nearby 🍴1km.

Bergum 🚐 S | 3C5

Camperterrein Prinses Margriet Kanaal, Opperdijk van Veenweg 22. **GPS**:
n53,18643 e6,00176.
20 🚐 € 10 ⊞📶 Ch ⚓ € 2. **Surface:** metalled. 🅾 01/01-31/12
Distance: 🏊on the spot.

Bergum 🚐 S | 3C5

Jachthaven Burgumerdaam, Bergumerdaam 51. **GPS**: n53,18667 e5,99194.

7 🚐 € 6 + € 0,80/pp tourist tax ⊞📶 Ch ⚓ € 1 WC ⊟ € 0,50. **Surface:**
metalled. 🅾 15/03-01/11
Distance: 🚶300m 🏊5km ⚓on the spot 🛒500m 🍴500m.
Remarks: Max. 72h.

Brantgum 🚐 S | 3C5

Camperplaats Veldzicht, Veldbuurtsterweg 9. **GPS**: n53,35556 e5,93632. ⬆.

15 🚐 € 10 ⊞📶 Ch ⚓ included. 🏕 **Location:** Rural, comfortable, isolated,
quit. **Surface:** grassy/metalled. 🅾 01/01-31/12
Distance: 🚶Dokkum 7km ⚓2km 🛒3km 🍴3km 🚴on the spot 🚶on the
spot.
Remarks: Ferry boat to Ameland 3km.

NL

Drachten 3D5

VV Drachten, Gauke Boelensstraat. **GPS:** n53,10289 e6,08832. ⬆️
5 🏕️free. **Surface:** asphalted.
Distance: 500m 🚂500m.

Earnewâld 3C5

Eilansgrien. **GPS:** n53,12958 e5,93630. ⬆️➡️

5 🏕️€ 5,20 + € 0,80/pp tourist tax 🚰€ 0,50 Ch 🔌€ 0,50/kWh WC 🚻€
0,50 🔲 washing machine/dryer € 3,50 📶. **Surface:** asphalted.
🅾️ 01/01-31/12
Distance: 200m 🚫500m 🚂200m.
Remarks: Sanitary/washing machine at tourist office (Summer season), max.
72h.

Harlingen 3C5

Tsjerk Hiddesluizen, Nieuwe Vissershaven 17. **GPS:** n53,17938 e5,41731. ⬆️

10 🏕️€ 5 🚰Ch 🔌 (16x) WC 🚻. 📱 **Surface:** asphalted.
Distance: 500m 🚫500m 🚂500m 🚂100m.
Remarks: Max. 72, laundromat/toilets/shower 500m.

Harlingen 3C5

Citycamp De Zeehoeve, Westerzeedijk 45. **GPS:** n53,16216 e5,41754. ⬆️➡️
56 🏕️€ 23,50 🚰Ch 🔌 WC€ 0,50 🍽️included 🔲against payment.
Location: Rural.
Surface: grassy/metalled.
🅾️ 01/04-01/11
Distance: 1km 🏊200m ➤on the spot 🚫on the spot 🚂500m 🚂1km.
Remarks: Tel: +31-(0)517-413465.**Tourist information Harlingen:**
ℹ️ VVV, Voorstraat 34, www.friesekust.nl.Historical city and port.

Heerenveen 3C6

Thialf, Pim Mulierlaan 1. **GPS:** n52,93843 e5,94495. ⬆️

4 🏕️free.
Surface: metalled. 🅾️ 01/01-31/12 🔲 during event.
Distance: 2km 🚫2km 🚂2km.
Remarks: Max. 72h, on parking ground of skating rink.

Heerenveen 3C6

De Koningshof, Prinsenweg 1. **GPS:** n52,94759 e5,94438. ⬆️

4 🏕️free. **Surface:** asphalted. 🅾️ 01/01-31/12
Distance: 1km 🚫on the spot 🚂4km 🚂500m.
Remarks: Large parking near A32, max. 72h.

Heerenveen 3C6

Gemeentewerf, Venus 4. **GPS:** n52,96663 e5,93502.
🚰free. 🅾️ Mon-Fri 9-15u

Hogebeintum 3C5

Bezoekerscentrum Terp Hegebeintum, Pijpkedijk 4. **GPS:** n53,33609 e5,85244.

4 🏕️free. **Surface:** asphalted.
Distance: 4km.
Remarks: Parking information centre/VVV, highest mound in the Netherlands,
max. 2 days.

Joure 3C6

Jachthaven, Grienedyk. **GPS:** n52,97210 e5,78836.

4 🏕️€ 12,50 🚰€ 0,50/70liter 🔌€ 1,50 🍽️€ 1. **Surface:** metalled. 🅾️
01/03-01/11
Distance: 500m 🚫50m.
Remarks: Max. 72h.

Joure 3C6

Sauna de Woudfennen, Woudfennen 10, Boornzwaag.
GPS: n52,96383 e5,76627.

🏕️use of sauna obligatory. **Surface:** asphalted.
Remarks: A7 exit 23, Joure west.
Tourist information Joure:
👁️ In de Witte Os, Midstraat 97.Nostalgic store. 🅾️ mo 13.30-17h, thue-sa

NL

10-17h.

M Museum Joure, Geelgietersstraat 1-11.Frisian trades. ◻ sa-mo 14-17h, thue-fri 10-17h |●| holiday.

🏊S Langweer ⚓🌳 3C6
Passantenhaven Langweer, Buorren 5. **GPS**: n52,96091 e5,72240.⤊.

3 🏕 € 12,50 ⚡ € 0,20 ▣ Ch ⚘ WC included ◻ € 0,50 ◉ washing machine/dryer € 3,50 🚰.
Surface: grassy. ◻ 01/04-31/10
Distance: 🛒500m ⛱on the spot ⛽on the spot ⊗500m 💊500m 🚌500m.

🏊 Langweer ⛱🌳 3C6
Brandweerkazerne, Pontdyk. **GPS**: n52,96000 e5,71972.⤊.

4 🏕free. **Surface:** metalled. ◻ 01/01-31/12
Distance: 🛒500m ⛱500m ⊗500m 💊500m.
Remarks: Max. 72h.

🏊S Leeuwarden 🌿 3C5
Leeuwarder Jachthaven, Jachthavenlaan 3. **GPS**: n53,19902 e5,83041.⤊.
5 🏕 € 12,50 ⚡ ▣ Ch ⚘ WC included ◻ € 1. 🐾 **Surface:** gravel. ◻ 01/01-31/12
Distance: 🛒2,5km ⛱on the spot ⛽on the spot ⊗500m 💊500m.

🏊S Lemmer 3C6
Jachthaven, Plattedijk 6. **GPS**: n52,84708 e5,69696.

8 🏕 € 10 ⚡ ▣ Ch ⚘ WC ◻against payment. **Surface:** metalled. ◻ 01/04-01/10
Distance: 🛒1km ⛱on the spot 💊1km.

Tourist information Lemmer:
👁 Ir. D.F. Woudagemaal.The biggest steam pumpingstation of Europe.
M Oudheidkamer.History of the Lemster barges. ◻ Mo-Fri 9.30-16h.

🏊S Makkum 3C5
Workumerdijk. **GPS**: n53,05322 e5,40312.⤊.
2 🏕 € 10 Ch ⚘ WC ◻included.
Surface: metalled. ◻ 01/01-31/12
Distance: ⛽on the spot ⊗400m 💊950m.
Remarks: Free from 01/11-01/04, no service. At marina.

Tourist information Makkum:
👁 Koninklijke Tichelaar, Turfmarkt 65.Making of tin-enamel earthenware. ◻

---

guided tour Mo-Thu 11h, 13.30h, 15h, Fri 11h, 13.30h, shop Mo-Fri 9-17h.30, Sa 10-17h.

M✓ Aldfaers Erf.Museum route, the life and working in 1900. ◻ 01/04-31/10 10-17h.

🍴 Nij Beets 3C5
Pier's Hiem, Domela Nieuwenhuisweg 114. **GPS**: n53,07027 e5,95398.
🏕.

Tourist information Nij Beets:
👁 Sudergemaal.Pumping-engine, working on Sa 13.45h. ◻ 06/05-30/09 Fri-Sa 13.30-16.30h, 21/06-13/09 Fr-Su.
M It Damhûs.Open air museum. ◻ 06/05-30/09 Fri-Sa 13.30-16.30h, 21/06-13/09 Fr-Su.

Nijetrijne 3C6
Paviljoen Driewegsluis, Lindedijk 2a. **GPS**: n52,83261 e5,92467.
🏕.

🏊S Oudega ⛵ 3C5
Jachthaven Oudega, Roundeel. **GPS**: n53,12315 e5,99961.⤊.

2 🏕 € 7 ⚡ € 1/100liter ⚘ € 2,50 ◻ € 0,50. **Surface:** grassy.
◻ 01/04-01/11
Distance: 🛒200m ⛱200m 💊200m.
Remarks: Max. 48h.

🏊S Oudemirdum 3C6
Landgoed de Syme, Jan schotanuswei 106a. **GPS**: n52,85989 e5,51853.
2 🏕 € 9 ⚡ ▣ Ch ⚘included.
Remarks: Entrance Oude Balksterweg.

🏊S Rohel 3C6
Aktiviteitenboerderij, Vierhuisterweg 29. **GPS**: n52,90337 e5,84540.
5 🏕 € 15 ⚡ ▣ Ch ⚘ WC ◻included. **Location:** Quit. **Surface:** metalled.
◻ 01/01-31/12
Distance: ⛱on the spot ⛽on the spot ⊗on the spot 💊on the spot.

🍴 Sexbierum 3C5
Restaurant Liauckama State, Liauckamaleane 2. **GPS**: n53,22028 e5,47656.

5 🏕 € 10, free for clients. ◻ 01/01-31/12
Distance: 🛒1km 💊1km 🚌1km.

Surhuisterveen 3D5
Zwembad Wettervlecke, Badlaan 3. **GPS**: n53,17987 e6,16124.⤊.

NL

5 🎞€5 ⌐ WC ⌐. **Surface:** grassy.
Distance: ⌐on the spot.

🏄 S	Tersoal	3C5

Watersportbedrijf Lege Geaen, Buorren 2. **GPS:** n53,07704 e5,74301.⬆.
6 🎞€10 ⌐ ⌐Ch ⌐ WC ⌐included. 🏊 **Location:** Rural, quit. **Surface:** grassy/gravel. ◐ 01/01-31/12
Distance: ⌐on the spot ⌐on the spot.

🏄 S	Wartena	3C5

Jachthaven Wartena, Bûtenstreek 3. **GPS:** n53,15044 e5,90398.

10 🎞€10 + €1/pp ⌐⌐Ch ⌐ WC ⌐€1 ◉€6 〰. **Surface:** grassy/metalled. ◐ 01/01-31/11
Distance: ⌐200m ⌐on the spot ⌐on the spot ⊗500m ⌐500m ⌐on the spot.

🏄 S	Wommels	3C5

Jachthaven Wommels, Terp 14. **GPS:** n53,10957 e5,58765.

5 🎞€10 ⌐⌐Ch ⌐ WC included ⌐€0,50. **Surface:** grassy/metalled. ◐ 01/04-01/10
Distance: ⌐300m ⌐on the spot ⌐100m.
Remarks: Market 100m, museum 200m.

Tourist information Wommels:
Ⓜ Museum It Tsiispakhûs, Keatsebaen 1.Dairy museum. ◐ 01/04-31/10 Tue-Su 13.30-16.30.
⌐ Weekmarkt. ◐ Tue-morning.

🏄 S	Woudsend	3C6

Recreatiecentrum De Rakken, Lynbaen 10. **GPS:** n52,94649 e5,62732.

5 🎞€16,50 + €0,65 tourist tax ⌐⌐Ch ⌐ WC ⌐included ◉€4,40, dryer €2,25 〰€6. **Surface:** grassy/metalled. ◐ 15/03-15/10
Distance: ⌐1km ⌐100m ⌐100m ⊗1km ⌐1km.

🏄 S	Ypecolsga	3C6

Camperplaats Waterloo, Nr. 19. **GPS:** n52,92758 e5,59549.⬆.

10 🎞€8, 2 pers.incl, tourist tax €1/pp ⌐⌐Ch ⌐included WC ⌐ Use sanitary €1,50/pp ◉€4,50, dryer €2.
Surface: grasstiles. ◐ 01/01-31/12
Distance: ⌐3km ⌐1km ⌐1km ⊗3,5km ⌐3,5km ⌐nearby.

🍴 S	Zurich	3C5

Wegrestaurant Zurich, Viaduct 3. **GPS:** n53,09870 e5,38466.

🎞 WC ⌐.
Remarks: Max. 48h.

🏄 S	Zwaagwesteinde	3D5

Camperpark Kuikhorne, Kuikhornsterweg 31. **GPS:** n53,24124 e6,01875.

25 🎞€8, 2 pers.incl ⌐€0,50 ⌐Ch ⌐€1 WC ⌐€0,50 ◉€4, dryer €3. **Surface:** grassy. ◐ 15/03-01/11
Distance: ⌐2km ⌐on the spot ⊗2km, pizzeria within walking distance ⌐2km.
Remarks: Max. 72h.

Groningen

🏛 S	Den Horn	3D5

Tempelboerderij, Nieuwbrugsterweg 4. **GPS:** n53,23814 e6,47053.⬆.

3 🎞€7 ⌐Ch ⌐€1 WC ⌐€0,50 ◉€2,50. **Surface:** metalled. ◐ 01/01-31/12
Distance: ⌐2km ⌐600m.

Tourist information Den Horn:
⌐ Schansenroute.Route along defensive works from the 80-year's War.

NL

Doezum 3D5

Landgoed Jonker, Provincialeweg 133a. **GPS:** n53,20411 e6,26018.

60 € 8,50, 2 pers.incl € 0,50 € 0,50 Ch (20x)€ 2/night WC included.
Surface: grassy.
01/01-31/12 facilities 01/10-31/03.
Distance: 1km on the spot.
Tourist information Doezum:
Abel Tasman Kabinet, Kompasstraat 1, Grootegast.Local archaeological museum seafarer Abel Tasman. Mo-Fri 13-17h, Sa 9-12h, 13-16h.

Eenrum 3D5

Jachthaven De Dobbe, Dobbepad. **GPS:** n53,36311 e6,45151.

4 € 13,50 Ch WC € 0,50.
Surface: grassy/metalled.
Distance: 500m on the spot 500m 500m.
Remarks: Check in at harbourmaster.
Tourist information Eenrum:
Abrahams Mosterdmakerij, Molenstraat 5.Groninger mustard factory, restaurant. Wed-Su >11h. € 2.

Garnwerd 3D5

Restaurant Ad Nooren, Hunzeweg 38a. **GPS:** n53,30503 e6,49427.

6 € 10 Ch € 2 WC € 1 € 6 5/h. **Surface:** grassy.
Distance: 500m on the spot on the spot on the spot.
Remarks: Bread-service.

Groningen 3D5

Sportcentrum Kardinge, Bieskemaar. **GPS:** n53,23946 e6,59680.

15 free. **Surface:** metalled. 01/01-31/12
Distance: 3km 1km on the spot.
Remarks: Max. 72h.

Groningen 3D5

Citycamp Stadspark, Campinglaan 1. **GPS:** n53,20489 e6,53306.
20 € 23,70 Ch € 2,50 WC included against payment.
Surface: metalled.
15/03-15/10
Distance: 2,7km 2km 500m 500m 2,7km.
Remarks: Tel:+31(0)50-5251624.
Tourist information Groningen:
VVV, Grote Markt 25, www.vvvgroningen.nl.Former residence of the prefects Maurits and Willem.
Prinsenhof en prinsenhoftuin. 15/03-15/10.
Noordelijk Scheepvaartmuseum/ Niemeyer Tabaksmuseum, Brugstraat 24.
Tue-Sa 10-17h, Su 13-17h.

Haren 3D5

Jachthaven Zuidwesthoek, Meerweg 247. **GPS:** n53,15883 e6,56648.
10 € 7 + € 1,38/pp tourist tax Ch € 1. **Surface:** asphalted.
01/01-31/12
Distance: on the spot.

Harkstede 3D5

Grunopark, Hoofdweg 163. **GPS:** n53,21135 e6,66161.

10 € 5 On demand WC .
Surface: metalled. 01/01-31/12
Distance: 3km 100m.
Tourist information Harkstede:
Hortus in Haren.Garden, exposition, restaurant. 9-17/18h.

Lauwersoog 3D5

Lauwersmeerplezier, Kustweg 30. **GPS:** n53,40625 e6,20044.
6 € 15, 2 pers.incl WC included € 3. **Surface:** grassy/metalled.
01/01-31/12
Distance: 500m on the spot on the spot 500m 500m.
Tourist information Lauwersoog:
Lauwersmeergebied.Breeding area for birds and recreation area. 01/04-31/10 Tue-Su 11-17h.

Leens 4A5

Leenstertillen. GPS: n53,34990 e6,87710.
15 € 5/pp WC . **Location:** Rural, quit.
Surface: grassy. 01/01-31/12
Distance: 1,5km 50m 50m 1,5km 1,6km.

Losdorp 4A5

Restaurant Eemshaven, Schafferweg 29. **GPS:** n53,37214 e6,84411.

NL

4 🗑consuming is appreciated 🖢🍳⚡WC 🧽. ⬛ 01/01-31/12 🔘 Mo.
Distance: 🚲2km 🚍2km.
Remarks: Delfzijl-Eemshaven.

6 🗑€ 6 + € 1/pp 🖢Ch ⚡ (6x) WC 🍳€ 0,50. **Surface:** grassy/metalled.
Distance: 🚲500m 🏊on the spot 🚶on the spot ⊗500m 🚍500m.

📷S	Sellingen	4A6

De Bronzen Eik, Zevenmeersveenweg 1. **GPS:** n52,95482 e7,13848.
10 🗑€ 9, € 0,80/pppd tourist tax 🖢Ch WC 🍳. **Surface:** gravel.
⬛ 01/01-31/12
Distance: 🚲1km 🚶on the spot 🚍1km.
Remarks: Arrival after 7pm.

🗑	Lutjegast	3D5

't Kompas, Kompasstraat 1. **GPS:** n53,23498 e6,25972.

🍴	Sellingen	4A6

Café Lunchroom De Heksenketel, Westerkamp 33. **GPS:** n52,94490 e7,13997.
7 🗑free.

📷S	Slochteren ⛪	4A5

Duurswoldje, Edserweg. **GPS:** n53,19412 e6,80556.⬆

5 🗑free. **Surface:** metalled. ⬛ 01/01-31/12
Distance: 🚲on the spot ⊗on the spot 🚍200m 🚌on the spot.
Remarks: Behind the club-building.

📷S	Musselkanaal 🌿🍽	4A6

Jachthaven Spoordok, Havenkade 1. **GPS:** n52,92694 e7,01389.⬆➡

7 🗑€ 5 🖢🍳Ch ⚡ included. **Surface:** grassy. ⬛ 01/01-31/12
Distance: 🚲500m 🚶on the spot ⊗on the spot 🚍1km 🚌on the spot.
Remarks: Covered picnic area, small stock accommodation.

🗑S	Stadskanaal	4A6

Pagedal, Dwarsweg. **GPS:** n52,98973 e6,98499.⬆

25 🗑€ 7,50 🖢€ 0,50/100liter 🖢Ch ⚡(25x) WC 🍳included. **Surface:**
grassy/metalled. ⬛ 01/05-01/10
Distance: 🚲500m 🏊on the spot 🚶on the spot ⊗on the spot 🚍nearby
🚌on the spot.
Remarks: Max. 72h. At new marina, on spit of land.

Tourist information Musselkanaal:
ℹ️ Former peat colony.
🏛 Plattelandsklooster, Boslaan 3-5, Ter Apel.Ecclesiastical art and history. ⬛
Tue-Sa 10-17h, Su 13-17h.

5 🗑free 🖢🍳Ch.
Surface: metalled.
⬛ 01/04-15/10
Distance: 🚲3km 🏊on the spot 🚶on the spot ⊗on the spot 🚍3km 🚌3km.
Remarks: Sa market. Recreation area.

Tourist information Stadskanaal:
ℹ️ Pagedal, www.stadskanaal.nl.Daytime recreation.
🏛 Musica, Scheepswerfkade 34-35.Collection antique musical instruments. ⬛
01/04-31/10: Sa/Su 14-17, 01/07-31/08 Tue-Su 14-17.

🍴	Nieuwe Schans 🌿	4A5

Restaurant Golden Tulip Fontana, Weg naar de Bron 7. **GPS:** n53,17900
e7,20437.
🗑.
Remarks: Max. 1 night. At the thermal spa Fontana.

Tourist information Nieuwe Schans:
🌀 Fontana.Thermal baths and sauna. ⬛ thermae 9-23, sauna 14-23h, 01/10-
31/03 Sa-Su 11-23h.

🍴	Termunterzijl	4A5

't Golden Zieltje, Plankpad 7. **GPS:** n53,30163 e7,03376.
🗑€ 7,50.

🍴	Nieuwediep	4A5

Huize Bareveld, Bareveld 1. **GPS:** n53,04990 e6,84659.
🗑.

📷S	Veendam	4A5

Borgerswold, Flora 2. **GPS:** n53,10637 e6,84826.⬆➡

📷S	Onderdendam	3D5

Watersportvereniging Onderdendam, Warffumerweg 2. **GPS:** n53,33652
e6,58600.⬆

NL

60 ⛺ € 9/night 🚰🔧 Ch 🔌 WC 📶 included. 🛁
Location: Rural.
Surface: grassy.
🅿 01/01-31/12
Distance: 🚲2km 🏖beach 50m 🚏on the spot ⊗2km 🍴1km.

Tourist information Veendam:
🚂📷 Museumspoorlijn STAR, Parallelweg 4, Veendam.Museum railway line, tickets available at railwaystation. 🅿 01/04-31/10, 27/12-03/01. 🎫 round trip € 9,50.
🏛 Veenkoloniaalmuseum, Museumplein 5.History of the peat, schipping and industry. 🅿 Tue-Fri 11-17h, Sa-Su 13-17h 🌙 01/09-30/06 Mo.

♿ S	Wildervank	4A5

J. Geerling, Wildervanksterdallen 69. **GPS:** n53,04316 e6,89637.

5 ⛺ € 5 🚰🔧 🔌. **Surface:** grassy. 🅿 01/01-31/12
Distance: 🚏500m 🍴7km.
Remarks: Max. 72h.

♨ S	Wildervank	4A5

Sauna 't Dalhuus, Wildervanksterdallen 59. **GPS:** n53,05479 e6,88384.⬆
4 ⛺ customers free 🚰 € 1. **Surface:** metalled. 🅿 01/01-31/12
Distance: 🚲5km.
Remarks: Max. 24h. Some kilometres south-east of Wildervank.

🍴 S	Winschoten 🎳🚣	4A5

Hotel Café Restaurant Bowling In den Stallen, Oostereinde 10. **GPS:** n53,15371 e7,06528.⬆ .

10 ⛺ consuming is appreciated 🚰🔧 🔌 On demand 📶📹.
Surface: asphalted/metalled.
Distance: 🚲1km ⊗600m 🚏600m ⊗on the spot 🍴1km 🚌600m.
Remarks: A7 Groningen-Nieuweschans, exit Winschoten, then dir Beerta.

Tourist information Winschoten:
👁 Stoomgemaal, Winschoter Oostereinde.Steam-engine 1895.

♿ S	Zoutkamp	3D5

Jachthaven Hunzegat, Strandweg 17. **GPS:** n53,34083 e6,29000.

---

10 ⛺ € 10 excl. tourist tax 🚰🔧 Ch dump chem.toilet only with biodegradable liquid 🔧 (10x) WC 🔌🖥 washing machine/dryer € 7,40 📶.
Surface: grassy/metalled. 🅿 01/01-31/12
Distance: ⊗500m 🍴500m 🚌300m.
Remarks: Bread-service.

Tourist information Zoutkamp:
👁 Waddencentrum, Hoofdstraat 83, Pieterburen. Exhibition mud-flats and wading in the mudflats. 🅿 01/04-30/11 Tue-Su 13-17h, 01/11-31/03 Sa-Su 13-17h. 🎫 free.
👁 Zeehondencrèche, Hoofdstraat 94a, Pieterburen.Sanctory to cure sick seals. .

♿ S	Zuidbroek	4A5

De Broeckhof, W.A. Scholtenweg 18. **GPS:** n53,16103 e6,86235.

3 ⛺ free 🚰🔧 WC 🔌. **Surface:** metalled. 🅿 01/04-30/09
Distance: 🚲500m 🍴1km.
Remarks: Max. 72h. Parking community centre.

Drenthe

♿ S	Assen 🚮	3D6

Van Hobokenstraat 5. GPS: n53,00030 e6,57123.⬆.

5 ⛺ free 🚰 € 0,50 🔌 € 1. **Surface:** metalled. 🅿 01/01-31/12
Distance: 🚲1km ⊗50m 🍴500m.
Remarks: Max. 72h.

🏕	Assen 🚮	3D6

Citycamp Witterzomer, Witterzomer 7. **GPS:** n52,97997 e6,50296.⬆➡
8 ⛺ € 12. 🅿 01/01-31/12
Remarks: Departure < 10h, tel:+31(0)592-393535.

Tourist information Assen:
ℹ VVV, Marktstraat 8-10.

🕛 S	Barger Compascuum	4A6

Nationale Veenpark, Berkenrode 4. **GPS:** n52,75504 e7,02546.⬆.

50 🛏€5 🚰 🔧 included. **Surface:** grassy. ⭕ 01/01-31/12, 01/11-31/03 weekend, Mo-Fri by request
Distance: ✖100m.
Remarks: Max. 3x24h.

Tourist information Barger Compascuum:
😊 Veenpark-Wereld van Veen, Berkenrode 4.Life and Work in peat area, 160 acres of nature, peat and villages. ⭕ 01/04-31/10 10-17h, 01/07-31/08 10-18h. 🎫 >5: € 12,75.

| 🏕️ | **Eelderwolde** | **3D5** |

Scandinavisch Dorp, Oude Badweg 1. **GPS**: n53,17044 e6,55610.
5 🛏. **Surface:** asphalted.
Distance: 🚶2km ⛰500m 🚆on the spot ✖on the spot 🍽2km 🚌200m.

| ©S | **Eext** 🌿 | **4A6** |

Schaopvolte, Stationsstraat 60a. **GPS**: n53,00007 e6,72862.⬆

6 🛏€7 🚰€ 1 🚿Ch 🔧 (6x)€ 1 WC ⬛€ 0,50 🔌€ 4,50 📶€ 2/day.
Surface: grassy/gravel. ⭕ 01/04-01/11
Distance: 🚶2km.

| 🏕️S | **Elim** | **3D6** |

De Barswieke, Barsweg 9. **GPS**: n52,67144 e6,57821.⬆

10 🛏€6 🚰 🍽Chincluded 🔧€ 1,50 WC ⬛. **Surface:** grassy. ⭕ 01/01-31/12
Distance: 🚶1km 🍽1km.

| 🏕️ | **Emmen** | **4A6** |

Kerkhoflaan- van Schaikweg. **GPS**: n52,78091 e6,90330.⬆

5 🛏free. ⭕ 01/04-30/10

Distance: 🚶1km ✖Albert Heijn 600m.
Remarks: Max. 72h, Zoo Emmen 900m. Public parking place, behind hotel Eden

| △S | **Emmen** | **4A6** |

Citycamp De Bult, Bultseweg 7, Schoonebeek. **GPS**: n52,66967 e6,87824.⬆➡
54 🛏€15 🚰 🍽Ch 🔧€ 2,50 WC ⬛included ⬛against payment.
Surface: metalled.
⭕ 01/01-13/12
Distance: 🚶15km ⛰on the spot 🚆on the spot ✖on the spot 🍽on the spot 🚲on the spot 🏊on the spot.

Tourist information Emmen:
ℹ VVV, Hoofdstraat 22, www.vvvemmen.nl.
😊 Noorder Dierenpark, Hoofdstraat 18.Zoo. ⭕ from 10h.

| 🏕️ | **Hoogeveen** | **3D6** |

Terpweg 3. **GPS**: n52,72639 e6,50040.⬆

3 🛏free. **Surface:** metalled. ⭕ 01/01-31/12
Distance: 🚶2km 🚴2,2km ✖100m 🍽1km 🚌1km.
Remarks: At sports park, max. 72h.

Tourist information Hoogeveen:
Ⓜ Museum de 5000 Morgen, Hoofdstraat 9.Town history. ⭕ Tue-Su 13-17h. 🎫 € 2.

| ©S | **Matsloot** | **3D5** |

Camping Pool, Matsloot 1a. **GPS**: n53,19354 e6,44980.

10 🛏€ 5,50 🚰 🍽Ch 🔧 WC ⬛included ⬛€ 5. **Surface:** grassy. ⭕ 01/04-15/10
Distance: 🚶5km ⛰200m.
Remarks: On Leekster lake.

| 🏕️S | **Meppel** | **3D6** |

Jachthaven, Westeinde 32. **GPS**: n52,69615 e6,18096.

5 🛏€ 3,50/pp 🚰 🍽Ch 🔧 ⬛€ 3, dryer € 3. **Surface:** grassy.
Distance: 🚶500m ⛰on the spot 🚆on the spot ✖on the spot 🍽400m.

| 🏕️S | **Nieuwlande** | **3D6** |

Bonenstee, Brugstraat 87. **GPS**: n52,67889 e6,61194.⬆

NL

20 ⬛€6 ⬛ ⬛Ch ⬛ (6x)€ 1,50 WC included. **Location:** Rural. **Surface:** grassy/metalled. ⬛ 01/04-31/10

Distance: ⬛2km ⬛4km ⬛4km ⬛2km ⬛2km ⬛100m ⬛ bike junction ⬛ on the spot.

Remarks: Max. 72h.

⬛	**Norg**	3D5

Hotel restaurant De Klokbeker, Westeind 7. **GPS:** n53,06723 e6,45756. 2⬛.

⬛	**Oosterhesselen**	4A6

Sauna Hesselerbrug, Verlengde Hoogeveensevaart 32. **GPS:** n52,73535 e6,72029.⬛.

10 ⬛ use of sauna obligatory. **Surface:** metalled. ⬛ 01/01-31/12

Distance: ⬛4km ⬛on the spot ⬛on the spot ⬛on the spot ⬛4km.

⬛	**Roden**	3D5

Restaurant de Pompstee, Brink 25. **GPS:** n53,13577 e6,43312. 2⬛.

⬛	**Rouveen**	8D1

De Roustap, Dedemsvaartseweg 35, N377. **GPS:** n52,58620 e6,21180. ⬛.

Remarks: Between A28 and Dedemsvaart.

⬛	**Schoonebeek**	4A6

Kegelhuis Dorgelo, Europaweg 93. **GPS:** n52,66025 e6,88951. 3 ⬛ free for clients.

Tourist information Schoonebeek:

⬛ Hunebedden.Megalithic monuments.

⬛ S	**Wijster**	3D6

Grondsels, Grondselweg 7. **GPS:** n52,80246 e6,48667.⬛.

6 ⬛€5 ⬛ ⬛Ch WC ⬛. **Surface:** grassy/metalled. ⬛ 15/03-31/12

Distance: ⬛3km ⬛on the spot ⬛3km ⬛6km.

Overijssel

⬛ S	**Almelo**	9A1

De Grenzen, Havenkade. **GPS:** n52,36000 e6,65694.⬛.

3 ⬛€ 4,50 Ch WC ⬛ included ⬛ washing machine/dryer € 2,25. **Surface:** metalled. ⬛ 01/01-31/12

Distance: ⬛300m ⬛on the spot ⬛200m ⬛200m ⬛100m.

Remarks: Parking marina (in centre) north side, max. 72h, check in at harbourmaster.

Tourist information Almelo:

⬛ VVV, Rosa Luxemburgstraat 8, www.vvvalmelo.nl.

⬛ De Meelzolder/Bolletjewinkel, Grotestraat Zuid 182.Baker's shop and bakery museum. ⬛ Tue-Fri 10-17.30h, Sa 10-17h.

⬛ Weekmarkt, Centrumplein. ⬛ Thu 8-16h, Sa 8-17h.

⬛	**Bathmen**	8D1

De Uutvolg, Prinses Margrietlaan 14. **GPS:** n52,25066 e6,30004.

2 ⬛ free. **Surface:** metalled. ⬛ 01/01-31/12

Distance: ⬛1km ⬛2,5km.

Remarks: Parking gymnasium.

⬛ S	**Belt Schutsloot**	3D6

Café-Restaurant de Belt, Havezatheweg 4. **GPS:** n52,66774 e6,05189.

10 ⬛ free for clients WC ⬛. **Surface:** asphalted. ⬛ 01/01-31/12

Distance: ⬛3km ⬛1km ⬛1km ⬛on the spot ⬛3km.

Remarks: North of Zwartsluis, at Belter- and Beulakerwijde.

⬛	**Borne**	9A1

Parking de Koem, De Koem. **GPS:** n52,29957 e6,75800.⬛.

1 ⬛€ 5/24h. **Surface:** metalled. ⬛ 01/01-31/12

Distance: ⬛on the spot ⬛50m ⬛on the spot.

Remarks: Max. 72h.

NL

🏕S ▲ **De Lutte** 🎱 9A1
Erve Velpen, Beuningerstraat 25. **GPS:** n52,33224 e7,01197.⬆️.

9 🏕€6 + tourist tax € 0,90/pp 🚿€ 1 🔌Ch 🧹€ 2 📶included. 🚰
Location: Rural, comfortable, isolated, quit.
Surface: grassy. ⭕ 01/01-31/12
Distance: 🛒4km ⊗300m 🚲 bike junction 🚶on the spot.

🏕S **Dedemsvaart** 8D1
Camperplaats Dedemsvaart, Langewijk 112. **GPS:** n52,60435 e6,45108.⬆️.

20 🏕€5 🚿€ 2,50 🔌🧹€ 2,50 📶. 🚰 **Surface:** metalled.
⭕ 01/01-31/12
Distance: 🛒700m ⊗300m 🚲200m.
Remarks: Max. 48h.

🏕S **Deventer** 🍃 8D1
Zeil- en Motorbootvereniging Deventer, Rembrandtkade. **GPS:** n52,26660 e6,12828.

4 🏕€10 🚿€ 0,50 🔌Ch 🧹WC 🚰€ 0,50 📶included.
Surface: metalled.
Distance: ⚓on the spot.
Remarks: Check in at harbourmaster, park right after turning into road (end of the road too small to turn).

Tourist information Deventer:
ℹ️Ⓜ️ VVV/Historisch museum, Brink 56, www.vvvdeventer.nl.Hanseatic city with historical centre.

🍴S **Diepenheim** 🏕🎱 8D2
't Holt, Hengevelderweg 1A. **GPS:** n52,19500 e6,59186.⬆️.

3 🏕€ 5, free for clients 🚿🔌Ch free.
Surface: metalled. ⭕ 01/01-31/12
Distance: 🛒3km ⊗on the spot 🚲3km.
Remarks: Golf court (pitch+putt).

🍴 **Diepenheim** 🏕🎱 8D2
In de Kokkerieje, Grotestraat 94. **GPS:** n52,19923 e6,55452.⬆️.

🏕free with a meal.
Distance: 🛒on the spot 🚌1km 🚲500m.
Remarks: Parking behind restaurant.

🏕 **Enschede** 🏕🎱 9A2
Diekmanterrein, Weggelhorstweg. **GPS:** n52,20543 e6,90096.⬆️.

5 🏕free. **Location:** Urban, very simple, isolated, quit. **Surface:** asphalted. ⭕ 01/01-31/12
Distance: 🛒2km 🚴1,4km 🚌on the spot.

🛖S **Enschede** 🏕🎱 9A2
Citycamp De Twentse Es, Keppelerdijk 200. **GPS:** n52,21028 e6,95139.⬆️➡️.
80 🏕€ 27 🚿🔌Ch 🧹WC 🚰included 🅿️against payment.
Surface: grassy.
⭕ 01/01-31/12
Distance: 🛒5km 🏊on the spot 🚌on the spot ⊗on the spot 🚲1km 🚌1km.
Remarks: Tel:+31 (0)53-4611372.

🏕 **Enter** 8D1
Werfstraat. **GPS:** n52,29812 e6,58310.⬆️.
3 🏕free. **Location:** Very simple.
Surface: metalled/sand. ⭕ 01/01-31/12
Distance: 🛒600m ⊗600m 🚲700m 🚲on the spot 🚶on the spot.

🍴S **Geesteren** 9A1
Zalencentrum Spalink, Koelenbeekweg 10. **GPS:** n52,44060 e6,69555.

🏕15 guests free 🚿🔌Ch 🧹WC.
Surface: grassy/gravel. ⭕ 01/01-31/12
Distance: 🛒3,5km ⊗on the spot 🚲3,5km 🚲on the spot 🚶on the spot.

🏕S **Giethoorn** 🍃 3D6
Passantenhaven Zuidercluft, Vosjacht 1G. **GPS:** n52,72134 e6,07449.

NL

30 ⬛€ 10, 2 pers.incl., 1/11-1/4 €5 ⚡€ 0,50/100liter ⬛Ch ✦€ 1/2kWh WC ⬛€ 0,50. **Surface:** grassy. ◗ 01/01-31/12
Distance: ⬛1km ⬛on the spot ⬛on the spot.
Remarks: Water closed during wintertime, check in at harbourmaster.

| | | Giethoorn 🌿 | 3D6 |

Camperplaats Haamstede, Kanaaldijk 17. **GPS:** n52,72828 e6,07570.⬆➡.

35 ⬛€ 11, 2 pers.incl ⚡€ 0,50 ⬛Ch ✦€ 2 WC ⬛€ 0,50.🚌
Location: Rural, comfortable, central, quit.
Surface: grassy.
◗ 01/04-31/10
Distance: ⬛2km ⬛1km ⬛20m ⬛1km ⬛1km ⬛on the spot ⬛on the spot.

Tourist information Giethoorn:
ℹ VVV, Eendrachtsplein 1, www.kopvanoverijssel.nl.Village in nature reserve De Weerribben, Dutch Venice, boat trips possible.

| | | Haaksbergen | 9A2 |

Henk Pen Caravans en Kampeerauto's, Westsingel 2. **GPS:** n52,14917 e6,71167.

2 ⬛free ✦. **Surface:** asphalted. ◗ 01/01-31/12
Distance: ⬛1km ⬛on the spot ⬛on the spot ⬛1km.
Remarks: Motorhome dealer.

| | | Hardenberg | 8D1 |

De Kuserbrink, Parkweg. **GPS:** n52,57746 e6,62927.⬆.

4 ⬛€ 10 ⚡€ 0,50/100liter ⬛Ch ✦(4x)€ 1/kWh. 📧 **Location:** Rural,

comfortable, central, quit. **Surface:** grasstiles. ◗ 01/01-31/12
Distance: ⬛centre 500m ⬛on the spot ⬛on the spot.
Remarks: Max. 72h.

| | | Hardenberg | 8D1 |

Fam. Pullen, Allemansweg 1a, Collendoorn. **GPS:** n52,58845 e6,59146.⬆.

20 ⬛€ 8,50 ⚡ ⬛Ch ✦ 🛜included. 🚌 **Location:** Rural, comfortable, isolated, quit. **Surface:** grassy. ◗ 01/01-31/12
Distance: ⬛3km ⬛3km ⬛bike junction ⬛on the spot.
Remarks: Dogs on leads.

| | | Hasselt | 8C5 |

Jachthaven de Molenwaard, Van Nahuysweg 151. **GPS:** n52,59309 e6,08706.

5 ⬛€ 8, tourist tax excl ⚡⬛Ch ✦€ 1,50 WC ⬛€ 0,50.
Surface: metalled.
◗ 01/01-31/12
Distance: ⬛500m ⬛on the spot ⬛on the spot ⬛500m ⬛500m ⬛500m.
Remarks: Check in at harbourmaster.

| | | Heeten | 8D1 |

De Baanbreker, Speelmansweg 8. **GPS:** n52,36026 e6,31190.⬆.

10 ⬛€ 3,50 ⚡€ 1 ⬛€ 0,50 Ch€ 0,50 ✦€ 1,50. **Surface:** metalled. ◗ 01/01-31/12
Distance: ⬛2km ⬛2km ⬛2km.

| | | Hellendoorn | 8D1 |

Camperplaats Hancate, Ommerweg 150/a. **GPS:** n52,43420 e6,44072.⬆➡.

10 ⬛€ 8 ⚡⬛Ch ✦🛜included. **Surface:** grassy. ◗ 01/01-31/12
Distance: ⬛Hellendoorn 5km ⬛100m ⬛200m.

NL

Hertme 9A1
Camperpark Rabo Scheele, Hertmerweg 37. GPS: n52,32663 e6,74698. ↑→.

25 🅟 € 10, 2 pers.incl ⚡ Ch ✎ WC ⌐included. **Surface:** grassy/metalled.
🅞 01/01-31/12
Distance: Hertme 500m, Borne 2km 100m ✕500m ⚡2km.

Kampen 8C1
Burgemeester Berghuisplein 1. **GPS:** n52,55274 e5,91306.

25 🅟 free ⚡ free Ch WC ⌐€ 0,50.
Surface: metalled. 🅞 01/01-31/12
Distance: historical centre 500m ⚡ on the spot ⚡ on the spot.
Remarks: Max. 72h.

Tourist information Kampen:
🄸 VVV, Oudestraat 151, www.vvvkampen.nl.Former Hanseatic town on the Ijssel.

Losser 9A1
Brilmansdennen, Bookholtlaan. **GPS:** n52,26917 e7,01361. ↑→.

3 🅟 free. **Surface:** metalled. 🅞 01/01-31/12
Distance: 1km.
Remarks: At sports park, max. 72h.

Nijverdal 8D1
De Wilgenweard, Sportlaan 6. GPS: n52,37139 e6,46568. ↑.

3 🅟 € 5 + €0,50/pp tourist tax ⚡ Ch ✎ WC ⌐included. **Surface:** grasstiles/metalled. 🅞 01/01-31/12, service 01/05-31/10
Distance: 500m ⚡ on the spot ⚡ on the spot ✕on the spot ⚡500m.

Tourist information Nijverdal:
Ⓜ Amerikaans Motorfiets Museum, Zwolsestraat 63C, Raalte.Collection of motorcycles, Harley Davidson and curiosa. 🅞 Fr-Sa 11-17, Su 13-17, 01/05-31/10: Mo-Sa 11-17, Su 13-17.

Oldemarkt 3C6
Vaartjes partycentrum, Kruisstraat 86-88. GPS: n52,82095 e5,96698. ↑→.

10 🅟 free for clients. **Surface:** asphalted. 🅞 01/01-31/12
Distance: 200m ⚡ on the spot ⚡ on the spot ✕on the spot ⚡200m.
Remarks: A32, exit 7, north of Weerribben.

Ommen 8D1
Landgoed De Stekkenkamp, Beerzerweg 3. **GPS:** n52,50722 e6,49806.

8 🅟 € 7,50/night, € 0,80pp tourist tax ⚡ ⚡ included.
Distance: 1,2km.
Remarks: Max. 72h, at historical farmhouse.

Ommen 8D1
De Lindenberg, Balkerweg 17a. GPS: n52,53527 e6,40993. ↑.

10 🅟 free for clients ⚡.
Surface: metalled. 🅞 01/01-31/12 ◉ Mon, Tue.
Distance: ✕on the spot ⚡80m.

Tourist information Ommen:
🄸 VVV, Kruisstraat 6.
Ⓜ Oudheidkamer, Den Oordt 7.Historical costumes, jewellery, school interior. 🅞 Tue-Fri 10-17h, Sa 12.30-16h.
Ⓜ Tinnen Figuren Museum, Markt 1.Tinware. 🅞 Apr-Oct Tu-Sa 11-17h, Su/holidays 13-17h.

Saasveld 9A1
Café-Restaurant Het Molenven, Bornsestraat 60. **GPS:** n52,32814 e6,78360.

Remarks: At road Borne-Weersело.

Steenwijk 3D6
Jachthaven, Houthaven. **GPS:** n52,78627 e6,10006. ↑→.

NL

20 📷€10 ⛽🍽🚿€ 1. **Surface:** grassy. 🅾 01/01-31/12
Distance: 🚲1km 🛒on the spot 🚤on the spot 🚉300m.
Remarks: Check in at harbourmaster.

Tourist information Steenwijk:
Ⓜ Kermis- en Circusmuseum, Onnastraat 3. 🅾 Tue-Fri 10-12h, 14-16.30h,
01/07-31/08 Mo-Fri 11-16.30h.

10 📷€10 ⛽🍽Ch🚿 included. 🅾 15/02-15/12 ⬛ during wet period.
Distance: 🚲2km 🏊3km 🚤2km 🚌700m.
Remarks: Max. 3 nights, max 3,5t.

| 🚐Ⓢ | Wierden 🌿⛲🎡 | 8D1 |

Wijngaard Baan, Kloosterhoekweg 15, Rectum. **GPS:** n52,32172 e6,56709.
6 📷€6 ⛽€ 1 🍽Ch🚿€ 2.

| 🚐Ⓢ | **Tubbergen** | 9A1 |

De Vlaskoel, Sportlaan 3. **GPS:** n52,41043 e6,78316.⬆.

| 🚐Ⓢ | Wijhe 🛶 | 8D1 |

Passantenhaven, Loswal. **GPS:** n52,38611 e6,12750.

2 📷free. **Location:** Very simple. **Surface:** metalled. 🅾 01/01-31/12
Distance: 🚲500m ⊗600m 🚤600m 🚴on the spot 🎣on the spot.
Remarks: At swimming pool.

5 📷€5 ⛽🍽Ch WC🚿€ 0,50. **Surface:** metalled. 🅾 01/05-01/10
Distance: 🚲500m 🛒on the spot 🚤500m.
Remarks: Max. 72h. At the dike from Zwolle to Deventer, marina at IJssel, N337.

Tourist information Wijhe:
ℹ Village on the river IJssel, signposted cycle and hiking routes.
🎡 Weekmarkt, Marktplein. 🅾 Tue-morning.

| 🚐Ⓢ | Vollenhove 🌿⛲ | 3C6 |

De Haven. GPS: n52,68277 e5,94862.⬆.

| 🍴 | Zalk | 8C1 |

Wegrestaurant Hotel Zalkerbroek, Rijksweg 3. **GPS:** n52,50619 e5,97004.
🚿.
Remarks: N50, south of Kampen.

| 🚐Ⓢ | Zwartsluis | 3D6 |

Voetbalvereniging DESZ, Clingellanden. **GPS:** n52,64437 e6,07810.

6 📷€10 ⛽🍽Ch🚿€ 1 WC🚿€ 0,50. **Surface:** metalled.
🅾 01/01-31/12
Distance: 🚲100m ⊗100m 🚤1km.
Remarks: Check in at harbourmaster.

| ©Ⓢ | Vollenhove 🌿⛲ | 3C6 |

Recreatiecentrum 't Akkertien, Op de Voorst, Noordwal 3. **GPS:** n52,67609
e5,93914.

15 📷€5 ⛽🍽Ch. **Surface:** gravel.
Remarks: Service at marina.

Tourist information Zwartsluis:
ℹ VVV, Stationsweg 32.
👁 Stoomgemaal Mastenbroek, Kamperzeedijk 5, Genemuiden.Pumping-engine, 1856.

| 🚐Ⓢ | Zwolle 🌿 | 8D1 |

Jachthaven de Hanze, Holtenbroekerdijk. **GPS:** n52,53012 e6,07410.⬆.

20 📷€8 ⛽🍽Ch🚿 included. 🅾 01/01-31/12
Distance: 🚲900m 🛒on the spot 🚤on the spot 🚉400m 🚌peak season.

| 🚐Ⓢ | Wierden 🌿⛲🎡 | 8D1 |

De Huurne, Zandinksweg 22. **GPS:** n52,34899 e6,57191.

10 🛏8 ⛽ Ch ⚡€ 1/kWh WC 🚻. 🛥 **Location:** Comfortable, isolated, quit. **Surface:** grassy. 🅾 01/05-01/11
Distance: 🚶2,5km ⚓2km 🚉1km 🚲bike junction 500m.
Remarks: Max. 72h.

2 🛏€ 1,05/m per night ⛽ Ch WC 🚻€ 0,50. **Surface:** metalled. 🅾 02/05-04/09
Distance: 🚶on the spot ⚓1km 🚤on the spot ⊗on the spot 🚉1km.
Remarks: Max 72h, check in at harbourmaster.

🏛	Zwolle 🌿	8D1

Turfmarkt. **GPS:** n52,51333 e6,10369.

🏛S	Almere-Haven	8B1

WSV Almere, Sluiskade 11. **GPS:** n52,33257 e5,21715.
8 🛏€ 11, 2 pers.incl ⛽ Ch included ⚡€ 0,50/2kWh WC 🚻🔊. 🅾 01/01-31/12
Distance: ⚓on the spot ⊗150m 🚉200m.

Tourist information Almere-Haven:
🎪 Weekmarkt, De Brink. 🅾 Fri 9-16h.

🏅	Lelystad	8C1

P Houtribhoek, Houtribslag. **GPS:** n52,54630 e5,45750. ⬆➡

3 🛏mo-sa 8-18h € 5/day, free overnight stay. **Surface:** metalled.
Distance: 🚉650m.

△S	Zwolle 🌿	8D1

Citycamp De Agnietenberg, Haersterveenweg 27. **GPS:** n52,53698 e6,13066. ⬆➡
10 🛏from € 16 ⛽ Ch ⚡ WC included 🚻€ 0,50.
Surface: grassy/gravel.
🅾 01/04-01/11
Distance: 🚶3km ⚓on the spot 🚤on the spot ⊗on the spot 🚃800m.
Remarks: Tel: +31 (0)38-4531530.

Tourist information Zwolle:
ℹ VVV, Grote Markt 20, www.vvvzwolle.nl.Former Hanseatic town on the IJssel.
👁 Sassenpoort, Koestraat 46.Medieval gate building. 🅾 Wed-Fri 14-17h, Sa-Su 12-17h.
😊 Ecodrome, Willemsvaart 19.Theme park, history of nature, geology. 🅾 01/04-31/10 10-17, 01/11-31/03 Wed, Sa, Su 10-17h.

Flevoland

🏛S	Almere 🌿🍃	8B1

Marina Muiderzand, IJmeerdijk 4. **GPS:** n52,34302 e5,13521. ⬆➡

4 🛏free.
Surface: metalled.
🅾 01/01-31/12
Distance: 🚶2km ⚓on the spot 🚤on the spot ⊗on the spot 🚉2km.
Remarks: Max. 48h.

Tourist information Lelystad:
👁 Bataviawerf, Oostvaardersdijk 01-09.Ship-historical museum, reconstruction VOC-ships, historical dutch trading ships. 🅾 Mo-Su 10-17h.
Ⓜ Nieuw Land Erfgoedcentrum.Reclamation of land of the former Zuiderzee.
🌿 Oostvaardersplassen.6000 acres of lakes, mud fields, reed swamps, hiking route 5km and cycle route 35 km.
🛍 Batavia Stad, Bataviaplein 60.Outlet-shopping. 🅾 daily 10-18h. 🅿 free, parking € 2,50/4h.

Ⓒ	Luttelgeest	3C6

Recreatie en Horeca bedrijf Craneburcht, Kuinderweg 52. **GPS:** n52,78304 e5,84331.
10 🛏€ 10. **Surface:** metalled. 🅾 01/03-31/11 🌙 winter: Mo-Tue.
Distance: 🚶200m ⊗on the spot 🚉7km.
Remarks: >17h <10h.

🏵S	Nagele	3C6

Afslag Nagele, Han Stijkelweg 11. **GPS:** n52,65278 e5,68417. ⬆

10 🛏€ 11 ⛽ Ch ⚡€ 2 WC 🚻included. 🛥 **Location:** Comfortable,

10 🛏€ 12,50 ⛽ Ch ⚡ WC 🚻included 🔌€ 5, dryer € 3 🔊 🧺.
Surface: asphalted. 🅾 01/05-30/09
Distance: 🚶8km ⚓on the spot 🚤on the spot ⊗on the spot 🚉on the spot 🚃1km.
Remarks: Check in at harbourmaster.

🏛S	Almere-Haven	8B1

Haven, Sluis. **GPS:** n52,33366 e5,22170. ⬆

NL

isolated, quit. **Surface:** grassy/metalled. 🅾 01/01-31/12
Distance: 🚶3km.
Remarks: Max. 72h.

Urk 🌊 3C6
Haven, Burgemeester Schipperkade. **GPS:** n52,66040 e5,59975.⬆

24 🛏€13 🚰🔌Ch 🧹 (18x) WC 🚽📷📶included. 🚿
Surface: metalled.
🅾 01/01-31/12
Distance: 🚶200m ⊗100m 🛒100m, bakery 300m.

Tourist information Urk:
ℹ VVV, Wijk 3 2, www.vvvflevoland.nl.Old fishermen's village, former island.
🏛 Het Oude Raadhuis, Wijk 2 2.Regional museum. 🅾 01/04-31/10 Mo-Fr
10-17h, Sa 10-16h, 01/03-30/11 Mo-Sa 10-16h.
🌾 Weekmarkt, Urkerhard. 🅾 Sa 8.30-13h.
✏ Stegentocht/Ginkiestocht.Guided walk, reservation at Touristinfo Urk.
🎫 € 4.

Zeewolde 8C1
Camperpark De Wielewaal, Wielseweg 9. **GPS:** n52,25981 e5,43727.

50 🛏€11 🚰🔌Ch 🧹 WC 🚽against payment. **Surface:** metalled. 🅾
01/01-31/12
Distance: 🚶7km ⊃on the spot 🚐on the spot 🛒7km.

Gelderland

Aalten 8D2
't Noorden, Lichtenvoordsestraatweg 44. **GPS:** n51,93326 e6,58221.⬆

4 🛏€10 🚰€ 1/80liter 🔌Ch 🧹included WC free.🏠 **Location:** Rural.
Surface: gravel. 🅾 01/01-31/12
Distance: 🚶700m ⊗on the spot.

Tourist information Aalten:
ℹ VVV, Landstraat 24, www.vvvaalten.nl.
👁 Wijngoed De Hennepe, Romienendiek 3.Guided tour and tastery. 🅾 shop
Tue-Fr 13.30h-sunset, Sa 10h, guided tour/tasting Jul/Aug We 15h.
🌾 Weekmarkt, Hoge Blik. 🅾 Thu 8-12h.

Aerdt 8D2
De Aerdtse Wacht, Heuvelakkersestraat 18. **GPS:** n51,88634 e6,08861.⬆

4 🛏€10 🚰€ 1/80liter 🔌Ch 🧹.🏠 **Location:** Rural. **Surface:** metalled.
🅾 01/01-31/12
Distance: 🚶on the spot 🚐on the spot 🐟on the spot 🎣on the spot.

Almen 🐾 8D2
De Nieuwe Aanleg, Scheggertdijk 10. **GPS:** n52,16639 e6,29750.⬆

10 🛏€10 🚰€ 0,75/100liter 🔌 🧹 WC 🚽€ 0,75. **Surface:** metalled. 🅾
01/01-31/12
Distance: 🚶3km ⊃on the spot 🚐on the spot ⊗on the spot 🚐on the spot.
Remarks: Behind restaurant, at the Twentekanaal.

Tourist information Almen:
👁 Mosterdmakerij Boesveld, Dorpsstraat 39. 🅾 Tue-Fri 13.30-17h, Sa 9-16h.

Beek 8D2
De Sprokkelaar, Sint Jansgildestraat 77. **GPS:** n51,90440 e6,19073.
3 🛏.
Remarks: N335, Didam-Zeddam.

Beek 8D2
Hotel-Café-Restaurant 't Heuveltje, Sint Jansgildestraat 27. **GPS:** n51,91413
e6,19423.
🛏.
Remarks: N335, Didam-Zeddam.

Bemmel 8C2
Dijkstraat/Wardstraat. **GPS:** n51,88972 e5,90972.⬆

3 🛏free. **Surface:** metalled. 🅾 01/01-31/12
Distance: 🚶400m.
Remarks: Max. 72h.

Bemmel 8C2
Het wapen van Bemmel, Dorpsstraat 52. **GPS:** n51,89116 e5,89791.
🛏.

Borculo 8D2
Hambroekplas, Hambroekweg 10. **GPS:** n52,11573 e6,53758.⬆

4 € 10 € 1/80liter Ch included. **Location:** Rural, comfortable, quit. **Surface:** gravel. 01/03-31/10
Distance: 500m 150m 50m on the spot on the spot.

S Borculo 8D2

Bruggink Campers, Kamerlingh Onnestraat 19. **GPS**: n52,12281 e6,52682.

6 free On demand. **Surface:** metalled. 01/01-31/12, 18-9h
Distance: 1,5km 2km 500m 1,5km 1,5km.

S Braamt 8D2

De Blonde Hoeve, Braamweg 2. **GPS**: n51,92789 e6,26084.

4 € 10 € 1/80liter Ch included. **Location:** Rural, quit.
Surface: grassy. 01/01-31/12 bike junction on the spot.

S Bredevoort 9A2

P2, recreatieplaats Slingeplas, Kruittorenstraat 10b. **GPS**: n51,94536 e6,61977.
4 € 10 € 1 Ch included.
Location: Rural, isolated, quit.
Surface: gravel. 01/01-31/12
Distance: 100m 3km on the spot 500m.
Remarks: Max. 72h.

Tourist information Bredevoort:
City with half-timbered houses.
Book market. 3rd Sa of the month 10-17.

Breedenbroek 8D2

Café-Restaurant Koenders, Terborgseweg 61. **GPS**: n51,87324 e6,47406.
01/01-31/12
Remarks: North of Dinxperlo.

S Culemborg 8B2

Jachthaven de Helling, Helling. **GPS**: n51,96117 e5,22148.

2 € 10 € 0,50/100liter Ch € 1/kWh WC washing machine/dryer € 4. **Surface:** grassy/sand. 01/04-01/11
Distance: 500m on the spot on the spot on the spot 500m 1,5km.
Remarks: Check in at harbourmaster.

S De Heurne 8D2

De Haar, Caspersstraat 14. **GPS**: n51,89802 e6,50035.

± 10 € 10 € 1/80liter Ch included. **Location:** Rural, quit.
Surface: grassy. 01/01-31/12
Distance: 1km 8km.
Remarks: Filling station gas bottles 300m.

Dinxperlo 8D2

P2, Europastraat 2. **GPS**: n51,86361 e6,49833.

3 free. **Surface:** metalled. 01/01-31/12
Distance: 200m on the spot 200m.
Remarks: Crowdy during weekends, Max. 72h. Parking at country park, follow Eurohal.

S Dinxperlo 8D2

Tankstation Wikkerink, Antholtseweg 30. **GPS**: n51,85640 e6,47643.
Ch.

Tourist information Dinxperlo:
VVV, Aaltenseweg 2, www.vvvdinxperlo.nl.
Grenslandmuseum, Markt 3.Life near the border area. 01/04-31/10 Tue-Sa 15-17h. € 1.
Kerkje de Rietstap.Smallest church of the country. So 14-17h. free.
Weekmarkt. Fri 13-20h.

Eerbeek 8D2

De Korenmolen, Kanaalweg 3. **GPS**: n52,10820 e6,07531.

Eibergen 9A2

Café-Restaurant Grenszicht, Vredenseweg 2, Holterhoek. **GPS**: n52,05381 e6,68445.
5
Remarks: Dir Zwillbrock.

NL

S | Elburg | 8C1
Havenkade 1. **GPS:** n52,45081 e5,82972. ⬆.

5 🅅 € 7,50 + € 0,90/pp tourist tax ⬛ 🅆 Ch WC included 🅆 € 0,50. **Surface:** metalled. ⬛ 01/01-31/12
Distance: 🚶250m ⚓on the spot ⚓on the spot ⊗300m.
Remarks: Max. 3 days.

S | Emst | 8C1
Recreatiepark 't Smallert, Smallertsweg 8. **GPS:** n52,30910 e5,98126. ⬆.

20 🅅 € 5 ⬛ free. **Surface:** metalled. ⬛ 01/01-31/12
Distance: 🚶2km ⊗on the spot.

S | Epe | 8C1
Pastoor Somstraat. **GPS:** n52,34965 e5,98331. ⬆.
3 🅅 free. **Location:** Urban, very simple.
Surface: metalled. ⬛ 01/01-31/12
Distance: 🚶on the spot ⚓3km ⊗on the spot 🍷on the spot.

S | Ermelo | 8C1
Surfcamping Horst, Buitenbrinkweg 82. **GPS:** n52,31222 e5,56611. ⬆.

40 🅅 € 7 ⬛ € 3 🅆 Ch 🅆 WC 🅆 € 0,50 🅆 free. **Surface:** grassy. ⬛ 01/03-31/10
Distance: 🚶4km ⚓200m ⚓200m ⊗500m 🍷4km.

🍴 | Garderen | 8C2
Hotel Restaurant Overbosch, Hooiweg 23. **GPS:** n52,22483 e5,70702.

10 🅅 € 5 🅆 € 5. **Surface:** gravel.
Remarks: Use of a meal appreciated, not obliged.

🍴 | Garderen | 8C2
Gasterij Zondag, Apeldoornsestraat 163-165. **GPS:** n52,21419 e5,70972. 🅅.
Remarks: Cross roads N344 and N310.

S | Geldermalsen | 8B2
Kostverlorenkade. **GPS:** n51,88421 e5,28985.

1 🅅 free. **Surface:** metalled.
Distance: 🚶100m ⚓3,6km ⚓on the spot ⚓on the spot ⊗on the spot.
Remarks: Parking at departure excursion boat.

S | Gendringen | 8D2
Willem Alexanderplein. **GPS:** n51,86999 e6,37948. ⬆.

3 🅅 free. **Location:** Very simple. **Surface:** asphalted. ⬛ 01/01-31/12
Distance: 🚶200m ⊗100m 🍷500m.
Remarks: Max. 72h.

S | Gendringen | 8D2
Dieckhuus, Ulftseweg 4a. **GPS:** n51,87397 e6,38489. ⬆.

4 🅅 € 10 ⬛ 🅆 🅆 included. 🅂 **Location:** Rural. **Surface:** gravel. ⬛ 01/01-31/12
Distance: 🚶600m ⊗600m.
Remarks: At manege.

S | Groenlo | 9A2
Camping Marveld, Elshofweg. **GPS:** n52,03698 e6,63187. ⬆.

4 🅅 € 10 ⬛ € 1/80liter 🅆 Ch 🅆 . **Surface:** metalled. ⬛ 01/01-31/12

⛺Ⓢ Groesbeek 8C3

Hotel-Restaurant Rozenhof, Nijmeegsebaan 114, Heilig Landstichting. **GPS**: n51,81659 e5,88220.

2 🅿 € 5, free with a meal ⛽ ⚡ € 5/night 🚿.
🅾 05/01-27/12

Tourist information Groesbeek:

Ⓜ Afrikamuseum, Postweg 6, Berg en Dal.Africa museum. 🅾 Mo-Fri 10-17h, Sa-Su 11-17h 🅾 01/11-31/03 Mo.
Ⓜ Bevrijdingsmuseum 1944, Wylerbaan 4.Liberation museum. 🅾 10-17h, Su 12-17h.
😊 Amusementspark Tivoli, Oude Kleefsebaan 116, Berg en Dal.Amusement park. 🅾 01/04-31/10 10-17.30h, 01/04-30/04, 01/09-31/10 Wed, Fri-Su. Ⓣ € 11.

🅿 Harderwijk 8C1

P Parkweg. **GPS**: n52,34088 e5,62977. ⬆️
3 🅿 free. **Location:** Very simple. **Surface:** metalled. 🅾 01/01-31/12
Distance: 🚂1,2km 🚲3km ⊗1,3km 🏪800m.

🅿Ⓢ Hattem 🌿 8D1

Jachthaven Hattem, Geldersedijk 20. **GPS**: n52,47750 e6,06981.

10 🅿 € 10 + € 0,85 tourist tax ⛽ 🔌Ch ⚡ WC 🍴 📶 included. **Surface:** grassy/metalled. 🅾 01/01-31/12
Distance: 🚂200m 🏊on the spot 🛒on the spot ⊗200m 🏪200m 🚌50m.
Remarks: Max. 72h, check in at harbourmaster.

Tourist information Hattem:

Ⓜ Bakkerijmuseum 'Het Warme Land', Kerkhofstraat 13. 🅾 Tue-Sa 10-17.

⛺Ⓢ Heerde 🌿🏊⚡ 8D1

Restaurant De Keet Van Heerde, Eperweg 55. **GPS**: n52,37084 e6,02079.

10 🅿 free, use of a meal desired ⛽ ⚡ (2x)included WC 📶 🚿. **Surface:** grassy/gravel.
Distance: 🚂3km 🏊1,5km 🛒1,5km ⊗on the spot 🏪2km 🚌100m.
Remarks: A50, exit 28, Heerde south, then after ±200m.

🅿 Hengelo-Gld 8D2

Sportvelden/zwembad, Elderinkweg 1-9. **GPS**: n52,04457 e6,30377. ⬆️

2 🅿 free. **Surface:** asphalted. 🅾 01/01-31/12
Distance: 🚂500m 🚌100m.
Remarks: Max. 24h.

🅿 Heteren 8C2

Boterhoeksestraat/Nijburgsestraat. **GPS**: n51,95450 e5,73072.

3 🅿 free. **Surface:** metalled.
Distance: 🚂2km.
Remarks: Max. 72h. Metalled motorhome parking nearby former castle.

🅿 Huissen 🌿🏊⚡🛒 8C2

Looveer. **GPS**: n51,93674 e5,94505. ⬆️

3 🅿 free. **Surface:** metalled.
Distance: 🚂200m 🏊Bathing 200m 🛒200m ⊗200m 🏪200m.
Remarks: Max. 72h.

🅿Ⓢ Kerkwijk 8B3

Hippisch Centrum Bommelerwaard, Jan Stuversdreef 1-3. **GPS**: n51,78876 e5,19929.
4 🅿 € 10 ⚡ 📶 included. **Surface:** metalled. 🅾 01/01-31/12

⛺ Laren (GE) 8D2

Hotel-Café-Restaurant Stegeman, Dorpsstraat 1. **GPS**: n52,19222 e6,36614.
2 🅿.
Remarks: Between Lochem and Deventer.

🅿Ⓢ Lathum 8D2

Jachthaven 't Eiland, De Muggenwaard 16. **GPS**: n51,98890 e6,04921. ⬆️
6 🅿 € 8,50 ⛽ 🔌Ch ⚡ WC 🍴 📶 🚿 **Location:** Rural, comfortable, quit.
Surface: grassy. 🅾 01/01-31/12
Distance: 🚲5km 🏊on the spot 🛒on the spot ⊗on the spot 🚴on the spot 🎣on the spot.
Remarks: At marina, max. 48h.

🅿 Lichtenvoorde 8D2

't Meekenesch, Kerkhoflaan 5. **GPS**: n51,99305 e6,56831. ⬆️

NL

3 🗺 free. **Surface:** metalled. ⬛ 01/01-31/12
Distance: 🚶1km 🚰100m.
Remarks: Parking swimming pool, max. 72h.
Tourist information Lichtenvoorde:
Ⓜ Museum Erve Kots, Eimersweg 4, Lievelde.Open air museum. ⬛ 10-17, inn 10-19.30/20.

🅿 S   Maasbommel 🌿🍴🏖   8C3
Saletmeubelen, Kapelstraat 30. **GPS:** n51,82459 e5,53193.⬆.

5 🗺 € 8 🚰🔌🛜 included. ⬛ 01/01-31/12
Distance: 🚶300m ⛵1km 🛥1km ⊗1km 🚲300m.

🍴 Meteren   8B2
Restaurant den Tol, Rijksstraatweg 80. **GPS:** n51,85759 e5,28009.

5 🗺 free.
Remarks: A15 Rotterdam-Nijmegen, exit Meteren.

🅿 S   Millingen a/d Rijn   8D2
't Crumpse Hoekje, Crumpsestraat 28. **GPS:** n51,85624 e6,03145.⬆➡.

6 🗺 € 6,50 + tourist tax € 0,75/pp 🚰 € 1/90liter 🔧 Ch 🛠 (6x)€ 2/day
WC free 🗑 1.🛝 **Location:** Rural, luxurious, quit. **Surface:** gravel. ⬛
01/01-31/12
Distance: 🚶1,4km 🛥2km ⊗1,4km 🚲1,4km.

🍴 S   Neede   8D2
Café restaurant De Olde Mölle, Diepenheimseweg 21. **GPS:** n52,14153 e6,61035.

4 🗺 € 10 🚰 € 1/80liter 🔌 Ch 🛠. **Surface:** metalled.
Distance: ⊗on the spot.

🍴 S   Neede   8D2
Partycentrum 't Haantje, Borculoseweg 111. **GPS:** n52,13437 e6,59886. ⬆.

5 🗺 € 5, free with a meal 🚰🔌🛠 WC included. **Surface:** gravel.
Distance: 🚶600m ⊗on the spot 🚲500m 🚰on the spot.
Remarks: Rental of electric scooters and bicycles.

🗺 S   Nijmegen 🌿🍴🏖   8C2
Lindenberghaven, Waalkade. **GPS:** n51,84889 e5,86936.⬆.

6 🗺 € 20 🚰🛠 (6x)€ 0,50/kWh. 🔌🛝 **Location:** Urban, very simple, central, noisy. **Surface:** metalled. ⬛ 01/05-01/09 ⬤ during the Four Days Marche.
Distance: 🚶on the spot ⛵on the spot 🛥on the spot.
Remarks: Along the river Waal, max. 72h.

🔺 S   Nijmegen 🌿🍴🏖   8C2
Citycamp Heumens Bos, Vosseneindseweg 46, Heumen. **GPS:** n51,76941 e5,81927.⬆⬆➡.
6 🗺 € 23 - € 31 🚰🔌 Ch 🛠 WC 🗑included 🔌against payment. **Surface:** grassy/sand. ⬛ 01/01-31/12
Distance: 🚶3km ⊗on the spot 🚲on the spot 🛝on the spot 🧗on the spot.
Remarks: Tel± +31 (0)24-3581481.

🗺 S   Nunspeet 🌿🍴🏖🍴   8C1
Camperplaats De Zwaan, Hardenbrinkweg 46. **GPS:** n52,37901 e5,75363. ⬆➡.

25 🗺 € 12 🚰🔌 Ch 🛠 4Amp WC 🗑included 🛜. **Surface:** grasstiles. ⬛
01/01-31/12

Distance: 🚶1,5km 🚲1km 🚉1,5km.
Remarks: No arrival on Sunday.

| 🏪 S | Nunspeet ☀🎣🍴🍺🏚 | 8C1 |

Routiers Nunspeet, Rijksweg A28. **GPS:** n52,36199 e5,77061. ⬆.

🚐free WC 🚽. **Surface:** asphalted.

| 🏪 S | Otterlo 🏕🍴 | 8C2 |

De Wije Werelt, Arnhemseweg 100-102. **GPS:** n52,08592 e5,77319.
16 🚐 18 🔌 Ch 🚰 WC 🚽 📶. **Surface:** metalled. 🅾 01/04-01/11
Remarks: Max. 2 nights.

Tourist information Otterlo:
Ⓜ Kröller Möller Museum.Collection.
🌿 De Hoge Veluwe.Nature reserve, signposted cycle and hiking routes. 🅾
01/04-31/08 8h-sunset, 01/09-31/03 9h.

| 🚐 | Putten | 8C1 |

Brinkstraat. **GPS:** n52,26254 e5,60758. ⬆.

2 🚐free. **Surface:** metalled. 🅾 01/01-31/12
Distance: 🚶200m 🚲300m 🚉300m 🚌250m.
Remarks: Max. 48h.

| 🍴 | Rekken | 9A2 |

Grensovergang, Oldenkotseweg. **GPS:** n52,09783 e6,75568. ✈.

5 🚐 € 5. **Surface:** metalled. 🅾 01/01-31/12
Distance: 🚶on the spot 🚲on the spot 🚉on the spot.
Remarks: Max. 72h, cycle and hiking routes.

| 🏪 S | Ruurlo | 8D2 |

Camping Tamaring, Wildpad 3. **GPS:** n52,10239 e6,44257. ⬆.

2 🚐 € 10 🔌 € 1/80liter 🧺Ch 🚰 included. 🚐 **Location:** Isolated. **Surface:** forest soil. 🅾 01/01-31/12
Distance: 🚶3km.
Remarks: Max. 8m.

| 🏪 S | Sinderen | 8D2 |

Biezenhof, Kapelweg 42a. **GPS:** n51,90370 e6,45285. ⬆.

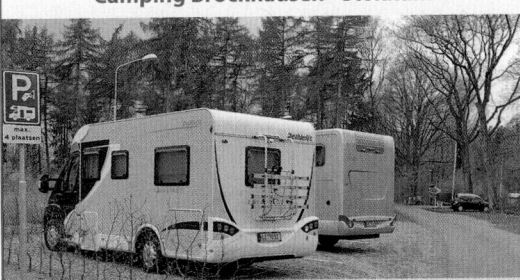

4 🚐 € 10 🔌 € 1/80liter 🧺Ch 🚰 included. 🚐 **Location:** Rural. **Surface:** gravel. 🅾 01/01-31/12

| 🏪 S | Stokkum 🍴 | 8D2 |

Camping Brockhausen - Stokkum

info@brockhausen.nl - www.brockhausen.nl
Paved and flat motorhome pitches
Walking and bicycle area
Good satellite reception

Camping Brockhausen, Eltenseweg 20. **GPS:** n51,87778 e6,21167. ⬆.
4 🚐 € 10 🔌 € 1/80liter 🧺Ch 🚰 included 📶 4/day. 🚐 **Location:** Rural.
Surface: gravel. 🅾 01/01-31/12
Distance: 🚶800m 🚲500m 🚉2,5km 🚌2km 🚴 on the spot 🚶on the spot.
Remarks: Max. 2 nights, bread-service.

| 🚐 | Tiel ☀🎣🍴🍺 | 8C2 |

Parking Waalkade, Waalkade. **GPS:** n51,88518 e5,44079. ⬆.

4 🚐 € 3. **Surface:** asphalted. 🅾 01/01-31/12
Distance: 🚶500m 🚤on the spot 🚲on the spot 🚲on the spot 🚉500m

NL

🚐on the spot.
Remarks: Max. 2 nights.

| 🏕 | Tolkamer | 8D2 |

Europakade, Europakade. **GPS:** n51,85130 e6,09927. ⬆️.

10 🛏 € 7,40. **Surface:** metalled. 🅾 01/01-31/12
Distance: ⊗150m 🚰200m.
Remarks: Max. 48h.

| 🍴 | Tolkamer | 8D2 |

De Swaenebloem, Bijland 3. **GPS:** n51,86268 e6,07800.

🛏free with a meal. 🅾 01/01-31/12
Distance: 🚶Lobith 3,5km 🚤100m 🚐on the spot ⊗on the spot.
Remarks: Max. 2 nights, charging point for electric bicycles. Along rivier, follow recreation area Bijland.

| 🏕 | Twello | 8D2 |

Jachtlustplein 7. **GPS:** n52,23424 e6,09810.

2 🛏free. **Surface:** metalled.
Distance: ⊗within walking distance 🚰within walking distance.
Remarks: Max. 24h.

| 🏕 | Vaassen 🌿🍴 | 8C1 |

Julianalaan. **GPS:** n52,29040 e5,96550. ⬆️.
4 🛏free. **Surface:** asphalted.
Distance: 🚶on the spot ⊗100m.
Remarks: Max. 48h.

| 🏕 | Varsseveld | 8D2 |

Pallandtbad, Pallandstraat 4. **GPS:** n51,94444 e6,46639.

4 🛏free. **Surface:** metalled. 🅾 01/01-31/12
Distance: 🚶200m ⊗200m 🚰200m 🚐200m.
Remarks: Max. 24h.

| 🌿S | Voorst | 8D2 |

De Adelaar - Voorst

info@campingdeadelaar.nl - www.campingdeadelaar.nl

Comfortable motorhome stopover
Beautiful view
Sanitary facilities

De Adelaar, Rijksstraatweg 49. **GPS:** n52,17760 e6,14150. ⬆️.
10 🛏 € 12,50 🚐🔌Ch 💧 (10x)€ 2 WC 🚰€ 0,50 🚿€ 4, dryer € 4 📶.
Location: Rural. **Surface:** grassy/metalled. 🅾 01/01-31/12
Distance: 🚶500m 🚲7km 🚤on the spot 🚐on the spot ⊗150m 🚰1km.
Remarks: Use camp-site facilities incl.

| 🌿S | Voorst | 8D2 |

Boerderij de Kolke, Klarenbeekseweg 30. **GPS:** n52,17355 e6,13318.
16 🛏 € 6 🚐🔌Chincluded 💧€ 1. **Surface:** grassy/metalled.
Remarks: Regional products.

| 🍴 | Voorthuizen | 8C2 |

Hooghe Hof, Brugveenseweg 25. **GPS:** n52,18268 e5,63172.
🛏.

| 🏕S | Westendorp 🍴 | 8D2 |

Recreatieoord Hippique, Doetinchemseweg 141. **GPS:** n51,94964 e6,42084. ⬆️.

4 🛏 € 10 🚐€ 1/80liter 🔌Ch 💧included WC 🚰€ 2 🚿 washing machine/
dryer € 5 📶. 🏪 **Surface:** grasstiles. 🅾 01/01-31/12
Distance: 🚶500m ⊗500m 🚰3km 🚐600m 🐾on the spot.
Remarks: Arrival 9><20h.

| 🍴S | Wilp | 8D2 |

Eetcafé De Kroon, Kerkstraat 28. **GPS:** n52,21909 e6,15317.

8 🛏 € 5 🚐🔌Ch 💧€ 2,50 WC 🚰€ 1 🚿€ 4,50. **Surface:** metalled. 🅾
01/01-31/12
Distance: 🚶500m 🚤800m ⊗on the spot 🚰500m 🚐200m.
Remarks: Check in at bar. Parking between restaurant and dike.

🏕️S Winterswijk 9A2
Landgoed Kreil, Heenkamppieperweg 1. **GPS:** n51,93573 e6,67907.⬆️

2 🛢️€10 🚰€ 1/80liter 🚽Ch 🧹included 📶against payment. 🚗
Location: Rural, isolated. **Surface:** metalled. 🅾️01/03-31/10
Distance: ♿Breedevoort 4,5km 🚶Located on estate.

🆔S Winterswijk 9A2
Camping Ten Hagen, Waliënsestraat 139A. **GPS:** n51,99131 e6,71898.⬆️

4 🛢️€10 🚰€ 1/80liter 🚽Ch 🧹included. **Location:** Rural, very simple, isolated, quit. **Surface:** grassy. 🅾️01/01-31/12
Distance: ♿city centre 3km ⛵lake.
Remarks: Max. 24h, Manufacturer of wooden clogs.

🆔S Winterswijk 9A2
Vreehorst, Vreehorstweg 43. **GPS:** n51,95028 e6,69251.⬆️

4 🛢️€10 🚰€ 1/80liter 🚽Ch 🧹included. 🚗 **Location:** Rural, comfortable.
Surface: gravel. 🅾️01/01-31/12
Distance: ♿3,6km.

🛢️ Zelhem 8D2
Carpoolplaats, Stikkenweg/N330. **GPS:** n51,99893 e6,34541.⬆️

2 🛢️free. **Surface:** asphalted. 🅾️01/01-31/12
Distance: ♿1km.
Remarks: Max. 24h.

🛢️S Zutphen 🍴 8D2
Houtwal. GPS: n52,13565 e6,19866.⬆️

8 🛢️€10 🚰€ 1/80liter 🚽Ch 🧹included. **Surface:** metalled. 🅾️01/01-31/12
Distance: ♿1km.
Remarks: Nearby police station, beautiful view, max. 48h.

Zutphen 🍴 8D2
IJsselkade. GPS: n52,14037 e6,19119.⬆️

2 🛢️€ 7,80. **Surface:** metalled. 🅾️01/01-31/12
Distance: ♿1km.
Remarks: Max. 48h, motorhome max. 6m.

Tourist information Zutphen:
ℹ️ VVV, Stationsplein 39, www.vvvzutphen.nl.Tour past art and antique stores.
🌾 Biologische boerenmarkt, Lange Hofstraat. 🅾️Thu 8-13h.
🌾 Weekmarkt, Groenmarkt-Houtmarkt-Zaadmarkt. 🅾️Thu 8-12h, Sa 8-17h.

Utrecht

🛢️S Amersfoort 🍴 8C2
Aan de Eem, Klein Koppel. **GPS:** n52,16210 e5,37829.⬆️
3 🛢️€ 1,10/meter 🚰🚽🧹WC included. **Surface:** metalled. 🅾️01/01-31/12
Distance: ♿600m ⛵on the spot ⊗500m 🚊500m.
Remarks: At fire-station, max. 24h.

🆔S Baarn 🍴 8B2
De Zeven Linden, Zevenlindenweg 4. **GPS:** n52,19721 e5,24838.⬆️
2 🛢️€10 🚰€ 1,25 🚽Ch. **Surface:** metalled. 🅾️01/04-01/11

Tourist information Baarn:
ℹ️ VVV, Brinkstraat 12.The most famous house the Palace Soestdijk, dwelling hous of Queen Mother.

🆔S Bunnik 🍴 8B2
Camping de Boomgaard, Parallelweg 9. **GPS:** n52,06065 e5,19943.⬆️

6 🛢️€ 7,50 🚰Ch WC 🧹€ 2.
Surface: metalled. 🅾️01/04/31/10
Distance: ♿3km 🚊800m.
Remarks: Use camp-site facilities allowed, >17h <10h check in at reception next morning.

Tourist information Bunnik:

〰 Natuurgebied De Brakel.Nature reserve, information VVV Zeist (52,08271 5,24013). 🅞 guided tour 01/04-30/09 Wed 10.30h, Sa 13.30h, Su 10.30h, 13.30h.

| 🄢S | IJsselstein 〰🏕🌊 | 8B2 |

Jachthaven Marnemoende, Noord IJsseldijk 107b. **GPS**: n52,04583 e5,01861. ⬆.

3 ⌇€ 14 ⛽€ 0,50 🄒Ch ⚡WC ⬛🔌📶📹.
Surface: grassy/gravel.
🅞 01/01-31/12
Distance: 🚶2km 🏊on the spot 🛒on the spot ⊗on the spot 🍴2km 🚌2km.

| 🍴 | Leersum | 8C2 |

Touché, Rijksstraatweg 54. **GPS**: n52,00974 e5,43507.
⌇.
Remarks: N225, milestone 27.

| 🍴 | Leusden | 8C2 |

De Mof, Arnhemseweg 95. **GPS**: n52,10654 e5,41445.

| 🄢 | Mijdrecht | 8B2 |

Rondweg. **GPS**: n52,20804 e4,86879.⬆➡.

4 ⌇free. **Surface:** metalled. 🅞 01/01-31/12
Distance: 🚶500m ⊗500m 🛒500m 🚌500m.
Remarks: Max. 48h.

| 🄢S | Oudewater 〰🏕 | 8B2 |

Trekkerscamping Statenland, Statenland 1. **GPS**: n52,01778 e4,87306.🔼.

6 ⌇€ 10 ⛽ ⚡€ 2 WC ⬛🔌.
Surface: grassy. 🅞 01/05-15/09
Distance: 🚶3k
m 🛒on the spot ⊗3km 🛒3km 🚌500m.
Remarks: Check in at swimming pool (<17h), max. 3 nights.

Tourist information Oudewater:
ℹ VVV, Leeuweringerstraat 10, www.vvvgroenehart.nl.Historical little town.
🅞 01/04-31/10 Tue-Sa 10-17h, Su 12-17h.

| 🍴 | Overberg | 8C2 |

De Holle Boom, Dwarsweg 63. **GPS**: n52,02992 e5,49502.
⌇.

| 🍴 | Rhenen 〰 | 8C2 |

Restaurant La Montagne, Kerkewijk-zuid 115. **GPS**: n52,00682 e5,54006.
⌇free.
Remarks: N233, Veenendaal-Ochten, milestone 49.

| 🌙 | Veenendaal | 8C2 |

Sauna de Heuvelrug, Dijkstraat-West 189. **GPS**: n52,02496 e5,51990.🔼.

⌇free. **Surface:** gravel. 🅞 01/01-31/12
Distance: 🚶2km.
Remarks: Use of sauna obligatory. On ring-road N233 exit Overberg and campsite, entrance sauna after ±2km.

| 🄢 | Vianen 〰 | 8B2 |

Kanaalweg, P1. **GPS**: n51,99549 e5,09620.

4 ⌇free.
Surface: metalled. 🅞 01/01-31/12
Distance: 🚶500m.
Remarks: Max. 48h, during events: Hazelaarplein.

Tourist information Vianen:
ℹ VVV, Voorstraat 97, www.vvv-vianen.nl.Historical centre.
🕊 Voorstraat (zuid). 🅞 Wed 10-16h.

South Holland

| 🄢S | Alblasserdam 🏕🌊 | 8A2 |

Haven 4. **GPS**: n51,86106 e4,65799.⬆.

10 ⌇€ 10 ⛽€ 0,50 🄒Ch WC ⬛.🚗
Surface: asphalted. 🅞 01/01-31/12
Distance: 🚶500m 🚲1,3km ⊗on the spot 🛒500m.
Remarks: At cultural centre 'Landvast', Kinderdijk ± 4,5km, sanitary in harbour building against payment.

Tourist information Alblasserdam:
ℹ VVV, Cortgene 2, www.alblasserdam.nl.
👁 Molens, Nederwaard 1, Kinderdijk.World famous mill-area. 🅞 01/07-31/08 Sa, 1st Sa of the month.
🕊 Weekmarkt, Wilgenplein. 🅞 Mo-afternoon.

| 🄫S | Barendrecht | 8A3 |

Camping de Oude Maas, Achterzeedijk 1a. **GPS**: n51,83494 e4,54273.
7 ⌇€ 25, dog € 2,50 ⛽ 🄒Ch ⚡WC included 📹. **Surface:** metalled. 🅞

NL

01/01-31/12
Distance: 🚶1km ⊗on the spot 🛒1km.
Remarks: Pitches at marina.

△ S — Delft — 8A2

Citycamp Delftse Hout, Korftlaan 5. **GPS:** n52,01740 e4,37882. ⬆➡.
46 🚐 € 24 - € 28 ⚡ Ch 💧 € 4,50 WC ▯included ▯against payment 📷.
Surface: grasstiles. 🔌 22/03-01/11
Distance: 🚶1km 🏊300m 🛒300m ⊗on the spot 🛒on the spot 🚌300m.
Remarks: Tel:+31(0)15-2130040.

Tourist information Delft:
🅸 VVV, Hippolytusbuurt 4, www.delft.nl.Historical centre with canals and merchant houses. ⛪ church 01/03-31/10 Mo-Sa 9-18h, 01/11-28/02 Mo-Sa 11-16h.

🚐 — Dordrecht — 8A3

Weeskinderendijk 5. **GPS:** n51,80861 e4,65611. ⬆

2 🚐free. **Surface:** metalled. 🔌 01/01-31/12
Distance: 🚶500m ⊗500m 🛒500m 🚌100m.
Remarks: Max. 72h.

🚐 S — Giessenburg — 8B2

Boerenterras De Groot, A.M.A. Langeraadweg 9. **GPS:** n51,85327 e4,92205. ⬆
8 🚐 € 10 ⚡ Ch 💧 included. **Surface:** metalled. 🔌 01/01-31/12

🚐 S — Giessenburg — 8B2

Halfomhoeve, Bovenkerkseweg 78. **GPS:** n51,84632 e4,87610. ⬆
3 🚐 € 10 ⚡ Ch 💧 included. **Surface:** grassy/metalled.

🚐 S — Giessenburg — 8B2

Landscheiding Giessenburg, Landscheiding 1. **GPS:** n51,47370 e4,92320. ⬆
10 🚐 € 10 ⚡ Ch 💧 📶included. **Surface:** grassy/metalled. 🔌 01/01-31/12

🚐 S — Giessenburg — 8B2

Stal Vonk, Binnendamseweg 18. **GPS:** n51,83367 e4,86345. ⬆
3 🚐 € 10 ⚡ Ch 💧 included. **Surface:** concrete. 🔌 01/01-31/12

🚐 S — Gorinchem — 8B3

WSV Merwede, Buiten de Waterpoort 8. **GPS:** n51,82697 e4,96477. ⬆

8 🚐 € 7,50 ⚡ Ch 💧 € 2,50 ▯€ 0,70.
Surface: gravel/metalled.
🔌 01/01-31/12
Distance: 🚶500m 🏊on the spot 🛒on the spot ⊗300m.
Remarks: Max. 72h, check in at harbourmaster.

Tourist information Gorinchem:
🅸 VVV, Grote Markt 17, www.gorinchem.nl.Historical centre with city walls.
🗿⊗ Slot Loevestein, Loevestein 1, Poederoijen.Castle, 14th century. 🔌
01/05-30/09 Tue-Fri 11-17h Sa-Su-Mo-holidays 13-17h, 01/10-30/04 Sa-Su 13-17h.
🏛 Weekmarkt, Grote Markt. 🔌 Mo 8.30-12.30h.

🚐 S — Gouda — 8B2

Parking Klein Amerika, Fluwelensingel. **GPS:** n52,01185 e4,71576. ⬆

25 🚐 € 7,50 ⚡ Ch 💧 WC included.
Surface: metalled.
🔌 01/01-31/12
Distance: 🚶1km.
Remarks: Max. 3 days.

Tourist information Gouda:
🅸 VVV, Markt 27, www.vvvgouda.nl.Historical centre with 300 monuments, famous for its Gouda-cheese. 🔌 01/04-30/09 13-17h, Thu 10-17h.
⊛ Kaaswaag, Markt.History of the Gouda cheese. 🔌 01/04-30/09 13-17h, Thu 10-17h.
🏛 Montmartre, Markt.Antiques and flea market. 🔌 01/05-30/09 We 9-17h.
🏛 Weekmarkt, Markt. 🔌 Thu 8.30-13h, Sa 8.30-17h.

🚐 S — Goudriaan — 8B2

Boerderij de Verwondering, De Hoogt 14. **GPS:** n51,89150 e4,90741. ⬆

3 🚐 € 7,50 🚽 € 2,50 Ch 💧 € 2,50. **Surface:** concrete.

🚐 S — Hellevoetsluis — 8A3

Camping 't Weergors, Zuiddijk 2. **GPS:** n51,82908 e4,11918.
4 🚐 € 10 ⚡ Ch 💧 WC ▯. **Surface:** metalled. 🔌 01/04-01/11
Distance: 🚶2km.
Remarks: Max. 24h.

🚐 S — Hoogblokland — 8B2

Landwinkel De Bikkerhoeve, Bazeldijk 66. **GPS:** n51,89716 e4,99563. ⬆
6 🚐 € 10 ⚡ Ch 💧 included. **Surface:** gravel/metalled. 🔌 01/01-31/12

🚐 S — Leerdam — 8B2

De Galgenwaard, Lingedijk 8a, Oosterwijk. **GPS:** n51,87451 e5,07311. ⬆

3 🚐 € 8 ⚡ WC. **Surface:** asphalted. 🔌 01/04-01/10
Distance: 🚶Leerdam 2km 🏊on the spot 🛒on the spot ⊗300m..
Remarks: Opening hours 7-22h, passenger ferry across the Linge.

🚐 — Leerdam — 8B2

Groenzoom, Lingedijk. **GPS:** n51,88296 e5,08671. ⬆
2 🚐. **Surface:** metalled. 🔌 01/01-31/12
Distance: 🚶1km ⊗1km.

🚐 — Leerdam — 8B2

Jachthaven Oude Horn, Sundsvall 1. **GPS:** n51,88984 e5,09532. ⬆

NL

3 🛏free. **Location:** Very simple. **Surface:** gravel.
Distance: 🚶300m ⊗300m 🚲300m.

Leiden 8A2

P Haagweg, Haagweg 6. **GPS:** n52,15963 e4,47852.⬆.

15 🛏€ 10/24h. **Surface:** metalled.
Distance: 🚶800m ⊗800m 🚲800m 🚌Free bus to centre.
Remarks: Video surveillance, free shuttle (till 2am).

Maasdam 8A3

De Fruitgaarde, Polderdijk 47. **GPS:** n51,79814 e4,53125.

20 🛏€ 14 🚰🗑Ch 🔌€ 2 WC 🚻.🐑 **Location:** Rural, comfortable, quit.
Surface: grassy/metalled. 🔵 01/04-01/11
Distance: 🚶1km ⊛2km 🛒2km ⊗on the spot 🚲2km 🚌2km 🚴on the spot 🚶on the spot.
Remarks: Teahouse, sheep breeding, small shop with farm products.

Mijnsheerenland 8A3

Café-Restaurant 't Stamineeke, Brabersweg 10. **GPS:** n51,80838 e4,44144.
3 🛏.

Nieuwland 8B2

De Grienduil, Geer 25. **GPS:** n51,90106 e5,02622.
8 🛏€ 10-12 🚰🗑Ch 🔌WC 🚻. **Surface:** metalled. 🔵 01/01-31/12
Distance: 🚶on the spot ⊗2km 🚲4km.
Remarks: In winter limited services.

Oud Beijerland 8A3

De Oude Tol, Randweg 31a. **GPS:** n51,82933 e4,39585.⬆.
4 🛏free. **Surface:** asphalted. 🔵 01/01-31/12
Distance: 🚶2km ⊗100m.

Ouddorp 7D3

Drive-in Camperpark Klepperduinen, Vrijheidsweg 1. **GPS:** n51,81724 e3,89850.⬆➡.
51 🛏€ 8-10/12h, € 14,50-18/24h + tourist tax € 0,81/pp 🚰100liter 🗑
Ch 🔌€ 4/24h WC 🚻against payment 📶included ♻.📦 **Location:**
Rural, luxurious, quit. **Surface:** grassy/metalled. 🔵 01/01-31/12
Distance: ⊛1km ⊗on the spot 🚲on the spot.

Rotterdam 8A2

Routiers Distripark Eemhaven, Willembarentzstraat 1a, Albrantswaard. **GPS:** n51,87016 e4,42030.
🛏.
Remarks: A15, exit 18 (havens 2780), between Rotterdam and Spijkenisse.
Tourist information Rotterdam:
ℹ VVV, Coolsingel 5, www.rotterdam.info.World famous harbour, large city with modern centre, shops open on Sunday 12-17.
Ⓜ Mueum Boymans-Van Beuningen, Museumpark 18-20.Art museum. 🔵 Tue-Su 11-17h.

Schiedam 8A2

Nieuwe Haven 97. **GPS:** n51,91135 e4,40050.⬆.

2 🛏free 🚰. **Surface:** metalled. 🔵 01/01-31/12
Distance: 🚶5 min 🚲1,8km ⊗50m.
Remarks: Max. 72h. A20 exit 11 centrum, end of the road to the right at roundabout to the left, in front of restaurant Le Pêcheur.

Schiedam 8A2

Doelenplein. **GPS:** n51,91972 e4,40111.

2 🛏€ 5,50. **Surface:** metalled. 🔵 01/01-31/12
Distance: 🚶500m 🚲1,5km 🏊on the spot 🛒on the spot ⊗500m 🚲500m 🚌500m.
Remarks: Max. 72h.
Tourist information Schiedam:
ℹ VVV, Buitenhavenweg 9, www.ontdekschiedam.nu.
Ⓜ Het Jenever Museum, Lange Haven 74-76.Making distilled spirits. 🔵 Tue-Sa 12-17h, Su 13-17h.
🎪 Weekmarkt, Lange Kerkstraat. 🔵 Fri 9-16h.

Strijensas 8A3

Jachthaven Strijensas, Sassendijk 6. **GPS:** n51,71472 e4,58735.⬆.

6 🛏€ 7,50 🚰€ 0,50/100liter 🗑Ch 🔌€ 2,50 WC 🚻€ 1. **Surface:** asphalted. 🔵 01/01-31/12
Distance: 🚶500m ⊗on the spot 🚴on the spot 🚶on the spot.
Remarks: Max. 72h.

Vlaardingen 8A2

Parking Deltabrug, Oosthavenkade 81. **GPS:** n51,90364 e4,34769.⬆.

NL

4 🛏free. **Surface:** metalled. ⬛ 01/01-31/12
Distance: 🚉1km 🏊on the spot ⊗50m 🍴100m 🚍500m.
Remarks: Max. 48h. Nearby sluices, along railwayline.

| | S | Zevenhoven | 8B2 |

Camperplaats Zevenhoven, Noordeinde 36. **GPS:** n52,19475 e4,77305.
5 🛏€ 10 🔌🍴Ch 🛠 included. 🚲 **Location:** Rural, comfortable, isolated.
Surface: grassy/metalled. ⬛ 01/01-31/12
Distance: 🍴1km.

| 🍴 | 's-Gravenzande | 8A2 |

Hoeve de Viersprong, Nieuwlandsedijk 10-12. **GPS:** n51,99703 e4,13378.➡️
🛏.
Remarks: Free, use of a meal desired.

Zealand

| 🅿 | Axel | 7D4 |

P Watertoren, Kinderdijk 4. **GPS:** n51,25972 e3,91028.⬆️

2 🛏free. **Surface:** metalled. ⬛ 01/01-31/12
Distance: 🚉500m 🏊on the spot ⊗on the spot 🍴500m.
Remarks: Max. 24h.

Tourist information Axel:
🎪 Weekmarkt, Noordstraat. ⬛ Sa 8-16h.

| 🚐 | Emmadorp 🌿 | 8A4 |

Bezoekerscentrum Saeftinghe, Emmaweg 4. **GPS:** n51,32833 e4,14867.⬆️➡️
3 🛏free. ⬛ 01/01-31/12
Distance: 🏊on the spot.
Remarks: Max. 48h.

| 🚐 | Graauw | 8A4 |

Zandbergsestraat. **GPS:** n51,32519 e4,10420.
1 🛏free. **Location:** Rural. **Surface:** metalled. ⬛ 01/01-31/12
Distance: 🚉400m 🚍400m.

| © | S | Groede | 7D4 |

De Ploeg, Parking Zuid, Voorstraat 47. **GPS:** n51,38194 e3,51138.⬆️

25 🛏€ 5 17-10h, € 12,50/24h 🔌🍴Ch 🛠€ 2,50. **Surface:** metalled. ⬛
01/04-01/10 ⬛ 22-7h.
Remarks: >17h <10h.

Tourist information Groede:

🅜 Museumstraatje van het Vlaemsche Erfgoed, Slijkstraat 1. ⬛ summer
Mo-Sa 10-17h.

| 🚐 | Hansweert | 7D3 |

Westhavendijk. **GPS:** n51,44505 e4,00629.
5 🛏free. **Surface:** asphalted. ⬛ 01/01-31/12
Distance: 🚉250m.

| 🚐 | S | Hengstdijk | 7D4 |

De Zeeuwse Adelaar, Heernisse kerkpad 2. **GPS:** n51,32597 e4,01383.

4 🛏€ 7,50 🔌🍴Ch 🛠. **Surface:** metalled.
Remarks: Max. 72h.

| 🚐 | Hulst 🌿⛵🎁 | 8A4 |

Parkeerterrein Havenfort, Havenfort. **GPS:** n51,27700 e4,04912.

15 🛏€ 0,80/h, mo-sa 9-17h, su 12-18h. 🚌 **Surface:** metalled. ⬛ 01/01-
31/12
Distance: 🚉on the spot 🚍25m ⊗150m 🍴150m 🚍200m.
Remarks: Max. 72h, shops open on Sunday.

Tourist information Hulst:
ℹ️ VVV, Grote Markt 19, www.bezoekhulst.nl.Fortified city with city walls, shops
open on Sunday.
🅜 Streekmuseum "De vier Ambachten", Steenstraat 28. ⬛ Easter-autums
holiday 14-17h, winter changing visiting hours.

| © | S | Kamperland | 7D3 |

Roompot Beach Resort, Mariapolderseweg 1. **GPS:** n51,58972 e3,71666.

20 🛏€ 6 10-17h, € 14 17-10h 🔌🍴Ch 🛠 WC 🍴⬛ € 4,50, dryer € 1,20
📶🧺. **Surface:** asphalted. ⬛ 01/01-31/12
Distance: 🚉3km 🏊500m 🚍500m ⊗500m 🍴500m 🚍1km.

| △ | S | Kruiningen | 8A4 |

Den Inkel, Polderweg 12. **GPS:** n51,43485 e4,04448.
6 🛏€ 16-22 🔌🍴Ch 🛠 WC included. ⬛ 01/01-31/12

| 🚐 | S | Middelburg 🌿 | 7D3 |

Oude Veerseweg. **GPS:** n51,50071 e3,62842.⬆️
5 🛏free 🔌€ 1 🍴Ch 🛠€ 1. **Surface:** metalled.
Distance: 🚉1km 🚍100m ⊗500m 🍴1km.

| 🚐 | S | Middelburg 🌿 | 7D3 |

Hof van Tange. **GPS:** n51,49688 e3,60474.⬆️
5 🛏€ 8,50. **Surface:** metalled. ⬛ 01/01-31/12 ⬛ 1st week Aug.

NL

Distance: ⊗500m 🚰300m.
Remarks: Max. 48h.

🏕 Middelburg 〰   7D3
Kanaalweg. **GPS:** n51,49432 e3,61519.⬆.
3 🏕 € 8,50. **Surface:** concrete. 🅾 01/01-31/12
Distance: 🚶500m ⚓on the spot 🛒on the spot 🚰500m.
Remarks: Max. 48h.

🍴 Oosterland   8A3
Wok van Zeeland, Rijksweg 6. **GPS:** n51,65767 e4,05336.
3 🏕.
Remarks: N59, Oosterland, Duiveland, between Bruinisse and Zierikzee.

©S Oostkapelle   7D3
De Pekelinge, Landmetersweg 1.
GPS: n51,56525 e3,55058.
20 🏕 € 18,50-27,50 🚰 🔌 Ch 🔧 included.
Surface: metalled.
🅾 27/03-01/11
Distance: 🚶nearby ⚓nearby ⊗on the spot 🚰on the spot.
Remarks: Max. 1 night >20h <10h.

Tourist information Oostkapelle:
🛈 VVV Domburg, Schuitvlotstraat 32, www.vvvwnb.nl.Family seaside resort.
🅾 01/03-30/11 Tue-Su 13-17h.
Ⓜ✖ Kasteel Westhove.Medieval castle. 🅾 01/11-31/03 Tue-Su 12-17h,
summer 10-18h.

🏕 Paal ⛵   8A4
Jachthaven, Zeedijk van de van Alsteinpolder. **GPS:** n51,35331 e4,10937.⬆.
1 🏕free. **Surface:** metalled.
Distance: ⚓on the spot 🛒on the spot.

🏕 Sas van Gent 〰⛴   7D4
Kanaaleiland, Oostkade. **GPS:** n51,22527 e3,80246.⬆.

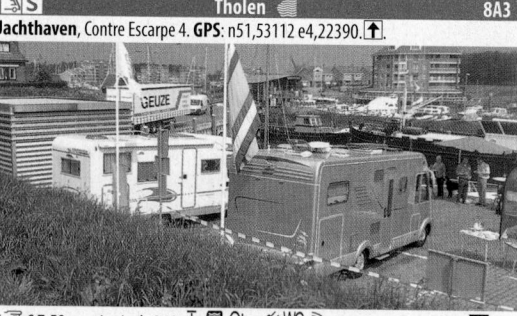

2 🏕free. **Surface:** metalled.
Distance: 🚶100m ⊗100m 🚰100m.
Remarks: Max. 24h.

Tourist information Sas van Gent:
⛺ Weekmarkt, Keizer Karelplein. 🅾 Tue 9-16h.

🏕 Terneuzen   7D4
Oostsluis, Binnenvaartweg. **GPS:** n51,33555 e3,82117.⬆.
4 🏕free. **Location:** Very simple. **Surface:** asphalted. 🅾 01/01-31/12
Distance: 🚶500m ⚓on the spot ⊗500m.

Tourist information Terneuzen:
⛺ Weekmarkt, Markt. 🅾 Sa 9-16h.

🏕S Tholen ⛵   8A3
Jachthaven, Contre Escarpe 4. **GPS:** n51,53112 e4,22390.⬆.

4 🏕 € 7,50, service incl. € 10 🚰 🔌 Ch 🔧 WC 📶. **Surface:** metalled. 🅾
01/03-01/10
Distance: 🚶100m ⊗100m 🚰100m.

🏕 Vogelwaarde   7D4
Schakeldreef. **GPS:** n51,32562 e3,97758.⬆.
2 🏕free. **Surface:** metalled.

🏕 Westdorpe   7D4
De Baeckermat, Bernhardstraat. **GPS:** n51,22917 e3,82167.⬆.

2 🏕free. **Surface:** metalled. 🅾 01/01-31/12
Distance: 🚶500m ⚓on the spot ⊗100m 🚰500m 🚐on the spot.
Remarks: Max. 24h.

©S Wolphaartsdijk   7D3
Camping 't Veerse Meer. GPS: n51,54325 e3,81253.
5 🏕 € 14 🚰 🔌 Ch 🔧 WC 📶 included.
🅾 01/01-31/12 🔘 15/11-15/12.
Distance: 🚶1,5km ⚓100m ⚓100m 🚰100m.

Tourist information Wolphaartsdijk:
🛈 VVV, Singelstraat 13, Goes, www.vvvzuidbevelandentholen.nl.Historical
centre.

©S Yerseke 〰   8A3
Camping Zon en Zee, Burenpolderweg 30A. **GPS:** n51,49871 e4,05319.
10 🏕 € 12,50 🚰 🔌 Ch 🔧 included.
Surface: metalled. 🅾 20/03-26/10

Tourist information Yerseke:
🛈 VVV, Kerkplein 1, www.vvvzuidbevelandentholen.nl.Oyster and mussel
culture.

🍴 Zaamslag   7D4
Kraaghof, Terneuzensestraat 89. **GPS:** n51,31284 e3,90869.
🏕. 🅾 12-21h 🔘 Mon, Tue.

North Brabant

🏕S Asten   8C4
Camperpark Wetland, Tureluurweg 7. **GPS:** n51,36687 e5,84214.⬆➡.

35 🏕 € 8,30, 2 pers.incl 🚰 🔌 Ch included 🔧 € 1,50 WC 🅾 € 2, dryer €
2 📶. **Surface:** grasstiles/metalled. 🅾 01/01-31/12
Distance: 🚶2km ⚓km ⚓20km ⚓8,5km ⊗2km 🚰2km.
Remarks: Located in nature reserve De Groote Peel.

Tourist information Asten:
Ⓜ Nationaal Beiaardmuseum, Ostaderstr 23.Collection bells and bell-founding.
🅾 Tue -Fri 9.30-17h, Sa-Mo 13-17h.

🏕S Beers   8C3
Kerkeveld 10. **GPS:** n51,73302 e5,82955.⬆.

10 �}€5 🔌🔧Ch🔧WC included. **Surface:** metalled. ⊙ 01/01-31/12

⌘free. **Surface:** grassy. ⊙ 01/01-31/12

Bergen op Zoom 8A3
De Boulevard Noord. **GPS:** n51,48735 e4,27708.⬆.

Etten-Leur 8A3
Jachthaven Turfhout, Westerpolderpad 6. **GPS:** n51,59556 e4,65444.

5 ⌘free. **Surface:** metalled. ⊙ 01/01-31/12
Distance: 1km 3,8km on the spot on the spot.
Remarks: Max. 72h. On the level of restaurant 'La Playa'.

Bergen op Zoom 8A3
Citycamp Uit en Thuis, Heimolen 56. **GPS:** n51,46912 e4,32129.⬆➡.
8 ⌘€15 🔌Ch🔧WC included 🔧€ 0,50.
Surface: metalled. ⊙ 01/04-31/10
Distance: 5km 4km on the spot 3,5km 1,5km on the spot on the spot.
Remarks: Tel: +31(0)164-233391.

Tourist information Bergen op Zoom:
ℹ VVV, Kortemeestraat 19, www.bergenopzoom.nl. Historical centre with 700 monuments.
De Markiezenhof, Steenbergsestraat 8. Medieval city palace. ⊙ Tue-Su 11-17h.

Best 8C3
Carpoolplaats De Wilg. **GPS:** n51,52106 e5,39423.⬆.
3 ⌘free. **Surface:** metalled. ⊙ 01/01-31/12
Distance: 150 m.
Remarks: Max. 24h.

Breda 8B3
Citycamp Liesbos, Liesdreef 40. **GPS:** n51,56504 e4,69618.⬆➡.
6 ⌘from €17,95 🔌Ch🔧WC included 🔧€ 0,15/1minutes ⬛against payment.
Surface: grassy.
⊙ 01/04-01/10
Distance: 3,5km 8km 6km on the spot 3,5km 700m.
Remarks: Tel:+31(0)76-5143514.

Tourist information Breda:
ℹ VVV, Willemstraat 17-19, www.vvvbreda.nl. Many historical bldg. And castles.

Eindhoven 8C4
Citycamp 't Witven, Runstraat 40, Veldhoven. **GPS:** n51,39930 e5,41200.⬆➡.
14 ⌘€24,50 🔌Ch🔧WC included ⬛against payment. **Surface:** metalled. ⊙ 01/010-31/12
Distance: 3km on the spot on the spot on the spot on the spot on the spot on the spot on the spot.
Remarks: Tel:+31 (0)40-2300043.

Escharen 8C3
Bar Bistro De Brouwketel, Hoogeweg 9. **GPS:** n51,74152 e5,73376.⬆.

18 ⌘€10 🔌Ch🔧WC included 🔧€ 1 ⌘free. **Surface:** grassy. ⊙ 01/01-31/12
Distance: 1,5km on the spot 500m.
Remarks: Max. 72h.

Tourist information Etten-Leur:
🔧 ⊙ Mo-morning.

Geertruidenberg 8B3
Statenlaan 2. **GPS:** n51,70333 e4,86333.⬆.

2 ⌘free 🔧. **Surface:** metalled. ⊙ 15/03-31/10
Distance: 500m 500m.
Remarks: Max. 24h. Parking in front of marina, nearby centre.

Tourist information Geertruidenberg:
ℹ VVV, Markt 46, www.geertruidenbergdigitaal.nl. Fortified city with historical centre.

Gemert 8C3
Koksehoeve, Koksedijk 25. **GPS:** n51,57380 e5,65846.
🔧.

Grave 8C3
Pater van den Elsenstraat. **GPS:** n51,76170 e5,73580.⬆.

⌘free. **Surface:** sand. ⊙ 01/01-31/12
Remarks: Max. 72h.

NL

Heusden 🏵   8B3
Wijkse poort, 't Ravellijn. **GPS**: n51,73472 e5,13417.

2 🚰free.
Surface: metalled. ◻ 01/01-31/12
Distance: 🚻200m ⚓on the spot 🛒on the spot ⊗on the spot 🛒200m.
Remarks: Max. ^3m. Parking within the fortifications, at the Wijksepoort, in village follow signs centre, not P-vesting.

Tourist information Heusden:
ℹ️ VVV, Pelsestraat 17, www.heusden.nl.Fortified city.
🏛 Vismarkt. ◻ Thu 13-18h.

🏠S   Hoogerheide   8A4
Fa. Broos, Buitendreef 4. **GPS**: n51,42522 e4,34656.
5 🚰free 🚿🔌Ch 🔧free. **Surface**: metalled. ◻ 01/01-31/12
Remarks: Industrial area 'de Kooi'.

🍴S   Hulten   8B3
Restaurant Stad Parijs, Rijksweg 6. **GPS**: n51,56996 e4,96446.
🚰free 🗄against payment. ◻ 01/01-31/12
Remarks: Free, use of a meal obligated. N282 provincial route Tilburg-Breda.

🏠S   Linden ⚓   8C3
Jachthaven Brasker, Hardweg 15. **GPS**: n51,75182 e5,82740.⬆

2 🚰free 🚿🔧. **Surface**: metalled. ◻ 01/01-31/12

🏠   Raamsdonksveer   8B3
De Uilendonck, Lageweg 8, Raamsdonk. **GPS**: n51,68540 e4,91380.⬆
3 🚰free. **Surface**: metalled. ◻ 01/01-31/12

🏠   Raamsdonksveer   8B3
Kloosterweg 1. **GPS**: n51,68908 e4,87582.⬆

4 🚰free. **Surface**: metalled.
Distance: 🚻800m ⊗on the spot 🛒800m.
Remarks: Parking at sports park.

🍴S   Reusel   8B4
Café-Restaurant de Klok, Turnhoutseweg 32. **GPS**: n51,35564 e5,14272.
3 🚰free 🚿🔧 WC. **Surface**: metalled. ◻ 01/01-31/12
Distance: 🚻2km.

🍴   Reusel   8B4
De Wekker, Wilhelminalaan 97. **GPS**: n51,36187 e5,17339.
5 🚰.

🏠S   Roosendaal 🏵   8A3
Mobildrôme, Argon 31-33. **GPS**: n51,56333 e4,46278.

11 🚰€ 10 🚿🔌Ch 🔧€ 1,50/day WC 🗄€ 1 🚽€ 2/day. **Surface**: grassy.
◻ 15/04-15/10
Distance: ⚓on the spot 🛒on the spot ⊗on the spot 🛒on the spot.
Remarks: Check in at harbourmaster 9-12h, 15-18h, caution key sanitary building € 20.

🍴   Maarheeze   8C4
Restaurant De Ark, Stationsstraat 75. **GPS**: n51,31336 e5,61996.
🚰.

🔺S   Mierlo 🍴   8C4
Boscamping 't Wolfsven, Patrijslaan 4. **GPS**: n51,43888 e5,59000.
6 🚰from € 16 🚿🔌🔧 WC 🗄€ 4,50, dryer € 1,20 🚽♻. **Surface**: asphalted. ◻ 26/03-21/10
Distance: 🚻3km ⚓150m 🛒150m ⊗1km 🛒on the spot 🚗1km.

🏠S   Oosteind   8B3
Van Dongen, Ter Horst 19. **GPS**: n51,64705 e4,88326.
4 🚰€ 8 🚿🔌Ch 🔧included. **Surface**: grassy.
Distance: 🚻2km ⊗500m.

🏠S   Oss   8C3
Van Venrooy Motorhomes, Galliërsweg 39. **GPS**: n51,75981 e5,55642.⬆

8 🚰free 🚿€ 0,50 🔌Ch 🔧€ 0,50. **Surface**: metalled.
Distance: 🚻2km 🚲1,1km 🛒2km.

Tourist information Roosendaal:
ℹ️ VVV, Markt 71, www.vvvroosendaal.nl.
🧺 Rosada, A17, afrit 19.Factory outlet.

🍴   Soerendonk   8C4
De Valk, Dorpsstraat 36. **GPS**: n51,30360 e5,57314.
20 🚰. **Surface**: gravel.
Remarks: Max. 48h.

Ⓢ | Vessem | 8B4

Eurocamping Vessem - Vessem

info@eurocampingvessem.com - www.eurocampingvessem.com

Open all year
Flat motorhome pitches
Comfortable motorhome stopover

Eurocamping Vessem, Zwembadweg 1. **GPS**: n51,41197 e5,27490.⬆️.
40 🛏️€ 9 🚰€ 0,50/80liter 🔌Ch 💧€ 0,60/kWh 🚽 0,50 📶€ 5/day.
Surface: grassy. ◻️ 01/01-31/12
Distance: 🚲5km 🏊7km ⛰️5km ⚓on the spot ⊗5km 🛒on the spot.

Ⓢ | Wijk en Aalburg | 8B3

Bakkerij Hardeman, Torenstraat 4. **GPS**: n51,75976 e5,13123.

3 🛏️€ 5 🚰 🔧free. ◻️ 01/01-31/12
Remarks: Parking bakery, next to church of Wijk.

🍴 | 's-Gravenmoer | 8B3

Samen Eten en Drinken, Hoofdstraat 75. **GPS**: n51,65147 e4,94172.
🛏️free for clients.

Limburg

Ⓢ | Brunssum | 8D5

Schutterspark P1, Heidestraat 20. **GPS**: n50,94582 e5,98385.

12 🛏️free 🚰free. **Surface**: metalled. ◻️ 01/01-31/12
Distance: 🚲1,5km ⊗100m Schuttershuuske.
Remarks: Max. 72h, barefoot path.

📷 | Gronsveld | 8C5

A2 Campeercentrum, Veilingweg 13. **GPS**: n50,80632 e5,72201.
4 🛏️.
Distance: 🚲500m.
Remarks: Max. 24h. Near A2, industrial area.

Ⓢ | Grubbenvorst | 8D4

Het Kompas, Meerlosebaan 7. **GPS**: n51,42861 e6,12889.⬆️.

40 🛏️€ 10 🚰€ 2 🔌Ch 💧 included 📶. **Location**: Rural. **Surface**:
grasstiles/grassy. ◻️ 01/03-30/11
Distance: 🚲2km ⚓500m ⊗2km 🛒2km.

🍴 | Heel | 8C4

Koffieterras De Tump, Heelderweg 13. **GPS**: n51,17698 e5,88315.⬆️.

5 🛏️€ 6. **Surface**: grassy. ◻️ 01/05-31/10 ◻️ Mo.
Distance: 🚲1km ⛰️on the spot.
Remarks: Max. 48h.

🍴Ⓢ | Heerlen | 8D5

Auberge De Rousch, Kloosterkensweg 17. **GPS**: n50,86652 e5,97591.
5 🛏️ 🚰 📷.
Remarks: Via A76 Eindhoven-Aken, exit Heerlen south, hospital.

🍴 | Kronenberg | 8D4

Restaurant Nieuw Kronenbergerhof, Kronenbergweg 19. **GPS**: n51,40951
e5,99669.⬆️.
30 🛏️.
Remarks: Dir Sevenum, exit Toverland.

ⒸⓈ | Landgraaf | 8D5

De Watertoren, Kerkveldweg 1. **GPS**: n50,91016 e6,07300.
6 🛏️€ 10 + € 0,90/pp tourist tax 🚰 🔌Ch 💧 included. **Location**: Quit. ◻️
01/01-31/12

Ⓢ | Lottum 🍴 | 8D3

Camperplek IndeVerte, Horstdijk 97. **GPS**: n51,45130 e6,13144.⬆️.
50 🛏️€ 10 🚰 🔌Ch 💧 📶included. 🚲 **Location**: Rural, comfortable, quit.
Surface: grassy. ◻️ 01/01-31/12
Distance: 🚲3km 🚴bike junction 🚶on the spot.

🍴 | Maasbree | 8D4

Restaurant Boszicht, Provincialeweg 2. **GPS**: n51,36395 e6,07980.
🛏️.
Remarks: Between Maasbree and Blerick/Venlo.

Ⓢ | Milsbeek | 8C3

Toeristisch knooppunt de Diepen, Zwartweg 60. **GPS**: n51,73788 e5,95510.
⬆️.

🛏️free. **Surface**: sand.
Remarks: Next to Eethuis de Diepen.

NL

Neer 8D4

Jachthaven Hanssum, Hanssum 40b. **GPS**: n51,25778 e6,00361.

5 €7,50 ⚡Ch ⚡WC. **Surface:** grassy/metalled.
Distance: 3km on the spot 200m.
Remarks: Max. 48h, service near marina. At the edge of village.

Neer 8D4

Café Restaurant Boothuis de Troost, Hanssum 47. **GPS**: n51,25964 e6,00380.

4 €7,50, guests free. **Surface:** metalled.

Nieuw Bergen 8D3

Camperplaats Bos&Heide, Op de Paal 4. **GPS**: n51,59008 e6,07269.

25 €6,50 + €0,93/pp tourist tax ⚡€ 1/100liter Ch (15x)€ 1,50
WC. **Surface:** grassy. 01/03-31/10
Distance: 1,5km 2km 1,5km 1,5km.
Remarks: Located in nature reserve Maasduinen.

Ottersum 8D3

Bier-Café Restaurant Old Inn, Siebengewaldseweg 13. **GPS**: n51,68935 e6,00728.

3 €6, 9-18h. **Surface:** gravel. 01/01-31/12
Distance: 150m 150m.
Remarks: Max. 24h. Special part for motor homes.

Tourist information Thorn:
ℹ️ VVV, Wijngaard 14, www.lekker-genieten.nl.The white village, with historical centre and Gothic collegiate church.

Valkenburg 8C5

Camperplaats Valkenburg aan de Geul, Heunsbergerweg 1.
GPS: n50,86037 e5,83148.
30 €15-21 ⚡Ch (30x)€ 0,60/kWh WC €0,70 €4,75, dryer €2,25 €5/day.
Location: Rural, comfortable, quit. **Surface:** grassy/metalled.
01/01-31/12
Distance: centre 500m 1km 1km on the spot on the spot on the spot on the spot on the spot.

Valkenburg 8C5

Burgemeester Henssingel. **GPS**: n50,86361 e5,83725.

4 €1,50/h 10-20h. **Surface:** metalled. 01/01-31/12
Distance: 300m.

Tourist information Valkenburg:
ℹ️ VVV, Th.Dorrenplein 5, www.vvvzuidlimburg.nl.Popular holiday resort.
👁 Gemeentegrot, Cauberg 4.Marl caves.
Ⓜ Steenkolenmijn, Daalhemerweg 31.Visiting a gallery of a mine. 01/04-30/11 10-17, 01/11-07/01 + weekend, guided tour 12h, 13.30h, 15h, remaining 14h.

Siebengewald 8D3

Routiers Gennep, Gennep Autoweg 41. **GPS**: n51,67537 e6,03287.

Remarks: Frontier station A77, Boxmeer-Gogh.

Thorn 8C4

Waterstraat. **GPS**: n51,15860 e5,84403.

20 free. **Surface:** metalled. 01/01-31/12
Remarks: Near Maria Roepaan.

⊠S | **Venlo** ☼ | 8D4

Jachthaven, Jachthavenweg 50. **GPS**: n51,39245 e6,14854. ⬆️.

10 ⌰€ 10 ⛽🍽✒ 10Amp WC ◻included ▣€ 3, dryer € 2 📶.
Surface: metalled.
🅾 01/04-30/10
Distance: 🚶Venlo centre 4km 🚤3,5km 🚌500m.
Remarks: Max 48h, check in at harbourmaster. Parking marina.

▥S | **Venlo** ☼ | 8D4

De Kraal, Kaldenkerkerweg 186.
GPS: n51,34870 e6,18518.
10 ⌰€ 6 ⛽🍽Ch✒.
Surface: metalled.
Remarks: Max. 72h.

Tourist information Venlo:
ℹ️ VVV, Nieuwstraat 40-42, www.lekker-genieten.nl.Historical centre.

⊠S | **Well** ☼🌳 | 8D3

Camperplaats De Wellsche Hut, Wezerweg 13. **GPS**: n51,58687 e6,12344. ⬆️.

18 ⌰€ 10 ⛽🍽Ch✒ WCincluded 🛒.
Surface: metalled. 🅾 01/01-31/12
Distance: 🚶4km 🚲6km ⊗on the spot.
Remarks: Dogs on leads, at mountainbike trail, nature reserve Maasduinen. Near German border at road from Well to Weeze.

⊠ | **Well** ☼🌳 | 8D3

Camperplaats Seurenheide, 't Leuken 3a. **GPS**: n51,56721 e6,07919. ⬆️.

⌰€ 5/24h. **Surface:** grassy.

🍴 | **Well** ☼🌳 | 8D3

Hotel-Auberge de Grote Waay, Kevelaarsedijk 1. **GPS**: n51,55267 e6,10701.
⌰.

NL

BELGIUM

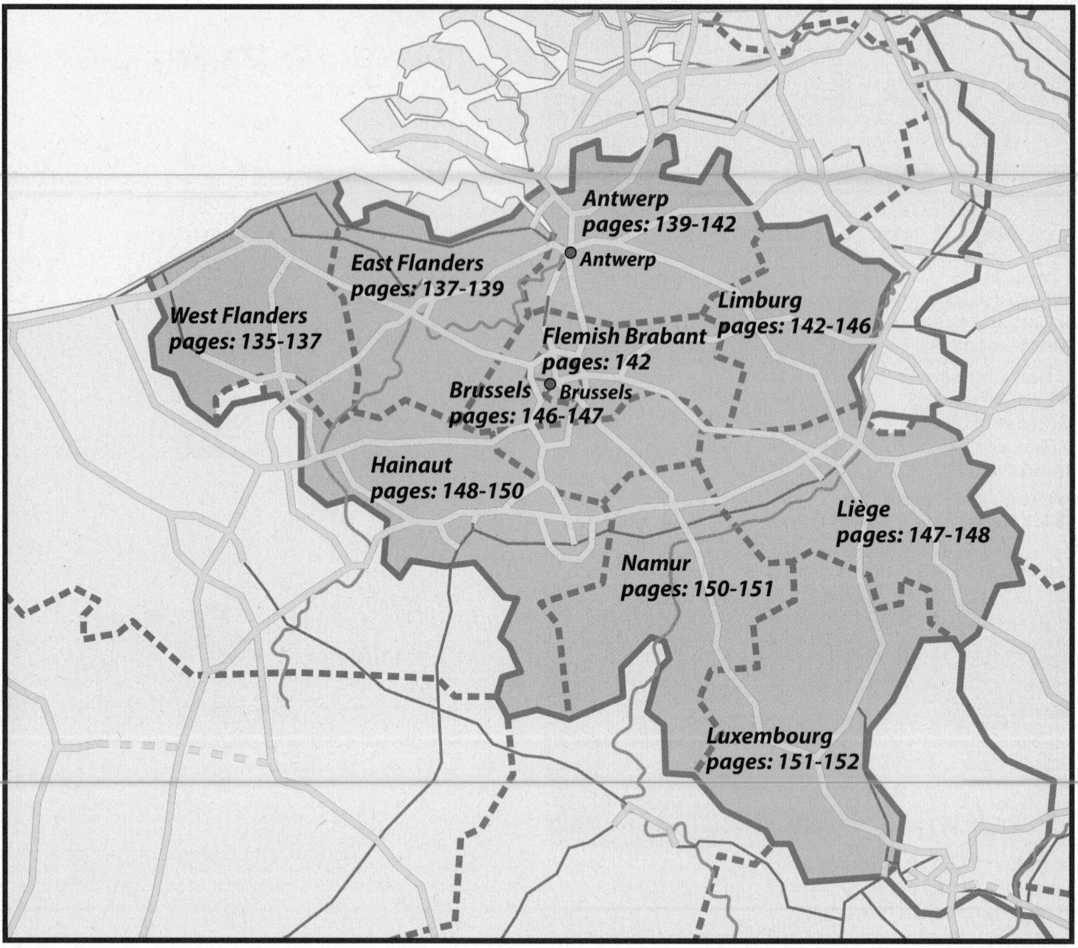

East Flanders
pages: 137-139

West Flanders
pages: 135-137

Antwerp
pages: 139-142

Antwerp

Limburg
pages: 142-146

Flemish Brabant
pages: 142

Brussels
pages: 146-147

Brussels

Hainaut
pages: 148-150

Liège
pages: 147-148

Namur
pages: 150-151

Luxembourg
pages: 151-152

Belgium
Capital: Brussels
Government: Constitutional monarchy
Official Language: Dutch/Flemish, French and German
Population: 11,007,000 (April 2011)
Area: 30,518 km

General information
Dialling code: 0032.
Currency: Euro

Regulations for overnight stays
Wild camping is forbidden.

Opening hours
Shops: Monday-Saturday 9am-6pm.
Banks: Monday-Friday 9am-12noon and 2pm-4.30pm.

West Flanders

Beernem 7C4

Kanaaloever Beernem, Oude Vaartstraat. GPS: n51,13482 e3,33427.

6 € 10/24h Ch WC included, sanitary at harbour building.
Surface: metalled. 01/01-31/12
Distance: 1,9km.
Remarks: Max. 72h.

Bredene 7C4

Sportcentrum Ter Polder, Spuikomlaan 21. GPS: n51,23074 e2,96340.

4 free. **Surface:** metalled. 01/01-31/12
Remarks: Small pitches, max. 24h.

Brugge 7C4

Ringlaan/Bargeweg. GPS: n51,19654 e3,22664.

60 € 15, € 22,50 01/04-30/09 Ch included. **Location:**
Urban, central. **Surface:** metalled. 01/01-31/12
Distance: within walking distance on the spot.
Remarks: Monitored parking, <3,5T parking allowed on all parkings.

Brugge 7C4

Citycamp Klein Strand, Varsenareweg 29, Jabbeke. GPS: n51,18490 e3,10573.

118 € 21 - € 38 Ch WC included € 0,20/1minutes against
payment. **Surface:** grassy/metalled. 01/01-31/12
Distance: 500m on the spot on the spot on the spot.
Remarks: Tel:+32(0)50-811440.

Tourist information Brugge:

Toerisme Brugge, 't Zand 34, www.brugge.be.City with medieval character,
hiking itinerary available at Dienst voor Toerisme.

Boat excursion from Bruges to Damme with the `Lamme Goedzak', departure
Noorweegse Kaai.

Brugs Brouwerij-Mouterijmuseum, ingang Verbrand Nieuwland 10.Brewery
museum. 01/04-30/09 Wed-Su 14-18h. € 3.

Huisbrouwerij Brugse Bierkaai, Nieuwstraat 9.Brewery museum.
restaurant/bar 11-23h, guided tour Tue-Fri 15.30h, 16.30h, Sa 15.30h, 16.30h,
19.30h, Su 12.30h, 15.30h. € 6.

Diamantmuseum, Katelijnestraat 43.Diamond museum. 10.30-17.30h.
€ 9.

Boudewijnpark, Alfons De Baeckerstraat 12, Sint-Michiels.Attractions park
with dolphinarium, seal island etc., in winter large skating rink covered

Geluveld 7C5

Oude Kortrijkstraat 97. GPS: n50,84592 e2,96806.

10 € 6 Ch included. **Surface:** grassy/metalled. 01/03-31/12
Distance: Geluveld 3km 2,6km on the spot on the spot.
Remarks: Amusement park Bellewaerde 500m, Ieper 8km.

Gistel 7C4

Sportstraat. GPS: n51,16112 e2,96495.

2 free Ch free. **Surface:** metalled.
Distance: 3,3km.
Remarks: Parking behind swimming pool, key service at swimming pool, many
walking and bicycle area.

Harelbeke 7C5

Sporthal de Dageraad, Stasegemsesteenweg 21. GPS: n50,84396 e3,31057.

8 € 5 Ch WC free. **Surface:** metalled. 01/01-31/12
Distance: 4,5km.
Remarks: Parking next to midget golf, service during opening hours: 8-20.

Tourist information Harelbeke:

Dienst Toerisme Harelbeke, Marktstraat 98, www.harelbeke.be.Historical city.
Museum voor Pijp en Tabak, Marktstraat 100.Pipes and tobacco. 10-12h,
14-17h Mo, Fri and 01/12-01/03. € 2

Knokke-Heist 7C4

Holiday, Natiënlaan 72. GPS: n51,33612 e3,28866.
10 € 17 01/10-31/03 € 19 01/04-30/09 Ch WC included.
Surface: metalled.

Kortemark 7C5

Sporthal Kortemark, Ichtegemstraat 2a. GPS: n51,03166 e3,04194.

BE

2 ⌂free ⚡€ 2 ⚡Ch ⚡€ 2. **Surface:** metalled. ⭕ 01/01-31/12
Distance: 🚶500m �

🚙on the spot.
Remarks: Max. 48h.

⚡S Kortrijk ♨ 7C5
Lagaeplein, Heule. **GPS:** n50,84473 e3,23569.

1 ⌂free ⚡.
Remarks: Next to swimming pool.

Tourist information Kortrijk:
ℹ️ Dienst Toerisme, Sint-Michielsplein 5, www.kortrijk.be.Historical little town .
Ⓜ️ Nationaal Vlasmuseum, E. Sabbelaan 4.Flax-growing and working demonstration. ⭕ 01/03-30/11 9.30-12.30h, 13.30-18h, Sa-Su 14-18h 🔵 Mo, holiday.

⚡S Mesen 7C5
Kerkstraat. **GPS:** n50,76391 e2,89825.⬆️.

3 ⌂free. **Surface:** metalled. ⭕ 01/01-31/12
Distance: 🚶on the spot ✖️frituur 200m 🍺100m.
Remarks: In opposite of church, max. 24h.

⚡S Nieuwpoort ♨⚓ 7C4
De Zwerver, Brugsesteenweg 29, N367. **GPS:** n51,12931 e2,76576.⬆️.

28 ⌂€ 1/1h, >1 hour € 0,50/h ⚡€ 0,50 ⚡Ch ⚡WC ⚡. **Surface:** grassy.
⭕ 01/01-31/12
Distance: 🚶within walking distance ⚡3,3km.

Tourist information Nieuwpoort:
ℹ️ Dienst Toerisme, Marktplein 7.

⚡S Oudenburg 7C4
Carpool, Stationsstraat. **GPS:** n51,19527 e3,00632.

⌂free ⚡ ⚡Ch.
Distance: ⚡800m.
Remarks: P service max. 30 min.

Tourist information Oudenburg:
⚡ ⭕ Wed-afternoon.

⚡S Poperinge ♨ 7B5
Oudstrijdersplein. **GPS:** n50,85300 e2,72300.

⌂.
Distance: ⚡50m.

Tourist information Poperinge:
ℹ️ Dienst Toerisme, Grote Markt 1, ww.poperinge.be.Centre of hop, beer and lace.

Roeselare 7C5
O.L. Vrouwenmarkt. **GPS:** n50,94786 e3,13450.⬆️.

4 ⌂free. **Surface:** metalled. ⭕ 01/01-31/12
Distance: 🚙on the spot.
Remarks: Max. 1 night.

⚡S Veurne ♨ 7B4
Kaaiplaats/Lindendreef. **GPS:** n51,07052 e2,66484.⬆️.

6 ⌂free WC€ 0,50 ⚡€ 1,50, sanitary at harbour building. **Surface:** metalled.
Distance: 🚶on the spot ⚡2km.

Remarks: Motorhome max. 6,50m.

S Westende 7C4
Kompas kampeerautoterrein, Strandjuttersdreef. **GPS:** n51,15594 e2,76019.

35 ⚐20h € 9,50-14,50, 44h € 17,50-27,50 Ch included.
Surface: grasstiles/metalled. 01/01-31/12
Distance: Taverne, Frituur on the spot.

Westende 7C4
Sint Laureinsstrand, Koning Ridderdijk. **GPS:** n51,16655 e2,76447.

⚐€ 5/day. **Surface:** asphalted. 01/01-31/12
Distance: Westende 1,4km on the spot on the spot Coast Tram.
Remarks: Beach parking.

East Flanders

S Aalst 8A5
Zwembadlaan 2. **GPS:** n50,93825 e4,05829.

2 ⚐free 100liter Ch 1h. **Surface:** metalled.
Distance: city centre ± 1km 3,8km.
Tourist information Aalst:
Dienst Toerisme, Grote Markt.
M Oud-Hospitaal, Oude Vismarkt 13. Tue-Fri 10-12h, 13-17h, Sa-Su 14-18h.
Thu-morning.

Aalter 7D4
Vaart-Zuid, Bellem. **GPS:** n51,09864 e3,49300.

25 ⚐free. **Surface:** asphalted.
Distance: Canal.

Aalter 7D4
Vaart-Noord, Bellem. **GPS:** n51,09875 e3,49468.
25 ⚐free.

Aalter 7D4
Bellemdorpweg. **GPS:** n51,09323 e3,48308.

2 ⚐free. **Surface:** metalled.
Remarks: At football ground.
Tourist information Aalter:
Kasteel Poeke, Kasteelstraat 26, Poeke. weekend, holidays, 01/04-31/10 Su 14-17h.
Wed-morning.

Bazel 8A4
Sporthal De Dulpop. GPS: n51,14778 e4,30583.

⚐free. **Surface:** asphalted.
Distance: 200m.
Remarks: Barn-museum 200m.
Tourist information Bazel:
M Dienst Toerisme, Kasteel Wissekerke, Koningin Astridplein 17.Castle can be visited. Mo-Fri.

Berlare 7D5
Donklaan, Berlare-Overmere. **GPS:** n51,04258 e3,98293.

4 ⚐free. **Surface:** grasstiles. 01/01-31/12

BE

Distance: ⚓Donkmeer ⊗on the spot.

| 🛁S | **Buggenhout** | **8A5** |

Vierhuizen, Platteput 14. **GPS:** n51,01195 e4,18998.⬆️.

2 🚐free ⚡free. **Surface:** metalled.
Remarks: At gymnasium, max. 48h, service on demand.

| 🅿️S | **Eeklo** 🌿 | **7D4** |

Jachthaven Eeklo, Nijverheidskaai. **GPS:** n51,17884 e3,54959.⬆️.

12 🚐€7 ⚡€ 0,50 🚰Ch ⚡€ 3, 10Amp WC 🚿. 🅾️ 01/01-31/12
Distance: 🚂1,5km ⊗1,5km 🛒800m.
Remarks: Use of showers only during the weekend, check in at harbourmaster. Follow signs jachthaven.

Tourist information Eeklo:
👁 Provinciaal Domein "Het Leen", Gentsesteenweg 80.Nature reserve. 🅾️ 9-12h, 13-17h. 🔴 Mo.
Ⓜ Heemkundig museum, Gentsesteenweg 80.Regional museum. 🅾️ Tue-Fr 10-17h, 01/09-30/05 Su 14-17h, 01/06-31/08 Sa/Su 14-17h.

| 🅿️ | **Gavere** 🌿 | **7D5** |

Sportdreef. GPS: n50,92823 e3,65810.⬆️.

12 🚐free. **Surface:** asphalted. 🅾️ 01/01-31/12
Distance: 🛒on the spot.
Remarks: Behind sports complex.

Tourist information Gavere:
ℹ️ VVV 't Gaverland, Markt 1.

| 🅿️ | **Gentbrugge** | **7D5** |

Sportcentrum Driebeek, Driebeekstraat 22. **GPS:** n51,03762 e3,76628.⬆️➡️.

5 🚐free. **Surface:** asphalted. 🅾️ 01/01-31/12
Distance: 🚂900m, Gent 4,5km ⚓1,5km 🚋Tram Ghent-centre.
Remarks: Ghent Festival the week of July 21.

Tourist information Gentbrugge:
🏕 Ledebergplein, Ledeberg. 🅾️ Su 7.30-13h.
🏕 Schooldreef. 🅾️ Mo 7.30-13h.
🎉 Lazy River, Arsenaal.Jazz festival and village fair. 🅾️ Whitsuntide.

| 🅿️ | **Geraardsbergen** 🌿 | **7D5** |

Jeugherberg 't Schipken, Kampstraat 59, N460, dir Ninove. **GPS:** n50,79500 e3,90412.⬆️➡️.

4 🚐free. **Surface:** grassy. 🅾️ 01/01-31/12
Distance: 🚂Geraardsbergen 3,7km 🛒on the spot.
Remarks: Max. 1 night.

Tourist information Geraardsbergen:
ℹ️ Dienst Toerisme, Markt, www.geraardsbergen.be.
Ⓜ Manneke Pis museum, StadhuisMarkt. 🎫 free.
⊕ Provinciaal Domein "de Gavers", Onkelzelestraat 280.Recreation area; swimming, watersports, fishing, boat trips and tennis.Free entrance, payment per attraction.

| 🅿️ | **Hamme** | **8A4** |

Camperplaats Hamme, Mirabrug, Hamveer. **GPS:** n51,10418 e4,14246.⬆️.

3 🚐free. **Surface:** metalled.
Distance: ⊗400m.
Remarks: Max. 48h.

| 🅿️ | **Lokeren** 🌿 | **7D4** |

Veerstraat. **GPS:** n51,11013 e3,97163.⬆️.
5 🚐free. **Surface:** asphalted. 🅾️ 01/01-31/12
Remarks: Max. 48h, parking in front of church.

Tourist information Lokeren:
ℹ️ Dienst Toerisme, Markt 2, www.lokeren.be.City with a number of medieval bldg.
🏕 Rommelmarkt, Stationsplein. 🅾️ Su 7-12h.
🌿 Molsbroek.Protected European Nature Reserve, 80ha marsh area with many birds, asphalted hiking trail. 🅾️ Su 14-17h, 01/07-31/08 Wed-Su 14-17h.

BE

Maldegem 🕭   7D4
🛁S

Zwembad St.Anna, Gidsenlaan. **GPS:** n51,21160 e3,44172. 🔼 .

🏕free 🚰. **Surface:** asphalted/metalled.
Remarks: Check in at swimming pool.

Maldegem 🕭   7D4
🍴

't Brigandje, Urselweg 100. **GPS:** n51,16907 e3,47099. 🔼 .

🏕customers free. **Surface:** gravel.

Tourist information Maldegem:
ℹ️ Dienst Toerisme, Oud Schepenhuis, Marktstraat 38, www.maldegem.be.
Ⓜ️ Stoomcentrum, Station.Steam museum. 🕐 01/07-31/08 10-18h, 01/09-30/06 Su.

Oudenaarde 🕭   7D5
🛁S

Heylbroekstraat 39. **GPS:** n50,80648 e3,55788.

8 🏕€5 🚰€ 1/100liter 🔌Ch🔌€ 0,50/kWh. **Surface:** grassy.
Distance: 🚉Oudenaarde 6km ⛵15km.
Remarks: Check in at nr. 39.

Rupelmonde   8A4
🛁

Mercator-eiland. **GPS:** n51,12556 e4,29250.

🏕free. **Surface:** sand. 🕐 01/01-31/12
Distance: 🚉100m ⊗100m 🛒600m.
Remarks: Along the Scheldt river, tide mill and castle ruins Graventoren, adjacent walking and bicycle area.

Tourist information Rupelmonde:
ℹ️ Dienst Toerisme, Nederstraat 2.

St.Laureins   7D4
🍴

Taverne 't Oud Gemeentehuis, Sint Margrietestraat 44, Sint-Margriete. **GPS:** n51,28065 e3,54677.

4 🏕free. **Surface:** grassy.

Temse 🕭   8A4
🛁

De Zaat. **GPS:** n51,12466 e4,21007. 🔼 .
🏕free. **Surface:** asphalted.
Distance: 🚉400m.
Remarks: Temporary stopover, behind police station.

Temse 🕭   8A4
🛁S

Camperbedrijf Alpha Motorhomes, Kapelanielaan 13a, N16. **GPS:** n51,13699 e4,18017.🔼.

🏕free 🚰 🔌Chfree. **Surface:** metalled.
Distance: 🚉city centre 3km.

Tourist information Temse:
ℹ️ Informatiekantoor 'De Watermolen', Wilfordkaai 23, www.temse.be.
Ⓜ️ Gemeentemuseum, Kasteelstraat 16.Regional museum. 🕐 Sa-Su 14-18h.
🎪 free.
⛺ Warenmarkt, Grote Markt. 🕐 Fri-morning.

Zulte 🕭   7D5

Leihoekstraat, Machelen. **GPS:** n50,96058 e3,48446. 🔼 .
8 🏕€5 🚰€ 1 🔌Ch🔌 included. **Surface:** metalled. 🕐 01/01-31/12
Distance: 🚉150m ⊗50m 🛒150m.
Remarks: Max. 72h.

Antwerp

Antwerpen 🕭   8A4
🛁S

Vogelzang, Vogelzanglaan 7-9, Antwerp (Antwerpen). **GPS:** n51,18983 e4,40074.🔼.

140 🏕€ 8, July-Aug € 10 🚰€ 0,50 🔌Ch🔌€ 1. **Surface:** grassy/metalled.
🕐 01/01-31/12 🔵 24/10-31/11, 07/01-28/02.
Distance: 🚉city centre 3km ⛵1km 🚌3km ⊗500m 🛒1km 🔵3km
🚐200m.

Tourist information Antwerp (Antwerpen):
ℹ️ Toerisme Antwerpen, Grote Markt, 13, www.visitantwerpen.be.Large port city, worth seeing is the city centre.
👁 Rubenshuis, Wapper 9-11.Living and work place of P. Rubens. 🕐 Tue-Su

BE

10-17h ⬛ holiday-Feiertag-jours de fête-giorni di festa.
Ⓜ Diamantmuseum, Koningin Astridplein.Diamond museum. ⬛ 01/05-31/10 10-18h, 01/11-30/04 10-17h.
Ⓜ Nationaal Scheepvaartmuseum "Steen", Steenplein.Shipping history. ⬛ Tue-Su 10-17h.
Ⓜ Provinciaal museum Sterckshof-zilvercentrum, Groendomein Rivierenhof Cornelissenlaan.Regional museum. ⬛ Tue-Su 10-17h. Ⓣ free.
🛖 Antiekmarkt, Lijnwaadmarkt. ⬛ Easter-Ostern-Pâques-Pasqua-Oct-Okt Sa 9-17h.
🛖 Brocantemarkt, St. Jansvliet. ⬛ Su 9-17h.
🛖 Exotische markt, Theaterplein. ⬛ Sa.
🛖 Vogelenmarkt, Theaterplein.Famous flea market. ⬛ Su-morning.
🛖 Warenmarkt, Dageraadsplaats. ⬛ Thu 8-13h.
🛖 Warenmarkt, St. Andriesplaats. ⬛ Tue 8-13h.
🛖 Warenmarkt, St. Jansplein. ⬛ Wed, Fri 8-13h.
🌀 Antwerpse Zoo.City-zoo. ⬛ 10h-sunset.

⛽Ⓢ	**Arendonk**	8B4

De Vloed. **GPS**: n51,32253 e5,08610.⬆.

🛏free 🚰.
Distance: 👟400m ⊗on the spot 🚌100m.
Remarks: Parking in front of swimming pool, water during openinghours swimming pool, max. 24h.

⛽Ⓢ	**Boom**	8A4

Recreatiedomein De Schorre. **GPS**: n51,08836 e4,37706.⬆.

4 🛏free 🚰 € 1 🍺Ch 🔌. **Surface:** metalled.
Distance: ⊗De Schorre.
Remarks: Follow 'De Schorre'.

⛽	**Brasschaat**	8A4

P5a, Elshoutbaan. **GPS**: n51,28485 e4,50335.⬆.

🛏free. **Surface:** metalled. ⬛ 01/01-31/12
Distance: 👟1,7km 🚲6km 🚏2km.
Remarks: Parking sports and recreation centre.

Tourist information Brasschaat:
🛖 Armand Reusensplein. ⬛ Mo 8-13h.

⛽	**Brecht**	8A4

Mudeausstraat, A1 Antwerpen-Breda afrit 3. **GPS**: n51,34829 e4,64222.⬆.

4 🛏free. **Surface:** metalled.
Distance: 👟on the spot 🚲1,2km ⊗150m 🚏150m.

Tourist information Brecht:
🛈 Dienst Toerisme, Mudaeusstraat 2.Walking and bicycle area.
Ⓜ Kempisch museum, Museumstraat. ⬛ 01/04-30/09 3rd Su 14-17h.

⛽Ⓢ	**Grobbendonk**	8B4

Vaartkom. **GPS**: n51,18954 e4,73638.⬆.

6 🛏free. **Surface:** asphalted.
Distance: 👟200m 🚲3,6km ⊗frituur 200m.

Tourist information Grobbendonk:
🛈 Infokantoor Toerisme, Kabienstraat 2a.

⛽Ⓢ	**Herentals** 🌿	8B4

Herenhoutseweg. **GPS**: n51,16586 e4,82664.⬆.

🛏 🚰. **Surface:** asphalted.
Distance: 👟1,5km 🚲2,8km 🚏bakery 200m.
Remarks: Parking multipurpose area, next to footballstadium VC Herentals.

⛽	**Herentals** 🌿	8B4

Jachthaven, Noordervaart 45. **GPS**: n51,17666 e4,85694.⬆.

🛏€ 10. **Surface:** metalled. ⬛ 01/01-31/12
Distance: 🚲3,9km.

Tourist information Herentals:
🛈 Dienst Toerisme, Grote Markt 41.Historical little town.

⌖ Augustijnenlaan. ⬛ Su-morning.
⌖ Grote Markt. ⬛ Fri-morning.

| 🍴S | Herselt 🌿🎐 | 8B4 |

Taverne Herberg Mie Maan, Diestsebaan 28. **GPS**: n51,06025 e4,92897.
6 🗐free ⌂. **Surface**: gravel. ⬛ 01/01-31/12
Distance: 🚶3km ⊗on the spot 🍺3km.
Remarks: Restaurant visit appreciated, intersection hiking and biking trails

| 🗐 | Koningshooikt | 8A4 |

Donderheide. **GPS**: n51,08439 e4,56541.⬆➡.

🗐free. **Surface:** unpaved.
Distance: 🚶on the spot.
Remarks: In front of 'Het Fort'.

| 📷 | Koningshooikt | 8A4 |

Motorhomes Konings, Sander de Vosstraat 141. **GPS**: n51,08774 e4,62816.⬆.

🗐€ 2,50 ⌂€ 2 💧€ 2,50. **Surface:** asphalted.
Remarks: Apply during openinghours.

| 🗐S | Lichtaart | 8B4 |

Vagevuur, Vinkendreef. **GPS**: n51,20559 e4,89701.
10 🗐free ⌂🍴Ch. **Surface:** grassy. ⬛ 01/01-31/12
Distance: 🚶2,5km.
Remarks: Caution key service € 5, at taverne Vagevuur.

Tourist information Lichtaart:
🎡 Bobbejaanland.Attractions park and shows. ⬛ 01/04-30/09 10-18h, 01/10-31/03 Sa-Su.

| 🗐S | Lier 🌿 | 8A4 |

Parking Mol Poort, Aarschotsesteenweg. **GPS**: n51,12525 e4,57332.

3 🗐⌂€ 1 🍴Ch. ⬛ 01/01-31/12

| 🗐 | Lier 🌿 | 8A4 |

Zaat, Leuvense Poort. **GPS**: n51,13013 e4,58232.⬆.

2 🗐free. **Surface:** metalled. ⬛ 01/01-31/12

Tourist information Lier:
ℹ Dienst Toerisme, Grote Markt 57.City with old centre worth a visit.
👁 City walls, prison tower and Zimmertoren. ⬛ 10-12h, 14-17/18h.
⌖ Grote Markt/Eikelstraat. ⬛ Sa 6-13h.
⌖ Duivernmarkt, Grote Markt. ⬛ Su 6-12h, Easter, Whitsuntide, Christmas.
☀ Kerststallentocht. ⬛ Dec.

| 🗐 | Mechelen 🌿 | 8A5 |

De Nekker, Nekkerspoel-Spuibeekstraat. **GPS**: n51,02667 e4,50367.⬆.

🗐free. **Surface:** unpaved. ⬛ 01/01-31/12
Distance: 🚶city centre 1,5km.
Remarks: Parking at sports and recreation centre 'de Nekker', max. 1 night.

Tourist information Mechelen:
ℹ Dienst Toerisme Stad Mechelen, Hallestraat 2-4, www.mechelen.be/.
Historical city, city of carillons.
Ⓜ Brouwerijmuseum Het Anker.Old brewery, 1369. ⬛ 01/04-30/09 14-18h, guided tour 15h. ⓣ € 3,30.
🎡 De Nekker.Sports and recreation area with ponds, sports grounds etc.
🎡 Dierenpark Planckendael.Zoo. ⬛ 10-18h.
🎡 Technopolis.Interactively "discover" museum.
🚶 Caroluswandeling.City walk along historical bldg. And breweries, information Dienst Toerisme.

| 🗐S | Putte | 8A5 |

Ixenheuvel, Heuvel. **GPS**: n51,04678 e4,62564.⬆.

2 🗐free ⌂🍴Chfree. **Surface:** asphalted. ⬛ 01/01-31/12
Distance: 🚶1,5km.
Remarks: Max. 48h.

| 🗐S | Puurs | 8A4 |

Eeuwfeeststraat/ Kerkhofstraat. **GPS**: n51,07476 e4,28337.⬆➡.

2 ⛺free ⚡ Ch ✎ free. **Surface:** metalled. 🔵 01/01-31/12
Distance: 📍5,3km.
Remarks: Max. 48h, intersection hiking and biking trails.

St.Amands 8A4
Parking Noord, Emile Verhaerenstraat. **GPS:** n51,05917 e4,20472.

3 ⛺free ✎ free. **Surface:** metalled.
Distance: 🚌 Good bus connection for Brussels.
Remarks: Next to cemetery and sports fields, no camping activity.

Limburg

Bilzen 8C5
Parking Lanakerdij, Lanakerdij. **GPS:** n50,86985 e5,52215.

2 ⛺free ⚡ Ch free. **Surface:** metalled. 🔵 01/01-31/12

Willebroek 8A4
Dijlelaan. **GPS:** n51,06028 e4,34472.

7 ⛺free ⚡€ 2 Ch ✎. **Surface:** asphalted. 🔵 01/01-31/12
Distance: 🚶300m ⊗300m 🚰300m on the spot on the spot.
Remarks: Max. 24h.

Tourist information Bilzen:
ℹ️ Toerisme Bilzen, Markt, toerisme.bilzen.be.
👁 Landcommanderij Alden Biesen, Rijkhoven. 10-18h, Nov-Easter 11-18h Mo.
👁 Zuivelhoeve 't Wanthof.Dairy farm. Tue-Fri 10-22h, Sa-Su 9-23h.
Ⓜ Apostelhuis, Bosselaar 11, Rijkhoven.Nature centre. 10-18h, Nov-Easter 11-18h Wed.
⛺ Weekmarkt. Wed.

Bocholt 8D2
Heuvelzicht, Schipperstraat 1. **GPS:** n51,17722 e5,58500.

3 ⛺free ⚡€ 1 Ch. **Surface:** metalled. 🔵 01/01-31/12
Distance: 📍300m.
Remarks: Max. 2 nights. A12, exit 7, first road to the left.

Flemish Brabant

Diest 8B5
De Halve Maan, Omer Vanaudenhovelaan. **GPS:** n50,98607 e5,06373.
4 ⛺€ 15 ⚡ ✎. **Surface:** asphalted.
Distance: 🚶1,2km, beguine convent 350m.
Remarks: Check in at pay-desk.

Tourist information Diest:
ℹ️ Socio-Cultureledienst, Stadhuis, Koning Albertstraat 16a, www.diest.be.
👁 Begijnhof.Beguine convent. Art studios open: sa/so afternoon and in july/aug each afternoon. Beguine convent daily, Angel convent Sa/Su 14.30-17h, church Easter-Oct Su 14-17h.
Ⓜ Stadsmuseum De Hofstadt, Grote Markt 1. 10-12h, 13.30-17h holiday-Feiertag-jours de fête-giorni di festa.

Merchtem 8A5
Brusselsesteenweg. **GPS:** n50,95553 e4,24011.

10 ⛺€ 6,50/24h ⚡ Ch ✎ WCincluded €1. **Surface:** asphalted. 01/01-31/12
Distance: 🚶on the spot ⊗50m 🚰100m 50m 50m.
Remarks: Parking marina at Zuidwillemsvaart, max. 48h.

Tourist information Bocholt:
ℹ️ Toerisme Bocholt, Dorpsstraat 16, www.bocholt.be/toerisme/. opening hours library.
Ⓜ Brouwerijmuseum, Dorpsstraat 53.Large brewery. Individual visits only in july and august. 01/07-31/08 13-17h. €5.

Bolderberg 8B5
Domein Bovy, Galgeneinde. **GPS:** n50,98690 e5,27048.

3 ⅀free ⎚€ 2 Ch ⎚€ 2/1h. **Location:** Rural. **Surface:** metalled.
Distance: 🚶500m ⊗150m 🚲bike junction 🚶on the spot.
Remarks: Estate with i.e. restaurant, bar, brasserie, marked hiking trails, herb garden, petting zoo, old tools.

Bree 🌿 8C4
N721, Opitter. **GPS:** n51,11844 e5,64358.⬆.

5 ⅀free. ◯ 01/01-31/12
Remarks: Parking next to church, in front of petrol station, max. 48h.

Tourist information Bree:
ℹ Toerisme Bree, Markt, www.bree.be.Small historical city.
Ⓜ De Gulden Tas, Ter Rivierenwal 18.Coffee-roasting factory. ◯ Tue-Fri 9-12h, 13-17h. ⊤ € 2,50.
🔆 Vrijthof. ◯ Fri.
✳ Sint-Antoniuskapel, Opitter.

Diepenbeek 8C5
Demerstrand, Stationsstraat. **GPS:** n50,91392 e5,42209.⬆.

4 ⅀free ⎚€ 2/100liter Ch € 2/8h. **Surface:** asphalted. ◯ 01/01-31/12
Distance: 🚶500m ⊗250m 🚶1km.
Remarks: At gymnasium.

Dilsen-Stokkem 8C5
De Wissen, Burg. Prevotlaan. **GPS:** n51,02451 e5,74950.⬆.

4 ⅀free. **Surface:** metalled. ◯ 01/01-31/12
Distance: 🚶500m 🏊on the spot 🚣on the spot ⊗Taverne Maascentrum

🚣500m 🚲on the spot.
Remarks: Parking at tourist office De Wissen, starting point of cycle routes.

Genk 🌿 8C5
Parking Kattevennen, Planetariumweg 19. **GPS:** n50,95728 e5,53337.

8 ⅀free ⎚Ch 🚲. **Surface:** asphalted.
Distance: 🚶3km ⊗taverne 🚲on the spot.
Remarks: National park Hoge Kempen, mountainbike and hiking trails.

Tourist information Genk:
ℹ Uit in Genk, Europalaan 34, www.uitingenk.be.Tourist information. ◯
Mo-Fri 9.30-16.30h, Sa 9-12h, 13-16h.
🔆 Zondagsmarkten.Flea market. ◯ 01/06-31/08 9-13h.

Hamont 8C4
Kerkplein. **GPS:** n51,25152 e5,54612.⬆.

5 ⅀free. **Surface:** metalled. ◯ 01/01-31/12
Distance: 🚶on the spot ⊗50m 🚣50m 🚲50m.
Remarks: Behind church, max. 24h.

Hamont 8C4
Michielsplein, Achel. **GPS:** n51,25423 e5,47985.

⅀free.
Remarks: Behind church of Achel, max. 24h, at bicycle trail Limburgse Kempen.

Hamont 8C4
Stadpark. **GPS:** n51,25085 e5,55200.

BE

free. **Surface:** unpaved.
Remarks: Large parking in the centre behind tennis-courts, max. 24h.
Tourist information Hamont:
VVV, Generaal Dempseylaan 1, www.hamontachel.com.Historical little town.
Mo-Fri 9-12h, 13-16h, Sa 9-12h.

free. **Surface:** asphalted.

| | Hechtel/Eksel | 8C4 |

Pijnven, Bosmuseum, Kiefhoekstraat. **GPS**: n51,16133 e5,31091.

| S | Hasselt | 4A6 |

Sporthal Alverberg, Herkenrodesingel. **GPS**: n50,93998 e5,32072.

>5 free € 2 Ch. **Surface:** metalled. 01/01-31/12
Distance: city centre 3km Carrefour Free bus to centre.

free. **Surface:** asphalted.
Remarks: Parking in the forest.
Tourist information Hechtel/Eksel:
Dienst Toerisme, Don Boscostraat 5, www.hechtel-eksel.be. Mo-Fri 9-12.

| | Hasselt | 4A6 |

Restaurant Myosotis, Overdemerstraat 20, Kuringen. **GPS**: n50,94663 e5,30877.

| | Helchteren | 8C4 |

Parking de Dool, Sportstraat. **GPS**: n51,06087 e5,38650.

8 guests free.
Distance: on the spot bakery 50m.

| | Hechtel/Eksel | 8C4 |

Kamertstraat. **GPS**: n51,13273 e5,35641.

10 free. **Surface:** asphalted. 01/01-31/12
Distance: 1km 500m 500m.
Remarks: Next to castle.

| S | Herk-de-Stad | 8B5 |

Park Olmenhof, Pikkeleerstraat. **GPS**: n50,93361 e5,16654.
7 free € 1/100liter Ch € 0,60/kWh WC. **Location:** Rural.
Surface: asphalted. 01/01-31/12
Distance: 400m 7km 50m 300m.
Remarks: Max. 48h.

| | Hoepertingen | 8B5 |

De Verborgen Parel, Hoenshovenstraat 5. **GPS**: n50,80170 e5,28944.
6 €7 Ch . **Surface:** metalled. 01/01-31/12
Distance: 1,5km 1,5km 1,5km.

| | Houthalen | 8C5 |

Parking Kelchterhoef, Kelchterhoefstraat. **GPS**: n51,03015 e5,44063.

free. **Surface:** sand.
Distance: 1,5km.
Remarks: N73 dir Leopoldsburg, nature reserve 'In de Brand'.

| | Hechtel/Eksel | 8C4 |

Parking CC De Schans, Rode Kruisplein 10, Hechtel. **GPS**: n51,12391 e5,36271.
.

BE

6 ⌇free. **Surface:** metalled. ◻ 01/01-31/12
Distance: ⛨6km ⊗on the spot.
Remarks: In front of abbey farm.

Kortessem 〰 8C5
Kapittelstraat. **GPS:** n50,85724 e5,39126. ⬆⬆→.

5 ⌇free. **Surface:** asphalted. ◻ 01/01-31/12
Distance: ⛨200m ⊗200m 🍺bakery 200m.
Remarks: At gymnasium, max. 2 nights.

Tourist information Kortessem:
🛈 Toerisme Kortessem, Kerkplein, 12, www.kortessem.be.
🏰 't Rood Kasteel, Guigoven.Former medieval water castle.

Leopoldsburg 〰 8B4
Jachthaven, Antwerpsesteenweg 129. **GPS:** n51,12765 e5,25113. ⬆.

10 ⌇€6-8 ⛽ ✦€ 2 WC ◻€ 1. **Surface:** asphalted. ◻ 01/01-31/12
Distance: ⛨2km ⚓on the spot ⊗on the spot 🍺2km.
Remarks: Check in at harbourmaster.

Leopoldsburg 〰 8B4
Reigersvliet, Reigervlietstraat. **GPS:** n51,10972 e5,25556. ⬆.

75 ⌇€8 ⛽ 🍽included ✦(10x)€ 2/24h. **Surface:** concrete. ◻ 01/01-31/12
Distance: ⛨1km.
Remarks: Market on Sa, Su flea market.

Leopoldsburg 〰 8B4
De Lido, Campaniëstraat. **GPS:** n51,13633 e5,24179.
⌇€7 ✦included. **Location:** Rural, isolated. **Surface:** gravel.
Distance: ⛨3km 🎣fish pond ⊗on the spot.

Tourist information Leopoldsburg:
🛈 Dienst Toerisme, Hechtelsesteenweg 7. ◻ Mo-Fri 9-12.30h, 14-17h.

Lommel 8C4
Taverne Haven de Meerpaal, Boskantstraat 60. **GPS:** n51,24266 e5,36891. ⬆.

15 ⌇€ 10 ⛽€ 0,50 🍽Ch ✦(6x)€ 1 WC ◻€ 1. **Surface:** asphalted.
Distance: ⊗on the spot.
Remarks: At marina.

Maaseik 〰 8C4
Sportlaan P4. **GPS:** n51,10108 e5,78964. ⬆.
20 ⌇free. **Surface:** asphalted. ◻ 01/01-31/12
Distance: ⛨historical centre 200m.
Remarks: Parking gymnasium behind swimming pool.

Tourist information Maaseik:
🛈 Toerisme Maaseik, Markt 1, www.maaseik.be.
Ⓜ Catharinakerk. ◻ Tue-Su 10-17h, 01/07-31/08 Mo-Su, 01/10-31/03 Sa-Su.
♫ Marktplein. ◻ Wed 9-12h.

Meeuwen-Gruitrode 8C4
CC Gruitrode, Royerplein 1, Gruitrode. **GPS:** n51,08939 e5,58949. ⬆.
⌇free. **Surface:** gravel/sand. ◻ 01/01-31/12
Distance: ⛨200m ⊗on the spot 🍺200m 🚗200m.
Remarks: Max. 24h.

Neeroeteren 〰 8C4
Cultureel Centrum, Borglaan. **GPS:** n51,08745 e5,69977. ⬆.

20 ⌇free. **Surface:** asphalted. ◻ 01/01-31/12
Distance: ⛨800m ⊗on the spot 🍺on the spot 🚗on the spot.
Remarks: Parking cultural centre, max. 24h.

Neerpelt 8C4
De Welvaart, Jaak Tassetstraat. **GPS:** n51,23290 e5,43206. ⬆.

10 ⌇free ⛽ 🍽Ch ✦free. **Surface:** metalled. ◻ 01/01-31/12
Distance: ⛨500m.
Remarks: Parking marina, on the canal, max. 48h, coin waste dump € 1.

Tourist information Neerpelt:
🛈 Dienst Toerisme, Kerkstraat 7, www.neerpelt.be.

P Peer 8C4
P1 Aan den Boogaard. **GPS:** n51,13193 e5,45741.
⌇free.
Distance: ⛨100m.
Remarks: Max. 24h.

P | **Peer** | 8C4

P2 Noordervest. **GPS:** n51,13422 e5,45511.
free.
Distance: 150m.

S | **Rekem** | 8C5

Kanaalstraat. **GPS:** n50,92297 e5,70622. .

free. **Surface:** unpaved.
Distance: 1km on the spot on the spot 500m 1km 100m.
Remarks: Walking and bicycle area, max. 48h. N78, exit Rekem-centrum, follow Oud Rekem, along canal.

Tourist information Rekem:
Oud-Rekem with museum-church, city walls and castle, marked walking route 2km.

S | **Schalkhoven** | 8C5

Nollekes Winning, Schalkhovenstraat 79. **GPS:** n50,84531 e5,44687.

4 WC . **Surface:** gravel. 01/01-31/12
Distance: 200m on the spot.

S | **St.Truiden** | 8B5

Kampeerautoterrein Sint Truiden, Speelhoflaan. **GPS:** n50,82118 e5,18935. .

20 free € 0,50/100liter Ch (20x)€ 0,50/kWh. **Surface:** metalled. 01/01-31/12
Distance: 750m 100m 500m 100m.
Remarks: Max. 72h.

Tourist information St.Truiden:
Toerisme Sint-Truiden, Stadhuis, Grote Markt, www.sint-truiden.be.Abbey-town.
Grote Markt, Groenmarkt, Trudoplein, Minderbroedersplein. Sa 7.30-13h.
Veemarkt, Speelhoflaan.Antiques and flea market. Sa 6-12h.

S | **Tongerlo** | 8C4

De Kieper, Keyartstraat. **GPS:** n51,12397 e5,65449.

5 free. **Surface:** metalled.
Distance: 10 min walking.

S | **Veldwezelt** | 8C5

Omstraat 20. **GPS:** n50,86195 e5,62696. .

2 free. **Surface:** metalled. 01/01-31/12
Distance: 800m 200m 500m.
Remarks: Parking gymnasium.

Bruxelles

P | **Bruxelles/Brussel** | 8A5

Bruparck, Wemmel/Heizel, Brussels (Bruxelles/Brussel). **GPS:** n50,89745 e4,33826.
.
Remarks: Overnight stays with a motorhome are not possible in Brussels, not even on the campsite (only tents). Ring road Brussels exit 8.

P | **Bruxelles/Brussel** | 8A5

GPS: n50,84052 e4,36165.
.
Remarks: In front of royal palace.

P | **Bruxelles/Brussel** | 8A5

Heizel/Heysel Metro, Brussels (Bruxelles/Brussel) . **GPS:** n50,89736 e4,33827.

Remarks: Nearby Bruparck.

Tourist information Brussels (Bruxelles/Brussel):
Bureau van Toerisme, Office de Tourisme, Grote Markt 1, Grand Place, www.brucity.be.Capital of Belgium, with a history of more than 1000 years. A lot of buildings worth seeing and historical places.
Koninklijke Serres van Laken, Les serres royales à Laeken.Park, garden, nature area.
M Autoworld, Jubelpark, Parc du Cinquantenaire.Motorcar history from 1886 up to 1970s. 01/04-30/09 10-18h, 01/10-31/03 10-17h.
M Koninklijk Legermuseum, Musée royal de l'armée et d'histoire militaire, Jubelpark, Parc du Cinquantenaire.Army museum. Tue-Su 9-12h, 13-16.45h.
M Museum van de stad Brussel Broodhuis, Musée de la ville Bruxelles, Grote Markt 44, Grand Place.History of the city. Tue-Su 10-17h.
Basiliek van Koekelberg, basilique de Koekelberg.The fifth largest church of the world. 01/10-18/10 Su 14-17.45h, 01/07-31/08 Sa-Su. T € 2,50.
Grote Markt, Grand place.Flowers and plant market. 8-18h.
Grote Zavel, Place du Grand Sablon.Antiques and book market. Sa 9-17h, Su 9-13h.
Vossenplein. 7-14h.
Kunstmarkt, marché d'art, Boterstraat, rue au Beurre.Painters and portraitists. 11-18h.
Atomium, Bruparck, Boulevard du Centenaire, Laeken.Built for the occasion of the 1958 Brussels World Fair, symbolising a crystallised iron molecule to the scale of its atoms enlarged 160 thousand million times. 10-18h, 01/04-31/08 9-20h. T € 5.
Bruparck, Boulevard du Centenaire 20, Laeken.Family park with among other things Mini-Europe, paradise pool and The Village with restaurants, cafés and

BE

shops. ☐ 01/01-31/12.

🌐 Mini-Europe, Bruparck, Boulevard du Centenaire, Laeken.Europe in miniature, 300 monuments. ☐ 30/03-03/01.

🌐 Oceade, Bruparck, Boulevard du Centenaire, Laeken.Subtropical leisure pool park. ☐ holidays, Sa-Su 10-22h.

Liège

| 🌐S | Blégny-Mine | 8C5 |

Domaine de Blégny-Mine, Rue Lambert Marlet. **GPS:** n50,68617 e5,72367.⬆️

8 🅿️free 🚰💧Chfree 🧹 (8x)€ 2/12h. **Location:** Rural, comfortable, isolated, quit. **Surface:** gravel. ☐ 01/01-31/12

Distance: ⚓4,6km ⊗on the spot 🐾on the spot 🧍on the spot.

Remarks: At former coalmine, UNESCO World Heritage, access € 9,30, 1 day all inclusive € 29,50, coins electricity at reception park.

| 🅿️ | Eupen 🌿 | 8D6 |

Langesthal 164. **GPS:** n50,62180 e6,09148.

🅿️free. **Surface:** asphalted.

Distance: ⚓Eupen 4km ⊗150m Taverne.

Remarks: At weir, isolated.

Tourist information Eupen:

🅜 Chocolademuseum, Rue de l'Industrie 16. ☐ Mo-Fri 9-17h.

🅜 Stadtmuseum, Gospert 52.Regional museum. ☐ Tue-Fri 10-12h, 13-16h, Sa 14-17h, Su 10-12h, 14-17h.

🎪 Rommelmarkt, Eupen/Keltenis. ☐ Su 7-16h.

🎪 Weekmarkt, Benedenstad. ☐ Wed 7-12.30h.

| 🅿️S | Hamoir | 8C6 |

Complexe Sportif, Quai du Batty. **GPS:** n50,42463 e5,53522.⬆️

10 🅿️free 🚰💧Chfree. **Surface:** grassy/gravel. ☐ 01/01-31/12

Remarks: Parking at the Ourthe River.

Tourist information Hamoir:

🅸 Office du Tourisme, Place del Cour 1.

| 🅿️ | Huy 🌿 | 8B6 |

Avenue Godin Pamajon. **GPS:** n50,52379 e5,24310.⬆️

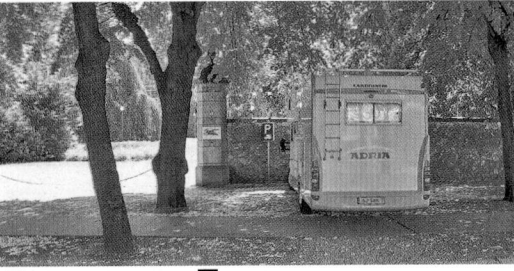

2 🅿️free. **Surface:** asphalted. ☐ 01/01-31/12

Distance: ⚓500m ⊗on the spot 🍴500m.

Remarks: Parking in front of restaurant Quick.

| 🅿️ | Huy 🌿 | 8B6 |

Quai de Namur. **GPS:** n50,51895 e5,23759.⬆️

2 🅿️free. **Surface:** asphalted. ☐ 01/01-31/12

Distance: ⚓500m ➔on the spot ⊗on the spot 🍴500m.

Remarks: Under the citadel, along the Meuse River, in front of Hôtel du Fort to the right to the quay.

Tourist information Huy:

🅸 Office du Tourisme, Quai de Namur,1, www.huy.be.Tourist town, citadel above the city.

🅜🍴 Fort en museum. ☐ Easter-Sep 10-17/18/19h.

| 🅿️S | Malmedy 🌿❄ | 8D6 |

Avenue de la Gare, N62. **GPS:** n50,42282 e6,03080.⬆️➔

30 🅿️€ 5/24h 🚰💧Ch 🧹 (8x)included. **Surface:** gravel/metalled. ☐ 01/01-31/12

Distance: ⚓300m ⊗300m 🍞bakery 100m, supermarket 800m 🚴Waimes 5km.

Remarks: At cycle route (former railroad).

Tourist information Malmedy:

🅸 Maison du Tourisme, Place Albert I, 29 A, www.malmedy.be.Small tourist town at the south edge of nature reserve Hautes Fagnes, high fens.

🅜 Musée National du Papier et musée du carnaval, Maison Cavens, Place de Rome 11.Museum of paper and the carnival museum. ☐ 14-17h 🔘 Mo.

🎪 Weekmarkt, Place St. Géréon. ☐ Fri 7-13h.

🌿🌱🐾 Hautes Fagnes.Nature reserve Hautes Fagnes.

| 🅿️ | Sourbrodt | 8D6 |

Signal de Botrange, Rue de Botrange. **GPS:** n50,50148 e6,09312.⬆️

20 ⌚free. **Surface:** gravel. ⏰ 01/01-31/12
Distance: ⊗on the spot ⚓on the spot.

| ⛴S | St.Vith | 8D6 |

An den Weyern, Rodter Strasse 9a. **GPS:** n50,28091 e6,12240.
20 ⌚free 🔌♨Ch against payment. **Surface:** asphalted. ⏰ 01/01-31/12
Distance: ⚓on the spot.
Remarks: At sports centre.

Hainaut

| ⛴ | Antoing ☀ | 7D6 |

Parking, Place Bara. **GPS:** n50,56550 e3,44838.
⌚free.
Remarks: Max. 24h.

| ⛴ | Antoing ☀ | 7D6 |

Parking, Place de Péronnes. **GPS:** n50,56413 e3,45093.
⌚free.
Remarks: Max. 24h.

| ⛴ | Antoing ☀ | 7D6 |

Parking, Rue de la Pêcherie. **GPS:** n50,56728 e3,44505.
⌚free.
Remarks: Max. 24h.

Tourist information Antoing:
🛈 Office de Tourisme, Place Bara 18, www.antoing.net.

| ⛴ | Aubechies | 7D6 |

Parking Archéosite, Rue de l'Abbaye 1Y. **GPS:** n50,57419 e3,67546.
⌚.

Tourist information Aubechies:
🛈 Archéosite d'Aubechies.Archeological open air museum. ⏰ Easter-01/11
Mo-Fri 9-17h, Sa, Su 14-18h.

| ⛴ | Basècles | 7D6 |

Place de Basècles. **GPS:** n50,52580 e3,64885.
⌚free.

| ⛴ | Beloeil ☀ | 7D6 |

Château Beloeil. **GPS:** n50,55000 e3,73242.
⌚free. ⏰ 01/01-31/12
Remarks: Parking castle.

| ⚠S | Beloeil ☀ | 7D6 |

Camping à la Ferme, Rue de la Hunelle 16. **GPS:** n50,55165 e3,73275.
12 ⌚€ 6 + € 2/pp 🔌♨Ch ✎€ 1 WC. ⏰ 15/03-15/11
Remarks: Minicamping.

Tourist information Beloeil:
🏰 Château de Beloeil, www.beloeil.be/. ⏰ 01/06-30/09 10-19h, 01/04-31/05
Sa,Su 10-19h.

| ⛴ | Bernissart ☀ | 7D6 |

Musée de l'Iguanodon, Ruelle des Médecins. **GPS:** n50,47530 e3,64958.

⌚free.
Remarks: Parking 100m of dinosaur museum.

Tourist information Bernissart:
Ⓜ Musée de l'Iguanodon, Ruelle des Médecins, www.bernissart.be/.Prehistoric
museum. ⏰ 10-17h.

| ⛴ | Binche ☀ | 8A6 |

Pastures, Rue des Pastures. **GPS:** n50,41557 e4,16810.
⌚free. **Surface:** asphalted. ⏰ 01/01-31/12
Remarks: Parking just outside centre.

Tourist information Binche:
🛈 Office du Tourisme, Parc communal, rue des Promenades, 2, www.binche.
be.Medieval city with ramparts.
Ⓜ Musée International du Carnaval et du Masque, Rue Saint Moustier
10.Carnivals and maskmuseum. ⏰ 9.30-12.30h, 13.30-18h ⏺ Fri + Sa
morning-, Ash Wednesday, 01/11, Christmas.

| ⛴ | Blaton | 7D6 |

Place de Feignies. **GPS:** n50,50179 e3,66135.

⌚free.
Remarks: Nearby Romanesque church.

| ⛴S | Bouffioulx | 8A6 |

Rue du Général Jacques. **GPS:** n50,39075 e4,51456.
⌚🔌♨Ch ✎against payment. **Surface:** metalled.
Remarks: Next to Centre d'Interprétation de la Poterie.

| ⛴S | Boussu-lez-Walcourt ⛵ | 15C1 |

Route de la Plate Taille. **GPS:** n50,19265 e4,37958. 🚲 .

20 ⌚free 🔌♨Chfree. **Surface:** asphalted. ⏰ 01/01-31/12
Distance: ⚓on the spot ⚓on the spot ⊗on the spot 🎣on the spot.

| ⛴ | Brugelette | 7D6 |

Parc Paradisio, Domaine de Cambron. **GPS:** n50,58892 e3,88670.

⌚€ 4.

Tourist information Brugelette:
🌐 Parc Paradisio, Domaine de Cambron,.Park with bird paradise and monkey
island. ⏰ Easter-Oct 10-18h.

| ⛴ | Charleroi ☀ | 8A6 |

Quai de la Gare Sud. **GPS:** n50,40537 e4,44199.
10 ⌚free.
Remarks: Parking behind station south.

⬛	**Charleroi** ♨	8A6

Rue des Rivages. **GPS:** n50,40867 e4,43673.

⬛free. **Surface:** metalled.

Remarks: Parking for tram-cars, next to the ministry of finance.

⬛	**Charleroi** ♨	8A6

Rue Montignies. **GPS:** n50,40900 e4,44405.

2 ⬛free.

Remarks: Parking in front of swimming pool.

Tourist information Charleroi:

ℹ️ Office du Tourisme, 100 avenue Mascaux, Marcinelle, www.charleroi.be.Former centre of the coal mines.

P	**Chimay**	15C1

Place Froissart. **GPS:** n50,04728 e4,31307.

⬛.

P	**Chimay**	15C1

Place Léopold. **GPS:** n50,04747 e4,31784.

⬛.

⬛	**Comines**	7C5

Parking Pont-Neuf. **GPS:** n50,76580 e3,00371.

⬛free. **Surface:** metalled.

Distance: ⊗100m.

⬛	**Comines**	7C5

Place Sainte Anne. **GPS:** n50,76855 e2,99914.

⬛free. **Surface:** metalled.

Distance: ⊗150m.

◉	**Comines**	7C5

Musée de la Rubanerie, Rue du Fort 50. **GPS:** n50,76576 e3,00471.

4 ⬛free. **Surface:** metalled.

Distance: ⊗100m.

Tourist information Comines:

ℹ️ Office du Tourisme, Chemin du Moulin Soete 21.

⬛	**Courcelles**	8A6

Rue du château d'eau, Place Franklin Roosevelt. **GPS:** n50,46250 e4,37654.

⬛.

Remarks: Behind Centre Culturel de la Posterie.

⬛ S	**Dottignies**	7C5

Rue des Écoles 75b. **GPS:** n50,72821 e3,30011.

⬛ 🚐🍽free. 🔲 01/01-31/12

Distance: ⟋ 1,3km.

Remarks: Square behind fire-station.

⬛ S	**Ecaussines**	8A6

Fort Château, La Grand-Place, Place des Comtes, Rue de Seneffe. **GPS:** n50,56868 e4,17676.

⬛free Ch.

⬛	**Ecaussines**	8A6

Château de la Folie, Rue de la Folie. **GPS:** n50,57443 e4,17851.

⬛free.

⬛	**Ecaussines**	8A6

Eglise Sainte Aldegonde, Rue Jacquemart Boulle 28, Ecaussines-Lalaing. **GPS:** n50,57085 e4,18107.

⬛free.

⬛	**Fleurus**	8A6

Parking Gare, Avenue de la Gare. **GPS:** n50,48215 e4,54433.

⬛.

⬛	**Fleurus**	8A6

Stade Communal, Rue de Fleurjoux. **GPS:** n50,47852 e4,55237.

⬛free.

⬛	**Harchies**	9A6

Place du Rivage. **GPS:** n50,47106 e6,69619.

⬛.

⬛	**Hornu**	7D6

Le Site du Grand Hornu, Rue Sainte-Louise 82. **GPS:** n50,43488 e3,83707.⬆️

⬛free.

Tourist information Hornu:

👁 Grand-Hornu.Old industrial mining complex, a remarkable reminder of the Industrial Revolution. 🔲 Tue-Fri 10-18h. 🎫 € 6.

⬛	**Houdeng Aimeries**	8A6

Musée de la Mine de Bois-du-Luc, Rue Saint-Patrice. **GPS:** n50,47081 e4,14952.

⬛free.

⬛	**La Louvière** ♨	8A6

Boulevard de Roi Baudouin. **GPS:** n50,46619 e4,19055.

⬛free.

Remarks: P Station Sud.

Tourist information La Louvière:

Ⓜ Ascenseur Funiculaire de Strépy-Thieu, Strépy-Bracquegnies.Gain boat lift, 19th century. 🔲 01/02-27/11 9.30-18.30.

Ⓜ Site ouvrière et musée de la mine, Rue Saint-Patrice 5bis.Coal town and mining museum. 🔲 Easter-Oct Tue-Fri 9-17h, Sa-Su 10-18h.

⛺ Weekmarkt, Rue du Marché. 🔲 Sa 8-13h.

⬛	**Lahamaide**	7D5

Place Plada. **GPS:** n50,69521 e3,72709.

⬛.

Remarks: At Ecomuseum.

⬛	**Le Roeulx**	8A6

Grand Place. **GPS:** n50,50019 e4,10919.

⬛.

⬛	**Le Roeulx**	8A6

Place de la Chapelle. **GPS:** n50,50294 e4,10874.

⬛.

⬛	**Le Roeulx**	8A6

Place de la Tannée. **GPS:** n50,50339 e4,10819.

⬛.

⬛	**Le Roeulx**	8A6

Place du Château. **GPS:** n50,50406 e4,11024.

⬛.

Remarks: Parking at castle.

⬛	**Lessines**	7D5

Rue des 4 fils Aymon. **GPS:** n50,71280 e3,83403.

⬛free.

⬛	**Leuze-en-Hainaut**	7D6

Rue du Pont de la Cure. **GPS:** n50,59924 e3,61347.

⬛free.

⬛	**Marchienne-au-Pont**	8A6

Musée d'Histoire et d'Archéologie Industrielle, 134 rue de la Providence. **GPS:** n50,41301 e4,40450.

⬛free.

Remarks: In front of museum.

⬛	**Mons/Bergen** ♨	7D6

Maison Van Gogh, Rue de Pavillon 3, Cuesmes, Mons (Mons/Bergen). **GPS:** n50,44174 e3,92630.

⬛free.

Remarks: In case of city-visit use parking nearby station or bypass.

Tourist information Mons (Mons/Bergen):

ℹ️ Maison du Tourisme, Grand-Place, 22, www.mons.be.Old university city with many art treasures.

Ⓜ Chapelle Saint Calixte, Square du Château.Museum of the Count's Castle with archeological discoveries, medieval iconography etc. 🔲 12-18h ⏺ Mo.

Ⓜ Maison Van Gogh, Rue du Pavillon 3, Cuesmes.Former place of residence of painter Van Gogh 1879/80, exhibition of reproductions. 🔲 10-18h ⏺ Mo.

Ⓜ Musée des Arts Décoratifs François Duesberg, Square Franklin Roosevelt

BE

12.Decorative arts museum. ⬜ Tue-Su 13.30-18h.
Ⓜ Musée des Beau-Arts.Museum of Fine Arts.
✝ Château Havré, Havré.Castle, 12-13th century.

	Morlanwelz-Mariemont	8A6

Musée Alex Louis Martin, Place de Carnières, 52, Carnières. **GPS**: n50,44402 e4,25416.
10 ⌂free.

	Mouscron	7C5

Musée du Folklore, Rue des Brasseurs, 3. **GPS**: n50,74217 e3,21795.
⌂free.
Remarks: Possibility make a reservation tel 02.56.33.23.36.

	Nimy	7D6

Musée de la Pipe et du Vieux Nimy, Rue Mouzin. **GPS**: n50,47499 e3,95853.
⌂free. **Surface:** metalled.
Remarks: Museum closed: Nov-Mar.

	Quaregnon	7D6

La Grand Place. **GPS**: n50,44369 e3,86428.
2 ⌂.

	Quevaucamps	7D6

Musée de la Bonneterie, Rue Paul Pastur. **GPS**: n50,52671 e3,68776.⬆➡

⌂free. ⬜ 01/01-31/12
Remarks: Parking in front of museum, via N527.

	Roisin	7D6

Musée Verhaeren, Rue Emile Verhaeren, 23, Honnelles. **GPS**: n50,34285 e3,71044.
⌂free.
Remarks: Parking nearby museum.

	Ronquières ☼	8A6

Grande tour et promenade en Bateau Mouche, Route de Baccara. **GPS**: n50,59121 e4,22115.
⌂free.

Tourist information Ronquières:
Ⓜ Site de Ronquières.Inclined plane of Ronquières. The life of a bargee, boat-trip. ⬜ 01/04-31/10 10-19h.

	Sivry	15C1

Observatoire de Sivry, Route de Mons 52. **GPS**: n50,17897 e4,22646.
2 ⌂.
Remarks: Centre for nature studies.

	Soignies	8A6

Collégiale et vieux cimentière, La Grand Place, la Place Vert, la Place Van Zeeland. **GPS**: n50,57832 e4,06869.
⌂free. **Surface:** gravel/sand.
Distance: on the spot.
Remarks: Thu closed because of market.

	Solre-Sur-Sambre	8A6

Château-Fort, Rue du Chateau Fort. **GPS**: n50,30918 e4,15585.
⌂free.
Remarks: At castle.

	Thuin	8A6

Drève des Alliés. **GPS**: n50,33951 e4,29860.
⌂.
Remarks: Max. 24h.

	Thuin	8A6

L'Abbaye d'Aulnes, Rue Vandervelde. **GPS**: n50,36592 e4,33324.
⌂free.

Remarks: Near abbey, max. 24h.

	Thuin	8A6

Place du Chapitre. **GPS**: n50,33980 e4,28724.
⌂.
Remarks: Max. 24h.

S	Tournai/Doornik ☼	7C6

Maison de la Culture, Boulevard Frère Rimbaud, Tournai (Tournai/Doornik). **GPS**: n50,60432 e3,38199.⬆
15-20 ⌂free ⌂ Ⓒh free. **Surface:** metalled. ⬜ 01/01-31/12
Distance: 5 min walking. ⊗5 min walking. 5 min walking.

Tourist information Tournai (Tournai/Doornik):
ℹ Dienst Toerisme, Vieux Marché aux Poteries, 14, www.tournai.be.One of the oldest cities of Belgium.
Ⓜ Musée Royal d'armes et d'histoire militaire, Rue Roc Saint-Nicaise 59-61. Military museum. ⬜ 10-12h, 14-17.30h ⬤ Tue.

	Trazegnies	8A6

Place Albert I 32. **GPS**: n50,46248 e4,33025.
⌂.
Distance: 1,5km.
Remarks: Parking at castle.

Namur

🍴	Alle-sur-Semois ⚘	15D2

Recreatiecentrum Recrealle, restaurant les Pierres du Diable, Rue Léon Henrard 16. **GPS**: n49,84648 e4,97579.⬆

10 ⌂free. **Surface:** unpaved. ⬜ Apr-Oct daily, Febr-Mar, Oct-Nov fr-su ⬤ 01/01-31/01.
Distance: on the spot fishing permit obligatory ⊗on the spot.
Remarks: Max. 1 night. E411 exit Wellin, dir Gedinne, Bièvre then follow Recrealle.

Tourist information Alle-sur-Semois:
ℹ Region with slate mines.
Ⓜ Ardoisalle, Rue de Reposseau 12.Slate mine with museum. ⬜ 01/05-30/06, 01/09-31/10 Wed-Su 10-12h, 14-17h, 01/07-31/08 daily.
☻ Recrealle.Canoe rent; departures for canoe and kayaks, fishing and swimming possibilities, bowling, tennis, play ground, restaurant.

S	Ave-et-Auffe	16A1

Camping Le Roptai - Ave-et-Auffe

info@leroptai.be - www.leroptai.be

Paved and flat motorhome pitches
Open all year

Le Roptai, Rue du Roptai 34. **GPS**: n50,11101 e5,14084.
10 ⌂ € 16 01/02-06/07, 20/08-31/12 Ⓒh (10x)€ 3/24h WC included
⌂ € 1 ⬤€ 4 € 3,50/24h. **Location:** Rural, comfortable, quit. **Surface:** grassy/gravel. ⬜ 08/01-31/12

Distance: 🚶4km 🚲2km ⊗1km 🍴5km 🚌1km.
Remarks: Han 5km.

| 🚐S | Han-Sur-Lesse 🌿⛰ | 16A1 |

Rue de la Lesse. **GPS:** n50,12730 e5,18660.⬆.

30 🚐€ 7,50, Jul/Aug € 10 🚰Ch 🔌WCincluded. **Surface:** asphalted. 🅾 01/01-31/12
Remarks: Parking nearby caves and centre.

Tourist information Han-Sur-Lesse:
ℹ Tourist centre around the caves.
👁M Belgacom, rue de l'Antenne 63 Lessive (Rochefort).Ground station telecommunication by means of satellites. 🅾 Easter-Oct 9.30-17h.
👁 Grottes de Han.Caves, son-et-lumière and boat trip on underground river. 🅾 01/04-31/10 10-16/18h, 01/11-31/03 11.30-16h.
M Musée du Monde Sousterrain, Place Theo Lannoy 3.Exposition of archeological findings. 🅾 01/04-15/11 11-17h, 01/07-31/08 11-19h.
😊 Réserve d'Animaux.European animals alive today and those which lived previously in this area. 🅾 01/03-31/12 10-17h, 01/07-31/08 9.30-18h.

| | Profondeville | 8B6 |

Chaussée de Namur. **GPS:** n50,37644 e4,87106.⬆.

4 🚐free. **Surface:** asphalted. 🅾 01/01-31/12
Distance: 🚶50m 🚲150m 🍴50m.
Remarks: Max. 24h.

| | Rochefort | 20B5 |

Route de Marche. **GPS:** n50,15742 e5,22562.⬆.

🚐free. **Surface:** metalled.
Remarks: From Marche N86 on entering the city, at roundabout follow 'toutes directions', 1st small street to the right, nearby centre.

| 🚐S | Saint-Hubert | 16A1 |

Chemin des Etangs/ Rue de Lavaux. **GPS:** n50,02689 e5,38088.⬆.

3 🚐🚰 Chfree. **Location:** Comfortable. **Surface:** gravel. 🅾 01/01-31/12
Distance: 🚶500m ⊗500m 🍴500m 🚲 on the spot 🚶 on the spot.
Remarks: 10 parking places tolerated, european capital of hunting, events: 1st weekend September and November 1st Saint Hubert.

| 🚐S | Viroinval 🍴 | 15D1 |

Rue Longue. **GPS:** n50,07075 e4,54879.

🚐free 🚰€ 1,50 Ch. **Surface:** asphalted.
Distance: 🚶Nismes 600m.
Remarks: Coins at Tourist Info.

Luxembourg

| 🚐S | Arlon 🌿 | 16B2 |

Casserne Callemeyn, Rue de Redange, N882. **GPS:** n49,68990 e5,81929.⬆.

4 🚐free 🚰🔌 🔌free. **Surface:** asphalted. 🅾 01/01-31/12
Distance: 🚶600m 🚲5,8km.
Remarks: At fire-station, max. 48h.

Tourist information Arlon:
ℹ Maison du Tourisme du Pays d'Arlon, rue des Faubourgs, 2.The historical capital of the province, founded by the Romans.
M Musée Luxembourgeois, Rue des Martyrs.Exposition of Gallo-Roman findings. 🅾 Mo-Sa 9-1h2, 14-17h.
⌒ Parc Archéologique, Rue des Thermes.Archeological site. 🅾 9-12h, 14-17h.
⚒ Antiekmarkt. 🅾 01/03-31/10 1st Su of the month 7-19h.

| 🚐S | Bastogne 🌿 | 16A1 |

Avenue Albert I. **GPS:** n49,99825 e5,71526.⬆.

BE

± 10 🅿free ⛽🚿free. **Location:** Central. **Surface:** asphalted.
Distance: 🚶300m 🚲3km ⊗300m 🚉300m.

🚐S **Durbuy** 🌿⛲👥 8C6

P Mobilhome Le Vedeur, Rue Fond de Vedeur. **GPS:** n50,35320 e5,45543. ↑→

20 🅿€ 15, 2 pers.incl ⛽🚿Ch 🔧 WC included. **Surface:** gravel. 🅿 Easter-Ostern-paques-Pasqua-31/10
Distance: 🚶750m 🏊on the spot ⛵fishing permit obligatory ⊗750m.

Tourist information Durbuy:
ℹ Tourisme Durbuy, Place aux Foires, 25.Small tourist town with old centre.
👁 Confiturerie Saint Amour, Rue St Amour 13.Production of traditional products.
🅿 10-18h ● 01/10-31/03 Mo. 🅣 free.
👁 Diamour, Rue de la Prevoté.Ardeens centrum van de diamant en edelsmeedkunst. 🅿 10.30-19.30h ● Tue-Wed. 🅣 free.
👁 Parc des Topiaires, Rue Haie Himbe.Model garden 🅿 10-18h ● 01/01-31/01. 🅣 € 4,50.
🌂 Antiques and flea market. 🅿 01/03-30/09, 9-17h, 2nd Sa of the month.

🚐S **Herbeumont** 🌿 16A2
Avenue de Combattants. **GPS:** n49,77800 e5,23600. ↑.

🚐free.
Distance: 🚶on the spot ⊗100m.
Remarks: Parking places in front of 'hall omnisports'.

Tourist information Hotton:
ℹ Office du Tourisme, Rue Haute 4.Small tourist town.
👁 Grottes de Hotton.Caves. 🅿 01/04-31/10 10-17h, 01/07-31/08 10-18h.

🚐 **La Roche** 🌿🏔 16A1
Rue du Harzé. **GPS:** n50,19075 e5,57432.

5 🅿free. **Surface:** asphalted. 🅿 01/01-31/12
Distance: 🚶300m.
Remarks: Parking at sports park.

Tourist information La Roche:
ℹ Syndicat d'Initiative, Place du Marché, 15, www.la-roche-tourisme.com.Small town totally destroyed during the battle of the Ardennes, 1944/45.
Ⓜ Musée de la Roche, Rue Châmont 5.War museum, Battle of the Ardennes.
✖ Medieval citadel. 🅿 10-12h, 14-17h, 01/07-31/08 10-19h, winter Sa-Su
● frost.

🚐 **Nisramont** 👥 16A1
Barrage de Nisramont, Rue de barrage. **GPS:** n50,14089 e5,67118. ↑.

50 🅿free ⛽🚿Ch free.
Distance: 🚶500m 🚉500m.
Remarks: Parking of old station.

Tourist information Herbeumont:
ℹ Royal Syndicat d'Initiative, Avenue des Combattants, 7, www.herbeumont.be.Beautiful position in the Ardennes landscape. Ruins of medieval castle, free entry.
👁 Grottes, 7 km di Bertrix.Caves. 🅿 01/04-30/09 daily, 01/11-31/03 Sa-Su. 🅣 € 7.

🚐 **Hotton** 🌿 8C6
Rue des Vergers. **GPS:** n50,26853 e5,44759.

10 🅿free. **Location:** Isolated, quit. **Surface:** metalled. 🅿 01/01-31/12
Distance: 🚶3,7km 🚲15km 🏊on the spot ⛵on the spot ⊗on the spot 🎣on the spot.
Remarks: At artificial lake.

🚐 **Redu** 16A1
Place de l'Esro. **GPS:** n50,00733 e5,16000.
🚐free. **Surface:** gravel.
Distance: 🚶250m.
Remarks: Parking in front of church.

🚐 **Redu** 16A1
Rue de Saint Hubert. **GPS:** n50,00877 e5,16348.
🚐free.
Distance: 🚶on the spot.
Remarks: Parking before entering the village.

LUXEMBOURG

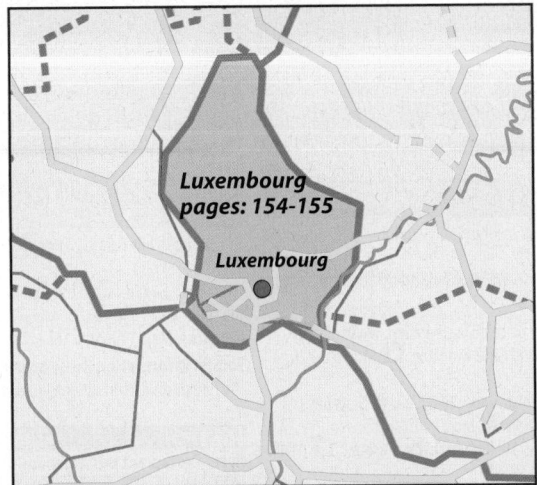

Luxembourg

Capital: Luxembourg
Government: Grand duchy
Offi cial Language: French, German, Luxembourgish
Population: 498,000 (2010
Area: 2,586 km²

General information

Calling code: 00352.
Currency: Euro

Regulations for overnight stays

Parking overnight and camping by public road is
forbidden. Motorhome-service only on campsites.

Luxemburg

Luxembourg

ⒼⓈ Bleesbrück 16B1
Camping Bleesbrück, 1, Bleesbreck. **GPS**: n49,87270 e6,18940.
2+2 🏕from € 9 💧🚿Ch.

ⒼⓈ Diekirch 🎿 16B1
Camping de la Sûre, Route de Gilsdorf. **GPS**: n49,86597 e6,16489.⬆️➡️.

8 🏕€ 12 💧🚿Ch 🚿 WC ⌐included, sanitary only summer ▣€ 3 📶free
🚮. **Surface**: grasstiles. 🅞 01/01-31/12
Distance: 🚶100m ⛱100m 🚋100m (permit € 4/month) ⊗100m 🚰100m.

Tourist information Diekirch:
ℹ️ Syndicat d'intitiative et de Tourisme, place de la Libération, www.diekirch.
lu/fr/index.htm.Itinerary biking and hiking cards available. 🅞 Mo-Fri 9-12h,
14-17h, Sa 14-16h.
Ⓜ Conservatoire National de véhicules historique, 20-22, rue de Stavelot.
Exhibition of historical vehicles. 🅞 10-18h 🅞 Mo.
Ⓜ Musée National de l'histoire militaire, 10, Bamertal.War museum. 🅞 01/04-
31/10 10-18h, 01/11-31/03 14-18h.
🎪 Weekmarkt, Rue St.Antoine. 🅞 Tue 8-12h.
🎊 Al Dikkirch.Folk festival. 🅞 2nd week Jul.

🚐Ⓢ Dudelange 16B2
Parking Gare-Usines. **GPS**: n49,47176 e6,07772.⬆️.

6 🏕free 💧🚿Chfree. **Surface**: asphalted. 🅞 01/01-31/12
Distance: 🚶1km 🚲4,1km 🚋near train station.
Remarks: Max. 3 nights, Luxemburg city 20min with train.

Tourist information Dudelange:
Ⓜ Musée National des Mines de Fer, carreau de la Mine, Rumelange.History of
the mines. 🅞 14-17h. 🎟 € 7,50.

🅛 Echternach 🎿🌿 16C2
Villa Romaine, Route de Luxembourg. **GPS**: n49,80500 e6,40750.⬆️.

🏕free. **Surface**: asphalted/metalled. 🅞 01/01-31/12
Distance: 🚶1,5km ⊗500m 🚰on the spot.

Tourist information Echternach:
ℹ️ Syndicat d'intitiative et de Tourisme, 9-10, Parvis de la Basilique, www.

mullerthal.lu.
🎊 Sprangprossessioun.Dancing procession. 🅞 Tue after Whitsuntide.

Ⓖ Ermsdorf 16B2
Neumühle. **GPS**: n49,83917 e6,22503.
2 🏕. 🅞 01/01-31/12

ⒼⓈ Heiderscheid 16B1
Quickstop, Fuusekaul 4. **GPS**: n49,87806 e5,99278.

34 🏕€ 8,50, July-Aug € 12 💧🚿Chincluded 🚿 6Amp🚮. **Surface**: gravel.
🅞 01/01-31/12
Distance: 🚶8km ⛱on the spot 🚲8km ⊗on the spot 🚰on the spot 🚋on
the spot.
Remarks: Max. 1 night, >16h <11h.

Tourist information Heiderscheid:
🎊 Heischter Mart.Traditional market. 🅞 end Jul.

🍴Ⓢ Hoscheid ⛰ 16B1
Hotel-Restaurant Des Ardennes, Haaptstrooss. **GPS**: n49,94676 e6,08036.

4 🏕free with a meal 💧🚿 WC 📶included 🚮. **Surface**: asphalted. 🅞
01/02-15/12
Distance: ⊗on the spot 🚋on the spot.
Remarks: Parking behind hotel.

Larochette 🎿✈🎎 16B2
Camping Birkelt, Um Birkelt 1. **GPS**: n49,78483 e6,21068.⬆️➡️.

8 🏕€ 15,25 💧🚿 Ch 🚿 WC ⌐included ▣€ 5 📶🚮. **Surface**: grasstiles.
🅞 01/03-31/10
Distance: 🚶1km ⊗on the spot 🚰on the spot 🚋1km.
Remarks: Quick-Stop: >17-9h, max. 1 night.

🛖Ⓢ Larochette 🎿✈🎎 16B2
Camping Auf Kengert. **GPS**: n49,80021 e6,19788.
6 🏕from € 18,50 💧🚿Ch. 🅞 carnival 31/10
Remarks: Quick-Stop: >19-09h.

Tourist information Larochette:
ℹ️ Syndicat d'intitiative et de Tourisme, 4, rue de Medernach, www.luarochette.
lu. 🅞 Mo-Fri 10-12h, 13.30-16h.
👁 Schiessentümpel.Waterfall with three cascades.
🏰 Château. 🅞 Easter-Oct, 10-18h, daily.

LU

△	Maulusmühle	16B1

Woltzdal. GPS: n50,09266 e6,02869.
2 ⌂. ⬛ 01/04-31/10

△	Mersch	16B2

Um Krounebierg. GPS: n49,74403 e6,09075.
5 ⌂ € 15-19,80. ⬛ 15/03-31/10

△	Obereisenbach	16B1

Kohnenhof. GPS: n50,01630 e6,13682.
⌂. ⬛ 31/03-01/11

⌂ S	Redange/Attert	16B2

Rue de la Piscine 24. **GPS**: n49,76918 e5,89459. ⬆.

12 ⌂ free ⌁ ⬛ Ch free. **Surface:** asphalted. ⬛ 01/01-31/12
Distance: ⬛800m ⬛ on the spot.
Remarks: Max. 72h.

⌂ S	Schwebsange	16B2

Camport, Rue du Port. **GPS**: n49,51163 e6,36249. ⬆.

18 ⌂ € 9 ⌁ ⬛ Ch included ⌁ € 1,50 WC ⌁ ⬛ € 2,50 ⬚ at restaurant
⬛. **Surface:** grasstiles. ⬛ 01/04-15/10
Distance: ⬛500m ⬛ fishing permit obligatory ⊗ on the spot ⬛ on the spot
⬛500m.
Remarks: At marina.

Tourist information Schwebsange:
Ⓜ A Possen, 1 rue Aloyse Sandt, Bech-Kleinmacher. Folkore and wine museum.
⬛ 01/05-31/10 14-19h, 01/03-30/04, 01/11-31/12 Fri-Su 14-19h ⬤ Mo.

⬛	Vianden ⬛ ⬛ ⬛ ⬛	16B1

39, rue du Sanatorium. **GPS**: n49,93717 e6,20556. ⬆.

⌂ free. **Surface:** asphalted. ⬛ 01/01-31/12
Distance: ⊗500m ⬛500m.
Remarks: At the chair-lifts (télésiege).

Tourist information Vianden:
ℹ Syndicat d'intitiative et de Tourisme, 1,a rue du vieux Marché, www.tourist-info-vianden.lu. ⬛ Mo-Fri 8-12h, 13-17h, summer daily.
👁 SEO. Large hydro-electric power-station. ⬛ Easter-Sep 10-20h. Ⓣ free.
Ⓜ Bakkerij museum, Grand rue 96-98. ⬛ Easter-Oct 11-17h ⬤ Mo.
✠ Château de Vianden. ⬛ 01/04-30/09 10-18h, 01/10-31/03 10-16h ⬤
02/11, 25/12, 01/01.

⬛ Nessmoort. Nuts market. ⬛ 2nd Su Oct.
⬚ Télesiège. Chair-lift. ⬛ Easter-Oct.

FRANCE

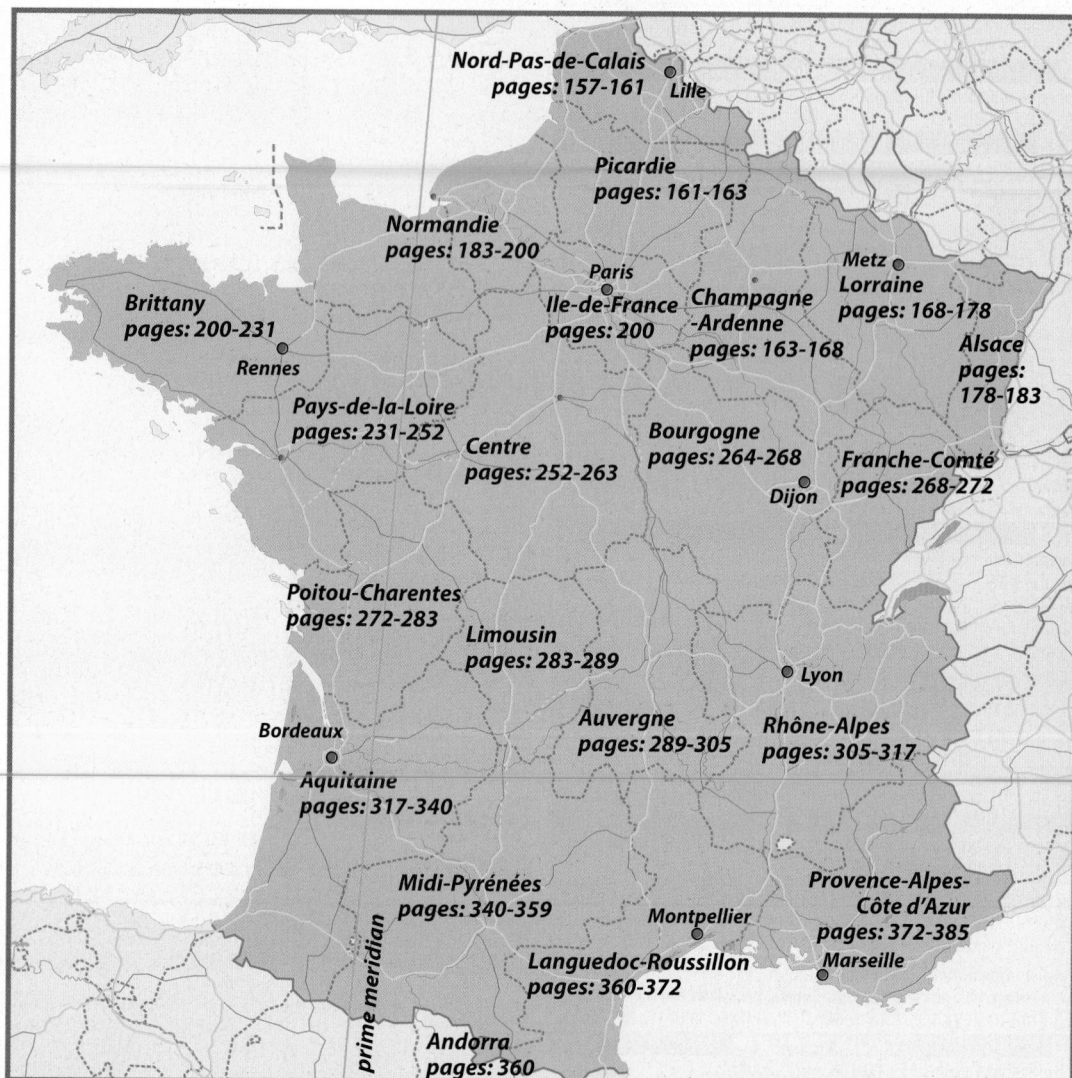

Nord-Pas-de-Calais
pages: 157-161
Lille

Picardie
pages: 161-163

Normandie
pages: 183-200

Metz
Lorraine
pages: 168-178

Paris

Alsace
pages:
178-183

Brittany
pages: 200-231

Ile-de-France
pages: 200

Champagne
-Ardenne
pages: 163-168

Rennes

Pays-de-la-Loire
pages: 231-252

Bourgogne
pages: 264-268

Centre
pages: 252-263

Franche-Comté
pages: 268-272

Dijon

Poitou-Charentes
pages: 272-283

Limousin
pages: 283-289

Lyon

Bordeaux

Auvergne
pages: 289-305

Rhône-Alpes
pages: 305-317

Aquitaine
pages: 317-340

Midi-Pyrénées
pages: 340-359

Provence-Alpes-
Côte d'Azur
pages: 372-385

Montpellier

Marseille

Languedoc-Roussillon
pages: 360-372

prime meridian

Andorra
pages: 360

Capital: Paris
Government: Unitary republic
Official Language: French
Population: 62,814,000 (July 2011)
Area: 543,965 km².

General information
Dialling code: 0033.
Currency: Euro
Payments by credit card are accepted almost
everywhere, however chip and pin systems are non-
compatible with British cards and fuel for example can
only be bought at supermarkets during opening
hours.

Regulations for overnight stays
Wild camping is accepted almost everywhere
throughout inland France. Special regulations for
motor homes you can find on signs by entering
thetown. It is permitted to stopover at motorway
services, be aware that toll roads often issue time-
constrained tickets.

Opening hours
Shops: Monday-Saturday 9am-12noon and 2pm-
7pm, supermarkets Monday-Saturday 9am-7/8pm,
Hypermarchés Monday-Saturday 9am-9.30pm
Banks: Monday-Friday 9am-4.pm.

Nord-Pas de Calais

Ambleteuse 7A5
D940 > Wimereux. **GPS**: n50,80638 e1,61484.⬆️.

7 🛒€3. **Surface**: grassy.

Arques 7B5
Rue Michelet. **GPS**: n50,74551 e2,30459.⬆️➡️.

20 🛒€2 ⛽€ 2,50. **Surface**: gravel. 🅿️ 01/04-31/10
Distance: 🛒100m.
Remarks: Behind camp site Beauséjour.

Arras 7C6
Rue des Rosati. **GPS**: n50,29497 e2,78824.⬆️.

10 🛒free ⛽€ 2/100liter 🚿Ch🔌€ 2/1h. **Surface**: asphalted. 🅿️ 01/01-31/12
Distance: 🛒700m ⊗500m.

Tourist information Arras:
ℹ️ Office de Tourisme, Hôtel de Ville, Place des Héros, www.ot-arras.fr.City, fortified by Vauban, became French territory in 1659.
👁 Hôtel de Ville.Town hall in Gothic style. Also guided tours of the subterranean passages of Arras.
🎭 🅿️ Wed, Sa.

Bailleul 7B5
Rue du collège. **GPS**: n50,74010 e2,73170.

20 🛒free. **Surface**: asphalted. 🅿️ 01/01-31/12
Distance: 🛒700m 🏖2,8km.

Remarks: At commemorative monument.
Banteux 15A1
GPS: n50,06259 e3,20106.⬆️.

5 🛒€5 ⛽🚿Chfree. **Location**: Rural. **Surface**: grassy/gravel. 🅿️ 01/01-31/12 🔵 service 01/11-31/03.
Distance: 🛒500m 🏖2,5km 🚲on the spot 🚶on the spot.

Bavay 7D6
Chemin de Ronde. **GPS**: n50,30004 e3,79551.⬆️.
10 🛒free ⛽🚿Chfree. **Surface**: gravel. 🅿️ 01/01-31/12
Distance: 🛒200m ⊗200m.

Berck-sur-Mer 7A6
Baie d'Authie, Chemin aux Raisins. **GPS**: n50,39701 e1,56431.⬆️➡️.

80 🛒€6, 01/10-01/04 free ⛽🚿Chfree. **Surface**: gravel. 🅿️ 01/01-31/12
Distance: 🛒1,5km 🏖100m 🍟frituur 100m.
Remarks: Baker every morning.

Berck-sur-Mer 7A6
Parking Terminus, Rue Dr. Calot, Berck-Nord. **GPS**: n50,42361 e1,56750.⬆️.

40 🛒€5,50/24h ⛽🚿Chincluded. **Surface**: gravel. 🅿️ 01/01-31/12
Distance: 🏖beach 200m.

Tourist information Berck-sur-Mer:
🎡 Bagatelle, CD 940.Amusement park. 🅿️ Easter-Sep 10-18.30h.

Bergues 7B5
Rue Maurice Cornette. **GPS**: n50,96543 e2,43596.⬆️➡️.

FR

50 🛏free. **Surface:** gravel. 🅾 01/01-31/12
Distance: 🚶500m 🚲 2,2km.
Remarks: Behind football ground, max. 48h.

🅢 **Boulogne-sur-Mer** 🛬🍵🍺 7A5
Parking Moulin Wibert, Boulevard Sainte Beuve, D940. **GPS:** n50,74308
e1,59688.⬆.

40 🛏€ 5,10/24h ⛽€ 3/10minutes 🔌Ch 🚿. **Surface:** metalled.
Distance: 🚶centre 2,5km 🚲 5,5km 🚌on the spot.
Remarks: Max. 48h, at sports grounds.

🅢 **Boulogne-sur-Mer** 🛬🍵🍺 7A5
Boulevard Chanzy. **GPS:** n50,72194 e1,60027.⬆.

🛏free. **Surface:** asphalted.
Distance: 🚶500m 🚲 4,5km.
Remarks: Nearby casino.

Tourist information Boulogne-sur-Mer:
ℹ Office de Tourisme, 24, quai Gambetta, www.coteo.com.Lively city with large
fishing port and historical city centre.
🎪 Boulevard Clocheville. 🅾 Wed-morning.
🎪 place Dalton, centre. 🅾 Wed + Sa morning.
🎪 place Vignon. 🅾 Su-morning.

🅢 **Calais** 7A5
Digue Gaston Berthe. **GPS:** n50,96688 e1,84406.

60 🛏free, 01/04-31/10 € 7/24h ⛽🔌Ch 🚽WCincluded.
Surface: asphalted.
Distance: 🚶500m 🏊100m ⊗100m 🚱100m.
Remarks: At the end of beach in front of the ferry terminal.

🅢 **Calais** 7A5
Quai Edmond Pagniez. **GPS:** n50,96050 e1,84466.⬆.

100 🛏free, 01/04-31/10 € 7/24h ⛽🔌Ch 🚽 included. **Surface:** asphalted.
🅾 01/01-31/12
Distance: 🚶300m ⊗350m.
Remarks: Service: Digue Gaston Berthe.

Tourist information Calais:
ℹ Office de Tourisme, 12, boulevard Clemenceau, www.coteo.com.Port city.
Ⓜ✖ Fort Nieulay.Fortress, 13th century, war museum.
Ⓜ Centre d'Information Eurotunnel.Exhibition about the Channel tunnel.
🎪 🅾 Wed, Thu, Sa.

🅢 **Cassel** 〰 7B5
Route d'Oxelaere, C301. **GPS:** n50,79328 e2,48852.⬆➡.

5 🛏free ⛽€ 2 🔌Ch 🚽€ 2.
Surface: gravel. 🅾 01/01-31/12
Remarks: At sports park, a little isolated, coins at Office de tourisme.

🅢 **Catillon-sur-Sambre** 15B1
N43. **GPS:** n50,07624 e3,64615.⬆.

5 🛏€ 5 ⛽🔌Ch 🚿free. **Surface:** asphalted. 🅾 01/01-31/12
Distance: 🚶200m 🚌on the spot.
Remarks: At the canal, max. 72h.

🅢 **Catillon-sur-Sambre** 15B1
Rue de la Gare. **GPS:** n50,07699 e3,64404.⬆➡.

20 🛏free. **Surface:** gravel. 🅾 01/01-31/12
Distance: 🚌on the spot.

🅢 **Embry** 7A6
Les Salons de l'Embryenne, D108. **GPS:** n50,49534 e1,96610.

8 🛏6 ⚡€ 2,50 🚰Ch 🚿€ 2,50/4h WC 🚽€ 2,50 🗑. 🐕 **Surface:** gravel. ◻ 01/01-31/12

🛏free. **Surface:** asphalted. ◻ 01/01-31/12
Distance: ⚓1,7km.

📷S | Equihen-Plage | 7A5
Plage de la Crevasse, Rue du Beurre Fondu. **GPS**: n50,67910 e1,56884. ⬆➡

📷 | Hondschoote | 7B5
Impasse Spinnewyn. **GPS**: n50,97628 e2,58033. ⬆➡

20 🛏€ 5 ⚡€ 3/10minutes 🚰Ch 🚿 (6x)€ 3/12h. **Surface:** grassy/gravel. ◻ 01/01-31/12
Distance: 🚶100m ⛱100m 🛒100m.

Tourist information Equihen-Plage:
ℹ Office de Tourisme, Place Albert Bécard.

8 🛏free ⚡€ 2/100liter 🚰Ch 🔌€ 2/1h. **Surface:** asphalted.
Distance: 🚶800m 🛒nearby.
Remarks: Behind Moulin de la Victoire, coins available, addresses indicated on the spot.

📷 | Gravelines | 7B5
Parking des Miaules, Rue des Islandais/Rue du Port. **GPS**: n50,98766 e2,12232. ⬆.

📷S | Le Portel | 7A5
Rue des Champs. **GPS**: n50,71188 e1,57485. ⬆➡

20 🛏€ 3, 01/04-01/10 € 6. 🗑

Location: Rural, quit. **Surface:** gravel.
Distance: 🚶500m 🛒nearby ⊗300m.
Remarks: From Dunkerque at entry straight on to small harbour, behind fort, parking at marina.

30 🛏€ 3, 01/06-30/09 € 4 ⚡€ 2/100liter 🚰Ch 🚿€ 2/4h 🗑. 🚌 🗑
Surface: metalled. ◻ 01/01-31/12
Distance: 🚶200m ⛱300m ⊗300m 🛒300m.
Remarks: Next to sports fields, 300m from beach (stairs).

📷S | Gravelines | 7B5
Rue de la Gendarmerie. **GPS**: n50,99342 e2,13177. ⬆➡
⚡€ 2 🚰Ch 🗑.

📷S | Le Touquet-Paris Plage | 7A6
Centre Nautique du Touquet Base Nord, Avenue Jean Ruet. **GPS**: n50,53588 e1,59285. ⬆➡

Tourist information Gravelines:
ℹ Office de Tourisme, 11, rue de la République, www.tourisme.fr/gravelines. Bathing resort and water sports centre.
Ⓜ L'Arsenal.Arsenal.

📷 | Hardelot | 7A5
Place R.L. Peeters. **GPS**: n50,63500 e1,59888. ⬆.

60 🛏€ 9 ⚡€ 2/100liter 🚰Ch 🔌€ 2/55minutes. **Surface:** asphalted. ◻ 01/01-31/12
Distance: 🚶10 min walking ⛱on the spot ⊗on the spot 🛒on the spot 🚌on the spot.
Remarks: Next to marina, at beach, follow signs.

📷S | Le Touquet-Paris Plage | 7A6
Parc International de la Canoke, Boulevard de la Canche. **GPS**: n50,52648 e1,59869. ⬆.

FR

100 ☐€7,50 ☐€ 2/100liter ☐Ch ☐€ 2/1h ☐. **Surface:** grassy/gravel. ☐ 01/01-31/12 **Distance:** ☐10 min walking ☐on the spot ☐on the spot ☐on the spot ☐on the spot.

Tourist information Le Touquet-Paris Plage:
☐ Office de Tourisme, Palais de l'Europe, Place de l'Hermitage, www.letouquet.com/.Popular bathing resort.
☐ Aqualud.Leisure pool park. ☐ 15/02-30/11 10-18h.

☐☐ Le-Cateau-Cambrésis 15B1
Avenue du Maréchal Leclerc, N43. **GPS:** n50,10256 e3,55429.☐

5 ☐free ☐ ☐Ch ☐free. **Surface:** asphalted. ☐ 01/01-31/12 **Distance:** ☐1km.

☐☐ Longfossé 7A5
Ferme du Louvet, 5, Route de Wierre, D52 Desvres > Samer. **GPS:** n50,64667 e1,79062.

8 ☐€6 ☐€ 3 ☐Ch ☐included. **Surface:** gravel.
Remarks: Narrow entrance.

☐ Merlimont 7A6
Place de la Gare. **GPS:** n50,46026 e1,58053.☐ .

12 ☐free. **Surface:** gravel. ☐ 01/01-31/12

☐☐ Nunq-Hautecôte 7B6
La Pommeraie, 13, route nationale. **GPS:** n50,30516 e2,29375.☐ .

5 ☐€5 ☐€ 2 ☐Ch ☐€ 5 ☐free.
Surface: gravel. ☐ 01/01-31/12
Distance: ☐50m.
Remarks: Covered pool € 3.

☐☐ Oye-plage ☐ 7A5
Les Huttes d'Oye Plage. GPS: n50,99703 e2,04228.☐.

10 ☐free ☐☐Ch.
Surface: gravel. ☐ 01/01-31/12
Distance: ☐on the spot ☐100m.
Remarks: Beach parking, service Oye-Plage: 50,97713 2,03966.

☐☐ Richebourg ☐ 7B6
Rue de la Briqueterie. **GPS:** n50,58028 e2,74639.☐☐.

6 ☐free ☐€ 2/100liter ☐€ 2/55minutes. **Location:** Rural, comfortable.
Surface: grasstiles. ☐ 01/01-31/12
Distance: ☐500m ☐ on the spot ☐ on the spot.
Remarks: Max. 48h.

☐ Stella-plage 7A6
Cours des Champs Elysées. **GPS:** n50,47470 e1,57726.☐.

30 ☐free. **Surface:** asphalted.
☐☐ Tardinghen 7A5
Le site des 2 caps, La Ferme d'Horloge, 1615 Route d'Ausques, D249. **GPS:** n50,86250 e1,64890.☐.

30 ⬛€ 5/24h 🔌€ 3 ♨Ch ⚓ included. **Surface:** metalled. 🅾 01/01-31/12
Distance: 🛒1,6km.
Remarks: Swin-golf € 5.

🏕 **Tardinghen** **7A5**
Le site des 2 caps, La Fleur des Champs. **GPS:** n50,85639 e1,65139.⬆.

50 ⬛€ 5/24h. **Surface:** grassy. 🅾 01/01-31/12
Distance: 🛒2km ⛱2km.

🏕 **Tardinghen** **7A5**
Le site des 2 caps, Le Fond de Sombre, Hervelinghen > Wissant. **GPS:** n50,89361 e1,68972.⬆.

10 ⬛€ 5/24h. **Surface:** grassy. 🅾 01/01-31/12
Distance: ⛱1km.

⬛S **Wissant** 🏖 **7A5**
Parking Wissant, Avenue Georges Clémenceau. **GPS:** n50,88684 e1,67064.⬆➡.

30 ⬛free ♨Ch free. **Surface:** metalled. 🅾 01/01-31/12
Distance: 🛒700m ⛱1,1km.

Picardie

⬛S **Ault** **14C1**
Rue Gest. **GPS:** n50,10333 e1,45083.⬆➡.

---

10 ⬛free 🔌€ 2 ♨Ch ⬛€ 2. **Surface:** asphalted. 🅾 01/01-31/12
Distance: 🛒within walking distance ⛱5 min walking ⊗200m ⬛200m.
⬛S **Bellicourt** **15A1**
Hameau de Riqueval, D1044. **GPS:** n49,95156 e3,23519.⬆.

2 ⬛free 🔌 ♨Ch ⬛ Service € 4. **Surface:** asphalted. 🅾 01/01-31/12 ⬛
service: 01/10-31/03.
Distance: 🛒300m ⊗on the spot ⬛on the spot.
Remarks: Coins at Tourist Info.
⬛S **Bourseville** **14C1**
Lotissement le Village. **GPS:** n50,10350 e1,52702.⬆➡.

35 ⬛free 🔌€ 2 ♨Ch ⚓€ 2. **Surface:** asphalted. 🅾 01/01-31/12
Distance: 🛒500m ⛱3km ⊗500m ⬛500m.
⬛S **Cayeux-sur-Mer** 🏖 **14C1**
Rue Faidherbe. **GPS:** n50,20300 e1,52612.⬆➡.

30 ⬛€ 5 🔌€ 3 ♨Ch. **Surface:** gravel. 🅾 01/01-31/12
Distance: 🛒2km ⛱At the sea, no beach ⊗2km ⬛2km.
Remarks: In front of campsite.
⬛S **Cayeux-sur-Mer** 🏖 **14C1**
Route blanche, Le Hourdel, D102. **GPS:** n50,21448 e1,55208.➡.

FR

30 🛏free. **Location:** Very simple, isolated, quit. **Surface:** gravel. ▢ 01/01-31/12
Distance: 🚶500m, Cayeux 6km ⚓sea 50m ⊗500m ⚍3km.

60 🛏€8 ⚐🔌 Ch WC free. **Surface:** gravel. ▢ 01/01-31/12
Distance: 🚶200m ⚓5 min walking.

🛏S	Château-Thierry	15B4

Aire de Château. GPS: n49,03657 e3,38365. ⬆➡.

🛏S	Le Crotoy	7A6

Aire Camping-car, Bassin des Chasses. **GPS:** n50,21800 e1,63300. ⬆.

13 🛏€6 ⚐🔌Ch ⚒ WC ⊿included. 🛋 ⚑ **Location:** Urban, comfortable.
Surface: asphalted. ▢ 01/01-31/12
Distance: 🚶centre ±1,8km ⚓on the spot ⊶on the spot ⊗on the spot ⚍on the spot 🛒on the spot 🍴on the spot.
Remarks: Along the Marne river.

🛏S	Conty	14D2

Rue du Marais. **GPS:** n49,74333 e2,15583.

50 🛏€5/24h ⚐€ 2/100liter 🔌Ch⚌€ 2/1h. **Surface:** sand. ▢ 01/01-31/12
Distance: 🚶5 min walking ⚓15 min walking ⊞Laverie Crotelloise, 20, avenue du Gal de Gaulle.
Remarks: In harbour.

🛏S	Le Crotoy	7A6

Aire Camping-car, Chemin du Marais. **GPS:** n50,22886 e1,61253. ⬆.

20 🛏free ⚐🔌 Ch WC free. ▢ 01/01-31/12
Distance: 🚶200m ⚑ 6,5km ⊶300m ⊗300m ⚍300m.
Remarks: In front of fire-station, baker every morning.

🛏S	Doullens	14D1

Rue du Pont à l'Avoine, N25-Arras-Amiens. **GPS:** n50,15390 e2,34260. ⬆.

35 🛏€5/24h ⚐€ 2/10minutes 🔌Ch⚌€ 2/1h. **Surface:** sand. ▢ 01/01-31/12
Distance: 🚶10 min walking ⚓on the spot ⊞Laverie Crotelloise, 20, avenue du Gal de Gaulle.

Tourist information Le Crotoy:
ℹ Office de Tourisme, 1, rue Carnot, www.tourisme-crotoy.com.Seaside resort at the mouth of the river Somme.

🛏S	Mers-les-Bains	14C1

Chemin de la Petite Allée. **GPS:** n50,06175 e1,40150. ⬆.
50 🛏€5,50 ⚐€ 2 🔌Ch. **Location:** Comfortable. **Surface:** gravel. ▢ 01/01-31/12
Distance: 🚶1,3km ⚓sandy beach 1,5km ⚍Auchan 600m.

🛏S	Morienval	15A3

Route de Pierrefonds 32. **GPS:** n49,30352 e2,92309.
🛏€8 ⚐€ 2/100liter 🔌Ch⚌€ 2/1h.
Surface: gravel. ▢ 22/03-16/11
Distance: 🚶500m ⊗500m ⚍500m.

🛏S	Picquigny	14D1

Rue de la Cavée d'Airaines. **GPS:** n49,94388 e2,13496. ⬆.

4 🛏free ⚐🔌Ch free. **Surface:** asphalted.
Distance: ⊞on the spot.

🛏S	Fort Mahon Plage	7A6

Plage Parking de la Dune, Rue de la Bistouille. **GPS:** n50,33833 e1,55611. ⬆.

8 ⬛€5 🚐🔌Ⓒincluded. ✴€ 2.🛒 **Location:** Rural.
Surface: grassy.
Distance: 🛒500m. 🚰500m.

| Ⓦ S | Quend | 7A6 |

Ferme de la Grande Retz. GPS: n50,32893 e1,61811.⬆️➡️.

10 ⬛€5 🚐Ⓒh ✴€ 3. **Surface:** grassy. ⭕ 01/01-31/12
Distance: 🛒3km 🏊9km 🚴9km 🚰2km.

| Ⓦ S | Quend-plage-les-Pins | 7A6 |

Plage des Pins. GPS: n50,32410 e1,55545.⬆️.
100 ⬛€7/24h 🚐 2/10minutes 🔌Ⓒh🚐€ 2/1h. **Surface:** gravel. ⭕
01/01-31/12
Distance: 🛒800m 🏖️beach 900m.

| Ⓦ S | St.Valéry-sur-Somme 🌿⚓ | 14C1 |

Rue de la Croix l'Abbé. GPS: n50,18220 e1,62881.⬆️➡️.

180 ⬛€ 9/24h 🚐🔌Ⓒhincluded. 🚗🛒 **Location:** Rural. **Surface:** gravel.
⭕ 01/01-31/12
Distance: 🛒1km ⊗nearby 🚰nearby.
Remarks: Su market.

Tourist information St.Valéry-sur-Somme:
ℹ️ Office de Tourisme, place Guillaume le Conquérant.Fishing town and family
bathing resort in the bay of the Somme river.

| 🏞️ | Villers-Cộtterets | 15A3 |

Grand Bosquet Parc du Château, Place Aristide Briand. **GPS:** n49,25483
e3,09400.⬆️.

⬛free. **Surface:** grassy/metalled. ⭕ 01/01-31/12

Champagne Ardenne

| Ⓒ S | Arc-en-Barrois | 15D6 |

Camping municipal, D3/D159. **GPS:** n47,95056 e5,00528.

25 ⬛€3 🚐🔌Ⓒh ✴included. **Surface:** gravel. ⭕ 01/01-31/12
Distance: 🛒500m 🚰500m 🚰500m.

| Ⓦ S | Attigny | 15D2 |

D987. **GPS:** n49,48583 e4,58077.
4 ⬛free 🚐🔌Ⓒhagainst payment.

| Ⓦ S | Avize | 15C4 |

Place du Bourg Joli. **GPS:** n48,97175 e4,00999.

⬛free 🚐🔌Ⓒhfree. **Surface:** asphalted. ⭕ 01/01-31/12
Distance: 🚰bakery 50m.
Remarks: Next to town hall.

| Ⓦ S | Beaunay | 15B4 |

Ferme Du Bel Air. GPS: n48,88177 e3,87475.⬆️.

12 ⬛€6 🔌Ⓒh ✴included 🛒. **Surface:** gravel. ⭕ 01/01-31/12
Distance: 🛒2km ⊗2km 🚰2km.

| Ⓦ S | Brienne le Château | 15D5 |

Rue de la Gare. **GPS:** n48,39617 e4,53130.➡️.

15 ⬛free 🚐 3 🔌Ⓒh🚐 3. **Surface:** asphalted.
Distance: 🛒300m ⊗400m 🚰bakery 300m.
Remarks: Coins at Office de Tourisme.

| Ⓦ S | Chamery | 15C3 |

Salle Polyvalente, Rue du Château Rouge. **GPS:** n49,17475 e3,95446.

FR

FR

5 🅂free 🚰€ 2/100liter 🅲h💺€ 2/55minutes. **Surface:** asphalted. ⬛
01/01-31/12
Remarks: In front of community centre.

🅂🅂 **Champigny-lès-Langres** 16A6

Rue du Port, D74. **GPS:** n47,88167 e5,33861.

6 🅂free 🚰 ✕ WC. **Surface:** gravel. ⬛ 01/01-31/12
Distance: ⊗400m 🪵800m.

🅂🅂 **Chaource** 15C6

Chemin de Ronde. **GPS:** n48,05944 e4,13861.⬆.

+5 🅂free 🚰€ 2/100liter 🅲h💺€ 2/1h.
Surface: gravel.
Remarks: Coins at Tourist Info, 2, Grande rue, mo.morning market.

🅂🅂 **Charleville-Mézières** 15D2

Rue des Pâquis. **GPS:** n49,78056 e4,72056.

8 🅂free 🚰🅲h ✕€ 5.
Surface: asphalted.
Distance: 800m.
Remarks: Motorhome parking next to campsite Mont Olympe.

Tourist information Charleville-Mézières:
ℹ Office de Tourisme, 4, place Ducale.Big city with historical centre.
Ⓜ Musée Ardennes.Regional museum. ⬛ Sa 21.15h all 12 scenes ⦿ Mo.
✝ Nôtre Dame de l'Espérance.Gothic basilica.
🛍 place Ducale.Regional products. ⬛ Tue, Thu, Sa.

🅂🅂 **Chaumont** 16A6

Port de la Maladière, RN74 Neufchâteau > Chaumont. **GPS:** n48,11815
e5,15437.⬆.

12 🅂€ 6,50, € 0,20/pp tourist tax 🚰🅲h ✕ ⬛€ 2, dryer € 2,80.
Surface: metalled. ⬛ 01/04-31/10
Distance: ⊘on the spot ⊗100m 🪵nearby.

Tourist information Chaumont:
ℹ Office de Tourisme, Place du Général de Gaulle.

🅂🅂 **Chavanges** 15D5

Ruelle du Fief Berthaux. **GPS:** n48,50691 e4,57627.⬆➡.

8 🅂free 🚰€ 3 🅲h💺. **Surface:** asphalted/gravel. ⬛ 01/01-31/12
Distance: 300m 🪵400m.
Remarks: Coins available at the shops.

🅂🅂 **Colombey-les-deux-Eglises** 15D6

Rue de Général de Gaulle. **GPS:** n48,22316 e4,88619.⬆.

10 🅂free 🚰 🅲h WC free. **Surface:** asphalted/gravel. ⬛ 01/04-31/11
Distance: on the spot ⊗50m 🪵50m.
Remarks: At museum and memorial Général de Gaulle.

🅂🅂 **Corgirnon** 23A1

Allée du Parc. **GPS:** n47,80681 e5,50308.⬆➡.

8 🅂€ 4 🚰🅲h ✕ WC ⬛included. 🌿 **Location:** Rural, isolated, quit.
Surface: gravel. ⬛ 01/01-31/12
Distance: 500m ⊘10km 🪵500m.
Remarks: Bread-service.

⊙Ⓢ **Dolancourt** 15D6

Nigloland, RN19. **GPS:** n48,26086 e4,60945. ⬆.

28 ⌇€ 5/24h ⚡⚑Ch⚓included. **Surface:** asphalted. ◻ 03/04-03/11
Remarks: Parking amusement park.

Ⓢ **Donjeux** 16A5

Halte Nautique, D67a. **GPS:** n48,36586 e5,14891.

5 ⌇free ⚡⚑Ch⚓(4x)free.
Surface: gravel/metalled. ◻ 01/01-31/12
Distance: ⚓1km ⌇on the spot ⚡on the spot ⊗1km ⚐800m.
Remarks: Baker every morning.

Ⓢ **Épernay** 15C4

Rue Dom Pérignon. **GPS:** n49,03602 e3,95130.

3 ⌇free ⚡€ 2 ⚑Ch⚓€ 2.
Surface: asphalted.
Distance: ⚓within walking distance ⚐Avenue Jean Jaurès.
Remarks: Behind church St.Pierre-St.Paul,coins at Tourist Info.

Tourist information Épernay:
ⓘ Office de Tourisme, 7, avenue de Champagne. ◻ 01/10-30/04 Mo-Fr 9.30-12.30h 13.30-17.30h, 01/05-30/09 Mo-Sa 9.30-12.30h 13.30-19h.
👁 Cave de Catellane, 154, avenue de Verdun.
👁 Coöperative des Premiers crus de la Marne, 5, rue de la Brèche. ◻ Tue-Fri 8.30-11.30h, 13.30-17h, Aug closed.
👁 Mercier, 70, avenue de Champagne. ◻ Mo-Sa 9.30-11.30h, 14-16.30h, Su/holidays 9.30-11.30h, 14-17.30h.
Ⓜ Musée de la Préhistoire d'Archéologie Régionale et du Vin de Champagne. ◻ 01-03/11.

Ⓢ **Esternay** 15B4

Place des Tilleuls, D48, Rue de la Paix. **GPS:** n48,73196 e3,55719.

5 ⌇free ⚡⚑free. **Surface:** gravel. ◻ water: 15/03-15/11
Distance: ⚓within walking distance.
Remarks: Behind church.

Ⓢ **Froncles** 16A5

Halte Nautique. GPS: n48,29954 e5,15246. ⬆.

10 ⌇€ 1,50 ⚡€ 1 ⚑Ch⚓(8x)€ 1,50 ᴡᴄ⌇€ 2 ▣€ 3, dryer € 3.
Surface: gravel. ◻ 01/01-31/12
Distance: ⚓on the spot ⚓on the spot ⊗on the spot ⚐1km.

Ⓢ **Giffaumont-Champaubert** ⚓⚓ 15D5

Site de Chantecoq, Rue du grand Der. **GPS:** n48,56880 e4,70294. ⬆.

50 ⌇free ⚡€ 3,50/80liter ⚑Ch⚓€ 3,50/45minutes ᴡᴄ.
Surface: metalled.
◻ 01/01-31/12
Distance: ⚓on the spot.
Remarks: At lake Der de Chantecoq, oins at Tourist Info.

Ⓢ **Giffaumont-Champaubert** ⚓⚓ 15D5

Station Nautique, Rue du Port. **GPS:** n48,55354 e4,76715. ⬆.

⌇free ⚡€ 3,50/80liter ⚑Ch⚓€ 3,50/45minutes. **Surface:** asphalted.
◻ 01/01-31/12
Distance: ⚓on the spot.
Remarks: Coins at Tourist Info.

Givet 15D1

Quai des Fours, D949. **GPS:** n50,13497 e4,82190.
± 4 ⌇free. **Location:** Very simple. **Surface:** asphalted. ◻ 01/01-31/12
Distance: ⚓50m ⊗50m ⚐50m.

© S | **Givet** | 15D1

Rue Berthelot. **GPS:** n50,14291 e4,82611.⬆️.

5 🅿️free ⛽€ 3 🚰Ch🔌(2x)€ 3. **Surface:** asphalted. ⬛ 01/01-31/12
Remarks: Coins electricity at campsite.

🅿️ S | **Goncourt** | 16A6

Rue des Lottes, D74. **GPS:** n48,23685 e5,60998.⬆️.

18 🅿️free ⛽€ 2 🚰Ch.
Location: Rural.
Surface: asphalted/gravel. ⬛ 01/01-31/12
Distance: 🏊on the spot.
Remarks: Voluntary contribution € 2, baker at 8am, along the Meuse.

FR

🅿️ S | **Joinville** | 16A5

Halte Nautique, Rue des Jardins. **GPS:** n48,44583 e5,15000.⬆️.

12 🅿️free ⛽€ 2 🚰Ch 🔌€ 2/55minutes 🧺. **Surface:** gravel/metalled.
⬛ 01/01-31/12
Distance: 🏪500m 🏊on the spot 🍽️on the spot ⊗800m 🚂100m.

🅿️ S | **Juzennecourt** | 15D6

Place de la Mairie. **GPS:** n48,18429 e4,97890.

4 🅿️free ⛽Ch🔌. **Surface:** metalled.
Distance: 🏪on the spot.
Remarks: Parking townhall.

🅿️ S | **La Cheppe** | 15C4

Champ d'Attila, Rue de Champo d'Attila. **GPS:** n49,04892 e4,49377.⬆️.

5 🅿️free ⛽€ 2 🚰Ch�☰€ 2 WC. **Surface:** gravel. ⬛ 01/01-31/12
Distance: 🏪500m.

🅿️ S | **La Gault-Soigny** | 15B4

Rue de la Liberté, D373. **GPS:** n48,81758 e3,59072.

4 🅿️free ⛽🚰Chfree. **Surface:** asphalted. ⬛ 01/01-31/12
Distance: 🏪on the spot.
Remarks: Near Salle des Fêtes.

🅿️ S | **Langres** | 23A1

Ruelle de la Poterne. **GPS:** n47,85795 e5,32989.⬆️.

15 🅿️free ⛽🚰free. **Surface:** asphalted.
Distance: 🏪800m.

| **Langres** | 23A1

Parking Panorama, Allée des Marronniers. **GPS:** n47,86104 e5,33674.⬆️.

🅿️free. **Surface:** asphalted. ⬛ 01/01-31/12
Remarks: Free elevator to old town, inclining pitches.

| **Langres** | 23A1

Place de Bel Air. **GPS:** n47,85885 e5,33225.⬆️.

🚿free. **Surface:** asphalted. 🅾 01/01-31/12

Tourist information Langres:
ℹ Office de Tourisme, Square Olivier Lahalle-place Bel'Air, www.tourisme-langres.com.City worth a visit, the city centre surrounded by a wall of 4 kilometres.
✝ Cathédrale St Mammes.
🏕 🅾 Fri.

🚻🆂	Les Riceys	15C6

D452. **GPS:** n47,99222 e4,36458.⬆➡.

20 🚿free 🚰€ 2 ♻Ch🔌€ 2. **Surface:** asphalted. 🅾 01/01-31/12
Distance: 🛒500m ⊗500m 🛢500m.

🚻🆂	Mareuil-sur-Ay	15C4

Place Charles de Gaulle. **GPS:** n49,04522 e4,03490.⬆.

8 🚿free 🚰€ 2 ♻Ch🔌€ 5. **Surface:** asphalted. 🅾 01/01-31/12
Remarks: On the canal.

🚻🆂	Monthermé	15D1

Rue du Général de Gaulle, D989. **GPS:** n49,88278 e4,73000.

🚿free 🚰€ 3,80 ♻Ch🔌. 🅾 01/01-31/12
Remarks: Coins at Mairie, office de tourisme. On edge from village, dir D1 Rocroi follow.

🚻🆂	Montier-en-Der	15D5

Rue de l'Isle. **GPS:** n48,47861 e4,76861.

6 🚿free 🚰€ 2,60 ♻Ch🔌€ 2,60 WC. **Surface:** gravel.
Distance: 🛒on the spot.
Remarks: Coins at Tourist Info.

🄲🆂	Nogent-sur-Seine	15B5

Parking camping/piscine, Rue du camping. **GPS:** n48,50388 e3,50888.⬆.

2 🚿free 🚰♻Ch🔌free. **Surface:** asphalted. 🅾 01/01-31/12
Distance: 🛒1,5km ⊗1,5km 🛢1,5km.

🄲🆂	Peigney	16A6

Lac de la Liez, D284, rue Côté de Recey. **GPS:** n47,87272 e5,38077.⬆➡.

8 🚿€ 10,50 🚰♻Ch🔌.
Surface: asphalted. 🅾 01/01-31/12
Distance: 🛒500m ⊘on the spot 🛒on the spot ⊗on the spot 🛢on the spot.

🚻🆂	Piney	15C5

Place des Anciens Combattants, Rue du Général de Gaulle. **GPS:** n48,35878 e4,33442.⬆.

3 🚿free 🚰€ 2 ♻Ch🔌€ 2. **Surface:** metalled. 🅾 01/01-31/12
Distance: 🛒500m ⊗500m 🛢500m.
Remarks: Closed when frosty.

🚻🆂	Reims	15C3

Parc du CIS de la Comédie, Esplanade André Malraux, chaussée Bocquaine. **GPS:** n49,24881 e4,02110.⬆➡.

9 ⌐free ╦ ☐Chfree. **Surface:** metalled.
Distance: ▲15 min walking ✈1,4km ⊗350m ═100m.
Remarks: Max. 48h, noisy place, call for entrance code (5270A). A4, exit Reims-centre.

| 🏭S | **Sapignicourt** | 15D5 |

Rue Deperthes à Larzicourt. **GPS:** n48,65111 e4,80583.

⌐ ╦€ 2,50/10minutes ☐Ch▦€ 2,50/55minutes.
Remarks: Coins at mairie and Mr. Bauer, 14, grande rue.

| 🏭S | **St.Dizier** | 15D5 |

Centre Loisirs Caravanning, Route de Villiers en lieu. **GPS:** n48,64255 e4,91035.

6 ⌐free ╦☐Ch ✎WCfree. **Surface:** asphalted. ☐ 01/01-31/12
Remarks: Motorhome dealer.

| 🏭S | **Vendeuvre-sur-Barse** | 15C6 |

Grande Rue/Passage Mesgrigny. **GPS:** n48,23750 e4,46932.⬆.

5 ⌐free ╦€ 3 ☐Ch▦. **Surface:** asphalted.
Distance: ▲100m ⊗on the spot ☐on the spot ═on the spot.

| 🏭S | **Viéville** ⚓ | 16A6 |

Halte Nautique La Licorne. **GPS:** n48,23825 e5,12988.⬆.

6 ⌐free ╦☐Ch ✎(6x) ⌐free. **Surface:** gravel.

| 🏭S | **Villeneuve-Renneville-Chevigny** | 15C4 |

Champagne Leclère-Massard, 12, rue du Plessis. **GPS:** n48,91488 e4,05959.

⌐€4 ╦☐Ch ✎included. **Surface:** asphalted.
Remarks: Champagne tastery, Tu-Su fresh bread.

| 🏭S | **Villers-sous-Châtillon** | 15B3 |

Halte camping-cars, Rue du Parc. **GPS:** n49,09642 e3,80078.

5 ⌐free ╦€ 3/100liter ☐Ch▦€ 3/1h. **Surface:** metalled. ☐ 01/01-31/12

Lorraine

| 🏭 | **Ancerville** | 15D5 |

Impasse des Pransons. **GPS:** n48,63641 e5,01582.⬆.

2 ⌐free. **Location:** Urban, very simple, quit.
Surface: metalled. ☐ 01/01-31/12
Distance: ⊗400m ☐400m.

| 🍴 | **Avocourt** | 16A3 |

Restaurant La Terrasse, Rue du Moulin. **GPS:** n49,20417 e5,14227.⬆.
4 ⌐free. **Location:** Rural, very simple.
Surface: unpaved. ☐ 01/01-31/12

| 🏭S | **Baccarat** | 16C5 |

Place du General Le'Clerc. **GPS:** n48,44667 e6,74000.⬆.

15 🛏€ 4/night ⚡€ 2/100liter 🔌Ch🔋€ 2/3minutes WC. **Surface:** asphalted. 🅿 01/01-31/12 ⊙ Fri-morning market.
Distance: 🚶300m 🏊on the spot 🛒on the spot ⊗300m 🍴300m.
Remarks: Along river, max. 24h.

Tourist information Baccarat:
ℹ Office de Tourisme, 2, rue Adrien Michaut, www.ville-baccarat.fr.Important French crystal manufacture (not to visit). Many shops with crystal.
Ⓜ Musée du Cristal.Crystal museum. 🅿 Mo-Sa 10-18h. 🎫 € 2,50.

| 🛏S | **Bar-le-Duc** | 16A4 |

Halte du port fluvial, Rue du débarcadère. **GPS:** n48,77536 e5,16654. ⬆➡.

8 🛏free ⚡€ 2/100liter 🔌Ch🔋€ 2/55minutes.
Location: Urban, noisy.
Surface: asphalted. 🅿 01/01-31/12
Distance: 🏊on the spot 🛒on the spot ⊗150m 🍴150m 🚲150m 🏍on the spot.
Remarks: On the canal, coins available at office de tourisme, 7 rue Jeanne d'Arc.

| 🛏 | **Beaulieu-en-Argonne** 🌿🌲🏚 | 15D4 |

Parking Mairie, Grande Rue, D2B. **GPS:** n49,03183 e5,06665. ⬆.

6 🛏free. **Location:** Urban, central, quit.
Surface: asphalted. 🅿 01/01-31/12
Distance: 🚶on the spot ⊗50m 🏍on the spot 🚶on the spot.
Remarks: In opposite of police station.

| 🛏 | **Beaulieu-en-Argonne** 🌿🌲🏚 | 15D4 |

Parking St. Rouin, D2. **GPS:** n49,03554 e5,02975.⬆.

4 🛏free. **Location:** Isolated. **Surface:** gravel.

Distance: 🚶Beaulieu 6km.
Remarks: Isolated parking.

| ⚡S | **Bonzée** | 16A3 |

Base de Loisirs du Colvert. **GPS:** n49,09619 e5,60950.
6 🛏€ 12, € 5 without service ⚡€ 4 🔌Ch🔋€ 5. **Surface:** grassy.
Distance: 🏊on the spot.

| 🛏S | **Bruley** | 16B4 |

D118, rue Saint-Martin. **GPS:** n48,70640 e5,85554.⬆.

10 🛏free ⚡€ 3/10minutes 🔌Ch🔋 (2x)€ 3/8h. **Surface:** gravel. 🅿 01/01-31/12
Distance: 🚶200m ⊗300m 🍴300m.

| 🛏S | **Bulgnéville** | 16B6 |

Étang des Récollets, Rue des Récollets. **GPS:** n48,20733 e5,83899. ⬆➡.

10 🛏€ 3/24h ⚡🔌Ch🔋 WC included.
Surface: asphalted.
🅿 01/01-31/12
Distance: 🚶700m 🚴1,8km 🏊on the spot 🛒on the spot ⊗100m 🍴700m.

| 🛏S | **Certilleux** | 16A5 |

rue de l'englise. **GPS:** n48,31193 e5,72679.⬆.

8 🛏free ⚡free. **Surface:** asphalted. 🅿 01/01-31/12

| 🛏 | **Champougny** | 16A5 |

D145f. **GPS:** n48,54410 e5,69277.⬆.

3 🛏free. **Surface:** grassy. 🅿 01/01-31/12
Distance: 🚶200m.

Charmes 16B5

Port de plaisance. GPS: n48,37334 e6,29542. ↥.

100 ⌁ € 6 ⌁ included ⌁ Ch ⌁ (80x)€ 2 WC ⌁€ 1,50 ⌁ € 3/day.
Surface: gravel/metalled. ◻ 01/01-31/12
Distance: ⌁1km ⌁1,5km ⌁on the spot ⌁on the spot ⌁within walking distance.
Tourist information Charmes:
⌁ Motorhome friendly village on the Mosel river.
⌁ Fri-morning.

Commercy 16A4

Rue du Docteur Boyer. **GPS:** n48,76374 e5,59616. ↥.

4 ⌁free ⌁€ 2/15minutes ⌁ Ch ⌁ (4x)€ 2/4h. **Surface:** asphalted. ◻
01/01-31/12
Distance: ⌁800m ⌁on the spot ⌁on the spot ⌁600m.
Remarks: On the canal.

Contrisson 15D4

Ballastière. GPS: n48,80530 e4,94714. ↥.

10 ⌁free WC. **Location:** Rural, very simple, isolated, quit. **Surface:** unpaved.
◻ 01/01-31/12
Distance: ⌁800m ⌁1km ⌁1km.
Remarks: At small lake.

Damvillers 16A3

Rue de L'île d'Envie, D905. **GPS:** n49,33790 e5,39752.

4 ⌁free ⌁€ 2 ⌁Ch⌁€ 2. **Surface:** asphalted. ◻ 01/01-31/12
Distance: ⌁on the spot ⌁on the spot.

Damvillers 16A3

Ballastière, D905. **GPS:** n49,35861 e5,40167.
10 ⌁free. **Surface:** grassy. ◻ 01/01-31/12
Distance: ⌁Damvillers 1,9km.
Remarks: Isolated parking, at Etangs de Monti.

Darney 16B6

Champ de Foire. **GPS:** n48,08727 e6,04287.

5 ⌁free. **Surface:** asphalted. ◻ 01/01-31/12

Dieue-sur-Meuse 16A3

Port de plaisance, Route des Dames. **GPS:** n49,07110 e5,42634. ↥.

15 ⌁free ⌁⌁Ch⌁free. **Location:** Rural, quit. **Surface:** gravel. ◻
01/01-31/12
Distance: ⌁200m ⌁on the spot ⌁on the spot ⌁200m ⌁200m.
Remarks: On the canal.

Dun-sur-Meuse 16A3

Rue du Vieux Port. **GPS:** n49,38919 e5,17787. ↥.

16 ⌁€ 7 ⌁⌁Ch⌁ (8x) WC ⌁included ⌁.⌁ **Location:** Rural,
comfortable, central, quit. **Surface:** gravel. ◻ 01/01-31/12 ◻ sanitary
building: 1/11-1/4.
Distance: ⌁600m ⌁on the spot ⌁on the spot ⌁400m ⌁600m ⌁on the
spot.

Épinal 16C6

Port d'Épinal, Quai de Dogneville, D12. **GPS:** n48,18671 e6,44493. ↥.

5 ⌁summer € 5, winter € 8 ⌁⌁Ch⌁ Service € 3/15min ⌁. **Surface:**
asphalted.

FR

Distance: 🛒1km ⛵ 3,5km.
Remarks: Max. 48h.

| 🅿 | Etain | 16A3 |
Allée du champ de foire, D631. **GPS:** n49,20942 e5,63755.
6 🅿 free. **Surface:** metalled. 🔲 01/01-31/12

| 🅿 | Etain | 16A3 |
La Sirène, D631. **GPS:** n49,21010 e5,63587. ⬆️
6 🅿 free. **Surface:** unpaved. 🔲 01/01-31/12
Remarks: Behind hotel de la Sirène.

| 🅿 S | Etival-Clairefontaine | 16C5 |
Rue du Vivier. **GPS:** n48,36355 e6,86504.

20 🅿 free ⛽ 🔧 Ch free. **Surface:** asphalted. 🔲 01/01-31/12 ⬤ water disconnected in winter.

| 🅿 | Fains-Veel | 15D4 |
Halte Fluviale, Rue du Stade. **GPS:** n48,79298 e5,12503. ⬆️

2 🅿 free.
Location: Very simple, quit.
Surface: metalled. 🔲 01/01-31/12
Distance: 🛒450m 🏊 on the spot ⊗ on the spot 🍴 on the spot.

| 🅿 S | Fénétrange | 16D4 |
Wally Services, Route de Sarre Union. **GPS:** n48,85365 e7,02723. ⬆️
5 🅿 free ⛽ € 2 🔧 Ch € 2. **Surface:** grassy/metalled.
Remarks: Max. 48h.

| 🅿 S | Fraize | 16D6 |
Impasse de la Gare/ Place Jean Sonrel. **GPS:** n48,18188 e7,00360.

6 🅿 free ⛽ € 2 🔧 Ch 🚻 € 2 WC. **Surface:** asphalted. 🔲 01/01-31/12
Distance: 🛒100m ⊗100m 🍴 100m.
Remarks: Behind Tourist Office.

| 🅿 S | Gérardmer 🏖 🚠 ❄ | 16C6 |
Parking de la Prairie, Boulevard d'Alsace. **GPS:** n48,07173 e6,87296. ⬆️

100 🅿 € 4 ⛽ 🔧 Ch WC free 🚿. **Surface:** asphalted/gravel. 🔲 01/01-31/12
Distance: 🛒 on the spot.

| 🅿 | Gérardmer 🏖 🚠 ❄ | 16C6 |
Chemin de la Rayée, La Mauselaine. **GPS:** n48,05846 e6,88862. ⬆️

🅿 € 4/24h. **Surface:** asphalted. 🔲 01/01-31/12
Distance: 🛒 Gérardmer 1,7km.
Remarks: Parking at skipistes.

Tourist information Gérardmer:
ℹ️ Office de Tourisme, 4, Place des Déportés, www.gerardmer.net.Lively holiday destination on lake of same name, watersports in the summer several wintersports during winter, 20 ski runs.
🏖 🔲 Thu, Sa.

| 🅿 | Gondrecourt-le-Château 🧁 | 16A5 |
Parking Musée du Cheval, Rue Saint Blaise. **GPS:** n48,51390 e5,50975.
2 🅿 free. **Surface:** metalled.
Distance: ⊗50m 🚆50m.

| 🅿 | Gondrecourt-le-Château 🧁 | 16A5 |
Rue du Général Leclerc. **GPS:** n48,51373 e5,50386.
3 🅿 free. **Location:** Urban. **Surface:** unpaved. 🔲 01/01-31/12
Distance: 🚆 on the spot.

| 🅿 S | Greux | 16A5 |
Rue Jeanne d'Arc. **GPS:** n48,44972 e5,67639.

10 🅿 free ⛽ 🔧 free. **Surface:** gravel. 🔲 01/01-31/12
Distance: ⊗500m 🚆500m.

| 🅿 S | Haironville 🌿 ⚓ | 15D4 |
GPS: n48,68438 e5,08586. ⬆️

5 🛏free ➡€ 2/10minutes 🚰Ch⏚€ 2/50minutes. **Location:** Rural, central, quit. **Surface:** gravel. ⬛ 01/01-31/12
Distance: 🚶200 🛒200m.
Remarks: Coins available at the shops.

| 🅢 | Heudicourt sous les Côtes 🏵 | 16A4 |

GPS: n48,93549 e5,71548.

🛏first night € 8, € 5 each additional night ➡🚰ChWC🗑. **Surface:** grassy/gravel.
Remarks: View on Lac de Madine.

| 🅢 | Issoncourt | 16A4 |

Parking Relais de la Voie Sacrée. GPS: n48,97070 e5,28776. ⬆.

4 🛏free. **Location:** Rural, very simple, quit. **Surface:** gravel.
Distance: 🚶50m.

| 🅢 | La Bresse | 16D6 |

Route de Lispach. **GPS:** n48,04354 e6,93348.
🛏free. **Surface:** unpaved. ⬛ 01/01-31/12
Remarks: At cross-country skiing circuit.

| Ⓒ🅢 | La Bresse | 16D6 |

Camping Belle Hutte. GPS: n48,03500 e6,96268.

20 🛏€ 12,50-22,50 ➡🚰Ch⚡ WC🗑against payment. **Surface:** grassy/gravel. ⬛ 01/01-31/12
Distance: 🚶9km 🚲100m 🏊500m.
Remarks: Summertime on campsite, wintertime in front of campsite.

| Ⓒ🅢 | La Bresse | 16D6 |

Camping du Haut Des Bluches, 5, route des Planches. **GPS:** n48,00005 e6,91718.

18 🛏€ 5 12.00-12.00h ➡🚰Ch⚡WC🗑included. ⬛ 01/01-31/12 ◉ 05/11-14/12.
Remarks: Zone camping-car.

| 🅢 | La Bresse | 16D6 |

Route de Niachamp. **GPS:** n47,99430 e6,85431.
➡€ 2/100liter 🚰Ch. ⬛ 01/01-31/12

| 🅢 | La Croix-sur-Meuse | 16A4 |

Auberge de la Truite, Route de Seuzey. **GPS:** n48,98267 e5,53393.⬆.

4 🛏free ➡⚡ (4x)€ 3 WC📶. **Surface:** grassy. ⬛ 01/01-31/12
Distance: 🚶2km 🏪on the spot ❌on the spot.

| 🍴 | Lachaussée | 16B4 |

Domaine du Vieux Moulin, Gr Grande Rue. **GPS:** n49,03507 e5,81735.
8 🛏. **Surface:** gravel.
Distance: 🏪on the spot.
Remarks: Along Étang de Lachaussée.

| 🅢 | Laheycourt 🏕🏵 | 15D4 |

Rue de la Gare. **GPS:** n48,88903 e5,02165.⬆.

3 🛏free. **Location:** Rural, very simple, quit. **Surface:** grassy/gravel. ⬛ 01/01-31/12
Distance: 🏊on the spot 🏪50m 🛒50m.
Remarks: Along the Chée river.

| 🅢🅢 | Les Islettes 🏕 | 15D3 |

Route du Lochères. **GPS:** n49,12122 e5,03684.⬆➡.

16 🛏€ 5/24h ➡€ 1 🚰Ch⏚€ 1 WC🗑.🚿 **Location:** Rural, comfortable. **Surface:** gravel. ⬛ 01/01-31/12

FR

Distance: 🚶3km 🚴10,5km ⊗3km 🚰3km.

🏕S **Liffol-le-Grand** 16A5

D427. **GPS:** n48,32500 e5,55817.

15 🏕free. **Surface:** gravel. 📅 01/01-31/12
Distance: 🚶2km ⊗2km 🚰1km.

🏕S **Ligny-en-Barrois** 16A4

Relais Nautique, Rue Jean Willemert. **GPS:** n48,68787 e5,31943. ⬆➡.

10 🏕free 🚰€ 2/80liter 🔌Ch🔌€ 2/50minutes. **Location:** Comfortable, central, quit. **Surface:** asphalted.
Distance: 🚶on the spot 🍴on the spot ⊗50m 🚰50m 🚲on the spot 🚶on the spot.
Remarks: Along Canal de la Marne au Rhin.

🏕 **Loison** 16A3

Parking Camp Marguerre. **GPS:** n49,28962 e5,56737.
6 🏕free.
Remarks: Isolated parking, Camp Marguerre: militair erfgoed '14-18.

🏕 **Longeville-en-Barrois** 16A4

Gr Grande Rue. **GPS:** n48,74201 e5,20645. ⬆.

10 🏕free. **Location:** Urban, very simple, quit. **Surface:** gravel.
Distance: 🚶on the spot ⊗100m 🚰100m 🚲on the spot 🚶on the spot.
Remarks: Along the Ornain river.

🏕S **Longuyon** 16A3

Parking Salvador Allende, N18. **GPS:** n49,44802 e5,59973. ⬆.

2 🏕free 🚰🔌Ch🔌WC 🧹.
Surface: asphalted.

Distance: 🚶on the spot ⊗on the spot 🚰100m.
Remarks: Parking next to Office du Tourisme, not suitable for big motorhomes.

🏕S **Lunéville** 16C5

Quai de la Vezouze. **GPS:** n48,59200 e6,49217. ⬆.

7 🏕free 🚰🔌Ch🔌free. **Surface:** asphalted.
Distance: 🚶500m ⚓on the spot ⊗500m 🚰500m 🚌500m.

Tourist information Lunéville:
Ⓜ🏰 Château Petit Versailles.Castle, 18th century and museum. 📅 10-12h, 14-18h 🔵 Tue.

🏕 **Marbotte** 16A4

Fort de Liouville. **GPS:** n48,82968 e5,61966.
2 🏕free. **Surface:** unpaved.
Distance: 🚶Marbotte 6km.

🏕 **Marbotte** 16A4

Parking de la Mairie, Rue Principale, D12. **GPS:** n48,83445 e5,58142. ⬆.
2 🏕free. **Surface:** unpaved.

🏕S **Maxey-sur-Meuse** 16A5

GPS: n48,44861 e5,69500. ⬆.

2 🏕free 🚰🔌free. **Surface:** gravel. 📅 14/05-31/12
Distance: 🚶2km 🚰2km 🚌500m.

🏕 **Maxey-sur-Vaise** 16A5

Gr Grande Rue. **GPS:** n48,53836 e5,66705.
6 🏕free.
Distance: 🚶on the spot.

🏕S **Metz** 16B3

Allée Metz Plage. **GPS:** n49,12371 e6,16887.

8 🏕free 🚰🔌Ch free. **Surface:** asphalted.
Distance: 🚶350m 🚴1,5km 🚰300m.
Remarks: At entrance campsite, max. 48h, inclining pitches.

Tourist information Metz:
ℹ Office de Tourisme, 2, place d'Armes, tourisme.mairie-metz.fr.Industrial city with old interesting centre.
👁 Église St Pierre-aux-Nonnains.One of the oldest French churches.
👁 Place St Louis.Square surrounded by houses from the 14th century.
Ⓜ Musée de la Cour d'Or.Collection of ceramics. 📅 10-17h, Sa-Su 11-17h 🔵 Tue, holiday. 🎫 € 4,60.

FR

✝ Cathédrale St Etienne.Cathedral.
☺ Fonds Saint Martin, Rombas.Climbing wall.
☻ Zoo, Amnéville.Zoo. ◯ 01/04-30/09 9.30-19.30h, 01/10-31/03 10h-sunset.

▣S Millery 16B4

Avenue de la Moselle, D40. **GPS:** n48,81507 e6,12716.⬆.

20 🛏free ⛽🍽Chfree. **Surface:** asphalted. ◯ 01/04-31/10 ◉ water: 01/11-31/03.
Distance: 🚶on the spot ⚓3,5km.
Remarks: Along Mosel.

▣S Monthureux-sur-Saône 16A6

D460. **GPS:** n48,15380 e5,58245.

8 🛏free ⛽🍽Ch WCfree 🚿against payment€ 3.
Distance: 🚶on the spot ➤on the spot ⊗200m ☕on the spot.
Remarks: At football ground.

▣ Montigny-lès-Vaucouleurs 🐑 16A5

Rue de la Côte. **GPS:** n48,58875 e5,63007.⬆.
4 🛏free. **Surface:** gravel.
Distance: 🚶700m.

Montplonne 🌳🌳 16A4

Rue du Four. **GPS:** n48,68630 e5,16934.⬆.

4 🛏free. **Location:** Rural, very simple. **Surface:** gravel.

▣ Morley 🌊 16A5

Parking Lavoir, D5A. **GPS:** n48,57848 e5,24878.⬆.

5 🛏free. **Location:** Rural, very simple, central, quit. **Surface:** .

FR

▣S Nancy 16B4

Port Saint Georges, N57, boulevard du 21ème Régiment d'Aviation. **GPS:** n48,69221 e6,19318.

6 🛏€ 10/night ⛽🍽Ch ⚡ WC🚿🍽included.
Surface: asphalted.
◯ 01/05-01/11
Distance: 🚶500m 🏊on the spot ➤on the spot ⊗100m ☕100m 🚌100m.
Remarks: Max. 5 nights, check in at harbourmaster.

▣S Nancy 16B4

Parking Faubourg les III Maisons, Rue Charles Keller. **GPS:** n48,70403 e6,17598.
⬆.
🛏€ 0,50-3,50. **Surface:** asphalted. ◯ 01/01-31/12
Distance: 🚶city centre ± 1km.

Tourist information Nancy:
ℹ Office de Tourisme, Place Stanislas, www.ot-nancy.fr.Art city, old capital of the Dukes of Lorraine.
Ⓜ Musée Historique Lorraine, Palais Ducal.Regional museum. ◯ 15/06-15/09 ◉ Tue.
Ⓜ Muséum Aquarium de Nancy, 34 rue Sainte-Catherine.Museum with a tropical aquarium.
☻ Zoo Haye, Velaine-en-Haye.Zoo with centre for wild birds.

▣ Nant-le-Grand 🌳🌳 16A4

Gr Grand Rue, D169A. **GPS:** n48,67530 e5,22382.⬆.

4 🛏free. **Location:** Rural, very simple, central, quit.
Surface: gravel.
Distance: 🚶on the spot.

▣S Niderviller 16D4

Marina Niderviller, Avenue de Lorraine. **GPS:** n48,71748 e7,09901.
12 🛏€ 10 ⛽€ 1/100liter 🍽Ch ⚡€ 0,50/kWh.

▣S Nonsard Lamarche 🌊 16B4

Base de Loisirs. GPS: n48,93064 e5,74873.⬆.
30 🛏€ 5 ⛽€ 3 🍽Ch.
Distance: 🏊on the spot ➤on the spot.
Remarks: At lake Madine, coins at campsite.

Nubécourt 16A4

D151, Rue Raymond Poincaré. **GPS:** n48,99704 e5,17256.⬆➡.

10 🛏free. **Location:** Rural, very simple, central, quit. **Surface:** metalled. 🅾
01/01-31/12
Distance: 🚶on the spot 🚲200m 🛶on the spot ⛲on the spot.

Phalsbourg 16D4
Avia, ZAC Louvois, Route du Luxembourg. **GPS:** n48,77047 e7,24198.
🛏free 🚰€ 2 🍽Ch 🚻€ 2. **Surface:** asphalted. 🅾 01/01-31/12
Distance: ⊗on the spot.

Pierre-Percée 16C5
D182A. **GPS:** n48,46723 e6,92911.

± 8 🛏free. **Surface:** asphalted.
Distance: 🏊on the spot 🚲on the spot.
Remarks: Picnic area at artificial lake.

Plombières-les-Bains ♨ 16C6
Avenue des Etats-Unis. **GPS:** n47,96208 e6,45411.⬆.

6 🛏€ 4/24h 🚰 🔌(5x)included. **Surface:** asphalted. 🅾 01/04-15/10

Pompierre 16A6
Chemin de la Corvée. **GPS:** n48,25417 e5,67050.⬆.

3 🛏free 🚰 🔌free. **Surface:** asphalted. 🅾 01/01-31/12
Distance: 🚶1km 🏊500m 🛒500m.

Pont-à-Mousson 🌿⚓🎣 16B4
Port de plaisance, Avenue des Etas Unis, D910. **GPS:** n48,90296 e6,06088.⬆.

42 🛏€ 7,50 🚰 🍽Ch 🔌 🚻⬚included ⬚.
Location: Luxurious.
Surface: asphalted. 🅾 01/04-31/10
Distance: 🚶400m 🚴3,4km 🚲on the spot ⊗400m 🛒400m 🚌on the spot.

Remarks: Check in at reception.

Rebeuville 16A5
Rue du Cougnot. **GPS:** n48,33530 e5,70128.⬆.

3 🛏free 🚰🍽Ch 🔌free. **Surface:** asphalted. 🅾 01/01-31/12
Distance: 🚶5km ⊗5km 🛒5km 🚌500m.

Revigny-sur-Ornain 15D4
Stade/Office de Tourisme, Rue de l'Abattoir. **GPS:** n48,82642 e4,98330.⬆➡.

2 🛏free 🚰€ 3 🍽Ch 🔌€ 3.
Location: Urban, central, quit.
Surface: asphalted. 🅾 01/01-31/12
Distance: 🚶on the spot 🚲100m ⊗on the spot 🛒on the spot 🚌on the spot.

Rhodes 16C4
Port Municipal, Rue Principale. **GPS:** n48,75784 e6,90053.
30 🛏€ 15/24h 🚰 🍽Ch 🔌 🚻included. **Surface:** grassy. 🅾
Easter-01/10
Distance: 🏊on the spot 🚲on the spot.
Remarks: Along Etang du Stock.

Richardmenil 16B5
Rue de Lac. **GPS:** n48,59457 e6,16078.⬆.

5 🛏free 🚰🍽Ch 🔌(4x)free. **Surface:** asphalted. 🅾 01/01-31/12
Distance: 🚶1km 🏊on the spot 🚲on the spot ⊗500m 🛒1km 🚌1km.

Rollainville 16B5
Rue de la Cure. **GPS:** n48,36185 e5,73842.

1 🛏free 🚰 🔌free. **Surface:** asphalted.

FR

Rupt-sur-Moselle 16C6

Quai de la Parelle. **GPS:** n47,92061 e6,66194.

6 🚐free 🔌€ 3/10minutes 🚰Ch 💧(4x)€ 3/3h WC.
Surface: asphalted.
Distance: ⊗350m 🚲on the spot 🚶Voie Verte.
Remarks: Coins available at the shops and town hall.

Saint-Nicolas-de-Port 16B5

Rue du jeu de Paune. **GPS:** n48,63515 e6,30048.⬆

10 🚐free 🔌€ 1 🚰Ch 💧€ 1/1h 💧(2x). **Location:** Urban, central, quit.
Surface: gravel. 🅾 01/01-31/12
Distance: 🚲on the spot ⊗150m 🛒200m 🚌100m.

Seuil-d'Argonne 15D4

Rue du Commandant Laflotte, D2/D20. **GPS:** n48,98294 e5,06215.⬆

5 🚐free. **Location:** Urban, very simple, quit.
Surface: gravel. 🅾 01/01-31/12
Distance: ⊗650m 🛒650m 🚲650m 🚶650m.
Remarks: In fron of sports fields.

Souilly 16A4

Route de St.André-en-Barrois, D159. **GPS:** n49,02730 e5,27985.⬆
6 🚐free. **Surface:** gravel. 🅾 01/01-31/12
Distance: 🚲600m.

Souslosse sous St.Elophe 16B5

Square Guy Bellamy. **GPS:** n48,40953 e5,73886.⬆

🚐free 🔌🚰Ch 💧free. **Surface:** gravel. 🅾 01/01-31/12
Distance: 🚲500m.

St.Mihiel 16A4

Chemin Gué Rapeau. **GPS:** n48,90227 e5,53960.⬆➡

4 🚐free 🔌€ 1 🚰€ 1 Ch🔲 1. **Surface:** asphalted. 🅾 01/01-31/12
Distance: 🚲1,5km ⊗1km 🛒1,5km.
Remarks: Directly beside river, nearby sluices, next to campsite municipal, max. 24h.

Tourist information St.Mihiel:
ℹ Office de Tourisme, Rue du Palais de Justice.

St.Nabord 16C6

Rue de la Croix Saint Jacques. **GPS:** n48,04527 e6,58175.⬆

3 🚐free 🔌€ 3/80liter 🚰Ch🔲€ 3. **Surface:** gravel. 🅾 01/01-31/12
Distance: 🚲300m ⊗200m 🛒50m.

Stenay 16A2

Aire Camping-car, D947. **GPS:** n49,48979 e5,18323.⬆➡

47 🚐€7 🔌🚰Ch 💧WC 🔲included 🔲€ 4, dryer € 4. **Surface:** metalled.
🅾 01/01-31/12
Distance: 🚲150m ⊗150m 🛒800m, bakery 300m.
Remarks: Musée Européen de la Bière, beer museum.

Stenay 16A2

Port de plaisance, Rue du Port. **GPS:** n49,49096 e5,18312.⬆➡

6 🚐€7 🔌🚰Chincluded 🔲€ 4, dryer € 4 📶. **Surface:** asphalted. 🅾 01/01-31/12
Distance: 🚲on the spot ⊗200m 🛒500m.

Tourist information Stenay:

🛈 Office de Tourisme, Place Raymond Poincaré 5.
Ⓜ Musée de la Bière.Beer museum.
⚔ Château, Louppy-sur-Loison.Renaissance castle, 17th century.

Tannois 〰🏕 16A4
Parking du Belvédère, D169. **GPS:** n48,71977 e5,22967.⬆️.

10 🛏free. **Location:** Rural, very simple, isolated, quit. **Surface:** gravel. ⬛ 01/01-31/12
Distance: 🚶1,3km 🚲1,5km 🏊on the spot 🏃on the spot.
Remarks: Isolated parking.

Thaon-les-Vosges 16C6
Aire du Coignot, Rue du Coignot. **GPS:** n48,24889 e6,42611.⬆️➡️.

20 🛏free 🚰🗑Chfree. **Surface:** asphalted/gravel. ⬛ 01/03-01/10
Distance: 🚲1,5km 🛒400m.
Remarks: Next to port fluvial.

Thierville-sur-Meuse 16A3
Thierville sur-meuse, Avenue de l,etangbleu. **GPS:** n49,17499 e5,36357.⬆️.

20 🛏free. **Location:** Rural, very simple, central.
Surface: . ⬛ 01/01-31/12
Distance: 🚶100m 🚲50m ⊗50m.
Remarks: Along the Meuse river.

Tilleux 16A5
Grande Rue. **GPS:** n48,29300 e5,72250.⬆️.

8 🛏free 🚰🗑free. **Surface:** gravel. ⬛ 01/01-31/12

Toul 16B4
Avenue du Colonel Péchot. **GPS:** n48,67939 e5,88806.

9 🛏€5 🚰🗑 Ch 🚿 (8x)included. **Surface:** asphalted. ⬛ 01/01-31/12
Distance: 🚶4km.
Remarks: In opposite of police station.
Tourist information Toul:
🛈 Office de Tourisme, Parvis de la Cathédrale, www.toul.fr.8-angular fortress city.
Ⓜ Salle Lapidaire du musée d'art et d'histoire de Toul, Chapelle de l'ancienne Maison-Dieu XIIIe siècle.Medieval ceramics and earthenware.
✝ Basilique Saint-Nicolas-de-Port.Basilica, 16th century, place of pilgrimage for Saint Nicolas.
✝ Cathédrale Saint Etienne.Cathedral, 13-16th century.

Vaucouleurs 16A5
Rue du Cardinal Lépicier. **GPS:** n48,60179 e5,66737.⬆️➡️.

4 🛏free 🚰€2 🗑Ch🚻€2 WC. **Surface:** asphalted. ⬛ 01/01-31/12
Distance: 🚶on the spot 🛒500m 🛒500m.

Vauquois 〰🏕 15D3
Parking municipal, D212. **GPS:** n49,20405 e5,07398.⬆️➡️.

8 🛏free. **Location:** Rural. **Surface:** gravel.
Distance: 🚶on the spot.

Velaines 16A4
D120A. **GPS:** n48,70589 e5,29804.⬆️.

4 🛏free. **Location:** Very simple, central. **Surface:** gravel.
Distance: 🚶on the spot.

Ventron 16C6
Route de Frère Joseph. **GPS:** n47,92495 e6,86364.⬆️.

🛏free. **Surface:** asphalted. ⬛ 01/01-31/12
Distance: 🚶Ventron 3,2km 🎿on the spot.
Remarks: Parking at skipistes.

| | Verdun | 16A3 |

Dragées Braquir, Rue du Fort de Vaux, D112. **GPS:** n49,15955 e5,39989. ⬆.

10🛏free. **Location:** Urban, very simple, central.
Surface: metalled.
Remarks: Max. 1 night.

| 🛏S | Void-Vacon | 16A4 |

Rue de la Gare. **GPS:** n48,68240 e5,61960. ⬆➡.

20🛏free 🚰€ 2 🔌Ch🔲€ 2. **Surface:** grassy/gravel. ⬛ 01/01-31/12
Distance: 🚶700m 🏊10m 🛒10m.
Remarks: Coins at shop/town hall.

Alsace

| 🛏S | Benfeld | 17A5 |

Concessionnaire CLC Alsace, 9, Rue de Hollande, RN83 dir Strasbourg-Colmar.
GPS: n48,37772 e7,59778. ⬆➡.
5🛏free 🚰🔌Ch 🚿free. **Surface:** gravel/metalled. ⬛ 01/01-31/12
Distance: 🚶2km 🛒2km 🛒2km.
Remarks: Motorhome dealer.

| 🛏S | Bourbach-le-Haut | 23D1 |

Route Joffre. **GPS:** n47,79463 e7,02868. ⬆.

5🛏€5 🚰🔌Ch🔲included. **Surface:** asphalted. ⬛ 15/03-15/11
Distance: 🚶50m 🛒100m 🛒100m 🎿5km.
Remarks: Nearby kindergarten.

| 🛏S | Chavannes-sur-l'Etang | 23D1 |

Aire pique-nique La Porte d'Alsace, RD419, Rue d'Alsace. **GPS:** n47,63325
e7,01858. ⬆➡.

15🛏€ 5 (19.00-09.00) 🚰🔌Ch 🚿 WCfree. **Surface:** asphalted. ⬛
01/01-31/12
Distance: 🚶900m 🛒1km.
Remarks: Parking picnic area, information: 16-19h.

| 🛏S | Colmar | 16D6 |

Rue de la Cavalerie/Rue des Brasseries. **GPS:** n48,08218 e7,35990. ⬆.

20🛏€ 2,40/4h, overnight stay free. **Surface:** asphalted.
Distance: 🚶200m ⊗on the spot 🛒on the spot 🛒on the spot.
Tourist information Colmar:
ℹ Office de Tourisme, 4, rue des Unterlinden, www.ot-colmar.fr.Old city with
historical centre.

| 🛏S | Eguisheim | 16D6 |

Bannwarth, Rue de Bruxelles 3. **GPS:** n48,04434 e7,30539.

6🛏free 🚰🔌Ch 🚿free.
Surface: metalled.
Distance: 🚶100m.
Remarks: On entering the village follow 'Poids Lourds', 3rd road on the right.

| 🛏S | Ferrette | 23D1 |

Route de Lucelle. **GPS:** n47,48882 e7,31118. ⬆.

4🛏free 🚰€ 2/10minutes 🔌Ch🔲€ 2/55minutes. **Surface:** asphalted.
Distance: 🚶700m ⊗2km 🛒2km.

| 🛏S | Fessenheim | 16D6 |

Allée de la Guyane. **GPS:** n47,91833 e7,53139. ⬆.

30 ⌗free ⌐⌐€ 2 ⌐Ch⌐⌐€ 2. **Surface:** asphalted. ⬛ 01/01-31/12
Distance: ⌐700m ⓦ700m ⌐200m.
Remarks: Coins available at swimming pool, supermarket.

| ⬛ | Guebwiller ⌐⌐⌐ | 16D6 |

Avenue Maréchal Foch. **GPS:** n47,90554 e7,21869. ⬆.

⌗free. **Surface:** gravel/metalled. ⬛ 01/01-31/12
Distance: ⌐300m ⓦon the spot ⓦ300m ⌐300m ⌐300m ⌐5km.

Tourist information Guebwiller:
ℹ Office de Tourisme, Hôtel de Ville, 73, rue de la République, www.ville-
guebwiller.fr.Industrial city with textile industry.

| ⒸⓈ | Guewenheim ⌐⌐ | 23D1 |

Le Doller. **GPS:** n47,75612 e7,09855.

10 ⌗free ⌐⌐€ 3,50 ⌐Ch⌐⌐WC⌐⌐.
Surface: gravel. ⬛ 01/01-31/12
Distance: ⌐2km ⌐1km ⓦ2km ⌐2km.

| ⌐Ⓢ | Harskirchen | 16D4 |

Port de Plaisance, Rue de Bissert. **GPS:** n48,93930 e7,02759. ⬆➡.
2 ⌗€ 6 ⌐⌐Ch⌐⌐included. **Surface:** gravel. ⬛ 15/03-15/11
Remarks: At canal Houillères de la Sarre.

| ⬛ | Heiligenstein | 16D5 |

Lieu-dit Lindel, D35. **GPS:** n48,42234 e7,45147. ⬆.

3 ⌗free. **Surface:** gravel. ⬛ 01/01-31/12
Distance: ⌐800m ⓦ300m ⌐500m.
Remarks: Hiking trails and wine tasting.

Tourist information Heiligenstein:
ℹ Village in wine-growing region.

| ⌐Ⓢ | Kaysersberg ⌐⌐ | 16D6 |

Aire Camping-car P1, Rue du 18 Décembre 1944. **GPS:** n48,13565 e7,26325. ⬆
➡.

80 ⌗€ 2/day, € 4/night ⌐⌐⌐Ch WC ⌐⌐free. **Surface:** asphalted. ⬛ 01/01-
31/12
Distance: ⌐300m ⓦ300m ⌐300m.
Remarks: Wifi at Office de Tourisme.

Tourist information Kaysersberg:
ℹ Office de Tourisme, 39 rue du Gal de Gaulle, www.kaysersberg.com.City with
half-timbered houses in a wine region.
Ⓜ Musée Albert Schweitzer.The life of Albert Schweitzer.

| ⬛ | Lautenbach ⌐⌐⌐ | 16D6 |

Parking Vivarium, Rue du Moulin, Lautenbachzell. **GPS:** n47,94167 e7,14972. ⬆.

10 ⌗free. **Surface:** grassy/metalled. ⬛ 01/01-31/12
Distance: ⌐1km ⌐on the spot ⌐on the spot ⓦ1km ⌐1km ⌐on the spot
⌐5km ⌐5km.

| ⬛ | Le Bonhomme ✳ | 16D6 |

Col du Bonhomme, D148, route des Crètes. **GPS:** n48,16495 e7,07971.

⌗free. **Surface:** gravel.
Distance: ⓦon the spot.

| ⬛ | Michelbach ⌐ | 23D1 |

Salle des polyvalente, Rue Principale. **GPS:** n47,75800 e7,11000. ⬆.

5 ⌗free. **Surface:** metalled. ⬛ 01/01-31/12

FR

Distance: 🚶250m ⚓2km 🚲2km ⊗1km 🚰1km.
Remarks: Behind community centre.

| 🏕 🅂 | **Mittelbergheim** | 16D5 |

Parking Zotzenberg. **GPS:** n48,39869 e7,44194. ⬆.

4 🅂free. **Surface:** asphalted.
Distance: 🚶300m 🚴3,1km ⊗300m 🚰300m.
Remarks: Hiking trails and wine tasting.

| 🏕 🅂 | **Munster** 🌿⚓ | 16D6 |

Place de la salle des Fêtes. **GPS:** n48,03944 e7,13944. ⬆.

8 🅂free.
Surface: asphalted. ⬛ 01/01-31/12
Distance: 🚶300m ⊗300m 🔲300m 🚐on the spot.

| 🏕 🅂 | **Murbach** 🌿⚓🎡❄ | 16D6 |

Abbaye de Murbach, Rue de Guebwiller. **GPS:** n47,92321 e7,16059. ⬆.

20 🅂free 🚰💧Ch🧺🛢. **Surface:** gravel/metalled. ⬛ 01/01-31/12
Distance: 🚶350m 🏊on the spot ⊗on the spot 🚰500m 🚲5km.

| 🏕 | **Obernai** 🌿⚓ | 16D5 |

Parking des Remparts, Rue Poincaré. **GPS:** n48,45972 e7,48667. ⬆➡.

12 🅂free. **Surface:** gravel. ⬛ 01/01-31/12
Distance: 🚶300m 🚴2,7km ⊗300m 🚰300m 🚐200m.
Remarks: Large parking in centre.

| 🅂 | **Obernai** 🌿⚓ | 16D5 |

Camping municipal Le Vallon de l'Ehn, 1, rue de Berlin. **GPS:** n48,46471 e7,46757. ⬆➡.
🚰€ 2 💧Ch. ⬛ 01/01-31/12

Tourist information Obernai:
ℹ Office de Tourisme, Place du Beffroi, www.obernai.fr.

| 🏕 🅂 | **Oltingue** ⚓🎡 | 23D1 |

Place Saint Martin. **GPS:** n47,49158 e7,39068. ⬆.

3 🅂free 🚰€ 2/10minutes 💧Ch🔌€ 2/55minutes. **Surface:** asphalted.
⬛ 01/01-31/12
Distance: 🚶100m ⊗200m.

| 🏔🅂 | **Orbey** | 16D6 |

Hôtel Restaurant Les Terrasses du Lac Blanc. GPS: n48,13540 e7,08957. ⬆.

8 🅂€ 5 🚰included 💧Ch🧺 (8x)€ 2,50. **Surface:** grassy/gravel.
Distance: ⚓500m 🚰500m 🚲on the spot.
Remarks: Customers free.

Tourist information Orbey:
😊 Pisciculture, La Blanc et Noir.Information centre about fish/trout. ⬛ 01/03-31/10 10-12h, 14-18h.

| 🏕 🅂 | **Orschwir** 🌿⚓🎡 | 16D6 |

Rue de la Source. **GPS:** n47,93722 e7,23083. ⬆➡.

4 🅂free 🚰💧Ch🔌€ 4,10 🛢. **Surface:** asphalted. ⬛ 01/01-31/12
Distance: 🚶200m ⊗200m 🚰500m.

| 🏔🅂 | **Pfaffenheim** | 16D6 |

Aire du Winzerhof, Rue de la Tuilerie. **GPS:** n47,98639 e7,29167.

5 🅂free 🚰€ 3 💧Ch🧺 (5x)€ 2 WC🚿. **Surface:** gravel/metalled. ⬛ 01/01-31/12
Distance: 🚶400m ⊗400m 🚰500m.

FR

Ribeauvillé ⓈⒶ 16D6
Route de Guémar. **GPS:** n48,19231 e7,32867. ⬆️.

15 🅿€ 1,50/5h, € 1,50/night ⚡€ 2 🔌Ch.
Surface: gravel. ⬛ 01/01-31/12
Distance: ⛽400m ⊗on the spot ⚡on the spot.
Remarks: Next to Cave de Ribeauvillé.
Tourist information Ribeauvillé:
ℹ️ Office de Tourisme, 1 Grand' Rue. Town on the Alsace wine road.
⚓ ⬛ Sa.

Riquewihr ⓈⒶ 16D6
Avenue Jacques Présis. **GPS:** n48,16608 e7,30175. ⬆️.

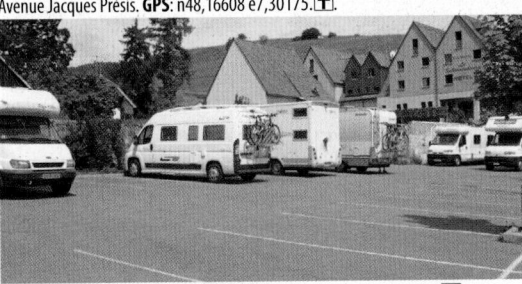

6 🅿€ 2/3h, € 4/night ⚡€ 2 🔌Ch🔌€ 2. **Surface:** asphalted. ⬛ 01/01-31/12
Distance: ⛽200m ⊗200m ⚡200m.
Remarks: Parking on entering the village, <7m.
Tourist information Riquewihr:
👁️ Office de Tourisme, Rue de 1ère Armée. Picturesque street with houses of the 16th century.

Saverne Ⓐ 16D4
Rue des Emouleurs. **GPS:** n48,74512 e7,36854.
🅿free. ⬛ 01/01-31/12
Distance: ⛽centre ±650m.

Ⓢ Saverne Ⓐ 16D4
Rue du Père Liebermann. **GPS:** n48,73131 e7,35504.
⚡🔌Chfree. ⬛ 01/04-30/09
Remarks: In front of campsite.
Tourist information Saverne:
ℹ️ Office de Tourisme, 37 Grand' Rue, voetgangerzône, www.ot-saverne.fr. Small touristic town with half-timbered houses on the border of nature reserve Vosges du Nord.
Ⓜ⚔ Château de Rohan. Museum, former summer residence of the bishops of Strasbourg.

ⓈⒶ Soufflenheim Ⓐ 17A4
Rue des Menuisiers. **GPS:** n48,82940 e7,95395. ⬆️➡️.

3 🅿free ⚡€ 2 🔌Ch🔌 2. **Surface:** asphalted. ⬛ 01/01-31/12
Distance: ⛽300m ⊗200m ⚡300m 🚌200m.

ⓈⒶ Soultz 16D6
Rue de la Marne. **GPS:** n47,88806 e7,23139. ⬆️.

30 🅿free ⚡🔌Ch🔌. **Surface:** asphalted. ⬛ 01/01-31/12
Distance: ⛽500m ⊗500m ⚡500m 🚌500m.
Remarks: Payment only by bank card.

Ste.Marie-aux-Mines ⓈⒶ❄ 16D6
Place des Tisserands. **GPS:** n48,24700 e7,18322. ⬆️⬆️.

4 🅿free. **Surface:** asphalted. ⬛ 01/01-31/12
Distance: ⛽300m ⊗300m ⚡300m.
Remarks: Max. 24h.
Tourist information Ste.Marie-aux-Mines:
ℹ️ Office de Tourisme, 86, rue Wilson, www.tourisme.fr/office-de-tourisme/sainte-marie-aux-mines-68.htm. Mineral city with silvermine, Mine d'Argent Sainte-Barthélemy.

ⓈⒶ Strasbourg ⓈⒶ 17A5
Parking Auberge de Jeunesse des Deux Rives (Parc du Rhin), Rue des Cavaliers. **GPS:** n48,56659 e7,79975. ⬆️.

40 🅿free ⚡🔌Ch🔌free. **Surface:** gravel. ⬛ 01/01-31/12
Distance: ⛽Strasbourg centre 5km 🚌bus 21 + tram.
Tourist information Strasbourg:
ℹ️ Office de Tourisme, 17, Place de la Cathédrale, www.ot-strasbourg.fr. City with a rich history and worth seeing centre.
👁️⊗ Maison Kammerzell. Restaurant, 1467-1589, one of the most beautifull half-timbered houses in the Alsace region.
Ⓜ⚔ Château Rohan. 18de Eeuws paleis met diverse musea.
Ⓜ Musée Alsacien. Folk art and handycrafts.
⛪ Cathédrale de Nôtre-Dame.

ⓈⒶ Thann ⓈⒶ 23D1
Place du Bungert, Rue des Pélerins. **GPS:** n47,81159 e7,10450. ⬆️➡️.

FR

20 ⌇free ⛽🚰Ch ✎free. **Surface:** asphalted. ◻ 01/01-31/12 ⦿
Sa-morning.
Distance: ⚓600m 🏊on the spot ⊗500m 🚉500m 🚌500m.
🏕S **Trois Épis** ⛷🚡⛄ 16D6
Place des Antonins. **GPS:** n48,10101 e7,22948. ⬆➡.

6 ⌇free ⛽€ 2 🚰Ch 🔌€ 2. **Surface:** asphalted. ◻ 01/03-30/11
Distance: 🍴nearby ⊗nearby 🚉on the spot.
Remarks: Max. 48h.
🏕S **Willer-sur-Thur** ((•)) 23D1
Place de l'Eglise. **GPS:** n47,84315 e7,07292. ⬆➡.

25 ⌇free ⛽€ 2 🚰Ch WC 🔌€ 1. **Surface:** asphalted. ◻ 01/01-31/12
Distance: ⚓150m ⊗150m 🚉150m.
🔄 **Turckheim** ⛵⛴ 16D6
Quai de la gare. **GPS:** n48,08555 e7,27739.

3 ⌇free ⛽🚰Ch free. **Surface:** asphalted. ◻ 01/01-31/12
Distance: ⚓250m ⊗500m 🚉500m, bakery 50m 🚌500m 🚲500m.

Normandie

🏕S **Agon-Coutainville** 🌊 13B3
Flot Bleu Park, Boulevard Louis Lebel-Jéhenne. **GPS:** n49,05176 w1,59123. ⬆.

6 ⌇free. **Location:** Noisy. **Surface:** metalled. ◻ 01/01-31/12
Distance: ⚓historical centre 250m ⊗250m 🚉300m 🚌on the spot.
S **Turckheim** ⛵⛴ 16D6
Camping municipal Les Cigognes, 4, quai de la Gare. **GPS:** n48,08539 e7,27535.
⛽€ 5,40 🚰Ch. 15/03-31/10

25 ⌇€ 6/24h ⛽🚰Ch ✎ included 📹🔌🛁 **Surface:** grassy. ◻ 01/01-31/12
Distance: 🚉800m.
Remarks: Service only € 2,50.

🏕S **Ungersheim** 16D6
Ecomusée. GPS: n47,85200 e7,28400. ⬆➡.

🏕S **Angiens** ((•)) 14B1
Aire de Château d'Iclon, Impasse des Roseaux. **GPS:** n49,84390 e0,81945. ⬆➡.

20 ⌇€ 5,50 ⛽🚰 ✎ included. **Surface:** gravel/metalled. ◻ 01/01-31/12
Distance: ⚓6km.

Tourist information Ungersheim:
Ⓜ Ecomusée d'Alsace.Largest open air museum of France. ◻ 01/03-31/12
10-17/18h.
🏕S **Westhalten** ⛴ 16D6
Rue St Blaise, D18, Vallée Noble, dir Soultzmatt.. **GPS:** n47,95189 e7,26389.

10 ⌇€ 5 + € 1/pp ⛽🚰Ch included ✎€ 3. **Surface:** grassy/gravel. ◻
01/01-31/12
Distance: ⚓3km.

Ardevon · 13B4
La Bidonnière - Ardevon

campingcar@ardevivre.fr - campingcar.ardevivre.fr

Paved and flat motorhome pitches
Beautiful view
Sanitary facilities

La Bidonnière, Route de la Rive 5. **GPS:** n48,60352 w1,47612. ⬆.
66 🅂€ 10/24h 🚰 Ch ✎€ 2/6h WC 🅂€ 2/4minutes 🔧. **Surface:** metalled. ⭘ 01/01-31/12
Distance: 🚶4km ⊗3km.
Remarks: View on Mt.St. Michel.

Argences · 13D3
Intermarché, Rue de la Gare, D80. **GPS:** n49,11889 w0,17528. ⬆➡.

🅂free 🚰€ 2 🅂Ch 🔲€ 2. **Surface:** asphalted. ⭘ 01/01-31/12
Distance: ⊗on the spot 🔧on the spot.
Remarks: Parking supermarket.

Arromanches · 13C3
Rue François Carpentier. **GPS:** n49,33904 w0,62553. ⬆➡.

14 🅂free 🚰€ 1 🅂Ch 🔲€ 1 🔧free15minutes. **Surface:** asphalted. ⭘ 01/01-31/12
Distance: 🚶150m ⊘on the spot ⊗100m 🔧250m.
Remarks: Next to campsite municipal.

Arromanches · 13C3
Arromanches 360, Cinéma Circulaire, Chemin du Calvaire. **GPS:** n49,33924 w0,61419. ⬆.

🅂€ 4/24h. ⭘ 01/01-31/12
Distance: ⊘on the spot.
Remarks: Beautiful view. On entering from dir Honfleur.
Tourist information Arromanches:
ℹ Office de Tourisme, 2, rue Maréchal Joffre, www.arromanches.com.Famous place, the invasion of allied forces on 6 June 1944.
Ⓜ Arromanches 360.Film of World War II.
Ⓜ Musée du Débarquement, place du 6 Juin.Memorial museum, World War II.
⭘ 01/02-30/11 10-13h, 14-17h, 01/05-31/08 9.30-18.30h.

Auffay · 14B2
Place de Bleckede. **GPS:** n49,71755 e1,10055. ⬆➡.

6 🅂free 🚰€ 3/100liter 🅂Ch. **Surface:** asphalted. ⭘ 01/01-31/12
Distance: 🚶on the spot ⊗100m 🔧100m.

Avranches · 13B4
Centre Culturel, Boulevard Jozeau Marigné. **GPS:** n48,68585 w1,367. ⬆➡.

8 🅂free 🚰€ 2 🅂Ch. **Surface:** metalled. ⭘ 01/01-31/12
Distance: 🚶200m ✎1,9km ⊗200m 🔧200m.
Remarks: Behind community centre, max. 1 night.

Tourist information Avranches:
ℹ Office de Tourisme, 2, rue Général de Gaulle, www.ville-avranches.fr.
👁 Jardins des Plantes.Garden with exotic plants.
Ⓜ Musée Bibliothèque.Manuscripts from the files of Mont Saint Michel.
✝ Basilique St Germain. ⭘ 9-12h, 14-16h.
🎪 place des Halles. ⭘ Sa + Tue-morning.

Bagnoles-de-l'Orne · 13C4
D235. **GPS:** n48,55821 w0,4129. ⬆.

FR

6 🛏free. **Surface:** gravel. ⬛ 01/01-31/12
Distance: 🚶on the spot.
Remarks: Behind Office de Tourisme, Place du Marché.

Tourist information Bagnoles-de-l'Orne:
ℹ️ Office de Tourisme, Place du Marché, www.bagnoles-de-lorne.com.Thermal centre.

🗺️S	Barfleur (50)	13B2

Route Alfred Rossel, D1. **GPS:** n49,66998 w1,26355.

8 🛏free 🚰 Ch WC. **Surface:** metalled.
Distance: 🚶200m.

🗺️	Barneville-Carteret	13A2

Quai Émile Valmy, rue du port. **GPS:** n49,37300 w1,789.

🛏free. **Surface:** asphalted.
Remarks: In front of the Gare Maritime.

🗺️S	Barneville-Carteret	13A2

Carrefour, Route du Pont Rose. **GPS:** n49,38553 w1,75239.

180 🛏free 🚰€ 2 🛢️ Ch 🚽€ 2. ⬛ 01/01-31/12
Distance: 🚶300m 🛒on the spot 🅿️centre.

🗺️S	Bayeux 🛒🚐🗑️	13C3

Place Gauquelin-Despallières. **GPS:** n49,28044 w0,70775.⬆️

5 🛏free 🚰🛢️Ch WC free. **Surface:** asphalted. ⬛ 01/01-31/12
Remarks: Max. 12h.

Tourist information Bayeux:
ℹ️ Office de Tourisme, Pont Saint Jean, www.bayeux-tourism.com.Medival city with half-timbered houses and small inner courts.
Ⓜ️ Centre Guillaume-le-Conquerant.Tapisserie de la Reine Mathilde, tapestry of 70m long.
Ⓜ️ Musée Memorial 1944.Battle of Normandy, June 6 till August 22, 1944. ⬛ 9.30-17h, 01/05-30/09 9-19h.
✝️ Cathédrale Nôtre Dame.Gothic cathedral.

	Beauvoir	13B4

Aire de camping-car du mont St Michel, Route de Mont St Michel. **GPS:** n48,59326 w1,51335.⬆️

122 🛏€ 12,50 🚰 🛢️ Ch 🚽 (122x)included 📶free. **Location:** Rural, comfortable, luxurious, quit. **Surface:** gravel. ⬛ 01/01-31/12
Distance: 🚶500m 🛒500m.
Remarks: Le Mont Saint Michel 5km.

🍴S	Beauvoir	13B4

La Ferme Saint Michel, Route du Mont Saint Michel, D976. **GPS:** n48,61112 w1,50978.

35 🛏guests free 🚰 🛢️Ch 📶 at restaurant. **Surface:** gravel. ⬛ 01/01-31/12 ⬤ Mo.
Distance: 🚶600m 🛒on the spot 🚐600m.

🗺️S	Beuvron-en-Auge	13D3

Parking de la Gare, Avenue de la Gare. **GPS:** n49,18560 w0,0495.

16 🛢️6 ⛲ 2 🚿Ch 💧 included. **Surface:** gravel. 🅿️ 01/01-31/12
Distance: 🚰200m ⊗on the spot 🚱on the spot.
Remarks: Pay and coins at Tabac-Presse.

🛢️S **Bréhal** 13B3
Rue des Pierres Foucard. **GPS:** n48,89818 w1,56626.⬆️.

25 🛢️€ 3/24h ⛲ 🚿Ch WC free. **Surface:** asphalted. 🅿️ 01/01-31/12
Distance: 🚰300m 🏖️beach 150m ⊗400m 🚱400m.

🚐S **Bretteville-sur-Odon** 13D3
Camping-car service, 4-6 Avenue des Carrières. **GPS:** n49,18449 w0,41465.⬆️
➡️.

🛢️free ⛲🚿Ch free. **Surface:** metalled. 🅿️ 01/01-31/12

🛢️S **Bréville-les-Monts** 13D3
Rue des Dentellières. **GPS:** n49,24167 w0,228.⬆️.

4 🛢️free ⛲€ 2/10minutes 🚿Ch. **Surface:** asphalted. 🅿️ 01/03-15/11
Remarks: Max. 72h, (may-july-aug) 48h, Coins at Office du Tourisme Merville and harbour.

🛢️S **Bricquebec** 🌿 13B2
Bas de Cattigny, D900, route de Cherbourg. **GPS:** n49,47402 w1,64674.

6 🛢️free ⛲🚿Ch 💧 free. **Surface:** gravel.

🛢️S **Broglie** 14A3
Parc de la bibliothèque. **GPS:** n49,00563 e0,52948.

8 🛢️€ 5/night ⛲€ 2,50/100liter 🚿Ch🚽€ 2,50/1h. **Surface:** grassy/metalled. 🅿️ 01/03-31/10 7-22h, 01/11-28/02 7.30-19h
Distance: 🚰200m ⊗200m 🚱200m, 7.30-19h.

Tourist information Broglie:
⛺ 🅿️ Fri 7-13h.

🛢️S **Buchy** 14B2
D919, Route de Forges. **GPS:** n49,58538 e1,36417.⬆️.

6 🛢️free ⛲€ 2 🚿Ch🚽€ 2. **Surface:** asphalted. 🅿️ 01/01-31/12
Distance: 🚰500m ⊗500m 🚱500m.

🛢️S **Cambremer** 13D3
Place de l'Europe. **GPS:** n49,15112 e0,04750.

7 🛢️free ⛲€ 2 🚿Ch🚽€ 2. **Surface:** asphalted. 🅿️ 01/01-31/12
Remarks: D50, exit 'poids lourds', nearby police station.

🛢️S **Campigny** 14A3
Chemin de la Motte. **GPS:** n49,31139 e0,55223.⬆️.

3 🛢️free ⛲🚿Ch free. **Surface:** grassy. 🅿️ 01/01-31/12
Remarks: On inner court of old presbytery, max. 24h.

🚐S **Carolles** 13B4
Rue du Mont Dol. **GPS:** n48,75931 w1,57062.⬆️.

FR

15 🛏€7 🚰€ 3/100liter 🚽Ch🚻€ 3/55minutes. **Surface:** grassy/sand. ◻ 01/01-31/12
Distance: 📶150m ⊗on the spot 🛒on the spot.
Remarks: Check in at restaurant O Gal'eau.

Carolles 13B4
La Guériniére, Residence les Jaunets. **GPS:** n48,74989 w1,55695.⬆
5 🛏free 🚰€ 2 🚽Ch🚻€ 2. **Surface:** asphalted. ◻ 01/01-31/12
Distance: 🛒on the spot 📶2km.
Remarks: Parking in front of town hall.

Caumont-l'Éventé 13C3
Souterroscope des Ardoisières, Route de Saint Lô, D71. **GPS:** n49,08868 w0,81645.➡
🛏free 🚰€ 2 🚽Ch🚻€ 2 WC. **Surface:** asphalted.

Cerisy-la-Forêt 13C3
GPS: n49,19806 w0,93389.⬆

10 🛏free 🚰€ 2 🚽Ch🚻€ 2. ◻ 01/01-31/12
Distance: 🛒on the spot.
Remarks: Next to the abbey.

Cherbourg 13B2
Musée Cité de la Mer, Llée du President Menut. **GPS:** n49,64740 w1,61782.

40 🛏free. **Location:** Very simple. **Surface:** asphalted.
Distance: 📶1km 🛒on the spot ⊗1km 🛒on the spot.
Remarks: Max. 1 night.

Tourist information Cherbourg:
ℹ Maison de Tourisme, 2, Quai Alexandre III, www.ot-cherbourg-cotentin.fr.Port city.
Ⓜ Musée Fort du Roule.War museum. ◻ 9.30-12h, 14-17.30h.
✝ Basilique Sainte Trinité.Basilica in gothic style.

Clères 14B2
Rue Edmond Spalikowski, Côte du Mont Blanc. **GPS:** n49,60228 e1,11667.⬆➡

10 🛏free 🚰€ 4 🚽Ch🚻. **Surface:** gravel. ◻ 01/01-31/12 ◉ service: 01/11-28/02.
Distance: 📶500m ⊗500m 🛒500m.
Remarks: Nearby football ground, max. 72h, coins available at bakery, butcher and Bar-Tabac.

Tourist information Clères:
☺ Zoo Clères.Zoo.

Colleville-Montgomery 13D3
Rue de Saint-Aubin. **GPS:** n49,27111 w0,29917.⬆➡

9 🛏€3 🚰🚽Chfree. **Surface:** grassy. ◻ 01/01-31/12
Distance: 📶100m 🛒450m.

Tourist information Colleville-Montgomery:
ℹ Office de Tourisme, Av. de Bruxelles, www.colleville-montgomery.fr/.
Ⓜ Musée Omaha Beach, St.Laurent-sur-Mer.Collection of military vehicles, weapons and costumes.

Cormeilles 14A3
Avenue de Chepstow, D810. **GPS:** n49,24830 e0,37446.➡

8 🛏free 🚰🚽Chfree. **Surface:** asphalted. ◻ 01/01-31/12
Distance: 📶400m 📶river 🛒400m.

Coudeville-Plage 13B4
Avenue de la Mer D351. **GPS:** n48,88707 w1,56607.⬆

10 🛏€ 5/24h 🚰🚽Ch 🔧 included 🗑.🚻 🚿 **Surface:** grassy/gravel. ◻ 01/01-31/12
Distance: 📶500m 📶200m 🚲200m ⊗500m 🛒500m.

🚐 [S] Courseulles-sur-Mer 13D3

Avenue de la Libération. **GPS**: n49,33440 w0,44551.⬆.

10 🚐 € 6 🚰 🚽 Ch. **Surface:** asphalted. ■ 01/01-31/12

Distance: 🏖 on the spot.

Remarks: Nearby entrance campsite, max. 24h.

🚐 [S] Couterne 13C5

Place de la Mairie. **GPS**: n48,51223 w0,41417.⬆➡.

10 🚐 free 🚰 🚽 Ch WC free. **Surface:** asphalted. ■ 01/01-31/12

Distance: 🏘 on the spot 🍴 nearby 🛒 nearby.

Remarks: Max. 1 night, closed when frosty.

🚐 Criel-sur-Mer 14B1

Rue de la Plage, D222. **GPS**: n50,03296 e1,31150.⬆.

75 🚐 free. **Surface:** grassy/gravel. ■ 01/01-31/12

Distance: 🏘 500m 🏖 on the spot 🎣 on the spot 🍴 500m 🛒 1km.

🚐 [S] Deauville 13D3

Boulevard des Sports. **GPS**: n49,35727 e0,08417.

6 🚐 free 🚰 🚽 Ch ⚡ free. ■ 01/01-31/12

Remarks: Behind stadium, max. 24h.

Tourist information Deauville:

ℹ Office de Tourisme, Place de la Mairie, www.deauville.org.Bathing resort.

🚐 [S] Dieppe 14B1

Quai de la Marne. **GPS**: n49,93139 e1,08667.⬆.

45 🚐 € 7/24h 🚰 🚽 Ch 📶 free. **Surface:** metalled. ■ 01/01-31/12

Distance: 🏘 500m 🏖 on the spot 🎣 on the spot 🍴 500m 🛒 500m.

Remarks: Motorhome parking right side of harbour, max. 48h, wifi card available at harbour master.

Tourist information Dieppe:

ℹ Office de Tourisme, Quai du Carenage, www.dieppetourisme.com.Seaside resort with fishing port.

👁 Porte des Tourelles.City gate, 15th century.

🏰 Château Dieppe.Castle, 15th century, with maritime museum. ■ 10-12h, 14-18h ◘ 01/10-31/05 Tue.

✝ Église Saint Jacques.

🛍 ■ Tue, Thu 8-14h.

🛍 Norman market. ■ Sa 8-14h.

🚐 [S] Doudeville 14B2

Place du Mont Criquet, centre-ville. **GPS**: n49,72000 e0,78750.⬆.

25 🚐 free 🚽 Ch. **Surface:** asphalted. ■ 01/01-31/12

Distance: 🏘 100m 🍴 100m 🛒 100m.

🚐 [S] Ducey 13B4

Rue St Quentin. **GPS**: n48,62513 w1,294.➡.

30 🚐 free 🚰 € 2 🚽 Ch ⚡ € 2 WC.

Surface: metalled. ■ 01/01-31/12

Distance: 🏘 500m 🍴 500m 🛒 500m.

🚐 Equeurdreville 13B2

Rue Jean Bart. **GPS**: n49,65465 w1,65044.⬆.

6 🚐 free. **Surface:** gravel.

FR

⟐S Etretat ⛴ 🏖 14A2

Aire de stationnement Maupassant, Rue Guy de Maupassant. **GPS:** n49,70009 e0,21579. ⬆➡.

30 ⟐ € 8/24h ⚡€ 3/100liter ⚑Ch 🚻€ 3/55minutes. **Surface:** gravel/metalled. ◻ 01/10-31/12
Distance: 🏖1km ⛵1,2km ⊗1km 🍴1km.
Remarks: Max. 24h, next to campsite municipal.

Tourist information Etretat:
ℹ Office de Tourisme, Place Maurice Guillard, www.etretat.net.The cliffs which have the shape of an arch are a well-known tourist attraction.
⚔ Château des Aygues, Rue offenbach.Castle, 1866, former summer residence of Spanish kings. ◻ 01/07-20/09 14-18 ◉ Tue.

⟐S Fécamp 14A2

Bassin Bérigny, Chaussée Edouard Levasseur et Fils. **GPS:** n49,76334 e0,36470. ⬆.

8 ⟐free ⚡€ 3 ⚑Ch.
Surface: asphalted. ◻ 01/01-31/12
Distance: 🏖200m ⛵on the spot 🍴on the spot ⊗50m 🍴200m.
Remarks: At entrance marina, coins at Office de Tourisme.

⟐ Fécamp 14A2

Quai Sadi Carnot. **GPS:** n49,76087 e0,37157. ⬆.

10 ⟐free. **Surface:** asphalted. ◻ 01/01-31/12
Distance: 🏖200m ⛵on the spot 🍴on the spot ⊗200m 🍴500m.
Remarks: Between pier and marina.

Tourist information Fécamp:
ℹ Office de Tourisme, 113, rue Alexandre le Grand, www.fecamptourisme.com. City against the chalk-cliff of the Côte d'Albâtre, fishing-port is now mainly a marina.
🏛⚔ Palais Bénédictine.Museum with Bénédictine distillery and tasting-pub. ◻ 01/07-31/08 10-18h, 01/09-30/06 10.30-11.30h, 14-17h.
🏛 Musée des Terres Neuvas, boulevard Clocheville.Fishery as from the Viking period. ◻ 10-12h, 14-17.30h, 01/07-31/08 10-19h.

⟐S Forges-les-Eaux ♨ 14C2

Boulevard Nicolas Thiessé. **GPS:** n49,60569 e1,54288. ⬆.

35 ⟐ € 6,12, 01/11-15/03 free ⚡ ⚑Ch ⚑ included. **Surface:** asphalted. ◻ 01/01-31/12 ◉ service in winter.
Distance: 🏖2km.
Remarks: Max. 15 days. Cross roads D919-D915.

⟐S Formigny 13C2

La Ferme du Lavoir, D517. **GPS:** n49,34041 w0,89654. ⬆.

6 ⟐ € 10/night ⚡ ⚑Ch ⚑WC ⚑ included. **Surface:** asphalted/grassy.

⟐S Gacé 🌿 14A4

Rue du Marché aux Bestiaux. **GPS:** n48,79500 e0,29583. ⬆.

30 ⟐free ⚡€ 2 ⚑Ch 🚻€ 2. **Surface:** asphalted. ◻ 01/01-31/12
Distance: 🏖on the spot 🚲 2,6km ⊗50m.
Remarks: In front of tourist office, max. 24h.

⟐S Gavray 13B3

D7. **GPS:** n48,91085 w1,35162. ⬆➡.

8 ⟐free ⚡ ⚑free. **Surface:** grassy/gravel. ◻ 01/01-31/12
Distance: 🏖100m ⊗100m 🍴100m.

⟐S Gisay-la-Coudre 14A4

D35. **GPS:** n48,95001 e0,62670. ➡.

6 ⬛free ⛽€ 2/100liter 🚽Ch 🔌 16Amp. **Surface:** asphalted. ⬛ 01/01-31/12
Distance: 🛒on the spot ✕300m.
Remarks: Coins available at restaurant La Tortue. Follow signs from La Barre and Ouche, D49.

📷 S	**Gournay-en-Bray**	14C2

Avenue Sadi Carnot. **GPS:** n49,48055 e1,72640.
10 ⬛free ⛽🚽Ch ✂free. **Surface:** asphalted. ⬛ 01/01-31/12 ⚫ Thu-morning closed because of market + 2nd weekend Sep.
Distance: 🛒on the spot ✕on the spot 📷on the spot 📷on the spot.
Remarks: Max. 48h.

📷	**Goury**	13A1

GPS: n49,71616 w1,94324.⬆️

20 ⬛free. **Surface:** grassy/sand. ⬛ 01/01-31/12
Distance: ✕nearby.

📷 S	**Gouville-sur-Mer**	13B3

Chemin du Beau Rivage. **GPS:** n49,09970 w1,60896.⬆️➡️

40 ⬛€ 4/19-10h ⛽€ 4/100liter 🚽Ch 🔌€ 4/55minutes WC. **Surface:** gravel. ⬛ 01/01-31/12
Distance: 🏊on the spot ✕on the spot.

📷 S	**Grainville-Langannerie**	13D3

Rue de Lapford. **GPS:** n49,01438 w0,26805.
⬛free ⛽€ 2 🚽Ch 🗑. **Surface:** metalled.

📷 S	**Grandcamp-Maisy**	13C2

Rue du Moulin Odo. **GPS:** n49,38620 w1,03782.➡️

---

14 ⬛free ⛽🚽Ch. **Surface:** asphalted.

📷 S	**Granville** 🌿🏖🌊	13B4

Haute Ville, Rue du Roc. **GPS:** n48,83530 w1,6095.⬆️

20-25 ⬛€ 6 ⛽€ 2,80/10minutes 🚽Ch 🔌€ 2,50/55minutes 🗑.
Surface: gravel.
⬛ 01/01-31/12
Distance: 🏊500m ✕500m 🛒500m.
Remarks: Motorhome parking behind sea aquarium, upper city, max. 24h, Atlantic Wall 50m.

Tourist information Granville:
ℹ️ Office de Tourisme, 4, Cours Jonville, www.ville-granville.fr. The old centre, Haute-Ville, is surrounded by ramparts. The lower city is a bathing resort.
Ⓜ️ Musée Vieux Granville, Grand Porte. Regional museum. ⬛ 10-12h, 14-18h.
⛪ 🏛 ⬛ Wed, Sa.

📷 S	**Gréville-Hague**	13A2

D402. **GPS:** n49,67509 w1,80127.⬆️

10 ⬛free ⛽€ 2 🚽Ch 🔌€ 2 WC. **Surface:** metalled.
Distance: 🛒100m.
Remarks: Next to sports fields.

📷 S	**Grigneuseville**	14B2

La Plaine d'Hermesnil, 7 rue de la Plaine. **GPS:** n49,64427 e1,19900.⬆️➡️

7 ⬛€ 6 ⛽🚽Ch ✂included. **Surface:** gravel.
Distance: 🏊2,5km ✕2,5km 🛒2,5km.

📷 S	**Guilberville**	13C3

D159. **GPS:** n48,98871 w0,94844.⬆️

20 🛏free 🚰 € 2/100liter ⚡Ch 🔌 € 2/1h. Surface: gravel. ⬛ 01/01-31/12 ◉ service: 01/11-01/03.
Distance: 🚶300m 🚲1,5km ⊗300m 🛒300m.
Remarks: Coins at Tourist Info, Bistro and bakery.

Hermanville-sur-Mer 13D3
Rue Verte. GPS: n49,28592 w0,31243.⬆.

6 🛏free 🚰⚡Chfree. Surface: asphalted. ⬛ 01/01-31/12
Distance: 🚶on the spot.

Tourist information Hermanville-sur-Mer:
🚻 ⬛ Tue morning.

Hérouvilette 13D3
Place l'Aiguillon, Avenue de Caen, D 513A. GPS: n49,21983 w0,24497.⬆➡.

10 🛏free. Surface: asphalted. ⬛ 01/01-31/12
Distance: 🚶on the spot 🍴on the spot.

Heurteauville 14B2
Les Cerisiers, Rue de Village. GPS: n49,44777 e0,81333.⬆➡.

12 🛏€5 🚰 € 3 ⚡Ch 💧 € 2. Surface: gravel. ⬛ 01/04-31/10
Distance: 🚶3km 🏊20m 🛒20m ⊗3km 🛒3km.
Remarks: Along the Seine river.

Honfleur 14A2
Bassin Carnot. GPS: n49,41916 e0,24166.

120 🛏€ 9/24h 🚰⚡Ch 💧included.
Surface: gravel.
⬛ 01/01-31/12 ◉ service in winter.
Distance: 🚶500m 🚲2,7km ⊗on the spot.

Remarks: Parking east of city, on entering from dir Pont de Normandie.
Tourist information Honfleur:
🚹 Office de Tourisme, Quai lepaulmier, www.ot-honfleur.fr.Smal port city with many tourists and artists.
🅜 Greniers à Sel.Former salt warehouses, exhibitions of Honfleur painters. ⬛ 01/03-31/10.
🅜 Musée de la Marine.History of navigation of Honfleur. ⬛ 01/02-30/11, 01/12-31/01 Sa-Su.

Isigny-sur-Mer 13C2
Quai Neuf. GPS: n49,32221 w1,10649.⬆.

6 🛏free 🚰 € 2 ⚡Ch. Surface: asphalted.
Distance: 🚶300m 🛒200m.

Jobourg 13A1
Nez de Jobourg, D202. GPS: n49,67722 w1,93806.

10 🛏free 🚰 WCfree. Surface: metalled. ⬛ 01/01-31/12
Distance: 🚶within walking distance.

Jumièges 14B2
Rue Alphonse Callais. GPS: n49,43106 e0,81452.⬆➡.

20 🛏free 🚰 € 3 ⚡Ch. Surface: gravel. ⬛ 01/03-30/11
Distance: 🚶1km 🏊500m ⊗200m 🛒200m.
Remarks: Coins at Tourist Info and bakery.

La Ferrière-aux-Etangs 13C4
Camping du Lac, Rue de l'Etang. GPS: n48,65931 w0,51706.➡.

7 🛏free 🚰 € 2 ⚡Ch 💧(3x)€ 2, 16Amp. Surface: metalled. ⬛ 01/01-31/12

Distance: ⛅400m ⊗400m ♨400m.
Remarks: At lake, near tennis-court.

| 🏕️S | La Ferté-Macé | 13D4 |

Ruelle des Fournelles, D916. **GPS:** n48,59018 w0,35528.⬆️

15 🏕️free ⛽🍴Ch free. **Surface:** asphalted. 🅾️ 01/01-31/12
Distance: ⛅on the spot ⊗on the spot ♨on the spot.
Remarks: Via D916.

| 🏕️S | La Lucerne-d'Outremer | 13B4 |

D35. **GPS:** n48,78437 w1,42727.⬆️

6 🏕️free ⛽🍴Ch WC free. **Surface:** asphalted. 🅾️ 01/01-31/12
Distance: ⛅on the spot ⊗100m ♨100m.
Remarks: Max. 2 days, next to castle.

| 🏕️S | La Mailleraye-sur-Seine | 14B2 |

Quai Paul Girardeau. **GPS:** n49,48444 e0,77333.⬆️

34 🏕️€ 5, 1/11-31/3 free ⛽€ 3/10minutes 🍴Ch. **Surface:** grassy. 🅾️
01/01-31/12
Distance: ⛅200m ⚓on the spot ⛵on the spot ⊗on the spot ♨200m.
Remarks: Coins at shops/town hall, along the Seine river.

| 🏕️ | La Poterie-Cap-d'Antifer | 14A2 |

GPS: n49,68317 e0,16480.⬆️➡️

4 🏕️free. **Location:** Very simple, quit.
Surface: grassy/gravel. 🅾️ 01/01-31/12
Distance: ⛅2km.

| 🏕️S | La-Rivière-Saint-Sauveur | 14A2 |

Chemin des Bancs, D580. **GPS:** n49,40856 e0,26926.⬆️

12 🏕️free ⛽🍴Ch € 5. 🅾️ 01/01-31/12
Distance: 🚤700m.
Remarks: Coins at the shops in the village. 4km from Honfleur.

| 🏕️S | Langrune-sur-Mer | 13D3 |

Rue du Colonel Pierre Harivel. **GPS:** n49,32474 w0,36814.⬆️
3 🏕️free. **Surface:** metalled. 🅾️ 01/01-31/12
Distance: ⚓beach 50m.

| 🏕️S | Le Billot | 13D4 |

GPS: n48,96920 e0,07190.⬆️➡️

4 🏕️free ⛽€ 2,50 🍴Ch€ 2,50 WC. **Surface:** metalled.
🅾️ 01/01-31/12
Distance: ⊗200m.
Remarks: Coins available at restaurant (200m).

| 🏕️S | Le Havre | 13D2 |

Chaussée John Kennedy. **GPS:** n49,48499 e0,10673.⬆️➡️

19 🏕️free ⛽🍴Ch € 5.
Location: Central.
Surface: asphalted. 🅾️ 01/01-31/12
Distance: ⛅5 min walking ⚓on the spot ⛵on the spot ⊗200m ♨200m.
Remarks: Max. 48h.

Tourist information Le Havre:
ℹ️ Office de Tourisme, 186 Boulevard Clémenceau, www.ville-lehavre.fr. Big port and industrial town.
Ⓜ️ Musée de l'Ancienne Havre, rue Jerome Bellarmato. History of the city. 🅾️ Wed-Su 14-18h.
Ⓜ️ Musée Maritime, Dock Vaubanquai Frissard. Maritime museum. 🅾️ 10-12h, 14-18h.
🎡 Canyon Parc, CD34, Epretot. Family park in western style.

| 🏕️S | Le Mesnil-Jumièges | 14B2 |

Base de loisirs UCPA, Route de Mesnil. **GPS:** n49,41172 e0,84494.⬆️

10 🥘free, July-Aug € 10 🚰🔌Ch 🧹. **Surface:** asphalted. 🚻 01/01-31/12
Distance: 🚶1km 🏖200m 🚲200m 🛒1km 🛍1km.
🅂 **Le Mont-Saint-Michel** 13B4
Aire Camping-car du Mont-Saint-Michel. GPS: n48,61381 w1,50576.

🥘€ 8,70/24h 🚰🔌Ch 🧹 🔲. **Surface:** grassy.
Distance: ⊗La Rotisserie 🛍on the spot.
Remarks: Cross roads D976-D275.
🅂 **Le Mont-Saint-Michel** 13B4
Parking Mont-Saint-Michel no.8. **GPS:** n48,62910 w1,50729.⬆

50 🥘€ 12,50/14-14h. **Location:** Very simple.
Surface: metalled.
🚻 01/01-31/12
Distance: 🏖on the spot ⊗100m 🚲on the spot.
Remarks: Overnight stay allowed, free shuttle to Le Mont-Saint-Michel.
Tourist information Le Mont-Saint-Michel:
ℹ Office de Tourisme, Corps de Garde des Bourgeois, www.mont-saint-michel.net. Town with abbey on a cliff in the sea.
🅂 **Le Noyer-en-Ouche** 14A3
Ferme Lesur, La Godinière, D140. **GPS:** n49,01017 e0,72444.⬆

8 🥘🚰🔌Ch. **Surface:** metalled.
🅂 **Le Sap** 14A4
Les Terriers, Rue Nicolas Lesieur, D12. **GPS:** n48,89525 e0,33249.⬆

4 🥘free 🚰🔌Ch 🧹 free. **Surface:** gravel. 🚻 01/01-31/12
Distance: 🚶500m 🚲on the spot ⊗500m 🛍500m.
Remarks: Next to fire station, dir Quimper.
🅂 **Le Tréport** 14C1
Du Funiculaire, Route Touristique, D126E. **GPS:** n50,05777 e1,36222.⬆

25 🥘€ 5,80 🚰€ 2,10/100liter 🔌Ch 🧹€ 2,10/55minutes 🔲.
Location: Comfortable, isolated, quit.
Surface: grasstiles.
Distance: 🚶Le Tréport centre 2km 🏖2km ⊗100m.
Remarks: Max. 48h, free transport to city centre. Le Tréport > Criel Plage.
🅂 **Le Tréport** 14C1
Parc Sainte Croix, Rue Pierre Mendès France. **GPS:** n50,05954 e1,38919.⬆➡

61 🥘€ 9,30, tourist tax incl 🚰🔌Ch 🧹(61x)included. **Location:** Comfortable, isolated, quit. **Surface:** asphalted. 🚻 01/01-31/12
Distance: 🚶700m 🏖700m 🛍500m Mr.Ed.
Remarks: Max. 48h, industrial area, near campsite.
Tourist information Le Tréport:
ℹ Office de Tourisme, Quai Sadi Carnot, www.ville-le-treport.fr. Bathing resort and fishing town on the mouth of the Bresle river.
🏰 Château d'Eu, Eu. Royal castle, 19th century. 🚻 15/03-01/11 ⚫ Sa.
🅂 **Les Pieux** 13A2
Plage Sciotot. GPS: n49,50722 w1,84731.

5 🥘€ 7,50 🚰€ 3 🔌€ 3. **Surface:** grassy. 🚻 01/01-31/12
🅂 **Le Rozel** 13A2
Camping Le Ranch. GPS: n49,48034 w1,84219.

free. **Surface:** metalled. 01/01-31/12
Remarks: Large parking, 50m from beach.

Les Pieux 13A2

Intermarché, Route de Cherbourg. **GPS**: n49,51736 w1,79797.

6 free € 2 Ch. **Surface:** asphalted.
Distance: on the spot.

Tourist information Les Pieux:
Château, Bircquebec.Castle, 13th century and museum. summer 10-12h, 14-18.30h Wed.

Lion-sur-Mer 13D3

Rue du General Gallieni. **GPS**: n49,30174 w0,31316.

4 free. 01/01-31/12
Distance: on the spot on the spot 100m.
Remarks: Parking townhall, at sea, only overnight stay allowed.

Lisieux 14A3

Parking du Carmel, Rue d'Alençon. **GPS**: n49,14413 e0,22788.

free € 2/100liter Ch WC.
Surface: asphalted. 01/01-31/12
Distance: on the spot river on the spot on the spot.

Marigny 13B3

Rue Auguste Eudeline, D53. **GPS**: n49,09911 w1,24776.

10 free Ch € 2. **Surface:** metalled. 01/01-31/12
Distance: 700m 700m 700m.

Merville Franceville 13D3

Boulevard Wattier. **GPS**: n49,28483 w0,21071.

6 free € 2 Ch. **Surface:** asphalted. 01/03-15/11

Montebourg 13B2

Parking Louis Lecacheux. **GPS**: n49,48486 w1,37449.

10 free Chfree. 01/01-31/12

Montfiquet 13C3

Hotel-Restaurant Relais de la Fôret, L'Embranchement, D572. **GPS**: n49,19400 w0,863.

60 € 14 Chincluded WC Use sanitary € 2. **Surface:** asphalted. 01/01-31/12
Remarks: Picnic tables available. Bayeux dir Mont Saint Michel.

Montmartin-sur-Mer 13B3

Rue du Clos d'Auguet. **GPS**: n48,98573 w1,51602.

5 free € 2/100liter Ch € 2, 16Amp. **Surface:** asphalted. 01/01-31/12
Distance: 1km 1km 1km.
Remarks: Parking at garage, car washing place.

Montville 14B2

Place de l'Abbé Kerebel. **GPS**: n49,54780 e1,07388.

FR

15 ⑤free ⚊€ 3 ⚌Ch⚋free,.
Surface: gravel. ⬛ 01/01-31/12
Distance: 🚶400m 📍400m.
Remarks: Coins at mairie, restauration Hexagone, museum.

Tourist information Montville:
⚓ ⬛ Mo-morning.

| | Mortain | 13C4 |

Place du Château. **GPS:** n48,64887 w0,94489.⬆.

6 ⑤free ⚊ ⚌Ch⚋free. **Surface:** asphalted. ⬛ 01/01-31/12
Distance: 🚶on the spot ⊗on the spot 🚻on the spot.
Remarks: Max. 48h.

Tourist information Mortain:
ℹ️ Office de Tourisme, Rue du Bourglopin, www.ville-mortain.fr.Hiking trail to the Grande and Petite Cascade, waterfalls.

| | Notre-Dame-de-Courson | 14A3 |

D4. **GPS:** n48,99021 e0,25922.
10 ⑤free ⚊€ 1 ⚌Ch⚋€ 1. **Surface:** gravel.
Distance: 🚶200m.

| | Oissel | 14B3 |

Rue du Bras St.Martin. **GPS:** n49,33783 e1,09183.⬆.

2 ⑤free ⚊€ 2/100liter ⚌Ch⚋€ 2/55minutes.
Surface: gravel.
⬛ 01/01-31/12
Distance: 🚶200m ⚓on the spot 🛒on the spot ⊗200m 🚻200m.
Remarks: <7m, Coins at the bakery: 1, Rue du Maréchal Foch.

| | Ouistreham | 13D3 |

Rue des Dunes. **GPS:** n49,28716 w0,24968.⬆.

20+20 ⑤€ 8 ⚊⚌Ch⚋ included. 🛏 ⚋ **Surface:** asphalted/gravel. ⬛
01/01-31/12
Distance: 🚶650m ⚓on the spot.
Remarks: Near car ferry.

| | Pirou-Plage | 13B3 |

Rue des Hublots. **GPS:** n49,16522 w1,58937.⬆➡.

6 ⑤free ⚊€ 2/10minutes ⚌Ch🚻€ 2/1h.
Surface: asphalted.
⬛ 01/01-31/12
Distance: 🚶500m.
Remarks: Coins available at campsite Le Clos Marin and restaurant La Marée.

| | Pont-d'Ouilly | 13D4 |

Rue de la Libération. **GPS:** n48,87794 w0,41304.⬆➡.

43 ⑤€ 10/24h ⚊⚌Ch⚋ (43x)included ⚋. **Surface:** gravel. ⬛ 01/01-31/12
Distance: 🚶550m 🛒on the spot ⊗550m 🚻550m.
Remarks: Along the Orne river.

| | Pont-l'Évêque | 14A3 |

GPS: n49,27324 e0,20642.
50 ⑤ ⚊⚌Ch.
Distance: ⚓5km ⚓on the spot 🛒on the spot.

| | Port-en-Bessin-Huppain | 13C2 |

Rue du 11 Novembre. **GPS:** n49,34583 w0,75861.

25 ⑤€ 3,40/night. **Surface:** sand.
Distance: 🚶400m.

⑤Ⓢ **Portbail** 🏕 13B2
Rue Gilles Poerier. **GPS**: n49,33776 w1,69273.⬆️.

4 🛏free ⚡€ 2 💧Ch🚽€ 2. **Surface**: asphalted.

⑤Ⓢ **Rauville-la-Bigot** 13B2
D900. **GPS**: n49,51723 w1,68368.

10 🛏free ⚡💧Chfree. **Surface**: asphalted.

⑤Ⓢ **Réville** 13B2
Ferme de la Froide Rue, 165, Rue des Monts. **GPS**: n49,62583 w1,25278.⬆️.

🛏first night € 7, € 4 each additional night ⚡💧Ch⚓. **Surface**: grassy/gravel. 🅿 01/01-31/12
Distance: 🏖1km.

⑤Ⓢ **Rots** 13D3
Centre Commercial Cora, Chemin de la Croix Vautier, RN13. **GPS**: n49,19985 w0,46027.⬆️.
🛏free ⚡💧Chfree. **Surface**: asphalted. 🅿 01/01-31/12
Distance: ⊗on the spot 🛒on the spot.

⑤Ⓢ **Rugles** 14A4
Place de la Liberté. **GPS**: n48,82230 e0,70846.

10 🛏free ⚡💧 WC. **Location:** Urban, comfortable, noisy. **Surface:** metalled.
🅿 01/01-31/12
Distance: 🏖1km🚉on the spot 🛒1km 🚌on the spot.
Remarks: Along railwayline.

⑤Ⓢ **Saint-Sever-Calvados** 13B4
Place de la Mairie. **GPS**: n48,84169 w1,04842.⬆️.

15 🛏free ⚡free. **Surface:** gravel. 🅿 01/01-31/12
Distance: 🏖100m 🚲15km 🛒100m.

⑤Ⓢ **Sainte-Saire** 14C2
Rue de la Gare, D7. **GPS**: n49,69677 e1,49476.⬆️.
🛏free ⚡💧Ch⚓. **Location:** Rural, comfortable, quit. **Surface:** asphalted/grassy. 🅿 01/01-31/12
Distance: 🏖300m 🚴 Avenue Verte.

⑤Ⓢ **Sallenelles** 13D3
Boulevard Maritime D514. **GPS**: n49,26474 w0,22694.⬆️.

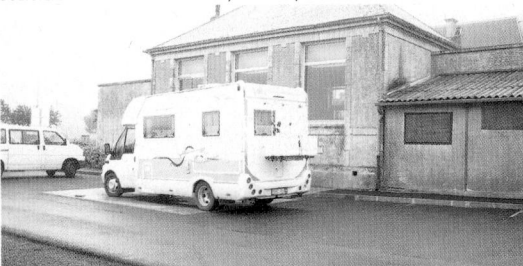

3 🛏free ⚡€ 2/10minutes 💧Ch. **Surface:** asphalted.
Distance: ⚓on the spot.
Remarks: Max. 48h.

⑤Ⓢ **Sideville-Lorimier** 13B2
Camping-car l'Orimier, Route du Pont Roger, D152. **GPS**: n49,58722 w1,69222.⬆️.

6 🛏€ 6/night ⚡💧Ch⚓included. **Surface:** asphalted/grassy.

⑤Ⓢ **Siouville-Hague** 13A2
Avenue des Peupliers. **GPS**: n49,56356 w1,8442.

4 🛏free ⚡💧Ch🚽free. **Surface:** metalled. 🅿 01/01-31/12
Distance: 🏖on the spot ⊗200m 🛒200m.
Remarks: Max. 48h.

⑤Ⓢ **Saint-André-de-l'Eure** 14B4
Boulevard Verdun. **GPS**: n48,90644 e1,26927.

FR

30 🛏free 🚰€ 2 💧Ch. **Surface:** grassy.
Distance: 🏊200m.

🅿S · · · · **Soumont-Saint-Quentin** 13D3
Rue de la Mine. **GPS:** n48,97840 w0,25.
🛏€ 5 🚰💧Ch🔌 included.

🅿S · · · · **Sourdeval** 13C4
Parc Saint-Lys, Rue Jean Baptiste Janin. **GPS:** n48,72603 w0,92308.⬆

10 🛏free 🚰💧Ch🗡free.
Surface: gravel/metalled. 🅾 01/01-31/12
Distance: 🚶100m ⊗400m 🍴400m.

🅿S · · · · **St.Fromond** 13C3
Place des Gabariers, D8. **GPS:** n49,22202 w1,08956.⬆

50 🛏free 🚰€ 2 💧Ch🔌€ 2. **Surface:** asphalted. 🅾 01/01-31/12
Remarks: Centre.

Tourist information St.Fromond:
ℹ🛕 Office de Tourisme, Bd de Verdun, Carentan, www.ot-carentan.fr.Old
bishop city with Gothic cathedral.

🅿S · · · · **St.Hilaire-du-Harcouët** 13B4
Place de la Motte. **GPS:** n48,57602 w1,09086.⬆

🛏free 🚰€ 2 💧Ch🔌€ 2. **Surface:** metalled. 🅾 01/01-31/12
Distance: 🚶on the spot ⊗on the spot 🍴on the spot.
Remarks: Behind church.

🅿S · · · · **St.Jouin-Bruneval** 14A2
Plage de Bruneval. **GPS:** n49,64970 e0,15349.⬆

10 🛏free. **Surface:** gravel. 🅾 01/01-31/12
Distance: 🚶4km 🏖pebbled beach ⮞on the spot ⊗nearby 🍴4km.

🅿S 🌊⚓🍴 **St.Lô** 13B3
Place de la Vaucelle. **GPS:** n49,11351 w1,10309.⬆➡

10 🛏free 🚰€ 2 💧Ch🗡€ 2 🧺. **Surface:** asphalted. 🅾 01/01-31/12
Distance: 🚶100m ⊗100m 🍴100m 🚌on the spot.
Remarks: Along the river.

Tourist information St.Lô:
ℹ Office de Tourisme, Place Général de Gaulle, www.saint-lo.fr.Modern city built
on the ruins of the bombardments 1944.
👁 Haras National, Rue du Maréchal Juin.National Stud farm established by
Napoleon in 1806. 🅾 01/06-30/09 14-18.
Ⓜ Musée de la Libération, place du Champ de Mars.Invasion in 1944. 🅾 10-
19h, winter 14-19h ● Tue. Ⓣ free.
🛕 Nôtre Dame.Renovated church 13th century.

🅿S · · · · **St.Nicolas d'Aliermont** 14B1
Place du 19 Mars 1962, Rue d'Arques. **GPS:** n49,88026 e1,22160.⬆

2 🛏free 🚰€ 2 💧Ch🔌€ 2.
Surface: asphalted. 🅾 01/01-31/12
Distance: 🚶200m 🚲12km ⊗200m 🍴200m.
Remarks: Behind town hall, coins available at town hall and library, max. 48h.

🅿S · · · · **St.Nicolas-de-Bliquetuit** 14A2
Route du Bac. **GPS:** n49,52083 e0,72777.⬆➡

12 🛏free 🚰€ 2 💧Ch🔌€ 2. **Surface:** asphalted. 🅾 01/01-31/12
Distance: 🚶1,4km 🏊on the spot ⮞on the spot ⊗2km 🍴2km.

Remarks: Coins at town hall, along river, hiking routes along the river Seine.

| 🛏️S | St.Pair-sur-Mer | 13B4 |

Avenue Léon Jozeau-Marigné. **GPS**: n48,81711 w1,56988.⬆️.

30 🛏️€ 5 🚰€ 2/10minutes 💧Ch 🔌€ 2/55minutes. **Surface:** asphalted/gravel. 🅿️ 01/01-31/12
Distance: 🚶500m 🏊beach 500m ⊗500m 🛒on the spot.
Remarks: Parking at tennis-court, max. 48h.

| 🛏️S | St.Pierre-Eglise | 13B2 |

Parking du 8 Mai 1945. **GPS**: n49,66897 w1,40387.➡️.

🛏️free 🚰€ 1,50 💧Ch. **Surface:** metalled. 🅿️ 01/01-31/12

| 🛏️S | St.Pierre-le-Vieux (((•))) | 14B1 |

Ferme du Moulin, D237. **GPS**: n49,85816 e0,88000.⬆️➡️.

5 🛏️€ 5 + € 1/pp 🚰💧Ch 🧹€ 3.
Surface: grassy/gravel. 🅿️ 01/01-31/12
Distance: 🚶1km ⊗1km 🛒1km.

| 🛏️S | St.Sauveur-le-Vicomte 🌿 | 13B2 |

Place Auguste Cousin. **GPS**: n49,38678 w1,52947.

🛏️free 🚰💧Chfree. **Surface:** asphalted.
Remarks: Next to town hall, max. 48h.

| 🛏️S | St.Vaast-la-Hougue 🚤⚓ | 13B2 |

Aire de la Gallouette, Rue Galouette. **GPS**: n49,58400 w1,267.⬆️.

27 🛏️€ 7 🚰€ 2/10minutes 💧Ch 🔌€ 2/1h. **Surface:** metalled.
🅿️ 01/01-31/12
Distance: 🚶300m 🛒300m.
Remarks: Near campsite Gallouette.

| 🛏️S | St.Vaast-la-Hougue 🚤⚓ | 13B2 |

Quai du Commandant Albert Paris. **GPS**: n49,58972 w1,26583.

🛏️free. **Surface:** metalled.
Distance: 🚶on the spot.

Tourist information St.Vaast-la-Hougue:
🛈 Office de Tourisme, 1, place Gen. de Gaulle, www.saint-vaast-reville.com.
Important port for allied forces in 1944. Now large marina.
👁️ Île de Tatihou, Port.Island in front of the coast, maritime museum and bird
hide. 🅿️ 01/04-30/09 10-18h.

| 🛏️S | St.Valéry-en-Caux | 14A1 |

Quai d'Aval. **GPS**: n49,87220 e0,70898.⬆️.

40 🛏️free, peak season € 5/day + € 0,20/pp 🚰€ 3 💧Ch.
Surface: asphalted.
🅿️ 01/01-31/12
Distance: 🚶600m 🏊on the spot 🛒on the spot ⊗500m 🛒bakery 600m.
Remarks: Max. 48h, coins available at office de tourisme.

Tourist information St.Valéry-en-Caux:
🛈 Office de Tourisme, Maison Henri IV, www.cauxmaritime.com.Popular seaside
resort with pleasant marina.

| 🛏️S | Ste.Honorine-des-Pertes | 13C2 |

Garage Vally, Route d'Omaha Beach, D514, dir Colleville-sur-Mer. **GPS**: n49,34868 w0,81635.

20 €6 Ch€ 1 included WC.
Distance: 500m on the spot.
Remarks: Passerby € 2,50.

Ste.Marie-du-Mont 13B2

Utah Beach, La Madeleine, D913. **GPS**: n49,41417 w1,17917.

50 free. **Location:** Quit. **Surface:** grassy/gravel. 01/01-31/12
Distance: 500m.

S Ste.Marie-du-Mont 13B2

La Madeleine. **GPS**: n49,41765 w1,18644.
€ 4 Ch.

Tourist information Ste.Marie-du-Mont:

M Musée du Débarquement, Utah-Beach.Landing museum.

Ste.Mère-Eglise 13B2

Rue du Général Koenig. **GPS**: n49,40830 w1,3159.

25 free, € 5/night.
Surface: asphalted. 01/01-31/12
Remarks: Parking behind church, max. 24h, bell-ringing every 15min.

S Ste.Mère-Eglise 13B2

Super U, ZA les Crutelles. **GPS**: n49,40461 w1,32223.
€ 2 Ch.
Distance: on the spot.
Remarks: Motorhome washing place max. ^3.80m.

Tourist information Ste.Mère-Eglise:

i Borne 0 de la voie de la Liberté.Pile 0, the starting point of the way to freedom.

i Office de Tourisme, 2, Rue Eisenhower, www.sainte-mere-eglise.info.Village well-known for the paratrooper who landed on the church-tower.

M Musée Airborne.Exhibition about the invasion at St.-Mère-Eglise. 10-12h, 14-18h.

S Surtainville 13A2

Rue des mielles. **GPS**: n49,46373 w1,82871.

10 free € 3 Ch. **Surface:** metalled.
Distance: 100m.

S Tourlaville 13B2

Espace Loisirs Colignon, piscine-camping municipal, Rue des Algues. **GPS**: n49,65398 w1,56606.

free € 2 Ch. **Surface:** asphalted.
Remarks: Coins at campsite or swimming pool.

Tourlaville 13B2

Quai Amiral Kniskern/Boulevard Maritime. **GPS**: n49,64549 w1,59976.

.
Remarks: Parking at ferry-boat.

S Tréauville 13A2

1, La Chaussee, D65. **GPS**: n49,54444 w1,83472.

10 €6,50 Ch included. **Surface:** grassy/metalled.
Distance: 2,5km.

S Valognes 13B2

Place Félix Buhot. **GPS**: n49,51159 w1,47813.

FR

7 🛏free 🚰 2 🔌Ch🏳️€ 2. **Surface:** asphalted.
Distance: 🛒on the spot.
Remarks: Next to supermarket Champion.

▦S	Valognes	13B2

Zone Artisanale d'Armanville, Chemin de la Brique. **GPS:** n49,51433 w1,50004.

🛏€ 5/24h 🚰 2 🔌Ch🏳️€ 2 WC. **Surface:** asphalted.
Remarks: Station de lavage Eléphant Bleu.

▦S	Varaville	13D3

Etang Saint Georges. **GPS:** n49,26916 w0,15874.
🛏€ 10/night, € 15/24h 🚰.
Distance: 🏊on the spot, sea 2,3km 🛒on the spot.
Remarks: Narrow road from direction Le Hôme, fishing lake.

▦	Veules-les-Roses 🌿🏖️	14B1

Parking des Falaises. GPS: n49,87555 e0,79269.⬆️➡️.

🛏free. **Surface:** grassy. 🅿️ 01/01-31/12
Distance: 🛍️500m 🏊on the spot 🛒on the spot ⊗500m 🚰500m.

©S	Veules-les-Roses 🌿🏖️	14B1

Camping des Mouettes, Avenue Jean Moulin. **GPS:** n49,87640 e0,80420.⬆️➡️.

15 🛏€ 5/24h 🚰 3 🔌Ch. **Surface:** metalled. 🅿️ 01/01-31/12
Distance: 🛍️300m 🏊500m 🛒500m ⊗300m 🚰300m 🚐on the spot.
Remarks: Parking next to campsite des Mouettes, max. 48h, coins available at campsite, 12-14h closed.

Tourist information Veules-les-Roses:
ℹ️ Office de Tourisme, 12, rue du Marché, www.veules-les-roses.fr.

▦S	Veulettes-sur-Mer	14A1

Chemin des Courses. **GPS:** n49,85233 e0,60165.⬆️.

15 🛏€ 4,50 🚰 3,50/100liter 🔌Ch 🔧(16x). **Surface:** asphalted. 🅿️ 01/01-31/12
Distance: 🛍️200m 🏊200m 🛒200m ⊗200m 🚰200m.
Remarks: Side-street D10, behind Syndicat d'Initiative.

▦S	Veulettes-sur-Mer	14A1

D10. **GPS:** n49,85488 e0,60702.⬆️.

50 🛏€ 4,50 🚰 3,50/100liter 🔌 🔧(18x). **Surface:** grassy. 🅿️ 01/01-31/12
Distance: 🛍️200m 🏊50m 🛒50m.
Remarks: Beach parking, max. 24h.

▦S	Villedieu-les-Poêles	13B4

Parc de la Commanderie, Rue Taillemarche. **GPS:** n48,83682 w1,22436.⬆️.

5 🛏free. **Surface:** asphalted. 🅿️ 01/01-31/12
Distance: 🛍️on the spot 🚲2,4km ⊗100m 🚰100m.

▦S	Villers-Bocage	13C3

Rue du Canada. **GPS:** n49,07973 w0,6609.

5 🛏free 🚰 2 🔌Ch🏳️€ 2. **Surface:** asphalted. 🅿️ 01/01-31/12
Distance: 🚲1,5km 🚰400m.

▦S	Villers-sur-Mer 🏖️	13D3

Rue des Martois. **GPS:** n49,32910 e0,01273.
14 🛏€ 8 🚰 4 🔌Ch. **Surface:** metalled. 🅿️ 01/01-31/12
Distance: 🏊beach 250m 🚰bakery 1,5km.
Remarks: Max. 48h.

⛟S **Vimoutiers** 14A4

D916, Avenue du Dr. Dentu. **GPS:** n48,93152 e0,19604.⬆️
8 ⛟free ⚡🍴Ch🚿 WC free. **Surface:** asphalted. ⬛ 01/01-31/12
Distance: 🛒Champion 200m.

⛟S **Vire** 13C4

Place du champ de foire. **GPS:** n48,84084 w0,88862.⬆️

50 ⛟free ⚡🍴Chfree. **Surface:** asphalted. ⬛ 01/01-31/12 ⚫ Fri-Sa.
Distance: 🛒on the spot ✖on the spot 🍽on the spot.
Remarks: Fri-Sa market, no water during winter time.

Ile-de-France

⛟S **Bray-sur-Seine** 15A5

Parking du Tapis Vert, Quai de l'Ile. **GPS:** n48,41713 e3,23745.

20 ⛟free ⚡🍴Chfree ⬛. **Surface:** asphalted.
Distance: 🛒100m ✖100m.
Remarks: Max. 72h.

Tourist information Bray-sur-Seine:
🚶 ⬛ Fri 8-13h.

⛟S **Coupvray** 15A4

Parking Disneyland Paris, Boulevard du Parc. **GPS:** n48,87500 e2,79700.⬆️

⛟€13/day ⚡🍴Ch🚿 WC🍽included.
Surface: asphalted. ⬛ 01/01-31/12
Remarks: Motorhome area at amusement park, note: tariffs will be charged per day, even if you arrive in the evening.

Tourist information Coupvray:
🎪 Crescend'O, Marne-la-Vallée.Water show in circus ambiance. ⬛ Mo, Tue, Wed, Fri 19.30, Sa 18, 21, Su 15, 18.
🎪 Disneyland Paris, Marne-la-Vallée.Attractions and themepark.

⛟S **Provins** 15A5

Parking Office de Tourisme, Chemin de Villecran. **GPS:** n48,56090 e3,28112.

30 ⛟€4 ⚡€ 2,50 🍴Ch🚿€ 2,50 ⬛.🚮 🗑 **Surface:** asphalted. ⬛
01/01-31/12 ⚫ service: frost.
Distance: 🛒500m ✖500m.
Tourist information Provins:
🚶 ⬛ Sa 8-14h.

⛟S **Souppes-sur-Loing** 15A6

GPS: n48,18083 e2,72343.⬆️➡️

5 ⛟€5 🍴Ch🚿included. 🛁 **Surface:** asphalted.
Remarks: Max. 72h.

⛟S **St.Cyr-sur-Morin** 15A4

Avenue Daniel Simon. **GPS:** n48,90641 e3,18463.
4 ⛟free ⚡🍴Chfree. **Surface:** grassy. ⬛ 01/01-31/12
Distance: 🛒nearby.
Remarks: Behind church.

Britanny

⛟S **Antrain** 13B5

Route de Pontorson. **GPS:** n48,46307 w1,47938.⬆️

2 ⛟free ⚡🍴Ch🚿 WC free. **Surface:** asphalted.

⛺S **Arradon** 12D4

Camping municipal, Rue de la Mairie. **GPS:** n47,62245 w2,82495.⬆️

12 ⛟free, 15/6/15/9 € 15 ⚡€ 2 🍴Ch🚿€ 2. **Surface:** asphalted. ⬛
01/01-31/12
Remarks: ± 12 pitches free on campsite if campsite is closed.
Tourist information Arradon:

i Syndicat d'Initiative Municipal, 2, place de l'Eglise.Seaside resort in the Gulf of Morbihan.

	Arzal	12D4

Barrage d'Arzal, D139. **GPS**: n47,50089 w2,38074. ⬆.

15 🛏free. **Surface:** asphalted. 🅿 01/01-31/12
Distance: 🚶1,5km ⚓50m 🚉50m ⊗50m 🛒50m.

S	Arzon	12D4

Aire d'accueil des Camping-cars de Kermor, Avenue de Kerlun, Kerjouanno. **GPS**: n47,53886 w2,88028. ⬆➡.

49 🛏€ 6,70/24h 🚰🚻Ch 🔌(16x)included. **Surface:** asphalted.
Remarks: Nearby Plage du Fageo, max. 72h.

S	Audierne ⚓	12B3

Rue Lamartine. **GPS**: n48,02733 w4,53721. ⬆.

🛏free 🚰10liter 🚻Ch 🚮. **Surface:** unpaved. 🅿 01/01-31/12
Distance: 🚶1,5km ⊗1,5km.

S	Auray ❀⚓	12C4

Chemin de Bellevue. **GPS**: n47,66365 w2,97393. ⬆➡.

🛏free 🚰€ 3/20minutes 🚻Ch 🚮. **Surface:** asphalted.
Distance: 🚶200m.

S	Auray ❀⚓	12C4

Place du Golhéres. **GPS**: n47,66524 w2,99036. ⬆➡.

3 🛏free 🚰🚻Chfree. **Surface:** asphalted.
Distance: 🚶500m ⊡on the spot.
Remarks: Follow Culturel Athena and Piscine.

Tourist information Auray:
✈ 🅿 Mo.

	Baud	12C3

Rue du Champ de Foire. **GPS**: n47,87375 w3,02008.

20 🛏free. **Surface:** metalled.

S	Baud	12C3

Route de Locminé. **GPS**: n47,88112 w2,97465.
🚰🚻Ch 🚮free. 🅿 01/01-31/12

S	Bédée	13A5

Rue de Dinan. **GPS**: n48,18099 w1,94416. ⬆.

6 🛏free 🚰🚻Chfree. **Surface:** asphalted.
Distance: ⊗200m 🛒50m.
Remarks: Nearby cemetery.

S	Belle-Isle-en-Terre	12C2

Rue Guerveur, D33. **GPS**: n48,54332 w3,39417. ⬆➡.

10 🛏free 🚰🚻Ch 🚮 free. **Surface:** gravel. 🅿 01/01-31/12
Distance: 🚶100m ⚓10m.

	Belz	12C4

Rue des Sports. **GPS**: n47,66940 w3,17744. ⬆➡.

FR

10 ⊠free. **Surface:** gravel/metalled. ☐ 01/01-31/12

⚓S | **Berric** | 12D4

Chemin de l'Étang. **GPS:** n47,63365 w2,52806.⬆➡.

6 ⊠€5 ⏚€ 2/10minutes ⚙Ch ⏚€ 2/55minutes. **Surface:** asphalted.
Distance: ⬅500m ⤢on the spot ⟵on the spot ⊗500m ⏚500m.
Remarks: Access via Rue du Grand Pont, parking fee being collected, coins at the shops in the village.

⚓S | **Binic** ⛱♨⚶ | 12D2

Aire camping-car de l'Ic, Rue de l'Ic. **GPS:** n48,60059 w2,83573.⬆➡.

50 ⊠free ⏚ ⚙Chfree. **Location:** Urban, central, quit. **Surface:** gravel. ☐ 01/01-31/12
Distance: ⬅500m ⊗700m ⟵500m ⚲500m.

Tourist information Binic:
ℹ Office de Tourisme, Avenue du Général de Gaulle, www.ville-binic.fr.Seaside resort with marina.
⛱ ☐ Thu.

⚓S | **Bourg-Blanc** | 12B2

Rue de Brest. **GPS:** n48,49194 w4,50256.⬆.

6 ⊠free ⏚ ⚙Chfree. **Surface:** grassy. ☐ 01/01-31/12
Distance: ⟵fish pond ⏚100m.

⚓S | **Brech** ⛱ | 12C4

Rue de Pont Douar/Avenue des Pins, D768. **GPS:** n47,71917 w3,00111.⬆➡.

6 ⊠free ⏚€ 1,50 ⚙Ch. **Surface:** grassy. ☐ 01/01-31/12
Distance: ⬅100m ⤢Small lake ⊗200m ⏚200m.
Remarks: Parking nearby small lake, plan d'eau.

| **Brest** | 12B2

Parking Océanopolis, Rue du Cormoran. **GPS:** n48,38893 w4,43535.⬆.

24 ⊠free. **Surface:** asphalted. ☐ 01/01-31/12
Distance: ⤢on the spot ⟵on the spot ⟵300m.
Remarks: Busy parking during the day, gate closes at 18h.

S | **Brest** | 12B2

Port du Moulin Blanc, Rue Eugène Berest. **GPS:** n48,39202 w4,43553.

⏚ ⚙Ch ⏚free.
☐ 01/01-31/12

Tourist information Brest:
ℹ Office de Tourisme, Place de la Liberté, www.mairie-brest.fr/.Modern city with natural harbour, important naval harbour.
👁 Tour Tanguy.Diorama old Brest. ☐ daily, 01/10-31/05 Wed, Su afternoon.
Ⓜ Musée de la Marine, Château de Brest.Navy museum. ☐ 01/02-31/03, 01/09-15/12 10-12h, 14-18h, 01/04-31/08 10-18.30h ⬤ Tue.
🐧 Océanopolis.Sea-centre, penguin and seals. ☐ 01/04-31/08 9-18h, 01/09-31/03 10-17h ⬤ Mo.

⚓S | **Callac (22)** | 12C2

Av Ernest Renan. **GPS:** n48,40200 w3,43737.✈ .

8 ⊠free ⏚€ 2 ⚙Ch ⏚€ 2. **Surface:** gravel. ☐ 01/01-31/12
Distance: ⤢200m ⟵200m.
Remarks: Lac Verte Vallée.

FR

⬚⬚S | **Camaret-sur-Mer** | 12B2

Rue Georges Ancey. **GPS:** n48,27513 w4,60793.⬆➡.

75 ⬚01/04-31/10 € 6 ⌇€ 2/100liter ⬚Ch⬚€ 2.⬚ **Location:** Rural, comfortable, quit. **Surface:** gravel. ⬚ 01/01-31/12
Distance: ⬚1km ⬚500m ⬚500m ⬚500m ⬚ on the spot ⬚ on the spot.
Remarks: Max. 72h.

⬚⬚S | **Campénéac** | 12D3

Rue de l'Étang. **GPS:** n47,95736 w2,29039.⬆➡.

30 ⬚free ⬚€ 2 WC. **Surface:** grassy. ⬚ 01/01-31/12
Distance: ⬚250m.
Remarks: Coins available at Fauchoux, rue nationale 32.

S | **Campénéac** | 12D3

Rue de la Fontaine. **GPS:** n47,95667 w2,29332.⬆➡.
⬚⬚Chfree.

⬚⬚S | **Cancale** ⬚⬚ | 13A4

Aire camping-car Ville Ballet, Rue des Français Libres. **GPS:** n48,67004 w1,86583.⬆.

50 ⬚€ 0,60/h, € 6/24h ⌇€ 2,80/100liter ⬚Ch⬚€ 2,80/55minutes ⬚.
Surface: grassy. ⬚ 01/01-31/12
Distance: ⬚on the spot ⬚1km ⬚800m ⬚100m.
Remarks: Bread-service.

⬚⬚S | **Cancale** ⬚⬚ | 13A4

Super U, ZA la Bretonnièrre. **GPS:** n48,67891 w1,8648.

50 ⬚free ⌇€ 2,50/100liter ⬚Ch⬚€ 4. **Surface:** asphalted.
Distance: ⬚on the spot.

Remarks: Coins at supermarket.
Tourist information Cancale:
⬚ Office de Tourisme, 44, rue du Port, www.ville-cancale.fr.Centre of the oyster culture.
⬚ La Ferme Marine.Guided tour oyster farm. ⬚ summer 11h,15h,17h Français, 14h English, 16h Deutsch.
⬚ St Meloir des Ondes, l'Atelier du Verre.Glass studio with demonstrations. ⬚ 10.30-12.30h, 14.30-18.30h, 01/07-31/08 10-13h, 14-19h. ⬚ free.

⬚⬚S | **Carantec** ⬚⬚ | 12B2

Aire du Meneyer, Rue Castel an Dour. **GPS:** n48,65967 w3,9138.

20 ⬚free ⌇€ 3/15minutes ⬚Ch⬚€ 3/55minutes. **Surface:** gravel/metalled. ⬚ 01/01-31/12
Distance: ⬚500m.
Remarks: Max. 48h.

⬚ | **Carantec** ⬚⬚ | 12B2

Chemin du Roch Glaz. **GPS:** n48,65235 w3,90308.

10 ⬚free. **Surface:** asphalted. ⬚ 01/01-31/12
Distance: ⬚beach 300m ⬚on the spot.
Remarks: Seaview.

⬚ | **Carantec** ⬚⬚ | 12B2

Rue Pen Al Lann. **GPS:** n48,66861 w3,895.

15 ⬚free. **Surface:** asphalted. ⬚ 01/01-31/12
Distance: ⬚500m ⬚150m ⬚150m ⬚1km ⬚1km.
Remarks: At tennis-courts, max. 48h.

⬚ | **Carantec** ⬚⬚ | 12B2

Square du Grand Sacconex, Rue du Kélenn. **GPS:** n48,66980 w3,91335.

10 🛏free. **Surface:** unpaved.
Distance: 🛒300m ⛱on the spot ⛽on the spot ⊗on the spot 🚰300m ▣on the spot.
Remarks: At gymnasium.
Tourist information Carantec:
ℹ️ Office de Tourisme, 4, rue Pasteur, www.ville-carantec.com/.Seaside resort with marina.
Ⓜ️ Musée Maritime.Navigation museum.

⛴Ⓢ	Carhaix-Plouguer	12C3

Rue de Bazeilles/Rue des Augustins. **GPS:** n48,27829 w3,57257.⬆️.

10 🛏free 🚰🍽Ch▪️free. **Surface:** metalled. 🅾️ 01/01-31/12
Distance: 🛒200m ⊗200m 🚰200m.

⛴Ⓢ	Carnac ⛱	12C4

Square d'illertissen. **GPS:** n47,58505 w3,08242.⬆️➡️.

±30 🛏free 🚰€ 2 🍽. **Surface:** asphalted. 🅾️ 01/01-31/12
Distance: 🛒50m ⊗50m 🚰50m.
Remarks: Max. 1 night.
Tourist information Carnac:
ℹ️ Office de Tourisme, 74, avenue des Druides, www.carnac.fr.Seaside resort and important place of finding of 30.000 prehistoric menhirs.
Ⓜ️ Musée de la Préhistoire.Prehistoric museum. 🅾️ 12-18h, Sa-Su 10-12.30h, 14-18h. 🎫 € 5.

⛴Ⓢ	Caulnes	13A5

Lavoir Fontaine, Rue de Dinan. **GPS:** n48,28655 w2,15517.⬆️.

---

10 🛏free 🚰€ 2/10minutes 🍽Ch▪️€ 2/1h WC. **Surface:** gravel. 🅾️ 15/03-15/11
Distance: 🛒500m ⊗100m 🚰100m 🚌200m.
Remarks: Max. 24h.

⛴Ⓢ	Cesson-Sévigné	13A5

Route de La Valette. **GPS:** n48,11802 w1,59121.⬆️.

8 🛏free 🚰€ 2/10minutes 🍽Ch▪️€ 2/55minutes ✎. **Surface:** metalled. 🅾️ 01/01-31/12

⛴Ⓢ	Châtillon-en-Vendelais	13B5

D108. **GPS:** n48,23112 w1,17959.

10 🛏free 🚰🍽Chfree. **Surface:** asphalted.
Distance: ⛱lake.
Remarks: At the lake, next to campsite.

⛴Ⓢ	Cléden-Cap-Sizun	12A3

Place du 19 mars 1962, Rue de la ville d'ys. **GPS:** n48,04803 w4,65008.⬆️.

20 🛏free 🚰€ 1/10minutes 🍽Ch WC. **Location:** Rural, quit. **Surface:** asphalted/metalled. 🅾️ 01/01-31/12
Distance: 🛒on the spot.

⛴Ⓢ	Cléden-Cap-Sizun	12A3

Pointe du Van, D7. **GPS:** n48,05936 w4,70727.⬆️.

20 🛏free WC. **Surface:** gravel. 🅾️ 01/01-31/12
Distance: 🛒Cléden-Cap-Sizun ± 5km ⛱on the spot.

⛴Ⓢ	Cléden-Cap-Sizun	12A3

Route de Kastel Koz, Beuzec-Cap-Sizun. **GPS:** n48,08473 w4,51844.⬆️.

10 ⃒free. **Location:** Rural, very simple, isolated. **Surface:** grassy/gravel. ▢ 01/01-31/12
Distance: ⌁on the spot ⅄ on the spot.

20 ⃒€ 2 ⚒ Ch ⚒ WC ⚒. **Surface:** asphalted. ▢ 01/01-31/12
Distance: ⌁on the spot.
Remarks: Foot ferry to centre.

⌗S **Clohars-Carnoët** 12C3
D16, Rue de Quimperlé. **GPS:** n47,79810 w3,58516.⬆.
4 ⃒free ⚒ € 2 ⚒Ch ⚒€ 2. **Surface:** asphalted. ▢ 01/01-31/12
Distance: ⌁200m ⚒ 10km ⌁beach 4,5km ⚒bakery 200m.

⌗S **Concarneau** 12B3
Parking de la Gare, Avenue de la Gare. **GPS:** n47,87864 w3,9202.⬆.

⌗S **Clohars-Carnoët** 12C3
Place de NAVA, Rue de Quimperlé. **GPS:** n47,79790 w3,585.

3 ⃒free ⚒€ 2 ⚒Ch ⚒€ 2. **Surface:** asphalted. ▢ 01/01-31/12

47 ⃒€ 2 ⚒ ⚒Ch ⚒ ⚒. **Surface:** metalled. ▢ 01/01-31/12
Distance: ⌁500m ⌁beach 1,4km.
Remarks: Parking station.

Tourist information Concarneau:
ℹ Office de Tourisme, Quai d'Aiguillon, www.ville-concarneau.fr.Important fishing-port, old city with city walls.
Ⓜ Ville-Close.History and techniques of the international offshore fishing. ▢ 10-12h, 14.30-18.30h, summer 9.30-20h.
⚒ Ⓜ Mo, Fri.

⌗S **Combrit** 12B3
Place du 19 mars 1962, Hent Ty Plouz. **GPS:** n47,88755 w4,1546.

⌗S **Crac'h** 12C4
Intermarché, AC Les Alizés. **GPS:** n47,60421 w2,99669.⬆➡.

10 ⃒free ⚒€ 2/10minutes ⚒Ch ⚒€ 2. **Location:** Quit. **Surface:** metalled. ▢ 01/01-31/12
Distance: ⌁on the spot.
Remarks: Coins available at the shops.

8 ⃒free ⚒€ 2/10minutes ⚒Ch. **Surface:** asphalted. ▢ 01/01-31/12
Distance: ⊗on the spot ⚒on the spot.

⌗S **Commana** 12B2
Place du salles de Sports, D11. **GPS:** n48,41611 w3,96139.⬆➡.

⌗S **Crozon** 12B2
Parking du Loc'h, Rue de l'Atlantique, Morgat. **GPS:** n48,22523 w4,50851.⬆.

5 ⃒free ⚒ ⚒free. **Location:** Rural, very simple, isolated, quit. **Surface:** grassy. ▢ 01/01-31/12
Distance: ⌁200m ⊗300m ⚒bakery 300m ⚒on the spot ⅄on the spot.

30 ⃒€ 4,08 ⚒€ 3,20/10minutes ⚒Ch ⚒€ 3,20/55minutes. ⚒ **Surface:** asphalted. ▢ 01/01-31/12
Distance: ⌁300m ⚒on the spot ⊗on the spot ⚒100m.
Remarks: Market on We.

⌗S **Concarneau** 12B3
Le Porzou, Allée Jean Bouin. **GPS:** n47,86320 w3,9051.

⚿⚿ S   **Crozon** 🏖️🌊   12B2

Le Fret, Le Sillon, D55. **GPS:** n48,28457 w4,50934. ⬆️.

6 🚐free 🚰€ 2,08/10minutes 🍺Ch. **Location:** Rural, very simple, quit.
Surface: unpaved. ⭕ 01/01-31/12
Distance: 🛒on the spot ⊗Resto 250m.

⚿⚿ S   **Crozon** 🏖️🌊   12B2

Parking office de tourisme, Boulevard de Pralognan, D887. **GPS:** n48,24770 w4,4934. ⬆️.

20 🚐free 🚰€ 2 🍺🔌€ 2 💳. **Location:** Urban. **Surface:** asphalted. ⭕ 01/01-31/12
Distance: 🛒on the spot.
Remarks: Nearby Office de Tourisme.

⚿⚿ S   **Damgan**   12D4

Parking de Kervoyal, Boulevard de l'atalante. **GPS:** n47,51465 w2,56038. ⬆️

76 🚐€ 6 🚰🍺Ch 🔌included. **Surface:** metalled/sand. ⭕ 01/01-31/12
Distance: 🛒600m ⛱️sandy beach.
Remarks: Parking at the beach, max. 48h.

⚿⚿   **Dinan**   13A5

Rue du Port, D12. **GPS:** n48,45450 w2,0389. ⬆️.

16 🚐🚰€ 2 🍺Ch🔌€ 2. **Surface:** asphalted.
Distance: 🛒nearby ⊗100m 🛒100m 🚌150m.

⚿⚿ S   **Elven**   12D4

Avenue des Martyrs de la Résistance, Le Guého. **GPS:** n47,73278 w2,58972. ⬆️➡️.

7+25 🚐€ 1 + € 1,50/pp 🚰€ 3 🍺Ch🔌€ 2/20minutes ⚡(12x)€ 2,50.
Surface: grassy/gravel. ⭕ parking 01/01-31/12 service 01/07-31/08
Distance: 🛒nearby ⊗nearby 🛒nearby.

⚿⚿ S   **Erdeven**   12C4

Boulevard d'Atlantique. **GPS:** n47,61429 w3,15958.

20 🚐€ 6,50/24h 🚰€ 2,50/4minutes 🍺Ch🔌€ 2,50/4minutes 💳.🚐
Surface: grassy.
Distance: ⛱️500m ⊗200m 🛒200m.

⚿   **Erdeven**   12C4

Place de St Margen. **GPS:** n47,64200 w3,157. ⬆️.

10 🚐free. **Surface:** metalled. ⭕ 01/01-31/12
Distance: 🛒50m ⊗50m 🛒50m.
Remarks: Parking in centre.

🏨⚿ S   **Erdeven**   12C4

Rue des Menhirs. **GPS:** n47,63750 w3,15156. ⬆️➡️.

30 🚐€ 0,30/30min 9-19h, overnight stay free. **Surface:** asphalted. ⭕ 01/01-31/12
Distance: 🛒800m ⊗500m.

⚿⚿ S   **Dol-de-Bretagne** 🌿🏖️   13A4

Place Jean Hamelin. **GPS:** n48,54736 w1,75442.

10 ⊠5 ⊏€ 3 🔌Ch❌. **Surface:** grassy/metalled.
Distance: 🚲500m ⊗on the spot 🛒Lidl 300m.

| ♿S | **Erquy** | 12D2 |

Caroual Plage, Rue des Hirondelles. **GPS:** n48,62120 w2,4724.⬆

47 ⊠6/24h ⊏€ 2 🔌Ch⊞€ 2. **Surface:** metalled. ⭕ 01/04-15/11
Remarks: Beach parking, max. 48h.

Tourist information Erquy:
ℹ Office de Tourisme, Boulevard de la Mer, "Le Rial",, www.erquy-tourisme.com. Fishing-port.

| ©S | **Étel** | 12C4 |

Camping municipal, Rue de la Barre. **GPS:** n47,65100 w3,202.⬆➡
25 ⊠€ 6,50/night ⊏€ 2 🔌Ch. **Surface:** grassy. ⭕ 01/04-30/09
Remarks: Baker every morning (Jul/Aug).

| ♿ | **Fouesnant** | 12B3 |

Chemin de Kerlosquen. **GPS:** n47,85444 w3,99255.

10 ⊠free. **Surface:** grassy/sand. ⭕ 01/01-31/12
Distance: 🏖beach 50m.
Remarks: Beach parking.

| ♿ | **Fouesnant** | 12B3 |

Plage Mousterlin, Chemin de Kerneuc. **GPS:** n47,85144 w4,04662.⬆

15 ⊠free. **Surface:** grassy/sand.
Distance: 🏖beach 50m.
Remarks: Beach parking, max. 48h.

| S | **Fouesnant** | 12B3 |

Leclerc, D45, Route de Quimper. **GPS:** n47,90234 w4,02938.⬆

12free ⊏€ 2/10minutes 🔌Ch⊞€ 2/55minutes. **Surface:** asphalted. ⭕ 01/01-31/12
Distance: 🛒on the spot.

| ♿S | **Fougères** | 13B5 |

Allée des Fêtes. GPS: n48,35660 w1,20242.⬆

⊠free ⊏ 🔌Ch WC free. **Surface:** asphalted. ⭕ 01/01-31/12
Distance: 🚲500m ⊗200m 🛒200m.

| ♿S | **Fougères** | 13B5 |

Parking de la Poterne, Ruelle des Anglais. **GPS:** n48,35524 w1,2113.⬆

16 ⊠free ⊏ 🔌Ch free. ⭕ 01/01-31/12
Distance: 🚲on the spot ⊗250m.
Remarks: Castle of Fougères 500m.

| ♿S | **Fréhel** | 12D2 |

La Ville Oie, Rue des Sports, D117, Pléhérel-plage. **GPS:** n48,65032 w2,35241.
⬆➡

40 ⊠free ⊏€ 2,50/100liter 🔌Ch⊞€ 2,50/30minutes 🗑. **Surface:** unpaved. ⭕ 01/01-31/12
Distance: 🚲1,1km 🏖beach 1,2km.

| ♿S | **Gâvres** | 12C4 |

Aire de la presqu'île de Gâvres, Boulevard de l'Océan, D158. **GPS:** n47,69583 w3,34778.

25 ⛺free ⚰€ 2 ⚑Ch. ☐ 01/01-31/12
Distance: 🚲100m.

Ⓒ Ⓢ Glomel 12C3
Etang du Coronc, Rue du Lac. **GPS:** n48,22052 w3,38972.⬆➡.

5 ⛺free ⚰⚑ Ch WC free. **Surface:** metalled. ☐ 01/01-31/12
Distance: ⛵on the spot 🚲on the spot 🛒bakery 150m.

Ⓢ Guidel 12C4
Guidel plage. GPS: n47,76640 w3,5258.⬆.

12 ⛺free ⚰€ 2/100liter ⚑Ch 🔌€ 2/1h 🗑. **Surface:** asphalted. ☐
01/01-31/12
Distance: ⛵150m.
Remarks: At lake.

Ⓢ Goulven 12B2
Aire Naturelle Ty Poas. GPS: n48,63109 w4,30833.⬆➡.

22 ⛺free ⚰⚑Ch 🚿free. **Surface:** metalled. ☐ 01/01-31/12
Remarks: Behind yachting school, max. 24h.

Ⓢ Guidel 12C4
Plage du Loc'h, D152, Guidel-Plage > Fort-Bloqué. **GPS:** n47,75052 w3,50654.
⬆➡.

FR

15 ⛺€ 5 + tourist tax ⚰€ 2 ⚑Ch 🔌€ 2 WC 🗑. 🧺 **Location:**
Comfortable, quit. **Surface:** grassy/metalled. ☐ 15/06-30/09
Distance: 🚲500m ⛵beach 200m 🛒500m.

Ⓢ Gueltas 12D3
Cité des Écureuils, D125. **GPS:** n48,09667 w2,80111.⬆➡.

20 ⛺free. **Surface:** sand.
Distance: ⛵on the spot.
Remarks: Behind Résidence Maéva.

Ⓢ Guidel 12C4
Arc-en-Ciel, ZA de Pen Mané. **GPS:** n47,80980 w3,4633.

10 ⛺free ⚰⚑Ch free. **Surface:** gravel.
Distance: ⛵200m.
Remarks: Nearby sports park.

Ⓢ Guichen 13A6
Le Boel, Pont Réan. **GPS:** n48,00221 w1,77336.⬆➡.

⛺⚰ service € 2, during opening hours ⚑Ch 🚿WC. ☐ 01/01-31/12

Ⓢ Guimiliau 12B2
Parking Salle Polyvalente, Rue des Bruyeres. **GPS:** n48,48676 w3,99665.⬆➡.

15 🛏free 🚰 🔌free. **Location:** Central, noisy. **Surface:** metalled. ⬛ 01/01-31/12
Distance: 🚶on the spot ⊗400m 🚲400m 🚌on the spot ✝on the spot.
Remarks: Max. 2 nights.

🔳S **Guingamp** 12C2
Place du Vally. **GPS:** n48,56024 w3,1489. ⬆➡.

🛏free 🚰 🔌Ch 🔌free. **Surface:** asphalted.
Distance: 🚶on the spot.
Remarks: Max. 24h.

🔳S **Guissény** 12B2
Rue de Plouguerneau. **GPS:** n48,63299 w4,41127. ⬆.

🛏free 🚰€ 2 🔌Ch. **Location:** Comfortable. **Surface:** gravel. ⬛ 01/01-31/12
Distance: 🚶on the spot 🏖beach 550m 🥖250m bakery.
Remarks: Coins available at the shops and town hall.

🔳S **Hillion** 12D2
Le Tertre Piquet, Lermot-plage. **GPS:** n48,53098 w2,66387. ⬆➡.

20 🛏free 🔌Ch WC free. **Surface:** grassy. ⬛ 01/01-31/12
Distance: 🏖sandy beach 100m.
Remarks: Beach parking.

🔳S **Hillion** 12D2
Rue Olivier Provost. **GPS:** n48,51743 w2,66772. ⬆.

7 🛏free 🚰 🔌Ch free. **Surface:** gravel. ⬛ 01/01-31/12
Distance: 🚶500m 🚌100m.

🔳S **Hirel** 13A4
D155. **GPS:** n48,60841 w1,82032. ⬆.

100 🛏€ 6 🚰€ 2/100liter 🔌Ch 🔌€ 2/55minutes. **Surface:** grassy.
Distance: 🚶700m 🌲200m.

🔳S **Huelgoat** 12C2
Place du Campiong-cars, Route du Fao, D769a. **GPS:** n48,36027 w3,75681. ⬆➡.

30 🛏free 🚰€ 5/10minutes 🔌Ch 🔌1h. **Location:** Rural, quit. **Surface:** metalled. ⬛ 01/01-31/12
Distance: 🚶500m 🌲on the spot 🚂on the spot ⊗500m 🚌500m 📺500m 🚲500m ✝500m.
Remarks: In front of campsite municipal, service 100m.

🔳 **Huelgoat** 12C2
Rue du Général de Gaulle. **GPS:** n48,36200 w3,75323. ⬆.

15 🛏free. **Surface:** metalled. ⬛ 01/01-31/12
Distance: 🚶100m 🌲on the spot ⊗100m 🚌100m.

🔳S **Janzé** 13B6
Aire du Hardier, D41. **GPS:** n47,97258 w1,53825.

FR

5 🚰free ⛽€ 2 🔧Ch. **Surface:** asphalted.

🏕️S | **Josselin** | 12D3

Josselin, Place St.Martin. **GPS:** n47,95639 w2,55056.

50 🚰free ⛽€ 2,50 🔧Ch WC. **Surface:** metalled. 🅿️ 01/01-31/12
Distance: 🛒300m N24 900m ⊗300m 🥖bakery 300m.
Remarks: Castle of Josselin 400m.

Tourist information Josselin:
ℹ️ Office de Tourisme, Place de la Congregation, www.paysdejosselin.com.City is dominated by the castle of Rohan.
Ⓜ️ Musée de Poupées, Château de Rohan.Private collection of antique dolls. 🅿️ 01/04-31/05, 01/10-31/10 Wed,Sa,Su 14-18h, 01/06-30/09 daily.

🏕️S | **Kerlouan** | 12B2

GPS: n48,66952 w4,36161.

🚰free ⛽€ 2 🔧Ch. **Surface:** grassy. 🅿️ 01/01-31/12
Remarks: Former campsite.

🏕️ | **Kerlouan** | 12B2

La Digue, La Digue. **GPS:** n48,66195 w4,37879. ⬆️

4 🚰free. **Location:** Isolated. **Surface:** gravel. 🅿️ 01/01-31/12
Distance: 🏊100m 🚲on the spot 🚶on the spot.

🏕️S | **La Chèze** | 12D3

Chemin d'Aliénor, Allée du 19 Mars 1962. **GPS:** n48,13419 w2,65787. ⬆️➡️

10 🚰free ⛽🔧Ch 🔧(6x)WC free. **Surface:** asphalted. 🅿️ 01/01-31/12
Distance: 🛒200m 🥖200m.
Remarks: Parking at small lake.

🏕️S | **La Martyre** | 12B2

Route de Ploudiry, D35. **GPS:** n48,44861 w4,15694. ⬆️

10 🚰free ⛽🔧Ch 🔧WC free. **Surface:** gravel. 🅿️ 01/01-31/12
Distance: 🛒100m ⊗100m 🥖100m.
Remarks: Nearby Maison du Plateau.

🏕️ | **La Roche-Bernard** | 12D4

Place du Dôme. **GPS:** n47,51753 w2,29733. ⬆️

>20 🚰free. **Surface:** asphalted. 🅿️ 01/01-31/12
Distance: 🛒50m ⊗100m 🥖50m.

🏕️S | **La Roche-Bernard** | 12D4

Halte Camping-car, Rue du Patis. **GPS:** n47,52012 w2,30466. ⬆️➡️

15 🚰€ 7,50, 1/7-22/8 € 9 ⛽🔧Ch 🔧€ 4 WC🔧. **Surface:** grassy. 🅿️ 02/04-16/09
Distance: 🛒100m 🏊50m 🚣50m ⊗100m 🥖100m.
Remarks: Next to campsite du Patis.

Tourist information La Roche-Bernard:
ℹ️ Small town especially known for the beautiful hanging bridge over the Vilaine river, 50m high and over 400m long.

🏕️S | **La Roche-Derrien** | 12C2

Rue du Jouet. **GPS:** n48,74696 w3,25976. ⬆️

12 ⬛€ 2 🚰 2 🗑 Ch 🧹 (6x). 🛒 **Location:** Rural, very simple, central, quit. **Surface:** gravel. 🅿 01/01-31/12
Distance: 🛒100m ⊗100m 🚶100m.
Remarks: In centre, next to bank Crédit Agricole.

Aire de Porspaul, Dir Beg ar Vir. **GPS:** n48,44667 w4,77722. ⬆➡.

50 ⬛free, 01/04-15/10 € 3,50, Jul/Aug + € 0,40/pp 🚰 € 2/20minutes 🗑 Ch 🗑 € 2/55minutes WC 🗑€ 1,60 🛁 € 3, dryer € 3,50. **Location:** Comfortable. **Surface:** grassy. 🅿 01/01-31/12
Distance: 🛒150m 🏖100m 🌊200m 🛒500m 🏊 on the spot 🚶 on the spot.
Remarks: Shower and washing machine Jul/Aug.

Rue du Calvaire. GPS: n48,44694 w4,25667. ⬆.

25 ⬛€ 5, incl. electricity 🚰€ 2 🗑 Ch 🧹 included 🛒. 🚐 **Location:** Comfortable. **Surface:** grassy/gravel. 🅿 01/01-31/12
Distance: 🛒500m 🏖river ⊗500m 🛒500m 🚶 on the spot.

P de Keravel, Rue du Manoir. **GPS:** n48,51015 w4,0758.

3 ⬛free 🚰 🗑 Ch free. **Surface:** asphalted. 🅿 01/01-31/12
Distance: 🛒on the spot ⊗on the spot 🛒100m 🏙centre.

Super U, Rue des Écoles. **GPS:** n48,00143 w4,34088. ⬆.

5 ⬛free 🚰€ 2/10minutes 🗑 Ch 🗑 € 2. **Location:** Rural. **Surface:** asphalted. 🅿 01/01-31/12
Distance: 🛒1km ⊗on the spot 🛒on the spot.
Remarks: Motorhome washing place.

Étang du Pas, Le Pas, D7. **GPS:** n48,34982 w2,90116. ⬆.

6 ⬛free 🗑 Ch WC free. **Surface:** asphalted/grassy. 🅿 01/04-31/10
Distance: 🏊on the spot 🚤on the spot.
Remarks: Parking at small lake.

Zone Lanveur, Place du Bouilleur de Cru. **GPS:** n47,83722 w3,16188. ⬆➡.

20 ⬛free 🚰 🗑 Ch free. **Surface:** metalled. 🅿 01/01-31/12
Distance: 🛒700m 🏍N24 300m.

Aire Fontaine Rouge. GPS: n48,55667 w4,50528. ⬆➡.

12 ⬛free 🚰 🗑 Ch WC.
Surface: metalled. 🅿 01/01-31/12
Distance: 🛒1km ⊗1,5km 🛒1,5km.
Remarks: D13/D11, from church dir Brest straight on, till end of dead end street.

Rue Haie Blanche. GPS: n48,57125 w4,52151.

FR

⏚free 🚰 🔧 Ch free. **Surface:** asphalted. ◐ 01/01-31/12
Distance: 🚶100m 🥖bakery 150m.
Remarks: In front of cemetery.

⏚ S | **Lanvallay** | 13A5
Rue du terrain des sports. **GPS:** n48,45420 w2,03028.

5 ⏚free 🚰€ 2 🔧Ch 🔌€ 2. **Surface:** asphalted. ◐ 01/01-31/12
Distance: 🚶50m.

⏚ | **Larmor-Baden** | 12D4
Route d'Auray. **GPS:** n47,58816 w2,89868. ⬆️➡️

3 ⏚free. **Surface:** asphalted. ◐ 01/01-31/12
Distance: 🚶50m 100m 🥖100m.

⏚ S | **Larmor-Plage** | 12C4
Parking les Pins, Rue des Pins. **GPS:** n47,70970 w3,3791.

4 ⏚free 🚰 🔧Ch WC free. **Surface:** asphalted. ◐ 01/01-31/12
Distance: 🏖50m 100m 🥖100m.
Remarks: Nearby plage de Toulhars, max. 72h.

⏚ S | **Le Conquet** 🏳️ | 12A2
Parking Parklec'H, Rue Général Leclerc. **GPS:** n48,36055 w4,7701. ⬆️

+10 ⏚free 🚰€ 2/100liter 🔧Ch 🔌€ 2/1h.
Surface: gravel.
◐ 01/01-31/12
Distance: 🚶200m 🏖beach 800m ⊗400m 🥖bakery 300m 🚲on the spot.

⏚ S | **Le Croisty** | 12C3
Aire de pique-nique, D132, Kergoff. **GPS:** n48,06510 w3,38144.

8 ⏚free 🚰€ 2 🔧Ch 🔌€ 2 WC. **Location:** Comfortable, isolated, quit.
Surface: asphalted. ◐ 01/01-31/12
Distance: 🚶1,5km 🏃on the spot.

⏚ S | **Le Folgoët** | 12B2
Parking Frepel, Route de Gorrékear. **GPS:** n48,56002 w4,33507. ⬆️➡️

30 ⏚free 🚰 🔧Ch 🛴free.
Surface: gravel/metalled. ◐ 01/01-31/12
Distance: 🚶on the spot ⊗100m 🥖100m.
Remarks: Nearby basilica.

⏚ S | **Le Trévoux** | 12C3
Rue des Sports. **GPS:** n47,89683 w3,64228.

⏚free 🚰 🔧Ch 🔌free. **Surface:** gravel. ◐ 01/01-31/12
Distance: 🚶on the spot.
Remarks: Max. 48h, nearby tennis-court.

⏚ S | **Le Vivier-sur-Mer** | 13A4
Rue de la Grève, D155. **GPS:** n48,60383 w1,7799. ⬆️➡️

FR

10 ⌇€5 🚰€ 2/100liter 🅲h🔌€ 2/1h. **Surface:** metalled. 🔲 01/01-31/12
Distance: 🚶200m 🛒on the spot ⊗on the spot 🍴on the spot.

| 🛏️S | Les Forges | 12D3 |

Place de l'Église, D117. **GPS:** n48,01820 w2,6482. ⬆️

5 ⌇free 🚰🍴 ✦WC free. **Surface:** metalled. 🔲 01/01-31/12
Distance: 🚶100m 🛒100m.

| 🛏️ | Lézardrieux | 12C2 |

Rue de l'Île à Bois. **GPS:** n48,83002 w3,08165. ⬆️

5 ⌇free. **Location:** Very simple, isolated, quit. **Surface:** gravel/sand. 🔲 01/01-31/12
Distance: 🚶Lézardrieux 6km 🛒50m 🍴on the spot.
Remarks: Max. 24h.

| 🛏️S | Lézardrieux | 12C2 |

Camping Municipal. GPS: n48,78021 w3,1147. ⬆️

4 ⌇€3 🚰€ 3,20 🅲h ✦WC 🔌€ 1,26. **Surface:** asphalted. 🔲 01/01-31/12
Distance: 🚶500m 🛒200m ⊗300m 🍴300m 🍴on the spot.

| 🛏️S | Liffré | 13B5 |

Intermarché. GPS: n48,22459 w1,50165. ⬆️➡️

⌇free 🚰Ch🔌free. **Surface:** asphalted. 🔲 01/01-31/12
Distance: ✏️300m 🍴on the spot.

| 🛏️S | Locmaria-Plouzané | 12B2 |

Plage de Portez, Rue de Portez, Porsmilin. **GPS:** n48,35501 w4,67269. ⬆️➡️

8 ⌇€ 4,40 🚰🍴Ch included. **Surface:** gravel. 🔲 01/01-31/12
Distance: 🚶3,5km 🛒beach 50m 🍴on the spot 🍴on the spot.
Remarks: To be paid at campsite.

| 🛏️S | Locmaria-Plouzané | 12B2 |

Zône détente Ty Izella, Rue de la Fontaine. **GPS:** n48,37306 w4,64306. ⬆️

12 ⌇free 🚰€ 2 🍴Ch🔌€ 2. **Location:** Quit. **Surface:** gravel. 🔲 01/01-31/12
Distance: 🚶100m ⊗250m 🍴250m.
Remarks: Coins at town hall.

| 🛏️S | Locmariaquer | 12C4 |

Aire de Pierres Plates, > Route des Plages. **GPS:** n47,55720 w2,9486. ⬆️➡️

±30 ⌇free. **Surface:** metalled. 🔲 01/01-31/12
Distance: 🛒beach 500m 🚌on the spot.
Remarks: 500m from 'Les Pierres Plates', max. 24h.

| 🛏️S | Locmariaquer | 12C4 |

Camping La Falaise. GPS: n47,55639 w2,94139. ⬆️➡️
🚰€ 2 🍴Ch.
Remarks: 6/6/11 during inspection service point out of order.

Tourist information Locmariaquer:
🛈 Office de Tourisme, Rue de la Victoire, www.ot-locmariaquer.com. Port city

with many megalithics, signed dolmen.

ℹ Office de Tourisme, Place de la Mairie. Historical town.

Locminé   12D3
Rue Laennec / rue du Pont Person. **GPS:** n47,88788 w2,83174.

free Ch free.
Distance: N24 1,4km.
Remarks: Max. 48h.

Loctudy   12B3
Plage des Sables Blancs, Rue du Beau Rivage. **GPS:** n47,79883 w4,19739.

3 free. **Location:** Rural, very simple.
Surface: asphalted. 01/01-31/12
Distance: 4km beach 80m.
Remarks: Beach parking.

Locmiquelic   12C4
Port de Ste. Catherine, Quai Rallier du Baty. **GPS:** n47,72364 w3,34958.

free. **Surface:** asphalted.
Distance: on the spot.
Remarks: Max. 1 night.

Loudéac   12D3
Parking de la Gare, Boulevard de la Gare. **GPS:** n48,18058 w2,76277.

3 free Ch free. **Surface:** metalled. 01/01-31/12
Distance: 600m 50m 200m 200m.

Locqueltas   12D4
Rue de la Fontaine. **GPS:** n47,75841 w2,76901.

Maël-Carhaix   12C3
Place de l'école, Route de Rostrenen. **GPS:** n48,28344 w3,42148.

5 free € 2 Ch WC. **Surface:** asphalted. 01/01-31/12
Distance: 100m 100m 100m.
Remarks: Coins at town hall.

6 free Ch free (4x)€ 3,05.
Surface: grassy.
01/01-31/12
Distance: 100m 600m 100m 100m.
Remarks: Max. 24h, coins at Bar-Tabac, 18 Place de la Mairie, town hall.

Malansac   12D4
Rue Saint Fiacre. **GPS:** n47,67820 w2,29942.

5 free Ch free. **Surface:** grassy.
Distance: 100m 100m 100m.

Locronan   12B3
Rue du Prieuré. **GPS:** n48,09811 w4,21245.

10 free, 01/06-15/10 € 5/24h € 2 Ch € 2 WC.
Surface: grassy/sand.
01/01-31/12
Distance: 50m.
Tourist information Locronan:

Malestroit   12D4
Chemin des Tanneurs. **GPS:** n47,80772 w2,37885.

12 🛏free ⚡🔧 Ch free. **Surface:** gravel/metalled. 🅿 01/01-31/12
Distance: 🚲500m ⊗on the spot ⊗350m.

🛏free ⚡🔧 Ch free. **Surface:** asphalted.
Distance: 🚲150m 🛢150m.

🅂🆂 Malestroit 〰🎣🏕 12D4
Rue de Narvik. **GPS:** n47,80896 w2,37591. ⬆➡.

🅂🆂 Mellé 13B5
Rue Rouviel. **GPS:** n48,48919 w1,18814. ⬆.

🛏free ⚡🔧 Ch free. **Surface:** asphalted.
Distance: 🚲1,5km ⊗600m 🚲600m ⊗2km 🛢1km.

6 🛏free ⚡🔧 Ch WC free. **Surface:** metalled.
Distance: 🚲200m 🛢200m.
Remarks: Nearby football ground, max. 48h.

🅂🆂 Malestroit 〰🎣🏕 12D4
Chemin de l'Écluse. **GPS:** n47,81250 w2,38197. ⬆➡.

🅂🆂 Meslin 12D2
Allée des Loisirs, D28. **GPS:** n48,44363 w2,56994. ⬆.

12 🛏free. **Surface:** metalled/sand. 🅿 01/01-31/12
Distance: 🚲100m ⊗on the spot 🚲on the spot ⊗100m 🛢100m.
Remarks: Max. 48h.

10 🛏free ⚡🔧 Ch free. **Surface:** metalled.
Distance: ⊗bar/crêperie 50m 🛢50m.

🅂🆂 Marzan ✝ 12D4
Rue de la Source. **GPS:** n47,54023 w2,32383. ⬆.

🅂 Moëlan-sur-Mer 12C3
Rue de Beg Tal Gward. **GPS:** n47,77749 w3,64404. ⬆➡.

+20 🛏free ⚡🔧 Ch WC free. **Surface:** asphalted.
Distance: 🚲50m 🛢20m.

4 🛏free. **Location:** Isolated, quit. **Surface:** asphalted. 🅿 01/01-31/12
Distance: 🚲Moëlan 5km ⊗sea 50m.

🅂🆂 Mauron 12D3
Rue de la Libération. **GPS:** n48,08472 w2,2833.

🅲🆂 Moncontour 12D3
Camping la Tourelle, Rue François Lorant. **GPS:** n48,35271 w2,63719. ⬆➡.

4 🍴€2 🚰 € 2 ♨Ch🚽€ 2/55minutes 🛏. **Surface:** gravel. ⏱ 01/01-31/12
Distance: 🛒1,5km ⊗1,5km ♨1,5km.
Remarks: Max. 48h.

| 📷S | Montertelot 🛶 | 12D3 |
Lieu-dit le Quai. **GPS:** n47,88155 w2,4239.⬆.

10 🍴free 🚰 ♨Chfree. **Surface:** metalled/sand.
Distance: 🛒200m ⚓on the spot ⊗200m.
Remarks: Along canal of Nantes à Brest.

| 📷S | Morlaix 🚻 🛶 | 12C2 |
Rue de Brest. **GPS:** n48,57422 w3,8316.⬆.

5 🍴free 🚰 ♨Chfree. **Location:** Urban, central, noisy. **Surface:** asphalted.
⏱ 01/01-31/12
Distance: 🛒on the spot 🚌on the spot ⊗200m 🏧100m 🚲200m 🛴on the spot 🧍on the spot.

| 📷S | Neulliac | 12D3 |
Rue des Deux Croix, D767. **GPS:** n48,12812 w2,98552.⬆➡.

3 🍴free 🚰 € 2 ♨Ch🚽€ 2. **Surface:** asphalted.
Distance: 🛒300m ⊗300m.

| 📷S | Névez | 12B3 |
Rue de Port Manech, Impasse du Stade. **GPS:** n47,81560 w3,7894.⬆.

20 🍴free 🚰 € 2 ♨Ch🚽€ 2. **Surface:** asphalted. ⏱ 01/01-31/12
Remarks: Parking next to stadium, max. 24h.

| 📷 | Névez | 12B3 |
Plage de Dourveil, Rue de Dourveil, D1. **GPS:** n47,79407 w3,8101.
4 🍴free. **Surface:** sand.
Remarks: No camping activity.

| 📷 | Névez | 12B3 |
Plage de Tahiti, Kerstalen. **GPS:** n47,79287 w3,79011.⬆.
20 🍴free. **Surface:** sand. ⏱ 01/01-31/12
Distance: 🏊beach 150m.
Remarks: Beach parking, max. 24h.

| 📷 | Névez | 12B3 |
Route de la Plage. **GPS:** n47,80499 w3,74261.⬆.
5 🍴free. **Surface:** asphalted. ⏱ 01/01-31/12
Distance: 🏊50m.
Remarks: Max. 24h.

| 📷 | Névez | 12B3 |
Rue des Iles, Raguénez. **GPS:** n47,78908 w3,80174.⬆.
10 🍴free. **Surface:** asphalted. ⏱ 01/01-31/12
Distance: 🏊sea 10m, beach 150m.
Remarks: Max. 24h.

| 📷S | Paimpol | 12D2 |
Parking Pierre Loti, Rue Pierre Loti. **GPS:** n48,78404 w3,0463.

15 🍴free, summer € 5 🚰 € 3,30/100liter ♨Ch🚽€ 3,30/55minutes.
Surface: gravel/sand. ⏱ 01/01-31/12
Distance: 🛒on the spot 🏊1km 🚌400m 🏧100m 🚲on the spot 🧍on the spot.
Remarks: Service 100m.

| 📷S | Paimpol | 12D2 |
Rue Pierre Loti/ D7. **GPS:** n48,78278 w3,0475.⬆.

15 🍴free 🚰 € 3,30/100liter ♨Ch🚽€ 3,30/55minutes 🛏. **Location:**
Urban, central, noisy. **Surface:** gravel. ⏱ 01/01-31/12
Distance: 🛒on the spot 🏊1km 🚌300m ⊗300m 🏧300m 🚲300m 🧍300m.
Remarks: Max. 48h. Access via roundabout Champ de Foire, 250m of harbour.

Paimpol 12D2
Parking de Goas Plat, Rue de Goas Plat. **GPS:** n48,77535 w3,04009.⬆.

6 🚐free. **Location:** Urban, very simple, central, quit.
 Surface: asphalted.
 Distance: 🏙centre 500m 🏖2km ⊗500m 🛒500m.
 Remarks: Max. 24h.

Paimpont 12D3
Rue de l'Enchanteur Merlin. **GPS:** n48,02286 w2,17128.⬆.

10 🚐free 🚰€ 2/10minutes 🗲Ch. **Surface:** gravel.

Pénestin 12D4
Allée du Grand Pré. **GPS:** n47,48111 w2,47361.⬆➡.

20 🚐free, € 5,30/night + € 0,20/pp 🚰€ 2/100liter 🗲Ch 🔌€ 2/1h.
 Surface: asphalted.
 Distance: 🏙500m 🏖1,5km ⊗500m.
 Remarks: Max. 48h, coins at Office de Tourisme, check in all aires in Pénestin: Office de tourisme; Bar-PMU Le Narval, Rue Calvaire; Café O 20 100 O, Port de Tréhiguier.

Pénestin 12D4
Alée de la Poudrantais. **GPS:** n47,46681 w2,48716.⬆.

4 🚐free, € 5,30/night + € 0,20/pp. **Surface:** gravel/metalled.
 Distance: 🏖50m.
 Remarks: Max. 48h.

Pénestin 12D4
Allée de Camaret. **GPS:** n47,49010 w2,49078.⬆.

4 🚐free, € 5,30/night + € 0,20/pp. **Surface:** gravel.
 Distance: 🏖100m.
 Remarks: Max. 48h.

Pénestin 12D4
Allée du Palandrin. **GPS:** n47,44955 w2,46351.⬆.

6 🚐free, € 5,30/night + € 0,20/pp. **Surface:** grassy/sand.
 Distance: 🏖50m.
 Remarks: Max. 48h.

Pénestin 12D4
Plage de la Source, Allée du Maro. **GPS:** n47,48158 w2,49005.⬆.

10 🚐free, € 5,30/night + € 0,20/pp. **Surface:** grassy/metalled.
 Distance: 🏖300m.
 Remarks: Max. 48h.

Pénestin 12D4
Plage du Palandrin, L'Isle du Clos Parc, Kerséguin. **GPS:** n47,45000 w2,46417.⬆➡.

6 🚐€ 5,30 + € 0,20/pp tourist tax. **Location:** Very simple, isolated. **Surface:** grassy. ⬛ 01/01-31/12
 Distance: 🏖sandy beach ⊗1km.
 Remarks: Pay at tourist office.

Pénestin 12D4
Route du Loguy. **GPS:** n47,49050 w2,49667.⬆.

20 🛏free, € 5,30/night + € 0,20/pp. **Surface:** grassy/metalled.
Distance: ⚓150m.
Remarks: Max. 48h.

5 🛏free 🚰 € 2 ⚑Ch🛁€ 2 WC. **Location:** Quit. **Surface:** asphalted. ⭘ 01/01-31/12
Distance: 🚿100m ⚓on the spot 🚐on the spot ⊗50m 🛒250m 🚲on the spot ⚓on the spot.
Remarks: Nearby port.

Penmarch   12B3
Aire de Port du Bouc, Route du Ster Kérity. **GPS:** n47,79981 w4,34794. ⬆.

Piré-sur-Seiche   13B6
Rue de Boistrudan. **GPS:** n48,00719 w1,42871.
15 🛏free 🚰⚑Chfree. **Surface:** metalled.
Distance: 🚿300m 🛒300m.
Remarks: To fish lake.

Plabennec   12B2
Rue de l'Aber. **GPS:** n48,50155 w4,43374. ⬆.

10 🛏€4/19-9h. 🐾 **Location:** Rural.
Surface: grassy. ⭘ 01/01-31/12
Distance: 🚿1,5km ⚓50m ⊗1km 🛒5km.

Penmarch   12B3
Aire du Viben, Rue de la Plage. **GPS:** n47,82390 w4,3708. ⬆.

5 🛏free 🚰⚑Chfree. **Location:** Very simple. **Surface:** metalled. ⭘ 01/01-31/12 🚲on the spot.
Remarks: Parking at small lake.

Planguenoual   12D2
Bien y Vient. GPS: n48,53447 w2,54506. ⬆➡.
6 🛏€5 🚰 € 2. **Surface:** grassy. ⭘ 01/01-31/12

Planguenoual   12D2
Ferme Gesbert, D786. **GPS:** n48,54883 w2,5556. ⬆➡.

30 🛏9-19h free, 19-9h € 4. 🐾 **Location:** Rural, quit. **Surface:** metalled. ⭘ 01/01-31/12
Distance: 🚿bakery 1km 🛒900m 🚐on the spot ⚓on the spot.

Penmarch   12B3
Aire de Kerameil, Rue du Pont Nevez. **GPS:** n47,81369 w4,36077. ⬆.

6 🛏free 🚰⚑Chfree. **Surface:** grassy/gravel. ⭘ 01/01-31/12
Distance: 🚿1km ⊗1km 🛒1km.

Plémet   12D3
Rue de l'Étang, D16. **GPS:** n48,17897 w2,58918. ➡.

🚰 € 2/10minutes ⚑Ch. **Location:** Rural.
Surface: . ⭘ 01/01-31/12
Distance: 🚿3km.
Remarks: Only overnight stays 19-9h.

Penzé   12B2
Rue du Dossen. **GPS:** n48,59811 w3,93439.

15 🛏free 🚰⚑Ch🛁free. **Surface:** gravel. ⭘ 01/01-31/12

Remarks: Parking at small lake.

S | **Pléneuf-Val-André** | 12D2

Port de Plaisance de Dahouët, Bassin des Salines, Chemin du Bignon. **GPS:** n48,57528 w2,56639. ⬆️➡️.

45 🗑️ € 3,60/24h, tourist tax € 0,20/pp 🚰 € 2 Ch 🔲 € 2 WC 🔲 € 2 📶 € 4/h. **Surface:** gravel. 🅿️ 01/01-31/12
Distance: 🏖️300m.

S | **Plérin** | 12D2

Sous la Tour, Rue de la Tour, D24. **GPS:** n48,53146 w2,72483. ⬆️.

20 🗑️free 🚰 Ch free. **Surface:** gravel. 🅿️ 01/01-31/12
Distance: 🏊on the spot ⊗300m 🛒1km.

S | **Pleslin-Trigavou** | 13A4

D28. **GPS:** n48,53631 w2,05009. ⬆️.

20 🗑️free 🚰 Ch free. **Surface:** asphalted.
Distance: 🏖️on the spot.
Remarks: Cycle and hiking routes: voie verte, Circuit des Mégalithes.

S | **Plessala** | 12D3

Rue de l'Étang. **GPS:** n48,27394 w2,62427. ⬆️➡️.

12 🗑️free 🚰 Ch free. **Surface:** gravel. 🅿️ 01/01-31/12
Distance: 🏖️200m 🎣on the spot.
Remarks: At fish lake, fishing permit available.

S | **Plestin-les-Grèves** | 12C2

Voie Communale de l'Armorique. **GPS:** n48,68157 w3,63411. ⬆️.

6 🗑️free. **Surface:** unpaved. 🅿️ 01/01-31/12
Distance: 🏖️3km 🏊50m ⊗2km 🎣on the spot.
Remarks: Beach parking.

Plestin-les-Grèves | 12C2

Route de la Corniche. **GPS:** n48,67235 w3,63602. ⬆️.

6 🗑️free. **Location:** Rural, very simple, quit. **Surface:** grassy/sand. 🅿️ 01/01-31/12
Distance: 🏖️1km 🏊on the spot ⊗300m 🛒Lidl 2km.
Remarks: Max. 24h.

S | **Plestin-les-Grèves** | 12C2

Rue de Guergay. **GPS:** n48,66232 w3,62562.
🚰 € 2/10minutes Ch 🔲 € 2/1h.
Remarks: Motorhome washing place.

Pleubian | 12C2

Port Béni. **GPS:** n48,84834 w3,17053. ⬆️.

4 🗑️free. **Location:** Rural, isolated, quit.
Surface: asphalted. 🅿️ 01/01-31/12
Distance: 🏖️Pleubian 2,5km 🏊on the spot ⊗2,5km 🎣on the spot.
Remarks: Max. 24h.

Pleubian | 12C2

Rue de Kermagen, Kermagen. **GPS:** n48,85667 w3,14194. ⬆️.

4 🗑️free. **Surface:** grassy. 🅿️ 01/01-31/12
Distance: 🏖️Pleubian 1,6km 🏊beach 100m 🎣on the spot.
Remarks: Max. 24h.

Pleubian — 12C2
Rue de Pen Lan, Lanéros. **GPS**: n48,85760 w3,07883. ⬆️

4 🛏 free. **Surface:** asphalted.
Distance: 🚶Pleubian 5,5km ⚓on the spot ⚡on the spot.
Remarks: Max. 24h.

Pleumeur-Bodou — 12C2
Parking de Toul ar Stang, Rue de Toul ar Stang, Ile Grande. **GPS**: n48,79868 w3,58342. ⬆️➡️

6 🛏 € 5/night ⚡€ 2/10minutes 🧺Ch 🚰€ 2/1h. 🚲
Location: Rural, quit.
Surface: grassy. ⏹ 01/01-31/12
Distance: 🚶Pleumeur-Bodu 6km ⚓sandy beach 150m ⊗150m ⚡on the spot.

Pleumeur-Bodou — 12C2
Cosmopolis-Parc Scientifique, Route du Radome. **GPS**: n48,78472 w3,52694. ⬆️

20 🛏 free ⚡🧺ChWC 🗑. **Surface:** gravel/sand. ⏹ 01/01-31/12
Distance: 🚶1km ⚓1km ⊗on the spot ⚡on the spot.

Plévenon — 12D2
Parking Cap Fréhel. GPS: n48,68174 w2,31811.

40 🛏 free, 1/6-30/9 € 2. **Surface:** metalled.
Distance: ⚓50m.

Ploemeur — 12C4
Rue Louis Lessart. **GPS**: n47,73790 w3,4314.
7 🛏 free ⚡🧺Chfree. **Surface:** asphalted. ⏹ 01/01-31/12
Remarks: Parking in the centre, max. 24h.

Ploemeur — 12C4
Aire du Courégant, D152, Boulevard de l'Atlantique. **GPS**: n47,71111 w3,47138.
7 🛏 free. **Surface:** asphalted. ⏹ Easter-01/11
Distance: ⚓200m ⊗on the spot.
Remarks: Only overnight stays 20-10h.

Ploemeur — 12C4
Golf Ploemeur, D152, Boulevard de l'Atlantique. **GPS**: n47,72316 w3,48156. ⬆️➡️
10 🛏 free. **Surface:** gravel. ⏹ 01/01-31/12
Distance: 🚶Ploemeur 5km 🛣N165 10km ⚓beach 300m 🍽1,8km.

Plogoff — 12A3
Aire Naturelle Kerguidy Izella, Rue Guillaume Pennamen. **GPS**: n48,03694 w4,68139. ⬆️

30 🛏€ 12 🚰🧺Ch ⚡WC 🗑 📶included. **Location:** Comfortable. **Surface:** grassy. ⏹ 01/01-31/12
Distance: 🚶2km.
Remarks: 9><20h.

Plogoff — 12A3
Parking de l'Eglise, Rue Cleder cap Sizum. **GPS**: n48,03752 w4,6657. ⬆️➡️

4 🛏 free ⚡€ 2/10minutes 🧺Ch. **Location:** Rural, comfortable. **Surface:** asphalted. ⏹ 01/01-31/12
Distance: 🚶centre.

Plogoff — 12A3
Aire de la Pointe du Raz, Route des Langoustiers. **GPS**: n48,03651 w4,7173. ⬆️

40 🛏€ 15-20. **Location:** Rural. **Surface:** metalled. ⏹ 01/01-31/12
Distance: 🚶3km ⚓50m.

Plogoff — 12A3
Parking du Stade, Rue du 19 Mars 1962. **GPS**: n48,03245 w4,66316. ⬆️

FR

15 ⌇free. **Location:** Rural, very simple. **Surface:** grassy/metalled. ⏻ 01/01-31/12

Distance: ⚊on the spot ⊗450m ⚑450m bakery.

⬚S **Plomelin** 12B3

Plomelin, Rue Hent Keramer. **GPS:** n47,93410 w4,1515.⬆

5 ⌇free ⚐€ 2/10minutes ⬚Ch⬚. **Location:** Rural, quit. **Surface:** asphalted. ⏻ 01/01-31/12

Remarks: Parking sports park, max. 24h.

⬚S **Plonévez-Porzay** 12B3

Plonévez-Porzay, Rue des Eglantines. **GPS:** n48,12469 w4,22414.⬆

15 ⌇free ⚐€ 2/10minutes ⬚Ch⬚. **Location:** Rural, comfortable. **Surface:** grassy. ⏻ 01/01-31/12

Distance: ⚊600m ⚑450m bakery + Spar.

⬚ **Plonévez-Porzay** 12B3

Kervel Izella. **GPS:** n48,11570 w4,28065.⬆

10 ⌇free. **Location:** Rural, very simple. **Surface:** grassy/sand. ⏻ 01/01-31/12

Distance: ⚊5,5km ⚓50m ⚐on the spot.

Remarks: Max 48h, beautiful view, beach parking.

⬚S **Plouarzel** 12A2

Aire de camping-car de Ruscumunoc, Route de Ruscumunoc. **GPS:** n48,42232 w4,78486.⬆➡

⌇free, 15/5-15/9 € 3,60 ⚐€ 2,20/10minutes ⬚Ch⬚€ 2,20/50minutes ⬚.⬚⚐ **Location:** Comfortable, quit. **Surface:** grassy. ⏻ 01/01-31/12

Distance: ⚊3km ⚓100m.

⬚ **Ploubalay** 13A4

Rue des Ormelets. **GPS:** n48,58057 w2,14524.⬆

3 ⌇free ⚐⬚Chfree. **Surface:** asphalted. ⏻ 01/01-31/12

Distance: ⊗100m ⚑500m. **Remarks:** D768 Dinard-Lamballe, at roundabout dir D768 Dinard-Lamballe, after 30m left.

⬚ **Ploubazlanec** ⚐⚐ 12D2

Pointe l'Arcouest, Route de l'Embarcadère. **GPS:** n48,82102 w3,01948.⬆

20 ⌇free, 30/06-30/09 € 6/24h. **Location:** Very simple, isolated, quit. **Surface:** grassy. ⏻ 01/01-31/12

Distance: ⚊2km ⚓50m ⚐on the spot.

⬚ **Plouescat** 12B2

Rue de Pen an Théven. **GPS:** n48,65902 w4,21863.⬆

6 ⌇free. **Surface:** metalled. ⏻ 01/01-31/12

Distance: ⚊3,5km ⚓100m.

⬚S **Plouescat** 12B2

Intermarché, La Rocade-Kerchapalain. **GPS:** n48,65083 w4,18444.⬆➡

FR

4 ⌇free ⚒€ 2 ⬛Ch⬛€ 2. **Location:** Comfortable. **Surface:** asphalted. ⬛ 01/01-31/12
Distance: ⬛500m ⊗600m ⬛on the spot ⬛on the spot.
Remarks: Parking supermarket.

⬛S **Plouézec** 12D2
Place du 19 mars 1962. **GPS:** n48,74788 w2,9853. ⬆.

6 ⌇free. **Surface:** asphalted. ⬛ 01/01-31/12
Remarks: Servicepoint at camping municipal.

⬛S **Plougasnou** 🌊⚓⛵🐚 12C2
Parking de la Métairie, Rue Charles de Gaulle. **GPS:** n48,69404 w3,79209. ⬆.

7 ⌇free ⚒€ 2/10minutes ⬛Ch⬛€ 2/1h WC. **Location:** Rural. **Surface:** gravel. ⬛ 01/01-31/12
Distance: ⬛on the spot ⬛sandy beach 1,4km ⊗200m ⬛250m bakery ⬛on the spot ⬛on the spot.
Remarks: Tue-morning market.

⬛S **Plougasnou** 🌊⚓⛵🐚 12C2
Rue des Grands Viviers, Le Diben. **GPS:** n48,70811 w3,82731. ⬆.

7 ⌇free ⚒€ 2 ⬛Ch⬛. **Location:** Rural, isolated, quit. **Surface:** asphalted. ⬛ 01/01-31/12
Distance: ⬛300m ⬛on the spot ⬛on the spot ⊗300m ⬛on the spot.
Remarks: Coins available at town hall.

⬛S **Plougasnou** 🌊⚓⛵🐚 12C2
Parking de la Baie, Rue du Grand Large, Primel-Trégastel. **GPS:** n48,71201 w3,81621. ⬆➡.

7 ⌇free. **Location:** Rural, central, quit.
Surface: gravel. ⬛ 01/01-31/12
Distance: ⬛50m.
Remarks: Max. 48h.

⬛S **Plougastel-Daoulas** 12B2
Rue de la Fontaine Blanche. **GPS:** n48,37111 w4,36428.

15 ⌇free ⚒ ⬛Ch ⬛ ⬛free. **Surface:** asphalted. ⬛ 15/05-15/10
Distance: ⬛450m ⊗450m ⬛450m.
Remarks: Parking at sports grounds.

⬛S **Plougonvelin** 12A2
Rue de Bertheaume. **GPS:** n48,33792 w4,70742. ⬆➡.

100 ⌇€6 ⚒ ⬛Ch ⬛ WC included. ⬛ **Location:** Comfortable, quit.
Surface: grassy/sand. ⬛ 01/01-31/12
Distance: ⬛1km ⬛beach 650m.

⬛S **Plougonvelin** 12A2
Intermarché, Rue du Stade. **GPS:** n48,34245 w4,72248.

⌇€6 ⚒€ 2/100liter ⬛Ch⬛€ 1/1h ⬛€ 5. ⬛⬛
Surface: asphalted.
Distance: ⬛on the spot.

⬛S **Plouguerneau** ⛵ 12B2
Lilia. **GPS:** n48,61891 w4,55341. ⬆➡.

10 ⌇free 🚰€ 4/10minutes ♨Ch☷€ 4/55minutes. **Location:** Comfortable. **Surface:** asphalted. 🅾 01/01-31/12
Distance: 🚶400m ⌇850m 🚰450m.

| 🅂 | **Plouha** 12D2 |

Plage de Palus, Route du Palus. **GPS**: n48,67667 w2,88556.⬆

20 ⌇free 🚰€ 2/10minutes ♨Ch☷€ 2/1h WC. **Location:** Rural, isolated, quit. **Surface:** grassy. 🅾 01/03-31/10
Distance: 🚶3km ⌇sandy/pebbled beach 100m ⊗50m ⚷on the spot.
Remarks: Max. 3 days, baker every morning.

| 🅂 | **Plouhinec** 12C4 |

Kervelue. **GPS**: n47,68116 w3,23633.⬆

45 ⌇€ 8 🚰♨Ch✎ (16x) WC.▯ 📇 **Surface:** metalled. 🅾 01/01-31/12
Distance: 🚶Plouhinec 2,5km.

| 🅂 | **Ploumoguer** 12A2 |

Rue Huon de Kermadec, D28. **GPS**: n48,40507 w4,72492.⬆➡

30 ⌇free, July-Aug € 3 🚰€ 2/80liter ♨Ch☷€ 2/45minutes WC▯€ 2 🅾€ 4, dryer € 2,30. **Surface:** metalled. 🅾 01/04-30/11
Distance: 🚶200m ⊗200m 🚰200m 🅾on the spot.
Remarks: Next to stadium, max. 48h, coins at town hall, supermarket, baker and Tabac.

| 🅂 | **Plouvorn** 12B2 |

Plan d'Eau de Lanorgant. **GPS**: n48,57722 w4,03056.⬆➡

15 ⌇free 🚰€ 2 ♨Ch☷€ 2 WC. **Location:** Quit. **Surface:** metalled. 🅾 01/01-31/12
Distance: 🚶500m ⌇100m ▬100m ⊗500m 🚰500m.
Remarks: Parking at small lake.

| 🅂 | **Pont-Aven** 12C3 |

Rue Louis Lomenech. **GPS**: n47,85401 w3,74333.

20 ⌇free 🚰€ 2,45 ♨Ch☷€ 2,45.
Surface: asphalted. 🅾 01/01-31/12
Distance: 🚶450m ⊗450m.
Remarks: Parking near stadium Sinquin, coins at Office de Tourisme (D783).

| 🅂 | **Pont-Aven** 12C3 |

Rue des Abbès Tanguy. **GPS**: n47,85646 w3,75203.
⌇free. **Surface:** asphalted. 🅾 01/01-31/12
Distance: 🚶400m.

| 🅂 | **Pont-Croix** 12B3 |

Place de la Métairie. **GPS**: n48,04207 w4,48549.⬆

40 ⌇free 🚰€ 2/10minutes ♨Ch☷.▯ **Location:** Urban. **Surface:** metalled. 🅾 01/01-31/12
Distance: 🚶10min ⊗on the spot.
Remarks: Thu (market).

Tourist information Pont-Croix:
ℹ Office de Tourisme, Rue Laënnec, www.chez.com/pontcroix/.Built as an anfiteatro. A number well-known artists stayed there.
⚷ 🅾 Thu.

| 🅂 | **Pont-l'Abbé** 12B3 |

Parking de la Gare, Rue de la Gare. **GPS**: n47,87070 w4,22506.⬆

5 ⌷free ⚲ ⬛Ch ⬛free. **Location:** Urban. **Surface:** asphalted. ◼ 01/01-31/12
Distance: ⟐on the spot.

35 ⌷free ⚲€ 2,10 ⬛Ch ⬛€ 2,10 ⬗. **Location:** Comfortable, quit. **Surface:** grassy. ◼ 01/01-31/12
Distance: ⟐on the spot ⟱350m ⊗200m ⟱200m.
Remarks: Max. 3 days.

		Pont-l'Abbé	12B3

Leclerc, Route de Saint Jean Trolimont. **GPS:** n47,86390 w4,2367. ⬆.

		Primelin	12A3

Camping Municipal de Kermaléro, Route de l'Océan. **GPS:** n48,02550 w4,61821.

13 ⌷free ⚲€ 2 ⬛Ch ⬛€ 2 ⬗. **Location:** Urban. **Surface:** asphalted. ◼ 01/01-31/12
Distance: ⟐on the spot ⟱on the spot.
Remarks: At supermarket, centre.

15 ⌷free ⚲€ 2 ⬛Ch ⬛€ 2. **Surface:** metalled. ◼ 01/01-31/12

		Port-Louis	12C4

Aire de la Côte Rouge, D781 Port-Louis > Riantec. **GPS:** n47,70873 w3,34295.

		Priziac	12C3

Base de Loisirs du Lac du Bel Air, Etang du Bel Air. **GPS:** n48,06183 w3,41132.

18 ⌷€ 5/24h, 01/06-15/09 € 10/24h ⚲ ⬛Ch ⬛included. ⬛ ⬗ **Surface:** asphalted. ◼ 01/01-31/12
Distance: ⟱on the spot ⟱on the spot.

⌷€ 5,50 ⚲ ⬛Ch ⬛included.
Distance: ⊗300m.

		Quiberon ⬆⬗	12C4

		Port-Louis	12C4

Aire des Remparts, Promenade Henri François Buffet. **GPS:** n47,70496 w3,35602.

Rue de Port Kerné. **GPS:** n47,49165 w3,13941. ⬆➜.

20 ⌷€ 5/24h, 01/06-15/09 € 10/24h ⚲ ⬛Chincluded. ⬛ ⬗ ◼ 01/01-31/12
Remarks: In front of campsite.

140 ⌷€ 5/24h ⚲€ 1/30liter ⬛Ch ⬛ ⬗ ⬛ ⬗ **Surface:** asphalted. ◼ 01/01-31/12, service 01/04-15/10
Distance: ⟐2km ⟱sea 250m.
Remarks: Next to campsite municipal, max. 72h, seaview.

Tourist information Quiberon:
🛈 Office de Tourisme, 14, rue de Verdun, www.quiberon.com. Lively bathing resort with boulevard and sandy beaches.

		Portsall	12B2

Aire camping-cars Kerros, Rue de Porsguen. **GPS:** n48,56583 w4,69944. ⬆➜.

		Quimperlé	12C3

Aire Saint Nicolas, Rue du Viaduc. **GPS:** n47,86640 w3,54334. ⬆.

FR

6 🅂free 🚰🔧Ch 🧹free. **Surface:** metalled. ⬛ 01/01-31/12

🅂S **Quintin** 12D2

Place du Champ de Foire. **GPS:** n48,40056 w2,90222. ⬆️➡️.

🅂free 🚰🔧Chfree. **Surface:** asphalted. ⬛ 01/01-31/12
Distance: 🛒on the spot ⚓on the spot.
Remarks: Near the lake.

Tourist information Quintin:
⛺ ⬛ Tue-morning.

🅂S **Redon** 20A1

Quai Robert Surcouf. **GPS:** n47,64510 w2,0897. ⬆️➡️.

10 🅂free 🚰🔧Chfree. **Surface:** asphalted. ⬛ 01/01-31/12
Distance: 🛒500m ⚓on the spot 🚲100m ⊗200m 🍴200m.
Remarks: In front of Bureau du Port de Plaisance.

Tourist information Redon:
👁 Manoir de l'Automobile de Loheac.Car collection: Ferrari, Lamborghini, Porsche, Maserati.

🅂S **Rennes** 13A5

Rue du Professeur Maurice Audin. **GPS:** n48,13531 w1,64542. ⬆️.

5 🅂free 🚰€ 2/100liter 🔧Ch🚰€ 2/1h 📶€ 1/30minutes. **Surface:** asphalted. ⬛ 01/01-31/12
Remarks: In park, near entrance of campsite, max. 48h.

Tourist information Rennes:
ℹ️ Office de Tourisme, 11, rue Saint Yves, www.tourisme-rennes.com/.University town with a historical centre.

Ⓜ️ Musée de Bretagne.Regional museum.
⛺ ⬛ Tue-Sa.

🅂S **Riantec** 12C4

Route de Plouhinec. **GPS:** n47,71111 w3,29889.

🅂🚰€ 4 🔧. ⬛ 01/01-31/12
Remarks: Parking lake.

🅿️ **Rochefort-en-Terre** 12D4

Parking des Grées. **GPS:** n47,69975 w2,33384. ⬆️.

>100 🅂€ 2/24h. **Surface:** gravel. ⬛ 01/01-31/12
Distance: 🛒200m.

🅂 **Rohan** 12D3

Port de Plaisance, Rue Saint-Gouvry. **GPS:** n48,07139 w2,755. ⬆️.

6 🅂free. **Surface:** asphalted. ⬛ 01/01-31/12
Distance: 🛒500m ⚓on the spot ⊗500m.
Remarks: At the Nantes-Brest Canal.

🅂S **Romagné** 13B5

Allée des Prunus, D812. **GPS:** n48,34409 w1,27415.

5 🅂free 🚰🔧Ch WCfree. **Surface:** metalled. ⬛ 01/01-31/12
Distance: 🛒100m 🚲1,7km 🍴200m 🛒50m.

🅂S **Roscoff** 12B2

Route du Laber. **GPS:** n48,71215 w3,99918. ⬆️.

30 ⬛free 🚰 🔧Chfree. **Location:** Isolated. **Surface:** asphalted. ⬤ 01/01-31/12
Distance: 🚲2km.
Remarks: Service 200m.

Tourist information Roscoff:
ℹ Office de Tourisme, 46, rue Gambetta, www.roscoff-tourisme.com.Seaside resort and former pirates town.
⛺ ⬤ Wed.

43 ⬛€ 5/24h 🚰 € 2/10minutes 🔧Ch 🔌 € 2/55minutes 🧺.🚐 🗑
Surface: asphalted. ⬤ 01/01-31/12
Distance: 🚲1km 🏊1,5km.
Remarks: Max. 48h.

�S	Saint-Rivoal	12B2

D42. **GPS:** n48,34930 w3,99782.⬆.
6 ⬛free 🔧Ch 🔌 free. **Surface:** grassy/metalled. ⬤ 01/01-31/12
Distance: 🚲200m.

🚻🚿S	Santec ⬤	12B2

Bistrot à Crèpes, Rue de Méchouroux. **GPS:** n48,70102 w4,03868.

🚿S	Rostrenen	12C3

Rue Rosa l'Hénaff, D23. **GPS:** n48,23318 w3,32019.⬆.

6 ⬛free 🚰 € 2/100liter 🔧Ch 🔌 € 2/1h. **Surface:** asphalted. ⬤ 01/01-31/12
Distance: 🚊100m.
Remarks: Coins at office de tourisme, town hall, maison de presse, tabac.

15 ⬛€ 3 🚰 € 2 🔧Ch 🔧included WC 🔊. **Location:** Quit. **Surface:** grassy. ⬤ 01/01-31/12
Distance: 🏊La plage du Staol 50 m ⊗on the spot 🚊800m.

🚿S	Sains	13B4

Rue du puits Rimoult. **GPS:** n48,55305 w1,58603.⬆➡.

🚿S	Sarzeau	12D4

Banastère, Rue du Palud Bihan. **GPS:** n47,51444 w2,66778.⬆➡.

10 ⬛€ 5 🚰 🔧Chfree. **Surface:** grassy/metalled. ⬤ 01/01-31/12
Distance: 🚲100m ⊗150m 🚊150m.
Remarks: Via RN176.

10 ⬛€ 5/18-8h 🚰 € 2 🔧Ch 🔌 € 2.
Surface: metalled. ⬤ 01/01-31/12
Distance: 🏊on the spot.

🚿S	Saint-Gelven	12C3

Rue de l'Ecole, D95. **GPS:** n48,22513 w3,09535.⬆.

🚿S	Sarzeau	12D4

Rue de Brénudel. **GPS:** n47,52969 w2,7598.⬆.

10 ⬛free 🚰 🔧Chfree. **Surface:** concrete. ⬤ 01/01-31/12

🚿S	Saint-Pierre-Quiberon 〰	12C4

Rue du Stade. **GPS:** n47,51160 w3,13903.⬆➡.

20 ⬛€ 5/24h 🚰 € 2 🔧Ch 🔌 € 2. **Surface:** asphalted. ⬤ 01/01-31/12 ⬤ school hours (8-16h).

🚿S	Sarzeau	12D4

Rue du Port St.Jacques, Kerbodo. **GPS:** n47,48906 w2,79297.⬆➡.

10 🏕€ 5/18-8h ☀🔌 Ch 🔲 free WC ⍾€ 2. **Surface:** asphalted. ⬤ 01/01-31/12
Distance: 🏖500m 🚉100m 🛒200m.
Remarks: Nearby port, max. 48h.

🏕S **Sarzeau** 12D4
Rue du Raker/Rue du Pont Neui, Plage du Rohaliguen. **GPS**: n47,49769 w2,76748. ⬆️➡️

10 🏕€ 5/18-8h ☀🔌 Ch WC free.
Surface: metalled. ⬤ 01/01-31/12
Distance: 🏖on the spot.

🏕S **Sarzeau** 12D4
Rue du Stang, St.Colombier. **GPS**: n47,54665 w2,72151. ⬆️➡️

5 🏕€ 5/18-8h ☀🔌 Ch free. **Surface:** asphalted.
Distance: 🚶St.Colombier 100m ⊗50m 🛒50m.

🏕 **Sarzeau** 12D4
Pointe de Penvins, Route de la Chapelle. **GPS**: n47,49472 w2,68139. ⬆️➡️

15 🏕€ 5. **Surface:** asphalted. ⬤ 01/01-31/12
Distance: 🏖on the spot.
Remarks: Follow Pointe de Penvins.

🏕S **Scaër** 12C3
Rue Louis Pasteur. **GPS**: n48,02774 w3,6951. ⬆️
🏕free ☀€ 2/10minutes 🔌 Ch 🔲€ 2/55minutes. **Surface:** gravel.
Distance: 🚶500m.
Remarks: Max. 72h, shady, coins at camping municipal.

🏕S **Sérent** 12D4
Du Pont Salmon, Rue du Général De Gaule,. **GPS**: n47,82445 w2,50194. ⬆️➡️

10 🏕free ☀€ 3 🔌 Ch 🔲. **Surface:** asphalted. ⬤ 01/01-31/12
Distance: 🚶400m ⊗400m 🛒400m.

🏕S **St.Aignan (Morbihan)** 12C3
Place de l'Église. **GPS**: n48,18306 w3,01361. ⬆️

6 🏕free ☀🔌 Ch ☀ WC free. **Surface:** metalled. ⬤ 01/01-31/12
Remarks: Square behind the church.

🏕S **St.Aubin d'Aubigné** 13A5
Rue de Rennes. **GPS**: n48,26147 w1,60621. ⬆️

5 🏕free ☀🔌 Ch WC free. **Surface:** asphalted. ⬤ 01/01-31/12
Distance: 🚶on the spot ⊗100m 🛒on the spot 🚌on the spot.

🏕S **St.Barnabé** 12D3
Place du Vieux Chêne, Rue Pierre Loti. **GPS**: n48,13672 w2,70146. ⬆️

10 🏕free ☀🔌 Ch free. **Surface:** gravel. ⬤ 01/01-31/12
Distance: 🚶200m 🛒bakery 50m.

🏕S **St.Benoit-des-Ondes** 13A4
Rue Bord de Mer. **GPS**: n48,61681 w1,84714.

FR

10 🛏free ⛽€ 3/80liter 🚿Ch 🚽€ 3/15minutes. **Surface:** asphalted.
🖼️S St.Brice-en-Coglès 13B5
Rue de Normandie, D102. **GPS:** n48,41150 w1,36283. ⬆️.

20 🛏free ⛽€ 3 🚿Ch 🚽€ 3 WC. **Location:** Quit. **Surface:** gravel/metalled. 🅾️ 01/05-31/10
Distance: 🛒100m 🏖️on the spot 🍽️on the spot ⊗300m 🚰300m.
Remarks: Nearby recreation area.
🖼️ St.Gildas-de Rhuys 12D4
Route de la Baie d'Abraham. **GPS:** n47,51359 w2,84627.

8 🛏free ⛽€ 2/100liter 🚿Ch 🚽€ 2/55minutes WC. **Surface:** asphalted/metalled. 🅾️ 01/01-31/12
Distance: 🛒300m ⊗500m 🚰400m 🛒300m.
🖼️S St.Carreuc 12D2
Rue de la Lande, D27. **GPS:** n48,40300 w2,73923. ⬆️.

20 🛏free. **Surface:** unpaved.
Distance: 🛒1,5km 🏖️beach 50m.
Remarks: Nearby beach des Goh-Velins, max. 48h.
🖼️S St.Gildas-de Rhuys 12D4
Camping municipal de Kervert, Route du Rohu. **GPS:** n47,52238 w2,85803.

12 🛏free ⛽€ 2/10minutes 🚿Ch 🚽€ 2/55minutes 🚿. **Surface:** grassy/gravel. 🅾️ 01/01-31/12
Distance: 🛒300m 🍽️on the spot.
Remarks: At Etang-du-Plessis, max. 24h.
🖼️ St.Cast-le-Guildo 12D2
Bois Bras. GPS: n48,61083 w2,26806. ⬆️.

20 🛏€ 6/24h ⛽€ 2 🚿Ch 🚿.🛒🚿 **Surface:** grassy/metalled. 🅾️ 01/01-31/12
Distance: 🛒4km 🏖️50m ⊗400m 🚰4km.
🖼️S St.Guyomard 12D4
Route de Bohal, D112. **GPS:** n47,78166 w2,51188. ⬆️➡️.

🛏free. **Location:** Very simple, isolated.
Surface: . 🅾️ 01/01-31/12
Distance: 🛒2,5km 🚲2,5km 🛒Intermarché 500m.
🖼️S St.Derrien 12B2
GPS: n48,54760 w4,18114.

20 🛏€ 5/night ⛽€ 3 🚿Ch 🚽€ 3. **Surface:** asphalted.
Distance: 🛒300m ⊗100m.
Remarks: Behind church, check in at town hall.
🖼️ St.Jacut-de-la-Mer 13A4
Rue de la Manchette. **GPS:** n48,58969 w2,18947. ⬆️.

26 🛏 € 5. **Surface:** grassy/gravel.
Distance: 🚶1km 🏊500m.
Remarks: Baker at 8am.

| S | St.Jacut-de-la-Mer | 13A4 |
Rue de Dinan. **GPS:** n48,58727 w2,19027.
🚰€ 2 🗑Ch🔋 € 2.

| S | St.Malo 🏰🌊 | 13A4 |
Les Iltots, Avenue de la Guimorais, Rothéneuf. **GPS:** n48,68109 w1,96348.

50 🛏 € 5, 01/07-31/08 € 4 🚰🗑Ch 🔌 included. **Surface:** grassy. 🅿
15/04-30/09
Distance: 🏊sandy beach 100m 🏪200m.

| S | St.Malo 🏰🌊 | 13A4 |
Parking Paul Féval, Rue Paul Féval. **GPS:** n48,64341 w1,99385.

200 🛏 € 7,40, 19.00-09.00h free 🚰 € 2 🗑Ch.
Surface: gravel.
🅿 holidays + 01/07-07/09
Distance: 🏪800m 🚌 Free bus to centre.
Remarks: 01/07-03/09 free shuttle bus to centre, 9am-12pm.

Tourist information St.Malo:
ℹ Office de Tourisme, Esplanade St-Vincent, www.saint-malo-tourisme.com.
City with restored centre.
🏛✖ Château.Castle, 14/15th century, historical museum. 🅿 10-12h, 14-18h.
🎫 € 4,50.
✖ Fort National.Fort designed by Vauban. At ebb accessoe by foot. 🎫 € 5.

| S | St.Pol-de-Léon | 12B2 |
Quai de Pempoul. **GPS:** n48,68361 w3,97083.⬆

30 🛏 free 🚰 € 2 🗑Ch🔋 € 2 WC.
Surface: metalled. 🅿 01/01-31/12
Distance: 🚶800m 🏊on the spot 🛒on the spot ⊗800m 🏪800m.
Remarks: At the sea.

| S | St.Pol-de-Léon | 12B2 |
Rue Hervé Mesguen. **GPS:** n48,67919 w3,99749.⬆

8 🛏 free 🚰 € 2/10minutes 🗑Ch🔋 € 2/55minutes. **Location:** Comfortable.
Surface: asphalted. 🅿 01/01-31/12
Distance: 🛒on the spot.
Remarks: In front of supermarket Leclerc.

| S | St.Rénan | 12B2 |
Route de l'Aber. **GPS:** n48,43878 w4,63063.

10 🛏 free 🚰 € 2 🗑Ch🔋 € 2 🚿. **Surface:** gravel. 🅿 01/01-31/12
Remarks: Jul/Aug max. 48h.

| S | St.Servais | 12B2 |
Cité Yan d'Argent. **GPS:** n48,50984 w4,15434.

10 🛏 free 🚰 🗑Ch 🔌 free WC. **Location:** Very simple, quit. **Surface:**
gravel/metalled. 🅿 01/01-31/12
Distance: 🚶200m ⊗200m 🏪200m.

| S | St.Thégonnec | 12B2 |
Park an Iliz, D118. **GPS:** n48,52215 w3,94637.⬆

25 ⌇free ⌇⌇ Ch ⌇free. **Location:** Urban, comfortable, central, quit.
Surface: gravel. ⬤ 01/01-31/12
Distance: ⌇on the spot ⊗150m ⌇150m ⌇on the spot ⌇on the spot.
Remarks: Coins available at the shops.
Tourist information St.Thégonnec:
⌇ ⬛ Fri.
⊗ Crêperie Steredenn, Rue de la Gare 6.

| | | Sulniac | 12D4 |

Salle des Fêtes, Rue des Écoles. **GPS:** n47,67756 w2,56642. ⬆➡.

15 ⌇free ⌇⌇ Ch free. **Surface:** grassy/sand. ⬤ 01/01-31/12
Distance: ⌇400m ⌇bakery 500m.

| | | Taden | 13A4 |

Salle Neuville, Rue de la Robardais. **GPS:** n48,47251 w2,02203. ⬆.

20 ⌇free ⌇⌇€ 2 ⌇Ch ⌇€ 2.
Surface: gravel. ⬤ 01/01-31/12
Distance: ⌇700m ⊗100m ⌇100m ⌇500m.

| | | Theix | 12D4 |

Allée de Noyalo. **GPS:** n47,62726 w2,66183.

4 ⌇free ⌇⌇ Ch free. **Surface:** asphalted.
Distance: ⌇500m ⊗500m ⌇500m.

| | | Tinténiac | 13A5 |

Quai de la Donac. **GPS:** n48,33168 w1,83202. ⬆.

10 ⌇free ⌇⌇ Ch free. **Surface:** grassy/gravel. ⬤ 01/01-31/12
Distance: ⌇500m ⌇Along river ⊗100m ⌇550m.

| | | Trébeurden | 12C2 |

Route de Lannion, D65. **GPS:** n48,76711 w3,5514. ⬆.

5 ⌇free ⌇⌇€ 2,05 ⌇Ch ⌇€ 2,05 ⌇. **Location:** Rural, comfortable,
central, quit. **Surface:** asphalted.
Distance: ⌇on the spot ⌇1,4km ⊗1,5km ⌇1km bakery, Intermarché
1,5km.

| | | Trébeurden | 12C2 |

Plage Goas-Treiz, Chemin de Crec'h Hellen. **GPS:** n48,78231 w3,57714. ⬆➡.

35 ⌇€ 5, Jul/Oct € 10. ⌇ **Location:** Rural, isolated. **Surface:** unpaved. ⬤
01/01-31/12
Distance: ⌇Trébeurden 2km ⌇sandy beach 80m ⊗2km ⌇on the spot.
Remarks: Beach parking.
Tourist information Trébeurden:
⬛ Office de Tourisme, Place de Crec'h Hery, www.ville-trebeurden.fr.st.Bathing
resort.

| | | Trégastel | 12C2 |

Rue de Poul-Palud. **GPS:** n48,82437 w3,49874. ⬆.

56 ⌇€ 4, 01/03-15/11 € 7,50 ⌇⌇ Ch free. ⌇⌇ **Location:** Rural,
comfortable, isolated, quit. **Surface:** asphalted. ⬤ 01/01-31/12
Distance: ⌇1km ⊗1km ⌇Super U ⌇on the spot.
Remarks: Max. 5 nights, Aug max. 3 nights.

| | | Tréguier | 12C2 |

Boulevard Anatole le Braz. **GPS:** n48,78932 w3,23144.

20 🛏free 🚱 Chfree. **Surface:** asphalted. 📅 01/01-31/12
Distance: 🛒100m 🏊20m ⛽20m 🍴100m 🚉100m.

<table>
<tr><td>S</td><td>Tréguier</td><td>12C2</td></tr>
</table>

Super U, Boulevard Jean Guehenno. **GPS:** n48,77892 w3,23346.⬆️.
🚰€ 1/10minutes 🚱Ch. 📅 01/01-31/12
Distance: ⊗200m 🚉on the spot.

<table>
<tr><td>🚱S</td><td>Trégunc</td><td>12B3</td></tr>
</table>

Parking Quentel, Place de la Mairie, Rue de Pont-Aven. **GPS:** n47,85472
w3,85139.⬆️.

6 🛏free 🚰€ 3 🚱Ch💶€ 3 🧹. **Surface:** metalled. 📅 01/01-31/12
Remarks: Parking behind town hall, max. 24h.

<table>
<tr><td>🚱</td><td>Trégunc</td><td>12B3</td></tr>
</table>

Parking de Pouldohan. GPS: n47,84435 w3,88832.
5 🛏free. **Surface:** grassy.

<table>
<tr><td>🚱</td><td>Trégunc</td><td>12B3</td></tr>
</table>

Plage Ster Greich. GPS: n47,84918 w3,88656.⬆️.
6 🛏free. **Surface:** sand. 📅 01/01-31/12
Remarks: Max. 24h.

<table>
<tr><td>🚱</td><td>Trégunc</td><td>12B3</td></tr>
</table>

Route de Kerlaëron. GPS: n47,82964 w3,8872.
5 🛏free. **Surface:** sand. 📅 01/01-31/12
Remarks: Max. 24h.

<table>
<tr><td>🚱</td><td>Trégunc</td><td>12B3</td></tr>
</table>

Rue de Porzh Breign. GPS: n47,84079 w3,89736.⬆️.
6 🛏free. **Surface:** asphalted. 📅 01/01-31/12
Remarks: Max. 24h.

<table>
<tr><td>🛒S</td><td>Trégunc</td><td>12B3</td></tr>
</table>

Supermarché Casino, Route de Concarneau, D783. **GPS:** n47,85633 w3,86343.
4 🛏free 🚰€ 2 🚱Ch💶€ 2 🧹. **Surface:** asphalted.

<table>
<tr><td></td><td>Tremblay</td><td>13B5</td></tr>
</table>

Route de Fougères. GPS: n48,42328 w1,47095.⬆️.

🛏free 🚰€ 2/10minutes 💶€ 2/55minutes. **Surface:** asphalted. 📅 01/01-
31/12
Distance: 🛒400m 🚉200m.

<table>
<tr><td>🚱S</td><td>Trémuson</td><td>12D2</td></tr>
</table>

Aire du Buchon, Rue de Brest, D712. **GPS:** n48,52250 w2,85278.

5 🛏free 🚰🚱Chfree. **Surface:** asphalted. 📅 01/01-31/12
Distance: ⊗50m 🚉500m.
Remarks: Max. 48h. RN12 exit La Barricade (from dir Brest) or exit Aéroport
(from dir Rennes).

<table>
<tr><td>🚱S</td><td>Vannes</td><td>12D4</td></tr>
</table>

Camping-car Parc, Avenue du Maréchal Juin. **GPS:** n47,63283 w2,77996.⬆️.

33 🛏€ 12/24h 🚰🚱Chincluded 🧹€ 4 📶.
Surface: asphalted.
📅 01/01-31/12
Remarks: In front of campsite Conleau, Note: access only after buying entrance
(3 formulas) via www.campingcarpark.com (wifi available).

Tourist information Vannes:
ℹ️ Office de Tourisme, 1, rue Thiers, www.tourisme-vannes.com.The old district
is surrounded by ramparts with gates and parks with historical wash places.
Ⓜ️ Château Gaillard.Archeological regional museum.
✝️ Cathédrale St Pierre.

Pays de la Loire

<table>
<tr><td>🚱</td><td>Angers</td><td>20C1</td></tr>
</table>

Parking Rochefoucault, Boulevard Arago. **GPS:** n47,47756 w0,55708.

🛏free. **Surface:** asphalted. 📅 01/01-31/12 ⚫ Nov.
Distance: 🚲2,2km.

<table>
<tr><td>S</td><td>Angers</td><td>20C1</td></tr>
</table>

Rue Olivier-Couffon. GPS: n47,46639 w0,56553.⬆️.
🚰🚱Chfree.

Tourist information Angers:
ℹ️ Office de Tourisme, 7, Place Kennedy, www.angers-tourisme.com.City with
historical centre, formerly the capital of ***Anjou.
👁 Haras National du Lion d'Angers.National stud-farm. 📅 15/04-11/09 daily,
12/09-14/04 Sa-Su 10.30h, 14.30h, 16h.
🏰 Château d'Angers.Fortified castle, museum for contemporary art. 📅 10-
17.30h. 🎫 € 6.

<table>
<tr><td>🚱S</td><td>Angrie</td><td>20B1</td></tr>
</table>

Route du Vieux Bourg. GPS: n47,57176 w0,97312.⬆️➡️.
10 🛏free 🚰🚱Chfree. **Surface:** gravel/metalled.

Remarks: Max. 48h.

Arnage 13D6

GPS: n47,93035 e0,18418.

2 free € 2 Ch . **Location:** Urban, quit. **Surface:** asphalted. 01/01-31/12
Distance: 250m on the spot 500m on the spot.

Assérac 12D4

Camping-Car Park de la Baie, Ker Avelo. **GPS:** n47,42446 w2,44688.
10 € 12 Ch WC included. **Location:** Rural, comfortable, quit. **Surface:** metalled. 01/01-31/12
Distance: Assérac 5km sandy beach 350m.

Assérac 12D4

Chemin de la Baie des Mulets. **GPS:** n47,42556 w2,45528.

5 free WC. **Surface:** grassy. 01/01-31/12
Distance: 50m 100m 100m 200m 200m.

Assérac 12D4

Route de la Grande Isle. **GPS:** n47,43111 w2,45194.

free WC. **Surface:** metalled.
Distance: 1km 300m 300m 2km 2km.

Aubigné-sur-Layon 20C2

Rue de 17 mars 1962. **GPS:** n47,21167 w0,46383.

3 free Ch free. **Surface:** metalled. 01/01-31/12
Distance: 100m.

Averton 13D5

Étang des Perles. **GPS:** n48,34744 w0,24468.

10 free € 2 Ch WC. **Location:** Rural. **Surface:** gravel. 01/01-31/12
Distance: lake on the spot on the spot on the spot.

Batz-sur-Mer 12D5

Route de la Govelle. **GPS:** n47,26747 w2,4537.

8 free € 2 Ch € 2 WC. **Surface:** metalled. 01/01-31/12
Distance: 1,5km 100m 100m 1,5km 50m.
Remarks: Max. 48h.

Baugé 20D1

Chemin du Pont des Fées. **GPS:** n47,53886 w0,09637.
10 free € 3/20minutes Ch € 3/20minutes.
Surface: gravel.

Beauvoir-sur-Mer 12D5

Rue de Nantes. **GPS:** n46,91685 w2,0465.

24 free, overnight stay € 5 € 2,50/10minutes Ch €
2,50/15minutes WC . **Surface:** asphalted. 01/01-31/12
Distance: 400m 800m 800m.

Belleville-sur-Vie 20A3

Rue des Écoliers. **GPS:** n46,78160 w1,42875.

15 free. **Surface:** gravel. 01/01-31/12
Distance: 500m 500m 200m.
Remarks: Near Salle des Fêtes.

Benet 20C4

Rue de la Gare. **GPS:** n46,36896 w0,59482.

FR

10 ⌂free ⌁ ⚑Ch WC free. **Surface:** asphalted.
Distance: 🚶300m ⊗300m 🛒on the spot 🥖50m.

| 🅂 | Blain | 20A1 |

Place Jollan de Clerville, Rue Victor Schoelcher. **GPS:** n47,47444 w1,76139.⬆️.

30 ⌂free ⌁ ⚑Ch free. **Surface:** gravel. 🚻 01/01-31/12
Distance: ⊗100m 🛒100m.

| 🅂 | Blaison-Gohier | 21A1 |

Rue de Thibaut de Blaison. **GPS:** n47,39923 e0,37515. ⬆️➡️.

5 ⌂free ⌁ ⚑Ch free. **Surface:** asphalted. 🚻 01/01-31/12
Distance: 🚶on the spot ⊗200m 🛒200m.

| 🅂 | Bouchemaine | 20C1 |

Rue Chevrière. **GPS:** n47,41913 w0,61117.⬆️.
40 ⌂free, 01/04-31/10 € 8 ⌁ 0,50/50liter ⚑Ch ⚡€ 2,50 🔌. **Surface:** grassy/gravel. 🚻 01/01-31/12
Distance: 🥖50m.
Remarks: Former campsite, along the river Maine, bread-service.

| 🅂 | Bourgneuf-en-Retz | 20A2 |

D758. **GPS:** n47,04028 w1,95704.⬆️.

10 ⌂free ⌁ ⚑Ch WC free. **Surface:** gravel. 🚻 01/01-31/12
Distance: 🚶300m 🚲200m ⊗300m 🛒300m.
Remarks: Parking office de tourisme, max. 48h.

| 🅂 | Boussay | 20B2 |

Place des Marronniers. **GPS:** n47,04240 w1,18648.⬆️➡️.

4 ⌂free ⌁ € 2 ⚑Ch ⚡€ 2. **Surface:** asphalted. 🚻 01/01-31/12
Distance: 🚶200m ⊗200m 🛒200m.
Remarks: Max. 48h, coins at mairie/poste.

| 🅂 | Briollay | 20C1 |

Plage de Briollay. **GPS:** n47,56766 w0,50733.⬆️.
10 ⌂free ⌁ ⚑Ch free. **Surface:** grassy/gravel. 🚻 01/01-31/12
Remarks: Along Sarthe River, closed when frosty and high water.

Tourist information Briollay:
ℹ️ Syndicat d'Initiative, 6 rue de la Mairie. Small historical place in the Loire-valley.

| 🅂 | Brissac-Quincé | 20C1 |

Rue de l'Aubance. **GPS:** n47,35465 w0,4463.⬆️➡️.

2 ⌂free ⌁ ⚑Ch. **Surface:** asphalted. 🚻 01/01-31/12
Distance: 🚶300m ⊗300m 🛒300m.

| 🅂 | Chailland | 13C5 |

Coccimarket. **GPS:** n48,22139 w0,86583.⬆️➡️.

4 ⌂free ⌁ ⚑Ch free. **Location:** Rural, very simple. **Surface:** asphalted. 🚻 01/01-31/12
Distance: 🚶300m ⊗300m 🛒on the spot.
Remarks: Max. 24h.

| 🅂 | Chaille-les-Marais | 20B4 |

Rue du 8 Mai 1945. **GPS:** n46,39228 w1,02127.⬆️.

20 ⌂free ⌁ € 3 ⚑Ch.
Surface: grassy. 🚻 01/01-31/12 ⬛ Thu-morning.
Distance: ⊗100m 🛒300m 🥖50m.

FR

Remarks: At fire-station and sports park.

🚐S **Challans** 20A3

Parking du Viaud Marais. **GPS:** n46,85027 w1,8742. ↑→

15 🗑free ⛽🚰 Ch free. **Surface:** asphalted. 🅾 01/01-31/12
Distance: 🚶1km ⊗500m 🛒500m 🚌100m.
Remarks: Max. 3 days.

🚐S **Chalonnes-sur-Loire** 20C1

Avenue de la gare. **GPS:** n47,34961 w0,74847. ↑

15 🗑free ⛽🚰 Ch free. **Surface:** forest soil. 🅾 01/01-31/12
Distance: 🚶1km ⊗1km 🛒on the spot.
Remarks: Parking nearby caveau the dégustation and swimming pool.

🚐S **Chambretaud** 20B3

Aire des Diamants, Rue Notre Dame. **GPS:** n46,92300 w0,9717. →

5 🗑free ⛽€ 2 🚰Ch WC. **Surface:** asphalted. 🅾 01/01-31/12
Distance: 🚶1km ⚓5km ⊗on the spot 🛒1km.

🚐S **Champtocé-sur-Loire** 20C1

Rue de la Hutte. **GPS:** n47,41143 w0,86958. ↑→

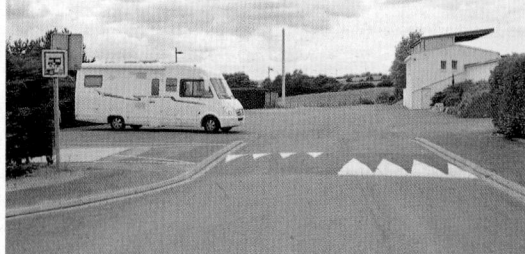

8 🗑free ⛽🚰 Ch free. **Surface:** asphalted. 🅾 01/01-31/12
Distance: 🚶300m ⚓5,7km ⊗400m 🛒400m.
Remarks: At stadium.

🚐S **Champtoceaux** 20B1

Parking Champalud, Place de Niederheimbach. **GPS:** n47,33816 w1,2649. ↑→

5 🗑free ⛽🚰Ch ⚓€ 3/24h WC.
Surface: asphalted. 🅾 01/01-31/12
Distance: 🚶150m ⚓23km.
Remarks: Square behind the church, max. 48h.

🍴S **Champtoceaux** 20B1

Le Port du Moulin, Le Cul du Moulin, D751. **GPS:** n47,33913 w1,27445. ↑

3 🗑free WC free. **Surface:** metalled. 🅾 01/01-31/12
Distance: 🚶1,5km ⚓on the spot 🛒on the spot ⊗on the spot 🛒1,5km.
Remarks: Along Dordogne river, max. 48h.

🚐S **Changé** 13C6

Parking du plan d'eau du Port, Rue du Bac. **GPS:** n48,10083 w0,78556. ↑

10 🗑free ⛽🚰Ch free. **Location:** Urban. **Surface:** gravel/sand. 🅾 01/01-31/12
Distance: ⚓5km 🛒800m.
Remarks: Along the Mayenne river.

🚐S **Chantonnay** 20B3

Rue de l'Arc en Ciel. **GPS:** n46,68754 w1,04104. ↑→

5 🗑free ⛽€ 2 🚰Ch €2. **Surface:** asphalted. 🅾 01/01-31/12
Distance: 🚶1km ⊗500m 🛒1km.
Remarks: Next to sports fields.

🚐S **Chanzeaux** 20C2

Aire de Ploizeau, D121. **GPS:** n47,25548 w0,63848. ↑

6 🛒free 🚰€ 2/100liter 🚽Ch. **Surface:** metalled. ⬛ 01/01-31/12
Distance: 🛒1km 🛒on the spot ⊗1km 🚽1km.

🛒Ⓢ   **Château-d'Olonne**   20A3
Rue des Plesses. **GPS:** n46,49132 w1,74293.⬆.
20 🛒€ 6/night 🚰€ 2/6minutes 🚽Ch 🔌€ 3/10minutes. **Surface:**
asphalted. ⬛ 01/01-31/12
Distance: 🚽500m.

🛒Ⓢ   **Château-d'Olonne**   20A3
Rue des Plesses. **GPS:** n46,49132 w1,74293.⬆.
20 🛒€ 6/night 🚰€ 2/6minutes 🚽Ch 🔌€ 3/10minutes. **Surface:**
asphalted. ⬛ 01/01-31/12
Distance: 🚽500m.

🛒   **Château-Gontier** 〰🏕🛶   13C6
Quai-du-Docteur Lefevre. **GPS:** n47,82450 w0,70206. ⬆ .

30 🛒free. **Location:** Urban, central.
Surface: asphalted. ⬛ 01/01-31/12
Distance: 🛒200m 🛒on the spot ⊗50m.
Remarks: Along the Mayenne river.
Tourist information Château-Gontier:
ℹ️ Office de Tourisme, Péniche l'Elan, Quai d'Alsace, www.sud-mayenne.com.
City on the Mayenne river, place for watersports.

🛒Ⓢ   **Chavagne-en-Paillers**   20B3
Place des Arcades. **GPS:** n46,89083 w1,24917.⬆➡.

3 🛒free 🚰€ 2/100liter 🚽Ch 🔌€ 2/55minutes. **Surface:** asphalted. ⬛
01/01-31/12
Distance: 🛒300m ⊗50m 🚽100m 🗑300m.
Remarks: Coins at Office de Tourisme.

🛒Ⓢ   **Chavagnes les Eaux**   20C2
Place de la Mairie. **GPS:** n47,27024 w0,45437.⬆➡.

3 🛒free 🚰🚽Ch free. **Surface:** metalled. ⬛ 01/01-31/12
Distance: 🛒on the spot 🚽150m.
Remarks: Behind church.

🛒Ⓢ   **Chênehutte-Trèves-Cunault**   20D2
Rue Beauregard, D751, Cunault. **GPS:** n47,32685 e0,19459.⬆➡.

40 🛒free 🚰€ 3/100liter 🚽Ch 🔌€ 3/6h 🧺. **Surface:** grassy. ⬛ 01/01-
31/12
Distance: 🛒500m ⊗500m 🚽500m.

🛒Ⓢ   **Chenillé-Changé**   20C1
Le Pin, D78. **GPS:** n47,69919 w0,66693.⬆.
8 🛒free 🚰€ 2,80 🚽Ch. **Surface:** gravel. ⬛ 01/01-31/12
Remarks: Coins at cafe.

🛒Ⓢ   **Coëx**   20A3
Rue des Goélettes. **GPS:** n46,69667 w1,76361.

4 🛒free 🚰€ 2 🚽Ch 🔌€ 2. **Surface:** asphalted. ⬛ 01/01-31/12
Distance: 🛒200m ⊗500m 🚽500m.
Remarks: Max. 48h, coins available at office de tourisme.

🛒Ⓢ   **Combrée** 🍴   20B1
Rue de Bretagne, Bel-Air. **GPS:** n47,71281 w0,9989.
🛒free 🚰🚽Ch WC free. **Surface:** unpaved. ⬛ 01/01-31/12

🛒   **Combrée** 🍴   20B1
D203. **GPS:** n47,70321 w1,02755.⬆.
🛒free. **Surface:** asphalted. ⬛ 01/01-31/12
Distance: 🛒200m.
Remarks: Behind tennis-court.

🛒Ⓢ   **Concourson-sur-Layon**   20C2
Aire de Repos, D960. **GPS:** n47,17405 w0,34317.➡.

FR

10 ⛅free ⟶ € 2 ⛿Ch WC. **Surface:** asphalted. ⬤ 01/01-31/12
Distance: 📍400m ⊗400m 🛒400m.

| 🛏S | **Dampierre-sur-Loire** | 20D2 |

L'Aigrette, Route de Montsoreau. **GPS:** n47,24157 w0,0232.⬆️.

40 ⛅free ⟶ ⛿Ch WC. **Surface:** forest soil. ⬤ 01/04-02/11
Distance: 📍on the spot ⊗on the spot 🛒on the spot.
Remarks: On the river Loire.

| 🛏S | **Deux-Evailles** | 13C5 |

Site de la Fenderie, Champ de Vigne, D129. **GPS:** n48,20203 w0,52018.➡️.

20 ⛅free ⟶ € 2 ⛿Ch € 2 WC. **Location:** Rural, comfortable, quit.
Surface: grassy/gravel. ⬤ 01/01-31/12
Distance: 📍1km ⛱20m ⟶20m ⊗20m 🛒5km Montsurs 🚶on the spot.
Remarks: Coins at Auberge.

| 🛏S | **Doué-la-Fontaine** | 20C2 |

Rue Jean Gaschet. **GPS:** n47,18280 w0,25742.
3 ⛅free ⟶ ⛿Ch free.

| 🛏S | **Durtal** | 20D1 |

Rue Beausite. **GPS:** n47,67139 w0,2406.⬆️.
2 ⛅free ⟶ € 2 ⛿Ch ➕ € 2. **Surface:** gravel. ⬤ 01/01-31/12
Distance: 🚲2,4km.

| 🛏 | **Durtal** | 20D1 |

Rue du Petit Port. **GPS:** n47,66842 w0,24172.
5 ⛅free. **Surface:** asphalted.
Distance: 🚲2,4km.

| 🛏S | **Ernée** | 13C5 |

Plan d'eau d'Ernée, Plan d'eau d'Ernée. **GPS:** n48,29670 w0,93997.

2 ⛅free ⟶ WC free. **Location:** Urban, very simple, quit. **Surface:** asphalted.
⬤ 01/01-31/12
Distance: 📍500m ⟶on the spot ⊗500m 🛒500m.
Remarks: Parking at small lake.

| 🛏S | **Faye d'Anjou** | 20C2 |

Chateau du Fresne, D55, Rue des Monts. **GPS:** n47,29923 w0,53806.⬆️➡️.

10 ⛅free ⟶ ⛿Ch free. **Surface:** gravel. ⬤ 01/01-31/12
Distance: 📍2km ⊗3km.

| 🛏S | **Fontenay-le-Comte** | 20B4 |

Avenue du Général de Gaulle. **GPS:** n46,46203 w0,80544.➡️.

10 ⛅free ⟶ € 3 ⛿Ch.
Surface: metalled. ⬤ 01/01-31/12
Distance: 📍500m ⊗500m 🛒500m.
Remarks: Max. 24h, centre, in front of police station.

Tourist information Fontenay-le-Comte:
ℹ️ Office de Tourisme, 8, rue du Grimouard, www.tourisme-sudvendee.com.Old
city, capital of the Southern Vendée, city walk 'mille ans d'histoire'.

| 🛏S | **Fontevraud l'Abbaye** | 20D2 |

Allée des Bruyères. **GPS:** n47,18444 e0,04917.⬆️➡️.

9 ⛅free ⟶ ⛿Ch WC free. **Surface:** asphalted.
Distance: 📍400m ⊗400m 🛒400m.

Tourist information Fontevraud l'Abbaye:
🍴 Abbaye Royale de Fontevraud. ⬤ daily 9-18.30h, 01/10-30/05 10-18h ⬤
01/01, 01/05, 01/11, 11/11, 25/12.

FR

Foussais-Payré — 20C4

Place du Prieuré. **GPS**: n46,53000 w0,68275. ↑.

20 ᴢfree 🔄 ⏚ Ch free. **Surface**: gravel. ⏱ 01/01-31/12
Distance: 500m ⊗500m 🚰200m.

Fresnay-sur-Sarthe — 13D5

Rue de la Gare. **GPS**: n48,28171 e0,02978. →.

8 ᴢfree 🔄 ⏚ Ch free. **Location**: Very simple. **Surface**: gravel. ⏱ 01/01-31/12
Distance: 600m ⊗600m 🚰50m.

Grez-en-Bouère — 13C6

Place A. Peigné. **GPS**: n47,87306 w0,52306. →.

6 ᴢfree 🔄 ⏚ Ch 🧹 free WC. **Location**: Rural, very simple. **Surface**: asphalted. ⏱ 01/01-31/12, service: 01/04-30/11
Distance: 50m ⊗50m 🚰100m.
Remarks: Max. 48h.

Grez-Neuville — 20C1

Rue du Port, D291. **GPS**: n47,60161 w0,68449.
8 ᴢfree 🔄 ⏚ Ch free. **Surface**: grassy. ⏱ 01/01-31/12
Remarks: Former campsite.

Guenrouet — 20A1

GPS: n47,52376 w1,95177.

2 ᴢfree 🔄€ 2 ⏚ Ch €€ 2. **Surface**: asphalted. ⏱ 01/04-31/10
Distance: 200m ⊷50m ⊗200m 🚰200m.
Remarks: Next to campsite Saint Clair, along canal of Nantes/Brest, max. 24h.

Guérande — 12D4

Geen naam, Rue du Parc Savary, D99E. **GPS**: n47,33389 w2,42083. ↑ →.

20 ᴢfree 🔄€ 5/100liter ⏚ Ch ▭€ 5/1h 🧹. **Location**: Noisy. **Surface**: asphalted/grassy. ⏱ 01/01-31/12
Distance: 1km.

Tourist information Guérande:
ℹ Office de Tourisme, 1, place du Marché au Bois, www.ot-guerande.fr. Fortified city.
ℹ Office de Tourisme, 8, Place de la Victoire, La Baule, www.labaule.fr. Mundane bathing resort to the Côte d'Armour.

Jans — 20A1

Route Tréffieux. **GPS**: n47,62222 w1,61222.

6 ᴢfree 🔄 ⏚ Ch WC free. **Surface**: gravel. ⏱ 01/01-31/12
Remarks: Behind town hall.

Jard-sur-Mer — 20A4

Route des Goffineaux. **GPS**: n46,41074 w1,59358. ↑ →.

20 ᴢ€ 6/24h, € 10/48h 🔄€ 2 ⏚ Ch 🧹. **Surface**: asphalted.
Distance: 1km 🏊50m ⊗1,5km 🚰1,5km.

Juvigné — 13B5

Plan d'Eau de Saint Martin, Rue de lCroixille, D29. **GPS**: n48,22806 w1,03806.
↑.

20 ᴢfree 🔄 ⏚ Ch WC free. **Location**: Urban. **Surface**: gravel. ⏱ 01/01-31/12
Distance: 200m ⊷20m ⊗200m 🚰100m 🚶 on the spot.
Remarks: Max. 24h.

FR

La Baconnière — 13C5
Place de l'Eglise. **GPS:** n48,18361 w0,89139.➡️

5 🛏free 🚰🗑Ch 🚿free. **Location:** Urban, very simple.
Surface: asphalted.
⬛ 01/01-31/12
Distance: 🚰on the spot 🚰100m.
Remarks: Behind church, service (winter) on demand.

La Barre-de-Monts — 12D5
Chemin de Querruy. **GPS:** n46,88500 w2,11889.⬆️

12 🛏free 🚰€ 2,30 🗑Ch. **Surface:** gravel. ⬛ 01/01-31/12
Distance: 🚰50m ⊗300m 🗑50m.
Remarks: Parking behind town hall, max. 48h.

La Baule — 12D5
Boulevard Guy de Champsavin, La Baule-Escoublac. **GPS:** n47,28196 w2,42509.
⬆️➡️

20 🛏free 🚰€ 3 🗑Ch 🚿(20x)€ 3/55minutes 🧺. **Location:** Urban,
comfortable, quit. **Surface:** metalled.
Distance: 🏖beach 700m.

La Bernerie-en-Retz — 12D5
Parking Wilson, Avenue de Jean d Arc. **GPS:** n47,07871 w2,03399.⬆️

36 🛏€4 🚰€ 3 🗑Ch📦WC. **Surface:** gravel. ⬛ 01/04-01/10
Distance: 🚰300m 🏊100m ⊗300m 🗑300m 🚌on the spot.
Remarks: Max. 48h.

La Chapelle-Saint-Florent — 20B1
Aire du Stade, Rue de l'Evre. **GPS:** n47,33411 w1,05178.⬆️➡️

6 🛏free 🚰🗑Ch. **Surface:** gravel. ⬛ 01/01-31/12
Distance: 🚰300m 🏊300m 🗑50m.

La Daguenière — 20C1
Chemin de Beausse. **GPS:** n47,42249 w0,43944.

12 🛏free 🚰🗑Chfree. **Surface:** asphalted. ⬛ 01/01-31/12
Distance: 🚰200m 🏊300m 🗑300m.

La Daguenière — 20C1
Port Maillard. GPS: n47,41772 w0,43745.
🛏free. **Surface:** unpaved.
Remarks: Along the Loire river.

La Flèche — 20D1
Promenade du Maréchal Foch. **GPS:** n47,69767 w0,07875.

10 🛏free 🚰free. **Surface:** asphalted.
Distance: 🚰100m ⊗100m 🗑100m.

La Fresnaye-sur-Chédouet — 14A5
La forêt de Perseigne, Les Ventes du Four, D236. **GPS:** n48,43469 e0,25972.⬆️

20 🛏free 🚰🗑Chfree. **Location:** Rural, quit. **Surface:** gravel. ⬛ 01/01-31/12
Distance: 🚰La Fresnaye 1,5km 🚶on the spot.

La Meilleraie-Tillay — 20B3
Rue des Ombrages. **GPS:** n46,73923 w0,84578.⬆️➡️

6 ⓈΞfree ⚡€ 2 ⚑Ch WC ⓘ€ 1. **Surface:** asphalted. ◘ 01/04-31/10
Distance: ⌂700m ⊗700m ☎700m.

10 ⓈΞfree ⚡€ 2/100liter ⚑Ch ☎ 2/1h WC. **Surface:** asphalted.
Distance: ⌂100m ⊗on the spot ☎50m.

| ⓈⓈ | La Plaine-sur-Mer | 12D5 |

Chemin de la gare. **GPS:** n47,13944 w2,19139.⬆.

| ⓈⓈ | La Suze-sur-Sarthe | 13D6 |

Rue du Camping. **GPS:** n47,88917 e0,03040.⬆➡.

8 ⓈΞfree ⚡⚑Ch free. **Location:** Very simple, isolated. **Surface:** asphalted.
◘ 01/01-31/12
Distance: ⌂300m ⊗800m ☎500m.
Remarks: Max. 24h.

10 ⓈΞ€3 ⚡⚑Ch ☎free WC. **Location:** Urban. **Surface:** grassy/gravel. ◘ 01/01-31/12
Distance: ⌂300m ⊗300m.
Remarks: Along Sarthe River.

| ⓈⓈ | La Poitevinière | 20B2 |

Place de la Fontaine, D15. **GPS:** n47,22723 w0,897.⬆.

| ⓈⓈ | La Tranche-sur-Mer | 20A4 |

Boulevard de la Petite Hollande. **GPS:** n46,34965 w1,44769.⬆.

4 ⓈΞfree ⚡⚑Ch ☎WC free. **Surface:** asphalted. ◘ 01/01-31/12
Distance: ⌂50m ⊗on the spot ☎50m.
Remarks: Coins available at bar.

20 ⓈΞfree ⚡€ 2,50 ⚑Ch 🏷. ◘ 01/01-31/12
Remarks: Max. 24h.

| ⓈⓈ | La Roche-sur-Yon | 20A3 |

Boulevard Italie. **GPS:** n46,66833 w1,41861.⬆.

| ⓈⓈ | La Tranche-sur-Mer | 20A4 |

Parking de la Baleine, Place des Baleines. **GPS:** n46,34340 w1,46222.⬆.

20 ⓈΞfree ⚡⚑Ch 🏷free.
Distance: ⌂500m ⊗500m ☎500m.
Remarks: Max. 36h.

| ⓈⓈ | La Séguinière | 20B2 |

Avenue de Nantes. **GPS:** n47,06005 w0,93668.⬆➡.

10 ⓈΞfree. **Surface:** gravel. ◘ 01/01-31/12
Distance: ⌂200m ⊗on the spot ☎on the spot.
Remarks: Max. 24h. Follow 'Le Phare'.

Tourist information La Tranche-sur-Mer:
ⓘ Office de Tourisme, Place de la Liberté, www.ot-latranchesurmer.fr.

| ⓈⓈ | La Turballe | 12D4 |

Boulevard de la Grande Falaise. **GPS:** n47,33106 w2,49919.⬆.
6 ⓈΞ€3 ⚡⚑Ch 🏷included. 🦽 **Surface:** gravel. ◘ 01/01-31/12
Distance: ⌂2km.

FR

La Turballe 12D4

Rue Alphonse Daudet. **GPS:** n47,34870 w2,50804.⬆.

22 € 3,00 Ch free. **Location:** Quit. **Surface:** gravel. 01/01-31/12
Distance: 200m 500m 100m 100m.
Remarks: Max. 5 days.

Lassay-les-Châteaux 13C5

Allée du Haut Perrin. **GPS:** n48,43777 w0,49822.⬆.

free € 2 Ch. **Location:** Urban, very simple, central. **Surface:** asphalted. 01/01-31/12
Distance: 100m.
Remarks: Coins at the bakery.

Laval 13C6

Parking de la Halte Fluviale, Rue du Vieux Saint-Louis. **GPS:** n48,07589 w0,77142.⬆➡.

10 free Ch free. **Location:** Urban, very simple. **Surface:** asphalted. 01/01-31/12
Distance: 300m on the spot on the spot on the spot.
Remarks: Parking nearby viaduct.

Tourist information Laval:
Office de Tourisme, 1, Allée du Vieux St-Louis, www.laval-tourisme.com. Historical art city with old centre, on the Mayenne river.
Vieux Château.Medieval castle, museum with collection of naive art. 10-12h, 14-18h.

Le Coudray Macouard 20D2

Route de Bron. **GPS:** n47,18806 w0,11722.⬆➡.

5 free **Surface:** grassy. 01/01-31/12
Distance: 800m 800m.

Le Croisic 12D5

Le Lin Gorzé, Rue du Lin Gorzé. **GPS:** n47,29917 w2,52194.⬆➡.

9 € 5,20 € 2 Ch. **Location:** Quit. **Surface:** asphalted. 01/01-31/12
Distance: 500m 500m 500m 800m.
Remarks: Max. 48h.

Le Croisic 12D5

Les Courlis, Rue des Courlis. **GPS:** n47,29000 w2,505.⬆➡.

15 € 5,30 € 2 Ch. **Surface:** gravel. 01/04-31/10
Distance: 500m 500m 500m 500m.
Remarks: Max. 48h.

Le Croisic 12D5

La Vigie, Avenue de Pierre Longue, D45. **GPS:** n47,28917 w2,53667.⬆.

9 € 5,30. **Surface:** asphalted. 01/01-31/12
Distance: 3km 50m 3km 3km.
Remarks: Max. 48h.

Le Croisic 12D5

Les Bassins, Rue du Bassin. **GPS:** n47,29194 w2,50741.⬆➡.

FR

9 🛏 € 5,30. **Location:** Urban, quit. **Surface:** asphalted. ⬛ 01/01-31/12
Distance: 🚶200m ⚓20m ⊗200m 🛒200m.
Remarks: Max. 48h.

🚱S Le Croisic 🌊⛲🍦🐚 12D5

P1 Kerdavid, Rue Kerclavid 1. **GPS:** n47,29835 w2,51995. ⬆️

8 🛏 € 5,30. 🚐 📦 **Location:** Urban, quit. **Surface:** asphalted. ⬛ 01/01-31/12
Distance: 🚶500m ⚓500m 🚌500m 🛒800m.

Tourist information Le Croisic:
ℹ️ Office de Tourisme, Place du 18 Juin 1940, www.ot-lecroisic.com.Seaside resort and fishing-port with old quay, coast line with cliffs and small beaches.
🔵 Océarium du Croisic.Sea aquarium. ⬛ 01/06-31/08 10-19h, 01/05-31/05, 01/09-30/09 10-12h, 14-18h, 01/10-30/04 14-18h.

🚱S Le Guédéniau 20D1

Rue du Lavoir. **GPS:** n47,49405 w0,04488. ⬆️

25 🛏 free 🚰 🚽 Ch free. **Surface:** metalled. ⬛ 01/01-31/12
Distance: 🚶on the spot.
Remarks: Recreation area at lake.

🚱S Le Mans 🌊⛲🍦🐚 13D6

Quai de l'Amiral Lalande. **GPS:** n48,00233 e0,18915. ⬆️

7 🛏 free 🚰 🚽 Ch free. **Location:** Urban, very simple. **Surface:** asphalted. ⬛ 01/01-31/12
Distance: 🚶centre ±1km 🔧8km.
Remarks: Along the river Sarthe.

Le Mans 🌊⛲🍦🐚 13D6

Quai Louis Blanc. **GPS:** n48,01111 e0,19750. 🚶

50 🛏 free. **Location:** Urban, very simple, noisy. **Surface:** asphalted. ⬛ 01/01-31/12
Distance: 🚶500m ⊗500m 🛒500m.
Remarks: Max. 24h, Sunday morning market.

Tourist information Le Mans:
ℹ️ Office de Tourisme, Hotel des Ursulines, Rue de l'Etoile, www.ville-lemans.fr.Historical centre.
Ⓜ️ Circuit Le Mans.Motorcar museum.
🍴 Place des Jacobins. ⬛ Wed + Su-morning, Fri.

🚱S Le Pallet 20B2

Rue Pierre Abelard. **GPS:** n47,13494 w1,3305. ⬆️

20 🛏 free 🚰 € 1 🚽 Ch. **Surface:** asphalted. ⬛ 01/01-31/12
Distance: 🚶500m ⊗500m 🛒500m.
Remarks: Wine museum, coins service at the shops in the village.

Le Pellerin 20A2

GPS: n47,20722 w1,78556.

🛏 free. **Surface:** metalled.
Distance: 🚶2km.
Remarks: Nearby sluices 'La Martinière'.

🚱S Le Poiré-sur-Vie 20A3

Rue de Roc. **GPS:** n46,76773 w1,51162. ➡️

5 🛏 free 🚰 🚽 Ch 🔧 free. **Surface:** gravel. ⬛ 01/01-31/12
Distance: 🚶500m ⊗500m 🛒500m.

FR

🅂 **Le Puy-Notre-Dame** 20D2
Place du Gâte Argent. **GPS**: n47,12390 w0,23155.⬆️.
🆓free 🚰🚻Chfree. **Surface**: metalled. 🔲 01/01-31/12
Distance: 100m ⊗200m 200m.
Remarks: Next to cemetery.

🅂 **Le Puy-Notre-Dame** 20D2
Cave-Champignonnière St.Maur, 1, Rue du Chateau, Sanziers. **GPS**: n47,11755 w0,20526.⬆️➡️.

8 🆓free 🚰🚻 WCfree. **Surface**: metalled. 🔲 01/03-30/10
Distance: 2km.
Remarks: At mushroom grower.

🅂 **Le Puy-Notre-Dame** 20D2
Domaine de la Renière, Les Caves. **GPS**: n47,13429 w0,24256.⬆️.

5 €5 🚰 included. **Surface**: metalled. 🔲 01/03-01/11
Distance: 700m.
Remarks: At wine-grower.

🅂 **Le Puy-Notre-Dame** 20D2
Domaine du Vieux Tuffeau, Les Caves. **GPS**: n47,13498 w0,24704.➡️.

6 🆓free 🚰. **Surface**: metalled. 🔲 01/01-31/12
Distance: 1km.
Remarks: At wine-grower.

🅂 **Le Puy-Notre-Dame** 20D2
Domaine de la Girardrie, Rue Fontaine de Cix. **GPS**: n47,11616 w0,24127.⬆️.

5 🆓free. **Surface**: gravel. 🔲 01/01-31/12
Distance: 1km ⊗1km 1km.

Tourist information Le Puy-Notre-Dame:
Ⓜ Champignonnière.Mushroom farm in cellar of the 16th century. 🔲 01/03-31/10.

🅂 **Le Vaudelnay** 20C2
Domaine du Vieux Pressoir, 235, Rue Château d'Oiré. **GPS**: n47,14669 w0,25239.➡️.

4 🆓free. **Surface**: metalled. 🔲 01/01-31/12
Distance: 3km ⊗3km 3km.
Remarks: At wine-grower.

🅂 **Les Epesses** 20B3
Le Puy du Fou, D27. **GPS**: n46,89425 w0,92506.⬆️.
€5 🚰€ 2 Ch. **Surface**: grassy.
Remarks: Baker every morning, free shuttle to Puy du Fou.

🅂 **Les Essarts** 20B3
Rue de la piscine. **GPS**: n46,77380 w1,23499.⬆️➡️.

10 🆓free 🚰€ 2 Ch. **Surface**: asphalted. 🔲 01/01-31/12
Distance: 600m 5,6km ⊗600m 600m.
Remarks: At swimmingpool and campsite.

🅂 **Les Sables-d'Olonne** 20A3
Centre Culturel, Rue Printanière. **GPS**: n46,49646 w1,77493.
€ 2/12h, € 4/24h, 06/11-31/03 free 🚰Ch included. **Surface**: metalled. 🔲 01/01-31/12 🔲 service 06/11-31/03.
Distance: beach 400m.

🅂 **Les Sables-d'Olonne** 20A3
Les Salines, 120 route de l'Aubraie. **GPS**: n46,50585 w1,78796.
20 €8 🚰Ch € 3 free.
Surface: sand. 🔲 01/04-30/09
Distance: 600m.
Remarks: July/Aug only overnight stays (18-11h), baker every morning.

🅂 **Les Sables-d'Olonne** 20A3
Parking de la Sablière. **GPS**: n46,50585 w1,78796.
🆓free. **Surface**: asphalted.

Tourist information Les Sables-d'Olonne:
ℹ️ Office de Tourisme, Centre de Congrès les Atlantes 1, Promenade Joffre, www.lessablesdolonne-tourisme.com.Important bathing resort in the Vendee.
Cours Dupont. 🔲 Wed + Sa morning.
☺ Zoo d'Olonne.Zoo.

🅂 **Liré** 20B1
Le Haut Fief, Square Espéranto. **GPS**: n47,34130 w1,16751.⬆️.

5 �
free ⌐ Ch ✎ WC free. **Surface:** asphalted. ⬛ 01/01-31/12
Distance: 500m ⊗250m ⚓50m.
Remarks: Max. 48h.

20 ⌐free ⌐€ 2 Ch. **Surface:** asphalted. ⬛ 01/01-31/12
Distance: 500m ⊗500m ⚓200m.

Longué-Jumelles 20D1
Boulevard Victor Hugo. **GPS:** n47,38046 w0,11488.

Maisdon-sur-Sèvre 20B2
Domaine des Croix, Les Croix. **GPS:** n47,10710 w1,38757.⬆
free ⌐ Ch ✎ € 4/24h. **Location:** Rural. **Surface:** gravel.
Distance: 1km.
Remarks: Max. 72h, wine tasting.

Mamers 14A5
Complexe de loisirs La grille, Rue de la Piscine. **GPS:** n48,35834 e0,37139.⬆➡

10 free ⌐ Ch WC free. **Surface:** gravel. ⬛ 01/01-31/12
Distance: on the spot ⚏3,3km ⊗on the spot ⚓on the spot.

Luçon 20B4
Domaine des Guifettes. **GPS:** n46,43339 w1,18189.
€ 10,50, dogs € 2,60 ⌐ Ch ✎ included.
Remarks: Free entrance swimming pool, jacuzzi, sauna, midget golf.

9 €5/night, € 12/3 nights ⌐ Ch ✎ included. **Location:** Rural, comfortable. **Surface:** grassy/gravel. ⬛ 01/01-31/12
Distance: 1km ⚓500m ⊗1km ⚓1km.
Remarks: Entrance code available at campsite.

Tourist information Luçon:
ℹ Office de Tourisme, Square Edouard Herriot, www.ville-lucon.fr.
Centre Ville. ⬛ Wed + Sa morning.

Martigné-Briand 20C2
Jardin des Vieux Pressoirs, Rue d'Anjou. **GPS:** n47,23584 w0,42851.⬆➡

L'Aiguillon-sur-Mer 20B4
Aire des Dunes, Point d'Aiguillon. **GPS:** n46,27673 w1,22399.
30 €5 ⌐ 2 Ch.
Remarks: Beach parking.

L'Aiguillon-sur-Mer 20B4
Centre de Voile, Avenue Amiral Coubert. **GPS:** n46,33238 w1,30726.⬆

4 free ⌐ Ch free. **Surface:** metalled. ⬛ 01/01-31/12
Distance: 200m ⊗200m ⚓100m.
Remarks: Closed when frosty.

Mayenne 13C5
Quai Carnot. **GPS:** n48,30000 w0,62.⬆

30 €5 ⌐ 2 Ch. **Surface:** asphalted. ⬛ 01/01-31/12
Distance: 300m ⚓on the spot ⊗300m ⚓300m.
Remarks: At lake, ecole de voile.

Maillé 20B4
La Petite Cabane. **GPS:** n46,34082 w0,79349.
€ 8 ⌐ Ch included.
Remarks: Check in at harbourmaster, service only € 3.

Maillezais 20C4
Rue de l'Ecole. **GPS:** n46,37081 w0,74123.➡

4 free ⌐€ 1,50 Ch. **Location:** Urban, very simple, noisy. **Surface:** asphalted. ⬛ 01/01-31/12
Distance: 1km ⚓10m.
Remarks: Max. 24h, coins at Office de Tourisme.

FR

Mervent 20C4
Chemin du Chêne Tord. **GPS**: n46,52304 w0,75737.

⌕free ⌁€ 2 Ch✄.
Remarks: At cemetery, coins available at Office du Tourisme.

Mesnard-la-Barotière 20B3
Base de Loisirs de la Tricherie. **GPS**: n46,85280 w1,11764.
⌕free ⌁ 3 Ch✄. **Surface:** grassy.
Distance: beach on the spot.
Remarks: At lake of Tricherie.

Mezeray 13D6
Parking, Rue de la Vezanne. **GPS**: n47,82300 w0,01485.

8 ⌕free ⌁€ 2 Ch€ 2. **Location:** Rural, very simple. **Surface:** gravel.
01/01-31/12
Distance: 300m.

Montfort-le-Gesnois 14A6
Parc des Sittelles, Parc des Sittelles. **GPS**: n48,03763 e0,41375.

16 ⌕€ 10 ⌁ Ch✄ included. **Location:** Rural, quit. **Surface:** forest soil.
01/01-31/12
Distance: 50m.

Montreuil-Bellay 20D2
Rue Georges Girouy. **GPS**: n47,13272 w0,15835.

20 ⌕free ⌁€ 2 Ch. **Surface:** gravel/metalled. 15/06-15/09 19-10h
Distance: 150m 150m 150m.
Remarks: Nearby campisite Les Nobis, along the river.

Montreuil-Bellay 20D2
Caveau de la Prévoté, Rue du Cohu 55, Méron. **GPS**: n47,13522 w0,11121.

3 ⌕free ⌁ Ch✄ free. **Surface:** metalled. 01/01-31/12
Distance: 50m 3km 3km.
Remarks: At wine-grower.

Tourist information Montreuil-Bellay:
Office de Tourisme, Place du Concorde, www.ville-montreuil-bellay.fr.City with a fortress from 1025.

Montreuil-Juigné 20C1
Rue Saint Jean Baptiste. **GPS**: n47,54132 w0,61526.

8 ⌕free ⌁ Ch free. **Surface:** gravel/metalled. 01/01-31/12
Distance: 1km 50m 800m.
Remarks: Along the Mayenne river.

Montsoreau 20D2
Domaine de la Perruche, 29, Rue de la Maumenière. **GPS**: n47,21828 e0,05079.
⌁.
⌕.
Distance: 500m 500m.
Remarks: At wine-grower, 10.30><18.30h.

Moutiers-sur-le-Lay 20B3
Palias. **GPS**: n46,55375 w1,15483.

6 ⌕free ⌁ Ch WC free. **Surface:** grassy. 01/01-31/12
Distance: 400m 400m 400m.
Remarks: At gymnasium.

Mouzillon 20B2
Route de la Vendée. **GPS**: n47,13944 w1,28194.

🅼 Musée de la Construction Navale. Naval architectural museum.
🅼 Musée de la Guériniere. Traditional folk art.
⛺ Place de la République. 🅿 Fri.
☺ Sealand Aquarium, Le Vieux Port.

🅢 Nort-sur-Erdre 20A1
13 Place du Bassin. **GPS:** n47,43746 w1,49546. ⬆️

12 📷 free 🚰 2 🐟 Ch. **Surface:** asphalted.
Distance: 🚶200m ⊗200m 🚰200m.

🅢 Noirmoutier-en-l'Ile 12D5
Place Florent Caillaud, Noirmoutier. **GPS:** n47,00139 w2,25167. ⬆️

150 📷 € 7, winter € 4,50 🚰 2 🐟Ch🔌 € 2. 🌙 01/01-31/12
Remarks: Motorhome parking south of the town, max. 8 days.

🅢 Noirmoutier-en-l'Ile 12D5
Place R. Ganachaud, l'Herbaudière. **GPS:** n47,02011 w2,30075.

15 📷 € 7, winter € 4,50 🚰 2 🐟 Ch🔌 € 2. **Surface:** asphalted.
Distance: ⚓on the spot ⊗350m.
Remarks: Parking behind town hall.

🅢 Noirmoutier-en-l'Ile 12D5
Route de la Chaussée, L'Epine. **GPS:** n46,98060 w2,26404.
40 📷 € 7/24h, € 13/48h, € 19/72h 🚰100liter 🐟 Ch🔌included50minutes
WC.🚻♿ **Surface:** metalled. 🌙 01/01-31/12
Distance: 🚶100m ⚓1,3km 🚴on the spot ⊗200m 🚰3km.
Remarks: Max. 72h.

🅢 Noirmoutier-en-l'Ile 12D5
Rue du Marché, La Guerinière. **GPS:** n46,99987 w2,24459.

📷 € 7, winter € 4,50 🚰 2 🐟Ch🔌 € 2. **Surface:** asphalted.
Distance: 🚶800m ⚓on the spot ⊗50m.

Tourist information Noirmoutier-en-l'Ile:
ℹ️ Office de Tourisme, Route du Pont, Barbatre, www.ile-noirmoutier.com. Island now accessed via a bridge.
🅼🏛 Château Noirmoutier. Regional museum. 🌙 daily.

30 📷 free 🚰 🐟Ch WC 🔌free. **Surface:** asphalted. 🌙 01/01-31/12
Distance: 🚶300m.

🅢 Notre-Dame-de-Monts 12D5
Aire de la Clairière, Rue de la Clairière. **GPS:** n46,83484 w2,14426. ⬆️

40 📷 € 5/20-8h 🚰 🐟Chfree. **Surface:** metalled. 🌙 01/01-31/12
Distance: 🚶800m ⚓200m 🚴200m ⊗800m 🚰800m.
Remarks: Motorhome parking at the beach, max. 48h.

🅢 Notre-Dame-de-Monts 12D5
Place du Marais. **GPS:** n46,83148 w2,13035. ⬆️

20 📷 € 5/20-8h 🚰 🐟 Ch WCfree. **Surface:** asphalted. 🌙 01/01-31/12
Distance: 🚶300m ⊗500m 🚰300m.
Remarks: Parking office de tourisme, max. 48h.

🅢 Nozay 20A1
Étang de Nozay. **GPS:** n47,57500 w1,62528. ⬆️

16 📷 € 5 🚰 🐟Ch♿ (16x) WC included. **Surface:** gravel. 🌙 01/01-31/12
⊙ service: frost.
Distance: 🚶200m 🎣2km 🚴10m ⊗200m 🚰200m.

FR

Olonne-sur-Mer 20A3

Le Fief des Grisses, Route de Brem, 43, route des amis de la nature, D80. **GPS:** n46,55667 w1,81139.

30 ⬛7 ⚡ Ch included ♨. **Surface:** grassy. ⬛ 01/03-31/12

Parnay 20D2

D947. **GPS:** n47,23146 e0,01098. ⬆

5 ⬛free ⚡€ 1,50 Ch. **Surface:** asphalted. ⬛ 01/01-31/12
Distance: 200m.
Remarks: Parking in the centre.

Pellouailles-les-Vignes 20C1

Rue Nationale, D323. **GPS:** n47,52141 w0,43698. ⬆
3 ⬛free ⚡ Chfree. **Surface:** gravel. ⬛ 01/01-31/12
Distance: on the spot 1,4km.

Piriac-sur-Mer 12D4

Parking de Brambel, Avenue du Général de Gaulle, D452. **GPS:** n47,39680 w2,51245.

12 ⬛€5 ⚡ Chfree WC. **Location:** Comfortable. **Surface:** metalled. ⬛ 01/01-31/12
Distance: 2km 50m 2km 2km.
Remarks: Parking to sea.

Piriac-sur-Mer 12D4

Parking de Lérat, Route de Mesquène, D99, Lieu-dit Lérat. **GPS:** n47,36770 w2,53196. ⬆

50 ⬛€5 ⚡ Chfree. **Surface:** metalled. ⬛ 01/01-31/12
Distance: 200m 600m 600m 500m 500m.

Remarks: Max. 48h.

Tourist information Piriac-sur-Mer:
🛈 Office de Tourisme, 7, rue des Cap-Horniers. Marina and seaside resort.
01/06-30/09 Mo + Wed + Sa-morning, 01/10-30/05 Tue.
Arts market. 01/07-31/08 Thu-evening.

Pornic 12D5

Le Val Saint-Martin. **GPS:** n47,12053 w2,09162. ⬆ ➡

7 ⬛free ⚡€ 2/100liter Ch. **Location:** Comfortable, isolated.
Surface: asphalted. ⬛ 01/01-31/12
Distance: city centre 1,5km.
Remarks: Next to swimming pool.

Pouancé 13B6

Rue de l'hippodrôme, Aubin. **GPS:** n47,75250 w1,18. ⬆

10 ⬛€ 2,50 ⚡ Ch WC free. **Surface:** grassy. ⬛ 01/01-31/12
Distance: on the spot 20m 1km 1km.
Remarks: In front of the church.

Pouzauges 20B3

Parking de la Vallée, D49/D203. **GPS:** n46,77639 w0,82861. ⬆

10 ⬛free ⚡ Chfree. **Surface:** asphalted. ⬛ 01/01-31/12
Distance: 1km 1km 1km.

Préfailles 12D5

Camping-Car Park de La Pointe, Chemin du Port aux Anes. **GPS:** n47,13872 w2,22213. ⬆

49 ⬛€ 12/24h ⚡ Ch included. **Location:** Comfortable. **Surface:** grassy/gravel. ⬛ 01/01-31/12

FR

ⓈＳ Préfailles 12D5

Rue de la Prée. **GPS:** n47,13388 w2,21221.

4 🍴free 🚰€ 2,50/100liter 🔧Ch. **Location:** Very simple. **Surface:** . ◻
01/01-31/12

Distance: 🚲500m.

Remarks: Coins at Tourist Info.

ⓈＳ Préfailles 12D5

Chemin de Biochon, Pointe de Saint Gildas. **GPS:** n47,13078 w2,18963.

75 🍴free, 15/4-15-10 € 3. 🛥 **Location:** Rural, quit. **Surface:** gravel/sand. ◻
01/01-31/12

Distance: 🚲3km 🏖500m 🛒500m ⊗3km 🚮3km.

Remarks: Max. 48h, baker every morning.

ⓈＳ Préfailles 12D5

D313, chemin des Pinettes. **GPS:** n47,13663 w2,23843.

45 🍴free, 01/05-30/09 € 3. 🛥 **Location:** Rural, quit. **Surface:** grassy/gravel.
◻ 01/01-31/12

Distance: 🚲3km 🏖50m ⊗200m 🚮3km.

Remarks: Max. 48h, baker every morning.

ⓈＳ Riaille 20B1

Rue de la Benate. **GPS:** n47,51412 w1,28803. ⬆➡

5 🍴free 🚰🔧Ch WC 🍴free. **Surface:** gravel.

Distance: 🚲700m ⊗700m 🚮700m.

ⓈＳ Rouans 20A2

Aire naturelle de Messan, Route des Marais. **GPS:** n47,19272 w1,85419. ⬆

8 🍴€ 5 🚰🔧Ch WC free. **Surface:** asphalted. ◻ 01/01-31/12

Distance: 🚲1km ⊗on the spot 🚮1km.

ⓈＳ Saint-Loup-du-Gast 13C5

Zone d'Activité du Creusot. **GPS:** n48,38750 w0,58548. ⬆➡

6 🍴free 🚰🔧Ch free. **Location:** Rural, very simple. **Surface:** asphalted/
grassy. ◻ 01/01-31/12

Distance: 🚲350m.

Remarks: Departure Vélorail, € 15 per bike for 4 pers.

ⓈＳ Saint-Nazaire 12D5

Route de l'Océan, D292, Saint-Marc-sur-Mer. **GPS:** n47,23700 w2,30033. ⬆

15 🍴free 🚰€ 3/100liter 🔧Ch🔌 € 3/1h 🧺 **Location:** Rural, quit.
Surface: gravel. ◻ 01/01-31/12

Distance: 🚲2km 🏖100m 🛒100m.

ⓈＳ Saint-Nazaire 12D5

Bois-Joalland, Route de Quelmer. **GPS:** n47,27669 w2,25771.

3 🍴free. **Location:** Rural, very simple, quit. **Surface:** unpaved. ◻ 01/01-
31/12

Distance: 🚲1km 🏖5m 🚴on the spot 🚶on the spot.

Remarks: Nearby base nautique.

ⓈＳ Saint-Nazaire 12D5

Boulevard Paul Leferme. **GPS:** n47,27760 w2,20362.

50 🍴free. **Location:** Urban, very simple, isolated. **Surface:** asphalted. ◻
01/01-31/12

Distance: 🚲on the spot 🚮500m 🛒50m.

ⓈＳ Saint-Nazaire 12D5

Route du Bois Joalland. **GPS:** n47,27954 w2,26229. ⬆

FR

5 ⌷free. **Location:** Central. **Surface:** gravel. ◻ 01/01-31/12 **Distance:** 500m 10m 10m on the spot on the spot.

| | S | Saulgé l'Hôpital | 20C2 |

Terrain de Loisirs, Chemin de la Planche. **GPS:** n47,29853 w0,38344. ⬆.

15 ⌷free Chfree. **Surface:** gravel. ◻ 01/01-31/12 **Distance:** 100m 100m 100m.

| | S | Segré | 20C1 |

Place du Moulin sous la Tour. **GPS:** n47,68862 w0,87167. ➡. 6 ⌷free Chfree. ◻ 01/01-31/12 ◯ Service: winter.

| | S | Sillé-le-Guillaume | 13D5 |

2, Place de la Gare. **GPS:** n48,18167 w0,13111. ⬆➡.

8 ⌷free € 2 Ch € 2. **Location:** Urban, very simple. **Surface:** asphalted. ◻ 01/01-31/12 **Distance:** 300m 300m 400m train 50m. **Remarks:** May 2012 during inspection service out of order.

| | | St.Aubin-de-Luigné | 20C2 |

Domaine La Biquerie, D17. **GPS:** n47,30843 w0,70211. ⬆.

30 ⌷free Chfree. **Surface:** grassy. ◻ 01/01-31/12 **Distance:** 5km. **Remarks:** At wine-grower.

| | S | St.Calais | 14A6 |

Boulevard du Docteur Gigon. **GPS:** n47,92416 e0,74459. ⬆➡.

4 ⌷free Ch WCfree. **Location:** Rural. **Surface:** asphalted. ◻ 01/01-31/12 **Distance:** 400m on the spot.

| | S | St.Calais | 14A6 |

Le Champ Long, D249. **GPS:** n47,93375 e0,74568. ⬆.

5 ⌷free WC. **Location:** Rural. **Surface:** asphalted. ◻ 01/01-31/12 **Distance:** 1,6km lake on the spot on the spot.

| | | St.Clément-des-Levées | 20D2 |

Rue de la Laiterie. **GPS:** n47,33089 w0,18015. ⬆➡.

10 ⌷free € 2 Ch. **Surface:** metalled. ◻ 01/01-31/12 **Remarks:** Coins available at the shops.

| | | St.Clément-des-Levées | 20D2 |

Port Poisson. **GPS:** n47,33004 w0,18393.

8 ⌷free. **Surface:** metalled. ◻ 01/01-31/12

| | S | St.Cyr-en-Bourg | 20D2 |

Cave de Saumur, Route du Mureau. **GPS:** n47,19642 w0,07266. ⬆➡.

15 ⌷free Ch WCfree. **Surface:** asphalted. ◻ 15/03-15/09 **Distance:** 3km. **Remarks:** Max. 48h, wine tasting 300m. Follow signs Cave de Saumur.

| | S | St.Georges-sur-Loire | 20C1 |

Rue de la Villette. **GPS:** n47,40610 w0,76301. ⬆.

20 🛏free 🚰🔌Chfree. **Surface:** asphalted. 🔲 01/01-31/12
Distance: 🍴300m ⛱100m ⊗300m 🛒300m.
Remarks: Next to the old abbey, max. 24h.

🛁Ⓢ **St.Gilles-Croix-de-Vie** ⚓🌊   20A3
La Rabalette, Rue de la Rabalette. **GPS:** n46,70302 w1,94728.⬆️.

35 🛏€5 🚰€ 2,60 🔌Ch.
Surface: asphalted. 🔲 01/01-31/12
Distance: 🍴500m ⛱1km ⊗500m 🛒500m.
Remarks: Nearby lake Soudinière, coins at Tourist Info.

🛁Ⓢ **St.Gilles-Croix-de-Vie** ⚓🌊   20A3
Stade de la Chapelle, Rue du Bois. **GPS:** n46,69449 w1,92716.
🛏€5 🚰€ 2,60 🔌Ch. **Surface:** asphalted. 🔲 01/04-30/09 weekend and
school holidays
Distance: 🍴centre 500m.
Remarks: Coins at Tourist Info.

Tourist information St.Gilles-Croix-de-Vie:
ℹ️ Office de Tourisme, Boulevard de l'Egalité, www.stgillescroixdevie.com.
Seaside resort with fishing port.
⛺ 🚗 🔲 St.Gilles: Tue, Thu, Su; Croix de Vie; Wed, Sa.

🛁Ⓢ **St.Hilaire de Riez** ⚓🌊   12D6
Allée de la Plage de la Parée Préneau. **GPS:** n46,72865 w1,99167.⬆️.

60 🛏free. **Surface:** sand.
Distance: ⛱on the spot.
Remarks: Beach parking.

🛁Ⓢ **St.Hilaire-de-Chaléons**   20A2
Rue Eloi Guitteny, D61. **GPS:** n47,10389 w1,86639.

2 🛏free 🚰🔌Ch 🔧 WCfree. 🔲 01/01-31/12
Distance: 🍴100m ⊗500m 🛒100m.
Remarks: Next to campsite de l'Etoile, max. 24h.

🛁Ⓢ **St.Jean-de-Monts**   12D6

Le Repos des Tortues - Saint-Jean-de-Monts

lereposdestortues@gmail.com - www.facebook.com/ReposDesTortues
Paved and flat motorhome pitches
Electricity at each pitch
Free wifi access

Le Repos des Tortues, Route de Notre Dame de Monts 38.
GPS: n46,79879 w2,07344.
49 🛏€ 8, 01/07-31/08 € 10 🚰🔌Ch🔌 🔧 (49x), 4Amp WC⊐€ 5/stay
💡€ 4 📶included 🗑.
Location: Comfortable. **Surface:** grassy/gravel. 🔲 01/01-31/12
Distance: 🍴800m ⛱1,5km 🚲50m 🛒2km.

🛁Ⓢ **St.Jean-de-Monts**   12D6
Rue de la Parée Jésus. **GPS:** n46,79250 w2,08029.⬆️.

28 🛏€5 🚰€ 2 🔌Ch. **Surface:** asphalted. 🔲 01/04-30/11
Distance: 🍴1km ⛱600m 🚲600m ⊗600m 🛒1km.
Remarks: At forest, in front of tennis-courts, nearby beaches, max. 48h.

Tourist information St.Jean-de-Monts:
⛺ 🔲 Wed, Sa.

🛁Ⓢ **St.Jean-sur-Mayenne** 🌊   13C6
Les Marchanderies. **GPS:** n48,12793 w0,75244.⬆️➡️.

25 € 6,20 Ch WC included. **Location:** Rural, luxurious, quit.
Surface: grassy/gravel. 01/01-31/12
Distance: 500m on the spot 300m 400m bakery.
Remarks: Along the Mayenne river.

S St.Lyphard 12D4

Route Herbignac, D47. **GPS**: n47,39900 w2,30091.

6 free € 2 Ch. **Surface:** grassy/metalled. 01/01-31/12
Distance: 500m 200m 500m.
Remarks: At small lake, max. 1 night.

S St.Mars-La-Jaille 20B1

Rue Neuve. **GPS**: n47,52327 w1,18357.

12 free Ch WC free. **Surface:** asphalted. 01/01-31/12
Remarks: Parking at small lake.

S St.Michel-Chef-Chef 12D5

Camping-Car Park Le Thar-Cor La Plaine sur Mer, Avenue Cormier. **GPS**: n47,16017 w2,16881.

22 € 12/24h Ch included. **Location:** Isolated, quit. **Surface:** . 01/01-31/12
Distance: sandy beach 400m 400m 400m.

S St.Michel-Chef-Chef 12D5

Chemin du Puits Martin. **GPS**: n47,18209 w2,14664.

30 free, 20-8h € 5 € 2,80/100liter Ch.
Surface: asphalted.
01/01-31/12
Distance: 300m 300m 300m.
Remarks: Parking townhall, oins at town hall, office du tourisme.

S St.Michel-Chef-Chef 12D5

Camping Clos Mer et Nature, Route de Tharon. **GPS**: n47,17309 w2,15779.

€ 5 € 2/100liter Ch € 2. **Location:** Quit. **Surface:** grassy. 01/01-31/12
Distance: 500m sandy beach 400m 300m.
Remarks: Check in at reception.

S St.Michel-Mont-Mercure 20B3

Place du Sommet. **GPS**: n46,83222 w0,88222.
20 free € 2/150liter Ch. **Surface:** gravel/sand.
Remarks: Near church.

S St.Philbert-de-Grandlieu 20A2

Chemin de la Plage. **GPS**: n47,04500 w1,64172.

10 free Ch free. **Surface:** gravel. 01/01-31/12
Distance: 1km on the spot on the spot 550m 1km.
Remarks: From Nantes first exit after Grande Surface, at roundabout dir city, first road to the right.

S St.Rémy-la-Varenne 20C1

Rue St Aubin-D132. **GPS**: n47,39805 w0,31612.

3 free Ch WC free. **Surface:** asphalted. 01/01-31/12
Distance: on the spot 100m 100m.

FR

St.Saturnin-sur-Loire 20C1
Route de Saumur, D751. **GPS**: n47,39267 w0,43285. ⬆️➡️.

10 🚰free ⌁€ 2,50 Ch. **Surface**: metalled. ⬛ 01/01-31/12
Distance: 🚶100m 🚲50m 🚌50m 🚆on the spot.
Remarks: Behind church, coins at the shops in the village.

3 🚰free ⌁ Chfree. **Surface**: metalled. ⬛ 01/01-31/12
Distance: 🚶on the spot ⊗100m 🚆100m.

St.Viaud 20A2
Rue du parc des sports. **GPS**: n47,25917 w2,015. ⬆️.

10 🚰free ⌁ Ch 🚿 (2x)free. **Location**: Rural, comfortable, quit. **Surface**: metalled. ⬛ 01/01-31/12
Distance: 🚶500m 🏊100m ⊗500m 🚆500m.
Remarks: At recreational lake, max. 8 days.

Vaiges 13C6
Rue Robert Gletron, D57. **GPS**: n48,04189 w0,48285. ⬆️.

5 🚰free ⌁€ 2 Ch. **Location**: Urban, very simple. **Surface**: gravel. ⬛ 01/01-31/12
Distance: 🚶500m 🚲1,7km 🚌20m 🚆700m bakery.

Valanjou 20C2
Aire de Plaisance, Rue de la Mairie. **GPS**: n47,21658 w0,60326.

St.Vincent-sur-Jard 20A4
Chemin des Roulettes, Le Goulet. **GPS**: n46,41038 w1,5413. ⬆️➡️.

18 🚰€ 5 ⌁€ 2/10minutes Ch ⚡€ 2/55minutes. **Surface**: metalled. ⬛ 01/01-31/12 🔘 Service: winter.
Distance: 🚶1km 🏊100m 🚆400m.

Ste.Gemmes-sur-Loire 20C1
Rue de l'Authion. **GPS**: n47,42343 w0,55092.
3 🚰free ⌁ Ch WC. **Surface**: asphalted/metalled.
Distance: ⊗500m 🚆100m.

6 🚰free ⌁ Ch WC free. **Surface**: metalled. ⬛ 01/01-31/12
Distance: 🚶200m.
Remarks: Nearby town hall.

Venansault 20A3
Rue Pierre Nicolas Loué. **GPS**: n46,68250 w1,51472.

Talmont-Saint-Hilaire 20A4
Parking des Gâtines, Rue des Gâtines. **GPS**: n46,46761 w1,61718. ⬆️.
16 🚰€ 5/24h ⌁€ 3/100liter Ch ⚡€ 3/50minutes. **Surface**: asphalted. ⬛ 01/01-31/12
Distance: 🏊Small lake (100m) 🚆100m.

Talmont-Saint-Hilaire 20A4
Parking du Château Guibert, Avenue de la Plage. **GPS**: n46,44098 w1,66351. ⬆️.
10 🚰€ 5/24h ⌁€ 3 Ch 🚿📷🚿
Surface: asphalted. ⬛ 01/01-31/12
Distance: 🏊1km.
Remarks: Max. 48h.

5 🚰free. **Surface**: sand. ⬛ 01/01-31/12
Distance: 🚶500m 🏊100m ⊗300m 🚆500m.

Vihiers 20C2
Rue Champ de Foire des Champs. **GPS**: n47,14355 w0,5358. ⬆️➡️.

Turquant 20D2
Rue des Ducs d'Anjou. **GPS**: n47,22393 e0,02858. ⬆️.

FR

5 🔲free ⌐ 🔲 Ch WC. **Surface:** asphalted. ◻ 01/01-31/12
Distance: ⌐50m ⊗100m 🔲100m.

🔲🔲 | **Villeveque** | 20C1
Rue du Port. **GPS:** n47,56222 w0,42257.
6 🔲free ⌐€ 1 🔲Ch WC.

🔲🔲 | **Villiers-Charlemagne** | 13C6
Village Vacances et Pêche, Rue des Haies. **GPS:** n47,92083 w0,68167.⬆.

25 🔲free ⌐ 🔲 Ch 🔲free.
Location: Rural, comfortable, quit.
Surface: grassy. ◻ 01/01-31/12
Distance: ⌐on the spot ⌐day pass available 🔲500m 🔲on the spot.
Remarks: Max. 24h.

FR

🔲🔲 | **Vouvant** | 20C3
Rue de Château Neuf. **GPS:** n46,57462 w0,77462.⬆➡.

20 🔲free ⌐ 🔲 Ch free. **Surface:** gravel. ◻ 01/01-31/12
Distance: ⌐500m ⊗500m 🔲500m.

Centre

🔲🔲 | **Allogny** (🔲) | 21D2
D944. **GPS:** n47,21913 e2,32329.⬆➡.

10 🔲free ⌐free. **Surface:** asphalted. ◻ 01/01-31/12
Distance: ⌐800m ⌐50m ⌐50m.

🔲🔲 | **Amboise** 🔲🔲🔲🔲 | 21B1
Vinci Park, Allée de la Chapelle Saint-Jean. **GPS:** n47,41761 e0,98742.⬆.

20 🔲€ 10/24h ⌐ 🔲 Ch included ⌐ (20x)€ 2 ⌐.⌐🔲⌐
Location: Rural, comfortable, central, quit. **Surface:** asphalted/grassy. ◻
01/01-31/12
Distance: ⌐200m ⌐200m ⊗200m 🔲200m ⌐on the spot 🔲on the spot.
Remarks: Next to campsite, castle 500m.

🔲🔲 | **Amboise** 🔲🔲🔲🔲 | 21B1
Parking St. Jean, Avenue Leonardo da Vinci 43 , D61. **GPS:** n47,40814 e0,98986.
⬆➡.

11 🔲free. **Location:** Urban, very simple, isolated, quit. **Surface:** asphalted. ◻
01/01-31/12
Distance: ⌐on the spot ⊗1,5km 🔲1,5km ⌐on the spot.

🔲🔲 | **Angé** | 21B2
Place de la Mairie. **GPS:** n47,33250 e1,24389.⬆.

20 🔲free ⌐ 🔲 Ch ⌐ free. **Surface:** metalled. ◻ 01/01-31/12

🔲🔲 | **Argent-sur-Sauldre** | 21D1
Super U, D940. **GPS:** n47,54916 e2,44797.⬆.

2 🔲free ⌐€ 2 🔲Ch. **Surface:** asphalted. ◻ 01/01-31/12
Distance: ⌐1,1km.

🔲 | **Argenton-sur-Creuse** | 21B4
Rue de la Grenouille. **GPS:** n46,58715 e1,52497.⬆➡.

50 ⌂free. **Surface:** gravel. ◻ 01/01-31/12
Distance: 50m 3,4km ⊗50m 50m.

S	Argenton-sur-Creuse	21B4

Alleé du Champ de Foire. **GPS:** n46,58556 e1,52222.
Ch WC free. ◻ 01/01-31/12
Distance: on the spot.

Tourist information Argenton-sur-Creuse:
Office de Tourisme, 13, place de la République, www.ot-argenton-sur-creuse.fr.
M Musée de Chemiserie, Rue Charles Brillaud.Textile museum. ◻ 01/03-31/12 9.30-12h, 14-18h ● Mo. T € 4.
M Musée Gallo Romain, Les Mersans, St. Marcel.Roman findings. ◻ 9.30-12h, 14-18h. T € 4.

	Athée-sur-Cher	21A2

Aire d'Athée-sur-Cher, D83, Rue de Cigogné. **GPS:** n47,31439 e0,91756. ↑→.

3 ⌂free Ch free. **Location:** Rural, very simple, isolated, quit. **Surface:** metalled. ◻ 01/01-31/12
Distance: 800m 11km ⊗1,5km 1km on the spot.
Remarks: Max. 24h.

S	Aubigny-sur-Nère	21D1

Parc des Sports, D7. **GPS:** n47,48201 e2,44995. ↑→.

12 ⌂free Ch free. **Surface:** asphalted. ◻ 01/01-31/12
Distance: 1km 1km 2km.

S	Aubigny-sur-Nère	21D1

Parking du Pré qui Danse, Mail Guichard. **GPS:** n47,49140 e2,43830. ↑.

40 ⌂free Ch WC free. **Surface:** asphalted. ◻ 01/01-31/12
Distance: 200m ⊗200m 200m.

S	Avoine	20D2

Avenue de la République. **GPS:** n47,21287 e0,17706. ↑.

11 ⌂€ 4 € 2/10liter Ch (11x)€ 2/24h Location: Rural, comfortable, luxurious, isolated, quit. **Surface:** asphalted/metalled. ◻ 01/01-31/12
Distance: 1km Lac Mousseau 300m ⊗300m.
Remarks: Max. 3 nights.

S	Azay-le-Rideau	21A2

Camping municipal Le Sabot, Rue du Stade. **GPS:** n47,25925 e0,46992. ↑→.

12 ⌂free € 3/100liter Ch € 1,70. **Location:** Urban, comfortable, central, quit. **Surface:** asphalted. ◻ 01/04-01/10
Distance: 200m ⊗300m on the spot on the spot.
Remarks: Max. 48h, coins at camping (9/16h), shower on campsite € 1,70, castle 300m.

S	Azé	14B6

M et Mme Hersant, Les Places, D957 Épuisay-Galette. **GPS:** n47,86451 e0,97659. ↑→.

6 ⌂€ 10 Ch included. Location: Rural, comfortable, isolated, quit. **Surface:** grassy. ◻ 01/01-31/12
Distance: 7km on the spot.

S	Barlieu	21D1

Base de loisirs de Badineau. **GPS:** n47,47918 e2,63168.

15 ⌂€ 2, first night € 3,50 Ch WC free. **Surface:** grassy/gravel.

⭕ Easter-01/11
Distance: 🚰1km ⚡nearby.

| 🚿S | Beaugency | 21C1 |

Quai Dunois. **GPS:** n47,77949 e1,63646.⬆️.

20 🚿free ⚡€ 2/10minutes 💧Ch🔌 2/55minutes WC 🗑️. **Surface:** metalled. ⭕ 01/01-31/12
Distance: 🚰100m ⛵8,8km 🏊100m ⚡50m ⊗100m 🛒100m.
Remarks: Quay along the Loire river, special place in front of motorhomes, max. 24h.

Tourist information Beaugency:
ℹ️ Office de Tourisme, 3, Place Dr Hyvernaud.Medieval city on the river Loire.

| 🚿S | Bessais-le-Fromental | 22A3 |

Base de loisirs de l'Étang de Goule, Champ de la Croix. **GPS:** n46,73402 e2,80034.⬆️➡️.

50 🚿free ⚡€ 2 💧Ch. **Surface:** asphalted/grassy.
Distance: 🚰4km 🏊on the spot ⚡on the spot ⊗on camp site ⚡on camp site.

| 🚿S | Blois 🌊🍴 | 21B1 |

P2, Rue Jean Moulin. **GPS:** n47,58677 e1,32615.⬆️.

20 🚿€ 5/24h ⚡💧Chfree. **Surface:** asphalted. ⭕ 01/05-30/09
Distance: 🚰on the spot ⛵6,9km ⊗100m ⚡100m ⚡on the spot.

Tourist information Blois:
ℹ️ Office de Tourisme, 23 place du Château.
👁️ Quartier juif.Rue Pierre de Blois leads to this medieval Jewish district.
❌ Château de Blois.
✝️ Cathédrale St Louis.
⛲ Quatier Coty. ⭕ Wed 7-13h.

| 🚿S | Boulleret | 22A2 |

Place des Charmes. **GPS:** n47,42304 e2,87244.⬆️➡️.

5 🚿free ⚡€ 2/100liter 💧Ch🔌 (2x)€ 2/6h WC. **Surface:** asphalted. ⭕ 01/01-31/12
Distance: 🚰nearby ⊗nearby ⚡nearby.
Remarks: Coins available at post office, restaurant, shops.

| 🚿S | Bourges | 21D2 |

Boulevard de l'Industrie. **GPS:** n47,07224 e2,39337.⬆️➡️.

5 🚿free ⚡💧Ch🔌free. **Surface:** metalled. ⭕ 01/01-31/12
Distance: 🚰500m ⊗500m ⚡500m.
Remarks: 100m from campsite.

| 🚿S | Bourges | 21D2 |

Rue Jean Bouin. **GPS:** n47,07597 e2,39897.⬆️.

50 🚿free ⚡💧Ch🔌free. **Surface:** asphalted. ⭕ 01/01-31/12
Distance: 🚰50m ⊗500m ⚡500m.
Remarks: Max. 48h.

Tourist information Bourges:
ℹ️ Office de Tourisme, 21, rue Victor Hugo, www.bourges-tourisme.com.Large historic city, centre of the armaments industry for centuries.
Ⓜ️ Hôtel Lallemant Musée des Arts Décoratifs, rue Bournonnoux.Collection of moquettes, porcelain and pieces of furniture.
Ⓜ️ Musée de Bery.Regional museum.
❌ Palais Jaques Coeur.Gothic palace named after the arms dealer Coeur.
🎆 Ballades de Bourges.Festivities and market in the city centre. ⭕ 01/07-31/08.

| 🚿S | Brézolles | 14B4 |

Rue de Verneuil, D939. **GPS:** n48,69083 e1,06972.

10 ⛺free 🚰 🔧Chfree. **Surface:** metalled. ⬛ 01/01-31/12
Distance: 🚶200m ⊗200m.

| 🅂 | | **Briare-le-Canal** | 22A1 |

Camping-Car Park. GPS: n47,64304 e2,72270.⬆.

12 ⛺€7/24h 🚰 🔧Ch 🔧 📶included. 🔲 ⬛ **Surface:** grassy. ⬛ 01/01-31/12
Distance: 🚶on the spot ⛰on the spot 🚲on the spot ⊗800m 🍴800m.
Remarks: Max. 72h.

| 🅂 | | **Briare-le-Canal** | 22A1 |

Rue des Vignes. GPS: n47,63215 e2,73981.⬆.

40 ⛺free 🚰 € 2 🔧Ch 📶 ⬛. **Surface:** gravel. ⬛ 01/01-31/12
Distance: 🚶300m 🚲50m ⊗on the spot.

| 🅂 | | **Briare-le-Canal** | 22A1 |

Port du Commerce, Quai de Mazoyer. GPS: n47,63470 e2,74030.⬆.

10 ⛺free 🚰 WCfree. **Surface:** asphalted. ⬛ 01/01-31/12
Distance: 🚶200m 🚲4,5km 🚲on the spot ⊗on the spot.

| 🅂 | | **Brou** 🍴 | 14B5 |

Madison Cars 28. GPS: n48,21379 e1,14681.⬆➡.

100 ⛺<7.90m € 6/day + € 20/night, >7.90m € 30/day + € 30/night. **Surface:** asphalted.
Distance: ⊗100m 🍴100m.
Remarks: Parking castle, max. 1 night.

| 🅂 | | **Chaon** | 21D1 |

D129. GPS: n47,60942 e2,16611.⬆➡.

10 ⛺free 🚰 🔧Chfree. **Surface:** grassy/metalled. ⬛ 01/01-31/12
Distance: 🚶200m.

| 🅂 | | **Châteaudun** 🔧🏠🍴 | 14B6 |

Aire de Châteaudun, Rue des Fouleries. GPS: n48,07172 e1,32421.⬆➡.

15 ⛺free 🚰€ 2/100liter 🔧Ch🔧€ 2/20minutes WC. **Location:** Urban, comfortable, central, quit.
Surface: asphalted. ⬛ 01/01-31/12
Distance: 🚶400m ⛰Canoe rental 🚲on the spot ⊗on the spot.
Remarks: Along Loir river, castel of Châteaudun 300m.

| △🅂 | | **Châteauneuf-sur-Loire** 🔧🍴 | 14D6 |

Camping municipal La Maltournée, Route de la Plage, Sigloy D11. GPS: n47,85671 e2,22963.⬆.
⛺€7,10 🚰 🔧Ch 🔧€ 3,90 WC 🔲🔲 📶included. **Surface:** grassy/metalled. ⬛ 01/04-31/10
Distance: 🚶800m ⛰on the spot 🚲on the spot ⊗800m 🍴800m.

| 🅂 | | **Châteauroux** | 21C3 |

17, Avenue de Parc des Loisirs. GPS: n46,82278 e1,69507.

5 ⛺free 🚰€ 2,50 🔧Ch🔧 € 2,50/1h.
Surface: asphalted. ⬛ 01/05-31/10

---

15 ⛺€5 🚰€ 1/100liter 🔧€ 1 Ch€ 1 🔧(4x)€ 3/24h 🔲€ 1.🚲
Location: Rural, comfortable, isolated, quit.
Surface: gravel. ⬛ 01/01-31/12
Distance: 🚶1km 🚲1km ⊗on the spot 🚲11,6km.
Remarks: Bread-service.

| 🅂 | | **Chambord** | 21B1 |

Château de Chambord, Place St.Louis. GPS: n47,61608 e1,51057.

FR

Distance: 3,6km 2km 2km.
Remarks: Parking at wave pool.

Tourist information Châteauroux:
Office de Tourisme, 1, Place de la Gare, www.ville-chateauroux.fr.

| S | **Chaumont-sur-Loire** | 21B1 |

Promendae de Trouillas. **GPS:** n47,48347 e1,19127.

20 free 2 Ch 2. **Surface:** grassy/metalled.

| **Chenonceaux** | 21B2 |

Aire de Chenonceaux, Chemin de la Varenne. **GPS:** n47,33053 e1,06824.

10 free. **Location:** Rural, very simple, isolated, noisy. **Surface:** grassy.
01/01-31/12
Distance: 500m 500m on the spot on the spot.
Remarks: Along railwayline.

| P | **Chenonceaux** | 21B2 |

Rue du Château. **GPS:** n47,33020 e1,06648.

20 free. **Location:** Rural, very simple, isolated. **Surface:** metalled.
01/01-31/12
Distance: 500m 500m on the spot.
Remarks: Parking at castle of Chenonceaux.

Tourist information Chenonceaux:
Castle.

| **Cheverny** | 21B1 |

Château Cheverny. **GPS:** n47,49762 e1,46097.

20 free.

Surface: metalled. 9.30-12h, 14.15-17h, Apr-Sep 9.30-18.15h
Distance: 100m 100m.

Tourist information Cheverny:
Château Cheverny.Castle. 9.30-12h, 14.15-17h, Apr-Sep 9.30-18.15h.

| S | **Chouzé-sur-Loire** | 20D2 |

Aire de Chouzé-sur-Loire, Rue de l'Église. **GPS:** n47,23809 e0,12649.

6 free 2 Ch. **Location:** Rural, comfortable, central, quit. **Surface:** gravel. 01/01-31/12
Distance: on the spot 250m on the spot on the spot.
Remarks: Coins available at the shops and town hall.

| S | **Courville-sur-Eure** | 14B5 |

Avenue Thiers. **GPS:** n48,44600 e1,24166.
6 free 2/100liter Ch 2/55minutes. **Surface:** asphalted.
01/01-31/12
Remarks: Coins at campsite and shops.

| S | **Culan** | 21D4 |

Place du Champ de Foire. **GPS:** n46,54714 e2,34521.

20 free 1,50 Ch 1,50 WC. **Surface:** asphalted.
01/01-31/12
Distance: 50m 50m 50m.
Remarks: Near office de tourisme.

| **Cuzion** | 21C4 |

Base de Loisirs Pont des Piles. **GPS:** n46,45639 e1,61167.

6 free. **Surface:** grassy/metalled. 01/01-31/12
Remarks: Max. 1 night.

| S | **Dry** | 21C1 |

Rue de Meung. **GPS:** n47,79824 e1,71419.

10 🛏free ⚡€ 1/10minutes 🚰Ch 🚽€ 1/55minutes. **Surface:** metalled.
⏻ 01/01-31/12
Distance: 🚲on the spot ⛰1km ⚓50m.
Remarks: Coins at town hall.

🛁S	**Esvres-sur-Indre** 🌳	21A2

Impasse Auguste Noyant. **GPS:** n47,28267 e0,78526.⬆️.

7 🛏free ⚡🛏free. **Location:** Urban, central, quit. **Surface:** gravel. ⏻ 01/01-
31/12 ⏻ water disconnected in winter.
Distance: 🚲on the spot ⊗100m ⚓250m 🚆on the spot 🚴on the spot 🚶on
the spot.

🛁S	**Genillé**	21B2

Ferme Jouvin, La Galerie, D 764 Loches> Montrichard. **GPS:** n47,21409 e1,10871.
⬆️.

🛏€2 ⚡ service € 3 🚰Ch 🚿included. 🚴 **Location:** Rural, very simple,
isolated, quit. **Surface:** grassy. ⏻ 01/01-31/12
Distance: 🚲2,7km 🚆on the spot.

🛁S	**Gien**	21D1

Route de Briare. **GPS:** n47,67985 e2,64308.⬆️.

8 🛏free ⚡€ 2 🚰Ch 🚽€ 2. **Surface:** asphalted. ⏻ 01/01-31/12
Distance: 🚲2km 🚆on the spot.
Remarks: Max. 48h, coins available at swimming pool.

🛁S	**Gizeux** 🌿🏊	20D1

Aire de Gizeux, Route du Lavoir. **GPS:** n47,39275 e0,19689.⬆️➡️.

20 🛏free ⚡€ 3/100liter 🚰Ch 🚽€ 3/1h. **Location:** Rural, comfortable,
central, quit. **Surface:** gravel.
Distance: 🚲on the spot 🚆500m ⊗In village 🚴on the spot 🚶on the spot.
Remarks: Château de Gizeux 400m, coins available at the shops and town hall.

🍴S	**Guilly**	21C2

Le Prieuré Chambres d'Hôtes, Rue du Prieuré. **GPS:** n47,07920 e1,72100.⬆️.

10 🛏€5 ⚡€ 3 🚰Ch 🚽. **Surface:** grassy/metalled.
Distance: 🚲150m ⊗10m ⚓150m.

🛁S	**Humbligny**	21D2

D44. **GPS:** n47,25451 e2,65850.⬆️.

10 🛏free ⚡€ 2/100liter 🚰Ch 🚽€ 2/10minutes. **Surface:** gravel. ⏻
01/01-31/12
Distance: 🚲on the spot.
Remarks: Coins at town hall (10m).

🛁S	**La Chapelle-Saint-Mesmin**	14C6

Aire camping-cars, Chemin de Fourneaux. **GPS:** n47,88550 e1,83990.

23 🛏€ 5/24h, € 9/48h, € 12/72h ⚡🚰Ch 🚿included. 🚐🚿 **Location:**
Urban, comfortable, quit. **Surface:** grassy. ⏻ 01/04-31/12
Distance: 🚲500m, Orléans 5km 🚴2,7km ⚓50m 🚆50m ⊗500m ⚓500m
🚴on the spot 🚶on the spot.
Remarks: Along the Loire river.

🛁S	**La Châtre**	21C4

Rue du Champ de Foire. **GPS:** n46,58250 e1,98250.

FR

10 ⒮ € 2. **Surface:** asphalted.
Distance: 50m 50m 50m.

La Châtre 21C4
Supermarché Super U, Avenue d'Auvergne, D943. **GPS:** n46,58278 e2,00139.
10 free € 2/10minutes Ch € 2/1h. **Surface:** asphalted.
01/01-31/12
Distance: 800m 50m.

La Ferte-Beauharnais 21C1
D922. **GPS:** n47,54455 e1,84882.

12 free € 2/10minutes Ch € 2/55minutes WC. **Surface:** grassy/metalled. 01/01-31/12
Distance: 300m on the spot 250m 100m.

Lailly-en-Val 21C1
GPS: n47,77023 e1,68544.

50 free Ch WC free. **Surface:** gravel.
Distance: 100m 50m 300m 200m.

Lamotte-Beuvron 21C1
Avenue de la Republique. **GPS:** n47,59795 e2,02524.

5 free Ch WC free. **Surface:** metalled. 01/01-31/12 Fri-morning, water disconnected in winter.
Distance: 200m 4,5km on the spot on the spot 300m 300m.

Tourist information Lamotte-Beuvron:
Avenue de la Republique. Market. Fri-morning.

Langon (Loir-et-Cher) 21C2
Parking Canal du Berry, D976. **GPS:** n47,28194 e1,82722.

7 free € 2/10minutes Ch € 2/1h. **Surface:** asphalted. 01/01-31/12 Service: winter.
Distance: 50m 20m 100m 100m.
Remarks: Coins at shops/town hall.

Le Châtelet 21D4
Le Tivoli, Avenue de la Gare. **GPS:** n46,64502 e2,27863.

5 free € 2 Ch. **Surface:** asphalted. 01/01-31/12
Distance: 50m 50m 300m.

Levet 21D3
Chemin du Crot A Thibault. **GPS:** n46,92306 e2,40639.

3 free Ch (3x)free. **Surface:** gravel. 01/03-31/10
Distance: 250m 250m 250m.
Remarks: Max. 24h.

Loches 21B2
Rue Amiral des Pointis. **GPS:** n47,13315 e1,00023.
8 free. **Surface:** gravel. 01/01-31/12
Distance: centre ±250m.
Remarks: Max. 24h.

Loches 21B2
Rue Aristide Briand. **GPS:** n47,12240 e1,00164.
Ch free. 01/01-31/12

Louzouer 15A6
Cidre Chivet, 323 Les Mussereaux. **GPS:** n48,02833 e2,87062.

5 ⬛€3 ⊓€ 3 ⬛Ch. **Surface:** asphalted/metalled. ⬛ 15/03-31/12
Distance: ⬛1,5km.

⬛⬛ **Marboué** ⬛ **14B6**
Aire de Marboué, Lieu-dit les 3 Fontaines. **GPS:** n48,11240 e1,32870. ⬆➡

8+5 ⬛free ⊓€ 2/100liter ⬛Ch⬛€ 2/1h. **Location:** Rural, comfortable,
central, quit. **Surface:** grassy/gravel. ⬛ 01/01-31/12
Distance: ⬛on the spot ⬛500m ⬛150m ⬛on the spot ⬛on the spot.
Remarks: N10 dir Châteaudun, before bridge to the right.

⬛⬛ **Martizay** **21B3**
Aire de Loisirs. GPS: n46,80528 e1,03806. ⬆

9 ⬛free ⊓⬛ Ch⬛ WCfree.
Surface: metalled/sand. ⬛ 01/01-31/12
Distance: ⬛on the spot ⬛bakery 500m.

⬛⬛ **Menetou-Salon** **21D2**
Rue de la Mairie. **GPS:** n47,23162 e2,49002. ⬆➡

6 ⬛free ⊓⬛Ch free. **Surface:** gravel/metalled. ⬛ 01/01-31/12
Distance: ⬛on the spot ⬛50m ⬛100m.

⬛⬛ **Mennetou-sur-Cher** ⬛ **21C2**
Place du 11 Novembre, N76. **GPS:** n47,26861 e1,86472. ⬆➡

8 ⬛free ⊓€ 2/10minutes ⬛Ch⬛€ 2/1h. **Surface:** sand. ⬛ 01/01-
31/12
Distance: ⬛150m ⬛100m ⬛150m ⬛150m.
Remarks: Small fortified town, coins at shops and tourist office.

⬛⬛ **Méry-sur-Cher** **21C2**
Chemin Lucien Bonneau/N76. **GPS:** n47,24586 e1,98989. ⬆

6 ⬛€ 5/24h, parking fee being collected ⊓⬛Ch ⬛ WCincluded. **Surface:**
metalled. ⬛ 01/01-31/12
Distance: ⬛150m ⬛100m.

⬛⬛ **Montoire-sur-le-Loir** ⬛⬛ **21A1**
Avenue de la République. **GPS:** n47,75750 e0,86928. ⬆

9 ⬛free ⊓⬛Ch free ⬛€ 1. **Location:** Urban, comfortable, quit. **Surface:**
asphalted. ⬛ 01/01-31/12
Distance: ⬛on the spot ⬛500m ⬛500m ⬛on the spot.
Remarks: At former station.

⬛⬛ **Montoire-sur-le-Loir** ⬛⬛ **21A1**
Aire de Montoire-sur-le-Loir, Boulevard des Alliés, Quartier Marescot. **GPS:**
n47,74990 e0,86317.

8 ⬛free. **Location:** Urban, central, quit.
Surface: asphalted. ⬛ 01/01-31/12
Distance: ⬛50m ⬛on the spot ⬛on the spot ⬛500m ⬛500m ⬛on the
spot ⬛on the spot.

⬛⬛ **Montrésor** ⬛ **21B2**
Rue du 8 Mai. **GPS:** n47,15750 e1,20169. ⬆
10 ⬛free ⊓⬛Ch free. **Surface:** asphalted. ⬛ 01/01-31/12
Distance: ⬛200m.

⬛⬛ **Neuillay-les-Bois** **21B3**
Route de Buzançais, D1. **GPS:** n46,76917 e1,47333.

5 ⬛free ⊓⬛Ch ⬛ WC free. **Surface:** metalled. ⬛ 01/04-31/10
Distance: ⬛50m ⬛50m ⬛50m ⬛50m.
Remarks: Max. 24h.

FR

Neuillé-Pont-Pierre 21A1
Parc Chauvin, Rue De Gaulle, D766. **GPS**: n47,54803 e0,55278. ⬆⬆ .

10 free ⌁ ⛏ Ch ⚡ (12x)free WC. **Location:** Urban, noisy. **Surface:** asphalted. ⬤ 01/01-31/12
Distance: 🚰on the spot ⚓ 3,5km ⊗on the spot 🛒on the spot.

Neuvy-Le-Barrois 22A3
Monsieur Thévenin, Le Pénisson, D45. **GPS**: n46,86159 e3,03930. ⬆➡ .

6 € 6 ⌁ ⛏ Ch ⊟ € 4 ⊡ € 2.
Surface: gravel/metalled. ⬤ 01/04-31/10
Distance: 🚰200m ⊗200m.

Neuvy-Pailloux 21C3
Les Gloux, RN151. **GPS**: n46,88278 e1,83682. ⬆ .
15 free ⌁ ⛏ ChWCfree. **Surface:** asphalted. ⬤ 01/01-31/12
Remarks: Isolated parking.

Tourist information Neuvy-Pailloux:
ℹ Small town.

Nogent-le-Roi 14C4
Rue du Pont des Demoiselles. **GPS**: n48,65059 e1,52894.
⛏ ⌁ Ch ⊟.

Nogent-sur-Vernisson 22A1
GPS: n47,84055 e2,73996. ⬆➡ .

6 grasstiles/metalled. ⬤ 01/01-31/12
Distance: 🚰300m ⊗300m 🛒300m.

Ouzouer-sur-Trézée 22A1
Parking halte nautique, Rue Saint-Roche/ Canal de Briare. **GPS**: n47,67000 e2,80888. ⬆ .

5 free ⛏. **Surface:** asphalted. ⬤ 01/04-31/10
Distance: 🚰500m 🛒on the spot ⊗500m.
Remarks: At canal 'de Briare', max. 48h.

Ouzouer-sur-Trézée 22A1
Camping municipal, Chemin du Rochoir. **GPS**: n47,66819 e2,80611.

6 free. **Location:** Quit. **Surface:** gravel. ⬤ 01/01-31/12
Distance: 🚰1km ⚓on the spot 🛒on the spot 🛒1km.

Nogent-sur-Vernisson 22A1
Rue Georges Bannery. **GPS**: n47,85363 e2,74014.
⛏ € 2,50 Ch⊟ € 2,50.
Remarks: Coins at office de tourisme, PMU Rue Bannery or bar in Rue A. Briand.

Nouan-le-Fuzelier 21C1
Rue Gauchoix. **GPS**: n47,53324 e2,03437. ⬆➡ .

6 € 4,50 ⛏ Ch ⚡ € 2,60 WC ⊟included 🗑. **Surface:** gravel. ⬤ 01/04-31/10

Reignac-sur-Indre 21A2
Rue Louis de Barberin, D58. **GPS**: n47,22922 e0,91585. ⬆ .

5 free ⛏ € 2/100liter ⛏ Ch. **Location:** Rural, central, noisy. **Surface:** asphalted/metalled. ⬤ 01/01-31/12
Distance: 🚰300m ⚓ 20km 🛒on the spot 🚲 on the spot 🎣 on the spot.
Remarks: Max. 24h, coins at the shops in the village.

Restigné 20D2
Rue Basse. **GPS**: n47,28041 e0,22614. ⬆➡ .

FR

10 🗂free 🚰€ 2/100liter ⚡Ch. **Location:** Rural, central, quit. **Surface:** gravel. ⬛ 01/01-31/12
Distance: 🚰on the spot ⊗on the spot 🎣on the spot 🎿on the spot.
Remarks: Coins at town hall.

Saint-Denis-les-Ponts 〽〒 14B6
Aire de Saint Denis-les-Ponts, Rue Jean Moulin. **GPS:** n48,06643 e1,28950.⬆️ ➡️.

+10 🗂free 🚰€ 2/100liter ⚡Ch.
Location: Urban, comfortable, central, quit.
Surface: gravel.
⬛ 01/01-31/12 ⬤ Service: winter.
Distance: 🚰Châteaudun 3km 🏊on the spot 🚴on the spot ⊗100m 🚂on the spot 🎿on the spot.
Remarks: Coins available at the shops, Châteaudun (city and castle) 4km.

Sainte-Maure-de-Touraine 🍴〽 21A2
Aire du Bois Chaudron, D910, Le Bois Caudron. **GPS:** n47,09315 e0,61275.⬆️➡️.

40 🗂€ 2,50, 2 pers.incl 🚰€ 1 ⚡€ 2 Ch€ 3 🧹(4x)€ 2/12h WC🗑⬤€
4 📶€ 2.🔌 **Location:** Rural, comfortable, isolated, quit. **Surface:** grassy. ⬛ 01/01-31/12
Distance: 🚰1,5km 🏊4,4km ⊗1,5km 🚂1,5km 🎿on the spot.
Remarks: Bread-service.

Sainte-Maure-de-Touraine 🍦〽 21A2
Parking Ronsard, Avenue Ronsard. **GPS:** n47,11056 e0,61750.⬆️➡️.

15 🗂free 🚰⚡Chfree WC. **Location:** Urban, central, quit. **Surface:** asphalted. ⬛ 01/01-31/12

Distance: 🚰200m 🏊3km ⊗200m 🚂200m 🚂on the spot.

Sancerre 〽🚡 22A2
Rempart des Abreuvoirs. **GPS:** n47,33062 e2,83638.⬆️.

10 🗂free. **Surface:** asphalted. ⬛ 01/01-31/12
Distance: 🚰on the spot ⊗on the spot.

Tourist information Sancerre:
ℹ️ Office de Tourisme, Rue de la croix de bois, www.ville-sancerre.com.City between the vintages with the famous white wine of the same name.

Sancoins 22A3
Quai du Canal. **GPS:** n46,83356 e2,91568.⬆️➡️.

20 🗂free 🚰⚡Ch WC free. **Surface:** gravel/metalled. ⬛ 01/01-31/12
Distance: 🚰200m 🏊on the spot 🚂200m.

Selles-sur-Cher 21C2
Avenue Kleber-Loustau. **GPS:** n47,27639 e1,55889.⬆️.

15 🗂€ 5 🚰⚡Ch. **Surface:** asphalted/grassy. ⬛ 01/01-31/12
Distance: 🚰500m 🏊200m ⊗500m 🚂500m.
Remarks: Coins at camping, office de tourisme, town hall.

St.Amand-Montrond 21D3
Quai Lutin, via Avenue Maréchal Foch. **GPS:** n46,71818 e2,50480.⬆️➡️.

12 🗂free 🚰⚡Ch WC free. **Surface:** asphalted/gravel. ⬛ 01/01-31/12
Distance: 🚰nearby 🏊on the spot 🚴on the spot ⊗300m 🚂300m.

St.Brisson-sur-Loire 21D1
Rue des Ruets, route d'Autry, D52. **GPS:** n47,64680 e2,68028.⬆️.

6 ⌘free ⛽🔌Ch📦free. **Surface:** asphalted. 🕐 01/01-31/12
Distance: 🏠100m ⊗100m 🍴100m 🚌50m.
Remarks: Parking nearby town hall.

10 ⌘free ⛽Chfree WC. **Location:** Rural, very simple, central, quit. **Surface:** gravel. 🕐 01/01-31/12
Distance: 🏠on the spot ⚓on the spot ⛽on the spot.

🏕 S	St.Georges-sur-Arnon	21C3

N151. **GPS:** n46,97740 e2,06908.

🏕 S	Theillay	21C2

Chemin du Ronaire. **GPS:** n47,31849 e2,03775. ⬆️

10 ⌘free ⛽🔌Ch WC free. **Surface:** asphalted.

🏕 S	St.Gondon	21D1

Rue de Sully. **GPS:** n47,69808 e2,53876. ⬆️

10 ⌘free ⛽🔌Chfree. **Surface:** gravel/metalled. 🕐 01/01-31/12
Distance: 🏠250m 🍴250m.

🏕 S	Thiron-Gardais 🚻	14B5

Aire de Thiron-Gardais, Avenue de la Gare. **GPS:** n48,31194 e0,99583. ⬆️➡️
10 ⌘free ⛽🔌Chfree. **Location:** Urban. **Surface:** asphalted.
Distance: 🏠100m 🚂300m ⊗300m 🍴300m 🚲on the spot 🚶100m.

🏕 S	Tour-en-Sologne	21B1

Rue de la Mairie. **GPS:** n47,53786 e1,49973.

3 ⌘free ⛽🔌Chfree. **Surface:** asphalted. 🕐 01/01-31/12
Distance: 🏠300m ⚓on the spot 🍴300m.
Remarks: Max. 48h.

🏕 S	Sully-sur-Loire 🌿⛲🍴	21D1

Chemin de la Salle Verte. **GPS:** n47,77139 e2,38451. ⬆️➡️

10 ⌘free ⛽€ 2 🔌Ch WC. **Surface:** metalled.
Distance: 🏠50m 🚂200m 🍴bakery 100m.

🏕 S	Vailly-sur-Sauldre	21D1

Rue du Pont. **GPS:** n47,45727 e2,64665. ⬆️

16 ⌘free ⛽🔌Ch📦free. **Surface:** gravel/metalled. 🕐 01/01-31/12
Distance: 🏠800m ⚓on the spot 🚂on the spot ⊗800m 🍴800m.
Remarks: Narrow entrance, nearby castle of Sully.

🏕 S	Ternay 🚻	21A1

Plan d'eau, Rue Saint Père. **GPS:** n47,73114 e0,77617. ⬆️

8 ⌘€ 3,50 ⛽🔌Chfree 🚿€ 2,50 WC ⬜€ 0,80. **Surface:** gravel/metalled.
🕐 01/04-31/10
Distance: 🏠300m 🚂on the spot ⊗nearby 🍴nearby.
Remarks: At D923 on entering the village from Aubigny, along river.
Tourist information Vailly-sur-Sauldre:
⛺ 🕐 Fri.

Avenue de la Résistance. **GPS**: n47,16080 e1,56163.⬆️.

10 🚿free. **Surface**: metalled. ⬛ 01/01-31/12
Distance: 🚶100m ⊗100m 🛒100m.
Remarks: Nearby entrance castle.
Tourist information Valençay:
ℹ️ Office de Tourisme, 2, Avenue de la Résistance, www.pays-de-valencay.com.
🏰 Château.Castle, 15th-18th century. ⬛ 01/03-30/11.

Veigné 🌿⚓🏠 21A2

Camping de la Plage, 'D50. **GPS**: n47,28921 e0,73436.
3 🚿free 🚰€ 2/100liter 🚿Ch🔌€ 2/10minutes. **Location**: Comfortable, noisy. **Surface**: metalled.
Distance: 🚶on the spot ⚓on the spot 🚲on the spot ⊗100m 🛒100m.

Vendôme 🌿⚓🏠🏠 21B1

Aie de Vendôme, Rue Geoffroy Martel. **GPS**: n47,79111 e1,07528.⬆️.

5 🚿free. **Location**: Urban, very simple, central. **Surface**: asphalted. ⬛ 01/01-31/12
Distance: 🚶500m.

Villaines les Rochers 🏠 21A2

Aire de Villaines-les-Rochers, Place de la Mairie/ Rue des Ecoles. **GPS**: n47,22083 e0,49583.⬆️➡️.

6 🚿free 🚰🚿Ch WC free. **Location**: Urban, comfortable, central, quit.
Surface: asphalted. ⬛ 01/01-31/12
Distance: 🚶on the spot ⊗100m 🛒100m 🚲on the spot 🏊on the spot.
Remarks: Max. 24h.

Villandry 🌿⚓🏠 21A2

Aire de Villandry, Rue Principale. **GPS**: n47,34100 e0,51127.⬆️. ,

25 🚿free 🚰€ 2/100liter 🚿Ch WC 🧽.
Location: Rural, comfortable, central, quit.
Surface: grasstiles. ⬛ 01/01-31/12
Distance: 🚶50m 🚲3,1km ⚓300 m ⊗90m 🛒90m 🚐on the spot 🏊on the spot 🏕on the spot.
Remarks: Coins at Office de Tourisme(100m), Château de Villandry 200m.

Villedômer 🏠 21A1

Aire de Villedômer, Rue du Lavoir. **GPS**: n47,54465 e0,88727.⬆️➡️.

5 🚿free, 15/06-15/09 € 5 🚰€ 2/100liter 🚿Ch🔌€ 2/1h. **Location**: Rural, central, quit. **Surface**: metalled. ⬛ 01/01-31/12
Distance: 🚶100m 🚲8,1km ⚓100m ⊗200m 🛒200m 🚐on the spot 🏕on the spot.
Remarks: Max. 24h, coins at town hall (200m), bakery (200m) and supermarket (50m).

Villequiers 22A2

L'Étappe Berrichonne, Le Petit Azillon. **GPS**: n47,08828 e2,77429.⬆️➡️.

6 🚿€6 🚰 3 🚿Ch🔌. **Surface**: gravel/metalled. ⬛ 01/01-31/12
Distance: 🚶3km.

Vouvray 🏠 21A1

Parking Bec de Cisse, Rue Bec de Cisse. **GPS**: n47,40929 e0,79735.⬆️➡️.

8 🚿free 🚰€ 2/100liter 🚿Ch🔌€ 2/1h WC.
Location: Rural, comfortable, central, quit. **Surface**: asphalted. ⬛ 01/01-31/12 ⬛ Service: winter.
Distance: 🚶on the spot 🚲8,5km ⚓500m ⊗150m 🛒150m 🚐on the spot 🏊on the spot.

Remarks: Coins at campsite (100m) and tourist office.

Bourgogne

Anost — 22C2

Place Centrale. **GPS:** n47,07778 e4,09869.⬆.

10 free Ch free. **Location:** Very simple. **Surface:** metalled. 01/01-31/12
Distance: on the spot.

Autun — 22C3

Route de Chalon. **GPS:** n46,95548 e4,31667.⬆.

18 free € 3,50 Ch. **Surface:** asphalted. 01/01-31/12
Distance: 500m on the spot on the spot nearby.
Remarks: Parking at small lake Le Vallon at N80.

Tourist information Autun:
Office de Tourisme, 2, Avenue Charles de Gaulle, www.autun.com.
Musée Rolin. Roman and Medieval excavations.
Wed, Fri, Su.

Auxerre — 22B1

Quai de la République. **GPS:** n47,79636 e3,57633.⬆.

free free. **Surface:** asphalted.
Distance: on the spot 100m on the spot.
Remarks: Along the Yonne river.

Tourist information Auxerre:
Office de Tourisme, 1-2, Quai de la République, www.ot-auxerre.fr.
Tue, Fri.

Beaune — 22D3

Parking Charles de Gaulle. **GPS:** n47,01731 e4,83628.⬆.

5 Ch € 3,50/1h. **Surface:** asphalted.
Distance: 500m 2,6km on the spot centre commercial 300m.
Remarks: 5 special pitches, all parking places permitted.

Tourist information Beaune:
Office de Tourisme, 1, Rue de l'Hôtel-Dieu, www.ot-beaune.fr. Tourist place worth seeing, old centre with ramparts.
Hôtel Dieu et Musée. Former hospital, 15th century, museum.
Château de Meursault, Meursault. Castle with vintage and wine tastery.

Chablis — 22B1

Route d'Auxerre, D235. **GPS:** n47,81711 e3,78425.⬆.

5 free free. **Location:** Very simple. **Surface:** asphalted.
Distance: centre 500m on the spot.

Chalon-sur-Saône — 22D3

P Ville Historique, Promenade Sainte Marie. **GPS:** n46,78365 e4,86046.⬆.

2 free Ch free. **Location:** Very simple. **Surface:** asphalted.
Distance: 500m 50m.
Remarks: Free shuttle to centre.

Tourist information Chalon-sur-Saône:
Office de Tourisme, Square Chabas - 29, Boulevard de la République, www.chalon-sur-saone.net.
Musée Nicéphore Niepce. Photography museum. 9.30-11.30h, 14.30-17.30h, 01/07-31/08 10-18h Tue, holiday.

Charolles — 22C4

Route de Viry. **GPS:** n46,43956 e4,28203.⬆.

5 🛒€3 ⚡🔌Ch📶€ 3. **Surface:** gravel. ⬛ 01/04-01/10
Distance: 🚶300m.
Remarks: Max. 48h.

Château-Chinon 22C3
Rue Jean Sallonnyer. **GPS:** n47,06304 e3,93627.⬆

10 🛒free ⚡🔌Chfree. **Surface:** metalled. ⬛ 01/01-31/12
Distance: 🚶on the spot ⊗250m 🚰250m.
Remarks: Max. 24h.

Châtillon-en-Bazois 22B3
Place Pierre Saury. **GPS:** n47,05310 e3,65511.⬆

5 🛒free. **Surface:** metalled. ⬛ 01/04-31/10
Distance: 🚰50m.

Chiddes 22C3
Le Bourg. **GPS:** n46,86108 e3,94091.⬆

4 🛒free ⚡🔌Chfree. **Surface:** gravel. ⬛ 01/01-31/12
Distance: 🚶on the spot ⊗on the spot.
Remarks: Max. 48h, coins at restaurant.

Clamecy 🌿 22B2
Rue de l'Abattoir. **GPS:** n47,46222 e3,52250.⬆

6 🛒free 🔌Chfree. **Location:** Very simple.
Surface: gravel. ⬛ 01/01-31/12
Distance: 🚶350m ⊗150m.

Décize 22B3
Esplanade des Halles, Allée Marcel Merle. **GPS:** n46,83223 e3,46133.⬆

± 15 🛒free ⚡€ 3 🔌Ch🧹. **Surface:** metalled. ⬛ 01/01-31/12
Distance: 🚶200m 🛶on the spot 🚣on the spot.
Remarks: On the river Loire.

Tourist information Décize:
Ⓜ Musée de la Mine, La Machine.Life of the coalminer. ⬛ summer 10-12h, 15-19h ⬤ Tue. Ⓣ € 1,60.

Digoin 22C4
Place de la Grève, Route de Vichy. **GPS:** n46,48102 e3,97288.⬆➡

± 15 🛒free ⚡🔌Ch🚿 (4x)free. **Location:** Central. **Surface:** asphalted.
⬛ 01/01-31/12
Distance: 🚶on the spot ⊗on the spot 🍴on the spot 🛒on the spot.
Remarks: Next to Office du Tourisme.

Tourist information Digoin:
ⓘ Office de Tourisme, 8, rue Guilleminot, perso.wanadoo.fr/office-de-tourisme-de-digoin.

Ecuisses 22C3
Place Marcel Pagnol, Route du Bourg. **GPS:** n46,76019 e4,52283.⬆

20 🛒free ⚡🔌free. **Surface:** metalled. ⬛ 01/01-31/12
Remarks: Max. 48h.

Étang-sur-Arroux 22C3
Place du Mousseau. **GPS:** n46,86631 e4,18946.⬆
🛒free ⚡🔌Chfree. **Location:** Rural.
Surface: asphalted. ⬛ 01/01-31/12
Distance: 🚶on the spot 🚰on the spot.

Fours 22B3
Rue des Saules, D981. **GPS:** n46,81720 e3,71806.⬆

10 ⌁free 🔧🔧 Ch 🔌free. **Surface:** gravel. 🚰 01/01-31/12
🔋S **Génelard** 🏖️🚣 22C4
Place du Bassin, D974. **GPS:** n46,57750 e4,23500.⬆️➡️.

2 ⌁free 🔧🔧Ch 🔌free. **Surface:** asphalted. 🚰 01/01-31/12
Distance: 🚣on the spot.
🔋S **Givry** 22D3
Relais camping-car, Rue de la Gare. **GPS:** n46,78000 e4,74830.⬆️.

15 ⌁free 🔧€ 2/100liter 🔧Ch🔧€ 2/10minutes. **Location:** Comfortable.
Surface: asphalted. 🚰 01/01-31/12
Distance: 🚣on the spot.
Remarks: Coins available at restaurant.

Tourist information Givry:
🏛️ Marché.Market. 🚰 Thu.
🚲 La Voie Verte de Givry à Cluny.Cycle route on former railway,.
🔋S **Gurgy** 15B6
Quai des Fontaines. **GPS:** n47,86348 e3,55376.⬆️➡️.

20 ⌁free 🔧€ 4/10minutes 🔧Ch🔧€ 4/1h. **Surface:** grassy/gravel. 🚰
01/04-31/10
Distance: 🚣50m 🚲7km 🛒on the spot ⊗500m 🍽️300m.
Remarks: Along the Yonne river, coints at supermarket.
🔋S **La Charité-sur-Loire** 22A2
Quai Romain Mollot. **GPS:** n47,17483 e3,01123.

5 ⌁free 🔧€ 4 🔧Ch🔧 🔌. **Surface:** asphalted. 🚰 01/01-31/12
Distance: 🚣250m 🛒on the spot 🔌on the spot ⊗on the spot 🍽️on the spot
🍺on the spot.
Remarks: Parking at river.
La Charité-sur-Loire 22A2
Quai de la Tête de l'Ourth. **GPS:** n47,17577 e3,01254.
3 ⌁free. **Surface:** asphalted. 🚰 01/01-31/12
Remarks: Parking at river.
Laignes 22C1
Chemin du Moulin Neuf, D965. **GPS:** n47,84850 e4,36132.⬆️➡️.
10 ⌁free. **Surface:** grassy/gravel. 🚰 01/01-31/12
Distance: 🚣1 km.
Remarks: Parking at river, max. 24h.
🔋S **Louhans** 23A4
Halte nautique, Rue du Port. **GPS:** n46,62952 e5,21302.⬆️.

15 ⌁free, 1/5-30/9 € 5 + € 0,20/pp tourist tax 🔧🔧 Ch 🔌 WC ⌁included.
Location: Comfortable, quit. **Surface:** gravel.
Distance: 🚣400m.
Remarks: Sanitary building: 1/5-30/9, to be paid at Halte Nautique.
🔋S **Louhans** 23A4
Boivin Claude, Rue de la Griffonnière. **GPS:** n46,63070 e5,24857.⬆️.
12 ⌁€5 🔧🔧Chincluded 🔌€ 5. **Surface:** gravel. 🚰 01/01-31/12
🔋S **Luzy** 22C3
Place du champ De Foire. **GPS:** n46,79028 e3,96840.⬆️.

4 ⌁free 🔧🔧 Ch WC free. **Surface:** metalled. 🚰 01/01-31/12
Distance: 🚣on the spot ⊗on the spot 🍽️200m 🍺500m.
Remarks: Max. 48h, coins at the shops and restaurant.
🔋S **Marsannay-la-Côte** 22D2
Rue du Rocher. **GPS:** n47,27099 e4,99224.⬆️➡️.

3 🛏free ⟟🚰€ 2,50 🍽Ch. ◻ 01/05-15/09
Distance: 🚶300m ⚓2,4km.

🛏S Prissé 22D4
Cave de Prissé. GPS: n46,32226 e4,75257.⬆️

5 🛏free ⟟🚰Chfree. **Surface:** asphalted. ◻ 01/01-31/12
Distance: ⚓3,5km 🛒750m.
Remarks: Via N74/D974.

5 🛏free ⟟🚰 Ch WC free. **Location:** Very simple. **Surface:** asphalted. ◻ 01/01-31/12
Distance: 🚶500m ⚓3km.
Remarks: Max. 24h.

🛏S Nolay 22D3
Avenue de la Liberté. **GPS:** n46,95016 e4,62828.⬆️

🛏S Pruzilly 22D5
La Croix Blanche, salle des Fêtes. GPS: n46,25708 e4,69792.

± 10 🛏free ⟟€ 2 🍽Ch🛏€ 2. **Surface:** gravel. ◻ 01/01-31/12
Remarks: Coins at Bar-Tabac, office de tourisme.

Tourist information Nolay:
🌿 Site Champetre du Bout du Monde, Vauchignon. Water falls.

6 🛏free ⟟🚰 Ch WC free. **Surface:** asphalted. ◻ 01/01-31/12
Distance: 🚶on the spot.
Remarks: Max. 48h, vins de Côte de Beaujolais.

🛏S Nuits-Saint-Georges 22D2
Rue de Cussigny. **GPS:** n47,13178 e4,95189.⬆️

🛏S Saint-Fargeau 🌿 22A1
Rue de Laveau, D18. **GPS:** n47,63968 e3,06999.⬆️

6 🛏free ⟟🚰 Chfree. **Location:** Very simple. **Surface:** metalled.
Distance: 🚶400m ⚓2,1km ✗500m 🛒Intermarché 300m.

Tourist information Nuits-Saint-Georges:
ℹ️ Office de Tourisme, 3, Rue Sonoys, www.ot-nuits-st-georges.fr. Small city the famous Burgundian vineyards, signposted wine routes.
⛱ ◻ Fri.

10 🛏free ⟟🚰 Ch WC free. ◻ 01/01-31/12
Distance: 🚶50m ✗50m.

🛏S Pouges-les-Eaux ⚓ 22A2
D907. **GPS:** n47,08315 e3,09382.⬆️

🛏S Savigny-le-Sec 22D2
Chemin de Saussy. **GPS:** n47,43365 e5,04607.⬆️

5 🛏free ⟟€ 2/10minutes 🍽Ch🛏€ 2/10minutes ♻. **Surface:** asphalted. ◻ 01/01-31/12
Distance: 🚶250m ⚓1,4km ✗100m.

🛏S Pouilly-en-Auxois 22D2
Rue du Vert Auxois. **GPS:** n47,26539 e4,54875.

10 🛏€ 3,50 ⟟€ 2 🍽Ch WC. **Surface:** gravel. ◻ 01/01-31/12

🛏S Semur-en-Auxois 22C1
Avenue Pasteur. **GPS:** n47,49306 e4,34472.
🛏free ⟟🚰Chfree.
Surface: asphalted.
◻ 01/01-31/12

Remarks: Behind stadium, near police station.
Tourist information Semur-en-Auxois:
🔔 Alise-Ste-Reine.Findings of Gallo-Roman city. ⬛ 01/04-31/10 daily.

Seurre — 23A3
Rue de la Perche à l'Oiseau. **GPS**: n47,00405 e5,14318. ⬆➡.

10 ⬛free 🚰€ 4 🔌Ch 🧹 ♻. **Surface:** asphalted. ⬛ 01/01-31/12
Distance: 🚶200m ⛵on the spot.

St.Gengoux-le-National — 22D4
GPS: n46,60624 e4,66844. ⬆.

16 ⬛free 🚰€ 3/15minutes 🔌Ch🔌€ 3/50minutes WC ♻. **Location:**
Quit. **Surface:** metalled. ⬛ 01/01-31/12
Distance: 🚶500m.
Remarks: At former station.
Tourist information St.Gengoux-le-National:
🚲 La Voie Verte.Cycle route on former railway,.

St.Honoré-les-Bains — 22B3
Allée de la Cressonnière. **GPS**: n46,90471 e3,84059. ⬆➡.

4 ⬛free 🚰€ 2 🔌Ch🔌€ 2. **Surface:** gravel. ⬛ 01/01-31/12
Distance: 🚶on the spot ⊗on the spot 🚌on the spot.
Remarks: Max. 48h, coins at mairie.

Franche Comté

Arc-et-Senans — 23B3
Grande rue. **GPS**: n47,03343 e5,78120. ⬆.

⬛free 🚰€ 1 🔌Ch. **Surface:** gravel. ⬛ 01/01-31/12

Remarks: Coints at mairie, supermarket, campsite.

Arinthod — 23A4
Rue de la Prélette. **GPS**: n46,39654 e5,57013.

6 ⬛6 🚰🔌Ch🧹 included. **Surface:** gravel. ⬛ 01/01-31/12

Arsure-Arsurette ❄ — 23B3
Châlet des Arches. **GPS**: n46,72168 e6,08402.

10 ⬛free 🚰€ 2 WC 🔌. **Surface:** asphalted. ⬛ 01/01-31/12

Baume-les-Dames — 23C2
Quai du Canal. **GPS**: n47,34000 e6,35806. ⬆.

32 ⬛€ 6,50 🚰🔌Ch🧹 WCincluded 🔌€ 1,50. **Surface:** asphalted/grassy.
⬛ 01/01-31/12
Distance: 🚶on the spot 🚲5,3km 🚌on the spot.
Remarks: Max. 24h.
Tourist information Baume-les-Dames:
ℹ Office de Tourisme, 6, rue de Provence.Small tourist town in the heart of
Doubs valley.
👁 Abbaye Nôtre Dame.Historical monument, 18th century.

Besançon — 23B2
Parking du Crous, Cité Carnot, Quai Veil Picard. **GPS**: n47,23702 e6,01644. ⬆.

12 ⬛free 🚰🔌Ch. **Surface:** asphalted. ⬛ 01/01-31/12
Distance: 🚶on the spot.
Tourist information Besançon:
ℹ Office de Tourisme, 2, place de la 1re Armée Française, www.besancon-
tourisme.com.City worth a visit along the Doubs river. Victor Hugo was born in

the house at Grande Rue number 40.

👁 Jardin Botanique, avenue de la Paix.Botanical gardens.
Ⓜ Citadelle; Musée de la Résistance et de déportation.War museum.
Ⓜ Musée Populaire Comtois, Citadelle.Folkore museum. 🅾 9-18/19h, winter 10-17h.
Ⓜ Muséum d'Histoire Naturelle comprenant le jardin zoologique, l'aquarium, l'insectarium et le noctarium, Citadelle.Natural museum.
✖ Château, Vaire-le-Grand. 🅾 15/08-18/09, 19/09-14/08 by agreement.
✝ Cathédrale St Jean.
⚅ 🅾 Tue, Fri, Su.
☻ Parc Zoologique de la Citadelle, Citadelle.Zoo. 🅾 10-17/19h. 🆃 € 7.

Bois-d'Amont 23B4
Musée de la Boisellerie, Impasse de l'Eglantine. **GPS:** n46,53771 e6,13934.

10 🅿 free 🔧 2 🍴Ch 🔌 € 2. **Surface:** asphalted.
Distance: ⊗on the spot 🍴on the spot 🛒on the spot.
Remarks: Service at town hall 300m.

Brognard 23C1
Base de Loisirs de la Savoureuse, Rue de Paquis. **GPS:** n47,52834 e6,85652. ⬆

3 🅿 free 🔧 🍴Ch free. **Surface:** asphalted. 🅾 01/01-31/12
Distance: ⚓50m ⚓1,3km.
Remarks: Max. 48h.

Champagnole 23B3
20, Rue Georges Vallerey. **GPS:** n46,74633 e5,89918. ⬆

5 🅿 free, 1/6-15/9 € 5 🔧 🍴Ch 🔌 € 5.
Surface: gravel. 🅾 01/01-31/12
Distance: ⚓500m ⚓250m.
Remarks: Max. 1 night, coins at campsite.

Clairvaux-les-Lacs 23B4
Route de Lons-le-Saunier, D678. **GPS:** n46,58246 e5,74660. ⬆

6 🅿 free 🔧🍴Ch free. 🅾 01/01-31/12
Distance: ⚓nearby.
Remarks: On entering village, nearby police station.

Conliège 23A4
Rue du Saugeois. **GPS:** n46,65270 e5,59981. ⬆➡

2 🅿 free 🔧🍴Ch WC free. **Surface:** asphalted.
Distance: ⊗100m.

Consolation-Maisonnettes 23C2
Parc du Seminaire du Cirque de Consolation.. **GPS:** n47,15848 e6,60600. ⬆

10 🅿 € 5/24h 🔧🍴Ch 🧹 WC included. **Surface:** asphalted.

Corre 16B6
Fluvial Loisirs, Pré le Saônier. **GPS:** n47,91402 e5,99308.

32 🅿 € 6 01/11-31/03, € 8 01/04-31/10 🔧🍴Ch 🧹 included 🔌 € 1,50 🔌 €
4 💧 € 3/day 🚿. **Surface:** gravel. 🅾 01/01-31/12
Distance: ⚓200m ⚓50m ⊗on the spot 🛒bakery 300m, supermarket 500m 🅿100m.

Cousance 23A4
Grande rue, Champs de foire. **GPS:** n46,52929 e5,39154. ⬆

4 🛏free ⚓ 🔌 Ch WC free. **Surface:** asphalted. 🅾 01/01-31/12
Distance: 🚶100m ⛵6,6km 🚊100m.

20 🛏free ⚓ 🔌 Ch free. **Surface:** asphalted.
Distance: 🚲on the spot 🚶on the spot.

Dôle 23A2
Avenue de Lahr. **GPS:** n47,08983 e5,49641.
🛏free.

Les Rousses 23B4
Parking l'Aube, Route du Lac. **GPS:** n46,48779 e6,06690.⬆

Tourist information Dôle:
ℹ Office de Tourisme, Place Grevy, www.dole.org.City on the Doubs river with many monuments.
Ⓜ Maison natale de Louis Pasteur, 43 de la rue Pasteur.Birth house Pasteur, museum. 🅾 1/4-31/10 10-12h, 14-18h, 01/11-31/03 Sa-Su 14-18h ⬤ Su-morning. 🇹 free.
Ⓜ Musée des Beaux-Arts, 85, rue des Arènes.Museum of Fine Arts.

Jeurre 23A4
35, Rue Principale. **GPS:** n46,36662 e5,70769.⬆➡

30 🛏free, €4/Winter ⚓ € 3,60/100liter 🔌Ch ➕ € 3,60/1h 🧺. **Surface:** asphalted. 🅾 01/01-31/12
Distance: 🚊200m.

Les Rousses 23B4
Porte du Balanciers, Route Blanche, N5. **GPS:** n46,44852 e6,07591.⬆

40 🛏€4 ⚓€ 2 🔌Ch ➕€ 2. **Surface:** grassy. 🅾 01/05-31/10
Remarks: From Lons le Saunier dir Saint Claude.

La Chapelle des Bois ❄ 23B4
Station de ski, Chemin du Marais Blanc. **GPS:** n46,60307 e6,11317.⬆
🛏free ⚓€ 3 🔌Ch. **Surface:** unpaved.
Distance: 🎿on the spot.

La Pesse 23B4
GPS: n46,28400 e5,84764.⬆

30 🛏free, €4/Winter ⚓€ 3,50 🔌Ch ➕ WC. **Surface:** asphalted. 🅾 01/01-31/12
Distance: ❌Restaurant 🚊5km.
Remarks: Ski station, ski rental, ski school, coins at Tourist Info.

Tourist information Les Rousses:
ℹ Jura community in an attractive green environment, also winter sports possibilities.
Ⓜ Musée de la Lunetterie, 5, rue Lamartine, Morez.Optical museum.

Longeville 23B3
Coulet, Grande Rue. **GPS:** n47,04148 e6,22678.

🛏free ⚓€ 2 🔌Ch WC. **Surface:** unpaved. 🅾 01/01-31/12
Distance: 🚊on the spot.
Remarks: At start of langlauf circuit.

La Pesse 23B4
Ferme Auberge de La Combe aux Bisons, Lieu-dit Pré Reverchon. **GPS:** n46,29278 e5,86011.
3 🛏guests free ⚓. 🅾 01/01-31/12
Distance: ❌on the spot.

Lamoura 23B4
Route de Prémanon, D25. **GPS:** n46,39810 e5,98300.

10 🛏€5 + € 1/pp ⚓🔌Ch 🔧 WC included. **Surface:** gravel/sand. 🅾 01/04-31/10

Luxeuil-les-Bains ♈ 23C1
Place de l'Etang de la Poche, rue Gambetta. **GPS:** n47,81679 e6,38659.

FR

20 free € 2/100liter Ch € 2/1h. **Surface:** asphalted.
Distance: on the spot Auchan/Aldi 500m.
Tourist information Luxeuil-les-Bains:
Fougerolles.Since the 16th century the small town is the centre of distilleries (Kirsch and cherry brandy).
Musée de la Tour des Echevins, 36, rue Victor Genoux.Art from 19th-20th century.

Maisod	23A4

La Mercantine. **GPS:** n46,46500 e5,68864.

40 €9 € 2 Ch. **Location:** Rural. **Surface:** gravel.
Distance: 100m 200m.
Remarks: At lake Vouglans.

Montbéliard	23C1

Parking du Champ de Foire. **GPS:** n47,50663 e6,79128.

4 free € 1,60 Ch € 1,60. **Surface:** asphalted.
Remarks: Max. 48h.

Montreux-Château	23D1

D11. **GPS:** n47,60283 e7,00252.

8 €5/24h Ch (8x) WC. **Surface:** gravel.

Moussières	23B4

GPS: n46,32111 e5,89778.

6 free € 2 Ch € 2. **Surface:** gravel. 01/01-31/12
Remarks: Cheese farm.

Mouthe	23B3

Place de l'Eglise. **GPS:** n46,71042 e6,19570.

20 free € 3 Ch. **Surface:** asphalted.
Remarks: Coins at the bakery, supermarket, tourist office.

Orgelet	23A4

Place Ancien Champ de Foire, Rue du Faubourg de l'Orme. **GPS:** n46,52232 e5,60860.
10 free Ch WC free. **Surface:** gravel. 01/01-31/12
Remarks: Closed when frosty.
Tourist information Orgelet:
Old Jura village in natural environment.

Salins-les-Bains	23B3

Rue de la République, D472. **GPS:** n46,93254 e5,87899.

8 free Ch free. **Surface:** asphalted.
Distance: 50m.
Remarks: Permitted to park/stay overnight on all parkings.

Sampans	23A2

Bidaut Caravanes, Route de Dijon, RN5. **GPS:** n47,12667 e5,45556.

3 free € 2 Ch. 01/01-31/12
Distance: 10km.

Sancey-le-Long	23C2

D31/D464. **GPS:** n47,30513 e6,59477.

FR

2 🛏free ⚡€ 2 Ch 🚰 2. **Surface:** gravel.
Remarks: Coins at supermarket, cafe, centre commercial.

| | | Saulx | 23B1 |

Place de l'Eglise. **GPS:** n47,69620 e6,28030.⬆️.

5 🛏free ⚡€ 0,50 🗑. **Surface:** metalled.

| | | Sermamagny | 23C1 |

Rue Alfred Lallemand. **GPS:** n47,67348 e6,81418. ⬆️ .

30 🛏free. **Surface:** grassy.

| | | St.Claude | 23B4 |

Avenue de la Libération, D436. **GPS:** n46,38049 e5,85209.
3 🛏free ⚡ 🗑 Ch 🚰free. **Surface:** asphalted. ⬤ 01/01-31/12

Tourist information St.Claude:
ℹ️ Tourist town, production of pipes.
👁 Musée du Pipe et Diamant.Pipes and diamond exhibition. ⬤ 01/06-30/09
9.30-12h, 14-18.30h, 01/10-31/05 14-18h ⬤ Su.

| | | St.Loup-sur-Semouse | 16B6 |

Rue de Champ de Tir. **GPS:** n47,88303 e6,26048.

Aire d'acceuil pour camping-cars, Rue du lac. **GPS:** n46,81268 e6,30375.

40 🛏€6 ⚡ Ch WC free. **Surface:** gravel/sand. ⬤ 01/03-30/11
Distance: 🏊 on the spot.
Remarks: Max. 1 night, no camping activity. Follow rive gauche.

| | | Thoirette | 23A5 |

Grande Rue. **GPS:** n46,26924 e5,53529.

7 🛏€6 ⚡ Ch 🚰included. **Surface:** gravel.
Distance: 🏊50m 🛒25m.

| | | Villers-le-Lac | 23C3 |

Rue du Clos Rondot. **GPS:** n47,05948 e6,67195.⬆️.

8 🛏free ⚡€ 2 Ch 🗑. **Surface:** concrete.

| | | Villers-le-Lac | 23C3 |

Bateaux du Saut du Doubs. **GPS:** n47,05500 e6,67000.

🛏free for clients ⚡. **Surface:** asphalted.
Remarks: Max. 1 night.

Poitou Charentes

| | | Aigre | 20D5 |

Parc Les Charmilles, Rue des Charrières. **GPS:** n45,89341 e0,00578.⬆️.

4 🛏free ⚡€ 3 Ch 🚰.
Surface: asphalted. ⬤ 01/03-30/11
Distance: 🚲on the spot 🏊500m ⊗on the spot 🛒on the spot 🚍on the spot.
Remarks: Behind church, max. 24h.

Tourist information St.Loup-sur-Semouse:
ℹ️ Office de Tourisme, 14, place Léon Jacquez, regionsaintloup.free.fr.

10 🍴€5 🚰 🔌 Ch 🚿 (4x)included WC 🚽. **Surface:** metalled. ⭘ 01/04-31/10
Distance: 🛒on the spot ⊗on the spot 🏊on the spot.
Remarks: 4th night free.

Angliers 20D3
Aire de repos de la Briande, D347. **GPS:** n46,95861 e0,10472. ⬆️➡️

8 🍴free 🚰€ 2 🔌Ch 🚿free WC.
Surface: asphalted. ⭘ 01/01-31/12
Distance: 🛒Angliers 1km ⊗50m.
Remarks: 5km south of Loudon.

Arçais 20C4
Aire camping-cars du Coursault, Rue de Coursault. **GPS:** n46,29583 w0,69. ⬆️

20 🍴free, 1/4-30/9 € 6 🚰 🔌 Ch WC free.
Surface: grassy. ⭘ 01/01-31/12
Distance: 🛒400m 🏊on the spot ⊗nearby 🏊nearby.

Aubeterre-sur-Dronne 🌿🏊 28C1
D2, Route de Ribérac. **GPS:** n45,26980 e0,17570. ⬆️

10 🍴free 🚰 🔌 Ch. **Surface:** metalled. ⭘ 01/01-31/12
Distance: 🛒500m 🏊on the spot ⊗300m 🏊500m.
Remarks: At tennis-courts, to be paid at Berthon, superette SAP.

Tourist information Aubeterre-sur-Dronne:
ℹ️ Office de Tourisme, Place du Château, aubeterresurdronne.free.fr.
Ⓜ Musée Papillon.Butterflies and African art. ⭘ Easter-Sep 9-20h, Oct-Easter Sa-Su 14-20h.
⛲ Place de Village. ⭘ Thu, Su.

Aulnay 20C5
Rue de Salles. **GPS:** n46,02239 w0,34528. ⬆️

10 🍴free 🚰 🔌 Ch free. **Surface:** gravel.
Distance: 🛒200m ⊗200m 🖥200m.
Remarks: Max. 24h.

Aulnay 20C5
Place Charles de Gaulle, Rue Haute de l'Eglise. **GPS:** n46,02306 w0,35444. ⬆️

10 🍴free. **Surface:** metalled. ⭘ 01/01-31/12
Distance: 🛒200m ⊗200m 🏊200m.
Remarks: Follow Église St.Pierre.

Aytré 🌊 20B5
Route de la Plage. **GPS:** n46,11311 w1,12331.
10 🍴free 🚰 🔌 Ch free. **Surface:** asphalted.
Distance: 🏊on the spot.

Bougon 🌿🏛 20D4
Musée des Tumulus, La Chapelle. **GPS:** n46,37845 w0,06825. ⬆️.

10 🍴free 🚰 🔌 Ch free. **Surface:** asphalted. ⭘ 01/01-31/12
Distance: 🛒3km.
Remarks: Parking museum.

Tourist information Bougon:
Ⓜ🔭 Tumulus de Bougon.Archeological site.

Bourcefranc 20B5
Port du Chapus, La Pointe du Chapus. **GPS:** n45,85511 w1,16905.
10 🍴 🚰€ 4 🔌Ch 🖥. ⭘ 01/01-31/12
Remarks: Coins at town hall, office du tourisme.

Bourcefranc 20B5
Bois de Pin. **GPS:** n45,82611 w1,14278.

20 �€ 5. **Surface:** asphalted/metalled. ⏹ 01/05-31/10

| | Bourcefranc | 20B5 |

Parking de la Plage. GPS: n45,82917 w1,14889.

8 ⌐€ 5. **Surface:** asphalted. ⏹ 01/05-31/10

| S | Bressuire | 20C3 |

Place de la Libération, Boulevard Joffre. **GPS:** n46,83811 w0,4918. ⬆
10 ⌐free ⛲🔌 Ch free. ⏹ 01/01-31/12
Distance: ⚡50m 🍴150m.
Remarks: Max. 24h.

| S | Cellefrouin | 20D5 |

D739. GPS: n45,89361 e0,38639. ⬆➡

50 ⌐free ⛲🔌 Ch WC free. **Surface:** gravel. ⏹ 01/01-31/12
Distance: ⚡300m.

| S | Celles-sur-Belle | 20C4 |

Rue du Bouchaud. GPS: n46,26278 w0,20806. ⬆

10 ⌐free ⛲🔌 Ch free. **Surface:** metalled. ⏹ 01/01-31/12
Distance: ⚡100m ⛵nearby ⊗nearby 🍴nearby.

| | Chabanais | 21A5 |

Chemin des Tanneries, N141. **GPS:** n45,87447 e0,72008. ⬆

4 ⌐free. **Location:** Rural. **Surface:** asphalted. ⏹ 01/01-31/12 ◉ Thu.
Distance: ⚡on the spot ⊗100m 🍴100m.
Remarks: Along the river Vienne.

| | Château-Larcher | 20D4 |

Val de Clouère. GPS: n46,41444 e0,31556. ⬆

10 ⌐€ 3 ⛺€ 3 🔌 Ch 🚽 WC. **Surface:** grassy/metalled. ⏹ 01/03-31/11
Distance: ⚡1km.

| | Châtelaillon-Plage | 20B5 |

Alléé du Stade. GPS: n46,07741 w1,08715.

⌐free. **Surface:** metalled. ⏹ 01/01-31/12

| S | Chef-Boutonne | 20D5 |

Aire camping-cars, Chemin du Parc. **GPS:** n46,10972 w0,07694. ⬆➡

20 ⌐free ⛲🔌 WC free. **Surface:** grassy/metalled. ⏹ 01/04-31/10
Distance: ⚡on the spot ⛵on the spot ⊗on the spot 🍴on the spot 🛒on the spot.

| S | Cherves-Richemont | 20C6 |

Allee des Coquelicots. GPS: n45,74030 w0,35607. ⬆➡

6 ⌷free ⌷⌷Chfree. **Surface:** asphalted. ⬛ 01/01-31/12 ⬤ service 01/11-15/04.
Distance: ⌷500m ⊗100m ⌷500m.

⌷€ 5/night ⌷⌷Ch ⌷WC ⌷included. **Surface:** metalled. ⬛ 01/01-31/12

| Chey | 20D4 |

Place de la Liberté. **GPS:** n46,30500 w0,04972. ⬆.

Tourist information Confolens:

ℹ Office de Tourisme, Place des Marronniers, www.tourisme-confolens.com.Old city on the Vienne river.

⌷ ⬤ Wed, Sa.

🎭 Festival international de Danses et Musiques du Monde.Internationally folk festival. ⬤ Aug.

| Couhé | 20D4 |

Place du Marché. **GPS:** n46,29906 e0,17882. ⬆➡.

⌷free ⌷WCfree. **Location:** Central, quit. **Surface:** asphalted. ⬛ 01/01-31/12
Distance: ⌷50m ⊗50m ⌷100m.

3 ⌷free ⌷⌷Ch WC free. **Surface:** gravel. ⬛ 01/01-31/12
Distance: ⌷on the spot ⊗on the spot ⌷on the spot.

| Clérac | 28C1 |

D261e. **GPS:** n45,17998 w0,22728. ⬆.

| Coulon | 20C4 |

Parking d'Autremont, Rue de l'Autremont. **GPS:** n46,32131 w0,58918. ⬆.

30 ⌷€ 6/night ⌷⌷Ch WC free. **Surface:** grassy. ⬛ 01/04-30/11
Distance: ⌷200m ⊗nearby ⌷200m.

| Criteuil la Magdeleine | 20C6 |

GPS: n45,53778 w0,21556. ⬆➡.

⌷free ⌷⌷Chfree. **Surface:** gravel.
Distance: ⌷200m ⌷on the spot ⊗100m ⌷100m.
Remarks: Behind bakery, at small lake.

| Cognac | 20C6 |

Place de la Levade, Quartier Saint-Jacques. **GPS:** n45,69847 w0,33265. ⬆.

5 ⌷free ⌷⌷Ch ⌷WCfree. **Surface:** asphalted. ⬛ 01/01-31/12
Distance: ⌷on the spot.
Remarks: In the village.

| Dolus-d'Oléron | 20B5 |

Parking du Cimetière, Rue des Chapelles. **GPS:** n45,91194 w1,265.

10 ⌷free ⌷⌷Chfree. **Surface:** asphalted. ⬛ 01/01-31/12
Distance: ⌷on the spot ⊗on the spot ⌷on the spot ⌷500m ⌷on the spot.

Tourist information Cognac:

ℹ Office de Tourisme, 16, rue du 14 juillet, www.ville-cognac.fr.Old place worth seeing which gave her name to the well-known spirits.

👁 Otard.Cognac distillery in 16th century castle. Guided tour and tasting. ⬛ daily ⬤ 01/10-31/03 weekend.

Ⓜ Cognac-musée.Culture around the Cognac. ⬛ 01/10-31/05 14-17.30h, 01/06-30/09 10-12h, 14-18h.

| Confolens | 21A5 |

Camping les Ribières, Avenue de Sainte-Germain. **GPS:** n46,01894 e0,67570.

8 ⌷free. **Surface:** asphalted. ⬛ 01/01-31/12

S **Echillais** 20B5
Place de la Carrière. **GPS:** n45,89753 w0,95545. ⬆.
⌗€4 🚰€ 3 🔧Ch. **Surface:** asphalted.
Remarks: Access via rue de l'église.

S **Fouras** 20B5
Place Jean Moulin. **GPS:** n45,98139 w1,0875.

15 ⌗€6 🚰€ 1/50liter ⊜Ch. **Surface:** asphalted. ⬛ 01/01-31/12
Distance: 🚶on the spot ⊗350m 🛒on the spot 🚌on the spot.
Remarks: Nearby Plages Sud and Espérance, max. 48h, coins available at campsite and office de tourisme, wastewater disposal: attention mark!.

S **Fouras** 20B5
Plage Nord, Avenue du Cadoret. **GPS:** n45,99194 w1,08694.

15 ⌗€6 🚰€ 1/50liter. **Surface:** metalled. ⬛ 01/01-31/12
Distance: 🚶on the spot ⊗on the spot 🛒on the spot.
Remarks: In front of campsite Cadoret, Fun golf, max. 48h, coins available at campsite and office de tourisme.

S **Fouras** 20B5
Prairie du Casino, Dir pointe de la Fumée. **GPS:** n45,99583 w1,10611.

20 ⌗€6 🚰€ 1/50liter. **Surface:** metalled. ⬛ 01/01-31/12
Distance: 🚶on the spot ⊗on the spot 🛒on the spot.
Remarks: Max. 48h. Parking on peninsula beyond Office du Tourisme.

Tourist information Fouras:
ℹ Bathing resort.

S **Gencay** 20D4
Place du Champs de Foire. **GPS:** n46,37315 e0,40638. ⬆ ➡.

10 ⌗free 🚰€ 2 ⊜Ch🚽€ 2 WC.
Surface: metalled. ⬛ 01/01-31/12
Distance: 🚶on the spot ⊗on the spot 🛒on the spot.
Remarks: Coins available at the shops.

S **Genté** 20C6
Rue de l'eglise. **GPS:** n45,62861 w0,315. ⬆ ➡.

6 ⌗free 🚰⊜Ch 🔧 (6x) WC free. **Surface:** asphalted. ⬛ 01/01-31/12
Distance: 🚶on the spot ⊗on the spot 🛒on the spot.

S **Hiers-Brouage** 20B5
GPS: n45,85167 w1,07317.

10 ⌗free 🚰€ 4 ⊜Ch🚽. ⬛ 01/01-31/12

S **Hiers-Brouage** 20B5
Rue Palissy, D3. **GPS:** n45,85284 w1,07745.
⌗free 🚰€ 4 ⊜Ch🚽. **Surface:** unpaved. ⬛ 01/01-31/12

P S **Jonzac** 20C6
Place du 8 Mai 1945. **GPS:** n45,44800 w0,433. ⬆.

8 ⌗free 🚰€ 1/100liter ⊜Ch🚽€ 1/1h. **Surface:** asphalted.
⬛ 01/01-31/12
Distance: 🚶on the spot ⊗on the spot 🛒on the spot 🚌on the spot.
Remarks: Behind police station, ± 200m from D2.

S **La Brée-les-Bains** 20A5
Rue de la Baudette. **GPS:** n46,01083 w1,35694.

50 ⌗free 🚰⊜Ch. **Surface:** asphalted. ⬛ 01/01-31/12
Remarks: Coins at Office de Tourisme.

La Couronne — 20D6
Rue du Champs de Foire. **GPS**: n45,60619 e0,10015.

free Ch WC free. **Surface:** asphalted. 01/01-31/12 Wed-morning, Sa-morning market.
Distance: on the spot on the spot.

La Roche-Posay — 21A3
Super U, ZA Les Chaumettes. **GPS**: n46,79361 e0,79750.

free Ch free. **Surface:** asphalted. 01/01-31/12
Distance: 1,5km.

La Rochelle — 20B4
Vieux Port, Avenue Jean Moulin. **GPS**: n46,15250 w1,13944.

50 € 10/24h Ch. **Surface:** asphalted. 01/01-31/12
Distance: 1,5km free.
Remarks: Shuttle to centre.

La Rochelle — 20B4
Esplanade des Parc, Chemin des Remparts. **GPS**: n46,16620 w1,1544.
24 free. **Surface:** asphalted. 01/01-31/12
Distance: 250m 100m 250m 50m.

La Rochelle — 20B4
Lycée hotelier, Les Minimes, Avenue des Minimes. **GPS**: n46,14417 w1,16083.

20 free. **Surface:** asphalted. 01/01-31/12
Distance: on the spot.
Remarks: Max. 48h.

Tourist information La Rochelle:
Office de Tourisme, Place de la Petite Sirène, Le Gabut, www.larochelle-tourisme.com.Old port city with marina.
Grosse Horloge, Centre ville.Old city gate, 13th century.
Tour de Lanterne, Centre ville.Monumental tower,15th century. 16/09-14/05 10-12.30h, 14-17.30h, 15/05-30/06, 01/09-15/09 10-12.45h 14-18.30h, 01/07-31/08 10-19h 16/9-14/5 Mo.
La Maison Henri II, Rue de Augustins.Archeological museum. 15/5-30/9 Sa-Fr 10-19h Sa-Su 14-19h.
Musée Maritime de la Rochelle, Bassin des Chautiers.Shipping museum. daily 10-19.30h.
Aquarium, Port des Minimes.Sea aquarium. 01/07-31/08 9-23h, 01/09-30/06 10-19/20h.

La-Mothe-St.Héray — 20D4
Rue du Pont l'Abbé. **GPS**: n46,35971 w0,11775.

4 free € 1/50liter Ch WC. **Surface:** metalled. 01/01-31/12
Distance: 500m 200m 200m.

Le Château d'Oléron — 20B5
Parking du Stade, Rue du Stade. **GPS**: n45,88867 w1,20505.

15 free. **Surface:** asphalted. 01/01-31/12
Distance: 800m 50m.

Le Grand Village Plage — 20B5
Rue de Puints Neuf. **GPS**: n45,85750 w1,2355.

7 free. **Surface:** asphalted. 01/01-31/12

Le Grand Village Plage — 20B5
Camping les Pins. GPS: n45,86222 w1,24111.
€ 4 Ch.
01/01-31/12
Remarks: Coins at office de tourisme, town hall or camping les Pins.

Le Pont d'Agris — 20D6
D6, Rue de Mansle. **GPS**: n45,78619 e0,33944.

FR

6 🅂free ⚷€ 2 🅂Ch🄼€ 2. **Surface:** asphalted. 🅾 01/01-31/12
Distance: 🚲10m 🚶10m 10m.
🅂🆂 **Les Mathes/La Palmyre** 🏖 (ⁱ) 🏊 20B6
Parking du Corsaire, Avenue de l'Atlantique. **GPS:** n45,68783 w1,187.

90 🅂€6/24h ⚷€ 4 🅂Ch 🄼. **Surface:** asphalted. 🅾 01/01-31/12
Distance: 🏖200m 🚶200m.
Remarks: Next to Office du Tourisme.
🅂🆂 **Les Mathes/La Palmyre** 🏖(ⁱ)🏊 20B6
Rue de la Garenne, Les Mathes. **GPS:** n45,71444 w1,1475.⬆
🅂€8 ⚷€ 2 🅂Ch🄼€ 2 WC.
Surface: metalled. 🅾 01/01-31/12
Remarks: Near centre, large flat parking, coins available at town hall Mo-Fri 9-18h and office de tourisme La Palmyre daily 9-19h in July/Aug.
🅂🆂 **Les Mathes/La Palmyre** 🏖(ⁱ)🏊 20B6
Boulevard de la Plage, La Palmyre. **GPS:** n45,68287 w1,17942.
🅂€ 8. **Surface:** gravel.
Distance: 🏖100m.

Tourist information Les Mathes/La Palmyre:
ⁱ Office de Tourisme, Av. de Royan, Les Mathes, www.la-palmyre-les-mathes.com.Seaside resort, signposted cycle routes.
ⁱ Parking de la Plage.
ⁱ Syndicat d'Initiative, Rond-Point de la Poste, Royan, www.royan-tourisme.com.Modern bathing resort with 5 large beaches.
⦿ Zoo de la Palmyre.Zoo, 1600 animals, 14Ha. 🅾 01/04-30/09 9-20.30h, 01/10-31/03 9-12h, 14-18h.
🅂🆂 **Les Portes-en-Ré** 🏊 20A4
Parking de la Patache, Route du Fier. **GPS:** n46,22925 w1,48315.

10 🅂€ 10/24h ⚷🅂Ch. **Surface:** metalled.
Distance: 🏊on the spot 🚶on the spot.
Remarks: Max. 24h.
🅂🆂 **Lezay** 🌿 20D4
Rue de Gâte Bourse. **GPS:** n46,26500 w0,01139.⬆.

15 🅂free ⚷🅂Chfree. **Surface:** asphalted. 🅾 01/01-31/12
Remarks: Next to Office du Tourisme.
🅂🆂 **Londigny** 20D5
Place de l'eglise. **GPS:** n46,08333 e0,13472.

5 🅂free ⚷🅂Ch 🄼 WCfree. **Surface:** gravel. 🅾 01/01-31/12
Remarks: Max. 48h.
🆂 **Loudun** 20D2
Place de la Porte Saint Nicolas. **GPS:** n47,01357 e0,07833.
⚷🅂Ch.
🅂🆂 **Lussac-les-Châteaux** 21A4
Place l'Amitié entre les Peuples. **GPS:** n46,40250 e0,72583.⬆.

20 🅂free ⚷🅂Ch WCfree.
Surface: metalled. 🅾 01/01-31/12 ⬛ Fri.
Distance: 🚲on the spot ⊗nearby 🍴nearby.
🅂 **Magné** 🌿🏊 20C4
Embarcadére Cardinaud, Avenue de la Repentie. **GPS:** n46,32130 w0,5803.

30 🅂free. **Surface:** grassy. 🅾 01/01-31/12
Distance: 🚲900m ⊗on the spot 🍴on the spot.
🆂 **Magné** 🌿🏊 20C4
Super U, Avenue du Marais Poitevin. **GPS:** n46,31632 w0,55656.
⚷€ 1,50 🅂Ch🄼€ 1,50. 🅾 01/01-31/12
🅂🆂 **Marennes** 20B5
1 Avenue William Bertrand. **GPS:** n45,82218 w1,13885.
🅂€ 5,50 ⚷🅂Ch.
Distance: 🏊on the spot.

Remarks: Near campsite Domaine des Pins.

🚐 [S] Mauzé-sur-le-Mignon 20C4

Le Port, Rue du Port. **GPS**: n46,20000 w0,67778.

10 🚐free 🚰€ 3 💦Ch 🚿WC. **Surface:** metalled. 🕒 01/01-31/12
Distance: 🏘1km ⛱on the spot.
Remarks: Coins at campsite and shops.

🚐 [S] Meschers-sur-Gironde 20B6

Capitainerie, 80, Avenue du Port. **GPS**: n45,55387 w0,94467. ⬆.

10 🚐€ 6 🚰💦Ch 🔌free. **Surface:** asphalted. 🕒 01/01-31/12
Remarks: Marina.

🚐 [S] Montguyon 🎈 28C1

Rue de Vassiac. **GPS**: n45,21796 w0,18368.

15 🚐free 🚰💦Ch WC free. **Surface:** gravel. 🕒 01/01-31/12
Distance: 🏘500m 🍴500m 🍞500m.

🏭 [S] Montmorillon 21A4

Leclerc, 2, Avenue de Provence. **GPS**: n46,41903 e0,85358. ⬆.
10 🚐free 🚰💦Ch free. **Surface:** asphalted. 🕒 01/01-31/12
Remarks: Parking supermarket.

🚐 [S] Mortagne-sur-Gironde 20B6

Rue de l'Europe. **GPS**: n45,47472 w0,79778.

🚐€ 6 🚰💦Ch 🔌WC 🚿free.
Surface: grassy. 🕒 01/01-31/12
Remarks: In harbour, in front of Capitainerie.

🚐 [S] Moulismes ⛱🌊 21A4

RN147. **GPS**: n46,33306 e0,81000. ⬆.

50 🚐free 🚰€ 3 💦Ch 🚿WC. **Surface:** metalled. 🕒 01/01-31/12
Distance: ⛱on the spot 🎣on the spot.
Remarks: At small lake (plan d'eau).

🚐 [S] Nersac 🌾 20D6

Rue d'Epagnac. **GPS**: n45,62578 e0,04776. ⬆➡.

7 🚐free 🚰💦Ch 🔌(4x)free. **Surface:** asphalted. 🕒 01/01-31/12
Distance: 🏘on the spot 🍴100m 🍞100m 🚌100m.
Remarks: Max. 48h.

🚐 [S] Nieuil-l'Espoir 🌾 21A4

Allée du champ de foire. **GPS**: n46,48505 e0,45417. ⬆➡.

10 🚐free 🚰€ 2 💦Ch 🚿€ 2.
Surface: grassy/metalled. 🕒 01/01-31/12
Distance: 🏘200m 🍞150m.
Remarks: At Base de Loisirs, oins at the shops.

🚐 [S] Nieulle-sur-Seudre 20B5

Place de la Mairie. **GPS**: n45,75185 w1,00204.

4 🚐free 🚰💦Ch 🚿. 🕒 01/01-31/12

🚐 [S] Niort 🌾⛱🧺🌊 20C4

Aire des camping-cars du Pré Leroy, Rue de Bessac. **GPS**: n46,32917 w0,46444. ⬆➡.

FR

16 �€7 🚰🗑 Ch🔌included. **Surface:** metalled. 🅾 01/01-31/12
Distance: 🚶1,2km ⊗150m 🛒300m.

Tourist information Niort:
ℹ️ Office de Tourisme, 16, rue du Petit Saint-Jean, www.niortourisme.com.
🎪 🅾 Tue, Sa.
🌿 Marais Poitevin.Swamp area, possibility of making boat trips.

🍴S	Oriolles	28C1

Ferme Auberge chez Baron, D131. **GPS:** n45,36180 w0,11784.⬆️.
8 ⌇€ 9,10, guests free 🚰🗑Ch included 🔌€ 1,50 🅾€ 3. 🅾 01/07-31/08

🅂S	Pamproux	20D4

Rue de la Cueille. **GPS:** n46,39625 w0,05874.⬆️.

3 ⌇free 🚰€ 2/20minutes 🗑Ch🔌€ 2/20minutes. **Surface:** asphalted.
🅾 01/01-31/12
Distance: 🚶100m 🚲5,2km 🛒100m.

🅂S	Parthenay	20C3

Aire base de loisirs Bois Vert, Rue de Boisseau 14. **GPS:** n46,64088 w0,26689.
⬆️➡️.

10 ⌇€ 6, Jul/Aug € 8 🚰🗑Ch included 🔌€ 3 🅾€ 4, dryer € 1,50
🔌€ 7/day. **Surface:** grassy/metalled. 🅾 22/03-31/10
Distance: 🚶2,5km on the spot ⊗nearby 🚲2km 🛒100m.
Remarks: Along the Sioule river, car rental € 5/day + € 0,19/km.

Tourist information Parthenay:
ℹ️ Service Tourisme-Accueil, 8, rue de la Vau St Jacques, www.cc-parthenay.fr.City with Medieval centre worth a visit.
🎪 Les Halles.Important cattle market. 🅾 Wed.

ⒼS	Pons	20C6

Avenue du Poitou. **GPS:** n45,57765 w0,55536.⬆️.
4 ⌇free 🚰🗑Ch🔌€ 6. **Surface:** asphalted.

🅂S	Port-des-Barques	20B5

Pré des Mays, Avenue des Sports. **GPS:** n45,94722 w1,09.⬆️.

⌇€6 🚰🗑free. **Surface:** metalled. 🅾 15/03-15/11
Remarks: In front of stadium, parking fee being collected.

🅂S	Rivedoux-Plage	20B4

125, Av Gustave Perreau. **GPS:** n46,15889 w1,27139.

10 ⌇€ 8,60 🚰 4 🗑Ch. **Surface:** asphalted. 🅾 01/01-31/12
Distance: 🚶100m.
Remarks: Next to campsite Le Platin.

🅂S	Rochefort	16B3

Port de Plaisance, Quai Lemoigne de Sérigny. **GPS:** n45,94444 w0,95556.

15 ⌇free 🚰🗑Chfree.
Surface: metalled. 🅾 01/01-31/12
Remarks: In marina, nearby Capitainerie, max. 24h.

Tourist information Rochefort:
ℹ️ Office de Tourisme, Avenue Sadi-Carnot, Porte de l'Arsenal, www.ville-rochefort.fr.Old city with seaport and river harbour.
👁 Corderie Royale.Old royal rope-walk.
Ⓜ Maison de Pierre Loti.House of the writer Pierre Loti. 🅾 daily guided tour 🅾 Tue-Su morning.
Ⓜ Musée de la Marine, place de la Galissonniere.Model boats and frigates. 🅾 daily 10-12h, 14-18h.
🎪 🅾 Tue, Thu, Sa.

🅂S	Rouillac	20D6

Super U, Rue de Genac. **GPS:** n45,77650 w0,06133.⬆️➡️.

8 ⌇€3 🚰€ 3 🗑Ch🔌. **Surface:** asphalted. 🅾 01/01-31/12
Distance: 🚶500m ⊗500m 🛒50m.

Remarks: Coins available at supermarket.

⊞ S **Roumazières-Loubert** 21A5

Aire de Détente de Ronmatiéres, RN141. **GPS:** n45,88275 e0,57287. ⬆️➡️

3 🅿free 🔧🔌 Ch 🚿 WC free. **Surface:** asphalted. ⬛ 01-01-31/12
Distance: 🚂500m ⊗100m 🛒300m.

⊞ S **Ruffec** 20D5

SARL Remy Frères Camping-Cars, D26. **GPS:** n46,03316 e0,18366.

10 🅿free 🔧🔌 Ch free. **Surface:** asphalted.
Distance: 🚂1km.
Remarks: Motorhome dealer.

Tourist information Ruffec:
ℹ️ Office de Tourisme, 18, place des Martyrs de l'Occupation.Old city.

⊞ S **Saint Césaire** 🚂🏖️ 20C6

Parking Paléosite, Rue de Groies. **GPS:** n45,75370 w0,50744. ⬆️➡️
20 🅿free 🔧🔌 Ch free. **Surface:** asphalted/metalled. ⬛ 01-01-31/12
Distance: 🚂on the spot ⊗500m 🛒300m.

Tourist information Saint Césaire:
◉ Paléosite, Route de la Montée Verte.Interactive park, in the footsteps of the Neanderthals. ⬛ 10.30-18.30, Jul-Aug 10-20 ⬛ January.

⊞ S **Saintes** 🏖️🚂🍺 20C5

Aire camping-cars, Rue de Courbiac. **GPS:** n45,75483 w0,62905. ⬆️

12 🅿free 🔧€ 5/10minutes 🔌 Ch 🔌€ 5/50minutes 🚿. **Surface:** asphalted. ⬛ 01-01-31/12
Distance: 🚂900m ⛴️4,4km.

🅿 **Saintes** 🏖️🚂🍺 20C5

Rue Geoffroy Martel. **GPS:** n45,74738 w0,63617.
10 🅿free. **Surface:** asphalted. ⬛ 01-01-31/12
Distance: 🚂on the spot 🛒300m.
Remarks: Follow abbay au Dames.

Tourist information Saintes:
ℹ️ Office de Tourisme, Villa Musso, 62 cours National, www.ot-saintes.fr.Historical city with Roman vestiges.
🎪 Place 11 November. ⬛ Tue + Fri morning.
🎪 Grande Foire.Large regional market. ⬛ 1st Mon of the month.

⊞ S **Saujon** 🐚 20B6

Route de Ecluses. **GPS:** n45,67503 w0,932.

10 🅿free 🔧🔌 Ch free. **Surface:** concrete. ⬛ 01-01-31/12
Distance: 🚂900m.

⊞ S **Sauzé-Vaussais** 20D5

Place des Halles. GPS: n46,13540 e0,10660.

🅿free 🔧🔌 Ch 🚿 WC free. **Surface:** asphalted. ⬛ 01-01-31/12 ⬤ water: Nov-March.
Distance: 🚂on the spot ⊗on the spot 🛒on the spot.

⊞ S **Segonzac** 🍇 20C6

Place Blanche. GPS: n45,61456 w0,22113. ⬆️➡️

4 🅿free 🔧🔌 Ch 🚿 (4x) WC free.
Surface: gravel. ⬛ 01-01-31/12
Distance: 🚂500m ⊗500m 🛒500m.
Remarks: Cognac 8km. Dir d'Archaic, RD736 next to the Jeu de Boules area.

⊞ S **Soubise** 20B5

Aire camping-car, Le Port/rue Colbert. **GPS:** n45,92833 w1,00666. ⬆️

17 🅿€ 6,50 🔧🔌 Ch 🚿 WC ⬛included. **Surface:** grassy/metalled. ⬛ 01-01-31/12
Distance: 🚂on the spot ⊗50m.
Remarks: Along river, max. 24h, incl. showers and warm water.

⊞ S **St.Agnant** 20B5

Place de Verdun. GPS: n45,86635 w0,9641.

10 🛏free 🚱🗑Chfree. **Surface:** asphalted. 🔌 01/01-31/12
Remarks: Next to town hall.

🛂S St.Amand-sur-Sèvre 20B3
Le Moulin Chaligny. GPS: n46,88493 w0,82342. ⬆.
7 🛏gift 🚱🗑Ch 🚿♿ € 3. 🔌 01/01-31/12

🛂S St.Clément-des-Baleines 20A4
Rue de la Forêt. GPS: n46,22756 w1,54644.

30 🛏€ 7, 2 nights € 12 🚱€ 4/100liter 🗑Ch 🔌€ 4/1h.
Distance: 250m 500m.
Remarks: Next to campsite.

🛂S St.Denis-d'Oléron 20A5
Aire du Moulin, Route des Huttes. **GPS:** n46,02750 w1,38306.

150 🛏€ 8 🚱🗑Ch 🚿 WC]included 🗑.
Surface: grassy. 🔌 01/01-31/12
Distance: 1km.
Remarks: Max. 4 nights.

🛂S St.Génis-de-Saintonge 20C6
Place Alcide Beauvais, N137. GPS: n45,47985 w0,56844. ⬆➡.

6 🛏free 🚱🗑Ch 🚿 (3x)WC]free.
Surface: asphalted. 🔌 01/01-31/12
Distance: 200m ✕300m 300m.
Remarks: Max. 48h.

🛂S St.Germain-de-Marencennes 20B5
Place Saint-André. GPS: n46,07719 w0,78747.

4 🛏free 🚱🗑Ch 🚿WCfree. **Surface:** metalled. 🔌 01/01-31/12
Remarks: 15/11-15/03 water disconnected.

🛂S St.Hilaire-la-Palud 20C4
Place de la Marie. GPS: n46,26444 w0,71306. ⬆.

10 🛏free. **Surface:** asphalted. 🔌 01/01-31/12
Distance: on the spot ✕on the spot on the spot.
Remarks: Parking in front of town hall, max. 2 nights.

🛂S St.Jean-d'Angély 20C5
Base de Plein Air, Avenue de Marennes, D18. **GPS:** n45,94537 w0,53735.⬆.

10 🛏free 🚱🗑Chfree. **Surface:** gravel. 🔌 01/01-31/12
Distance: 1km 100m 100m ✕200m 1km.
Remarks: Max. 2 nights.

🛂S St.Pochaire 20B5
Place du Champ de Foire. GPS: n45,81883 w0,7765.

10 🛏free 🚱🗑ChWCfree.
Surface: gravel. 🔌 01/01-31/12
Remarks: Max. 48h, play garden and picnic area present.

🛂S St.Trojan-les-Bains 20B5
Place de la Riberté. GPS: n45,84306 w1,21.⬆.

20 ⬛free ⌇€ 4 ▤Ch ✎. **Surface:** asphalted. ⬛ 01/01-31/12

Tourist information St.Trojan-les-Bains:
ℹ️ Bureau Municipal de Tourisme, Carrefour du Port, www.st-trojan-les-bains.
fr.Seaside resort on the island of Oléron, well-known for the mimosa and oyster culture.
⚓ place de Filles de la Sagesse.Food and drugs market. ⬛ Thu + Sa-morning,
summer daily.
⚓ Marche Nocturne, rue de la République.Evening market. ⬛ Thu from 17h.

△S	St.Yrieix-sur-Charente	20D6

Rue du Plan d'Eau, Impasse des Ooyères. **GPS:** n45,69176 e0,14517.⬆️➡️.

10 ⬛€ 6,80/8,60 ⌇▤Ch ✎free. **Surface:** asphalted. ⬛ 01/04-31/10
Distance: 🚶2km ⛵1km 🚲1km ⊗1km 🚉3km 🚌1km.
Remarks: Max. 24h.

⬛S	Thouars 🌿	20D2

Rue Felix Gellusseau. **GPS:** n46,97614 w0,21151.⬆️➡️.

⬛free ⌇▤Ch WC free. **Surface:** metalled. ⬛ 01/01-31/12
Distance: 🚶100m ⊗100m 🚉100m.

Tourist information Thouars:
ℹ️ Office de Tourisme, 3, bis Bd Pierre Curie, www.ville-thouars.fr/tourisme.City
with half-timbered houses.
Ⓜ️✖️ Château d'Oiron.Contemporary art.
⚓ ⬛ Tue, Fri.

⬛S	Thurageau	20D3

Fam. Turpeau, Agressais. **GPS:** n46,78388 e0,25644.⬆️.

5 ⬛free ⌇▤Ch free. **Surface:** gravel. ⬛ 01/01-31/12

Distance: 🚶2,5km.
Remarks: Goat farm, farm products.

⬛S	Tonnay-Charente	20B5

Quai des Capucins. **GPS:** n45,93921 w0,88171.
15 ⬛free ⌇▤Ch free. **Surface:** gravel.

⬛S	Vasles 🌿⚓	20D4

Mouton Village, Rue de la Cité. **GPS:** n46,57317 w0,02266.⬆️➡️.

10 ⬛free ⌇▤Ch WC free. **Surface:** gravel. ⬛ 01/01-31/12
Distance: 🚶400m 🚉400m.

⬛S	Vicq-sur-Gartempe	21A3

25, Route de la Roche Posay. **GPS:** n46,72414 e0,86189.

10 ⬛free ⌇▤Ch WC free. **Surface:** gravel. ⬛ 01/01-31/12
Distance: 🚶500m.

Limousin

⬛S	Allassac	29A1

Avenue du Saillant. **GPS:** n45,25897 e1,47358.⬆️.

4 ⬛free ⌇▤Ch ✎ (2x)free. **Surface:** gravel/sand. ⬛ 01/01-31/12
Distance: 🚶500m 🚲5km ⊗500m 🚉500m.
Remarks: Parking station.

⬛S	Aubusson (Creuse) 🌿⚓🍴	21C5

Parking Champ de Foire, Rue des Fusilles, D988. **GPS:** n45,95694 e2,17528.⬆️
➡️.

10 ⬛free ⌇€ 2 ▤Ch 🔌€ 2 WC. **Surface:** asphalted. ⬛ 01/01-31/12
Distance: 🚶500m ⊗500m 🚉500m.

FR

Auphelle 21C6
GPS: n45,80750 e1,84111. ⬆➡.

80 free. **Surface**: grassy.
Distance: Lac de Vassivière 300m.

Ayen 29A1
Route de la Noix, Ayen Bas. **GPS**: n45,24964 e1,32343. ⬆➡.

10 free 🚰 Ch free. **Surface**: gravel. 🅾 01/01-31/12
Distance: 300m.
Remarks: Nearby D39, campsite and sports grounds.

Beaumont du Lac 21C6
GPS: n45,78640 e1,87077. ⬆➡.

20 free 🚰€ 2/100liter Ch 🔌€ 4/1h.
Surface: gravel. 🅾 01/01-31/12
Distance: 5km on the spot on the spot 100m.
Remarks: At lake Vassivière.

Bessines-sur-Gartempe 21B5
Rue d'Ingolsheim. **GPS**: n46,10979 e1,37008. ✂.

10 free 🚰€ 2 Ch 🔌€ 2. **Surface**: asphalted. 🅾 01/01-31/12
Distance: 900m 100m.

Bort-les-Orgues 29B1
Rue Fort Grande/rue Prémontal. **GPS**: n45,39913 e2,49710. ⬆➡.

10 free 🚰 Ch free. **Surface**: asphalted. 🅾 01/01-31/12
Distance: 200m river 200m 200m.

Bourganeuf 21C5
Place de l'Etang, Avenue du Dr Butaud. **GPS**: n45,95444 e1,75750. ⬆➡.

5 free 🚰 Ch free. **Surface**: gravel. 🅾 01/01-31/12 tue-evening, wed-morning (market).
Distance: on the spot on the spot on the spot.
Tourist information Bourganeuf:
Tour de Zizim. 🅾 01/07-15/09.

Bujaleuf 21B6
Route du Champ de Foire. **GPS**: n45,79747 e1,63141. ⬆➡.

10 free 🚰 Ch free. **Surface**: gravel. 🅾 01/01-31/12
Distance: 500m 500m.
Remarks: Max. 24h.

Chambon-sur-Voueize 21D5
Rue du Stade. **GPS**: n46,18579 e2,43426. ⬆➡.

4 free 🚰€ 2 Ch 🔌€ 2. **Surface**: asphalted. 🅾 01/01-31/12
Distance: 500m 500m 200m.
Remarks: Near camping municipal.

Châtelus-le-Marcheix 21B5
Rue du Tursaud. **GPS**: n45,99894 e1,60339. ⬆➡.

FR

8 ⌁free ⚡€ 2 ⚑Ch ⎘€ 2. **Surface:** asphalted. ⬤ 01/01-31/12
Distance: ⚭300m ⊗300m ⚑300m.
Remarks: Next to campsite municipal.

5 ⌁free ⚡€ 2 ⚑Ch ⎘€ 2.
Surface: asphalted. ⬤ 01/01-31/12
Distance: ⚭100m ⚑500m.
Remarks: At fish lake, coins available at superette 'la Montagne' (500m).

⊞S | **Chénérailles** | 21C5
Route d'Aubusson, lotissement Marlaud, D990. **GPS:** n46,11058 e2,17753. ⬆➡.

⊞S | **Dampniat** | 29A1
Stade, Le Mas. **GPS:** n45,16262 e1,63728. ⬆.
⌁free ⚡€ 2/10minutes ⚑Ch ☀€ 2/55minutes. **Location:** Rural.
Surface: gravel.
Distance: ⚭850m.

⊞S | **Donzenac** | 29A1
Village de Vacance La Rivière, Rue du 19 Mars 1962. **GPS:** n45,21897 e1,51829. ⬆➡.

5 ⌁free ⚡€ 2 ⚑Ch ⎘€ 2. **Surface:** asphalted. ⬤ 01/01-31/12
Distance: ⚭200m ⊗50m.
Remarks: Coins available at restaurant le Coq d'Or (50m).

⊞S | **Collognes-la-Rouge** | 29A1
Parking le Marchadial. GPS: n45,05833 e1,65889. ⬆➡.

10 ⌁€3, 1/6-30/9 €9 ⚡ ⚑Ch ☀€ 3,10/night, peak season WCfree.
Surface: gravel. ⬤ 01/01-31/12
Distance: ⚭4km ⚓1,3km ⊗4m ⚑4km.
Remarks: Max. 48h.

⊞S | **Egletons** | 29B1
Parking Espace Ventadour, Rue Henri Dignac. **GPS:** n45,40406 e2,04791. ⬆.

20 ⌁€5/24h ⚡⚑Ch ☀ WCincluded.
Surface: gravel. ⬤ 01/01-31/12
Distance: ⚭500m ⊗500m ⚑500m.

⊞S | **Concèze** | 29A1
D56e. **GPS:** n45,35472 e1,34583. ⬆➡.

3 ⌁free ⚡⚑Chfree. **Surface:** gravel. ⬤ 01/01-31/12
Distance: ⚭on the spot.

20 ⌁free ⚡⚑Chfree.
Surface: gravel. ⬤ 01/01-31/12 ⬛ Service: winter.
Distance: ⚭300m ⚓3,5km ⊗300m ⚑300m.

⊞S | **Cressat** | 21C5
D990, rue de Laprade. **GPS:** n46,13956 e2,11015. ⬆➡.

⊞S | **Felletin** | 21C5
Parking Lagrange, Avenue Joffre. **GPS:** n45,88308 e2,17667. ⬆➡.

20 ⌁free ⚡⚑Chfree. **Surface:** gravel. ⬤ 01/01-31/12
Distance: ⚭on the spot.

FR

⟦S⟧ Gouzon 21D5
Place du champ de foire, Rue d'Alcantera. **GPS:** n46,19139 e2,24028. ⬆️➡️

6 ⟦free⟧ 🔧 Chfree. **Surface:** sand. ⬤ 01/01-31/12
Distance: 300m ⊗300m 🛒300m.

⟦S⟧ Jarnages 21C5
Route des Promenctes, D65. **GPS:** n46,18417 e2,08098. ⬆️➡️

6 ⟦free⟧ 🔧€ 2 💬 Ch 🔲€ 2. **Surface:** asphalted. ⬤ 01/01-31/12
Distance: 500m ⊗500m 🛒500m.
Remarks: At tennis-courts.

⟦S⟧ Javerdat 21A5
GPS: n45,95323 e0,98600. ⬆️

4 ⟦free⟧ 🔧 💬 Ch 🔲. **Surface:** gravel. ⬤ 01/01-31/12
Distance: ⊗100m.
Remarks: Coins at Auberge Limousine (100m).

⟦S⟧ Les Salles-Lavaugyon 21A6
Le Tilleul, Route de St Mathieu. **GPS:** n45,73972 e0,70278. ⬆️➡️

4 ⟦€4⟧ 🔧 💬 ✏️ included. **Surface:** gravel. ⬤ 01/01-31/12

⟦S⟧ Liginiac 29B1
Le Maury-Liginiac. **GPS:** n45,39158 e2,30387. ➡️

⟦free⟧ 🔧 💬 Ch 🔲free. **Surface:** gravel.
Distance: Liginiac 4,5km ⚓sandy beach ⊗on the spot.
Remarks: At lake Neuvic. Follow restaurant Le Maury.

⟦S⟧ Meuzac 21B6
Étang de la Roche, D243. **GPS:** n45,54933 e1,43869. ⬆️➡️

15 ⟦free⟧ 🔧 💬 Chfree. **Surface:** gravel. ⬤ 01/01-31/12
Distance: 100m ✎ 5km ⚓on the spot ⊗on the spot 🛒100m.

⟦S⟧ Meymac 21C6
Parking Lac de Sechemailles. **GPS:** n45,52500 e2,12761. ⬆️➡️

20 ⟦free⟧ 🔧€ 2,60 💬 Ch 🔲€ 2,60. **Surface:** gravel. ⬤ 01/01-31/12
Distance: 2km ⚓500m ⊗500m.
Remarks: Coins available at Office du Tourisme and bar.

⟦S⟧ Montboucher 21C5
GPS: n45,95056 e1,68083. ⬆️➡️

5 ⟦free⟧ 🔧 💬 Ch WC free. **Surface:** grassy/gravel. ⬤ 01/01-31/12

⟦S⟧ Nieul 21B5
Rue de la Gare, D28. **GPS:** n45,92564 e1,17236. ⬆️

5 ⛺free ⚡ 🚰 Ch WC free. **Surface:** asphalted. 🅿 01/01-31/12
Distance: 🚶400m ⊗400m 🚆400m.

🏕🆂 Objat 29A1
Parc Aquatique Espace Loisirs, Avenue Jules Ferry. **GPS:** n45,27110 e1,41147.
⬆➡.

20 ⛺€5 ⚡€ 2/50liter 🚰 Ch 🔌 included WC 🚻€ 2 🧺. 🗑 ♻
Surface: grassy/metalled.
🅿 01/01-31/12
Distance: 🚶500m ▣500m.
Remarks: Entrance code available at office de tourisme, max. 7 days, baker
Tue-Sa.

🏕🆂 Oradour-sur-Glane 21A5
Aire camping-car, Rue du Stade. **GPS:** n45,93570 e1,02471.⬆.

20 ⛺free ⚡€ 2 🚰 Ch 🔌€ 2 WC. 🅿 01/01-31/12
Distance: 🚆nearby.
Remarks: Metalled pitches, play ground.
Tourist information Oradour-sur-Glane:
ℹ Office de Tourisme, Place du Champ de Foire. Martyre town, was attacked by
200 SS-soldiers on 10 June 1944. They assassinated the population. Afterwards
the village was burned down. In commemoration a wall was built round the the
city after the war. 🕑 free.

🏕🆂 Pageas 21A6
GPS: n45,67758 e1,00224.⬆➡.

10 ⛺free ⚡€ 3 🚰 Ch 🔌 WC. **Surface:** grassy. 🅿 01/01-31/12
Distance: 🚶100m ≋on the spot ⊗on the spot 🚆on the spot.

Remarks: Near N21.
🏕🆂 Peyrat-le-Château 21C6
Parking Pré de l'Age. GPS: n45,81468 e1,77085.⬆.

20 ⛺free ⚡€ 2 🚰 Ch. **Surface:** gravel. 🅿 01/01-31/12
Distance: 🚶on the spot 🚆on the spot.
Remarks: Coins at town hall, office du tourisme.
Tourist information Peyrat-le-Château:
ℹ Office de Tourisme, 1, Rue du Lac, www.peyrat-tourisme.com. Tourist town
close water sports lake, Lac de Vassivière, marked cycle and hiking routes. 🅿
Sa-Su 15-17h. 🕑 free.

🏕🆂 Sadroc 29A1
Place du Château. GPS: n45,28362 e1,54806.⬆➡.

6 ⛺free ⚡ 🚰 Ch 🔌 free. **Surface:** asphalted. 🅿 01/01-31/12
Distance: 🚶on the spot 🚲5,2km 🚆50m.
Remarks: Max. 24h.

🏕🆂 Servières-le-Château 29A1
Centre touristique du lac de Feyt. GPS: n45,14415 e2,03665.⬆➡.

15 ⛺free ⚡€ 2/100liter 🚰 Ch 🔌€ 2/1h. **Surface:** asphalted. 🅿 01/01-
31/12
Distance: ≋sandy beach ⊗on the spot.

🏕🆂 St.Junien-la-Bregère 21C5
Rue du Chevalier de Châteauneuf. GPS: n45,88056 e1,75028.⬆.

3 ⛺free ⚡ 🚰 Ch free. **Surface:** asphalted. 🅿 01/01-31/12

FR

📶⚡🅂 **St.Laurent** 21C5
Rue des Cerisiers. **GPS:** n46,16639 e1,96167. ⬆️➡️.

4 🚐free 🚰🔧Ch 🧹free. **Surface:** metalled. ⭕ 01/01-31/12
Distance: 🚶on the spot.

📶🅂 **St.Laurent-sur-Gorre** 21A6
Les Chênes, Allée des Primevères. **GPS:** n45,76528 e0,95639. ⬆️➡️.

20 🚐€6 🚰🔧Ch 🧹WC 📶included.
Surface: grassy. ⭕ 01/01-31/12
Distance: 🚶300m 🏊20m 🚲20m 🛒300m 🍴300m.
Remarks: Special motorhome washing place.

📶🅂 **St.Merd-les-Oussines** 21C6
D109 > Tarnac. **GPS:** n45,63500 e2,03719. ⬆️.

6 🚐free 🚰€2 🔧Ch. **Surface:** gravel. ⭕ 01/01-31/12
Distance: 🚶400m.
Remarks: Coins at Auberge du Mont-Chauvet.

📶🅂 **St.Yrieix-la-Perche** 🏕️⚓ 21B6
Avenue de Lattre de Tassigny, D901. **GPS:** n45,51222 e1,20556. ⬆️.

5 🚐free 🚰€3,50 🔧Ch.
Surface: asphalted. ⭕ 01/01-31/12
Distance: 🚶300m 🛒300m 🍴300m.
Remarks: Coins available at Office du Tourisme, bar and maison de la presse.

📶🅂 **St.Yrieix-la-Perche** 🏕️⚓ 21B6
Ferme du Poumier, Lieu-dit Poumier, Marcognac. **GPS:** n45,52065 e1,26853. ⬆️.

4 🚐€3 🚰€ 4 🔧Ch 🧹. **Surface:** gravel. ⭕ 01/01-31/12
Distance: 🚶St.Yrieix 5km.
Remarks: Near D901 dir Coussac-Bonneval.

📶🅂 **Treignac** 21C6
Les Rivières, D940. **GPS:** n45,54341 e1,79950. ⬆️➡️.

25 🚐free 🚰🔧Ch WC free. **Surface:** grassy/gravel. ⭕ 01/01-31/12 🔘
service: frost.
Distance: 🚶2km 🏊on the spot.
Remarks: Along the river.
Tourist information Treignac:
ℹ️ Office de Tourisme, 1, Place de la République. Free itinerary city tour along all curiosities, available at OT.

📶🅂 **Turenne** 🏕️⚓ 29A1
Aire camping-cars, Avenue du Sénateur Labrousse, D8. **GPS:** n45,05391 e1,57988. ⬆️➡️.

10 🚐free 🚰€2 🔧Ch🛒€2 WC. **Surface:** gravel. ⭕ 01/01-31/12
Distance: 🚶on the spot 🛒100m 🍴100m.
Remarks: Narrow road, not suitable for motorhomes +7m, behind office de tourisme, coins at Office de Tourisme, supermarket.
Tourist information Turenne:
ℹ️ Office de Tourisme, Le Bourg, www.brive-tourisme.com. Small medieval town.
🕐 Tour de Cesar. ⭕ Easter-Oct daily, winter Su.

📶🅂 **Ussel** 21D6
Aire du lac de Ponty. **GPS:** n45,54762 e2,28330. ⬆️.

15 🛏free ⛽€ 2 🔌Ch🚻€ 2 WC. **Surface:** asphalted. ⬛ 01/01-31/12
Distance: 🚶Ussel 3km ⛵8,5km.
Remarks: At lake, in front of entrance campsite.

🅿🆂 **Uzerche** 29A1
Place de la Petite Gare, Rue Paul Langevin. **GPS:** n45,42477 e1,56696.⬆➡

20 🛏free ⛽🔌Ch🚻WCfree. **Surface:** asphalted. ⬛ 01/01-31/12
Distance: 🚶300m ⛵4,4km🏊little stream.

Tourist information Uzerche:
ℹ Office de Tourisme, Place de la Libération, www.uzerche.fr.Little town on the
Vézère river with ruins of the abbey of Saint Peter.

🅿🆂 **Vigeois** 29A1
D7, route de Brive. **GPS:** n45,36717 e1,53392.⬆➡

12 🛏free ⛽€ 2 🔌Ch🚻€ 2. **Surface:** grassy. ⬛ 01/01-31/12
Distance: 🚶2km ⛵7,2km🏊beach 150m.
Remarks: Coins at bars in the village.

Auvergne

🅿🆂 **Aigueperse** 🌿 22A5
Place du Foirail, Rue de la Porte aux Boeufs. **GPS:** n46,02634 e3,20313.⬆

15 🛏free ⛽€ 2/10minutes 🔌Ch🚻€ 2/1h. **Location:** Urban, central, quit.
Surface: asphalted.
Distance: 🚶on the spot ⊗nearby 🏊nearby.
Remarks: Market square.

🅿🆂 **Allanche** 🏔 29C1
Aire de la Gare, Chemin de la Roche Marchal. **GPS:** n45,23000 e2,93139.⬆

25 🛏free ⛽€ 2 🔌Ch.
Location: Rural, quit. **Surface:** gravel/sand. ⬛ 01/05-01/11, parking 01/01-
31/12
Distance: 🚶300m ⊗300m 🏊300m.
Remarks: Altitude ±1000m. Follow 'vélo gare du Cezalier'.

🅿🆂 **Arlanc** 29D1
Loumans. **GPS:** n45,41233 e3,71782.⬆➡

+10 🛏free ⛽🔌Chfree 📶. **Location:** Rural, quit. **Surface:** asphalted/
grassy. ⬛ 01/01-31/12
Distance: 🚶500m 🏊on the spot ⚓on the spot ⊗100m 🏊1km 🚶on the
spot.
Remarks: At swimming pool and small lake.

🅿🆂 **Arnac (Cantal)** 29B1
Aire camping-cars, RD61. **GPS:** n45,06056 e2,23389.⬆

2 🛏free ⛽€ 2/100liter 🔌Ch🚻€ 2/1h. **Location:** Rural, quit. **Surface:**
grassy/gravel. ⬛ 01/01-31/12
Distance: 🚶50m 🏊150m 🏊150m.

🅿🆂 **Aubusson-d'Auvergne** 💦 ❄ 22B6
Base de Loisirs-lac d'Aubusson. **GPS:** n45,75377 e3,61079.⬆

50 🛏€6 ⛽🔌Ch WC 📶free. **Location:** Rural, very simple, isolated, quit.
Surface: metalled. ⬛ 01/01-31/12
Distance: 🏊on the spot ⚓on the spot ⊗200m 🏊8km 🚶on the spot.

🅿🆂 **Aurillac** 🏛 29B2
Place du Champ de Foire, Cours d'Angoulême. **GPS:** n44,92944 e2,44963.⬆➡

10 🛏free ⛽€ 3,50 🔌Ch🚻€ 3,50. **Location:** Urban, noisy. **Surface:**

FR

asphalted. ⏹ 01/01-31/12 ◉ service: 31/10-01/05.
Distance: 🚲on the spot ⊗100m 🚰100m.
Remarks: Max. 24h, coins at Office de Tourisme.
Tourist information Aurillac:
ℹ️ Office de Tourisme, Rue de Carmes, www.iaurillac.com.Old city centre with alleys and half-timbered houses.
✳️ European street theatre and festival. ⏹ 3rd week Aug.

🏕️ S	Aydat 🚩	22A6

Aire camping-cars. GPS: n45,66025 e2,97778.⬆️➡️.

41 🗑️€ 8 🚰🔌 Ch 💦 WC ⏹included. 🛗 ♻️ **Location:** Rural, comfortable, quit. **Surface:** grassy. ⏹ 01/01-31/12
Distance: 🚲200m ⛵on the spot ⊷on the spot ⊗on the spot 🚰250m.
Remarks: Former campsite, max. 8,20m.

🏕️ S	Beaulieu	29D1

Zone d'Activité la Gerle. GPS: n45,12597 e3,94608.⬆️➡️.

15 🗑️free 🚰🔌 Ch 💦 (2x)free. **Location:** Rural, quit. **Surface:** gravel. ⏹ 01/04-31/10
Distance: 🚲400m.

🏕️ S	Beaulon 🚩	22B4

Écluse de Beaulon, La Curesse. **GPS:** n46,60443 e3,65840.⬆️➡️.

+10 🗑️free 🚰🔌 Ch 💦 (4x)free. **Location:** Rural, isolated, quit. **Surface:** gravel. ⏹ 01/01-31/12
Distance: 🚲1,2km ⛵Canal ⊷on the spot ⊗1,2km 🚰1,2km 🚴on the spot 🎣on the spot.

🏕️ S	Bellerive-sur-Allier	22B5

Riv'Air Camp, Rue Claude Decloitre. **GPS:** n46,11514 e3,43114.⬆️.

50 🗑️€ 10 🚰🔌 Ch 💦 (50x) WC ⏹included ◉. 🐕 **Location:** Urban, comfortable, isolated, quit. **Surface:** metalled. ⏹ 01/01-31/12
Distance: 🚲2,5km ⛵17km ⛰️on the spot ⊷on the spot ⊗on the spot 🚰800m.
Remarks: Along the Allier river.

🏕️ S	Billy	22B5

Rue de la Fontaine. GPS: n46,23586 e3,43044.⬆️⬆️.

🗑️free 🚰🔌 Chfree. **Surface:** asphalted. ⏹ 01/01-31/12
Distance: 🚲on the spot.
Remarks: Max. 48h.

🍴 S	Blesle 🏘️	29C1

Hôtel-Restaurant Le Scorpion, D909. **GPS:** n45,31219 e3,18677.⬆️.

25 🗑️€ 15 🚰🔌 Ch 💦 (8x) WC ⏹included. **Location:** Rural, comfortable, quit. **Surface:** grassy. ⏹ 01/01-31/12
Distance: ⛵5,8km ⊗on the spot.
Remarks: A75 exit 19, 22 or 23 from southern dir exit 20, 22 or 24.
Tourist information Blesle:
ℹ️ Office de Tourisme, Place de l'Eglise, www.tourismeblesle.fr.Ancient little town, 9th century, built around Benedictine monastery.

🏕️ S	Brioude 🏛️	29C1

Parking des Remparts, Avenue de Lamothe, D588. **GPS:** n45,29444 e3,38778.⬆️➡️.

30 🗑️free 🚰€ 2 🔌Ch🛗€ 2. **Location:** Urban, central, quit. **Surface:** asphalted. ⏹ 01/01-31/12
Distance: 🚲100m ⊗100m 🚰100m.

Remarks: Coins at Office du Tourisme (100m).
Tourist information Brioude:
ℹ️ Office de Tourisme, Place Lafayette, www.ot-brioude.fr.Old fortress city.
👁 L'aquarium-la Maison du Saumon et de la Rivière, Place de la Résistance.
Museum about the salmon. ⬛ 01/04-30/11.

| 🏕️ S | **Buxières-les-Mines** | 22A4 |

Le Boucher - Buxières-les-Mines

margabolmer@orange.fr - www.camping-leboucher.com

Electricity/water/drainage at each pitch
Sanitary facilities
Use swimming pool included

Le Boucher. GPS: n46,45464 e2,96791. ⬆️➡️.
6 🅿️€ 14,50 🚰 🍽️ Ch 🔌 (6x), 12Amp WC ⬜€ 5 📶 included. 🚿
Location: Rural, comfortable, isolated.
Surface: grassy. ⬛ 01/01-31/12
Distance: 🚶2km 🏊5km 🚲2km 🛒5km 🍽️2km.

| 🏕️ S | **Calvinet** | 29B2 |

Aire de Calvinet, Terrain de sport. **GPS:** n44,71023 e2,35914. ⬆️➡️.

6 🅿️free 🚰€ 2 🍽️Ch 🔌€ 2. **Location:** Rural, quit. **Surface:** gravel. ⬛
01/01-31/12 ⚫ service 01/11-31/03.
Distance: 🚶1,5km 🛒1,5km 🍽️1,5km.
Remarks: Nearby sports ground.

| 🏕️ S | **Cassaniouze** | 29B2 |

Aire camping-cars, Le Bourg. **GPS:** n44,69347 e2,38233. ⬆️➡️.

6 🅿️free 🚰€ 2/80liter 🍽️Ch 🔌 2/1h ⬜€ 1. **Location:** Rural, quit.
Surface: gravel. ⬛ 01/01-31/12 ⚫ service 01/11-31/03.
Distance: 🚶600m 🛒600m 🍽️600m.

| 🏕️ S | **Cayrols** | 29B2 |

Aire camping-cars, La Devèze, D51. **GPS:** n44,83000 e2,23278. ⬆️➡️.

10 🅿️free 🚰€ 3,80 🍽️Ch 🔌€ 3,80 WC.
Location: Rural, comfortable, quit. **Surface:** metalled.
⬛ 01/01-31/12 ⚫ service 01/11-31/03.
Distance: 🚶100m 🍽️200m.
Remarks: Max. 1 week, coins at the shops in the village.

| C S | **Chambon-sur-Lac** 🏊 ⛰️ ❄️ | 22A6 |

Camping Les Bombes, La Vergne. **GPS:** n45,56991 e2,90176. ⬆️➡️.

30 🅿️€ 6 🚰€ 3 🍽️Ch. 🚿 **Location:** Rural, quit. **Surface:** grassy/gravel. ⬛
01/01-31/12 ⚫ service: 15/09-01/05.
Distance: 🚶500m 🏊200m 🚲1km 🛒500m 🍽️500m bakery 🚴 on the spot
🚶 on the spot.
Remarks: Pay and coins at campsite.

| 🏕️ S | **Champeix** | 22A6 |

Champeix, Route de Montaigut, D996. **GPS:** n45,58845 e3,11568. ⬆️.

+10 🅿️free 🚰€ 2 🍽️Ch. **Location:** Rural, very simple, isolated, quit.
Surface: grassy/gravel. ⬛ 01/01-31/12
Distance: 🚶1,3km 🛒1,3km 🍽️500m.

| 🏕️ S | **Chanaleilles** ⛰️ | 29C2 |

Le Bourg. **GPS:** n44,85971 e3,49083. ⬆️.

5 🅿️free 🚰 🍽️Ch. **Location:** Rural, comfortable, isolated, quit. **Surface:**
grassy/gravel.
Distance: 🚶500m 🛒375m.

| 🏕️ S | **Charbonnières-les-Varennes** | 22A5 |

Route de Saint-Georges, Paugnat. **GPS:** n45,88457 e2,97993. ⬆️.

FR

10 🔥free 🚰€ 2/10minutes 🗑Ch📶€ 2/55minutes. **Location:** Rural, comfortable, quit. **Surface:** grassy. 🅾 01/01-31/12
Distance: 🚶500m 🛒bakery 500m 🏃on the spot.
Remarks: Coins available at the shops, trail to volcano crater.

10 🔥free. **Location:** Urban, very simple, quit. **Surface:** asphalted. 🅾 01/01-31/12
Distance: 🚶500m ⊗600m 🛒600m.

📷S | **Chaspuzac** | 29D1
Rue du Vol à Voile. **GPS:** n45,07491 e3,76131.➡.

📷S | **Chaudes-Aigues** | 29C2
Parking Beauredon, Avenue Georges Pompidou, D921. **GPS:** n44,84972 e3,00306.⬆➡.

6 🔥free 🚰€ 2 🗑Ch. **Location:** Rural, quit. **Surface:** asphalted.
Distance: ⊗50m.
Remarks: View on airport.

10 🔥free 🚰€ 2 🗑Ch📶€ 2/55minutes. **Location:** Urban, very simple. **Surface:** gravel. 🅾 15/04-15/10
Distance: 🚶100m ⊗300m 🛒300m.

📷S | **Chastreix** 🏔❄ | 21D6
Parking Station de Ski, Chastreix Sancy. **GPS:** n45,53507 e2,77695.⬆.

Tourist information Chaudes-Aigues:
ℹ Office de Tourisme, 1, avenue Georges Pompidou, www.chaudesaigues.com. Small town with warm thermal sources (82ºC).

📷S | **Chomelix** 🎏 | 29D1
Centre Multi Activités Les Marches d'Auvergne, Route d'Estables, D135. **GPS:** n45,26219 e3,82573.⬆.

14 🔥free 🚰Ch🧹€ 9, (winter) WC 🗑€ 2, (winter). **Location:** Rural, quit. **Surface:** metalled. 🅾 01/01-31/12
Distance: 🚶Chastreix 6km 🎿on the spot.
Remarks: Check in between 9-17h.

6 🔥free 🚰€ 4 🗑Ch. **Location:** Rural, quit. **Surface:** gravel. 🅾 01/01-31/12
Distance: 🚶on the spot ⊗on the spot 🚴mountainbike trail 🏃on the spot.

📷S | **Châtel-Guyon** 🎏 | 22A5
Place de la Musique Nationale. **GPS:** n45,92324 e3,06590.⬆➡.

📷S | **Clermont Ferrand** | 22A6
P&R Les Pistes, Rue de la Fontaine de la Ratte. **GPS:** n45,79810 e3,11222.⬆.

7 🔥€ 5/day 🚰€ 2 🗑Ch WC. **Location:** Urban, comfortable, central, quit. **Surface:** asphalted. 🅾 01/01-31/12
Distance: 🚶nearby ⊗400m 🛒400m.
Remarks: Check in at police station, coins at Tourist Info.

6 🔥€ 5 🚰🗑Chfree. 🚿 **Location:** Urban. **Surface:** asphalted. 🅾 01/01-31/12
Distance: 🚶historical centre 3km 🚌50m.
Remarks: Nearby Michelin museum, check in at parking attendant.

📷S | **Châtel-Guyon** 🎏 | 22A5
Parking des Roches, Chemin de Bussane. **GPS:** n45,91789 e3,06545.⬆.

Coltines 29C1

D40. **GPS:** n45,09612 e2,98555. ➡.

5 🛏free ⚡€ 2/100liter 🗑Ch➕€ 2.
Location: Rural.
Surface: gravel.
Distance: 🏊400m ⊗400m 🛒400m.
Remarks: Coins at Epicerie-Presse, Centre Chantarisaen de Maire.

Condat 29B1

Parking au Pont, D678. **GPS:** n45,33889 e2,76250. ⬆.

4 🛏free ⚡ Service € 2,50 🗑Ch➕. **Location:** Very simple. **Surface:** asphalted. ⬤ 01/01-31/12 ⬤ service: 01/10-01/05.
Distance: 🏊50m 🚲10m 🛒50m.
Remarks: Coins at campsite La Borie Basse (500m).

Coubon 29D1

Route du Plan d'Eau. **GPS:** n44,99735 e3,91742. ⬆.

5 🛏free 🗑ChWC. **Surface:** metalled. ⬤ 01/01-31/12
Remarks: Along river.

Crandelles 29B1

Aire camping-cars, Lac des Genevrières. **GPS:** n44,95877 e2,34289.

10 🛏free ⚡€ 3,50 🗑Ch. **Location:** Comfortable, central, quit. **Surface:** gravel. ⬤ 01/01-31/12 ⬤ service: 01/11-01/04.
Distance: 🏊300m 🏊50m 🚲50m ⊗50m 🛒300m.

Craponne-sur-Arzon 29D1

Avenue de la Gare. **GPS:** n45,33360 e3,85057. ⬆.

+20 🛏free ⚡€ 2 🗑Ch➕€ 2/1h. **Location:** Urban, very simple, quit.
Surface: asphalted/gravel. ⬤ 01/01-31/12
Distance: 🏊150m ⊗150m 🛒on the spot.

Drugeac 29B1

Aire de campingcars, La Gare SNCF. **GPS:** n45,16694 e2,38667. ⬆➡.

4 🛏free ⚡€ 2/100liter 🗑Ch➕€ 2/1h.
Location: Rural, very simple, quit. **Surface:** asphalted. ⬤ 01/01-31/12 ⬤ service: 01/11-01/05.
Distance: 🏊100m ⊗100m 🛒100m.
Remarks: At former station, now start Vélorail.

Tourist information Drugeac:
ℹ Office de Tourisme, Place Tyssandier d'Escous, Salers. Small town built from grey lava stones with ramparts from the 15th century.

Ebreuil 22A5

Parking du Stade, D915. **GPS:** n46,10954 e3,07606. ⬆.

10 🛏free. **Location:** Very simple. **Surface:** gravel. ⬤ 01/01-31/12
Distance: 🚲6,5km.
Remarks: Service 500m, in front of campsite municipal.

Ebreuil 22A5

Chemin des Nières. **GPS:** n46,11083 e3,08111. ⬆.
⚡🗑Ch free. ⬤ 01/01-31/12
Remarks: Next to campsite municipal, overnight stay on Parking du Stade.

Estivareilles 21D4

Salle Polyvalente, Via: rue de la République. **GPS:** n46,42471 e2,61529. ⬆➡.

20 🛏free ⚡🗑free. **Location:** Urban.

Surface: gravel. ⬛ 01/01-31/12
Distance: 🅿on the spot ⚪9km ⊗200m 🍺bakery 200m.

| 🖩S | Faverolles | 29C2 |

D248 Centre village. **GPS:** n44,93917 e3,14750.

6 🛏free ⟟€ 2/100liter ⊟Ch ▦€ 2/55minutes WC. **Location:** Rural.
Surface: gravel. ⬛ 01/01-31/12
Distance: 🅿on the spot ⊗100m 🍺200m.

| 🖩S | Jaligny-sur-Besbre 🏞 | 22B4 |

Rue de la Chaume. **GPS:** n46,38155 e3,59147. ⬆➡.

5 🛏free ⟟⊟Ch ▦(5x)free. **Location:** Rural, quit. **Surface:** gravel. ⬛
01/01-31/12
Distance: 🅿200m 🏊on the spot 🛒on the spot ⊗250m 🍺250m.
Remarks: Along the Besbre river.

| 🖩S | La Bourboule 🏞♨ | 21D6 |

Plateau de Charlannes. **GPS:** n45,57811 e2,73513. ⬆.

10 🛏free. **Location:** Rural, quit. **Surface:** asphalted. ⬛ 01/01-31/12
Distance: 🅿6,5km ⊗Snackbar ⛷on the spot 🚶on the spot.
Remarks: Parking at funicular railway.

| 🖩S | La Bourboule 🏞♨ | 21D6 |

Rue Fernand Forest, D130. **GPS:** n45,58984 e2,74953. ⬆.

10 🛏free. **Location:** Urban. **Surface:** asphalted. ⬛ 01/01-31/12
Distance: 🅿500m ⊗500m 🍺500m.

| 🖩S | La Chapelle-Laurent ❄ | 29C1 |

Aire camping-cars, D10. **GPS:** n45,18028 e3,24389. ⬆.

5 🛏free ⟟⊟Chfree. **Location:** Rural, very simple. **Surface:** grassy. ⬛
parking 01/01-31/12, service 01/04-15/11
Distance: 🅿50m 🛒nearby ⊗100m 🍺100m.

| 🖩S | La Roche-Blanche | 22A6 |

Madame BLAZANIN, La Pigné Sud, Route des Fours à Chaux. **GPS:** n45,71567
e3,14790. ⬆.

100 🛏€6 ⟟€ 2/100liter ⊟Ch ▦(4x)€ 6/6h. 🐾 **Location:** Rural,
isolated, quit. **Surface:** grassy. ⬛ 01/03-30/11
Distance: ⚪1,1km.

| 🖩S | La Tour-d'Auvergne 🏞🏞 | 21D6 |

-, Route de Bagnols. **GPS:** n45,53290 e2,68213. ⬆.

25 🛏free ⟟⊟Chfree. **Location:** Quit.
Surface: metalled. ⬛ 01/01-31/12
Distance: 🛒on the spot ⊗650m 🍺650m bakery.

| 🖩S | Lacapelle-Viescamp | 29B2 |

Aire camping-cars, D18. **GPS:** n44,92167 e2,26361. ⬆.

5 🛏free ⟟€ 3/100liter ⊟Ch ▦€ 3/1h. **Location:** Rural. **Surface:**
metalled. ⬛ 01/01-31/12
Distance: 🅿100m ⊗100m 🍺on the spot.
Remarks: Coins available at the shop.

| 🖩S | Lapalisse 🏞🏞❄ | 22B5 |

Place Jean Moulin, RN7 dir Roanne. **GPS:** n46,25000 e3,63500. ➡.

FR

50 🛏free 🚰€ 2 💧Ch 🚿€ 2 WC. **Location:** Urban, central, quit. **Surface:** asphalted. ⬛ 01/01-31/12
Distance: 🚶300m 🛒on the spot ⊗on the spot 🍴on the spot.

Lavaudieu 🌿🏛️ .   29C1

Le Bourg. **GPS:** n45,26297 e3,45606. 🔼 .

+10 🛏free. **Location:** Very simple, isolated, quit. **Surface:** grassy/gravel. ⬛ 01/01-31/12
Distance: 🚶200m 🚶on the spot.

Le Breuil-sur-Couze   29C1

Allée de Treize Vents. **GPS:** n45,46867 e3,26121. 🔼➡️ .

8 🛏free 🚰💧Chfree. **Location:** Urban, very simple. **Surface:** gravel. ⬛ 01/01-31/12
Distance: 🚲900m 🍴700m bakery, supermarket.
Remarks: Along railwayline.

Le Cheix-sur-Morge   22A5

D425. **GPS:** n45,95096 e3,17884. 🔼➡️ .

Remarks: Tue market.

Le Monastier-sur-Gazeille   29D2

Rue Augustin Ollier. **GPS:** n44,93720 e3,99250. 🔼➡️ .

10 🛏free. **Location:** Rural, very simple.
Surface: grassy. ⬛ 01/03-31/10
Distance: 🚶300m ⊗300m 🍴300m.

Le Monastier-sur-Gazeille   29D2

Le Moulin de Savin. **GPS:** n44,93680 e3,98600. 🔼➡️ .
🚰💧Ch.
Remarks: Next to campsite.

Le Puy-en-Velay   29D1

Avenue Charles Dupuy. **GPS:** n45,04358 e3,89240. 🔼➡️ .

12 🛏€ 8, € 2/3h. 🔌 **Location:** Urban, very simple, central, noisy. **Surface:** asphalted. ⬛ 01/01-31/12
Distance: 🚶500m.
Remarks: Max. 24h, behind bus terminal.

Le Puy-en-Velay   29D1

Boulevard de Cluny. **GPS:** n45,04963 e3,88976. 🔼 .
🚰€ 2 💧Ch.

Le Vernet   29D1

Le Bourg. **GPS:** n45,03560 e3,66952. 🔼 .

6 🛏free 🚰💧Chfree. **Location:** Rural, isolated, quit. **Surface:** gravel. ⬛ 01/01-31/12
Distance: 🚶500m.
Remarks: Max. 48h.

Le Donjon   22B4

Place du Champ de Foire, Rue Georges Gallay. **GPS:** n46,34940 e3,79473. 🔼 .
🛏free. **Location:** Very simple, central, quit.
Surface: gravel. ⬛ 01/01-31/12
Distance: 🚶100m 🍴50m.

10 🛏€ 2 🚰€ 2/80liter 💧Ch 🚿€ 2/10minutes. **Location:** Rural, very simple, isolated, quit. **Surface:** grassy/sand. ⬛ 01/01-31/12
Distance: 🚶50m 🚶on the spot.

Les Estables 🏛️⛄   29D2

Le Bourg. **GPS:** n44,90231 e4,15679. 🔼 .

FR

8 🛏free 🚰🔧Chfree 📶. **Location:** Rural. **Surface:** asphalted. ⬛ 01/01-31/12

Distance: 🚶50m ⊗50m 🏊 on the spot.

Remarks: Free wifi, code at office de tourisme.

🛏Ⓢ **Lezoux** **22B6**

Parking Musée départemental de la Céramique, Rue de la République. **GPS:** n45,82686 e3,38459.⬆️➡️.

30 🛏free 🚰🔧 Ch WC free. **Location:** Comfortable, central, quit. **Surface:** gravel. ⬛ 01/01-31/12 ⬤ water: 01/11-31/03.

Distance: 🚶500m 🚲3,5km ⊗500m 🛒500m.

🛏Ⓢ **Lurcy-Lévis** ⌛ **22A3**

Plan d'eau des Sézeaux, Rue de Fontgroix. **GPS:** n46,73797 e2,93863.⬆️➡️.

6 🛏free 🚰€ 3/100liter 🔧Ch🔌€ 3/55minutes WC. **Location:** Rural, comfortable, quit. **Surface:** grassy/gravel. ⬛ 01/01-31/12

Distance: 🚶800m ⌛Small lake 🎣on the spot⊗800m 🛒800m.

Remarks: Coins at cafe, in front of the church.

🛏Ⓢ **Mandailles-Saint-Julien** 🏔️ **29B1**

Aire de camping-cars, Le Mas, D17. **GPS:** n45,06916 e2,65611.➡️.

5 🛏free 🚰€ 3,50 Ch. **Location:** Rural, quit. **Surface:** metalled. ⬛ 01/01-31/12 ⬤ service: 30/09-01/05.

Distance: 🚶200m ⊗200m 🛒200m 🎣 on the spot.

Remarks: Max. 24h, coins at restaurants.

🛏Ⓢ **Manzat** **22A5**

Place du 14 Juillet. **GPS:** n45,96180 e2,93883.⬆️.

20 🛏free 🚰🔧Chfree. **Location:** Rural, quit. **Surface:** unpaved. ⬛ 01/01-

31/12

Distance: 🚶on the spot 🚲5,6km ⊗250m 🛒200m.

Remarks: In opposite of police station.

🛏Ⓢ **Marcolès** **29B2**

Aire camping-cars, Terrain de sport. **GPS:** n44,78028 e2,35389.⬆️.

5 🛏free 🚰🔧Chfree. **Location:** Rural, quit. **Surface:** gravel. ⬛ 01/01-31/12 ⬤ service 01/11-31/03.

Distance: 🚶100m ⊗100m 🛒100m.

Remarks: Artists village.

🛏Ⓢ **Massiac** **29C1**

Rue Jacques Chaban Delmas. **GPS:** n45,25278 e3,19667.⬆️➡️.

9 🛏free. **Location:** Rural, very simple.

Surface: grassy. ⬛ 01/01-31/12

Distance: 🚶200m 🚲1,3km ⊗200m 🛒200m.

🛏Ⓢ **Mauriac** ⌛ **29B1**

Aire de campingcars, Rue du Val Saint Jean. **GPS:** n45,21863 e2,32183.⬆️➡️.

10 🛏free 🚰€ 2/100liter 🔧Ch🔌€ 2/1h 🧹. **Location:** Rural, very simple, quit. **Surface:** metalled. ⬛ 01/01-31/12

Distance: 🚶1km ⌛beach 300m ⊗1,2km 🛒1,2km.

🛏Ⓢ **Maurs** **29B2**

Maurs La Jolie, Route de Quezac. **GPS:** n44,71442 e2,19615.⬆️➡️.

5 🛏free 🚰€ 2/100liter 🔧Ch🔌€ 2/1h. **Location:** Urban, central, quit. **Surface:** asphalted. ⬛ 01/01-31/12

Distance: 🚶300m ⊗300m 🛒300m 🎣300m.

Remarks: Coins at Papetterie and tourist office.

Messeix 21D6

-, Place des Pins. **GPS:** n45,61576 e2,55621.

6 free € 2/10minutes Ch € 2/55minutes. **Location:** Urban, quit.
Surface: asphalted. 01/01-31/12
Distance: 500m 18km 1,7km on the spot.
Remarks: Coins available at the shops.

Montluçon 21D4

Route de l'Etang de Sault, Prémilhat. **GPS:** n46,33469 e2,55855.

8 free € 6/150liter Ch (6x)€ 2,50/10h . **Location:** Rural,
comfortable. **Surface:** gravel. 01/01-31/12
Distance: 5km Montluçon 2,6km 150m 150m 500m.
Remarks: Max. 72h.

Montluçon 21D4

Place de la Fraternité, Rue des Marais. **GPS:** n46,35535 e2,58686.

15 free € 5/150liter Ch € 2,50/10minutes WC . **Location:**
Urban, very simple, noisy. **Surface:** asphalted. 01/01-31/12 water:
Nov-March.
Distance: on the spot A71 16km on the spot on the spot on the
spot.
Remarks: Thu-morning closed because of market (6-15h). From Châteauroux, on
entering the town.

Tourist information Montluçon:
 Office de Tourisme, Boulevard du Courtais, www.montlucontourisme.com.

Montmurat 29B2

Aire camping-cars, Le Bourg, D345. **GPS:** n44,62811 e2,19804.

10 free € 1 Ch. **Location:** Rural, very simple, isolated, quit. **Surface:**
gravel. 01/01-31/12
Distance: on the spot.

Montoldre 22B4

D21. **GPS:** n46,33272 e3,44727.

+10 free € 2 Ch. **Location:** Rural, quit. **Surface:** asphalted.
01/01-31/12
Distance: centre on the spot.
Remarks: Parking in front of town hall.

Montsalvy 29B2

Aire camping-cars, Route de Junhac. **GPS:** n44,70778 e2,49667.

11 free € 2 Ch € 2 WC 1. **Location:** Rural, comfortable,
quit. **Surface:** gravel. 01/01-31/12
Distance: 400m 400m 400m.

Moulins 22A4

Flot Bleu Park, Chemin de Halage. **GPS:** n46,55852 e3,32491.

92 € 0,10/h € 2 Ch € 2 € 2/20minutes (12x)€ 2/4h .
 Location: Urban, comfortable, central, quit. **Surface:** grassy/metalled.
01/01-31/12
Distance: city centre 1km 100m 300m on the spot.

Murat 29C1

Avenue d'Olonne-sur-mer. **GPS:** n45,10757 e2,85975.

free. **Location:** Urban, very simple. **Surface:** concrete. 01/01-31/12
Remarks: At sports park.

Murat   29C1

Parking du Stade, Rue du Stade. **GPS**: n45,10861 e2,87027.

free. **Surface:** asphalted. 01/01-31/12

S   Murat   29C1

Place du 19 mars. **GPS**: n45,10917 e2,86917.

€ 2 Ch € 2 WC. 01/05-31/10

Tourist information Murat:
Office de Tourisme, Place de l'Hôtel de Ville. Medieval city, city tour available at OT.
Fri-morning.

S   Murat-le-Quaire   21D6

Les Rives du Lac, Route de la Banne d'Ordanche. **GPS**: n45,60274 e2,73797.

37 € 8/24h Ch (8x) WC included € 1. **Location:** Rural, comfortable, quit. **Surface:** grassy/metalled. 01/01-31/12
Distance: 1,2km 12km 100m 100m day pass available on the spot on the spot 100m 5km.
Remarks: Bread-service.

S   Murol   22A6

Rue du Tartaret, D5. **GPS**: n45,57288 e2,94101.

20 free service € 2 Ch. **Location:** Urban.
Surface: asphalted.
Distance: 450m 300m.
Remarks: Service 100m, pay at tourist office.

Tourist information Murol:
Bureau de Tourisme Grande Vallée, Rue de Jassaguet, www.grandevallee.com. Holiday resort, dominated by the Château de Murol, 13th century.

S   Naucelles   29B1

Aire camping-cars, Rue du Terrou. **GPS**: n44,95694 e2,41757.

5 free € 3,50/100liter Ch € 3,50/1h. **Location:** Urban, very simple, quit. **Surface:** asphalted. 01/01-31/12
Distance: Spar 300m.
Remarks: Coins at supermarket in the village.

S   Néris-les-Bains   21D4

Camping du Lac, Avenue Marrx Dormoy, D155. **GPS**: n46,28673 e2,65235.

6 €7 Ch (6x) WC included. **Location:** Urban, comfortable.
Surface: gravel. 01/03-31/10
Distance: 500m 12km bakery 500m.
Remarks: Max. 3 nights, to be paid at campsite.

S   Neussargues-Moissac   29C1

Allée des Peupliers. **GPS**: n45,13438 e2,98130.

5 free € 2/100liter Ch € 2/2h. **Location:** Rural, comfortable, quit. **Surface:** gravel. 01/01-31/12 water disconnected in winter.
Distance: 300m 50m 300m.

Orcines   22A6

-, D941. **GPS**: n45,80394 e2,98726.

10 free. **Location:** Very simple, noisy. **Surface:** metalled. 01/01-31/12
on the spot.

FR

S | **Orcines** | **22A6**

D941B dir Orcines Vulcania. **GPS**: n45,78765 e3,00947. ⬆ .

4free ⛲ € 2/100liter 🗑Ch📦 € 2/1h. **Location**: Urban, noisy. **Surface**: .
⬛ 01/01-31/12

S | **Pierrefort** | **29C2**

Côte de Chabridet. **GPS**: n44,92172 e2,84199. ⬆➡ .

20 ⭕free ⛲ € 2/100liter 🗑Ch📦 € 2.
Surface: gravel. ⬛ 01/01-31/12
Distance: 🚶100m ⊗200m 🛒200m.

S | **Pleaux** | **29B1**

Parc des Auzerals, Place d'Empeyssine. **GPS**: n45,13556 e2,22833. ⬆➡ .

10 ⭕free ⛲ 🗑Ch WC free. **Location**: Urban, central, quit. **Surface**: asphalted/gravel. ⬛ 01/01-31/12
Distance: 🚶on the spot ⊗100m 🛒100m.

S | **Pradelles** | **29D2**

Aire de la Salaison, N88. **GPS**: n44,77540 e3,88752. ⬆➡ .

3 ⭕free ⛲ 🗑Ch📦free. **Location**: Rural, very simple, quit. **Surface**: gravel.
⬛ 01/01-31/12 ⬤ service 01/11-31/03.
Distance: 🚶300m ⊗300m.

S | **Randan** | **22A5**

Rue du Puy de Dôme. **GPS**: n46,01630 e3,35075. ⬆➡ .

5 ⭕free ⛲ € 2/15minutes 🗑Ch📦 € 2/15minutes. **Location**: Urban, quit.
Surface: gravel. ⬛ 01/01-31/12
Distance: 🚶500m ⊗500m 🛒200m.
Remarks: Coins at Maison de la Presse, Rue de Commerce.

S | **Raucoules** | **29D1**

Raucoules, Le Bourg. **GPS**: n45,18640 e4,29750. ⬆➡ .

4 ⭕free ⛲ € 2 🗑Ch🚿(4x)€ 2. **Location**: Rural, comfortable, central, quit. **Surface**: asphalted. ⬛ 01/01-31/12
Distance: 🚶200m ⊗300m.
Remarks: Coins available in village.

S | **Retournac** | **29D1**

Rue de la Loire. **GPS**: n45,20328 e4,04501. ⬆➡ .

20 ⭕free ⛲ 🗑Ch free. **Location**: Rural, isolated, quit. **Surface**: gravel. ⬛
01/01-31/12 ⬤ Service: winter.
Distance: 🚶city centre 1km 🚲on the spot 🚶on the spot ⊗650m 🚶on the spot.
Remarks: Along the Loire river.

S | **Riom** | **22A5**

-, Route d'Ennezat, D224. **GPS**: n45,89455 e3,12477. ⬆➡ .
4 ⭕free ⛲ € 2/15minutes 🗑Ch📦 € 2/15minutes. **Location**: Urban,

S | **Prunet** | **29B2**

Aire camping-cars, Le Bourg. **GPS**: n44,82049 e2,46398. ➡ .

central, noisy. **Surface:** gravel. ⬛ 01/01-31/12
Distance: 🚶700m 🚲2,5km ⊗nearby 🍴nearby.

ⓢ | Riom-es-Montagnes | 29B1
Rue du Champ de Foire. **GPS**: n45,28444 e2,65389.⬆➡.

🚰€ 2/100liter ♨Ch🚽€ 2/1h.
Location: Very simple.
Surface: metalled. ⬛ 01/01-31/12
Distance: 🚶on the spot ⊗100m 🍴100m.
Remarks: Overnight stay on Parking de la Piscine, GPS N 45,27902 E 2,66403.

ⓢ | Ruynes-en-Margeride | 29C1
GPS: n45,00111 e3,22389.➡.

6 🅿free 🚰€ 2/10minutes ♨Ch🚽€ 2/55minutes. **Surface:** asphalted.
⬛ 01/01-31/12
Distance: 🚶50m ⊗50m 🍴50m.

ⓢ | Salins | 29B1
Aire de campingcars, D722. **GPS**: n45,19167 e2,39361.⬆.

3 🅿free 🚰♨free. **Surface:** gravel. ⬛ 01/01-31/12
Distance: 🚶50m.

ⓢ | Sansac-de-Marmiesse | 29B2
Aire camping-cars, Rue de la Vidalie. **GPS**: n44,88389 e2,34639.⬆➡.

3 🅿free 🚰€ 3,50 ♨Ch🚽€ 3,50. **Location:** Urban, central. **Surface:**
asphalted. ⬛ 01/01-31/12 🅾 service: 01/10-30/04.
Distance: 🚶on the spot ⊗200m 🍴on the spot.
Remarks: Coins at the bakery.

ⓢ | Sauges | 29C2
Place du Brieul. **GPS**: n44,95940 e3,54395.⬆.

10 🅿free 🚰♨Chfree. **Surface:** asphalted.
Distance: 🚶on the spot.

ⓢ | Sauret-Besserve | 22A5
D523. **GPS**: n45,99389 e2,81001.

4 🅿free 🚰€ 2 ♨Ch€ 2. **Location:** Rural, isolated. **Surface:** .
⬛ 01/01-31/12
Remarks: Near church, June 2012 during inspection service out of order.

ⓢ | Ségur-les-Villas | 29C1
Aire de camping-cars, Le Bourg. **GPS**: n45,22311 e2,81818.⬆➡.

10 🅿free 🚰€ 2/100liter ♨Ch🚽€ 2/1h. **Location:** Rural, quit. **Surface:**
grassy. ⬛ 01/05-31/10
Distance: 🚶200m ⊗300m 🍴200m.
Remarks: Nearby football ground, coins available at shops.

ⓢ | Solignat | 22A6
Route des Dauphins d'Auvergne, D32. **GPS**: n45,51701 e3,17074.⬆.

+50 🅿free 🚰€ 2/100liter ♨Ch🚽€ 2/1h. **Location:** Rural, very simple,
quit. **Surface:** grassy. ⬛ 01/01-31/12
Distance: 🚶100m.

ⓢ | St Anthème | 22B6
Rambaud. **GPS**: n45,52354 e3,91464.⬆➡.

FR

30 🗒€2 ⌐🍴 Ⓒhincluded. **Location:** Rural, central, quit. **Surface:** grassy/gravel. 🅾 01/01-31/12 ⦿ Water when frosty.
Distance: 🚰200m 🏖beach 250m ⊗200m ⚡on the spot.
Remarks: Next to campsite Rambaud, water disconnected.

| 🗒Ⓢ | St.Bonnet-le-Froid | 30A1 |

Chemin de Brard. **GPS:** n45,14136 e4,43454.⬆.
6 🗒€4 ⌐🍴Ch ✂included. **Surface:** gravel. 🅾 01/03-01/11
Distance: 🚰150m ⊗150m ⚡150m.
Remarks: Access via D105.

| 🗒Ⓢ | St.Bonnet-Tronçais 🎣 | 21D3 |

Parking du Stade, Route de Tronçais, D39. **GPS:** n46,66096 e2,69442.
🗒free ⌐€ 3/50liter 🍴. **Surface:** gravel. 🅾 01/01-31/12 ⦿ water disconnected in winter.
Remarks: Coins at the bakery.

| 🗒Ⓢ | St.Bonnet-Tronçais 🎣 | 21D3 |

Rue de l'Étang. **GPS:** n46,65896 e2,69228.⬆➡.
10 🗒free. **Location:** Very simple, central.
Surface: gravel. 🅾 01/01-31/12
Distance: 🚰on the spot 🚲27km 🏊Lake 450m ⚡bakery 200m.

| 🗒Ⓢ | St.Christophe-sur-Dolaison | 29D1 |

Le Bourg. **GPS:** n44,99811 e3,82147.⬆.

6 🗒free ⌐€ 2 🍴Ch ➕€ 2. **Location:** Rural, very simple. **Surface:** asphalted.
Distance: 🚰100m ⊗150m.

| 🗒Ⓢ | St.Eloy-les-Mines | 22A5 |

Rue du Puy-de-Dôme, RN144. **GPS:** n46,15559 e2,83615.⬆➡.

30 🗒free ⌐€ 2 🍴Ch ➕€ 2. **Location:** Rural. **Surface:** metalled.
🅾 01/01-31/12
Distance: 🏊on the spot ⊗700m ⚡400m Carrefour Market.
Remarks: Max. 48h.

| 🗒Ⓢ | St.Flour 🎣⛲🏔 | 29C1 |

Place de l'Ander, ville basse. **GPS:** n45,03556 e3,09750.⬆.

8 🗒free ⌐€ 2 🍴Ch ➕€ 4. **Location:** Urban, very simple. **Surface:** asphalted. 🅾 01/01-31/12
Distance: 🚰300m 🚲4km ⊗300m ⚡300m.
Remarks: Lower part of the city, nearby campsite.

| 🗒Ⓢ | St.Flour 🎣⛲🏔 | 29C1 |

Cours Chazerat. **GPS:** n45,03389 e3,08750.⬆.

20 🗒free. **Location:** Urban. **Surface:** metalled. 🅾 01/01-31/12
Distance: 🚰on the spot 🚲4,6km ⊗50m ⚡50m.
Remarks: Higher part of the city.

Tourist information St.Flour:
ℹ️ Office de Tourisme, 17bis, place d'Armes, www.saint-flour.com.City with car-free historical centre, Vieux Saint Flour.
Ⓜ Musée de la Haute Auvergne, Place d'Armens.Regional museum. 🅾 01/05-30/09. Ⓣ € 3,50.

| 🗒Ⓢ | St.Georges | 29C1 |

GPS: n45,03167 e3,13500.⬆.

20 🗒free ⌐€ 2 🍴Ch ➕€ 2 WC. **Location:** Highway. **Surface:** asphalted.
🅾 01/01-31/12
Distance: 🚰3km 🚲1km ⊗200m ⚡on the spot.
Remarks: At petrol station Esso.

| ©Ⓢ | St.Just | 29C2 |

GPS: n44,88972 e3,20889.⬆.

10 🗒€8 ⌐€ 2/100liter 🍴Ch ➕€ 2/55minutes WC🍴. **Location:** Comfortable, quit. **Surface:** grassy. 🅾 01/01-31/12
Distance: 🚰50m 🚲6,2km ⊗100m ⚡100m.

FR

Remarks: Use camp-site facilities incl.

St.Mamet-la-Salvetat 29B2

Aire camping-cars, D20. **GPS:** n44,85714 e2,30981.

3 free € 2/100liter Ch € 2/1h WC. **Location:** Rural, quit.
Surface: asphalted. 01/01-31/12
Distance: 500m 350m.
Remarks: Coins available at the shops and town hall.

St.Marcel-en-Murat 22A4

-, D243. **GPS:** n46,32184 e3,00837.

10 free € 2/100liter Ch € 2/1h. **Location:** Rural. **Surface:** gravel.
01/01-31/12
Distance: 3,5km exit 11 A71 nearby.
Remarks: Coins at town hall and restaurant.

St.Paul-des-Landes 29B1

Aire camping-cars, Rue du Moinac. **GPS:** n44,94250 e2,31694.

3 free € 3,50 Ch € 3.50. **Location:** Rural, central, quit. **Surface:** asphalted. 01/01-31/12
Distance: 50m 200m 50m.
Remarks: Coins at petrol station.

St.Pourçain-sur-Sioule 22A4

Aire Camping-car de la Moutte, Rue de la Moutte. **GPS:** n46,31262 e3,29656.

60 free € 2 Ch 2 (8x)€ 2/4h. **Location:** Urban, comfortable,
central, quit. **Surface:** grassy. 01/01-31/12
Distance: 800m on the spot on the spot on the spot.

Remarks: Along the Sioule river.

St.Rémy-de-Blot 22A5

Place du Bourg. **GPS:** n46,07722 e2,93139.

7 free WC. **Location:** Rural, isolated, quit. **Surface:** grasstiles. 01/01-31/12
Distance: on the spot.

St.Romain-Lachalm 29D1

Rulière. **GPS:** n45,26399 e4,33576.
4 free Ch (4x)€ 2/4h. **Surface:** asphalted.
Distance: 100m bakery 200m.
Remarks: Coins available at the shops and town hall.

St.Sauves d'Auvergne 21D6

Domaine de Lavaux, D82. **GPS:** n45,61688 e2,68975.

50 €8 Ch (10x)€ 4/day WC included € 1,25 € 5.
Location: Rural, comfortable, isolated, quit.
Surface: grassy. 15/05-30/09
Distance: 1km on the spot.

Super Besse 22A6

Ronde de Vassivière. **GPS:** n45,50644 e2,85342.

172 € 5,10/24h € 36,20/8 days € 1/20minutes Ch (100x)€ 1/4h
Location: Comfortable, quit.
Surface: asphalted.
01/01-31/12
Distance: 300m 300m on the spot 300m.
Remarks: No camping activities.

Super Lioran 29B1

Aire de Laveissière, Parking Font d'Alagnon. **GPS:** n45,08856 e2,73819.

25 ⛊free. **Location:** Rural, very simple, quit. **Surface:** asphalted. ⬛ 01/01-31/12
Distance: ⊗200m ⛾200m ⚹50m ⚲30m ⚲30m.

⛊⛊ **Talizat** 29C1

Place du 19 mars 1962. **GPS:** n45,11417 e3,04583.

3 ⛊free ⛽€ 2 ⛋Ch⚏€ 2. **Location:** Rural, very simple, quit. **Surface:** asphalted. ⬛ 01/01-31/12
Distance: ⛲on the spot ⊗100m ⛾100m.
Remarks: Behind town hall.

⛊⛊ **Thiers** 22B6

Base de loisirs Iloa, D44 > Dorat. **GPS:** n45,87070 e3,48311.⬆

50 ⛊free ⛽⛊free. **Location:** Rural, very simple, isolated, quit. **Surface:** metalled. ⬛ 01/01-31/12
Distance: ⚡2,6km.
Remarks: D 44 dir Dorat.

⛊⛊ **Thiézac** ⛵ 29B1

Aire de camping-cars, D59. **GPS:** n45,01583 e2,66278.⬆➡

8 ⛊free ⛽€ 2 ⛋Ch⚏€ 2. **Location:** Rural, quit. **Surface:** asphalted. ⬛ 01/01-31/12
Distance: ⛲50m ⊗100m ⛾100m.
Remarks: Max. 24h, coins at Office de Tourisme and petro station.

⛊⛊ **Tiranges** 29D1

Accueil Camping Car, La Nerceyre. **GPS:** n45,30702 e3,99107.⬆➡

10 ⛊free ⛽€ 2 ⛋Ch. **Location:** Rural, very simple, quit. **Surface:** asphalted. ⬛ 01/01-31/12
Distance: ⛲400m.

⛊⛊ **Tourzel-Ronzières** 22A6

Aire camping-car, Chemin du Clos, D23. **GPS:** n45,52888 e3,13611.⬆

15 ⛊free ⛽⛋Ch⚏WC free. **Location:** Rural, very simple, isolated, quit. **Surface:** grassy/gravel. ⬛ 01/01-31/12
Distance: ⛲500m ⊗500m.

⛊⛊ **Treteau** ⚐ 22B4

Rue du Rosier, D21. **GPS:** n46,36800 e3,51758.⬆➡

+10 ⛊€ 3/night ⛽€ 2 ⛋Ch⚏€ 2 WC. ⚲ **Location:** Rural, quit. **Surface:** grassy/metalled. ⬛ 01/03-31/10
Distance: ⛲500m ⚖on the spot ⛨day pass available ⊗100m.
Remarks: At small lake.

⛊⛊ **Valette** ⚐ 29B1

Aire camping-cars, D678. **GPS:** n45,27000 e2,60222.⬆➡

5 ⛊free ⛽€ 2 ⛋Ch⚏€ 2. **Location:** Rural, comfortable, quit. **Surface:** gravel. ⬛ 01/01-31/12 ⬤ service: 01/11-01/05.
Distance: ⛲50m ⛾100m ⊗150m.
Remarks: Quiet place.

⛊⛊ **Valuéjols** 29C1

Place de 19 Mars 1962, D34. **GPS:** n45,05333 e2,92944.

FR

12 🛏free ⚡€ 3 🔌Ch WC ⬛. **Location:** Rural. **Surface:** asphalted. ⬛
01/01-31/12
Distance: 🛒400m ⊗400m 🚰400m ♿on the spot.

🏕S | **Varennes-sur-Allier** | 22B4
Place Hôtel de Ville, Rue de Beaupuy. **GPS:** n46,31288 e3,40476. ⬆➡

30 🛏free ⚡€ 2 🔌Ch WC. **Location:** Urban, very simple, central, noisy.
Surface: metalled. ⬛ 01/01-31/12
Distance: 🛒on the spot ⊗on the spot 🚰on the spot.
Remarks: Coins at town hall.

🏕S | **Velzic** 🏔 | 29B1
Lavernière, Rue de Fracort. **GPS:** n45,00166 e2,54638. ⬆➡

4 🛏free ⚡€ 3,50 🔌Ch. **Location:** Rural, isolated. **Surface:** asphalted. ⬛
01/01-31/12 ⬛ service: 30/09-01/05.
Distance: 🛒1km ⊗1km 🚰1km ♿on the spot.
Remarks: Coins at épicerie Pas de Peyrols.

🏕S | **Vézac** | 29B2
Aire de camping-cars, Route de Cavanière. **GPS:** n44,89028 e2,51806. ⬆➡

2 🛏 ⚡€ 3,50 🔌Ch. **Location:** Rural, very simple. **Surface:** asphalted. ⬛
01/01-31/12
Distance: 🛒100m ⊗50m 🚰700m.
Remarks: At golf court, coins at bar/tabac.

🏕S | **Vic-sur-Cère** | 29B1
Aire de camping-cars, Avenue des Tilleuls. **GPS:** n44,98194 e2,63111. ⬆➡

10 🛏free ⚡€ 2 🔌Ch ⬛€ 2. **Location:** Rural, comfortable, quit. **Surface:**
asphalted. ⬛ 01/01-31/12
Distance: 🛒200m ⊗200m 🚰150m.
Remarks: Coins at Office de Tourisme, Avenue Mercier.

🏕S | **Vieillevie** 🚣 | 29B2
Aire de Vieillevie, Le Bourg. **GPS:** n44,64432 e2,41773. ⬆➡

5 🛏free ⚡€ 2 🔌Ch ⬛€ 2. **Location:** Rural, comfortable, quit. **Surface:**
gravel. ⬛ 01/01-31/12
Distance: 🛒50m 🍞100m ⊗50m 🚰50m.

🏕S | **Villefranche-d'Allier** | 22A4
Avenue du 8 Mai 1945. **GPS:** n46,39565 e2,85672. ⬆

4 🛏free ⚡€ 2/10minutes 🔌Ch 🔌 (4x)€ 2/2h. **Surface:** asphalted. ⬛
01/01-31/12
Distance: 🛒150m 🚲12km ⊗150m 🚰150m.
Remarks: Coins available at the shops.

🅲S | **Viverols** | 29D1
Camping Le Pradoux, Le Ruisseau. **GPS:** n45,43257 e3,89299.

6 🛏free ⚡€ 2 🔌Ch ⬛€ 2. **Surface:** gravel. ⬛ 01/04-31/10

🏕S | **Vorey-sur-Arzon** | 29D1
Chemin de Félines. **GPS:** n45,18640 e3,90648.

5 🏕€ 2 🚰€ 3 🔌Ch📷. **Surface:** gravel. 🅾 service: 01/04-31/10
Distance: 🛒200m 🍴on the spot ⊗200m 🛒200m 🚲on the spot 🚶on the spot.
Remarks: Next to camping Les Moulettes, at river, coins and code wifi available at campsite.

🏕free 🚰🔌Chfree. **Surface:** asphalted.
Distance: ⊗150m 🛒150m.
Remarks: Next to old people's home.

| 🏕S | Albertville | 23C6 |

Montée Adolphe Hugues, Conflans. **GPS:** n45,67389 e6,39694.
6 🏕free 🚰€ 3,50 🔌Ch 🗑. **Surface:** asphalted.
Distance: 🛒10 min walking.

Tourist information Albertville:
ℹ Office de Tourisme, Place de l'Europe, www.albertville.com.
🚻 Quai des Allobroges. 🅾 Thu 6-18h.

| 🏕S | Ytrac | 29B2 |

Aire camping-cars, Impasse Jean de la Fontaine. **GPS:** n44,91417 e2,36389.⬆
➡.

| 🏕S | Alpe d'Huez | 30C1 |

Parking de Brandes. GPS: n45,08654 e6,07916.⬆
75 🏕€ 10/day + € 0,20/pp tourist tax 🚰🔌Ch📷 WC.
Surface: asphalted.
Distance: 🚲on the spot.
Remarks: First buy a parking ticket at Palais des Sports et des Congrès.

| 🏕S | Alpe d'Huez | 30C1 |

Parking l'Eclose, Rue du 93me Ram. **GPS:** n45,08709 e6,07983.⬆➡.

3 🏕free 🚰€ 3,50 🔌Ch📷€ 3,50. **Location:** Rural, central. **Surface:** asphalted. 🅾 01/01-31/12
Distance: 🛒150m ⊗100m 🛒150m.
Remarks: Coins at the shops in the village and tourist office.

Rhône Alpes

| 🏕S | Aiguebelle | 23C6 |

Place du Souvenir Français, N6. **GPS:** n45,54289 e6,30635.⬆

25 🏕€ 10/day + € 0,20/pp tourist tax 🚰🔌Ch📷 WC included. **Surface:** asphalted. 🅾 01/12-01/04, 11/07-31/08
Distance: 🛒200m ⊗200m 🛒200m 🚲on the spot.
Remarks: First buy a parking ticket at Palais des Sports et des Congrès.

| 🏕S | Ambierle | 22B5 |

Complexe sportif, Rue Sainte Claude. **GPS:** n46,10663 e3,89384.⬆➡.
3 🏕free 🚰🔌Chfree. **Location:** Rural. **Surface:** asphalted.
Distance: 🛒on the spot 🚶on the spot.
Remarks: At sports park.

| 🏕S | Annecy | 23B5 |

Parking de Colmyr, N508. **GPS:** n45,89125 e6,13936.⬆

30 🏕free 🚰🔌Chfree. **Surface:** asphalted/grassy. 🅾 01/01-31/12 🅾
Thu-morning closed because of market.
Distance: 🛒on the spot 🚤6,1km.

Tourist information Aiguebelle:
🚻 🅾 Tue-morning.

| 🏕 | Aix les Bains | 23B6 |

Avenue du Grand Port. **GPS:** n45,70498 e5,88785.⬆.
16 🏕free. **Surface:** gravel. 🅾 01/01-31/12
Distance: 🛒city centre 2km 🏊Lake 100m ⊗150m.

| 🏕S | Alba | 31A2 |

GPS: n44,55342 e4,35502.

10 🏕free 🚰🔌Chfree. **Surface:** asphalted. 🅾 01/01-31/12
Distance: 🛒700m 🏊100m 🍴on the spot ⊗700m 🛒700m.
Remarks: Max. 24h.

Tourist information Annecy:
ℹ Office de Tourisme, Bonlieu, 1 rue Jean Jaurès, www.lac-annecy.com.Located on lake of the same name and surrounded by mountain peaks. The old city centre exists of covered lanes, canals and bridges.

M✕ Musée du Palais de L'Isle.Regional museum.
⚐ Place de Romains. **O** Tue.

⬛S	**Arçon**	22B5

Le Bourg. **GPS**: n46,00977 e3,88793.⬆.
3 ⬛free ⟊⬛Ch free. **Location**: Rural, quit. **Surface**: .
Distance: ⛟on the spot.

	Aubignas	30A2

Aire camping-cars. **GPS**: n44,58732 e4,63177.

10 ⬛free ⟊€ 2 ⬛Ch WC.
Distance: ⛟300m.
Remarks: On entering the village from RN 102.

⬛S	**Banne**	29D3

Quartier l'Eglise, D251. **GPS**: n44,36709 e4,15513.

20 ⬛free ⟊€ 2/60liter ⬛Ch ⟊€ 2/1h. **Surface**: gravel/metalled. **O**
01/01-31/12
Distance: ⛟500m.
Remarks: Behind church.

⬛S	**Beausemblant**	30A1

Aire camping-cars. **GPS**: n45,21842 e4,83324.⬆➡.

5 ⬛free ⟊⬛Ch free. **Surface**: gravel.
Distance: ⛟100m ⊗100m.
Remarks: Max. 48h. Via D122.

⬛S	**Belmont-de-la-Loire**	22C5

Place de l'Eglise. **GPS**: n46,16543 e4,34634.

2 ⬛free ⟊⬛Ch ⟊WC free. **Surface**: metalled. **O** 03/03-19/07, 01/08-

31/10
Distance: ⛟on the spot ⊗100m ⛟100m.

⬛S	**Boulieu-lès-Annonay** 〰	30A1

Chemin du Lavoir. **GPS**: n45,26933 e4,66967.⬆➡.
5 ⬛free ⟊ Ch WC free. **Location**: Rural. **Surface**: gravel.
Distance: ⛟400m ⊗400m ⛟400m ⚲on the spot ⚲on the spot.
Remarks: Voluntary contribution, market on Su.

	Bourg-en-Bresse	23A5

Parking V.L./Bus, Boulevard de Brou. **GPS**: n46,19871 e5,23679.

10 ⬛free. **Surface**: asphalted.
Distance: ⊗100m ⛟200m.
Remarks: Follow signs monastère/musée.

⬛S	**Bourg-St.Andéol**	30A3

Chemin de la Barrière. **GPS**: n44,37520 e4,64327.⬆.

5 ⬛free ⟊⬛Ch free. **Surface**: asphalted.
Distance: ⛟750m ⛟50m.
Remarks: Max. 48h, along railwayline.

⬛S	**Bourg-St.Maurice** ⛱ ⛰ ❄	23C6

Arc1600. **GPS**: n45,59523 e6,78951.
20 ⬛⟊€ 2 ⬛Ch ⟊€ 2. **O** 01/01-31/12
Distance: ⛟Bourg St.Maurice 15km.

Tourist information Bourg-St.Maurice:
i Mountain city, centre of winter sports.
M Musée du Costume.Costumes of the region.

	Bourgneuf	23B6

Aire camping-cars, D925. **GPS**: n45,55257 e6,21091.⬆.

30 ⬛free ⟊€ 1,50 ⬛€ 1,50 Ch€ 1,50. **O** 01/01-31/12
Distance: 🚲5km ⊗Brasserie/Pizzeria ⛟bakery.
Remarks: Coins available at Pizzeria/Tabac.

⬛S	**Bouvante**	30B2

Font d'Urle. **GPS**: n44,89789 e5,32195.

10 🗂free 🔌€ 2/100liter 🔧Ch 💧€ 7 WC 🗑€ 2. **Surface:** gravel.
⭕ 01/06-01/10
Remarks: Coins available in village.

🗂S Chambéry 🏔⚓🏕❄ 23B6
Rue de la Cardinière. **GPS:** n45,56289 e5,93302.
6 🗂free 🔌🔧Chfree. **Surface:** asphalted.
Distance: 🚶500m 🚲1,2km ⊗500m 🚉500m.
Remarks: Service closed during wintertime.

Tourist information Chambéry:
ℹ Office de Tourisme, 24, Boulevard de la Colonne, www.chambery-tourisme.com.City with Italian influences.
👁 Les Charmettes.Rousseau museum.
👁 Vieux Cité.Historical centre with old mansions.
🏰 Château des Ducs de Savoie.Complex of buildings, 13-14th century.

🗂S Chamonix-Mont-Blanc 🏔⚓🏕❄ 23D5
Parking Grépon, Aiguille du Midi, D1506. **GPS:** n45,91578 e6,86970.

50 🗂€ 12/24h 🔌€ 2 🔧Ch WC 🗑🚻 **Surface:** asphalted. ⭕ 01/01-31/12, service only during summer period
Distance: 🚶5 min.

Tourist information Chamonix-Mont-Blanc:
ℹ Office de Tourisme, 85, Place du Triangle de l'Amitié, www.chamonix.com. Tourist town, summer and winter.
Ⓜ Musée Alpin.Museum of the Alps, the history of the winter sports.
🚠 Aiguille du Midi.Telpher carrier from Chamonix (1036 m.) To Aiguille de Midi (3842m).
🚠 Montenvers et mer de Glace.Tramline from Montenvers to the ice lake, a gletsjer of 7 km long and 1.2 km broad.

🗂S Charlieu 🏔🚣 22C5
Pouilly-sous-Charlieu, Place d'Eningen. **GPS:** n46,16031 e4,17813.⬆.

5 🗂free 🔌Ch WC free. **Surface:** asphalted. ⭕ 01/01-31/12
Distance: 🚶historical centre 500m ⊗500m 🚉500m.
Remarks: In opposite of police station.

Tourist information Charlieu:
ℹ Office de Tourisme, Place St Philibert, www.leroannais.com.Historical centre with old trade houses.

🗂S Charols 30A2
Aire municipal, D9. **GPS:** n44,59160 e4,95441.

10 🗂free 🔌🔧free. **Surface:** gravel. ⭕ 01/01-31/12
Distance: 🚶200m ⊗200m 🚉50m.

🗂S Chichilianne 30B2
Passière. **GPS:** n44,81226 e5,57532.

🗂free 🔌€ 3 🔧Ch. **Surface:** grassy. ⭕ 01/01-31/12 💧 water disconnected in winter.
Distance: 🚶on the spot ⊗on the spot.
Remarks: Coins at town hall or Maison du Parc.

🗂S Clansayes 🏔⚓🏕☕ 30A3
Aire de Toronne, Quartier Toronne RD133. **GPS:** n44,36975 e4,79901.⬆.

25 🗂€ 13 🔌🔧Ch 💧€ 4/day WC 🗑€ 4.🚿 **Location:** Rural, comfortable, luxurious, isolated, quit. **Surface:** grassy/gravel. ⭕ 01/01-31/12
Distance: 🚶2km 🚲10km ⊗buvette-menu rapide-restauration 🚉3km.
Remarks: Bread-service.

🗂S Crest 30A2
Place du Champ de Mars, Avenue Agirond. **GPS:** n44,72600 e5,02100.

80 🗂€ 3,50 🔌€ 2 🔧Ch 🚻€ 2 📶free. **Surface:** asphalted. ⭕ 01/01-31/12

Tourist information Crest:
ℹ Office de Tourisme, Place du Docteur Rozier, www.vallee-drome.com/ot-crest.
👁 Naturodrôme.Minerals and fossils.
🏰 Tour de Crest.Exhibitions. ⭕ 01/05-30/09 10-19h, 30/09-01/05 14-18h.

FR

🚐 [S] Die 30B2

Avenue du Maréchal Leclerc, D238. **GPS**: n44,75103 e5,37385.⬆.

30 🚐free 🚰 🚽 Ch WC free. **Surface:** grassy/sand. ☐ 01/01-31/12
Distance: 🏙300m 🍴on the spot 🛒1km.
Remarks: Max. 1 night.

🚐 [S] Donzère 30A3

GPS: n44,44060 e4,71899.⬆➡.
🚐free 🚰 🚽 Ch WC free. **Surface:** asphalted. ☐ 01/01-31/12
Distance: 🏙500m ⛽7km.
Remarks: Near RN7.

🍴 [S] Epercieux-St.Paul 22C6

Auberge de l'Eperon d'Or, D1082, Le Petit Bois. **GPS**: n45,78702 e4,21110.⬆➡.

5 🚐€ 3 🚰 🚽 Ch ⚡€ 5, guests free. **Surface:** gravel/metalled. ☐ 01/01-31/10, 01/12-31/12
Distance: 🏙2km 🍴on the spot 🛒2km.

🏭 [S] Feurs 22C6

Societé Notin, Z.A. Les Places, Civens, D1082. **GPS**: n45,77029 e4,22069.⬆.

3 🚐free 🚰€ 2 🚽 Ch 🔌€ 2. ☐ 15/01-15/12
Distance: 🏙2km 🍴1km 🛒2km.
Remarks: Guarded area motorhome factory, entrance code during opening hours 8.30-12, 13.30-17.30.

🚐 [S] Gervans 30A1

Place des Amandiers, Rue de l'école. **GPS**: n45,10932 e4,83031.⬆.

4 🚐free 🚰 🚽 Ch free.

Remarks: Max. 24h.

🚐 [S] Gresse-en-Vercors 30B2

D8D, La Ville. **GPS**: n44,89184 e5,54766.

🚐free 🚰 🚽 Ch. **Surface:** gravel.
Distance: 🏙on the spot.
Remarks: Max. 24h, service on campsite.

🚐 [S] Hauteluce 23C6

Parking de la Fôret, Tetras, D123. **GPS**: n45,74633 e6,53441.

5 🚐free 🚰€ 2 🚽 Ch 🔌€ 2. **Surface:** gravel. ☐ 01/01-31/12
Distance: 🏙3km 🍴3km 🛒3km.

🚐 [S] Hauteluce 23C6

Parking Du Col des Saisies, D218b. **GPS**: n45,76297 e6,53382.⬆➡.

40 🚐€ 7 🚰€ 2 🚽 Ch 🔌€ 2. **Surface:** asphalted. ☐ 01/01-31/12
Distance: 🏙500m 🍴on the spot 🛒500m ⛷200m ⛷200m.

Tourist information Hauteluce:
[i] Office de Tourisme, 316, Avenue des Jeux Olympiques, www.Lessaisies.com. Mountain village. Both in summer and winter an attractive touristic destination.

🚐 [S] Hauterives 30A1

D538. **GPS**: n45,25497 e5,03022.

🚐free 🚰€ 3/100liter 🚽 Ch. **Surface:** gravel.

Tourist information Hauterives:
👁 Palais Idéal du Facteur Cheval.

🚐 [S] La Balme de Sillingy 23B5

Aire de Camping-cars Domaine du Tornet, D508. **GPS**: n45,97124 e6,03135.

FR

30 € 5 Chfree. **Surface:** gravel. 01/04-30/11
Distance: 100m (fishing permit available) 100m.
Remarks: Max. 48h.

La Clusaz 23C5

Route des Confins. **GPS**: n45,92298 e6,48380.
free. **Surface:** asphalted. 01/01-31/12
Remarks: Parking at pistes.

La Féclaz 23B6

Aire Camping-cars de la Féclaz, D206a. **GPS**: n45,64210 e5,98411.

40 € 4 € 1,50 Ch € 1,50. **Surface:** asphalted. 01/01-31/12
Distance: on the spot on the spot on the spot 300m.

La Voulte 30A2

Place Jargeat, N86. **GPS**: n44,80053 e4,78210.

free.
Distance: on the spot 50m.
Remarks: Near office de tourisme.

Lamastre 30A1

Place Pradon. **GPS**: n44,98672 e4,58001.

20 free € 2 Ch. **Surface:** asphalted. 01/01-31/12

Larnas 30A2

GPS: n44,44871 e4,59781.

3 free € 2 Ch € 2. **Surface:** grassy/gravel. 01/01-31/12
Remarks: Parking behind town hall.

Le Bessat 30A1

Route de Chabouret. **GPS**: n45,36812 e4,52768.
4 free € 2,50/20minutes Ch € 2,50/6h.
Location: Rural.
Surface: asphalted. 01/01-31/12
Distance: 1km 100m mountainbike trail on the spot on the spot.
Remarks: Coins available at Chalet des Alpes and the shops.

Le Cheylard 30A2

Super U, Chemin du pre-jalla, ZI la Palisse. **GPS**: n44,91143 e4,44162.

20 free € 2 Ch € 2. **Surface:** asphalted. 01/01-31/12
Distance: on the spot.
Remarks: Max. 24h.

Le Lac d'Issarlès 29D2

D16. **GPS**: n44,81948 e4,06156.

16 € 8 Ch included.
Surface: metalled. 01/05-30/11
Distance: 100m.
Remarks: Attention: this town is not Issarlès!.

Le Teil 30A2

Alleé Paul Avon. **GPS**: n44,55138 e4,68972.

6 free Chfree. **Surface:** grassy/metalled.
Distance: on the spot on the spot 500m.
Tourist information Le Teil:

FR

✈ ⬛ Thu morning.

🏂 S **Les Carroz-Arâches** 🏔 ❄ 23C5

Télécabine Les Cluses. GPS: n46,02500 e6,64361.

🏂free 🚰🔌Ch🚿free. ⬛ 01/06-30/11
Remarks: Parking funicular railway.

🏂 S **Les Gets** ⛵🏔❄ 23C5

Route des Grandes Alpes. **GPS:** n46,14992 e6,65673.

6 🏂€4 🚰🔌Ch🚿€ 8. **Surface:** asphalted. ⬛ 01/04-01/11
Distance: 🚶500m ⊗on the spot.

🏂 S **Marsanne** 〽 30A2

Avenue de Bailliencourt, D57. **GPS:** n44,64568 e4,87175.⬆
🏂free 🚰🔌Chfree. **Location:** Rural. **Surface:** grassy.
Distance: 🚶300m 🍴300m.
Remarks: Max. 48h.

🏂 S **Megève** 23C6

Chemin des Ânes. **GPS:** n45,86401 e6,62010.
🏂free. ⬛ 01/01-31/12
Remarks: In front of parking Télécabine du Jaillet.

🏂 S **Meyras** 29D2

Aire camping-cars, Grande rue, D26. **GPS:** n44,67939 e4,26847.⬆

🏂€ 14/1 night, € 20/2 nights, € 0,90pp tourist tax 🚰🔌Ch🚽🧺. **Surface:** gravel. ⬛ 01/01-31/12
Distance: 🚶1km 🚲on the spot.
Remarks: Bus to centre every 30 minutes.

Tourist information Les Gets:
ℹ Office de Tourisme, Place de la Mairie, www.lesgets.com.Winter sports resort.
Ⓜ Musée de la Musique Mécanique.Collection of mechanical musical instruments.
Ⓜ Musée du Ski, Restaurant Belvedère.Exhibition of the history of the ski. Can only be reached by means of telpher carrier of Mont Chéry.
✈ Week market. ⬛ Thu-morning.

🏂 S **Les Granges-Gontardes** 30A3

Domaine de la Tour d'Elyssas, Quartier Combe d'Elissas. **GPS:** n44,41811 e4,75465.
15 🏂free 🚰🔌Ch🚿free. **Surface:** gravel. ⬛ 01/01-31/12
Distance: 🚲9km.
Remarks: At wine-grower. Follow Dôme d'Elyssas.

🏂 S **Les Karellis** 30C1

GPS: n45,22778 e6,40639.
🏂free. ⬛ 01/01-31/12
Remarks: Mountain station nearby St.Jean-de-Maurienne.

🏂 S **Les Menuires** ⛵🏔❄ 30C1

Les Bruyères, Dir Val Thorens. **GPS:** n45,31410 e6,53750.⬆➡
40 🏂€ 5<12h, € 10/24h, tourist tax € 0,20/pp 🚰🔌Ch🚿(7x)€ 2/4h 🧺.
Surface: asphalted. ⬛ 01/01-31/12
Distance: 🚶on the spot ⊗on the spot 🍴on the spot.
Remarks: Near the pistes.

Tourist information Les Menuires:
ℹ Office de Tourisme, Imm. Belledonne, www.lesmenuires.com.Winter sports resort.

🏂 S **Les Noës** 22B5

Le Bourg, D47. **GPS:** n46,04083 e3,85206.⬆
3 🏂free 🚰🔌Chfree. **Surface:** gravel.
Distance: 🚶on the spot.

🏂 S **Les Plans d'hotonnes** 23A5

La Grange des Plans, D396. **GPS:** n46,03968 e5,70320.⬆

10 🏂€4 🚰€ 3 🔌Ch🚽🧺. **Surface:** asphalted.
Distance: 🚶200m ⊗200m 🍴nearby.
Remarks: Coins at town hall.

Tourist information Meyras:
ℹ Office de Tourisme, Place du Champ de Mars, www.meyras-tourisme.com.

🏂 S **Mijoux** 〽⛱🏔👥❄ 23B4

D50, Route de la Combe-en-Haut. **GPS:** n46,36963 e6,00247.⬆➡

20 🏂free 🚰€ 2 🔌Ch🚿€ 2. **Surface:** gravel.
Distance: 🚶500m ⊗500m 🍴500m 🚲on the spot 🏊on the spot.

🏂 S **Mirabel-aux-Baronnies** 30A3

Aire camping-cars, Chemin des Grottes. **GPS:** n44,31260 e5,09968.⬆

FR

6+10 🛏️voluntary contribution 🚰🔌Chfree. **Surface:** grassy/metalled. ⬛
01/01-31/12
Distance: 🚶200m.

| 🚐S | Montalieu-Vercieu | 23A6 |

Chamboud. **GPS:** n45,82776 e5,42100.⬆️

6 🛏️free 🚰🔌Ch♻️🧹.
Surface: asphalted.
Remarks: Next to campsite /Bade de Loisirs de la Vallée Bleue, max. 2 nights.

| 🚐S | Montbrison-sur-Lez | 30A3 |

Place Publique. GPS: n44,43663 e5,01779.

6 🛏️free ♻️free. **Surface:** metalled. ⬛ 01/01-31/12
Distance: 🚶100m ⊗100m 🚰100m.

| S | Montbrison-sur-Lez | 30A3 |

GPS: n44,42751 e5,02438.⬆️
🚰€ 2 🔌Ch🍴€ 2.
Remarks: Coins at bar and garage.

| S | Montbrun-les-Bains 🌊♨️ | 30B3 |

Toscan. **GPS:** n44,17247 e5,43881.⬆️➡️
🛏️. **Location:** Rural. **Surface:** grassy.
Distance: 🚶500m.

| S | Montbrun-les-Bains 🌊♨️ | 30B3 |

Condamine. **GPS:** n44,17413 e5,44071.⬆️
🚰€ 2 🔌Ch🍴€ 2.

| 🚐S | Montélimar | 30A2 |

Domaine du Bois de Laud, Chemin du Bois de Laud. **GPS:** n44,56522 e4,75691. ⬆️➡️

50 🛏️€ 4,10 🚰🔌Ch♻️ included. 🧹 ♻️ **Surface:** grassy/metalled.
Distance: 🚶500m 🚰100m.
Remarks: Max. 48h, near Centre Commercial Leclerc.

| 🚐S | Morillon 🌊⛵🏔️🌲❄️❄️ | 23C5 |

GPS: n46,08289 e6,67968.⬆️➡️
10 🛏️free 🚰Ch WC free. **Surface:** asphalted.
Distance: 🚶200m ⊗100m 🚰300m 🎿100m.

| 🚐S | Nantua | 23A5 |

D74. **GPS:** n46,15497 e5,59656.⬆️➡️

6 🛏️€ 5 + tourist tax 🚰🔌Chfree.
Surface: unpaved. ⬛ 01/04-30/09
Distance: 🚶700m 🚲7km 🏊on the spot ⛵on the spot ⊗150m 🚰150m.
Remarks: North-west of Nantua to lake.

Tourist information Nantua:
ℹ️ Office de Tourisme, Place de la Déportation, www.nantua-tourisme.com.
Tourist town with historical centre.
Ⓜ️ Musée de la Résistance, Montée de l'Abbaye.War museum.

| 🚐S | Noirétable 🏖️🌲 | 22B6 |

Aire d'accueil de camping-cars, Lieu-dit La Roche. **GPS:** n45,80674 e3,77133.
⬆️➡️.

6 🛏️free 🚰€ 3 🔌Ch🍴♻️. **Surface:** metalled. ⬛ 01/01-31/12
Distance: 🚶800m 🏊100m ⊗100m 🚰800m.
Remarks: Next to campsite.

| 🚐S | Nyons | 30B3 |

Promenade la Digue. **GPS:** n44,35778 e5,13861.⬆️.

20 🛏️€ 9/24h 🚰🔌Ch♻️ WC included 🧹.🧹♻️ **Surface:** gravel.
Distance: 🚶250m ⊗250m 🚰250m ⛽on the spot.
Remarks: Max. 48h, next to Parc loisirs aquatique.

| 🚐S | Nyons | 30B3 |

Domaine Rocheville, D 538. **GPS:** n44,36850 e5,11775.⬆️.
6 🛏️€ 5, 2 pers.incl 🚰🔌Ch♻️€ 2,90 🔌included.

Tourist information Nyons:
ℹ️ Pavillon du Tourisme, Place de la Libération.Important Olive-city in the Provence.
Ⓜ️ Musée de l'Olivier.Museum about the olive-tree and production of olive oil.
⬛ daily ⬤ 01/11-28/02 Su.
🎪 Centre-ville.Regional market. ⬛ Thu-morning.

| 🚐S | Panissières | 22C6 |

Aire camping-cars, Allée des Acacias. **GPS:** n45,78835 e4,34355.⬆️.

FR

7 ⌇ € 5,80 ⚡ 🔌 Ch ⊞ included WC ⊐ Use sanitary € 3,10/pp ♨. **Surface:** metalled. ◘ 01/01-31/12
Distance: 🚶300m ✖300m 🚰300m.
Remarks: Use sanitary € 2,40/pp per day. Dir 'gîte La Ferme Seigne'.

4 ⌇free ⚡ 🔌 Ch WC free. ◘ 01/01-31/12
Distance: 🚶50m ⚓on the spot 🏊50m 🚰50m.

| 📷 S | Planfoy | 30A1 |

Chemin du Vignolet. **GPS:** n45,37445 e4,44910. ⬆➡.

| 📷 S | Prapoutel-les-Sept-Laux | 30C1 |

D281. **GPS:** n45,25775 e5,99551.

10 ⌇free ⚡ € 2 Ch 🔌 € 2/6h. **Surface:** asphalted. ◘ 01/01-31/12
Distance: 🚶1,3km ⚓7km 🚰1,3km.
Remarks: Coins available at the shops.

⌇free ⚡ WC. **Surface:** metalled. ◘ 01/01-31/12
Distance: 🚴50m.
Remarks: Parking at pistes.

| 📷 S | Poncin | 23A5 |

Rue de la Verchère. **GPS:** n46,08703 e5,40375.

| 📷 S | Privas | 30A2 |

Boulevard de la Chaumette. **GPS:** n44,73723 e4,60204. ⬆➡.

25 ⌇free ⚡ 🔌 Ch free. **Surface:** gravel/metalled.
Distance: 🚰200m.
Remarks: Nearby Stade Guy Drut.

10 ⌇free ⚡ 🔌 Ch free. **Surface:** asphalted. ◘ 01/01-31/12
Distance: 🚶300m ✖300m 🚰300m.

| 📷 | Pont-de-Veyle | 22D5 |

D933, Rue de la Poste. **GPS:** n46,26419 e4,88709.

| 📷 S | Puy-Saint-Martin | 30A2 |

Aire de camping-car. **GPS:** n44,62753 e4,97492. ⬆➡.
13 ⌇free ⚡ Ch. **Location:** Rural, comfortable. **Surface:** grassy.
Distance: 🚶on the spot.
Remarks: Max. 48h, former campsite.

| 📷 S | Renaison | 22B5 |

GPS: n46,04757 e3,92124. ⬆➡.
⌇free ⚡ 🔌 Ch free. **Location:** Rural. **Surface:** grassy.
Distance: 🚶400m 🚰700m.
Remarks: At little stream.

⌇free.
Distance: 🚰150m.

| 📷 S | Pontcharra-sur-Turdine | 22C6 |

Place A. Schweitzer. **GPS:** n45,87405 e4,49133. ⬆.

| ⛺ S | Renaison | 22B5 |

Auberge du Barrage, La Tâche, D41 dir les Barrages. **GPS:** n46,04519 e3,87272.

12 ⌇ € 4, free with a meal ⚡ 🔌 Ch ⊞ € 4, guests free ♨. **Surface:** grassy.
◘ 15/03-01/11 ● Mon, Tue (except Jul/Aug).

FR

Distance: Renaison ± 4km 100m on the spot 4km.

S | **Reventin-Vaugris** | 30A1

Rue Mouret. **GPS:** n45,46806 e4,84222.

6 free WC. **Surface:** gravel/metalled. 01/01-31/12
Distance: on the spot 6km 20m bakery 10m.

S | **Roanne** | 22C5

Port de Plaisance, Allée Amiral Vermeilleux du Vignaux. **GPS:** n46,03750 e4,08306.

10 6 € 2,10 Ch € 2,10 WC.
Surface: metalled. 01/01-31/12
Distance: 2km on the spot 500m 2km 2km.
Remarks: Max. 72h.

S | **Saillans** | 30B2

Montmartel. **GPS:** n44,69549 e5,19350.
free € 2 Ch. **Location:** Rural. **Surface:** unpaved.
Distance: 300m.
Remarks: Along the Drôme river, closed when high water.

S | **Saint-André-d'Apchon** | 22B5

La Prébande. GPS: n46,03385 e3,92705.
3 free Ch free. **Location:** Very simple. **Surface:** gravel.
Distance: 300m.

S | **Saint-Germain-Lespinasse** | 22C5

Place du 8 mai 1945. **GPS:** n46,10510 e3,96229.
2 free Ch free. **Location:** Very simple. **Surface:** gravel.
Distance: 200m 350m.

S | **Saint-Haon-le-Châtel** | 22B5

Fondanges, Route de la Croix du Sud, D39. **GPS:** n46,06362 e3,91313.
free Ch free. **Location:** Rural. **Surface:** metalled.
Distance: 400m.

S | **Samoëns** | 23C5

Le Fayet-Samoëns. **GPS:** n46,07278 e6,69895.

10 free Ch € 5. **Surface:** metalled. 01/01-31/12 Service: winter.
Distance: 2km 100m 2km.

S | **Samoëns** | 23C5

Parking du Giffre. GPS: n46,07666 e6,71899.

5 free Ch . **Surface:** asphalted. 01/01-31/12 Service: winter.
Distance: 100m 100m 100m Skibus to Samoëns 1600 100m on the spot.
Remarks: Near campsite du Giffre, parking 150m.

S | **Sixt-Fer-à-Cheval** | 23C5

Route du Cirque du Fer à Cheval. **GPS:** n46,05698 e6,78048.

30 free Ch € 4/12h. **Surface:** asphalted. 01/01-31/12
Distance: 500m on the spot 500m.

S | **St.Alban-Auriolles** | 29D3

Rue Marius Perbost. **GPS:** n44,42693 e4,30096.

free Ch free. **Surface:** gravel.
Distance: 300m 200m.

S | **St.Bonnet-le-Château** | 29D1

Parking du Musée International Pétanque et Boules, Place du Musée de la Boule. **GPS:** n45,42514 e4,06436.

50 free Ch WC free. **Surface:** metalled.
Distance: 200m 1km 200m 200m.

Tourist information St.Bonnet-le-Château:
M Musée de la Pétanque et des Boules, Esplanade de la Boule. All about the beloved French national sport. 01/04-31/10.
M Musée International Pétanque et Boules, Boulevard des Chauchères.
 Fri.

S | **St.Désirat** | 30A1

Musée de l'Alambic, D291. **GPS:** n45,25865 e4,79227.

FR

🏕free ⟵ 🚿 WC free. **Surface:** metalled.
Distance: ⊗300m.
Remarks: Max. 1 night.

Tourist information St.Désirat:
Ⓜ Musée de l'Alambic, D291.Museum with distillery, tasting and sales. ⬛
10-12h, 14-18.30h. ⊤ free.

| 🏕Ⓢ | St.Donat-sur-l'Herbasse | 30A1 |

Route de St.Bardoux. **GPS:** n45,11902 e4,98284.

🏕free ⟵ 🍴Chfree. ⬛ 01/01-31/12
Distance: 🚶400m ⊗400m 🛒400m.
Remarks: In front of gymnasium, max. 1 night.

| 🏕Ⓢ | St.Félicien | 30A1 |

Place du Pre Lacour. **GPS:** n45,08648 e4,62800.

🏕free ⟵€ 2 🍴Ch. ⬛ 01/01-31/12
Remarks: Max. 24h.

| 🏕Ⓢ | St.Georges d'Espéranche | 22D6 |

Chemin des Platières. **GPS:** n45,55584 e5,07520. ⬆➡.

12 🏕free ⟵ 🍴Chfree. **Surface:** metalled. ⬛ 01/01-31/12
Distance: 🛒500m.
Remarks: Max. 48h.

| 🏕Ⓢ | St.Gervais-les-Bains ⛷ | 23C5 |

77, impasse Cascade. **GPS:** n45,88864 e6,71287. ⬆.

---

20 🏕free ⟵€ 2 🍴Ch🔌€ 2. **Surface:** asphalted.
Distance: 🚶200m ⊗200m 🛒200m 🚲300m.
Remarks: Parking skating rink.

| 🏕Ⓢ | St.Jean d'Ardières | 22D5 |

Domaine de Grande Ferrière, 831 route des Rochons. **GPS:** n46,12954 e4,71581.

5 🏕free ⟵ 🍴Ch🚿 free. **Surface:** gravel.
Distance: 🚶3km 🍴6km 🏊5km 🛒500m ⊗3km 🛒3km.

| 🏕Ⓢ | St.Jean-de-Bournay | 23A6 |

Place du Marche. **GPS:** n45,50123 e5,13866.

4 🏕free ⟵ 🍴free. **Surface:** asphalted. ⬛ 01/01-31/12
Distance: ⊗100m 🛒100m.

| 🏕Ⓢ | St.Jean-de-Maurienne ⛷🚲❄ | 30C1 |

Place du Champ de Foire. **GPS:** n45,27962 e6,34687. ⬆.
10 🏕free ⟵€ 2 🍴Ch🔌€ 2 WC. **Surface:** asphalted. ⬛ 01/01-31/12
Distance: 🚲2,5km.
Remarks: Behind Hyper Géant.

Tourist information St.Jean-de-Maurienne:
ℹ Office de Tourisme, Ancien Evêché, Place de la Cathédrale, www.
saintjeandemaurienne.com.Mountain village.
Ⓜ Musée de l'Opinel.The history of the knife. ⬛ Mo/Sa 9-12h, 14-18h. ⊤
free.

| 🏕Ⓢ | St.Jean-en-Royans 🚲 | 30B1 |

Rue de la Gare. **GPS:** n45,02028 e5,29032. ⬆➡.

3 🏕free ⟵ 🍴Chfree.
Distance: 🚶200m ⊗200m 🛒200m.

⚅S St.Just-d'Ardèche 30A3
Domaine La Favette, N86, route des Gorges d'Ardèche. GPS: n44,30134 e4,60649.

6 🛇€5 🚰 2 ♨Ch🚽€ 2. ☐ 01/01-31/12
Remarks: At wine-grower, max. 24h.

Tourist information St.Just-d'Ardèche:
ℹ️ Good starting point to discover the Ardèche gorges.
⛩ ☐ Thu.

⚅S St.Just-en-Chevalet 22B5
Boulevard de l'Astrée. GPS: n45,91411 e3,84727.
5 🛇free 🚰 ♨Chfree. ☐ 01/01-31/12 ⦿ Thu-morning.

⚅S St.Paul-Trois-Châteaux 30A3
Parking Office de Tourisme, Le Courreau, Place Chausy. GPS: n44,34786 e4,76995.

🛇free 🚰 ♨WC. **Surface:** asphalted.
Distance: 🚶50m ✕50m.

Tourist information St.Paul-Trois-Châteaux:
ℹ️ Office de Tourisme, Place Chaussy, www.office-tourisme-tricastin.com.
⛩ Marché. ☐ Tue-morning.
⛩ Marché aux truffes du Tricastin. ☐ Dec-Mar Su-morning.

⚅S St.Pierre-en-Faucigny 23C5
Avenue de la Gare. GPS: n46,06096 e6,37874.

4 🛇free 🚰 ♨Ch🚽free. **Surface:** asphalted.
Distance: 🚶on the spot ✕60m 🚊nearby 🚌on the spot.
Remarks: Nearby railway station.

⚅S St.Rémèze 30A3
Les Chais du Vivarais, D362. GPS: n44,39536 e4,50576.⬆

🛇free 🚰 ♨Chfree. **Surface:** asphalted. ☐ 01/03-30/11
Distance: 🚶500m ✕200m.
Remarks: Max. 48h.

Tourist information St.Rémèze:
👁 Grotte de la Madelaine.Caves. ☐ Apr-Oct 10-18h.
👁 Grotte de Marzal.Caves. ☐ Sa/Su/Holidays, 01/04-30/09 10.30-18h.
Ⓜ Musée de la lavande.Museum and distillery with lavender fields. ☐ 01/05-30/09 10-17h, Apr + Oct Sa-Su-holiday 10-17h.

⚅S St.Romain-de-Lerps 30A1
Le Village, D287. GPS: n44,98029 e4,79596.⬆
🛇free 🚰 ♨Ch WC. **Surface:** gravel.
Distance: 🚶100m ✕100m 🚊100m.
Remarks: Panoramic view over the Rhône-valley 200m.

⚅S St.Thomé 30A2
N107, Les Crottes. GPS: n44,50430 e4,63414.⬆

🛇 🚰 ♨Chfree.

⚅S St.Victor-sur-Loire 29D1
Base Nautique du lac de Grangent. GPS: n45,44787 e4,25626.⬆

10 🛇free 🚰 ♨Chfree ⚓(4x)against payment. **Surface:** asphalted. ☐ 01/01-31/12
Distance: 🏊on the spot 🚤on the spot ✕on the spot.

⚅S Thueyts 29D2
Chemin d'Echelle du Roi, via N102. GPS: n44,67333 e4,21888.⬆➡

10 🛇free 🚰€ 2 ♨Ch🚽€ 2/10minutes. **Surface:** grassy/gravel. ☐ 01/01-31/12

Distance: 🚶200m 🚲200m.

🏕🅂 **Tournon-sur-Rhône** ⛵ 🌊 **30A1**

Chemin de la Beaume/D86. **GPS:** n45,07337 e4,82150.

🅂free 🚰🗑Chfree. **Surface:** asphalted. 🅾 01/01-31/12

Distance: 🚴5km.

Tourist information Tournon-sur-Rhône:

ℹ️ Office de Tourisme, Hôtel de la Tourette, www.ville-tournon.com.

🚶 🅾 Wed, Sa.

🚩 Route Panoramique, place Jean Jaurès.Starting point touristic route.

🏕🅂 **Treffort** 🏞 🏡 **30B2**

Plage de la Salette, D110b. **GPS:** n44,90732 e5,67208.⬆️

50 🅂€9 🚰🗑Ch 🛶 WCincluded. **Surface:** gravel. 🅾 01/05-31/10

Distance: 🚶3km ⛵lake 🎣lake ⊗on the spot.

Remarks: At lake Monteynard.

ℂ🅂 **Trévoux** 🌿 🏡 👁 **22D5**

Chemin du Camping. **GPS:** n45,94004 e4,76770.⬆️

5 🅂free 🚰€ 2 🗑Ch 🔌€ 2. **Surface:** gravel/sand. 🅾 01/01-31/12

Distance: 🚶1km 🚴7km ⊗1km 🚲1km.

Remarks: At entrance campsite, beside river, coins available at campsite or town hall.

🏕🅂 **Ugine** **23C6**

Place du 8 Mai 1945. **GPS:** n45,74614 e6,41962.⬆️

2 🅂free 🚰€ 2 🔌€ 2. **Surface:** asphalted. 🅾 01/01-31/12

Distance: 🚶50m ⊗50m 🚲50m.

Tourist information Ugine:

ℹ️ Syndicat d'Initiative, 15 Place du Val d'Arly, www.ugine.com.

🚶 🅾 Wed, Sa-morning.

📷 **Valloire** **30C1**

Rue de la Bonne Eau. **GPS:** n45,16824 e6,42893.

🅂free. **Surface:** gravel. 🅾 01/01-31/12

🅂 **Valloire** **30C1**

Route des Villards. **GPS:** n45,16566 e6,42978.

🚰🗑Ch 🛶. 🅾 01/01-31/12

Distance: 🚶± 800m.

Remarks: Nearby camping-municipal.

🏕🅂 **Vallon-Pont-d'Arc** ⛵ 🏡 🌊 **30A3**

Chemin du Chastelas. **GPS:** n44,40537 e4,39683.⬆️

20 🅂€7 🚰🗑Chfree. 🅾 01/01-31/12

Remarks: Max. 2 nights, excl tourist tax, guarded parking 9-19h.

ℂ🅂 **Vallon-Pont-d'Arc** 🏡 🌊 **30A3**

Domaine de l'Esquiras, Chemin du Fez. **GPS:** n44,41583 e4,37738.

5 🅂€7-8, € 0,60/pppd tourist tax 🚰🗑Ch 🛶€ 2.

Surface: gravel.

🅾 01/04-30/09

Tourist information Vallon-Pont-d'Arc:

ℹ️ Office de Tourisme, 1, place de l'ancienne gare, www.vallon-pont-darc.com. Small tourist town with the well-known Pont d'Arc, a natural arc over the Ardèche river.

👁 Grotte des Huguenots.Former shelter of the Huguenots. 🅾 15/06-31/08.

👁 Ma Magnanerie, Lagorce.Silkworm farm. 🅾 Easter -15/09 Mo/Sa 10-12h, 14-18h.

🚶 🅾 Thu-morning.

ℂ🅂 **Valvignères** **30A2**

Camping le Colombier. GPS: n44,49904 e4,57672.

🅂€ 7, 2 pers.incl 🚰🗑Chfree.

Remarks: In front of campsite municipal, service closed during wintertime.

🏕🅂 **Vassieux-en-Vercors** 🏡 ❄ **30B2**

Avenue du Mémorial, D76. **GPS:** n44,89703 e5,36927.🎿 .

50 🅂free 🚰🗑Chfree.

Distance: 🚶200m 🚲200m 🎿7km 🚶‍♂️on the spot.

Vaujany 30C1

Télécabine. **GPS**: n45,15694 e6,08011.

15 free Ch free € 5. **Surface**: gravel. 01/01-31/12
Distance: 300m 300m 300m 300m.
Remarks: Max. 24h, coins at Office de Tourisme (electricity).

Villards-de-Lans 30B1

Chemin des Bartavelles. **GPS**: n45,06681 e5,55584.

15 free. **Surface**: asphalted.
Remarks: Max. 48h.

Villars-les-Dombes 22D5

Parc des Oiseaux, RN83. **GPS**: n45,99177 e5,02520.

100 free free. **Surface**: asphalted/grassy. 01/01-31/12
sundays, holidays, winter.
Distance: 2km 1km 1km 2km 2km.
Remarks: Parking bird park, max. 1 night.

Tourist information Villars-les-Dombes:
Parc des Oiseaux.Bird park, 23ha. 8.30-19h, winter 8.30-17.30h. € 10.

Villerest 22C5

Aire camping-car du Grezelon, D18, Route de Seigne. **GPS**: n45,98610 e4,04300.

15 €3 4 Ch. 01/01-31/12
Remarks: Max. 48h.

Viviers 30A2

Capitainerie du port. **GPS**: n44,48632 e4,69290.

4 Ch included.
Distance: 800m 7km 500m.
Remarks: Dir. Châteauneuf du Rhône, before the bridge over the Rhône river to the left.

Tourist information Viviers:
Office de Tourisme, 5, Place Riquet.

Aquitaine

Aire-sur-l'Adour 28B4

Rue des Graviers. **GPS**: n43,70333 w0,25535.

50 €3 1 Ch. **Location**: Quit. **Surface**: gravel. 01/01-31/12
3rd week Jun.
Distance: 200m on the spot on the spot.
Remarks: Max. 72h, near campsite.

Amou 28B4

Stade de Sport, Promenade pour Piétons. **GPS**: n43,58917 w0,74083.

10 free Ch free. **Surface**: asphalted. 01/01-31/12
Distance: 1km on the spot on the spot 1km 1km.
Remarks: In front of campsite Digue.

Andernos-les-Bains 28A2

Port Ostréicole, Avenue du Commandant Allègre. **GPS**: n44,74400 w1,10823.

60 € 7,70 € 2,15/10liter Ch. **Surface**: grassy. 01/01-31/12
Distance: 50m.
Remarks: In harbour, max. 48h.

FR

🄢 S   Anglet   28A4

Parking des Corsaires, Boulevard des Plages. **GPS**: n43,50696 w1,53373. ➡️.

72 🄢 free, July-Aug € 7 🚰 ⬛ Ch ⚡ included. **Surface**: asphalted.
Distance: 🚂500m 🏊500m ⊗500m 🛒500m.
Remarks: Baker every morning, max. 24h, Biarritz 2km. D5, Boulevard des
Plages.

🄢 S   Anglet   28A4

Terroirs d'Aventures, Avenue de l'Adour, D405. **GPS**: n43,52608 w1,51488. ⬆️.

10 🄢 € 6 🚰 € 3 ⬛ Ch. **Surface**: sand. 🗓️ 01/07-31/08
Distance: 🚂1km 🏊300m 🚲50m ⊗500m 🛒500m 🚌100m.
Remarks: Private property.

🄢 S   Arcachon 🏖️ 〰️   28A2

Boulevard Mestrézat, D650. **GPS**: n44,65094 w1,15002. ⬆️.

20 🄢 free 🚰 ⬛ Ch free. **Location**: Urban, very simple, noisy. **Surface**: gravel.
🗓️ 01/01-31/12
Distance: 🚂1km 🛒50m.
Remarks: Max. 24h.

Tourist information Arcachon:
ℹ️ Office de Tourisme, Esplanade G. Pompidou, www.arcachon.com.Bathing
resort.
🏛️ place du XI Novembre.Covered market. 🗓️ 01/06-31/08 daily 7-13h.

🄢 S   Arzacq-Arraziguet   28B4

Aire de camping cars, Place du Marcadieu. **GPS**: n43,53481 w0,41035. ⬆️.

10 🄢 free 🚰 ⬛ Ch ⚡ free. **Surface**: asphalted. 🗓️ 01/01-31/12
Distance: 🚂on the spot 🏊500m 🚲500m ⊗100m 🛒100m.

Remarks: In village.

🄢 S   Azerat   28D1

Le Bourg. **GPS**: n45,14954 e1,12496. ⬆️ ➡️.

6 🄢 € 2 🚰 € 3 ⬛ Ch. **Location**: Quit.
Surface: gravel. 🗓️ 01/01-31/12
Distance: 🚂50m.
Remarks: Pay at town hall.

🄢 S   Badefols-sur-Dordogne   28D2

Le Bourg. **GPS**: n44,84254 e0,79160. ⬆️.

10 🄢 free 🚰 € 2 ⬛ Ch.
Surface: asphalted. 🗓️ 01/01-31/12 🛒 Sa market.
Distance: 🚂on the spot 🛒bakery 50m.
Remarks: Coins at town hall.

🄢 S   Bazas   28B2

Cours Gambetta/Allée des Tilleuls. **GPS**: n44,43389 w0,21509.

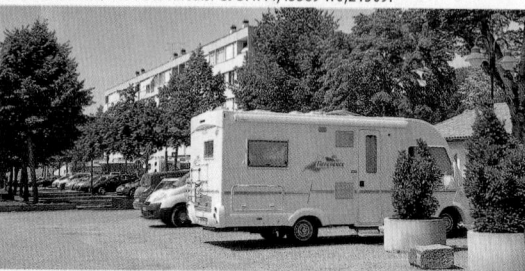

🄢 free 🚰 ⬛ Ch WC free. **Location**: Very simple, noisy. **Surface**: asphalted.
🗓️ 01/01-31/12
Distance: 🚂200m 🚲3,1km ⊗350m 🛒300m.

🄢 S   Beaumont du Périgord 🏖️   28D2

Avenue Rhinau, D660. **GPS**: n44,77469 e0,76559. ⬆️ ➡️.

40 🄢 free 🚰 ⬛ Ch free. **Surface**: asphalted. 🗓️ 01/01-31/12
Distance: 🚂800m.
Remarks: Behind community centre.

Bergerac 28C2

Aire camping-car La Pelouse, Rue Jean Jacques Rousseau. **GPS**: n44,84904 e0,47630. ⬆.

8 ⬛ € 6,10 ⬛ ⬛ Ch ⬛ WC.
Surface: asphalted/grassy. ⬛ 01/04-30/09
Distance: city centre 1,4km.

Tourist information Bergerac:
ℹ Office de Tourisme, 97, rue Neuve d'Argenson, www.bergerac-tourisme.com. Small port city, worth seeing is the old city centre.
Ⓜ Musée du Tabac, Maison Peyrarède, Place du Feu.History of tobacco. ⬛ Mo-Fri 10-12h, 14-18, Sa 10-12h, 14-17h, Su 14.30-17.30h, Nov-Mar Mo-Fr.
⛪ Église Notre Dame, Rue Saint Esprit. ⬛ Wed, Sa 7-13h.

Bernos-Beaulac 28B2
La Grande Route, N524. **GPS**: n44,36946 w0,24355. ⬆.

10 ⬛ free ⬛ € 2 ⬛ Ch. **Location:** Quit. **Surface:** metalled. ⬛ 01/01-31/12
⬛ water: frost.
Distance: river on the spot bakery 100m.
Remarks: Coins at petrol station.

Beynac-et-Cazenac 28D2
Le Parc, D703. **GPS**: n44,84466 e1,14560. ➡.

⬛ free. **Surface:** gravel. ⬛ 01/01-31/12
Distance: 100m, ville historique 500m.

Biarritz 37D4
Parking Milady, Avenue de la Milady, Biarritz-sud, D911dir Bidart. **GPS**: n43,46520 w1,57194. ⬆.

40 ⬛ € 10 ⬛ ⬛ Ch ⬛ included. **Surface:** asphalted. ⬛ 15/05-15/10
Distance: 500m 300m ⊗500m ⬛500m.

Tourist information Biarritz:
ℹ Office de Tourisme, Square d'Ixelles, www.biarritz.fr.Glamorous bathing resort with old centre. Important surf centre.
⛪ Rue des Halles. ⬛ daily.

Biron 28D2
Route de Vergt de Biron. **GPS**: n44,63080 e0,87055.

10 ⬛ free. **Surface:** grassy/metalled. ⬛ 01/01-31/12
Distance: ⊗250m.
Remarks: From Monpazier, dir Villéral then exit Biron, from Villérial dir Monpazier exit Biron.

Biscarrosse 28A2
Aire camping-cars, Rue des Viviers, Biscarrosse-plage. **GPS**: n44,46027 w1,24627. ⬆.

100 ⬛ free, € 12 (May-Sept) ⬛ ⬛ Ch ⬛ WC. ⬛
Location: Quit.
Surface: forest soil. ⬛ 01/05-31/10
Distance: 400m ⊗Superette 100m 50m.
Remarks: No camping activities, guarded (jul/aug), shady.

Biscarrosse 28A2
Biscarrosse Plage Sud, Chemin de Navarosse. **GPS**: n44,43223 w1,16566. ⬆.

30 ⬛ 1/7-31/8 € 8 ⬛ ⬛ Chfree. ⬛ **Surface:** metalled. ⬛ 01/05-31/10
Distance: 50m ⊗100m ⬛50m.
Remarks: No camping activities, guarded (jul/aug).

Biscarrosse 28A2
Centre Leclerc, Avenue Laouadie. **GPS**: n44,41063 w1,16803. ⬆.
free ⬛ ⬛ Chfree WC.
Surface: asphalted.
Distance: ⊗on the spot ⬛on the spot ⬛on the spot.

Tourist information Biscarrosse:
ℹ Office de Tourisme, 55, place G. Dufau, Biscarrosse-plage, www.biscarrosse.com.Bathing resort between lakes. Many beaches and water sports.

Blaye 28B1
Parking de la Citadelle. GPS: n45,12521 w0,66623.
⬛ free. **Surface:** metalled. ⬛ 01/01-31/12

FR

Distance: 🛒250m ⊗300m.

Bouglon 28C2

Le Clavier. **GPS**: n44,38599 e0,10271.

4 🛏free ☂ WC. **Location**: Quit. **Surface**: asphalted. ⬛ 01/01-31/12
Distance: 🛒500m ⊗500m 🛒500m.
Remarks: Picnic area.

Bourdeilles 28D1

Plaine de loisirs. **GPS**: n45,32270 e0,58260. ⬆

20+ 🛏€3 ☂€2 Ch. **Location**: Comfortable, quit. **Surface**: grassy. ⬛
01/01-31/12
Distance: ⊿on the spot 🛒on the spot ⊗200m 🛒200m.
Remarks: Coins at town hall.

Tourist information Bourdeilles:
🏠 Syndicat d'Initiative, Place des Tilleuls, www.bourdeilles.com.Historical small town around Château de Bourdeilles. ⬛ Wed-Mo, 01/07-31/08 daily.

Bourg-sur-Gironde 28B1

Quai Jean Bart. **GPS**: n45,03794 w0,55762.
🛏free. **Surface**: asphalted. ⬛ 01/01-31/12
Distance: 🛒on the spot ⊿On the river Gironde.

Brantôme 28D1

Chemin de Vert Galant. **GPS**: n45,36134 e0,64842. ⬆

80 🛏€4 ☂€2 Ch. **Location**: Quit.
Surface: grassy. ⬛ 01/01-31/12
Distance: 🛒200m ⊗100m 🛒300m.

Brantôme 28D1

Aire Camping-cars Font Vendôme, Route de Nontron. **GPS**: n45,37924 e0,64588. ⬆➡

4 🛏€5 ☂ Ch 🚿included.
Surface: asphalted. ⬛ 01/01-31/12
Distance: 🛒on the spot ⊗on the spot 🛒on the spot.
Tourist information Brantôme:
🏠 Office de Tourisme, Abbaye - Boulevard Charlemagne, www.ville-brantome.fr.
⛺ ⬛ Fri-morning.

Buzet-sur-Baïse 28C3

Port de Buzet-Val d'Albret. **GPS**: n44,25799 e0,30569.

20 🛏free ☂€2 Ch 🚿€2 WC 🚿 2/24h. **Surface**: grassy.
Distance: ⊿6,5km.

Cadillac 🌿⛺ 28B2

Allée du Parc. **GPS**: n44,63871 w0,31721. ⬆

10 🛏free ☂ Ch free 🚿€ 2/3h.
Surface: asphalted. ⬛ 01/01-31/12
Distance: 🛒on the spot ⊗on the spot 🛒on the spot ▣on the spot.
Remarks: Max. 3 nights, closed when frosty.

Cancon 28D2

GPS: n44,53638 e0,62562. ⬆➡

10 🛏free ☂ Ch 🚿 WC free. **Surface**: metalled. ⬛ 01/01-31/12
Distance: 🛒100m ⊗100m 🛒100m.
Remarks: Via N21.

Capbreton 28A4

Plage l'Océanide, Parking des Ortolans, Allée des Ortolans. **GPS**: n43,63578 w1,44681. ➡

120 ▤ € 9 ⌂ ▤ Ch ⚓ (120x)included. **Surface:** asphalted.
Distance: ▦1,5km ⚓on the spot ➤on the spot ⊗1,5km ▦1,5km.
Remarks: Beach parking.

▤S **Capian** 28B2
D13/Chemin de Lavergne. **GPS:** n44,71177 w0,33093. ⬆.

25 ▤. **Surface:** gravel.

▤S **Carcans** 28A1
Route de Bombannes, Maubuisson. **GPS:** n45,08545 w1,14866.

20 ▤ € 5,80/20-9h ⌂ ▤ Ch ⚓ free. ⚓ **Surface:** asphalted/metalled. ▢
01/06-31/09
Distance: ⚓on the spot.
Remarks: No parking, only overnight stays.

Tourist information Carcans:
🄸 Office de Tourisme, Maison de la Station, www.carcans-maubuisson.com.
Touristic town between the ocean and a wine region, 120km signposted cycle routes.

▤S **Casseneuil** 🌾 28D2
Rue Grande, D225. **GPS:** n44,44667 e0,61861. ⬆➤.

20 ▤ free ⌂ ▤ Ch free. **Surface:** gravel. ▢ 01/01-31/12
Distance: ▦100m ⚓on the spot ➤on the spot ⊗100m ▦800m.
▤S **Castelculier** 28D3
GPS: n44,17475 e0,69452. ⬆.

5 ▤ free ⌂ € 2 ▤ Ch. **Surface:** metalled. ▢ 01/01-31/12
Distance: ▦200m.
▤S **Casteljaloux** ♈ 28C3
Ste Castel Chalets, D933. **GPS:** n44,29230 e0,07361. ⬆.

20 ▤ € 10 ⌂ ▤ Ch ⚓ WC ▤ 📶 included. **Location:** Comfortable, quit.
Surface: gravel/sand. ▢ 01/10-31/10
Distance: ▦2km ⚓Lac de Clarens.
▤S **Casteljaloux** ♈ 28C3
Impasse de la Fôret. **GPS:** n44,31056 e0,07861. ⬆➤.

4 ▤ free ⌂ ▤ Ch free. **Location:** Quit.
Surface: asphalted. ▢ 01/01-31/12
Distance: ▦250m ▦250m.
Remarks: Parking at swimming pool.
▤S **Caumont-sur-Garonne** 🌾 28C2
Bourg de Caumont. **GPS:** n44,44202 e0,17887. ⬆.

9 ▤ free ⌂ € 1 ▤ Ch ⊞ € 1/2h. **Surface:** gravel. ▢ 01/01-31/12
Distance: ⚓8km.
▤S **Celles** 28C1
Le Bourg. **GPS:** n45,29364 e0,41065.
▤ free. **Surface:** unpaved.
Distance: ⚓Small lake.
▤S **Château-l'Evêque** 28D1
Place de la Fontaine. **GPS:** n45,24472 e0,68743. ⬆.

FR

8 🛏free 🚰 2 🔧Ch 🔌€ 2. **Surface:** gravel. ⬤ 01/03-31/10 ◉
summer: Su (flea market).
Distance: 50m 100m 🚉on the spot.
Remarks: Max. 12h, coins at shops in the village 08-21h.

🛏S **Contis-Plage** 28A3
Avenue du Phare. **GPS:** n44,09333 w1,31861.⬆.

76 🛏€ 7, 01/06-01/09 € 11/24h, 01/12-28/02 free 🚰 2 🔧Ch 🔌WC 🛒
🧽 **Surface:** gravel. ⬤ 01/01-31/12
Distance: 200m on the spot.
Remarks: Max. 72h.

🛏S **Créon** 28B2
Vélo-centre, Boulevard Victor Hugo, D20. **GPS:** n44,77663 w0,34815.⬆.

5 🛏free 🚰 2 🔧Ch 🔌€ 2. **Surface:** asphalted. ⬤ 01/01-31/12 ◉
tue-evening, wed-morning (market).

🛏S **Damazan** 28C3
Chambre D'Hôtes Constantine, Route Cap de Bosc. **GPS:** n44,28130 e0,26285.
6 🛏€5 🚰🔧Ch🔌€ 7 WC🛒. ⬤ 01/01-31/12
Distance: 500m 1km.

🛏S **Dax** ♨ 28A4
Parking du Pont des Arènes, Boulevard des Sports. **GPS:** n43,71427 w1,04931.
⬆.

8 🛏free 🚰 free. **Location:** Very simple, noisy. **Surface:** asphalted. ⬤
01/01-31/12
Distance: on the spot.
Remarks: Max. 72h, sa market in the halls.

Tourist information Dax:
ℹ Office de Tourisme, 11, cours Foch, www.dax.fr.Health resort with warm
water sources and medicinal mud.

🛏S **Domme** 28D2
Le Pradal. GPS: n44,80053 e1,22156.⬆➡.

20 🛏€5 🚰 2/10minutes 🔧Ch🔌€ 2/1h. **Location:** Quit. **Surface:**
asphalted. ⬤ 01/01-31/12 ◉ Service: winter.
Distance: 500m 500m.
Remarks: Note: follow the signs, no gps-coordinates.

Tourist information Domme:
ℹ Office de Tourisme, Place de la Halle, www.ot-domme.com.Fortified city
worth seeing, parking for motorhomes outside of the town, being indicated.

🛏S **Douchapt** 28C1
Beauclair. **GPS:** n45,25145 e0,44335.⬆➡.
🛏free 🚰 2 🔧Ch🔌€ 2. **Surface:** metalled. ⬤ 01/01-31/12
Distance: 1,5km Dronne river.
Remarks: Coins at Village Vacances Beauclair.

🛏S **Eaux-Bonnes** 28C5
Parking du Ley. GPS: n42,96304 e0,33933.⬆.

20 🛏free. **Surface:** asphalted. ⬤ 01/01-31/12
Distance: 1,4km 1,4km 1,4km 1,4km.

🛏S **Espés Undurein** 28A4
Etche Gochoki, D11. **GPS:** n43,26388 w0,88083.⬆.

6 🛏€8 🚰 2 🔧Ch 🔌€ 2. **Surface:** grassy/metalled. ⬤ 01/01-31/12
Distance: 500m 500m 400m.

🛏S **Excideuil** 28D1
rue Léon Barreau. **GPS:** n45,33605 e1,05239.

4 🚐€3 🚰€ 3 🚽 Ch 🔌. **Surface:** asphalted.

[S] Fontet 28C2

Base de Loisirs Fontet. GPS: n44,56118 w0,02282.⬆➡.

25 🚐€8 🚰 🚽 Ch ⚡ WC included 🚿€ 1. **Surface:** grassy/gravel. 🗓 01/01-31/12

Distance: 🏖on the spot 🛒bakery 500m, supermarket 4km.

Remarks: At lake.

Tourist information Fontet:

[M] Musée d'Artisanat et Monuments d'Allumettes, 2, Couture.Exhibitions, monuments of matches and maquettes. 🗓 01/02-30/09 14-18h, 01/10-30/11 Su 14-18h.

[S] Fourques-sur-Garonne 28C2

Halte Nautique d Pont des Sables, Pont des Sables, D933. **GPS:** n44,46081 e0,13932.

4 🚐free 🚰 🚽 Ch 🔌. **Surface:** metalled. 🗓 01/03-31/10

Distance: 🏘Fourques 2,5km 🚶3km.

[S] Frontenac 28C2

D236. **GPS:** n44,73781 w0,16308.

100 🚐€ 2,50 🚰 🚽free. **Surface:** grassy. 🗓 01/01-31/12

Distance: 🏘200m 🍴200m 🛒bakery 200m.

Remarks: Max. 48h, behind town hall.

[S] Fumel 28D2

Place Du Saulou, rue Massenet, D911. **GPS:** n44,49809 e0,97165.⬆.

10 🚐free 🚰 🚽 Chfree. **Surface:** asphalted. 🗓 01/01-31/12

Distance: 🏘200m 🍴200m.

Remarks: Château de Bonaguil 7km.

Tourist information Fumel:

[i] Office de Tourisme, Place Georges Escande, www.tourisme-fumelois.fr.

🏰 Château-fort de Bonaguil.Very well kept castle/fortress. 🗓 01/02-30/11, 10.30-12.30, 14-17.30h, 01/07-31/08 10-19h.

[S] Gastes 28A2

Port de Gastes, Avenue du lac. **GPS:** n44,32880 w1,15068.⬆.

100 🚐€ 2-4,50, 15/3-15/11 €7 🚰 🚽 Ch ⚡ WC 🚿included. 🚌 💳

Location: Comfortable.

Surface: grassy. 🗓 01/01-31/12 ⏺ service in winter.

Distance: 🏘Parentis-en-Born 7km 🏖on the spot 🎣on the spot 🍴800m 🛒800m.

Remarks: Along lake, baker every morning.

[C] [S] Gastes 28A2

Camping Les Echasses, 193 rue de Bernadon. **GPS:** n44,31871 w1,13879.⬆.

10 🚐€ 5-8 🚰€ 3 🚽 Ch ⚡ included. **Surface:** grassy. 🗓 01/01-31/12

Distance: 🏖Gastes Lac 2km 🚲on the spot.

Remarks: Max. 1 night, no camping activity.

[S] Grenade-sur-l'Adour 28B3

Place du 19 mars 1962. **GPS:** n43,77500 w0,43472.⬆.

40 🚐free 🚰 🚽 Ch WC free. **Surface:** asphalted/gravel.

Distance: 🏘100m 🍴100m 🛒100m.

Remarks: Next to cemetery, max. 24h.

[S] Hautefort 28D1

Route de Boisseuil. **GPS:** n45,25945 e1,14889.⬆.

FR

5 🌲free ⚡ € 2 🟦 Ch 🔲 € 2 WC. **Surface:** asphalted. 🅾 01/01-31/12
Distance: 🚶50m ⊗100m 🛒Intermarché 1km.

Tourist information Hautefort:
🅸 Office de Tourisme, Place du Marquis J. F. de Hautefort.
✖ Château Hautefort.Classified castle. 🅾 01/04-30/09 daily, 01/10-31/03 afternoons.
⚐ 🅾 Wed-morning.

🛁S	**Hendaye**	37D4

Gare des deux Jumeaux, Rue d'Ansoenia. **GPS:** n43,37019 w1,7648.⬆➡.

12 🌲free ⚡🟦 Chfree. **Surface:** asphalted. 🅾 01/01-31/12
Distance: 🚶on the spot ⊗800m ⊗450m ⊗450m 🚌on the spot.
Remarks: Railway-station Hendaye-plage.

🛁S	**Hostens** 🚻	28B2

Rue Chantegrue. **GPS:** n44,49321 w0,62898.

4 🌲free ⚡ service € 3 🟦Ch🔲 ♻. **Location:** Quit. **Surface:** . 🅾 01/01-31/12
Distance: 🚶1km ⊗on the spot 🚶on the spot ⊗on camp site 🛒on camp site.
Remarks: Next to campsite Ariales, June 2012 during inspection service out of order.

🛁S	**Houeillès**	28C3

Aire de Repos, Rue du 19 Mars 1962. **GPS:** n44,19611 e0,03250.

🌲free ⚡WC. **Location:** Quit. **Surface:** grassy/gravel. 🅾 01/01-31/12
Distance: 🚶100m 🛒250m.
Remarks: Max. 24h.

🛁S	**Hourtin**	28A1

Mombet, Hourtin-Port. **GPS:** n45,18083 w1,08056.⬆.

90 🌲€ 5, 01/04-30/09 € 8,15 ⚡€ 2 🟦Ch WC. 🚮 **Surface:** forest soil. 🅾 01/01-31/12
Distance: 🚶50m ⊗50m ⊗50m.
Remarks: Parking in harbour.

🛁S	**La Chapelle-Faucher**	28D1

Champignonnière de Rochevideau, D78. **GPS:** n45,36195 e0,74112.⬆.

6 🌲€ 3 ⚡🟦Ch 🌲free. **Location:** Quit.
Surface: concrete. 🅾 01/01-31/12
Distance: ⊗4km 🛒4km.

🛁S	**La Coquille**	21A6

N21, Place de l'église. **GPS:** n45,54250 e0,97778.⬆.

5 🌲free ⚡🟦 Ch WC free. **Location:** Central. **Surface:** asphalted. 🅾 01/01-31/12
Distance: 🚶100m ⊗200m 🛒200m.

🛁S	**La Pierre-Saint-Martin** 🏔 ❄	28B5

Aire de campingcar de la Pierre-Saint-Martin, Braça de Guilhers. **GPS:** n42,97918 w0,7487.⬆.

40 🌲free
⚡🟦Ch ⚡€ 10/2kWh, (winter).
Surface: asphalted.
🅾 01/01-31/12
Distance: 🚶300m ⊗300m ⊗150m.

🛁S	**La Réole**	28C2

Les Justices, Avenue Gabriel-Chaigne. **GPS:** n44,58057 w0,03018.⬆.
10 🌲€ 4 ⚡🟦Chfree. **Surface:** grassy. 🅾 15/04-01/10

Remarks: Centre ville, D1113 diri Marmande Agen, nearby Musée Automobile et Militaire.

⌧S **La Roche-Chalais** **28C1**

Parking Intermarché, d'Avenue d'Aquitaine. **GPS:** n45,15043 e0,01245.

🚱🚽Ch. **Surface:** asphalted. ◻ 01/01-31/12

⌧S **La Roque-Gageac** 🌿🎪🌊 **28D2**

D703. **GPS:** n44,82428 e1,18376. ⬆

20 🗑€7 🚱€ 2/10minutes 🚽Ch🚻€ 2/1h.

Surface: metalled.

◻ 01/01-31/12

Distance: 🚶on the spot 🏊on the spot 🚲on the spot ⊗200m 🚆200m.

Remarks: Along the Dordogne river.

Tourist information La Roque-Gageac:

ℹ www.cc-perigord-noir.fr.Small town worth seeing, in the Dordogne valley.

⌧S **Labastide-d'Armagnac** 🌿 **28B3**

Les Embarrats. **GPS:** n43,97205 w0,18602. ⬆

20 🗑free 🚱🚽Chfree. **Location:** Rural, quit. **Surface:** grassy.

Distance: 🚶300m.

⌧S **Labenne** **28A4**

Route Océane. **GPS:** n43,59616 w1,45492. ⬆

50 🗑€ 7,50 🚱🚽Ch🚿included. **Surface:** metalled. ◻ 10/04-02/10

Distance: 🚶1km 🏊2km 🚲2km ⊗1km 🚆1km.

Remarks: Max. 48h, camping forbidden.

⌧S **Lacanau** **28A1**

Le Huga, Rue des Sauviels. **GPS:** n45,00583 w1,16528. ⬆➡

125 🗑€ 13/24h 🚱🚽Ch🚻included. 📷🔌◻ 01/01-31/12

Remarks: In front of heliport, max. 48h.

⌧S **Ladaux** **28B2**

Vignobles Lobre & Fils, Le Bos. **GPS:** n44,69677 w0,24393.

5 🗑free 🚱🚽🚿WC. **Surface:** grassy/metalled. ◻ 01/01-31/12

Distance: 🚶300m.

⌧S **Lanouaille** **28D1**

Rue du Chemin Neuf. **GPS:** n45,39248 e1,14002. ⬆

6 🗑free 🚱🚽Ch🚿WCfree. **Location:** Comfortable, central, quit. **Surface:** asphalted. ◻ 01/01-31/12

Distance: 🚶50m ⊗100m 🚆100m.

Remarks: Max. 48h.

⌧S **Lanton** **28A2**

Allée Albert Pitres, Taussat. **GPS:** n44,71710 w1,06991. ⬆

10 🗑free 🚱🚽Chfree. **Surface:** asphalted. ◻ 01/01-31/12

Distance: 🏊sandy beach 100m.

⌧S **Laruns** 🎪🏔❄ **28B5**

Artouste Fabrèges. **GPS:** n42,87914 w0,39693. ⬆

FR

20 🅢free ⚡€ 4/100liter 🅒Ch💶€ 4/1h WC. **Surface:** asphalted. ⬛
01/01-31/12
Distance: 🚂200m ⛰on the spot 🛒on the spot ⊗on the spot 🍴on the spot
🚲1km.
Remarks: Coins at Office de Tourisme. Parking in centre, 20km from Laruns,
follow signs hamlet Artouste Fabrèges, along lake.

🅢S	Laruns 🚂⛰❄	28B5

Avenue de la Gare. **GPS:** n42,98819 w0,42458.⬆

25 🅢free ⚡€ 3,10 🅒Ch🔌 WC. **Surface:** asphalted. ⬛ 01/01-31/12
Distance: 🚂450m ⊗450m 🍴450m 🚐400m.
Remarks: Max. 24h, coins at Office de Tourisme.

🅢S	Laruns 🚂⛰❄	28B5

Parking Eaux-Chaudes. **GPS:** n42,95444 w0,43833.⬆

FR

5 🅢⚡€ 3 🅒Ch💶 WC. **Surface:** asphalted. ⬛ 01/01-31/12
Distance: 🚂on the spot ⛰on the spot 🛒on the spot ⊗on the spot 🍴100m
🚲100m 🚐100m.
Remarks: Coins at Office de Tourisme.

Tourist information Laruns:
ℹ Office de Tourisme, Maison de la Vallée d'Ossau, www.tourisme64.com, www.
station-artouste.com.Summer and winter destination, thermal centre. Route to the
Col d'Aubisque (Tour de France).
👁 Le Petit Train d' Artouste, Artouste Fabrèges.This sightseeing electric train, which
links Fabrèges lake with Artouste lake, 2,000 meters in altitude, enables you to
discover the highest and most beautiful summits of the Atlantic Pyrenees. That open
air electric train trots along for 10 kilometers. ⬛ 01/05-30/09.
👾 La Falaise aux Vautours, Aste Béon.Vultures being watched by camera and visible
on a huge screen. ⬛ 01/04-31/10 14-17/18, 01/06-31/08 10.30-12.30 14/17/18.

🅢S	Lavardac	28C3

Rue de la Victoire - Place du Foirail. **GPS:** n44,17883 e0,29928.⬆

3 🅢free ⚡🅒Chfree. **Location:** Very simple. **Surface:** asphalted.
Distance: 🚂on the spot 🍞22km 🍴bakery 150m.

🅢S	Layrac	28D3

Aire de Layrac, Rue du 19 Mars 1962. **GPS:** n44,13233 e0,65946.⬆.
6 🅢free ⚡🅒Ch WC free. **Surface:** asphalted.

🅢S	Layrac	28D3

Le Moulin, D129. **GPS:** n44,13675 e0,66533.⬆➡.

max. 4 🅢€ 10/24h ⚡🅒Ch🔌📶. **Surface:** grassy. ⬛ 01/01-31/12
Distance: 🚂on the spot.
Remarks: Call if no one is present.

🅢S	Le Bugue 🚂	28D1

Place Léopold Salme. **GPS:** n44,91679 e0,92775.⬆.

+50 🅢free ⚡🅒Chfree. **Surface:** metalled. ⬛ 01/01-31/12 ◉ Service:
winter.
Distance: 🚂200m ⛰20m ⊗100m 🍴Intermarché 100m.
Remarks: Along the river Vézère.

◎	Le Bugue 🚂	28D1

Aux Etangs du Bos, Audrix, St Chamassy. **GPS:** n44,86820 e0,96920.
🅢.
Distance: ⛰Etang de Bos.
Remarks: Recreation park, not accessible with heavy rainfall.

🅢	Le Porge	28A1

Avenue de l'Océan. **GPS:** n44,89437 w1,2131.

🅢free. **Surface:** forest soil. ⬛ 01/01-31/12
Distance: 🚂Le Porge 10km.

Remarks: Max. 24h.

Ⓢ **Le Porge** 28A1

Intermarché. GPS: n44,87574 w1,07883.
🚱€ 2 ♟Ch.

Le Temple-sur-Lot 28C2

Avenue de Verdun. **GPS:** n44,38000 e0,52639.⬆️➡️

4 🚐free 🚱♟Ch WC free. **Surface:** asphalted. ⬛ 01/01-31/12
Distance: 🚶50m 🚰100m.

Ⓢ **Le Verdon-sur-Mer** 20B6

Plage fluviale, Allée des Baïnes. **GPS:** n45,54582 w1,05433.⬆️➡️

30+20 🚐€ 5/24h, 01/06-30/09 € 8/24h 🚱€ 2 ♟Ch. 🚾 **Surface:** gravel.
⬛ 01/01-31/12
Distance: 🏖️50m ⊗500m 🛒2km 🚲 on the spot.
Remarks: Coins available at town hall, office de Tourisme and the shops at the
beach.

Ⓢ **Lège-Cap-Ferret** 28A2

Route des Pastourelles, Avenue Charles de Gaulle, D106, Claouey. **GPS:** n44,75127
w1,18033.⬆️
± 15 🚐free 🚱♟Ch 🔧 Service € 3,30/15min. **Surface:** forest soil. ⬛
01/01-31/12
Remarks: Coins at camping municipal, day parking also allowed, overnight stay
on motorhome stopovers.

Ⓢ **Lège-Cap-Ferret** 28A2

Avenue Edouard Branly. **GPS:** n44,75203 w1,18809.⬆️
15 🚐free. **Surface:** forest soil.
Remarks: Near campsite Les Embruns.

Ⓢ **Lège-Cap-Ferret** 28A2

D106, Avenue de Bordeaux, L'Herbe. **GPS:** n44,68655 w1,2451.⬆️
15 🚐free. **Surface:** unpaved.

Ⓢ **Léon** 28A3

Aire camping-cars, Route de Puntaou. **GPS:** n43,88444 w1,31861.⬆️

150 🚐€ 10 🚱♟Ch 🔧 included. 📇
Surface: grassy/gravel. ⬛ 01/04-31/10
Distance: 🚶1km 🏖️250m 🛥️50m ⊗50m 🛒50m.
Remarks: Nearby lake.

Ⓢ **Les Eyzies** 🌿🏖️🌊 28D1

Parking de la Vézère, Promenade de la Vézère. **GPS:** n44,93863 e1,00907.⬆️➡️

25 🚐€ 4/night 🚱€ 2/100liter ♟Ch. **Location:** Comfortable, quit. **Surface:**
grassy. ⬛ 01/01-31/12
Distance: 🚶100m ⊗100m 🛒100m.
Remarks: Along the river Vézère, summer max. 48h, parking fee being collected
at 9AM.

Tourist information Les Eyzies:

ℹ️ Office de Tourisme, 19, rue de la Préhistoire. Also called the prehistoric
capital.
👁️ Le Village Troglodytique de la Madeleine, Turzac. Troglodyte-village.
Ⓜ️ Le Village du Bournat, Le Bugue. Open air museum. ⬛ 01/04-31/10 10-
17/18h.
Ⓜ️ Musée Préhistorique National, 1, rue du musée. Collection of flint and other
objects. ⬛ 01/10-31/03. 🎫 € 5.

Ⓢ **Lhers** 🏔️ 28B5

La Nabe. **GPS:** n42,91028 w0,61939.⬆️

20-25 🚐€ 7 🚱♟Ch 🔧 WC 🔲included. 🚲 **Location:** Rural, comfortable,
isolated, quit. **Surface:** gravel.
Distance: 🚶7km 🐟100m 🚶 on the spot.

Ⓢ **Lit-et-Mixe** 🎏 28A3

Cap de l'Homy, 600, avenue Océan. **GPS:** n44,03846 w1,33764.⬆️

36 🚐€ 8-15 🚱♟Ch 🔧 WC. **Location:** Quit. **Surface:** forest soil. ⬛
01/01-31/12
Distance: 🏖️on the spot ⊗200m 🛒200m 🚲 on the spot.
Remarks: Next to campsite municipal.

Ⓢ **L'Hôpital-St.Blaise** 28B4

Parking l'Église. GPS: n43,25088 w0,76925. 🚶

FR

5 🛏free 🚰 WC. **Surface:** asphalted. ☀ 01/01-31/12
Distance: 🚰on the spot 🛒on the spot 🚰on the spot ✕on the spot.

📷	Macau	28B1

Domaine du Prat, 51, Avenue de la Coste. **GPS:** n45,00380 w0,60508. ⬆

5 🛏free. ☀ 01/01-31/12
Distance: 🚰on the spot.

S	Macau	28B1

Chemin du Mahoura. **GPS:** n45,00722 w0,61278. ⬆➡

🚰 Ch free. ☀ 01/01-31/12

S	Marmande	28C2

La Filhole, Rue de la Filhole. **GPS:** n44,49667 e0,16412.

50 🛏 €5 🚰 Ch. **Surface:** grassy. ☀ 03/06-05/09

S	Marmande	28C2

Place du Moulin. **GPS:** n44,49833 e0,16028. ⬆

2 🛏free 🚰 Ch free. **Surface:** asphalted. ☀ 15/09-15/05
Distance: 🚰150m 🛒on the spot.
Remarks: Max. 48h.

S	Mensignac	28D1

Combecouyere-Sud. **GPS:** n45,22309 e0,56553.
3 🛏free 🚰€ 2 🚰 Ch. **Surface:** gravel. ☀ 01/03-31/10

	Messanges	28A3

Plage principale, Avenue de la Plage. **GPS:** n43,81549 w1,40088. ⬆

10 🛏free. **Location:** Very simple. **Surface:** metalled/sand.
Distance: 🚰1,5km 🛒750m.
Remarks: Max. 48h.

S	Mimizan	28A3

Hélistation Plage Sud, Rue des Lacs, Mimizan-Plage. **GPS:** n44,20517 w1,29675. ⬆➡

85 🛏€ 8, 01/06-30/09 € 12 🚰 Ch 🔌 included. 🛒 📚 **Location:**
Comfortable. **Surface:** asphalted. ☀ 01/01-31/12
Distance: 🚰500m 🛒on the spot ✕500m 🛒200m.
Remarks: Parking at dune, no trailers allowed.

S	Mimizan	28A3

Route du C.E.L.. **GPS:** n44,21375 w1,28239. ⬆

100 🛏€6 🚰€ 3 🚰 Ch. **Location:** Very simple. **Surface:** grassy/gravel. ☀ summer
Distance: 🛒beach 1,5km 🚴on the spot.

FR

Mimizan 28A3

Camping du Lac, Avenue de Woolsack, Mimizan-lac. **GPS**: n44,21956 w1,22972.

21 € 10-15, 2 pers.incl, tourist tax excl., dog € 1,05-1,82 € 2
Ch . **Location**: Comfortable. **Surface**: gravel. 01/04-30/09

Moliets-et-Maa 28A3

Avenue de l'Océan, Moliets-Plage. **GPS**: n43,85091 w1,38188.

50 € 5, 1/6-50/11 € 11 Ch WC . **Location**: Comfortable, noisy. **Surface**: grassy/gravel.
Distance: 200m 750m 200m 200m.
Remarks: Shady.

Monbahus 28C2

Le Bourg, D124. **GPS**: n44,54738 e0,53517.
3 free Ch free. **Surface**: asphalted. 01/01-31/12 Service: winter.
Remarks: Steep entrance road, beautiful view.

Monbazillac 28C2

Château du Haut Pezaud, Les Pezauds. **GPS**: n44,78471 e0,48687.

10 free free € 1 WC € 1.
Surface: grassy. 01/01-31/12
Distance: table d'hôtes.
Remarks: Tasting of regional products.

Monbazillac 28C2

Domaine La Lande, Route de Ribagnac, D13. **GPS**: n44,78822 e0,49587.

10 free Ch WC free.

Surface: grassy. 01/01-31/12

Monflanquin 28D2

Zone commercial, D124. **GPS**: n44,52477 e0,75642.

5 free Ch free. **Surface**: gravel. 01/01-31/12
Distance: 1,3km 100m.

Tourist information Monflanquin:
Office de Tourisme, Place des Arcades, www.monflanquin-tourisme.com.
Medieval town.

Monpazier 28D2

La Duelle-nord. **GPS**: n44,68499 e0,89362.

10 free Ch free. **Surface**: gravel. 01/01-31/12
Distance: 200m.
Remarks: Square behind fire-station.

Monségur 28C2

Place du 8 mai. **GPS**: n44,65060 e0,08363.

5 free Ch WC free. **Surface**: asphalted. 01/01-31/12
Distance: nearby.
Remarks: Max. 48h. No access via La Bastide.

Montalivet-les-Bains 20B6

Avenue de l'Europe. **GPS**: n45,37349 w1,1442.

30 € 8 Ch included. **Location**: Quit.
Surface: forest soil. 01/05-30/09
Distance: 800m nearby nearby.
Remarks: Max. 48h.

FR

Montalivet-les-Bains 20B6

Boulevard de Lattre de Tassigny, Montalivet-sud. **GPS:** n45,37611 w1,15667.⬆️

30 🛏️€5 ⛽€ 1 🚰Ch. **Surface:** grassy/metalled. 🅿️ 01/05-30/09
Distance: 🏖️on the spot.
Remarks: Parking at sea, max. 48h.
Tourist information Montalivet-les-Bains:
⛺ 🅿️ Fri.

Montcaret 28C2

Le Chalet du Gourmet, D936. **GPS:** n44,85349 e0,03964.⬆️

16 🛏️€6,50 ⛽🚰Ch 💧€ 2 WC🚽€ 2 🔌€ 3.
Surface: grassy.
🅿️ 01/01-31/12
Distance: ⊗Resto Rapid.
Remarks: Bread-service, fruit-vegetables-wine-regional products for sale.

Monteton 28C2

D423. **GPS:** n44,62226 e0,25635.⬆️

25 🛏️free ⛽🚰Ch free. **Surface:** grassy. 🅿️ 01/01-31/12
Distance: ⊗on the spot.
Remarks: Beautiful view.

Montignac 28D1

Avenue Aristide Briand, D65. **GPS:** n45,06083 e1,15888.⬆️

20 🛏️free ⛽🚰Ch WC free. **Location:** Very simple. **Surface:** asphalted.
Distance: 🏖️on the spot ⊗300m 🚂500m.
Remarks: Along the river Vézère, next to sports fields.

Montignac 28D1

Avenue Alsace-Loraine. **GPS:** n45,06800 e1,16547.➡️

20 🛏️free. **Location:** Central. **Surface:** gravel. 🅿️ 01/01-31/12
Distance: 🚰200m ⊗200m 🚂200m.

Montignac 28D1

Ferme du Bois Bareirou, Les Baraques, Montignac-Lascaux. **GPS:** n45,09053 e1,11143.⬆️➡️

20 🛏️free ⛽€ 3 🚰Ch🔌€ 3. **Surface:** grassy. 🅿️ 01/01-31/12
Distance: 🚰5km.
Remarks: Max. 3 days.

Montpon-Ménestérol 28C1

Chez Lou Cantou, 46 rue Gustave Eiffel, D730. **GPS:** n45,02101 e0,15997.
5 🛏️€ 10/24h ⛽🚰Ch 💧. 🅿️ 01/01-31/12 🔌 frost.

Morcenx 28A3

Chemin des Abattoirs. **GPS:** n44,03811 w0,90914.⬆️

🛏️free ⛽🚰Ch free.
Distance: 🚰500m 🚂8,8km.
Remarks: Along railwayline.

Mugron 28B4

Avenue des Martyrs de la Résistance, D32e. **GPS:** n43,74846 w0,75063.⬆️

4 🛏️free ⛽🚰Ch 💧(4x)free. **Location:** Rural, very simple. **Surface:** gravel.
Distance: 🚰300m 🏕️on the spot.
Remarks: Max. 24h.

Nailhac 28D1

Ferme de la Jalovie. **GPS**: n45,23640 e1,13569. ⬆.

6 free ⚡ Ch free. **Surface**: metalled. ⬛ 01/01-31/12

Nérac 28C3

Place du Foirail. **GPS**: n44,13435 e0,33655.

10 free ⚡ WC. **Location**: Very simple. **Surface**: asphalted. ⬛ 01/01-31/12
Distance: 50m ⊗on the spot on the spot.

Nontron 21A6

Super U, 26, Avenue Jules Ferry. **GPS**: n45,53670 e0,66660.

3 free ⚡ € 2 Ch € 2. **Location**: Noisy. **Surface**: asphalted. ⬛ 01/03-31/10
Distance: 1km ⊗1km on the spot.
Remarks: Parking supermarket, max. 24h.

Oloron-Sainte-Marie 28B5

Parking Trivoli, Rue Adour Oloron. **GPS**: n43,18371 w0,60845. ⬆➡.

7 free ⚡€ 4/55minutes Ch € 4/55minutes. **Surface**: asphalted. ⬛ 01/01-31/12
Distance: 100m on the spot on the spot 400m 400m.
Remarks: Max. 48h.

Ondres 28A4

P3, Avenue de la Plage, Ondres-Plage. **GPS**: n43,57611 w1,48611. ⬆.

41 € 7, 01/07-31/08 € 9 ⚡ Ch WC free. ⚿ **Surface**: asphalted. ⬛ 01/06-30/09
Distance: 3km on the spot on the spot ⊗on the spot on the spot.
Remarks: Service also in winter available, 01/07-31/08 max. 48h. Third beach parking on the right.

Parentis-en-Born 28A2

Site du Lac, Route des Campings. **GPS**: n44,34432 w1,09879. ⬆.

30 €7 ⚡ Ch (4x)included. **Location**: Comfortable. **Surface**: gravel. ⬛ 01/01-31/12 ◉ service in winter.
Distance: 3km 50m ⊗50m.

Pau 28B4

Place de Verdun, Rue Ambroise Bordelongue. **GPS**: n43,29876 w0,37589. ⬆.

20 free. **Surface**: asphalted. ⬛ 01/01-31/12
Distance: on the spot ⊗on the spot 200m.

Pellegrue 28C2

Le Touran, Rue du Lavoir. **GPS**: n44,74498 e0,07528.

4 free ⚡ Ch free.
Surface: metalled. ⬛ 01/01-31/12
Distance: 100m.
Remarks: To edge of town.

Périgueux 28D1

Espace des Prés, Rue des Prés. **GPS**: n45,18770 e0,73081. ⬆➡.

FR

40 🛏€5 🚐🔌⚡ Ch ⚡ included. **Location:** Comfortable, central. **Surface:** asphalted. 🔵 01/01-31/12 ⬛ water disconnected in winter.
Distance: 🚶800m 🚃on the spot.
Remarks: Max. 2 nights.

Tourist information Périgueux:

ℹ️ Office de Tourisme, 26, place Francheville, Tour Mataguerre, www.tourisme-perigueux.fr.Old city, la Cité, the old Vesunna, with remainders, excavation of the old Roman city, many antique stores.

Ⓜ Le Musée d'art et d'archéologie du Périgord, 22 cours Tourny.Collection of prehistoric findings.

🛏S	Peyrehorade	28A4

Des Gaves, Route de la Pêcherie. **GPS:** n43,54300 w1,1071.⬆.
16 🛏€8 🚐🔌 Ch ⚡€ 2,50 WC 🚻.
Surface: grassy. 🔵 01/06-30/09
Distance: 🚶150m ⛱on the spot 🍴on the spot ⊗150m 🍺150m 🚃200m.

🛏S	Peyrehorade	28A4

Place Jean Bridart, Route de Sorde l'Abbaye D817. **GPS:** n43,54300 w1,09994. ⬆.

10 🛏free 🚐🔌 Ch free. **Surface:** metalled. 🔵 01/01-31/12
Distance: 🚶50m ⛱on the spot 🍴on the spot ⊗100m 🍺on the spot.
Remarks: In front of supermarket Carrefour.

🛏S	Preignac	28B2

Parking de la Mairie, D1113. **GPS:** n44,58551 w0,29597.⬆.

10 🛏free 🚐🔌 Ch free. **Surface:** asphalted. 🔵 01/01-31/12
Distance: 🚶on the spot 🛒6,8km ⊗250m.

🛏S	Ribérac	28C1

Place Pradeau. GPS: n45,24931 e0,33771.

4 🛏free 🚐🔌 Ch free.
Surface: asphalted. 🔵 01/01-31/12 ⬛ Fri-morning.

©S	Ribérac	28C1

Aux Deux Ponts Ouest, D708. **GPS:** n45,25704 e0,34255.⬆.

10 🛏free, 01/06-15/09 €5 🚐🔌 Ch free. **Surface:** gravel. 🔵 01/01-31/12
⬛ Water when frosty.
Distance: ⊗50m 🍺Leclerc 900m.

🛏S	Saint Estèphe	21A6

Etang de Saint Estèphe. GPS: n45,59008 e0,67396.⬆.

10 🛏free 🚐🔌 Ch free. **Location:** Comfortable.
Surface: gravel. 🔵 01/01-31/12
Distance: 🚶700m ⛱lake ⊗on the spot 🍺3km, bakery 800m.
Remarks: Summer: beach, bar, restaurant.

🛏S	Saint-Emilion	28C1

Château Gerbaud, St.Pey-d'Armens. **GPS:** n44,85310 w0,10699.⬆.

50 🛏€5 🚐🔌 Ch ⚡ (8x)€ 4. **Surface:** grassy. 🔵 01/01-31/12
Distance: ⊗200m 🍺bakery 200m, supermarket 2km.
Remarks: Max. 48h.

🛏S	Saint-Estèphe	28B1

Rue des Pêcheurs. GPS: n45,26460 w0,75784.⬆.

FR

5 ⛺free 🚰🔌Ch 🚽 Service € 5. **Surface:** metalled.
Remarks: Free, coins available at restaurant.

| 🏕️S | Sainte-Colombe-en-Bruilhois | 28C3 |

Lieu-dit Bécade. **GPS:** n44,17889 e0,51692.

4 ⛺free 🚰🔌Ch WC free. **Surface:** gravel. ⬛ 01/01-31/12
Distance: 🚶on the spot.

| 🏕️S | Sainte-Nathalène | 28D2 |

Les Ch'tis, Le Bourg, D47. **GPS:** n44,90409 e1,28765.

6 ⛺€ 10 🚰🔌Ch 🔌included. **Surface:** gravel. ⬛ 01/01-31/12
Distance: 🚶Sarlat 7km ⊗50m 🛒bread service 500m.

| 🏕️S | Salies-de-Béarn | 28A4 |

Aire Campincar du Herre, Quartiér du Herre. **GPS:** n43,47270 w0,9339.➡️

24 ⛺€ 6 🚰🔌Ch 🔌included. **Surface:** metalled. ⬛ 01/01-31/12
Distance: 🚶300m ⊘on the spot 🚶on the spot ⊗300m 🚌300m 🏪300m.

| 🏕️S | Salignac-Eyvigues | 29A1 |

Rue des Ecoles. **GPS:** n44,97257 e1,32061.⬆️

10 ⛺free 🚰🔌Ch free. **Location:** Comfortable, quit. **Surface:** grassy. ⬛
01/01-31/12
Distance: 🚶300m ⊗300m 🏪250m.

| 🏕️S | Sanguinet 🏕️ | 28A2 |

Aire du camping-car Les Bardets, 1131, Avenue de Losa. **GPS:** n44,48416
w1,09114.⬆️

15 ⛺free, € 7 (15/6-15/9) 🚰🔌Ch free. **Location:** Quit. **Surface:** metalled.
⬛ 01/01-31/12
Distance: 🚶800m ⊘on the spot 🚶on the spot ⊗50m 🏪on the spot.
Remarks: At lake, max. 48h.

| 🏕️S | Sanguinet 🏕️ | 28A2 |

Parking du Pavillon, 459, Avenue de Losa. **GPS:** n44,48579 w1,08479.⬆️

30 ⛺free, € 8 (15/6-15/9) 🚰WC. **Location:** Quit. **Surface:** forest soil. ⬛
01/01-31/12
Distance: ⊘on the spot ⊗Le Pavillon.
Remarks: Max. 48h.

| 🏕️S | Sare | 37D4 |

Place de Campingcars de Sare. GPS: n43,31307 w1,57679.⬆️ .

10 ⛺€ 6 🚰🔌Ch 🔌included. **Surface:** metalled. ⬛ 01/01-31/12
Distance: 🚶300m ⊗300m 🏪300m.
Remarks: Max. 48h.

Tourist information Sare:
ℹ️ Office de Tourisme, Bourg, www.sare.fr.Typical Basque village in Labourd-region.
👁️ Le petit train de la Rhune, Col de Saint Ignace.The little train runs through
the mountains in the Basque Country on the Franco-Spanish border. ⬛ 15/03-

FR

15/11 from 9h.

👁 Les Grottes de Sare.Caves, prehistoric park and museum. 🅾 01/02-31/12.

Sarlat-la-Canéda 〰🍽 28D2

Place Flandres Dunkerque. **GPS:** n44,89530 e1,21266.⬆➡.

50 🚐€ 5/24h, € 12/48h 🚰€ 2 🔧Ch🔌€ 2 🧺.🚗 **Location:** Noisy.
Surface: asphalted. 🅾 01/01-31/12 **Distance:** 🚶300m ⊗100m 🛒bakery 50m.

Tourist information Sarlat-la-Canéda:
ℹ Office de Tourisme, Ancien Evêché - Rue Tourny, www.sarlat-tourisme.com.
Small tourist and historical town. The streetscape is predominated by Lauzes, the
soft yellow flat stones of which the houses have been built. 🅾 Sa-morning.
🌳 Centre ville.Centre of the French trade in foie grass. 🅾 Sa-morning.

Sauvagnon 28B4

Aire du campingcars Champ de Foire, Rue du Béarn. **GPS:** n43,40361
w0,38635.⬆.
6 🚐free 🚰🔧Ch WC free. **Surface:** asphalted. 🅾 01/01-31/12
Distance: 🚶on the spot ⊗on the spot 🛒on the spot 🚌on the spot.

Sauveterre de Guyenne 28C2

Boulevard de 11 Novembre. **GPS:** n44,69051 w0,0867.

4 🚐free 🚰€ 0,50 🔧Ch🔌€ 1,50/90minutes. **Surface:** metalled. 🅾
01/01-31/12
Remarks: Coins at Office du Tourisme, supermarket.

Seignosse 28A4

Aire camping-cars, D79. **GPS:** n43,69089 w1,42539.⬆➡.

ENTREE ENTRADA ENTRANCE

75 🚐€8 🚰🔧Ch 🔧WC included 🧺.
Surface: grassy/gravel. 🅾 01/01-31/12
Distance: 🚶500m ⛰500m 🛒500m ⊗500m 🛒500m.
Remarks: Next to campsite municipal Hourn-Nao.

Sévignacq Méracq 28B5

Aire du gave d'Ossau, Quartier Raguette. **GPS:** n43,10712 w0,419.⬆➡.

20 🚐€7 🚰🔧Ch 🔧WC 🔌. **Surface:** grassy/gravel. 🅾 01/01-31/12
Distance: 🚶1km ⛰on the spot 🛒on the spot ⊗1km 🛒1km.

Sorges 28D1

Le Bourg. **GPS:** n45,30403 e0,87255.⬆.
🚐🚰🔧Ch free.

Sorges 28D1

Aire de repos Grangearias, RN21. **GPS:** n45,30486 e0,87273.⬆.

4 🚐free. **Surface:** metalled. 🅾 01/01-31/12

Soulac-sur-Mer 20B6

Boulevard de L'Amélie. **GPS:** n45,49938 w1,1373.⬆.
50 🚐€8 🚰€ 2 🔧Ch. 🅾 01/01-31/12
Distance: 🏊50m ⊗2,5km 🛒2,5km 🚴on the spot 🎣on the spot.

Sourzac 28C1

D6089. **GPS:** n45,05147 e0,39518.⬆.

8 🚐free 🚰🔧Ch 🔧free. **Location:** Comfortable, central. **Surface:** .
🅾 01/01-31/12 🅾 water disconnected in winter.
Distance: 🚶100m ⊗100m 🛒100m.
Remarks: Along the Isle river.

Soustons 28A3

Parking du Lac Marin, Avenue de la Pêtre, Soustons Plage. **GPS:** n43,77560
w1,41167.⬆.

82 🚐01/10-31/04 € 6, 01/05-30/09 € 12 🚰🔧Ch 🔧WC included. 🚗🧺
Surface: gravel/metalled. 🅾 01/01-31/12
Distance: 🚶city centre 3km ⛰lake 50m, ocean 300m ⊗50m 🛒50m 🚴on
the spot.

Remarks: Max. 72h.

⬛S St.Antoine-Cumond · 28C1
Le Bourg, D43. **GPS:** n45,25553 e0,19963.
5 🌊free 🚰🍽Ch WC free. **Surface:** gravel. ⬛ 01/01-31/12
Distance: ⊗300m 🏪300m.
Remarks: Max. 48h.

⬛S St.Caprais de Blaye · 28B1
Route de Saintes, RN137, Ferchaud. **GPS:** n45,29120 w0,5692.⬆

8 🌊free 🚰🍽Ch WC 🌊free, cold shower. **Surface:** asphalted. ⬛ 01/01-31/12
Distance: ◢6,4km ⊗on the spot 🏪on the spot.
Remarks: Tourist information and picnic tables available.

⬛S St.Cyprien (Dordogne) 🌿⛲ · 28D2
Place Mackenheim, Rue du Priolat. **GPS:** n44,86828 e1,04435.⬆

8 🌊free 🚰€ 3,50 🍽Ch 🌊(8x)€ 3,50/12h. **Surface:** asphalted. ⬛ 01/01-31/12
Distance: 🚰50m 🏪bakery 50m, supermarket 100m.
Remarks: Max. 48h, coins at supermarket, tourist office.

Tourist information St.Cyprien (Dordogne):
ℹ Office de Tourisme, Place Charles de Gaulle.
⊗ Marché repas gourmand. ⬛ summer Thu-evening.

⬛S St.Front-la-Rivière · 21A6
Place Louis Moreau, D83. **GPS:** n45,47450 e0,72430.

10 🌊free 🚰🍽Ch 🌊WC free. **Location:** Isolated. **Surface:** asphalted. ⬛ 01/01-31/12
Distance: ⊗500m.
Remarks: Picnic area.

⬛S St.Jean-de-Côle · 21A6
Le Bourg. **GPS:** n45,41984 e0,84048.

6 🌊free 🚰€ 2 🍽Ch. **Location:** Comfortable, quit. **Surface:** metalled. ⬛ 01/01-31/12
Distance: ⊗100m 🏪300m 🚏200m.
Remarks: At tennis-court, coins at tourist office.

⬛S St.Jean-de-Luz · 37D4
Pont Charles de Gaulle, N10. **GPS:** n43,38527 w1,6629.⬆

18 🌊free 🚰🍽Ch 🌊free. **Surface:** asphalted.
Distance: 🚉200m ◢2,2km ⛰300m 🚏300m ⊗100m 🏪100m.
Remarks: Max. 48h. Parking at station, via RN10.

Tourist information St.Jean-de-Luz:
ℹ Office de Tourisme, Place du Maréchal Foch, www.saint-jean-de-luz.com.
Tourist town with beautiful shops. The local speciality is chipirones, octopus cooked in its own ink.
⛲ Halles, Bd Victor Hugo. ⬛ morning.

⬛S St.Jean-Pied-de-Port 🌿⛲ · 28A5
Parking du Lai Alai. **GPS:** n43,16540 w1,23323.⬆

70 🌊€ 5,50/24h 🚰🍽Ch free. **Surface:** metalled. ⬛ 01/01-31/12
Distance: 🚉350m ⛰350m 🚏350m ⊗350m 🏪350m.
Remarks: Nearby stadium, max. 48h.

Tourist information St.Jean-Pied-de-Port:
ℹ Office de Tourisme, 14, Place Charles de Gaulle, www.pyrenees-basques.com. Fortified city on the foot of the Roncesvallespass on the road to Santiago de Compostela.
⬇ Forêt d'Iraty. Nature reserve, hiking trails available at OT.

⬛S St.Leon-sur-l'Isle · 28C1
Avenue de la République. **GPS:** n45,11515 e0,50034.⬆➡

4 ⍓free ⊨ Chfree. **Surface:** asphalted. ⬛ 01/01-31/12
Distance: 200m 5,3km 200m.

| 🏕️S | St.Léon-sur-Vézère 🌿⛺ | 28D1 |

Le Bourg, C201. **GPS:** n45,01230 e1,08978. ⬆.

30 ⍓€ 8,50/24h ⊨€ 2/120liter Ch € 2/4h.
Surface: asphalted. ⬛ 01/01-31/12
Distance: 3km on the spot 500m Restaurant Aintzira Le Lac.
Remarks: Parking at lake, max. 48h.

| 🏕️S | St.Saud-Lacoussière | 21A6 |

Domaine Sous Chardonnièras, 4, Impasse Sous Chardonnièras. **GPS:** n45,54053 e0,81909.

⍓free ⊨€ 2 Ch WC. **Location:** Quit.
Surface: grassy/gravel. ⬛ 01/01-31/12
Distance: 100m 200m 150m.
Remarks: Sanitary building 100m, shower € 0,50, coins available at tourist office.

4 ⍓€ 12 ⊨ WC ⎤included. **Surface:** unpaved. ⬛ 01/01-31/12
Distance: 500m 2km 2km 500m 500m.

| 🏕️S | St.Palais | 28A4 |

Parking Place Ste. Elisabeth. GPS: n43,32944 w1,0325. ⬆.

| 🏕️S | St.Sauveur | 28D2 |

Le Bourg, D21. **GPS:** n44,86850 e0,58834. ⬆.

10 ⍓free ⊨ Ch WCfree. **Surface:** asphalted. ⬛ 01/01-31/12
Distance: 200m 250m 250m.

| 🏕️S | St.Paul-les-Dax 🌿 | 28A4 |

Allée Salvador Allende. **GPS:** n43,73460 w1,07865. ⬆➡.

3 ⍓free ⊨ Ch WCfree. **Surface:** asphalted. ⬛ 01/01-31/12
Distance: 100m 100m 100m.

| 🏕️S | St.Savin | 28B1 |

Aire de Civrac-de-Blaye, Parc de la Mairie, D36, Civrac-de-Blaye. **GPS:** n45,11222 w0,44444. ⬆.

8 ⍓free ⊨ Chfree. **Surface:** gravel/sand. ⬛ 01/01-31/12
Distance: 500m 500m.
Remarks: Max. 72h, shady.

| 🏕️S | St.Pée-de-Nivelle | 28A4 |

Flot bleu park St. Pée sur Nivelle. GPS: n43,34945 w1,5215. ⬆➡.

1 ⍓free ⊨ WC free. **Surface:** grassy. ⬛ 01/01-31/12
Distance: 50m 100m.

| 🏕️S | St.Savin | 28B1 |

Aire de St.Girons d'Aiguevives, St.Girons d'Aiguevives. **GPS:** n45,13972 w0,5425.

2 🗗free 🚰. **Surface:** grassy/gravel. 🔲 01/01-31/12
Distance: 🔧on the spot ⊗4km 🛒10km.
Remarks: In front of the church.

| 🗗S | St.Savin | 28B1 |

Aire des Lacs du Moulin Blanc, St.Christoly-de-Blaye. **GPS:** n45,15167 w0,47583.

2 🗗free 🚰 WC free. **Surface:** gravel. 🔲 01/01-31/12
Distance: 🔧800m ⚓50m 🔧on the spot ⊗on the spot 🛒3km.
Remarks: Parking to lake.

| 🗗S | St.Savin | 28B1 |

Aire des Lagunes, St.Mariens. **GPS:** n45,11000 w0,39.

2 🗗free 🚰 WC free. **Surface:** asphalted. 🔲 01/01-31/12
Distance: 🔧on the spot ⚓6km 🔧6km ⊗2km 🛒3km.

| 🗗S | St.Savin | 28B1 |

Parking Centre Culturel. GPS: n45,13800 w0,4465.

2 🗗free WC. **Surface:** gravel. 🔲 01/01-31/12
Distance: 🔧on the spot ⚓3km 🔧3km 🔧150m 🛒800m.

| 🗗S | St.Savin | 28B1 |

Parking Maison des Jeunes, Cubnezais. **GPS:** n45,07500 w0,40861. ⬆➡.

12 🗗free 🚰 🧹 free. **Surface:** asphalted. 🔲 01/01-31/12
Distance: 🔧50m ⊗3km 🛒3km.

| 🗗S | St.Savin | 28B1 |

Aire de l'Église, Générac. **GPS:** n45,18000 w0,54.
2 🗗free. 🔲 01/01-31/12
Distance: 🔧on the spot ⊗6km 🛒10km.
Remarks: Church square.

| 🗗S | St.Savin | 28B1 |

Aire de Marcenais, Marcenais. **GPS:** n45,05000 w0,33.

2 🗗free. 🔲 01/01-31/12
Distance: 🔧on the spot ⊗6km 🛒6km.
Remarks: Next to community centre.

| 🗗S | St.Savin | 28B1 |

Aire de Saugon, Saugon. **GPS:** n45,17795 w0,50243.
2 🗗free. 🔲 01/01-31/12
Distance: 🔧on the spot ⚓6km 🔧6km ⊗3km 🛒6km.
Remarks: Behind town hall.

| 🗗S | St.Savin | 28B1 |

Aire de St. Vivien, RN137, St.Vivien-de-Blay. **GPS:** n45,09000 w0,51.

2 🗗free. 🔲 01/01-31/12
Distance: 🔧on the spot ⚓3km 🔧3km ⊗3km 🛒3km.
Remarks: Parking at church.

| 🗗S | St.Savin | 28B1 |

Aire du Dojo, Cézac. **GPS:** n45,09000 w0,41.

1 🗗free. 🔲 01/01-31/12

Distance: on the spot 6km 6km 3km 3km.
Remarks: Nearby town hall.

| St.Savin | 28B1 |

Aire du Lac des Vergnes, Laruscade. **GPS:** n45,10000 w0,34.
2 free. 01/01-31/12
Distance: 200m on the spot 500m 2km.
Remarks: Parking to lake.

| St.Savin | 28B1 |

Aire Maison de la Forêt, Donnezac. **GPS:** n45,24000 w0,44.

2 free. 01/01-31/12
Distance: on the spot 6km 6km.
Remarks: Next to community centre.

| St.Savin | 28B1 |

Parking communal Aire de Cavignac, Rue de Paix, Cavignac. **GPS:** n45,09976 w0,39048.

2 free. 01/01-31/12
Distance: on the spot 8km 50m 300m.

| St.Savin | 28B1 |

Parking communal Aire de Saint Yzan, Parking de la Gare, St.Yzan-de-Soudiac. **GPS:** n45,13000 w0,39.
2 free. 01/01-31/12
Distance: on the spot 12km 800m 3km 3km on the spot.

| St.Savin | 28B1 |

Parking de Marsas, Rue Chaignaud, Marsas. **GPS:** n45,06770 w0,3849.
2 free. 01/01-31/12
Distance: on the spot 4km 4km.

| S | St.Christoly-de-Blaye | 28B1 |

St.Christoly-de-Blaye. **GPS:** n45,15000 w0,47.

Ch free. 01/01-31/12
Distance: on the spot.
Remarks: Parking in front of town hall.

| St.Sylvestre-sur-Lot | 28D2 |

Place du Lot, Avenue Jean Moulin. **GPS:** n44,39621 e0,80499.

12 free. **Surface:** asphalted. 01/01-31/12
Distance: 150m, Penne d'Agenais centre 1,8km 100m 50m.

| S | St.Sylvestre-sur-Lot | 28D2 |

GPS: n44,39566 e0,80568.
Ch free.

| S | St.Vincent-de-Cosse | 28D2 |

Ferme d'Enveaux. **GPS:** n44,82669 e1,09822.

50 guests free Ch free.
Surface: unpaved.
01/01-31/12
Distance: pebbled beach 50m on the spot on the spot.
Remarks: Max. 48h, along the Dordogne river, key service at canoe rental.

Tourist information St.Vincent-de-Cosse:
Château de Milandes, Les Milandes.Former dwellinghouse of Josephine Baker, nowadays exhibition concerning her.

| S | St.Vincent-Jalmoutiers | 28C1 |

Le Bourg. **GPS:** n45,20055 e0,19091.
free Ch WC free. **Surface:** grassy/gravel. 01/01-31/12
Distance: 350m 350m.

| S | Ste.Alvére | 28D1 |

Rue de la Fontaine Saint Jean. **GPS:** n44,94500 e0,80499.

10 free € 2,50/100liter Ch € 2,50/1h. **Location:** Isolated.
Surface: metalled. 01/01-31/12
Distance: 500m 500m 500m.
Remarks: At sports centre, coins at town hall.

| S | Ste.Eulalie-en-Born | 28A2 |

Route du Port, D652. **GPS:** n44,30634 w1,18206.

FR

40 ⌇€ 6,50, 01/04-31/10 € 4 ⟟ ⬗ Ch ⟋ WC ⟩included ⟿ € 3. **Location:** Comfortable, quit.
Surface: grassy. ⬛ 01/04-31/10 ⬤ service 01/11-01/03.
Distance: ⬱50m ⊗50m ⬱on the spot ⬱ on the spot.
Remarks: At marina, to be paid at campsite.

| 🅢 | Ste.Livrade-sur-Lot | 28C2 |

Avenue René Bouchon. **GPS:** n44,39588 e0,59179.

8 ⌇free ⟟ ⬗ Ch free. **Surface:** asphalted. ⬛ 01/01-31/12
Distance: ⬱850m.
Remarks: At fire-station.

| 🅢 | Tournon-d'Agenais | 28D2 |

Base de Loisirs Camp Beau, Pont Roumio, Route de Libos, D102. **GPS:** n44,40444 e0,99833.

15 ⌇free ⟟ ⬗ Ch free. **Surface:** metalled. ⬛ 01/01-31/12

| | Valeyrac | 20B6 |

Port de Goulée, Route Castillonaise. **GPS:** n45,40500 w0,91028.

⌇free. **Surface:** asphalted/grassy.
Distance: ⬱50m ⬱on the spot ⊗20m.
Remarks: At harbour.

| 🅢 | Varaignes | 20D6 |

Place du Château. **GPS:** n45,59784 e0,31450. ⬆.

4 ⌇free ⟟ ⬗ Ch WC free. **Location:** Central. **Surface:** gravel. ⬛ 01/01-31/12
Distance: ⬱on the spot ⊗100m ⬱bakery 50m.

| 🅢 | Vertheuil | 28B1 |

Château Ferré, 3 rue des Aubépines. **GPS:** n45,26225 w0,82798. ⬆.

5 ⌇free ⟟ ⬗ Ch WC. **Surface:** gravel. ⬛ 01/01-31/12

| 🅢 | Veyrines-de-Domme | 28D2 |

Boutique des Bois d'Envaux, Route des Milandes, 6-102 Le Falgueyrat. **GPS:** n44,82090 e1,10394. ⬆.

30 ⌇free ⟟ free. **Surface:** grassy.
Distance: ⊗on the spot.
Remarks: Sale of foie gras and wine.

| 🅢 | Vielle St.Girons ⟟⟟ | 28A3 |

Lac de Léon, plage de Vielle. GPS: n43,90279 w1,30944. ⬆.

30 ⌇€ 9-12, dog € 4,70 ⟟ ⬗ Ch ⟋ (30x)€ 4,50/night WC ⟩. **Surface:** gravel/metalled. ⬛ 01/04-30/09
Distance: ⬱100m ⬱300m ⊗50m ⬱100m.
Remarks: Max. 48h.

| 🅢 | Vielle St.Girons ⟟⟟ | 28A3 |

Les Tourterelles, Saint Girons-Plage. **GPS:** n43,95278 w1,35778. ⬆.

FR

40 ⌇€ 8,90, July-Aug € 12,50 ⌇€ 2,70/10liter ⌇Ch ⌇ 55minutes WC ⌇.
Location: Comfortable. **Surface:** gravel/metalled. ⌇ 01/01-31/12 ⌇ Service 01/10-26/04.
Distance: ⌇300m ⌇500m ⌇500m.

10 ⌇free ⌇€ 3 ⌇Ch⌇WC. **Surface:** grassy/gravel. ⌇ 01/01-31/12
Distance: ⌇50m ⌇2km beach at Dordogne river ⌇200m.
Remarks: Coins available at restaurant Le Point Vue (200m).

Midi Pyrénées

| | Vieux-Boucau-les-Bains | 28A3 |

Aire camping-cars Village, Avenue des Pêcheurs. **GPS:** n43,77971 w1,40041.⌇

| | Albi | 29B3 |

Parking Cathédrale. GPS: n43,92750 e2,14111.⌇

120 ⌇€ 6, 01/05-30/09 € 12 ⌇⌇Ch ⌇ included. ⌇⌇**Location:** Comfortable. **Surface:** gravel/sand. ⌇ 01/01-31/12
Distance: ⌇500m ⌇200m ⌇500m ⌇500m ⌇on the spot.
Remarks: >3,5t not allowed.

9 ⌇free. **Surface:** asphalted.
Distance: ⌇50m ⌇50m ⌇100m.
Remarks: Parking nearby cathedral Sainte Cécile, max. 48h.

| | Vieux-Boucau-les-Bains | 28A3 |

Aire du Marensin Plage, Boulevard du Marensin. **GPS:** n43,79485 w1,4051.⌇

| | Albi | 29B3 |

Rue Michelet. GPS: n43,94583 e2,15111.⌇→.
⌇⌇Chfree. ⌇ 01/01-31/12

Tourist information Albi:

⌇ Office de Tourisme, Palais de la Berbie, place Sainte-Cécile, www.mairie-albi.fr.Old city with narrow streets round the cathedral, birth town of Toulouse Lautrec. Musée de Toulouse-Lautrec, Palais de la Berbie, is a complete collection of the painter.
⌇ Musé de Toulouse-Lautrec, Palais de la Berbie.Collection by the painter.

| | Alblas | 28D2 |

Pech del Gal. GPS: n44,47480 e1,23275.→.

35 ⌇€ 6, 01/05-30/09 € 12 ⌇⌇Ch ⌇.⌇**Location:** Quit. **Surface:** gravel. ⌇ 01/01-31/12
Distance: ⌇1,5km ⌇Ocean 500m ⌇1,5km ⌇1,5km ⌇on the spot.
Remarks: Max. 48h, >3,5t not allowed.

| | Villeton | 28C2 |

D120. **GPS:** n44,36386 e0,27279.

10 ⌇free ⌇⌇free. **Surface:** gravel.
Remarks: Near campsite.

| | Alvignac | 29A2 |

Route de Padirac. GPS: n44,82504 e1,69711.⌇

4 ⌇free ⌇€ 2 ⌇Ch⌇€ 2. **Surface:** gravel. ⌇ 01/01-31/12
Distance: ⌇10,5km ⌇on the spot ⌇on the spot ⌇on the spot.

| | Vitrac | 28D2 |

Montfort, D703. **GPS:** n44,83558 e1,24852.⌇

10 ⌇free ⌇⌇Ch. **Surface:** asphalted.

Distance: 🚰100m ⊗200m 🛒200m.

🅿🅢 **Aragnouet** ⛰❄ 28C5

P5, Piau Engaly. **GPS:** n42,78599 e0,15800. ⬆➡
100 🚐€6 🚰🚽Ch⚡(100x)€ 6 WC. **Surface:** asphalted. ⏹ 01/12-31/08
Distance: 🚰300m 🛒300m 🏪300m.
Remarks: A64 exit Tarbes, dir Spain (RD929).

🅿🅢 **Arfons** 29B4

Pierron-Les Escudiés. **GPS:** n43,43972 e2,19472.

4 🚐€5 🚰🚽Ch WC ⚡. **Surface:** grassy. ⏹ 01/01-31/12
Distance: 🚰4km 🚶1km ⊗4km 🛒4km.

🅿🅢 **Arreau** 28C5

Chemin de Fregel, Avenue de la gare. **GPS:** n42,90708 e0,35912. ⬆

27 🚐€2 🚰Ch free. **Surface:** asphalted. ⏹ 01/01-31/12
Distance: 🚰100m 🏊100m 🏪300m 🛒300m 🚌200m.

🅿🅢 **Arrens-Marsous** 28B5

GPS: n42,95806 w0,20722. ⬆

10 🚐free 🚰🚽Ch free. **Surface:** asphalted. ⏹ 01/01-31/12
Distance: 🚰1,5km ⊗1,5km 🛒1,5km.
Remarks: Behind 'services techniques'.

🅿🅢 **Arvieu** ⛰🏖 29B3

GPS: n44,19205 e2,65938. ⬆

11 🚐 🚰€ 2/80liter 🚽Ch WC. **Surface:** gravel. ⏹ 01/04-30/11
Distance: 🚰100m 🏊on the spot ⊗on the spot 🛒on the spot.

🅿🅢 **Aubrac** 29C2

D533. **GPS:** n44,62026 e2,98705.

10 🚐 🚰🚽Ch WC free. **Surface:** gravel. ⏹ 01/01-31/12
Distance: 🚰50m ⊗on the spot 🛒on the spot 🏪on the spot 🏊on the spot.

🅿🅢 **Auch** 🌿🏛🍞🏖 28C4

Camping municipal, Rue des Cormorans. **GPS:** n43,63654 e0,58854. ⬆➡

3 🚐free 🚰🚽Ch free. **Surface:** asphalted. ⏹ 01/01-31/12
Distance: 🚰15min ⊗15min 🛒15min.

🅿🅢 **Auterive** 29A4

Grande Allée du Ramier. **GPS:** n43,35025 e1,47730. ⬆

6 🚐free 🚰🚽free. **Surface:** asphalted. ⏹ 01/01-31/12
Remarks: At fire-station.

🅿🅢 **Auzas** 28D5

GPS: n43,17060 e0,88690.

5 🚐€3 🚰🚽Ch ⚡included. **Surface:** asphalted.
Distance: 🏊on the spot.
Remarks: At lake.

🅿🅢 **Ax-les-Thermes** 🏛⛰🌳❄♨ 29A6

Parc d'Espagne. **GPS:** n42,71504 e1,84142. ⬆

35 🚐free. **Surface:** metalled. ⏹ 01/01-31/12
Distance: 🚰500m ⊗500m 🛒500m.

🅿🅢 **Bagnac-sur-Célé** 29B2

Parking de la Planquette. GPS: n44,66806 e2,15861. ⬆

FR

6 🛏free ⚓ 🔧 Ch free. **Surface:** asphalted. 🌙 01/01-31/12
Distance: 🚶on the spot ⊗100m 🛒100m 🚌200m.
🔵S | **Bagnères-de-Bigorre** ⚓ | 28C5
Rue René Cassin. **GPS:** n43,07319 e0,15256. ⬆➡.

10 🛏free ⚓ € 3 🔧Ch WC. **Surface:** asphalted. 🌙 01/01-31/12
Distance: 🚶on the spot 🛒50m 🚴 on the spot 🧍on the spot.
Remarks: Inclining pitches, coins at the shops in the village.
🔵S | **Barbotan-les-Thermes** 🏖 | 28C3
Avenue des Thermes. **GPS:** n43,94884 w0,04344. ⬆➡.

10 🛏free ⚓ 🔧 Ch WC free. **Surface:** gravel. 🌙 01/01-31/12
Distance: 🚶500m ⊗1km 🛒1km.
🔵S | **Bagnères-de-Bigorre** ⚓ | 28C5
Place de la Gare. **GPS:** n43,06917 e0,14889.

6 🛏free, overnight stay against payment. **Surface:** asphalted. 🌙 01/01-31/12
Distance: 🚶500m ⊗50m 🛒500m.
🔵S | **Bardigues** 🌿⛺🌳 | 28D3
GPS: n44,03869 e0,89271. ⬆➡.

10 🛏free. **Surface:** asphalted.
Distance: 🚶200m ⊗200m 🛒200m.
Remarks: At station.
🔵S | **Bagnères-de-Luchon** ⚓ | 28C5
Allée du Corp Franc Pommiès. **GPS:** n42,79540 e0,59875.

4 🛏free ⚓ € 2 🔧Ch. **Surface:** gravel. 🌙 01/01-31/12
Distance: 🚶150m ⛽8,6km ⊗150m 🛒150m.
Remarks: Dir cemetery, A62 exit Valence d'Agen, dir Aurillac then Bardigues.
🔵S | **Barqnac** | 29A5
La Bastide-de-Sérou. **GPS:** n43,00194 e1,44556. ⬆.

30 🛏€ 4/24h ⚓ 🔧Ch 🔌€ 6. **Surface:** asphalted. 🌙 01/01-31/12 ⚫
service: 01/12-01/04.
🔵S | **Baraqueville** | 29B3
Rue du Val de l'Enne. **GPS:** n44,27850 e2,43407. ⬆.

15 🛏€ 13,60 ⚓🔧Ch 🧹 WC 🚿included. **Surface:** asphalted/gravel. 🌙
06/03-13/11
Remarks: Next to campsite.
🔵S | **Belmont sur Rance** 🏔⛺ | 29B4
Parking de la Mairie, Place de la Maririe RD 32. **GPS:** n43,81630 e2,75269. ⬆.

3 ⌾free ⊷ ⌁Ch free. **Surface:** asphalted. ◻ 01/01-31/12
Distance: ⚓on the spot.

⚿S **Boisse Penchot** 🏞 29B2
Rue du Chateau Bas. **GPS:** n44,59208 e2,20616. ⬆.

8 ⌾free ⊷€ 3/100liter ⌁Ch 🔋€ 3/1h.
Surface: asphalted.
◻ 01/01-31/12
Distance: ⚓100m ⚓on the spot ⚓on the spot ⊗on the spot ⚓on the spot.

⚿S **Bonac Irazein** 🏔 28D5
Lac Bonac. **GPS:** n42,87541 e0,97565. ⬆.

10 ⌾€ 5/night ⊷ ⌁Ch ⚑ included. **Surface:** grassy/gravel.
Distance: ⚓on the spot.
Remarks: At artificial lake of Bonac.

⚿S **Bouillac** 29B2
Aire pique-nique, D840. **GPS:** n44,57333 e2,15750. ⬆.

6 ⌾free ⊷€ 3 ⌁Ch. **Surface:** metalled. ◻ 01/03-30/11
Distance: ⚓on the spot ⚓on the spot ⊗on the spot ⚓600m.
Remarks: Max. 24h, coins at the shops.

⚿S **Branne** 28C2
Route de Cabara. **GPS:** n44,83191 w0,18448.
⌾free ⊷€ 2/100liter ⌁Ch 🔋€ 2/1h.
Distance: ⚓on the spot.

⚿S **Brassac** 29B4
Place Belfortès. **GPS:** n43,62968 e2,49434.
6 ⌾free Ch WC. **Surface:** asphalted. ◻ 01/01-31/12

Distance: ⚓on the spot.
Remarks: Access via RD622.

⚿S **Broquies** 🏔🐑 29B3
Rue du Lavoir. **GPS:** n44,00498 e2,69371.

30 ⌾free ⊷ ⌁Ch ⚑ WC ⌁free. **Surface:** gravel. ◻ 01/04-30/11
Distance: ⚓50m ⊗on the spot ⚓on the spot.

⚿S **Cadours** 28D4
Rue Malakoff. **GPS:** n43,72280 e1,04880. ➡.

5 ⌾free ⊷ ⌁Ch free. **Surface:** grassy. ◻ 01/01-31/12 ⚪ tue-evening, wed-morning.
Distance: ⚓1km ⊗1km.
Remarks: At football ground.

⚿S **Cahors** 🌊⚓🧁🏔🐑🏞 29A2
Parking Saint George, Rue Saint George, D920. **GPS:** n44,44062 e1,44170. ➡.

3 ⌾free ⊷ ⌁Ch free. **Surface:** gravel. ◻ 01/01-31/12
Distance: ⚓500m ⚓on the spot ⊗250m ⚓50m ⚓on the spot.
Remarks: Along river.

Tourist information Cahors:
ℹ Maison de Tourisme, Place François Mitterrand, www.quercy.net. The city is famous because of the wine. Moreover it has a rich architecture heritage.
⚓ ◻ Wed, Sa.

⚿S **Cahuzac-sur-Vère** 29A3
Place du Mercadial. **GPS:** n43,98194 e1,91111. ⬆➡.

5 ⌾free ⊷ ⌁Ch WC. **Surface:** gravel.
Distance: ⚓200m ⊗200m ⚓200m.

🅂 Cajarc 29A2

Place de la Gare. **GPS:** n44,48458 e1,84573. ⬆️➡️

8 🛏free ⚡€ 1 🔌Ch. **Surface:** grassy. ⬛ 01/01-31/12
Distance: 🚰100m ⊗200m 🛒200m.

🅂 Calès 29A2

D673. **GPS:** n44,81298 e1,53780.

4 🛏free ⚡🔌Ch against payment.
Distance: 🚰on the spot.

🅂 Camares 🏔️🎡 29C4

Base de loisirs des Zizines. **GPS:** n43,81654 e2,87988. ⬆️

10 🛏free ⚡🔌Ch WC 🛒free. **Surface:** gravel. ⬛ 01/04-31/10
Distance: 🚰100m 🏊on the spot.

🅂 Campagnac 🏔️ 29C3

GPS: n44,41903 e3,08210. ⬆️

5 🛏€3 ⚡🔌Ch. **Surface:** metalled. ⬛ 01/04-31/10
Distance: 🚰50m ⊗on the spot 🛒on the spot.

🅂 Campuac 🏔️🎡 29B2

GPS: n44,57027 e2,59162. ⬆️
10 🛏free ⚡🔌Ch WC free. **Surface:** gravel. ⬛ 01/01-31/12
Distance: 🚰100m 🛒on the spot.

🅂 Cardaillac 29A2

Le Pré del Prie. **GPS:** n44,67868 e1,99805. ⬆️

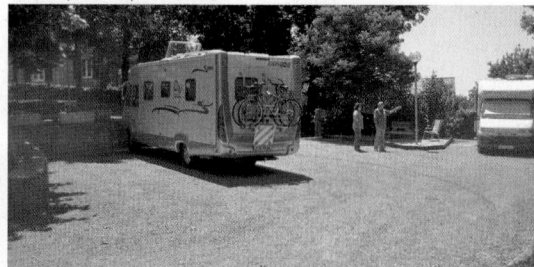

12 🛏free ⚡🔌Ch 🔧free. **Surface:** metalled. ⬛ 01/01-31/12
Distance: 🚰100m 🛒100m.
Remarks: Behind church.

🅂 Castanet 29B3

GPS: n44,27889 e2,28944. ⬆️➡️

4 🛏€3 ⚡🔌Ch 🔧included. **Surface:** gravel. ⬛ 01/01-31/12
Distance: 🚰on the spot ⊗on the spot.

🅂 Castelnau-de-Montmiral 29A3

Les Miquels. **GPS:** n43,96667 e1,80278. ⬆️➡️

6 🛏€ 9,50, 2 pers.incl ⚡🔌Ch 🔧. **Surface:** grassy. ⬛ 01/01-31/12
Distance: 🚰2,5km ⊗on the spot 🛒2,5km.

🅂 Castelnau-Durban 28D5

D117. **GPS:** n42,99994 e1,33976. ⬆️

10 🛏free ⚡€ 2 🔌Ch WC. **Surface:** metalled.
Remarks: In front of church.

🅂 Castelsarrasin 28D3

Allée de la Source. **GPS:** n44,03861 e1,10221. ⬆️➡️

FR

40 ⌧€ 3/24h ⌐ € 2,50/100liter ⌧Ch ⌐€ 2,50/24h. **Surface:** gravel. ○
01/01-31/12
Distance: 500m ⊗500m ⌧500m.
⌧S **Castelsarrasin** 28D3
Rue Louis Braille. **GPS:** n44,03833 e1,11473.⬆.

15 ⌧free ⌐⌧Ch⌧free. **Surface:** asphalted. ○ 01/01-31/12
Distance: 200m ⌀3km ⊗250m.
Remarks: Along Canal des 2 Mers.
⌧S **Castres** 29B4
Parc de Gourjade, Avenue de Roquecourbe, D89. **GPS:** n43,62049 e2,25357.⬆.

5 ⌧free ⌐⌧Ch free. **Surface:** metalled.
Distance: 2km.
⌧S **Castres** 29B4
Place Gerard Philipe. **GPS:** n43,60168 e2,24939.

⌧free. **Surface:** asphalted. ○ 01/01-31/12
Distance: 2km ⊗2km ⌧2km.
Remarks: Free shuttle to centre.

Tourist information Castres:
ℹ Office de Tourisme, 3, rue Milhau-Ducommun, www.ville-castres.fr.Centre of the textile industry.
✝ Palais Episcopal.Episcopal palace.
⚘ ○ Tue, Thu-Su.
⌧S **Caussade** 29A3
Place de la Halle, Boulevard Léonce Granier. **GPS:** n44,16111 e1,53583.

10 ⌧free. **Surface:** asphalted.
Distance: on the spot ⊗on the spot ⌧on the spot ⇌on the spot.
⌧S **Cauterets** 28B5
Place de la Patinoire, D920. **GPS:** n42,89361 w0,11256. ⬆→.

80 ⌧€ 8/24h ⌐⌧Ch ⌐free. **Surface:** asphalted. ○ 01/01-31/12
Distance: 300m ⊗300m ⌧300m.
Remarks: Max. 21 nights.
Tourist information Cauterets:
ℹ Office de Tourisme, Place Foch.Mountaineering village with thermal sources.
⌧S **Caylus** 29A3
Base de loisirs Labarthe. **GPS:** n44,23363 e1,77225.⬆.

6 ⌧free ⌐⌧Ch free. **Surface:** grassy/gravel. ○ 01/01-31/12
Distance: 200m ⊗200m ⌧200m.
Remarks: D19 dir St.Antonin, along lake.
Tourist information Caylus:
ℹ St.Antonin.Small town with the oldest town hall of France.
⌧S **Condom** 28C3
Ferme de Parette, Route de Nérac, RN930. **GPS:** n43,99944 e0,35639.⬆.

8 ⌧€ 8 ⌐⌧Ch ⌐⌧included ⌧against payment. **Surface:** grassy. ○
01/01-31/12
Distance: 2km ⊗2km ⌧2km.
Remarks: 800m from hamlet Parette.
Tourist information Condom:
ℹ Larressingle.Small fortified town, surrounded by ramparts and tower of defence.

FR

ℹ Office de Tourisme, Place Bossuet, www.tourisme-tenareze.com.Historical place and centre of the Armagnac.
Ⓜ Musée de l'Armagnac.All about Armagnac.

Cordes-sur-Ciel 29A3
Parking les Tuileries. GPS: n44,06453 e1,95802.⬆.

40 ⌇€ 3,50 ⚷ ⚏ Ch ⚙ included. ⬜ 01/01-31/12
Distance: 🚶250m.

Tourist information Cordes-sur-Ciel:
ℹ Office de Tourisme, Maison Fonpeyrouse, www.cordes-sur-ciel.org.Medieval city with renovated city walls and archways.

Coupiac 29B3
Route de Martin. **GPS:** n43,95174 e2,58464.⬆.
10 ⌇free ⚷ ⚏ Chfree. **Surface:** grassy. ⬜ 01/01-31/12
Distance: 🚶500m.
Remarks: Nearby petrol station at D60.

Cransac 29B2
Aire de Camping-car Cransac, Avenue de la Gare. **GPS:** n44,52278 e2,27444.

6 ⌇€5 ⚷ ⚏ Chfree. **Surface:** gravel. ⬜ 01/01-31/12
Distance: 🚶500m ⊗500m 🚰500m.
Remarks: In front of campsite.

Donzac 28D3
Lac de Sources, D30. **GPS:** n44,11308 e0,82044.⬆.

10 ⌇free ⚷ ⚏Chfree. **Surface:** gravel.
Remarks: Max. 48h.

Douelle 29A2
Domaine Marcilhac, D8. **GPS:** n44,47927 e1,34947.➡.

10 ⌇free ⚷€ 2 ⚏Ch. **Surface:** gravel. ⬜ 01/01-31/12
Distance: 🚶1km ⊗1km 🚰1km 🚗1km.

Entraygues-sur-Truyère 29B2
GPS: n44,64417 e2,56278.

5 ⌇free. **Surface:** gravel. ⬜ 01/01-31/12
Distance: 🚶50m ⊗150m 🚰150m.

Entraygues-sur-Truyère 29B2
Route de Villecomtal, D904. **GPS:** n44,64020 e2,56925.⬆.

⌇free. **Surface:** grassy. ⬜ 01/04-31/12
Distance: 🚶50m ⚓on the spot ➤on the spot ⊗50m 🚰50m.

Entraygues-sur-Truyère 29B2
Rue du 16 Août 1944. **GPS:** n44,64167 e2,56611.

⚷ ⚏Ch ⚙.

Figeac 29A2
Parking le Foiral, Boulevard Colonel Teulié. **GPS:** n44,60833 e2,03806.

5 🛏free ⛽€ 2 🔧Ch. **Surface:** asphalted. 🅾 01/01-31/12
Distance: 🚶100m ⛲400m 🛒100m 🚮100m.

Tourist information Figeac:
ℹ Office de Tourisme, Hôtel de la Monnaie, Place Vival, figeac.quercy-tourisme. com/.
Ⓜ Musée Champollion.Collection of old Egyptian art. 🅾 Tue-Su 10-12h, 14.30-18.30h.
✈ Marché régional.Regional market. 🅾 Sa-morning.

🛏 S	Fleurance	28D3

Boulevard de Metz. **GPS:** n43,85164 e0,66184.➡.

20 🛏free ⛽€ 2 🔧Ch🚰€ 2. **Surface:** gravel.
Distance: 🚶200m 🛒on the spot 🚮on the spot.

🍴 S	Frejairolles	29B4

Le Grand Chêne, D81. **GPS:** n43,86043 e2,24799.⬆.
5 🛏€5 ⛽🔧Ch🚿included.
Remarks: Free for clients.

🛏 S	Gaillac	29A3

Parking des Rives Thomas. **GPS:** n43,89951 e1,89494.⬆➡.

🛏free ⛽🔧Chfree. **Surface:** asphalted. 🅾 01/01-31/12
Distance: 🚶200m ⛲200m 🛒200m.

🛏 S	Gavarnie 🚡🏔❄	28B5

Parking Holle, D923. **GPS:** n42,73857 w0,01959.

20 🛏€ 4 ⛽🔧Ch 🚿included. 🅾 01/01-31/12
Distance: 🚶800m 🏊100m 🎣100m ⛲800m 🛒800m 🚌600m 🚲1,5km 🚶1,5km.

🛏 S	Gavarnie 🚡🏔❄	28B5

Parking du Cirque, Chemin du cirque. **GPS:** n42,73694 w0,01278.

20 🛏free. **Surface:** asphalted. 🅾 01/01-31/12
Distance: 🚶200m ⛲200m 🛒200m 🚮200m.

Tourist information Gavarnie:
ℹ Office de Tourisme, www.gavarnie.com.Village, World Heritage Site of UNESCO. Summer and winter destination.
👁 Cirque de Gavarnie.Can be reached with a donkey, a horse or by foot. A giant waterfall, snow pillars and mountain slopes.

🛏 S	Gignac	29A1

Le Moulin, Place des Troubadours. **GPS:** n45,00624 e1,45687.⬆.

10 🛏free ⛽🔧Ch. **Surface:** metalled. 🅾 01/01-31/12
Distance: 🚶50m ⛲150m 🛒150m.

🛏 S	Gimont 🌿🌳🍴	28D4

Avenue de Cahuzac, RN124. **GPS:** n43,62987 e0,87009.⬆.

12 🛏free ⛽🔧Ch🚿free.
🅾 01/01-31/12
Distance: 🚶100m 🏊on the spot 🎣on the spot ⛲300m 🛒300m 🚌300m.
Remarks: At lake, max. 48h.

🛏 S	Gourdon 🌿🌳🍴🌳	29A2

Esplanade du foirail. **GPS:** n44,73423 e1,38523.⬆➡.

8 🛏€6 ⛽🔧Ch 🚿included. **Surface:** gravel.
Distance: 🚶200m ⛲100m 🛒200m 🚮on the spot.

🛏 S	Gramat	29A2

La Garenne, Avenue Paul Mezet. **GPS:** n44,77972 e1,72833.⬆➡.

FR

10 free ⛽ 🔌 Ch 🚻. **Surface:** metalled. ◻ 01/01-31/12
Distance: 🛒400m ⊗400m 💧400m.
Remarks: Max. 24h.

Grenade-sur-Garonne 28D4
Quai de Garonne. **GPS:** n43,77201 e1,29673.⬆

4 free ⛽ 🔌 Ch. **Surface:** gravel.
Distance: 🛒100m ⊗100m 💧100m 100m.
Remarks: Service: Allées Alsace Lorraine (100m).

La Couvertoirade 29C3
GPS: n43,91171 e3,31478.

€ 2. **Surface:** gravel. ◻ 01/01-31/12
Distance: 🛒50m.
Remarks: Large parking on edge from village.

Tourist information La Couvertoirade:
ℹ Citadelle de l'Ordre de Tempeliers.Fortified city in original state. Now many old craft industries are exercised. There is a toll-house at the entrance of the village, entrance fee is charged.

Labastide-Murat 29A2
Route de Gramat. **GPS:** n44,64944 e1,57061.⬆
free ⛽ Ch. **Location:** Rural, very simple. **Surface:** asphalted.
Distance: 🛒300m 💧on the spot.
Remarks: At supermarket Carrefour.

Labruguiere 29B4
Domaine d'en Laure, Rue du Parc du Montimont. **GPS:** n43,53139 e2,25528.⬆➡

10 free ⛽€ 2/10minutes 🔌Ch🚻€ 2/minutes. **Surface:** grassy. ◻ 01/01-31/12
Distance: 🛒1km 🏊on the spot 🛒on the spot ⊗1,3km 💧1,3km.

Lacapelle Marival 29A2
Place de la Roque. **GPS:** n44,72806 e1,92944.

50 free ⛽Ch ♨free. **Surface:** asphalted. ◻ service 15/05-30/09
Distance: ⊗100m 💧50m.
Remarks: Follow dir Aurillac, in centre, between PTT and castle.

Lacaune 29B4
Rue de la Balme. **GPS:** n43,70795 e2,69010.

20 free. **Surface:** gravel. ◻ 01/01-31/12
Distance: 🛒on the spot ⊗on the spot.

Tourist information Lacaune:
ℹ Office de Tourisme, Place du Général De Gaulle, www.lacaune.com.

Lacroix-Barrez 29B2
GPS: n44,77793 e2,63086.⬆
10 €2,50 + € 0,30 tourist tax ⛽🔌Chfree. **Surface:** grassy. ◻ 01/01-31/12 ◉ service: 01/11-17/04.
Distance: 🛒400m.

Laguepie 29A3
Quai de l'Aveyron. **GPS:** n44,14485 e1,97226.⬆➡

6 free ⛽🔌Chfree. **Surface:** asphalted. ◻ 01/01-31/12
Distance: 🛒200m ⊗200m 💧on the spot.

Laguiole 29C2
Rue de Lavernhe. **GPS:** n44,68408 e2,85048.⬆➡

10 ⌂free ⚲🗑 Ch free. **Surface:** gravel. ⬛ 01/01-31/12, service: 17/04-15/10
Distance: 🚲on the spot.

10 ⌂free ⚲🗑 Ch WC free. **Surface:** asphalted. ⬛ 01/01-31/12 📷 tue-evening, wed-morning.
Distance: 🚲500m ⊗on the spot 🛒on the spot.

🚻S	Laissac	29B3

Place du Foirail des Ovins, RN88. **GPS:** n44,38584 e2,28215. ⬆.

🚻S	Lauzerte	28D3

D2, Vignals. **GPS:** n44,26750 e1,14083. ⬆.

6 ⌂free ⚲🗑 Ch free. **Surface:** asphalted. ⬛ 01/03-30/11
Distance: 🚲500m ⊗500m 🛒500m.
Remarks: Max. 24h.

🚻S	Lanuéjouls	29B2

Aire Campingcar Lanuéjouls. **GPS:** n44,42528 e2,16139. ⬆➡.

20 ⌂free ⚲🗑 Ch WC free.
Surface: grassy/gravel. ⬛ 01/01-31/12
Distance: 🚲Lauzerte 2km ⊗on the spot 🛒2km.

Tourist information Lauzerte:
ℹ Office de Tourisme, Place des Cornières.Medieval town.
⛺ ⬛ Wed-morning.

🚻S	Le Fossat	28D5

Aire des Lallières, Place de la Mairie. **GPS:** n43,17201 e1,41170. ⬆➡.

14 ⌂€5 ⚲🗑 Ch ⚡ WC included. **Surface:** gravel. ⬛ 01/01-31/12
Distance: 🚲100m ⊗100m 🛒100m.
Remarks: Via D1.

🚻S	Latronquière	29B2

Place du 19 mars 1962. **GPS:** n44,79917 e2,07917. ⬆.

20 ⌂€ 6,50 ⚲🗑 Ch ⚡ WC included. **Surface:** gravel.

🚻S	Le Garric	29B3

Cap Découverte. **GPS:** n44,01361 e2,13778. ⬆.

4 ⌂free ⚲🗑 Ch ⚡ WC free. **Surface:** asphalted. ⬛ 01/01-31/12
Distance: 🚲300m 🏊3km 🚶3km ⊗300m 🛒300m.

🚻S	Lauzerte	28D3

1, Place du Foirail. **GPS:** n44,25471 e1,13762.

18 ⌂€ 8 ⚲🗑 Ch ⚡ included. **Surface:** asphalted. ⬛ 01/01-31/12
Distance: ⊗300m.

🍴🚻S	Le Houga	28C4

Ferme aux Cerfs, Route de Mont de Marsan, D6. **GPS:** n43,78430 e0,20997.

FR

15 ⬛free 🚰 ⬛ Ch free. **Surface:** grassy. ⬛ 01/01-31/12
Distance: 🛒2,5km ⊗on the spot.

| 🏕️S | Le Ségur | 29A3 |

Place de Marie. **GPS:** n44,10889 e2,05861. ⬆️➡️.

20 ⬛free 🚰 ⬛ WC free. **Surface:** gravel.
Distance: 🛒200m ⊗150m ⬛200m.

| 🏕️S | Loudenvielle 🏔️ | 28C5 |

GPS: n42,79633 e0,40743.

3 ⬛free 🚰 ⬛ Ch WC free. **Surface:** metalled. ⬛ 01/01-31/12
Distance: 🛒50m ⊗100m ⬛100m.

| 🏕️S | Les Cabannes | 29A6 |

Quartier la Bexane. **GPS:** n42,78493 e1,68301. ⬆️➡️.

200 ⬛free, € 3/ski season + Jul/Aug 🚰 ⬛ 2 ⬛ Ch ⬛ € 2. **Surface:** asphalted/grassy.

| 🏕️S | Lourdes | 28B5 |

Parking Arrouza, Esplanade du Paradis. **GPS:** n43,08911 w0,05378. ⬆️.

30 ⬛€ 4/24h 🚰 € 2/100liter ⬛ Ch WC. **Surface:** asphalted.

| 🏕️S | Lisle sur Tarn | 29A4 |

Aire de Bellevue. GPS: n43,86167 e1,81833. ⬆️➡️.

⬛free. **Surface:** asphalted.
Distance: 🛒city centre 1km.

Tourist information Lourdes:

ℹ️ Office de Tourisme, Place Peyramale, www.lourdes-infotourisme.com.Lively place of pilgrimage.

⛪ Basilique St.Pius X.Underground basilica, of the largest sanctuaries in the world, there is place for 25,000 people.

| 🏕️S | Luzech | 28D2 |

Les Berges de Caïx, D9. **GPS:** n44,49121 e1,29348.

12 ⬛free 🚰 ⬛ Ch. **Surface:** gravel. ⬛ 01/01-31/12
Distance: 🛒1,5km ⊘on the spot ⬛on the spot ⊗1,5km ⬛1,5km.

| 🏕️S | Lombez 🍽️ | 28D4 |

Route de Toulouse, D632. **GPS:** n43,47417 e0,91592. ➡️.

50 ⬛€ 7,50 🚰 ⬛ Ch 🧹 WC ⬛included. ⬛ 01/01-31/12
Distance: 🛒2km.
Remarks: Along Lot river, opening hours 9-21h.

| 🏕️ | L'Hospitalet-près-l'Andorre 🏔️ | 29A6 |

N22. **GPS:** n42,58823 e1,79833.

5 ⌂ free. **Surface:** asphalted.
Distance: ⊗100m.

| ⌂ | Marbre 🏔️👣 | 28C5 |

Lac de Payolle, D918, Campan > Col de Aspin. **GPS:** n42,93528 e0,29222.

⌂ free. **Surface:** grassy/gravel.
Distance: ◲40m. ◦40m.

| ⌂ S | Martel 🌿⚓ | 29A1 |

La Fontanel, Avenue de Nassogne. **GPS:** n44,93505 e1,60656. ⬆️

12 ⌂ free. ⌐ 🗑️ Ch. **Surface:** gravel. ◻ 01/01-31/12
Distance: 🚰250m ⊗250m 🛒250m.

| ⌂ S | Mazamet | 29B4 |

Rue du Champ de la Ville. **GPS:** n43,49083 e2,37944. ⬆️➡️

⌂ free ⌐ 🗑️ Ch free. **Surface:** asphalted. ◻ 01/01-31/12
Distance: 🚰300m ⊗500m 🛒300m.

| ⌂ S | Mazamet | 29B4 |

Soulever la Grille, Rue Galibert-Ferret, Champ de la Ville. **GPS:** n43,49089 e2,37918. ⬆️
10 ⌂ free ⌐ 🗑️ Ch free. **Surface:** asphalted. ◻ 01/01-31/12 ◉ Fri-Sa market.

Distance: 🚰on the spot ⊗on the spot.
Remarks: At townhall, max. 24h.

| ⌂ S | Mazères-sur-Salat | 28D5 |

Rue de Vieux Ruisseau. **GPS:** n43,13457 e0,97633. ⬆️

---

15 ⌂ free ⌐ 🗑️ Ch 📷 free. **Surface:** metalled. ◻ 01/01-31/12
Distance: 🚲4,5km ⌁river.

| ⌂ | Millau ⛱️🏔️🌊 | 29C3 |

Rue de la Saunerie 19. **GPS:** n44,09601 e3,08576. ⬆️

31 ⌂ free. **Surface:** gravel/metalled.
Distance: 🚰500m.

| S | Millau ⛱️🏔️🌊 | 29C3 |

Parking de la Grave, Rue Cantarane. **GPS:** n44,09531 e3,08306. ⬆️
⌐ € 6 🗑️ Ch.
◻ 01/01-31/12
Distance: 🚰on the spot ⊗on the spot.
Remarks: Closed when frosty.
Tourist information Millau:
ℹ️ Office de Tourisme, 1, Place du Beffroi, www.ot-millau.fr.City tourist in the Valley of the Tarn and the Dourbie. Important for the leather trade.
👁️ Grands Causses.Limestone plateaus with ravines.
⌂ La Graufesenque.Archeological findings, 1st century.
🚶 Vieux Millau.Historical hiking route, info at Office de Tourisme.

| ⌂ S | Mirandol-Bourgnounce | 29B3 |

Place de Foirail. GPS: n44,14167 e2,16667. ⬆️

8 ⌂ free ⌐ 🗑️ Ch WC free. **Surface:** asphalted. ◻ 01/01-31/12
Distance: 🚰on the spot ⊗on the spot 🛒50m.

| ⌂ S | Mirepoix | 29A5 |

Parking des Capitouls, Alée des Soupirs. **GPS:** n43,08500 e1,87444. ⬆️

20 ⌂ free ⌐ 🗑️ Ch WC free. ◻ 01/01-31/12

FR

Remarks: Next to community centre.

Tourist information Mirepoix:

🛈 Office de Tourisme, Hôtel-de-Ville, Place Maréchal Leclerc, www.ot-mirepoix. fr.Village with half-timbered houses and square with arcades.
🐄 Cattle market. ☀ winter 2nd, 4th Mo of the month.
🐄 🅾 Thu, Sa.

🚐S	Mont Roc 🚶🚶	29B4

Salle de Fêtes. **GPS:** n43,80330 e2,37192.⬆.

8 🛏free 🚰€ 2 ♨Ch⬛€ 2 WC. **Surface:** metalled. 🅾 01/01-31/12
Distance: 🚶50m ⊗on the spot 🛒on the spot.

🚐S	Montauban 🌿⬆	28D3

Mr. Lacaze, aire camping-car, 225, route de Corbarieu, D21. **GPS:** n43,99188 e1,35196.⬆.

15 🛏€6 🚰€ 2 ♨Ch ✎ WC⬛€ 1.
Surface: gravel. 🅾 01/01-31/12
Distance: 🚶Montauban 3km 🛒1km.
Remarks: Motorhomes < 3,5t.

Tourist information Montauban:

🛈 Office de Tourisme, 2, rue du Collège, officetourisme.montauban.com.City of roses.
🐄 🅾 Sa.

🚐S	Montcuq 🚶🚶	28D3

Route de Cahors, D653. **GPS:** n44,34082 e1,20242.

4 🛏free 🚰⬛♨Chfree. **Surface:** gravel. 🅾 01/01-31/12
Distance: 🚶100m⊗100m 🛒50m.

🚐S	Montet-et-Bouxal	29A2

D653, La Vittarelle. **GPS:** n44,74111 e2,01944.

5 🛏free 🚰⬛Ch ✎ WCfree. **Surface:** asphalted. 🅾 01/01-31/12
Remarks: In village behind petrol station.

🚐S	Montézic ⬆🚶🚶	29B2

Les Prades Sud. GPS: n44,71054 e2,64413.⬆.

4 🛏free 🚰⬛Chfree. **Surface:** asphalted. 🅾 01/03-31/10
Distance: 🚶500m ⊗on the spot 🛒on the spot.

🚐S	Montréal (Gers)	28C3

Stade André Daubin, D29. **GPS:** n43,95375 e0,19730.⬆.

🛏free 🚰⬛Chfree. **Surface:** gravel. 🅾 01/01-31/12
Distance: 🚶200m ⊗500m 🛒500m.
Remarks: Parking at rugby ground.

Tourist information Montréal (Gers):

🛈 Office de Tourisme, place de l'Hôtel de Ville, www.montrealdugers.com/. Fortified city with ramparts, square with arcades and picturesque alleys.

🚐S	Mur de Barrez ⬆🚶🚶	29B2

Parc de la Caurette, Place du Foirail. **GPS:** n44,84842 e2,65980.⬆.

15 🛏free 🚰€ 2 ♨Ch ✎.
Surface: gravel. 🅾 01/01-31/12
Distance: 🚶250m ⊗250m 🛒250m.
Remarks: Coins at Tourist Info and petrol station.

🚐S	Monteils	29A3

D47. **GPS:** n44,26694 e1,99667.⬆.

FR

⑃free ⟲◥Ch free. **Surface:** asphalted. ☐ 01/01-31/12
Distance: 100m ⊗on the spot ⛽50m.

| ⑃S | Nages | 29B4 |

Rieu Montagné, Lac du Laouzas, D162. **GPS:** n43,64694 e2,78194.

15 ⑃€6,10 ⟲◥Ch ▦included. ☐ 01/01-31/12
Remarks: Nearby base nautique, quiet place with view at the lake.

| ⑃S | Najac | 29A3 |

GPS: n44,22167 e1,96778. ⬆➡

10 ⑃free ⟲€ 2 ◥Ch ▦. **Surface:** asphalted. ☐ 01/01-31/12
Distance: 1,8km ⊘on the spot ⛽1,8km.

| ⑃S | Naucelle | 29B3 |

Place du Ségala. GPS: n44,19723 e2,34175. ⬆

4 ⑃free ⟲◥Ch free. **Surface:** asphalted. ☐ 01/01-31/12
Distance: on the spot ⊘500m 🛒500m.

| ⑃S | Naussac | 29A2 |

Aire de Loisirs de Peyrelevade. GPS: n44,52167 e2,07944. ⬆➡

10 ⑃€4 ⟲◥Ch WC included. **Surface:** gravel. ☐ 01/01-31/12
Remarks: Recreation area, follow aire de loisirs.

| ⑃S | Oust | 28D5 |

Aire camping-car, Foute d'Aulus les Bains. **GPS:** n42,87167 e1,21833. ➡

10 ⑃€ 10,50/night ⟲◥Ch € 5,60 WC. **Surface:** grassy. ☐ 01/04-30/09
Remarks: Next to campsite Les 4 Saisons.

| ⑃S | Peyrusse le Roc | 29B2 |

D87. **GPS:** n44,49500 e2,13972. ⬆➡

8 ⑃free ⟲◥Ch free. **Surface:** sand. ☐ 01/01-31/12
Distance: 500m ⊗500m ⛽500m.

| ⑃S | Pierrefitte-Nestalas | 28B5 |

Place Lamartine. **GPS:** n42,96037 w0,07743.

10 ⑃free ⟲◥Ch free. **Surface:** asphalted. ☐ 01/01-31/12
Distance: 200m ⊗200m ⛽200m.
Remarks: Max. 1 night.

| ⑃S | Pinsac | 29A2 |

Parking Salle des Fêtes, D43. **GPS:** n44,85500 e1,51222.

FR

5 ☕free ⚡€ 2 ⬛Ch⬛€ 2. **Surface:** gravel. ⬛ 01/01-31/12
Distance: ⬛on the spot ⚡9,5km ⬛700m.

4 ☕free ⚡⬛ Ch WC free. **Surface:** gravel. ⬛ 01/01-31/12 ⬛ 05/08-14/08.
Distance: ⬛250m ⊗300m ⬛300m.
Remarks: In front of town hall, upper city, max. 24h.

⬛S	Pont-de-Salars	29B3

Place de la Rivière. **GPS:** n44,27822 e2,72853. ·

⬛S	Puylaurens	29A4

Rue Albert Thorel. **GPS:** n43,56861 e2,01194. ⬆➡

5 ☕free ⚡€ 2 ⬛ Ch WC. **Surface:** asphalted. ⬛ 01/05-31/10
Distance: ⬛100m ⬛1km ⬛1km ⊗on the spot ⬛nearby.
Remarks: Along river, max. 3 days.

10 ☕free ⚡⬛ Ch ⚡ WC ⬛. **Surface:** gravel. ⬛ 01/01-31/12
Distance: ⬛700m ⊗700m ⬛400m.
Remarks: Wifi at supermarket.

⬛S	Prayssac ⬛	28D2

Avenue des Acacias. **GPS:** n44,50352 e1,19197.

⬛S	Requista ⬛	29B3

Place François Fablé. **GPS:** n44,03465 e2,53599. ⬆

10 ☕free ⚡⬛ Ch WC. **Surface:** grassy/gravel.

⬛S	Preignan	28C4

Rue Emile Zola. **GPS:** n43,71243 e0,63378. ➡

6 ☕free ⚡⬛free. **Surface:** gravel. ⬛ 01/01-31/12
Distance: ⬛200m.

⬛S	Revel	29A4

Chemin de la Pergue. **GPS:** n43,45444 e2,01528. ⬆➡

30 ☕free ⚡⬛ Ch free. **Surface:** gravel.
Distance: ⬛1km.
Remarks: At sports park.

⬛S	Puy l'Eveque	28D2

Place de la Gendarmerie. **GPS:** n44,50536 e1,13808. ⬆

☕€ 7,60, 2 pers.incl. ⚡€ 3 ⬛Ch ⚡€ 3. **Surface:** grassy. ⬛ 01/01-31/12.
Distance: ⬛1km ⊗1km ⬛1km.

⬛S	Rignac ⬛	29B3

Hameau du Lac, La Peyrade. **GPS:** n44,40456 e2,28958. ➡

FR

12 ⛺free 🚰 🖳 Ch. **Surface:** grassy. ⬛ 01/01-31/12
Distance: ⚓600m ⊗600m 🍺600m.

🏕🆂 Rocamadour — 29A2
D673. **GPS:** n44,80000 e1,61528.

30 ⛺free. **Surface:** gravel.
Distance: ⊗100m.

🏕🆂 Rodez — 29B3
Z.I. Cantaranne, Rue de Salelles. **GPS:** n44,35731 e2,59374.⬆.

6 ⛺free 🚰 🖳 Chfree. **Surface:** asphalted. ⬛ 01/01-31/12
Distance: ⚓1km.
Remarks: Max. 72h.

🏕 Rodez — 29B3
Parking du Foirail, Avenue Victor Hugo. **GPS:** n44,35143 e2,56822.
4 ⛺. ⬛ 01/01-31/12
Distance: ⚓on the spot.
Remarks: In front of Avenue Victor-Hugo.

Tourist information Rodez:
ℹ Office de Tourisme, Place Foch, www.ot-rodez.fr.Medieval city.

🏕🆂 Roquecor (◐) — 28D3
GPS: n44,32346 e0,94496.⬆.

6 ⛺free 🚰 🖳 Chfree. **Surface:** asphalted. ⬛ 01/01-31/12
Distance: ⚓250m 🍺250m.
Remarks: Max. 48h.

🏕🆂 Roquefort-sur-Soulzon — 29C3
D23. **GPS:** n43,98120 e2,98163.

⛺free 🚰 🖳 Ch WC free. **Surface:** asphalted. ⬛ 01/01-31/12
Distance: ⚓100m.
Remarks: Parking behind Office du Tourisme, no water during winter time.

🏕🆂 Saint-Antoine — 28D3
GPS: n44,03587 e0,84209.⬆➡.

10 ⛺free 🚰 🖳 Chfree. **Location:** Rural, very simple, quit. **Surface:** asphalted.
Distance: ⚓200m 🚤4,3km.

🏕🆂 Samatan 🌿⚓🍺🌳 — 28D4
Base de Loisirs, Avenue de Lombez et Barave, D39. **GPS:** n43,48791 e0,92616.➡.

10 ⛺€ 3,80/24h 🚰 🖳 Ch ✂ WC included.
Surface: asphalted.
⬛ 01/01-31/12
Distance: ⚓500m 🏊on the spot ⛟on the spot ⊗250m 🍺250m 🚐250m.

🏕🆂 Sarrant — 28D4
Route de Solomiac. **GPS:** n43,77532 e0,92822.➡.

100 ⛺free 🚰 🖳 Chfree. **Surface:** grassy/gravel. ⬛ 01/01-31/12
Distance: ⚓150m 🍺150m.
Remarks: In front of football stadium.

🏕🆂 Sauveterre-de-Rouergue — 29B3
Le Sardou. **GPS:** n44,21613 e2,31700.
10 ⛺free 🚰 🖳 Ch ✂ € 1,50 WC ◈€ 1,50. **Surface:** grassy. ⬛ 01/01-31/12

FR

Distance: 🏘on the spot 🍴on the spot 🛒on the spot.
Remarks: Parking at D997.

🚐[S] Ségur 29B3

GPS: n44,29087 e2,83503.[↑].
5 🚐free 🚰 🚽 Ch 🔌 WC 🚿€ 2. **Surface:** asphalted. 📅 01/01-31/12
Distance: 🏘500m 🛒on the spot.
Remarks: Covered picnic area with electricity. Parking at D29.

🍇[S] Senergues ⛰ 🌳 29B2

La Ferme des Autruches, La Besse. **GPS**: n44,58861 e2,48361.[↑].
5 🚐free 🚰 🚽 Chfree. **Surface:** grassy/gravel. 📅 01/03-30/11
Distance: 🏘2km.

🚐[S] Serres-sur-Arget 29A5

GPS: n42,96990 e1,51972.

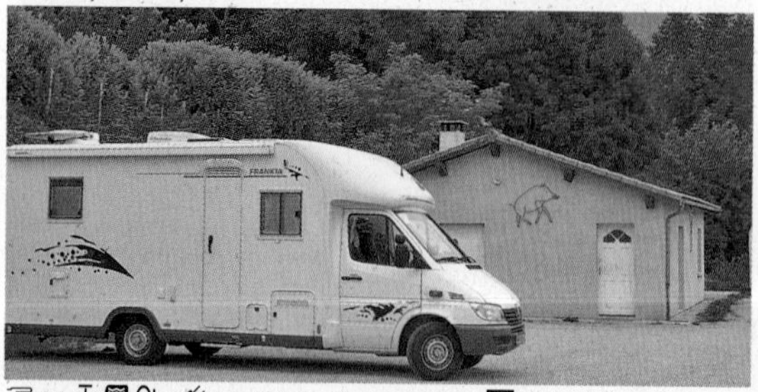

🚐€ 4 🚰 🚽 Ch 🔌included. **Surface:** metalled. 📅 01/01-31/12
Remarks: Next to community centre.

🚐[S] Souillac ⛱ 🌊 29A2

Parking de Baillot, Chemin de Baillot. **GPS**: n44,89139 e1,47667.[↑][→].

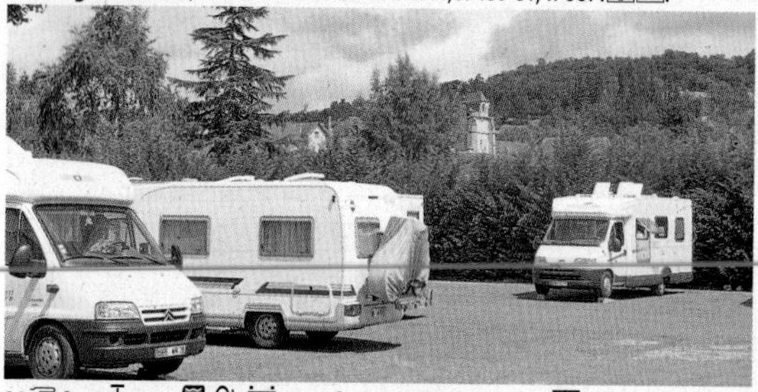

20 🚐free 🚰€ 3 🚽 Ch 🔌€ 3 🪙. **Surface:** asphalted. 📅 01/01-31/12
Distance: 🏘400m ⛽4,5km 🍴400m 🛒500m.

Tourist information Souillac:

[i] Bd Louis-Jean Malvy.Monastery-city, 12th century, between the regions Périgord and Quercy.

🚐[S] Soulom 28B5

Place des Fêtes, D921. **GPS**: n42,95611 w0,0725.

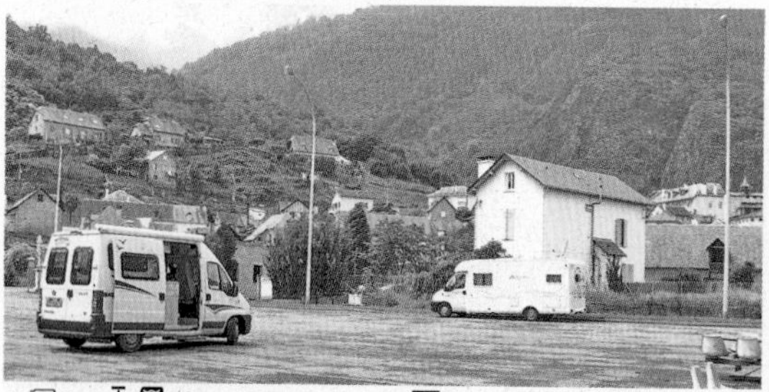

10 🚐free 🚰 🚽free. **Surface:** asphalted. 📅 01/01-31/12
Distance: 🏘200m 🏖500m 🍴200m 🛒200m.

🚐[S] Sousceyrac 🌊 ❄ 29A2

Place des Condamines. **GPS**: n44,87255 e2,03649.

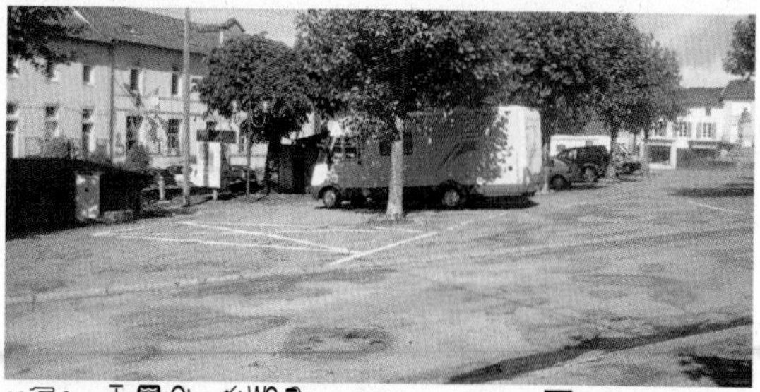

10 🚐free 🚰 🚽 Ch 🔌 WC 🚿free. **Surface:** asphalted. 📅 01/01-31/12
Distance: 🛒100m.
Remarks: Parking in front of town hall, max. 1 night.

🚐[S] St.Antonin Noble Val 29A3

Chemin de Roumégous. **GPS**: n44,15222 e1,75139.[↑][→].

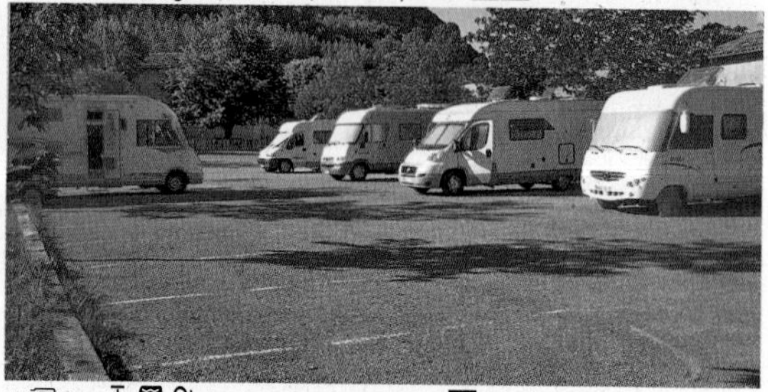

15 🚐free 🚰 🚽 Chfree. **Surface:** asphalted. 📅 01/01-31/12
Distance: 🏘200m 🍴300m 🛒100m.

🚐[S] St.Céré 29A2

D940. **GPS**: n44,86139 e1,88583.

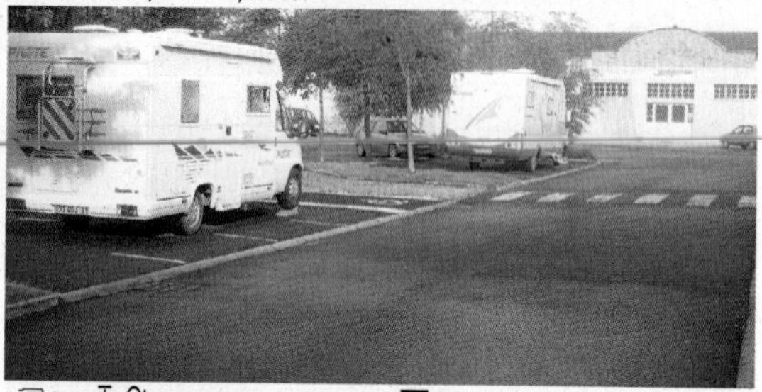

3 🚐free 🚰 Chfree. **Surface:** asphalted. 📅 01/01-31/12
Distance: 🏘200m 🍴200m 🛒150m.
Remarks: Behind stadium, nearby cemetery.

🚐[S] St.Cirque-Lapopie 🏞 ⛱ ⛰ 🌳 🌊 29A2

Porte Roques, halte nautique-plage, D662. **GPS**: n44,47055 e1,68050.[↑].

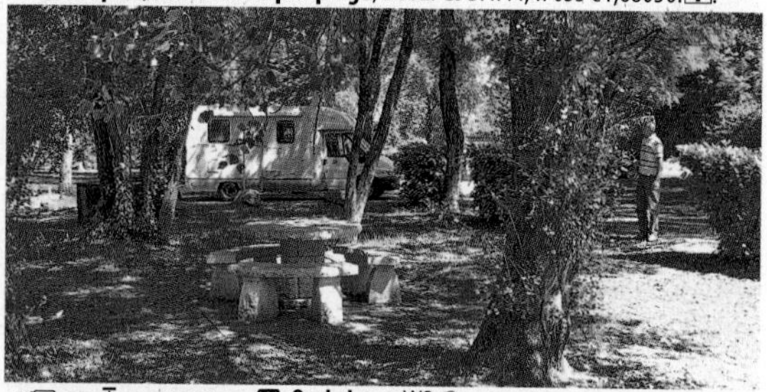

40 🚐€ 8 🚰€ 2/100liter 🚽 Ch 🔌€ 2 WC 🚿€ 2. **Surface:** grassy/gravel. 📅 01/01-31/12
Distance: 🏘1,5km 🏖on the spot 🍴50m.
Remarks: Along Lot River, nearby campsite de la Plage.

Tourist information St.Cirque-Lapopie:

[i] Village, entirely under preservation order, has been built on a rock above the river Lot.

[i] Cajarc.Village worth seeing with medieval houses.

⛰ Grotte de Pech-Merle, Cabrerets.Temple cave, monument from the Paleolithicum with images of mammoth, horses and bizons.

FR

⊞S St.Clar 28D3

Aire de repos, Route de Valence. **GPS:** n43,89111 e0,77250.

10 ⌂free ⌁ ⬡Ch WC ⌂free. **Surface:** gravel. ◻ 01/01-31/12
Distance: ⌂500m ⊗250m.

⊞S St.Felix-Lauragais 29A4

Lac de Lenclas, D622. **GPS:** n43,42667 e1,89806.

10 ⌂free ⌁ ⬡Ch WC. **Surface:** gravel. ◻ 01/01-31/12
Distance: ⌂nearby ⊗nearby.
Remarks: Max. 24h.

Tourist information St.Felix-Lauragais:
ℹ Office de Tourisme, Le Beffroi, place Philippe VI de Valois, Revel, www.revel-lauragais.com.
Ⓜ Musée Spéleologique du Grand Sud-Ouest, Revel.Speleology, the underground world. ◻ Tue-Sa 14-18h.

⊞S St.Geniez-d'Olt 29C2

Avenue de la gare. **GPS:** n44,46305 e2,97563. ⬆

10 ⌂free ⌁ ⬡Ch ⌁ WC free. **Surface:** gravel. ◻ 01/01-31/12
Distance: ⌂on the spot ⟵on the spot ⟵on the spot ⊗on the spot ⌂on the spot.
Remarks: Max. 24h.

Tourist information St.Geniez-d'Olt:
ℹ The river Lot seperates the old and new city.

⊞S St.Girons 28D5

Rue Aristide Berges. **GPS:** n42,98865 e1,13852. ⬆

7 ⌂free ⌁ Ch 3 ⬡Ch ✎. **Surface:** asphalted.
Distance: ⌂100m.

⊞S St.Jean et St.Paul 29C3

Saint Jean d'Alcas. **GPS:** n43,92646 e3,00887. →
⌂free ⌁ ⬡Ch WC free. **Surface:** gravel. ◻ 01/01-31/12
Distance: ⌂on the spot.

⊞S St.Just-sur-Viaur 29B3

Parking La Fabrie, D532. **GPS:** n44,12402 e2,37588. ⬆
5 ⌂free ⌁ ⬡Ch WC free. **Surface:** gravel. ◻ 01/04-30/11
Distance: ⌂100m ⌂on the spot.

⊞S St.Lary Soulan ⛵⛰❄ 28C5

Route de Vieille Aure. **GPS:** n42,82248 e0,32329. ⬆

10 ⌂€ 6/night ⌁€ 2 ⬡Ch ⊞€ 2. **Surface:** asphalted. ◻ 01/01-31/12
Distance: ⌂300m ⌂300m.
Remarks: Parking behind stadium.

Tourist information St.Lary Soulan:
ℹ Office de Tourisme, 37, rue Vincent Mir, www.saintlary.com.Mountain village in the Pyrenees with information centre of the Parc National des Pyrénées. Winter sports area with 100 km of skiruns.

⊞S St.Martory 28D5

Place Nationale, D52E, D117. **GPS:** n43,14141 e0,93033.

7 ⌂free ⌁ ⬡Ch WC free. **Surface:** asphalted.
Distance: ✎3km.
Remarks: Along the river, max. 1 night.

⊞ St.Maurice-en-Quercy 29A2

Place de l'église. **GPS:** n44,74306 e1,94722.

10 ⌂free. **Surface:** gravel. ◻ 01/01-31/12

⊞S St.Nicolas-de-la-Grave 28D3

Rue de la Calle. **GPS:** n44,06379 e1,02471. →

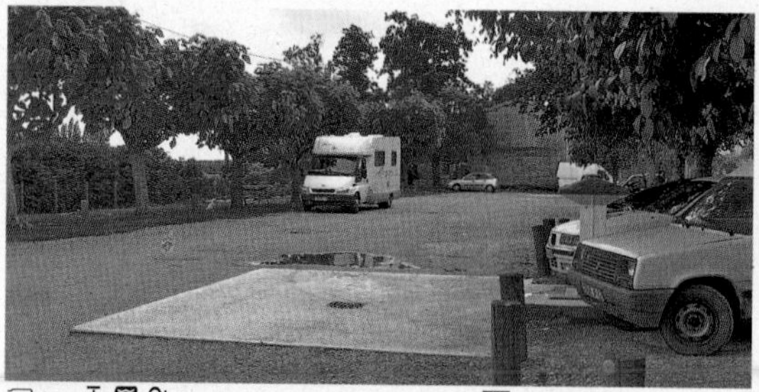

🚐free 🚰 🕳 Chfree. **Surface:** asphalted/gravel. ■ 01/01-31/12
Distance: 🏘100m 🏊50m 🍴100m.

🚐 [S] St.Puy 28C3

Grande Rue, D654. **GPS:** n43,87611 e0,46250.[↑].

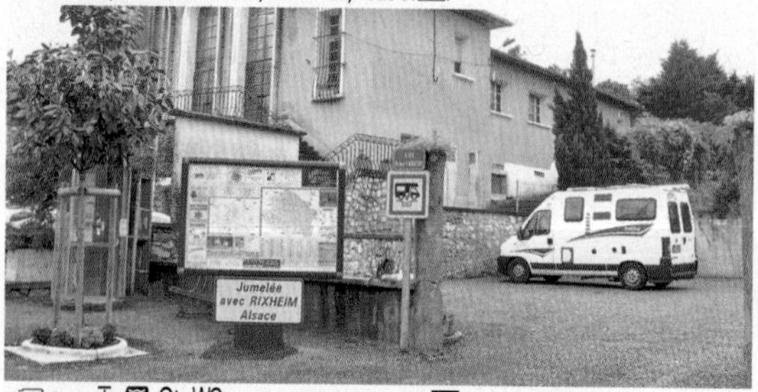

3 🚐free 🚰 🕳 Ch WC free. **Surface:** gravel. ■ 01/01-31/12
Distance: 🏘20m 🍴50m 🛒20m.

🚐 [S] St.Sulpice-sur-Lèze 28D4

Stade Municipal. **GPS:** n43,32924 e1,32944.[↑].

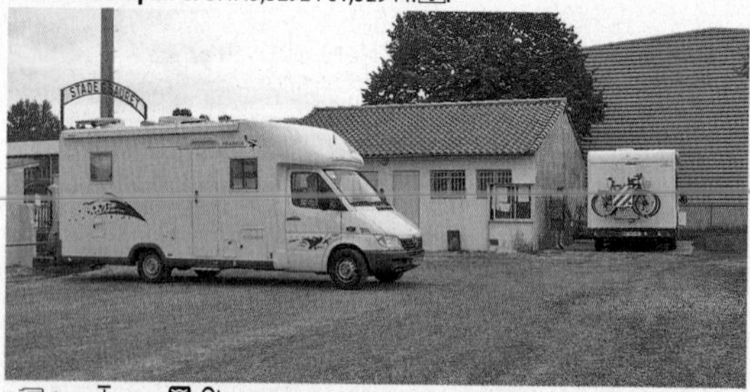

5 🚐free 🚰€ 2 🕳 Ch. **Surface:** gravel.

🍇 [S] St.Thomas 28D4

Ferme Le Gros, D58. **GPS:** n43,50190 e1,07451.[↑][→].
10 🚐€ 3 🚰 🕳 Ch 🔌 included. **Surface:** grassy/gravel.
Distance: 🏘2km.

🚐 [S] Ste.Croix-Volvestre 28D5

GPS: n43,12673 e1,17094.

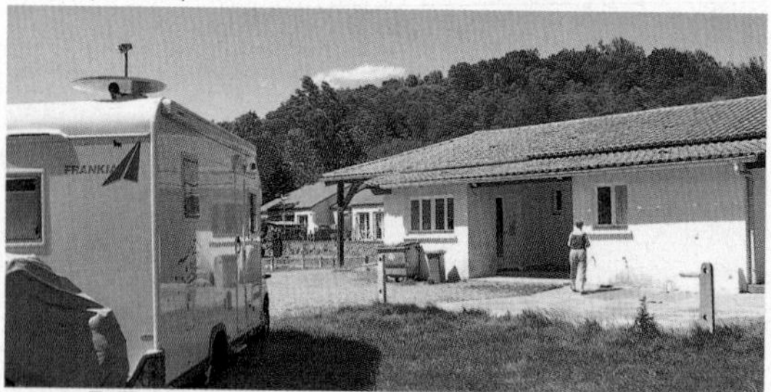

🚐free 🚰 🕳 Chfree. **Surface:** grassy/gravel. ■ 01/01-31/12
Remarks: Sports park, parking village square nearby lake.

🚐 [S] Ste.Geneviève-sur-Argence 29B2

Rue de l'Argence. **GPS:** n44,80194 e2,76222.

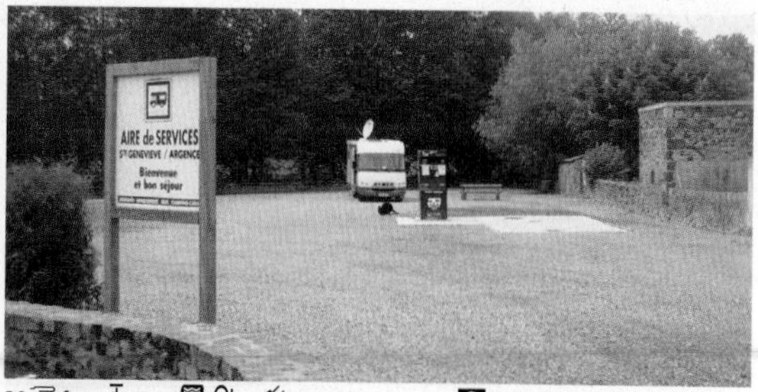

20 🚐free 🚰€ 1 🕳 Ch 🔌. **Surface:** gravel. ■ 01/01-31/12
Distance: 🏘300m 🏊500m 🐟500m 🍴300m 🛒300m.
Remarks: On entering the village.

🚐 [S] Tarbes ⛰ 28C5

Avenue de la Libération. **GPS:** n43,24316 e0,06785.[↑][→].

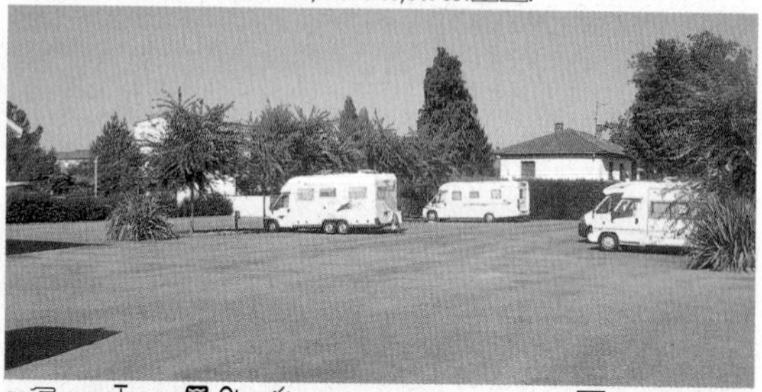

38 🚐€ 10 🚰€ 2 🕳 Ch 🔌 included. **Surface:** asphalted. ■ 01/01-31/12
Distance: 🏘500m 🍴500m 🛒500m.
Remarks: Service only € 2, water + electricity € 5.

🚐 [S] Thémines 29A2

Place de L'église. **GPS:** n44,74083 e1,82972.

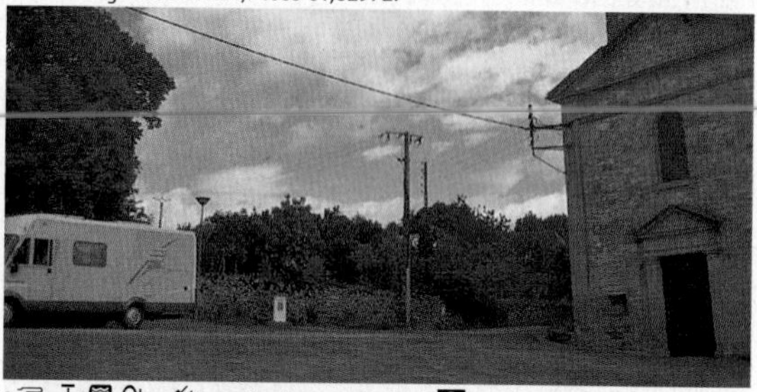

3 🚐 🚰 🕳 Ch 🔌 free. **Surface:** asphalted. ■ 01/01-31/12
Distance: 🏘on the spot 🍴100m 🛒100m.
Remarks: Nearby church.

🚐 [S] Therondels 🌳 ⛰ 🍴 29B2

GPS: n44,89474 e2,75807.[↑].
20 🚐free 🚰 🕳 Chfree. **Surface:** grassy. ■ 01/04-15/11
Distance: 🏘on the spot 🍴100m ◙100m.

🚐 [S] Vabres-l'Abbaye 29B3

Le Coustel, D999. **GPS:** n43,94575 e2,83779.[↑].
🚐free 🚰 🕳 Chfree. **Surface:** gravel. ■ 01/04-30/10
Distance: 🏘50m 🏊on the spot.
Remarks: 4Km from S. Affrique, near bridge.

🚐 Valcabrère 28C5

Parc de la Basilique Saint Just. **GPS:** n43,02812 e0,58370.
🚐free. **Surface:** asphalted. ■ 01/01-31/12
Remarks: Nearby Saint Bertrand de Comminges.

🚐 [S] Valderiés 29B3

Place de Mairie, D91. **GPS:** n44,01167 e2,23333.[↑].

5 ⌂free ⌐ Ch WC. **Surface:** asphalted. ▢ 01/01-31/12
Distance: ⚓on the spot ⊗on the spot ⚑on the spot.
Remarks: Weighbridge.

⌂⌂ S Valence (Tarn-et-Garonne) ⚘ 28D3
M. Cadot, aire privée, 341, Route des Charretiers, Valence-sud. **GPS:** n44,09907 e0,89013.
8 ⌂€8 ⌐ Chfree. **Surface:** gravel. ▢ 01/01-31/12
Remarks: Max. 24h. Dir campsite municipal, 500m before campsite.

⌂⌂ S Valence-sur-Baïse 28C3
Route d'Auch, D930. **GPS:** n43,87220 e0,38807.⬆.

7 ⌂free ⌐ Ch WC free. **Surface:** gravel. ▢ 01/01-31/12
Distance: ⚓500m ⊗500m ⚑500m ▭on the spot.
Remarks: On entering village from dir Auch, nearby police station.

Tourist information Valence-sur-Baïse:
🛈 Syndicat d'Initiative, Rue Jules Ferry. Fortified city, 13th century, with cistercian abbey of Flaran.

⌂⌂ S Vénerque 29A4
Allée du Duc de Ventadour. **GPS:** n43,43356 e1,44021.⬆.

10 ⌂free ⌐ Ch ▦free. **Surface:** metalled.
Distance: ⚓on the spot.

⌂⌂ S Vers ⚘ ⚘ ⚘ 29A2
Halte Nautique. GPS: n44,48551 e1,55503.

20 ⌂€5 ⌐ Ch WC ⌂free. **Surface:** grassy. ▢ 01/05-30/09
Distance: ⚓100m ⚓100m ⊗200m ⚑100m.

⌂⌂ S Vic-en-Bigorre 28C4
Rue du Stade, Avenue de Pau D6. **GPS:** n43,38472 e0,04917.⬆➡.

4 ⌂free ⌐ Chfree. **Surface:** grassy. ▢ 01/01-31/12
Distance: ⚓500m ⊗1km ⚑1km.

⌂⌂ S Vicdessos 29A6
GPS: n42,76891 e1,50257.

20 ⌂€6 ⌐ Ch ⚘included. **Surface:** metalled. ▢ 01/01-31/12
Distance: ⚓on the spot.

⌂⌂ S Villefranche-de-Rouergue 29A3
Parking des Ruelles, Boulevard de Gaulle. **GPS:** n44,35111 e2,03333.⬆.

3 ⌂free. **Surface:** asphalted. ▢ 01/01-31/12
Distance: ⚓100m ⊗100m ⚑100m.

⌂⌂ S Villefranche-de-Rouergue 29A3
Quai du Temple. **GPS:** n44,34937 e2,03917.⬆.

2 ⌂free. **Surface:** asphalted. ▢ 01/01-31/12
Distance: ⚓300m ⊗200m ⚑300m.
Remarks: At quay in front of the old bridge.

Tourist information Villefranche-de-Rouergue:
🛈 Maison de Tourisme, Promenade du Guiraudet, www.villefranche.com.
⚐ place Notre Dame. ▢ Thu.

⌂⌂ S Villeneuve (Aveyron) 29A2
Place du sol de la Dime. **GPS:** n44,43855 e2,03269.⬆.

FR

13 ⌛free 🚰 ⌛Ch WC free. **Surface:** asphalted. ⬛ 01/01-31/12
Distance: 🚶100m ⊗100m 🛒100m.

100 ⌛€ 1,60/h, max. € 9,40/24h WC. **Surface:** metalled.
Distance: 🚶100m.

Andorra

<table>
<tr><td>🅢S</td><td>Pas de la Casa</td><td>29A6</td></tr>
</table>

GPS: n42,54468 e1,73525.
⌛20-9h € 1 🚰. **Surface:** metalled.

<table>
<tr><td>🅢S</td><td>Aigues-Mortes 〰⚓</td><td>29D4</td></tr>
</table>

Rue du Port. **GPS:** n43,56631 e4,18575.[↑].

Languedoc Roussillon

<table>
<tr><td>🅢S</td><td>Agde 〰⚓</td><td>29C5</td></tr>
</table>

Les Peupliers. **GPS:** n43,29846 e3,45194.[↑][→].

30 ⌛€ 8, Jul/Aug € 10 🚰⌛Ch 🧹(30x)€ 2 📶. **Surface:** gravel/
metalled. ⬛ 03/04-14/11
Distance: 🚶2km ⚓1,7km 🛒on the spot.

50 ⌛01/10-14/03 € 7, 15/03-30/09 € 12 🚰⌛Ch free.
Surface: metalled.
Distance: 🚶600m.

Tourist information Aigues-Mortes:
ℹ Office de Tourisme, Place Saint Louis, www.ot-aiguesmortes.fr.Medieval
fortress, 13th century, in the swamp of the Camargue, tourist attraction.
🚾 free.
👁 La Tour Carbonnière, Place Saint Louis.Tower, guard-post for the defence of
the city.

Tourist information Agde:
ℹ Office de Tourisme, Cap d'Agde.Modern lively seaside resort with marina and
recreation island.
ℹ Office de Tourisme, Espace Molière, 1, place Molière.Pleasant tourist city with
medieval centre, Vieux Cité.
✝ Cathédrale Ste Étienne.Romanesque fortified cathedral, 12th century.

<table>
<tr><td>🅢S</td><td>Alzonne 〰</td><td>29B5</td></tr>
</table>

La Pujade, Route de Montolieu. **GPS:** n43,25412 e2,17745.[↑][→].

<table>
<tr><td>🅢S</td><td>Aigues-Mortes 〰⚓</td><td>29D4</td></tr>
</table>

Les Poissons d'Argent, CD62. **GPS:** n43,56476 e4,16289.[↑].

8 ⌛€ 8/24h 🚰⌛Ch 🧹€ 3 WC 🚻 Use sanitary € 3/pp per day. **Surface:**
grassy. ⬛ 01/01-31/12
Distance: 🚶1,5km ⊗1,5km 🛒1,5km.

<table>
<tr><td>🅢S</td><td>Amélie-les-Bains-Palalda 〰</td><td>29B6</td></tr>
</table>

GPS: n42,48063 e2,67951.
40 ⌛free 🚰€ 3 ⌛Ch. **Surface:** gravel. ⬛ 01/01-31/12
Remarks: Behind hotel du Lion D'Or.

80 ⌛€ 8/24h 🚰€ 2 ⌛Ch 🧹€ 3/24h, 5Amp. **Surface:** gravel.
Distance: 🚶2,5km ⚓3km 🛒on the spot ⊗on the spot 🛒1,5km Lidl.
Remarks: To fish lake.

<table>
<tr><td>🅒S</td><td>Amélie-les-Bains-Palalda 〰</td><td>29B6</td></tr>
</table>

Camping municipal, Avenue Beau Soleil, D115. **GPS:** n42,48035 e2,67847.[↑][→].

<table>
<tr><td>🅢S</td><td>Aigues-Mortes 〰⚓</td><td>29D4</td></tr>
</table>

P4, Boulevard Diderot. **GPS:** n43,56580 e4,19575.[↑][→].

5 ⌛free 🚰€ 3 ⌛Ch. **Surface:** grassy/gravel. ⬛ 01/01-31/12

FR

Distance: on the spot.
Remarks: Max. 48h.

Anduze 29D3
Place de la Gare. **GPS:** n44,05000 e3,98444.

20 free € 2 Ch € 2. **Surface:** asphalted. 01/01-31/12
Distance: on the spot.
Remarks: Max. 48h.

Anduze 29D3
Camping l'Arche. GPS: n44,06889 e3,97282.

5 € 12/night Ch WC included, sanitary at campsite.
Surface: asphalted.
01/04-31/09
Distance: 3km on the spot on the spot 100m.

Tourist information Anduze:
Office de Tourisme, Plan de Brie, www.ot-anduze.fr.Historical city, gate to the Cévennes.
Bamboosserie de Prafrance.Bamboo garden laid out in 1835, with a large variety of bamboo species. 01/03-15/11.
Train Touristique.Tourist train from Anduze to St. Jean-du-Gard. € 6,50.

Aniane 29C4
Le Pont du Diable. GPS: n43,70270 e3,55988.

€ 4/day, € 14/24h € 3 Ch . **Location:** Rural, isolated.
Surface: gravel. 01/01-31/12
Distance: 9km.
Remarks: Max. 48h, Pont du Diable 600m, St.Guilhem-le-Désert 4km, free shuttlebus Mai-Sept: weekend (11-19h), July-Aug daily (10-23h).

Aniane 29C4
Boulevard Saint-Jean. **GPS:** n43,68550 e3,58500.

+10 free. **Surface:** gravel. 01/01-31/12
Distance: 300m nearby 300m 300m.

Arre 29C3
D999. **GPS:** n43,96771 e3,52139.
free € 2/100liter Ch. **Location:** Rural. **Surface:** metalled.
Distance: on the spot bakery 50m.

Avèze 29C3
Aire du pont vieux, D999. **GPS:** n43,97517 e3,59899.
free € 2/100liter Ch € 2/1h. **Location:** Rural, comfortable.
Surface: metalled.
Remarks: Nearby sports park.

Bagnols-sur-Cèze 30A3
Av. de l Europe, D8086. **GPS:** n44,16820 e4,61958.

20 free Ch against payment. **Surface:** gravel.
Distance: 200m 200m 200m.
Remarks: Max. 24h.

Balaruc-les-Bains 29D4
Thermes Hespérides, Avenue des Hespérides. **GPS:** n43,44574 e3,67770.

30 € 7 Ch WC included. **Surface:** asphalted.
Distance: 1km.

Beaucaire 30A4
Les Marguilliers, Chemin des Marguilliers. **GPS:** n43,81667 e4,64107.

5 € 10/24h € 2 Ch € 2 included. **Surface:** gravel. 01/01-31/12
Distance: 500m 500m 500m 500m.

⅀Ⓢ **Bédarieux** 29C4
Avenue Jean Moulin. **GPS**: n43,61071 e3,15329.
10 ⅀€ 5/24h, € 8/48h ⌁€ 2 ⬛Ch.
Distance: ⌁on the spot.
Remarks: Along the Orb river.

⅀Ⓢ **Bélesta** 🌿⛰ 29B6
Rue des Loisirs. **GPS**: n42,71545 e2,60918.⬆

10 ⅀free ⌁ 2 ⬛Ch ⌁€ 1. **Surface:** grassy/gravel. ⬛ 01/04-31/10
Distance: ⌁100m.

⅀Ⓢ **Belpech** 29A5
Stade municipal, Rue du Stade. **GPS**: n43,19717 e1,75278.

15 ⅀free ⌁⬛Ch ⌁free WC. **Surface:** grassy. ⬛ 01/01-31/12
Distance: ⌁1km ⊗1km ⬛1km.

⅀Ⓢ **Cabanes de Fleury** 🚣 29C5
GPS: n43,21529 e3,23315.⬆

30 ⅀€ 5 ⌁⬛Ch ⌁included. **Surface:** metalled/sand. ⬛ 01/01-31/12
Distance: ⌁on the spot ⌁on the spot.
Remarks: Next to campsite municipal Rive d'Aude, max. 48h.

⅀Ⓢ **Carcassonne** 🌿⛰ 29B5
Parking Cité, P2. GPS: n43,20534 e2,37189.

⅀free from 20-08h. **Surface:** asphalted.
Distance: ⌁5km.

Ⓟ **Carcassonne** 🌿⛰ 29B5
Place Gaston-Jourdanne. **GPS**: n43,21000 e2,36028.

20 ⅀free.
Surface: asphalted/metalled.
Distance: ⌁900m.

Tourist information Carcassonne:
ℹ Office de Tourisme, 15, Boulevard Camille Pelletan, www.carcassonne-tourisme.com.Medieval fortified city, museum city with many curiosities.
🛍 The new city has a modern shopping centre.

⅀Ⓢ **Carnon** 29D4
Avenue Grassion Cibrand, Carnon-plage. **GPS**: n43,55097 e3,99417.⬆

15 ⅀€ 11 ⌁⬛Ch ⌁ WC on camp site ⬛€ 5. **Surface:** asphalted. ⬛ 01/06-15/09
Distance: ⌁1km ⊘80m ⬛50m.
Remarks: Next to campsite Les Saladelles.

⅀Ⓢ **Casteil** 29B6
D116. **GPS**: n42,53324 e2,39230.⬆

5 ⅀free. **Surface:** grassy/gravel. ⬛ 01/04-31/10
Distance: ⌁1km.

⅀Ⓢ **Chusclan** 30A3
Cave Chusclan, Route d'Orsan, D138. **GPS**: n44,14552 e4,67762.⬆

6 ⅀free ⌁⬛Chfree. ⬛ 01/01-31/12
Distance: ⊗500m ⬛500m.
Remarks: Max. 48h.

⅀Ⓢ **Clermont-l'Hérault** 29C4
GPS: n43,64694 e3,39000.⬆

8 ⌁€5 ⚡ 2 Ch. **Surface:** gravel. ◻ 01/01-31/12
Distance: ⬇7km ⬇on the spot.
Remarks: Next to campsite Campisol, at lake of Salagou, coins available at campsite.

Tourist information Clermont-l'Hérault:
ℹ Office de Tourisme, 9, Rue René Gosse.Medieval city on artificially lake, Lac de Salagou, 750ha.

| ⌁S | Collioure 🏖⚓🏰🐚 | 29C6 |
Route de Madeloc. **GPS:** n42,52566 e3,06861.⬆.

80 ⌁€10 ⚡ Ch ⚡ WC included. **Surface:** asphalted. ◻ 01/05-31/10
Distance: ⬇1km ⬇2,3km.

Tourist information Collioure:
ℹ Office de Tourisme, Place du 18 Juin, www.collioure.com.Seaside resort and Catalonian harbour, source of inspiration for many famous painters: Picasso, Juan Gris, Derain and Duffy.
👁 Quartier de Moure.District with small blank paved alleys.
✠ Château Royal.Castle of the Templars, 12th century.

| ⌁S | Comps | 30A4 |
Place des Arènes. **GPS:** n43,85402 e4,60724.⬆.

50 ⌁€2 ⚡ 2/10minutes ⚡Ch ◼€ 2/55minutes ⚡.🚗 **Location:** Rural, quit. **Surface:** unpaved. ◻ 01/01-31/12

| ⌁S | Duilhac-sous-Peyrepertuse | 29B5 |
GPS: n42,86160 e2,56527.⬆.

25 ⌁free ⚡ 2 ⚡Ch ◼€ 2 WC. **Surface:** asphalted. ◻ 01/04-31/10

Distance: ⬇200m ⊗200m.

| ⌁S | Fanjeaux | 29A5 |
Chemin des Fontanelles. **GPS:** n43,18611 e2,03222.⬆➡.

15 ⌁free ⚡ ⚡Ch ⚡ free. **Surface:** grassy/gravel. ◻ 01/01-31/12
Distance: ⬇100m.
Remarks: Next to maison de retraite (home for the elderly), max. 48h.

| ⌁S | Félines-Termenès | 29B5 |
Av. de Termenes, dir Mouthoumet. **GPS:** n42,98691 e2,61285.

3 ⌁free ⚡ ⚡Ch ⚡ free. **Surface:** gravel. ◻ 01/01-31/12
Distance: ⬇50m.
Remarks: Closed when frosty.

Tourist information Félines-Termenès:
👁 Cité Médiéval, Villerouge Termenes.Medieval village and castle from 12-14th century. ◻ 01/07-30/09.

| ⌁S | Florac 🌿 | 29C3 |
D16. **GPS:** n44,32582 e3,59032.

23 ⌁free ⚡ 2 ⚡Ch ◼€ 2. **Surface:** asphalted. ◻ 01/01-31/12
Distance: ⬇150m ⊗150m ⚓150m.
Remarks: Nearby cemetery.

Tourist information Florac:
ℹ Office de Tourisme, Av J. Monestier, www.mescevennes.com.Old town in the National Park of the Cévennes.
✠ Château de Florac. ◻ 01/01-31/12.

| ⌁S | Fonties d'Aude | 29B5 |
Rue de Matet, D3. **GPS:** n43,18595 e2,45263.⬆.

FR

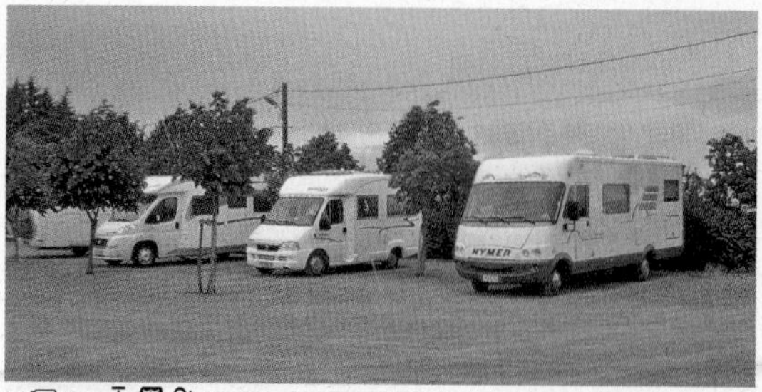

10 free Chfree. **Surface:** gravel.
Distance: 350m 6km bakery 25m.
Remarks: Max. 48h.

S Fraïsse-sur-Agout 29B4

Allée des Tilleuls. **GPS:** n43,60583 e2,79778.

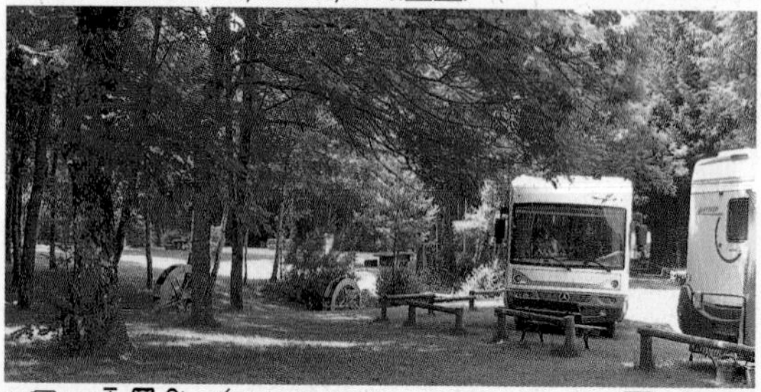

15 € 6 Ch (1x)included. **Surface:** asphalted/grassy. 01/01-31/12
Distance: 400m 20m 20m 400m.
Remarks: At the edge of village, on the Agout river.

S Gruissan 29C5

Aire des 4 Vents, Port sud, Quai deTramontane. **GPS:** n43,10444 e3,09944.

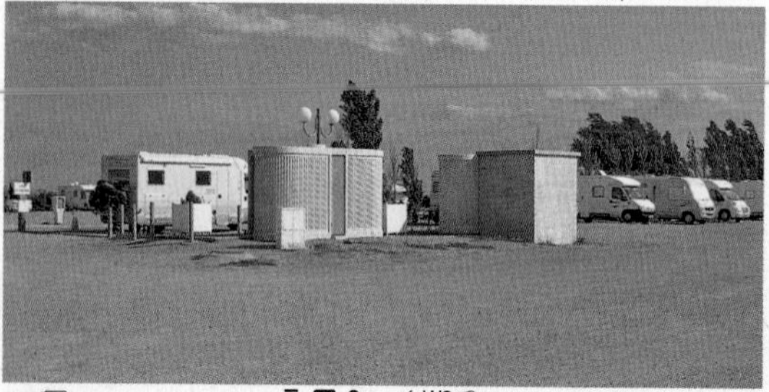

150 free, 01/03-30/11 € 8 Ch WC included. **Surface:** gravel.
01/01-31/12
Distance: on the spot on the spot on the spot on the spot on the spot.
Remarks: Next to the Gendarmerie Maritim, follow signs Gruissan Yacht Club.

S Gruissan 29C5

Étang de Mateille, Gruissan dir Narbonne-Plage, base de voile, D332. **GPS:** n43,12083 e3,11417.

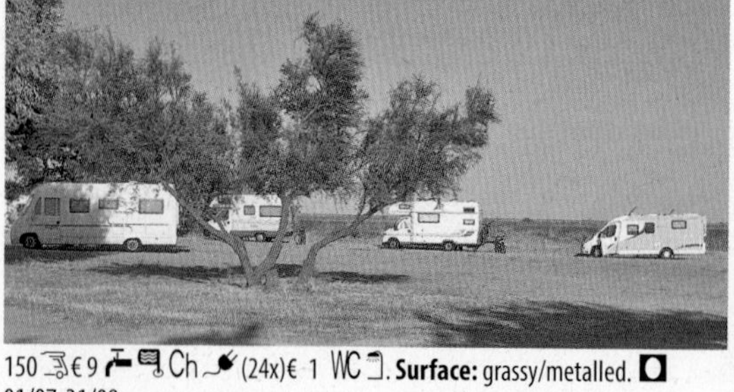

150 € 9 Ch (24x)€ 1 WC . **Surface:** grassy/metalled. 01/07-31/08
Distance: 4km on the spot on the spot 800m Lidl 2km.

S Gruissan 29C5

Plage des Châlets, Avenue de la Jetée, Gruissan-plage. **GPS:** n43,09583 e3,11111.

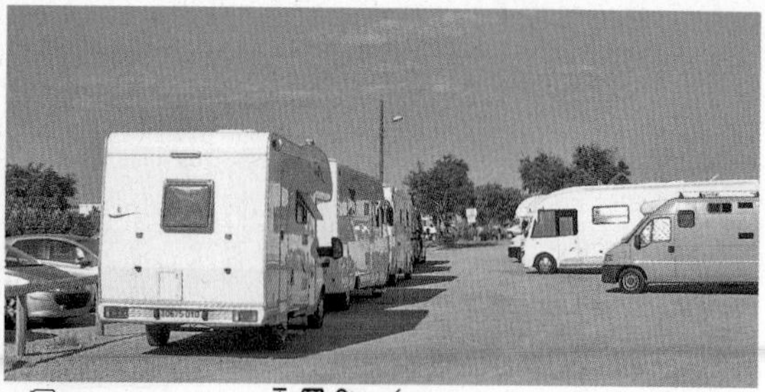

80 free, 01/03-30/11 € 8 Ch included.
Surface: gravel.
01/01-31/12
Distance: 2km on the spot on the spot 2km 2km.
Remarks: Next to Résidence Tahiti and Base de Voile.

Tourist information Gruissan:

Office de Tourisme, 1, boulevard du Pech-Maynaud, www.ville-gruissan.fr.Bathing resort and old town on the slope of the Clape.

L'Hospitalet.Probably the largest wine-cellar of the world.

Vieux Port.Old fishing-port.

S Ispagnac 29C3

Le Pavillon, D907. **GPS:** n44,37077 e3,53687.

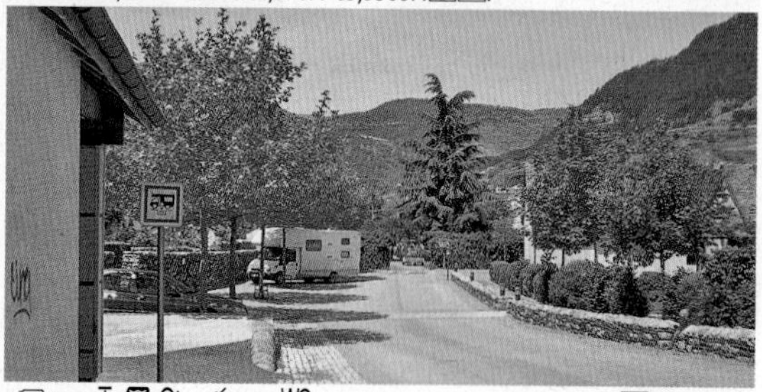

6 free Ch € 2 WCfree. **Surface:** asphalted/gravel. 01/04-31/10
Distance: 100m 100m 100m.
Remarks: Behind Office de Tourisme, coins at Office de Tourisme (electricity).

S La Grande Motte 29D4

Aire camping-car Les Cigales, Avenue de la Petite Motte. **GPS:** n43,56789 e4,07404.

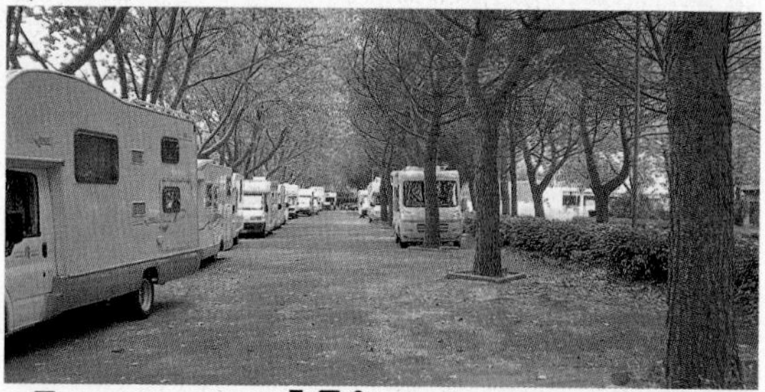

40 € 13, € 15 01/05-30/09 Ch. **Surface:** asphalted. 01/01-31/12
Distance: 2km 1,2km 2km 2km.

S Lagrasse 29B5

Parking de la Promenade, D3. **GPS:** n43,09273 e2,62004.

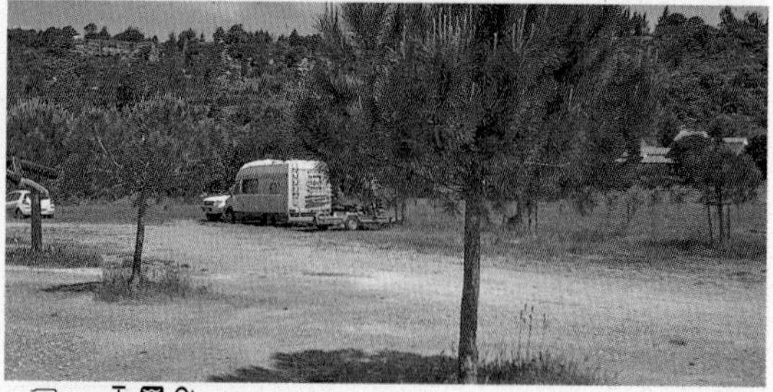

40 free Chfree.

Surface: gravel. ☐ 01/01-31/12 ◉ Market day.
Distance: on the spot on the spot on the spot ⊗on the spot on the spot.

🏕🅂 Langogne 🚣 29D2

Parking Base Nautique l'Espace Bleu. GPS: n44,73598 e3,83489.

50 €5 € 3 Ch. **Surface:** unpaved. ☐ 01/04-31/10
Distance: 2km.
Remarks: At lake Naussac.

Tourist information Langogne:
ℹ️ Office de Tourisme, 15, Bd des Capucins, www.langogne.com.

🏕🅂 Lapradelle Puilaurens 29B6

D117. **GPS:** n42,81003 e2,30854. ⬆️.

6 free Chfree. **Surface:** gravel.
Distance: on the spot ⊗on the spot on the spot.
Remarks: At fire-station.

🏕🅂 Latour-Bas-Elne 29C6

Aire de Latour Bas Elne, Route de la Mer. **GPS:** n42,60017 e3,00667. ⬆️➡️.

42 € 10/night Ch included.
Surface: grassy. ☐ 01/04-31/10
Distance: 3km.
Remarks: Monitored parking.

🏕🅂 Latour-de-Carol 29A6

Village Club Yravals, 2 Rue de Saneja. **GPS:** n42,45829 e1,89460. ⬆️.

5 €5 Ch WCincluded € 2/day. **Surface:** grassy. ☐ 01/04-31/10

Distance: 2km.

🏕🅂 Laudun 30A3

Place des Arènes. **GPS:** n44,10791 e4,65556. ⬆️.

3 free € 4 Ch. **Surface:** asphalted. ☐ 01/01-31/12
Distance: 300m ⊗300m 300m.

🏕🅂 Le Boulou 29B6

Chemin du Moulin Nou. **GPS:** n42,52719 e2,83704. ⬆️➡️.

21 free ChWCfree. **Surface:** asphalted. ☐ 01/01-31/12
Remarks: In front of cemetery, max. 24h.

🏕🅂 Le Cap d'Agde 29C5

Rue du Gouverneur. **GPS:** n43,28600 e3,51739. ⬆️➡️.

30 € 10 Ch included. **Surface:** asphalted/metalled.
Distance: on the spot 500m ⊗500m 500m.
Remarks: Near campsite la Clape.

🏕🅂 Le Monastir 29C2

GPS: n44,50896 e3,25162. ⬆️➡️.

4 free € 2,50 Ch WC.
Surface: asphalted. ☐ 01/01-31/12
Distance: 1km 1,5km 1km.
Remarks: Coins at petrol station, picnic area present. Motorhome parking, A75 Clermont Ferrand-Millau exit 39, 10km south of Marvejols.

🏕🅂 Le Ségala 29A4

Esplanade du Canal. **GPS:** n43,34089 e1,83544.

10 🛏free ⚡€ 1 🔌Ch 💧€ 2 WC. **Surface:** gravel. ⬛ 01/01-31/12
Distance: 🛒on the spot 🏊on the spot ⊗on the spot.
🏧S **Les Angles** 🏔🏕 **29A6**
Pla del Mir. GPS: n42,56365 e2,06599.⬆.

100 🛏free ⚡🔌Ch WC free. **Surface:** asphalted. ⬛ 01/01-31/12
Distance: 🛒2,6km.
🏧 **Les Mages** **29D3**
D904, St. Ambroix/Alés. GPS: n44,23444 e4,16936.⬆.

15 🛏free ⚡🔌Ch💧free. ⬛ 01/01-31/12
Remarks: Picnic area.
🏧 **Leucate** 🏔🏖 **29C5**
Aire camping-car, Chemin du Mouret, Leucate Plage. **GPS:** n42,90022 e3,05272.
⬆.

100 🛏€ 6,50 ⚡€ 2,50 🔌Ch. **Surface:** asphalted/gravel. ⬛ 01/01-31/12
Distance: 🛒300m 🏊on the spot 🛒on the spot.
Remarks: Beach parking.
🏧S **Leucate** 🏔🏖 **29C5**
Chemin des Coussoules, La Franqui. **GPS:** n42,94329 e3,02917.⬆.

70 🛏€ 6,50 ⚡🔌Ch 🖌 included. **Surface:** unpaved. ⬛ 01/01-31/12
Distance: 🛒2km 🏊on the spot 🛒on the spot ⊗2km 🍴2km.
Remarks: Next to campsite Coussoules, check in at reception.
Tourist information Leucate:
ℹ Office de Tourisme, Espace Culturel, www.leucate.net.
🏧S **Limoux** **29B5**
Esplanade François Mitterand. **GPS:** n43,05052 e2,21870.

3 🛏free ⚡🔌free. **Surface:** metalled. ⬛ 01/01-31/12
Distance: 🛒on the spot ⊗450m.
Remarks: In centre next to school ((lycée), parking 200m from service.
🏧 **Lodève** 🏔🏕 **29C4**
Parking Esplanade, Boulevard Général Leclerq. **GPS:** n43,73304 e3,31475.

200 🛏free. **Surface:** gravel.
Distance: 🛒on the spot ⊗on the spot 🍴on the spot.
Remarks: Parking in centre.
Tourist information Lodève:
ℹ Maison de Tourisme, 7, Place de la République, www.lodeve.com.Old city to
the gate of the Mediteranean.
🏧S **Lunas** **29C4**
Base de Loisirs Prade, D35. **GPS:** n43,70555 e3,18555.⬆.

75 🛏free ⚡🔌Ch free. **Surface:** asphalted. ⬛ 01/01-31/12
Distance: 🛒700m ⊗700m 🍴700m.
🏧S **Marseillan-Plage** 🏔🏖 **29C5**
Rue des Goélands. **GPS:** n43,31902 e3,54864.⬆➡.

FR

± 200 ⅏€ 4-6-10/24h 🚰€ 2/10minutes ⚡Ch ♨.🚿
Surface: gravel.
Distance: 🚮on the spot 🏖sandy beach 600m ⊗on the spot 🍴on the spot.

Matemale 29A6
Rue de la Truite. **GPS**: n42,57106 e2,10984.

10 ⅏free. **Location:** Rural. **Surface:** gravel. 🔲 01/01-31/12
Distance: 🚮500m ⚓20m 🏊20m ⊗500m 🍴500m.
Remarks: Parking at lake.

Matemale 29A6
Camping du Lac, Route des Cariolettes. **GPS**: n42,58197 e2,10584.
⅏€ 12 🚰€ 3 ⚡Ch 📶 WC 🚿. **Surface:** grassy. 🔲 01/01-31/12
Distance: 🚮1km.

Mende 29C2
Rue du Faubourg Montbel. **GPS**: n44,52063 e3,49660.

⅏free 🚰 ⚡Chfree. 🔲 01/01-31/12

Mèze 29C4
Complexe sportif des Sesquiers, Route de Villeveyrac. **GPS**: n43,44135 e3,59436.⬆.

6 ⅏free 🚰 ⚡Chfree. **Surface:** gravel.
Distance: 🚮2,5km ⚓10km.

Tourist information Mèze:
👁 Lagunage.Sea-farm for preservation of natural beauty and aquarium.
👁 Le Mourre Blanc, Bassin de Thau.Oyster culture houses.

Mont-Louis 29A6
Parking des Remparts. GPS: n42,50765 e2,12273.

20 ⅏€ 3 🚰 🔧 included. **Surface:** asphalted.
Distance: 🚮200m ⊗200m 🍴200m.
Remarks: Parking at city wall.
Tourist information Mont-Louis:
ℹ Fortified city, 17th century.

Montagnac 29C4
D613. **GPS**: n43,47520 e3,49129.⬆➡.

3 ⅏free 🚰 ⚡Chfree. **Surface:** gravel.
Distance: 🚮1km ⊗1km 🍴1km.

Montferrand 29A4
Col de Naurouze, Route du Ségala, N113> D218. **GPS**: n43,35238 e1,82390.⬆.

20 ⅏free 🚰 ⚡Ch 🔧. **Surface:** gravel. 🔲 01/01-31/12
Distance: 🚮2km ⊗on the spot 🍴2km.

Montpellier 29D4
Parking Joffre, Rue D'Argencour. **GPS**: n43,61316 e3,88608.
⅏€ 1/h. **Surface:** asphalted. 🔲 01/01-31/12
Distance: ⚓4km.
Remarks: Overnight stay possible. Via avenue Jean Mermoz.
Tourist information Montpellier:
ℹ Office de Tourisme, 30, Allée Jean de Lattre de Tassigny, Esplanade Comédie, www.ot-montpellier.fr.
👁 Corum.Opera-complex.
👁 Place de la Comédie.Square with many cafés.

Montpeyroux 22A6
D797C, Rue De l'Hume. **GPS**: n45,62373 e3,19911.⬆.

FR

+10 🌊free 🚰€ 2,50 ♨Ch📦€ 2,50/1h. **Location:** Rural, quit. **Surface:** gravel. 🅿 01/01-31/12
Distance: 🚶100m 🚲200m ⊗200m.

Tourist information Montpeyroux:
ℹ️ Small town with wine-cellar Cave de Montpeyroux. 🅿 Mo/Sa 8.30-12.30h, 14-18/19h, Su 10.30-12h, 16-19h.

🌊S	Mourèze	29C4

D8. **GPS:** n43,61728 e3,36111. 🔼

20 🌊€6 🚰 ♨Ch ✏️ included. **Surface:** gravel.

🌊S	Narbonne	29C5

Parking du Parc des Sports, Avenue de la Mer. **GPS:** n43,18017 e3,02294.

36 🌊€9/day 🚰€ 2 ♨Ch ✏️€ 2.
Surface: asphalted.
Distance: 🚲2,3km 🛒Carrefour.
Remarks: Free bus to centre every 30 minutes.

Tourist information Narbonne:
ℹ️ Office de Tourisme, Place Roger Salengro. Old Roman port city.
👁 Autorail Touristique du Minervois. Train tourist from Narbonne to Bize.
🅿 01/07-17/09.
Ⓜ Musée d'Archéologie et de Préhistoire.
Archeological findings.
⚔️ Palais des Archevêques. Palace, 11th century, with cathedral.
🎪 🅿 Thu, Su.
⚫ Résèrve Africain, Sigean. Safaripark, 200 ha. 🅿 daily from 9h.

🌊S	Narbonne-Plage	29C5

Narbonne-Plage>Gruissan. **GPS:** n43,14778 e3,15319.

🌊€ 10 🚰 ♨Ch ✏️ included.
Surface: gravel. 🅿 01/01-31/12
Distance: ⛵100m ⊗on the spot.
Remarks: Max. 24h. Just before Narbonne, next to restaurant and midget golf.

🌊S	Nîmes 🍷🎪🍴🛒	29D4

Domaine de Fontbespierre, 3359, route d'Anduze. **GPS:** n43,87142 e4,27746. 🔼

50 🌊€8 🚰€ 2 ♨Ch ✏️€ 2/day WC.
Surface: grassy. 🅿 01/01-31/12
Distance: 🚶6km ⊗6km 🛒6km.
Remarks: Terrain with video surveillance.

🌊	Octon 🏞	29C4

Avenue de la Molière. **GPS:** n43,65390 e3,30378.

🌊free.
Surface: gravel.
Distance: 🚶50m ⊗50m 🛒50m.
Remarks: Parking behind 'Clamery', walking and bicycle area, Lac du Salagou.

🌊S	Ouveillan	29C5

Place Cave Coopératieve. **GPS:** n43,29204 e2,97080. 🔼

7 🌊free 🚰 ♨Chfree. **Surface:** gravel/metalled. 🅿 01/01-31/12
Distance: 🚶2km ⊗2km 🛒2km.

🌊S	Palavas-les-Flots	29D4

Port Fluvial, Base Paul Riquet, Avenue de Lattre Tassigny. **GPS:** n43,53091 e3,92316. 🔼

FR

200 ⌁ € 10, Jul/Aug € 17,50 ⌁ € 3 🔌Ch 🛠 € 2 WC 🚽 📶. **Surface:** asphalted. ⬛ 01/01-31/12
Distance: 🛒1km ⊗1km 🚰1km.

Tourist information Palavas-les-Flots:
ℹ️ Office de Tourisme, Place de la Méditerranée, www.palavaslesflots.com. Bathing resort and fishermans village, separated by a canal and linked by a telpher carrier, Transcanal.

⌁S	Peyriac-de-Mer 🏖	29C5

Rue des Étangs. **GPS:** n43,09372 e2,96205. ⬆️.

20 ⌁free, July-Aug € 5 ⌁ 🔌Ch WC 🚽. **Location:** Rural. **Surface:** grassy/metalled. ⬛ 01/01-31/12
Distance: 🛒1km ⚓on the spot ⊗1km 🚰1km 🚴on the spot 🚶on the spot.
Remarks: Next to rugby ground.

⌁S	Pézenas 🌿🏖	29C4

Promenade du Pré St.Jean, Avenue du Maréchal Leclerc. **GPS:** n43,46054 e3,42622.

⌁free. **Surface:** metalled. ⬛ 01/01-31/12
Distance: 🛒on the spot 🚲1km.
Remarks: Parking in the centre.

Tourist information Pézenas:
ℹ️ Office de Tourisme, Place Gambetta, www.paysdepezenas.net.Artists village with historical centre.
👁 Barbier Gely.Barbers' boutique.
Ⓜ Musée Vulliode St German.Collection of tapestry.
🚻 ⬛ Sa.

⌁S	Pezens	29B5

Place de la Liberté. **GPS:** n43,25528 e2,26361.

5 ⌁free ⌁ 🛠 free. **Surface:** gravel. ⬛ 01/01-31/12
Distance: 🛒50m ⊗50m 🚰50m.
Remarks: Near (busy) RN113.

⌁S	Port Vendres 🏖	29C6

Plage des Tamarins, Route de la Jetée. **GPS:** n42,51778 e3,11375. ⬆️.

30 ⌁ € 4,90-8,60 ⌁ € 1 🔌Ch WC 🛠 **Surface:** gravel. ⬛ 01/01-31/12
Distance: 🛒1,3km ⚓100m ⊗on the spot.

Tourist information Port Vendres:
ℹ️ Port Venus.Old fishing-port, quay for cruise ships.

⌁S	Port-la-Nouvelle ⚓🏖	29C5

Chemin des Vignes. **GPS:** n43,01366 e3,04077. ➡️.

60 ⌁free ⌁ € 2/15minutes 🔌Ch ⌁ € 2/15minutes 🛠. **Surface:** grassy/gravel.
Distance: 🛒2km ⚓2km ⊗2km 🚰1km Huit-à-huit, Passage de l'Abbé Gavanon.

⌁S	Quillan	29B5

Parking Joseph Courjétaire, D117. **GPS:** n42,87366 e2,18266. ⬆️.

10 ⌁free ⌁ € 2 🔌Ch WC. **Surface:** asphalted. ⬛ 01/01-31/12
Distance: 🛒on the spot ⚓on the spot 🚴on the spot ⊗on the spot 🚰on the spot.
Remarks: Nearby railwayline.

⌁S	Remoulins	30A3

N86. **GPS:** n43,93789 e4,55851.

FR

🚰free 🚰€ 5/20minutes 🚽Ch. **Surface:** asphalted.
Distance: 🚶100m ⊗100m 🚰100m.
Remarks: Parking nearby river, service on the other side of the bridge: Route du Pont du Gare.
Tourist information Remoulins:
⌂ Pont du Gard.Roman aqueduct.

Rigarda 🏔🌳 29B6
Aire 66, Route de Finestret. **GPS:** n42,62585 e2,52898.⬆

30 🚰€5 🚰🚽Ch 🚿 included. 🚲 **Location:** Rural, isolated, quit. **Surface:** grassy/gravel. ◉ 01/01-31/12
Distance: 🚶Vinça 2,7km ⊗2,7km 🚰2,7km.

Routier 29A5
Place Malèbre. **GPS:** n43,10737 e2,12738.⬆➡

±7 🚰free 🚰free. **Surface:** gravel/metalled. ◉ 01/01-31/12
Distance: 🚶on the spot.
Tourist information Routier:
ℹ Corbières.Region is known for its wines and the Cathar citadels, the castle of Queribus in Cucugan is one of the last bastions of the Cathars.

Saillagousse 🏔🌳 29A6
Rue des Sports. **GPS:** n42,45764 e2,03766.⬆

7 🚰free 🚰€ 3 🚽Ch🚽WC. **Surface:** asphalted. ◉ 01/01-31/12
Distance: 🚶on the spot ⊗on the spot 🚰on the spot.
Remarks: Coins at Mairie, office de tourisme. N116, behind Hotel Christiannia.

Salles-sur-l'Herbs 29A5
Allée des Platanes. **GPS:** n43,29194 e1,78844.

10 🚰free 🚰🚽Ch🚽free. **Surface:** gravel. ◉ 01/01-31/12
Distance: 🚶on the spot ⊗100m 🚰100m.

Sauve 🌿 29D3
D999. **GPS:** n43,94017 e3,95218.⬆➡

5 🚰free 🚰🚽Chfree. **Surface:** metalled.
Distance: 🚶50m ⊗50m.

Sérignan-Plage 29C5
Parking Mini-Golf, Avenue de la Plage. **GPS:** n43,26892 e3,33629.
20 🚰€ 10, Jul/Aug € 15 🚰🚽Ch 🚿 WC included. **Surface:** unpaved. ◉ 01/01-31/12
Distance: 🚶150m 🚰150m.
Remarks: Behind restaurant, swimming pool.

Sernhac 30A4
Mas des Puits Blancs, 3215 rte Beaucaire, D986. **GPS:** n43,90658 e4,56798.⬆

25 🚰€ 10 🚰🚽Ch 🚿 WC included. **Surface:** grassy.
Distance: 🚶2km 🚲7,6km.

Sète 29C5
Parking Les 3 Digues. **GPS:** n43,36663 e3,61523.⬆

30 🚰free 🚰€ 2 🚽Ch 🚿 **Surface:** gravel. ◉ 01/01-31/12
Distance: 🚶50m 🚲on the spot 🧍on the spot.
Remarks: Beach parking.

Sommières 29D4
Chemin de la Princesse. **GPS:** n43,78701 e4,08717.⬆

25 🛏free 🚰€ 3 🔧Ch. **Surface:** gravel.
Distance: 🚶500m.
Remarks: In front of campsite municipal.

🅂 **St.André** 29C6
Parking de Taxo. **GPS:** n42,55248 e2,97303. ⬆️➡️.

6 🛏€ 2,30 🚰€ 2 🔧Ch 🔌€ 2. **Surface:** asphalted. ⬛ 01/01-31/12
Distance: 🚶on the spot.
Remarks: Max. 3 nights, coins at Office de Tourisme.

🅂 **St.Chély-d'Apcher** 29C2
Parking du Péchaud, Boulevard G. d'Apcher, N9. **GPS:** n44,80084 e3,27296. ⬆️ ➡️.

2 🛏free 🚰€ 2 🔧Ch. **Surface:** asphalted.
Distance: 🚶200m 🚲2,5km ⊗200m 🛒200m 🚌on the spot.
Remarks: Small pitches.

🅂 **St.Gilles** 30A4
Quai du Canal. **GPS:** n43,67154 e4,43281. 🚶.

🛏free. **Surface:** asphalted. ⬛ 01/01-31/12
Distance: 🚶500m ⊗200m 🛒500m.

Tourist information St.Gilles:
⬆ Abbay St.Gilles. Abbey with underground church.

🅂 **St.Jean-du-Gard** 29D3
Av. de la Resistance. **GPS:** n44,10210 e3,88347. ⬆️.

20 🛏free 🚰🔧Ch WC free. **Surface:** gravel. ⬛ 01/01-31/12
Distance: ⊗50m.
Remarks: Nearby railway station.

🅂 **St.Mamert-du-Gard** 29D4
Route du Stade. **GPS:** n43,88479 e4,19057.

6 🛏free 🚰🔧Ch free. **Surface:** metalled. ⬛ 01/01-31/12
Distance: 🚶200m.
Remarks: Between Uzès and Sommières.

🅂 **St.Marsal** 29B6
GPS: n42,53755 e2,62242. ⬆️.

25 🛏€ 2,50 🚰🔧Ch WC free. **Surface:** asphalted. ⬛ 01/01-31/12
Distance: 🚶on the spot ⊗nearby 🛒nearby.

🅂 **St.Mathieu-de-Tréviers** 29D4
D17. **GPS:** n43,76206 e3,86016. ⬆️➡️.

8 🛏€ 5 🚰🔧Ch ✂included.
Surface: gravel. ⬛ 01/01-31/12
Distance: 🚶1km.
Remarks: At sports complex, caution key service (gardien).

🅂 **St.Pierre-la-Mer** 29C5
Base de Loisirs Etang de Pissevache. **GPS:** n43,18972 e3,19694.

🛏€ 5 🚰🔧Ch ✂included. 🚽 ♻ **Surface:** unpaved. ⬛ 01/01-31/12
Distance: 🏖sandy beach 300m.
Remarks: Parking directly behind the beach, next to tennis park and small surf lake, follow Base de Loisirs.

FR

Thues-entre-Valls 29B6

Gorges de la Carança. **GPS:** n42,52320 e2,22203.

25 € 4 Ch included.
Surface: gravel. 01/01-31/12 frost.
Distance: 2km.

Tournissan 29B5

M. Bailly, Route de Saint Laurent B452, Lieu-dit la Paulette. **GPS:** n43,08068 e2,67280.

3 free Ch free. **Surface:** gravel. 01/04-31/10
Distance: 500m.

Vailhan 29C4

Parking de l'Eglise. GPS: n43,55527 e3,29882.

6 free Ch free. **Surface:** gravel. 01/01-31/12
Distance: 1km 200m 50m.

Valras-Plage 29C5

Avenue du Casino. **GPS:** n43,28162 e3,24230.

30 free € 2 Ch.
Surface: asphalted/metalled.
01/10-30/06 summer.
Distance: on the spot 200m on the spot on the spot on the spot.

Villeneuve-lès-Maguelone 29D4

Avenue René Poitevin. **GPS:** n43,52980 e3,86584.

26 € 14/24h Ch included. **Surface:** asphalted.
Distance: 500m 500m 250m 50m.
Remarks: Check in at tourist office (200m).

Villeneuve-Minervois 29B5

Avenue du Jeu de Mail. **GPS:** n43,31516 e2,46432.

20 free Ch WC. **Surface:** asphalted/metalled. 01/01-31/12
Distance: on the spot on the spot on the spot.
Remarks: Max. 48h, parking in front of town hall.

Provence-Alpes-Côte d'Azur

Allos 30D3

GPS: n44,24289 e6,62220.

30 € 5 Ch (9x)included WC. **Surface:** asphalted.
01/01-31/12
Distance: 500m 200m 500m 500m 200m 200m.
Remarks: Driving out of village dir Base de Loisirs.

Allos 30D3

Parking de la Cluite. GPS: n44,24677 e6,66918.

6 free. **Surface:** gravel.
Distance: Allos 6,5km.
Remarks: Isolated parking, Jul/Aug shuttle bus to Lac d'Allos.

Allos 30D3

La Foux d'Allos. **GPS:** n44,29583 e6,56944.

5 🛏free 🚰🗑Ch WCfree. **Surface:** asphalted.
Distance: 🚶1km ⊗100m ⊗100m 🚌Skibus 50m 🍴50m.
Remarks: Follow Col d'Allos.

🛏🅂 Annot 🏔 30D3
Chemin de la Colle Basse. **GPS:** n43,96351 e6,66386.⬆➡.

20 🛏free 🚰🗑Chfree. **Surface:** grassy/gravel. ⬛ 01/01-31/12
Distance: 🚶400m ⊗400m ⊗400m.

🛏🅂 Arles 🌊⛲🍷 30A4
Place Lamartine. **GPS:** n43,68151 e4,63046.⬆.

6 🛏free 🚰🗑Chfree. **Surface:** asphalted.
Distance: 🚶50m ⊿on the spot ⊗on the spot ⊗50m ⊗100m.

Tourist information Arles:
ℹ Office de Tourisme, Boulevard des Lices, www.tourisme.ville-arles.fr.City on the border of the nature reserve Camargue with Roman ruin. The painter Van Gogh lived in Arles, 1888-89.
✝ Église St.Trophine.Romanesque and Gothic construction.
⌂ Palais Constantin.Large Roman imperial palace of which only the baths are left.

🛏🅂 Avignon 🌊⛲🍷 30A3
Chemin de l'Ile Piot. **GPS:** n43,95167 e4,79361.⬆.

20 🛏free. **Surface:** asphalted. ⬛ 01/01-31/12
Distance: 🚶800m ⊗800m ⊗800m 🚌on the spot.
Remarks: Free bus to centre every ten minutes.

Tourist information Avignon:

ℹ Office de Tourisme, 41, cours Jean Jaurès, www.ot-avignon.fr.Roman city dominated by the Palais du Papes. ⬛ 01/04-31/08, 01/10-31/10 9-17h, 01/09-30/09 9-20h, 01/11-31/03 9-12.45h, 14-18h.
◉ Place d'Horloge.Cosy square in the old centre of the city.
◉ Pont Saint Bénézet.Known as the Pont d'Avignon, bridge over the river Rhône.
♜ Petit Palais.Former residence of the archbishop.

🛏🅂 Banon 30B3
Rue de la Grande Fontaine. **GPS:** n44,03982 e5,63006.⬆.

± 15 🛏€ 3/24h 🚰🗑Chfree WC.
Location: Rural. **Surface:** metalled.
Distance: 🚶250m ⊗250m ⊗100m.
Remarks: Tue-morning market.

🛏🅂 Barcelonnette 🏔 30D3
Parking du Bouguet, Chemin des Alpages. **GPS:** n44,38222 e6,65778.⬆➡.

15 🛏€6 🚰€ 2/100liter 🗑Ch 🔌€ 2/1h ⊘. **Surface:** grassy. ⬛ 01/01-31/12
Distance: 🚶500m ⊿200m ⊗500m ⊗500m.

🛏🅂 Bédoin 30B3
Chemin des Sablières. **GPS:** n44,12472 e5,17167.⬆.

🛏€ 3 🚰€ 2/100liter 🗑Ch. **Surface:** grassy.
Remarks: Max. 3 nights.

🛏🅂 Bollène 30A3
Centre Leclerc, Route de Saint Paul Trois Châteaux, D26. **GPS:** n44,32222 e4,74306.⬆.

🛏free 🚰🗑Chfree. ⬛ 01/01-31/12

FR

Distance: 4,3km.
Remarks: Service only during opening hours shop.

Tourist information Bollène:
Office de Tourisme, Place Reynaud de la Gardette, www.bollenetourisme.com.
Village Troglodyte.Cave dwelling village. 01/04-31/10 9.30-19h, 01/11-31/03 Sa-Su, holidays 14-18h 01/12-31/01.

Briançon 30D2
Parc des Sports, Rue Jean Moulin. **GPS:** n44,89010 e6,62824.
free Ch.
Remarks: At sports park.

Tourist information Briançon:
Office de Tourisme, 1, place du Temple, www.ot-briancon.fr.Highest city of Europe, fortress is now a tourist centre, in winter as winter sports resort and in summer parapente, rafting and biking.
Parc des Écrins.Nature reserve.

Caille 30D4
Aire de Caille, Chemin de la Plaine. **GPS:** n43,77893 e6,73331.

3 free € 2/15minutes Ch € 2/15minutes. 01/01-31/12
Distance: 50m 50m 100m.

Carpentras 30A3
Cours de la Pyramide. **GPS:** n44,05598 e5,04235.

free Chfree. **Surface:** metalled. 01/01-31/12
Distance: 500m 500m 500m.
Remarks: Near ring-road city centre (west).

Tourist information Carpentras:
Office de Tourisme, Place Aristide Briand, www.ville-carpentras.fr.Old city with historical centre. Mo-Fri Jewish holiday.
Hôtel Dieu.Former hospital, 18th century.
Centre-ville. Fri-morning.

Carro 30A5
Quai Jean Verandy. **GPS:** n43,32931 e5,04076.

70 01/06-01/11 € 8 Ch included. **Surface:** metalled. 01/01-31/12
Distance: on the spot on the spot 200m 200m.

Castellane 30C4
GPS: n43,84667 e6,51406.

28 € 5 Ch included. **Surface:** asphalted.
Distance: 100m on the spot.
Remarks: Directly at the river, near Pont du Roc.

Tourist information Castellane:
Office de Tourisme, Rue Nationale, www.castellane.org.Holiday resort and good starting point for a visit to the Gorges du Verdon.
Sa-morning.

Cavalière 30C5
GPS: n43,15242 e6,43221.

30 € 15 . **Surface:** sand.
Distance: 50m Plage-Restaurant-Bar Le Cannier 200m.
Remarks: Parking at beach, at coast road D559.

Chorges 30C2
Place du champ de foire. **GPS:** n44,54600 e6,28008.

10 free free. 01/01-31/12
Remarks: Max. 12h.

Tourist information Chorges:
Lac de Serre Ponçon, Serre Ponçon.Clear blue artificial lake, many water sports.
Office de Tourisme, Place Centrale, www.otchorges.com.

Colmars-les-Alpes 30D3
GPS: n44,17943 e6,62695.

FR

10 ⏻free ⛽€ 2 ⬛Ch ◇. **Surface:** asphalted. ◻ 01/01-31/12
Distance: 🚶300m ⛱50m 🛒50m ⊗300m 🚉300m.
Remarks: 31/7/10 during inspection service out of order.

🏕 S | **Comps-sur-Artuby** | 30C4
D955. **GPS:** n43,70652 e6,50678.⬆.

⏻free ⛽€ 3 ⬛Ch WC. **Surface:** gravel. ◻ 01/01-31/12
Distance: 🚶350m ⊗pizzeria/crêperie.
Remarks: Max. 12h.

🏕 S | **Cuges-les-Pins** | 30B5
Le Jardin de la Ville. **GPS:** n43,28114 e5,70592.

10 ⏻€ 3/12-12h ⛽⬛Ch ◄ included. ◻ 01/01-31/12
Distance: 🚶500m ⊗500m 🚉500m.
Remarks: Monitored parking.

Tourist information Cuges-les-Pins:
Ⓜ Musée Légion Etrangères, Aubagne.Museum about the French Foreign Legion.

🏕 S | **Dauphin** | 30B4
Route de la Rencontre. **GPS:** n43,90028 e5,78417.⬆.

⏻free ⛽⬛Chfree. **Surface:** metalled.
Remarks: Near Salle des Fêtes.

🏕 S | **Digne-les-Bains** 🏔♨ | 30C3
Le Vallon des Sources, Avenue des Thermes. **GPS:** n44,07998 e6,26091.

25 ⏻free ⛽€ 2 ⬛Ch. ◻ 01/01-31/12
Distance: 🚶2,5km ⊗750m 🚉2km 🚌100m.
Remarks: Coins available at pay-desk of theTherme. Follow Therme.

🏕 S | **Fayence** | 30D4
Allée des Jardins. **GPS:** n43,62308 e6,68982.
5 ⏻free ⛽€ 4 ⬛Ch.
Remarks: Max. 48h, at tennis-court and swimming pool.

🏕 S | **Fontaine-de-Vaucluse** | 30B3
D25, Avenue Robert Garcin. **GPS:** n43,91995 e5,11916.⬆.

60 ⏻€ 3/24h ⛽⬛Ch ◄ included. **Surface:** gravel. ◻ 01/01-31/12
Distance: 🚶touristic centre 700m ⊗700m 🚉700m.
Remarks: Along the river.

Tourist information Fontaine-de-Vaucluse:
ℹ Office de Tourisme, Chemin du Gouffre.

🏕 S | **Fontvieille** | 30A4
Parking du Moulin de Daudet, Allée des Pins. **GPS:** n43,72000 e4,71200.

⏻€ 3. **Surface:** gravel.
Distance: 🚶800m.

🏕 S | **Gap** | 30C2
Parking Dumont, Avenue Commandant Dumont, N85. **GPS:** n44,56544 e6,08447.➡.

3 ⏻free ⛽€ 3 ⬛Ch 🛢€ 3 ◇. **Surface:** asphalted.
Distance: 🚶500m ⊗on the spot 🚉on the spot.
Remarks: Stay overnight allowed at other pitches.

Tourist information Gap:
ℹ Office de Tourisme, 2a, Cours Frédéric Mistral, www.ville-gap.fr.

🏕 S | **Gémenos** | 30B5
Cours Sudre. **GPS:** n43,29772 e5,62953.

FR

3 ⛺ free ⛵ 🍽 Ch ⚓ free. **Surface:** metalled.
Distance: 🚰100m ⊗100m 💧100m.
Remarks: Max. 24h.

80 ⛺ € 7 ⛵ 🍽 Ch ⚓ WC included.
Surface: grassy. ⭘ 01/01-31/12
Distance: 🚰150m ⊗150m 💧150m.
Remarks: Max. 3,5t.

🏕 Ⓢ Gigondas 30A3
Domaine des Florets, Route des Dentelles, D80. **GPS:** n44,16220 e5,01725.⬆.

🏕 Ⓢ Grimaud 🏖 30C5
Saint Pons Les Mûres, D98. **GPS:** n43,28000 e6,57806.⬆.

3 ⛺ free ⛵ 🍽 free. **Surface:** gravel.
Distance: 🚰1,7km ⊗500m.
Remarks: Check in at tasting room.

12 ⛺ € 13 ⛵ € 2,50 🍽 Ch ⚡ € 2,50 💶. 🚐 **Location:** Very simple.
Surface: asphalted. ⭘ 01/01-31/12
Distance: 🚰800m ⊗200m 💧500m.
Remarks: Max. 72h.

🏕 Gordes 30B4
D2. **GPS:** n43,90056 e5,19306.⬆.

🏖 Grimaud 🏖 30C5
Plage du Gros Pin, N98. **GPS:** n43,28450 e6,59498.⬆.
10 ⛺. **Surface:** asphalted.
Distance: 🚰5km 🏊on the spot.

🏕 Ⓢ Guillaumes 30D3
D2202. **GPS:** n44,08861 e6,85285.⬆➡.

20 ⛺ free. **Surface:** gravel. ⭘ 01/01-31/12
Distance: 🚰2km ⊗2km 💧2km.

⭘ Ⓢ Greasque 30B4
Musée de la Mine, Route de Puits Hely d'Oissel. **GPS:** n43,43281 e5,53439.

10 ⛺ free ⛵ € 2/100liter 🍽 Ch ⚡ € 2/1h. ⭘ 01/01-31/12
Distance: 🚰50m 🏊on the spot 🛶on the spot ⊗50m 💧50m.
Remarks: Coins at Bar-Tabac, office de tourisme, town hall.

Ⓢ Guillestre 30D2
Quartier Saint James. **GPS:** n44,65731 e6,63306.
⛵ 🍽 Ch ⚡ € 5. ⭘ 01/01-31/12, 8-20h
Remarks: Nearby campsite Saint James les Pins.

Tourist information Guillestre:
ℹ Maison de Tourisme, Place Salva, www.pays-du-guillestrois.com.
⛺ ⭘ Mo.

15 ⛺ free ⛵ 🍽 Ch free. **Surface:** gravel. ⭘ 16/01-20/12
Distance: 🚰600m.

🏕 Ⓢ Gréoux-les-Bains 🏖 30C4
Aire Camping-car, Chemin de la Barque. **GPS:** n43,75562 e5,88862.⬆➡.

🏕 Ⓢ Hyères 🏖 30C5
Le Mérou, D42, L'Ayguade. **GPS:** n43,10897 e6,18117.⬆.

FR

6 🛁🚻€ 3/15minutes 🔌Ch 🚿.

🏕️S | **Hyères** 🏖️🌊⛵ | 30C5

Les Etangs de Sauvebonne, 566 Route de Pierrefeu. **GPS**: n43,16120 e6,12133. ⬆️

20 🛏️10 🛁🚻Chincluded 🔥€ 3/day. **Location:** Rural, quit. **Surface:** grassy. ⏹️ 01/01-31/12

Distance: 🏊on the spot 🚶on the spot.

🏕️S | **Jausiers** 🏔️🌊 | 30D3

Route de Jausiers-Barcelonette, D900. **GPS**: n44,41266 e6,72936.⬆️➡️

3 🛏️free 🛁€ 3 🔌Ch 🚻. **Surface:** metalled. ⏹️ 01/01-31/12

Distance: 🚶600m 🏊50m ⊗100m 🛒400m.

🏕️ | **Jausiers** 🏔️🌊 | 30D3

Lotissement des Neiges. **GPS**: n44,41278 e6,72472.

15 🛏️free. **Surface:** unpaved. ⏹️ 01/01-31/12

Distance: 🚶600m 🏊on the spot ⊗100m 🛒400m.

Remarks: Service 200m.

🏕️S | **La Bastide** 🏔️ | 30D4

GPS: n43,73806 e6,62583.

4 🛏️free 🛁🔌Ch. **Surface:** asphalted. ⏹️ 01/01-31/12

Distance: 🚶200m ⊗100m 🛒100m.

🏕️S | **La Bréole** 🏔️ | 30C2

Bourg La Bréole. **GPS**: n44,45777 e6,29194.➡️

6 🛏️free 🛁🔌Ch WC free. **Surface:** asphalted. ⏹️ 01/01-31/12

Distance: 🚶on the spot 🏊2km 🚶2km Lac de Serre Ponçon ⊗100m 🛒100m.

🏕️S | **La Crau** | 30C5

Espace Lavage Auto Grand Bleu, La Moutonne. **GPS**: n43,12417 e6,07444.

3 🛏️€ 4/night 🛁🔌Ch 🔥WCincluded.

Surface: concrete. ⏹️ 01/01-31/12

Remarks: Free after washing the motor home (€ 10).

🏕️S | **La Londe-les-Maures** | 30C5

Rond-point Ducourneau, chemin du Pansard. **GPS**: n43,13185 e6,23053.⬆️

4 🛏️free 🛁€ 3 🔌Ch 🚻.

Distance: 🚶800m.

Remarks: Max. 24h.

🏕️S | **La Motte** | 30C4

Moulin de Vallongues, Avenue Fréderique Mistral, D47. **GPS**: n43,49630 e6,53134.⬆️

10 🛏️free 🛁🔌Ch 🚻€ 6 🚿. **Surface:** gravel. ⏹️ 01/01-31/12

Distance: 🚶600m ⊗600m 🛒4km.

Remarks: Max. 24h.

🏕️ | **La Roche-des-Arnauds** | 30C2

D994, Chemin des Digues. **GPS**: n44,56134 e5,95637.⬆️

5 ⌥free. **Surface:** asphalted. 🅾 01/01-31/12
Distance: 🚶100m 🛒on the spot 🚰on the spot 🚰100m.
Remarks: Max. 24h.

6 ⌥free 🚿 WCfree. **Surface:** gravel. 🅾 01/01-31/12
Distance: 🚶50m 🛒50m ⊗50m 🚰100m.

| | La Salle-les-Alpes 🏔❄ | 30C2 |
Chemin de l'Oratoire, Villeneuve. **GPS:** n44,94417 e6,55583.

| | Les Arcs-sur-Argens | 30C4 |
Cellier des Archers. GPS: n43,45509 e6,47750.⬆.

16 ⌥€ 6, winter € 17 🚿🍴 Ch 🔌 included. **Surface:** gravel. 🅾 01/01-31/12
Distance: 🚶200m ⊗50m.
Remarks: Parking at skipistes.

10 ⌥free 🚿🍴 Chfree. **Surface:** gravel/sand. 🅾 01/01-31/12
Distance: 🚶1km 🚲8km ⊗100m 🚰Super U 1km 🏪1km 🚏200m.
Tourist information Les Arcs-sur-Argens:
🎪 🅾 Thu morning.

| | Laragne-Montéglin | 30B3 |
Avenue de Provence, D1075. **GPS:** n44,31212 e5,82543.⬆.

| | Les Issambres | 30D5 |
Chez Marcel, Plage La Gaillarde, N98. **GPS:** n43,36559 e6,71202.⬆.

15 ⌥free 🚿🍴 Ch 🔌free. **Surface:** asphalted.
Distance: 🚶300m ⊗300m 🚰300m.

50 ⌥€ 12/night, peak season € 15,50/night 🚿🍴 Chincluded 🔌€ 3/day 🍴€ 0,50 🔌€ 5 📶. **Location:** Comfortable. **Surface:** gravel/sand. 🅾 01/01-31/12
Distance: 🛒50m ⊗200m 🚰200m.

| | Laragne-Montéglin | 30B3 |
Intermarché, D1075. **GPS:** n44,30300 e5,83700.⬆.

| | Malaucène | 30B3 |
Avenue Charles de Gaulle. **GPS:** n44,17792 e5,12970.⬆➡.

30 ⌥free 🚿€ 2 🍴Ch. 🅾 01/01-31/12
Distance: 🚶2km.

| | Le Lauzet-Ubay 🏔🌲❄ | 30C3 |
D900. **GPS:** n44,42833 e6,43389.⬆.

15 ⌥free 🚿🍴 Chfree. **Surface:** asphalted/metalled. 🅾 01/01-31/12
Distance: 🚶150m ⊗150m 🚰150m.
Remarks: Between sports fields and gendarmerie.
Tourist information Malaucène:
🎪 Marché Provencal. 🅾 Wed-morning.

| | Malemort-du-Comtat | 30B3 |
Avenue Docteur Tondut, D5. **GPS:** n44,02175 e5,15714.⬆.
⌥free 🚿🍴 Chfree. **Location:** Rural. **Surface:** gravel.

FR

Distance: 200m on the spot.

| | Ménerbes | 30B4 |

GPS: n43,83193 e5,20828.

free.
Distance: 250m 100m.

| | Montgenèvre | 30D2 |

Parking le Collet. GPS: n44,93324 e6,72547.

250 € 10 Ch (80x)included.
Surface: metalled. 01/01-31/12
Remarks: Driving ou village dir Italy.

Tourist information Montgenèvre:
Office de Tourisme, Route d'Italie, www.montgenevre.com. Ski station on the border with Italy. In the summer canyoning.

| | Mouans Sartoux | 30D4 |

Allée des Magnans. **GPS:** n43,61806 e6,97035.

6 € 12, Jul-Aug € 15 Ch included. € 3. **Surface:** grassy. 01/01-31/12
Distance: 50m 50m 200m 50m.
Remarks: Private property.

| | Moustiers Ste.Marie | 30C4 |

P5, D952. **GPS:** n43,84361 e6,21874.

€ 6/night € 2 Ch € 2. **Surface:** gravel.
Distance: 10 min walking.
Tourist information Moustiers Ste.Marie:

Office de Tourisme, Place de l'église, ville-moustiers-sainte-marie.fr.City of faïence.
Musée de la Faïence, Mairie. summer: 09-12h,14-19h.

| | Oppède-le-Vieux | 30B4 |

GPS: n43,83107 e5,15911.

€ 5/day free.
Distance: 500m 500m.
Remarks: Parking on entering the village.

Tourist information Oppède-le-Vieux:
Hiking route through medieval top-hill village.

| | Orange | 30A3 |

Parking Sully. GPS: n44,14100 e4,80800.
10 free. **Surface:** asphalted.
Distance: 1km 2km.
Remarks: Via Avenue A.Artaud.

Tourist information Orange:
Office de Tourisme, 5, cours Aristide Briand, www.provence-orange.com. Roman city between the vineyards of the Côtes du Rhône.
Amfithéâtre.Open-air theater built under emperor August.
Arc d'Orange.Roman triumphal arch 20 after Christ.
Ruine de Château des Princes Oranges.Ruins of the castle of the Princes of Orange.
Thu.

| | Orcières-Merlette | 30C2 |

Camping-car Casse Blanche, Station d'Orcières, P3. **GPS:** n44,69465 e6,32098.
30 € 12/24h Ch included.
Surface: asphalted. 01/01-31/12
Distance: on the spot on the spot.

| | Pélissanne | 30B4 |

Chemin de la Prouvenque. **GPS:** n43,62805 e5,15307.

6 free Ch free.
Distance: 500m 8km.
Remarks: Parking stadium.

| | Plan-de-la-Tour | 30C5 |

Parking Boulodrôme, D74. **GPS:** n43,33827 e6,54902.

FR

🛁free. **Surface:** asphalted. ⬛ 01/01-31/12 ⬤ Thu.
Distance: 🚶100m ✖100m 🛒100m.
Remarks: At tennis-courts.

Tourist information Plan-de-la-Tour:
ℹ️ Office de Tourisme, Place du 19 Mars.
🎪 ⬛ Thu morning 6-12h.

🏊S | Port Saint-Louis-du-Rhône | 30A5
GPS: n43,38464 e4,82165. ⬆➡.

50 🛁€6 🔌🗑Ch🖍 included. **Surface:** asphalted/gravel. ⬛ 01/01-31/12
Distance: 🚶2km 🏖50m ✖2km 🛒2km.
Remarks: Baker every morning.

🏊S | Pra-Loup 🏔❄ | 30C3
Parking des Choupettes. **GPS:** n44,36806 e6,60611. ⬆.

50 🛁free 🔌🗑Ch▦consumption, WC. **Surface:** asphalted. ⬛ 01/01-31/12
Distance: 🚶400m ✖400m 🛒400m 🎿50m.
Remarks: Parking skiruns.

🏊S | Puget Theniers 🏔 | 30D3
Aire de la Condamine, Avenue Bisschofsheim. **GPS:** n43,95306 e6,89944. ⬆➡.

10 🛁€3,50 🔌🗑Ch🖍 included. **Surface:** asphalted. ⬛ 01/01-31/12
Distance: 🚶300m 🏖20m ✖300m 🛒300m.

🏊S | Puy-Saint-Vincent 🏔❄ | 30C2
GPS: n44,83245 e6,48331. ⬆.
20 🛁€6 🔌🗑Ch▦ included. ⬛ 18/12-25/04
Remarks: Max. 15 days, information at funicular railway. Follow signs Station 1600m, first parking on the right next to funicular railway.

Tourist information Puy-Saint-Vincent:
✒ Office de Tourisme, Chapelle St-Jacques, Les Alberts, www.puysaintvincent.com.

🏊S | Puyvert | 30B4
Super U, D118. **GPS:** n43,74689 e5,33644. ⬆.

5 🛁free 🔌🗑Ch🖍 (4x)free ⬤€ 4.
Surface: asphalted. ⬛ 01/01-31/12
Distance: 🚶1,5km 🛒on the spot ⬤on the spot.

🏊S | Quinson 🛶 | 30C4
Les Prés du Verdon. GPS: n43,69801 e6,03911. ⬆.

9 🛁free 🔌🗑Chfree. **Surface:** gravel/sand. ⬛ 01/01-31/12
Distance: 🏖100m 🚶100m ✖300m 🛒500m.

🏊S | Ramatuelle | 30D5
Parking de Tamaris, Plage de Pamplonne, Route des Tamaris. **GPS:** n43,23893 e6,66149. ⬆.

60 🛁€ 5/day, € 5/night, 1/7-31/8 € 9day, € 9/night, dog € 1 🔌🗑Ch🖍 (20x)€ 7/day. 🏕 **Location:** Rural. **Surface:** gravel.
Distance: 🏖on the spot ✖on the spot 🛒on the spot.
Remarks: Beach parking.

🏊S | Ramatuelle | 30D5
Parking Municipal, Plage de Pamplonne, Route de Bonne-Terrasse. **GPS:** n43,21126 e6,66217. ⬆➡.

90 🛁€ 7,70 🔌🗑Ch WC 🗑. 🏕 **Location:** Rural. **Surface:** gravel. ⬛ 01/04-31/10
Distance: 🏖200m ✖200m 🛒2km.
Remarks: Beach parking, bread service.

Tourist information Ramatuelle:
ℹ️ Office de Tourisme, Place de l'Ormeau, www.ramatuelle-tourisme.com.
🎪 La place de l'Ormeau.Provencal Market. ⬛ Thu, Su.

FR

Riez 30C4

Place Maxime Javelly. **GPS**: n43,81650 e6,09188.

7 free Ch free. **Surface**: asphalted/grassy.
Distance: 50m 100m 100m.

Roussillon 30B4

Parking Saint Joseph, D149. **GPS**: n43,89660 e5,29593.

10 € 2/day, € 5/night.
Distance: 800m 800m.

Tourist information Roussillon:

Office de Tourisme, Place de la Poste, www.roussillon-provence.com.
Sentier des Ocres.Hiking trail, 45 min.

Sablet 30A3

Domaine du Parandou, D977. **GPS**: n44,19325 e4,99522.
5 € 3 Ch included. **Surface**: unpaved.

Salin-de-Giraud 30A4

Rue de la Bouvine. **GPS**: n43,41222 e4,73056.

20 € 2 Ch € 0,80. 01/04-31/10

Sarrians 30A3

GPS: n44,07943 e4,97788.

10 free € 2 Ch € 2. **Surface**: metalled. 01/01-31/12
Distance: 800m.

Sault 30B3

P3, Route de Saint-Trinit. **GPS**: n44,09434 e5,41308.

15 free € 2/10minutes Ch € 2/1h. **Surface**: gravel. 01/01-31/12
Distance: 500m 500m.

Sausset-les-Pins 30B5

Avenue Pierre Matraja. **GPS**: n43,33890 e5,10916.

15 free € 2/100liter Ch € 2/1h. **Surface**: asphalted. 01/01-31/12
Distance: 1,2km 1,2km 1,2km 5m.
Remarks: At stadium.

Savines-le-Lac 30C2

Parking du Barnafret, Av. du Faubourg, D954. **GPS**: n44,52495 e6,40090.

30 € 7 € 2/120liter Ch (20x). **Surface**: asphalted.
Distance: 300m 100m.

Selonnet 30C3

Quartier de Boulangère. **GPS**: n44,36862 e6,31525.

7 free € 2/10minutes Ch € 2/55minutes . **Surface**: gravel.
01/01-31/12
Distance: 300m 300m 300m.
Remarks: Coins available at town hall/bakery/supermarket/bar-tabac, free wifi at town hall.

Sénas 30A4

Avenue des Jardins. **GPS**: n43,74403 e5,08020.

FR

6 ⌇free ⌐€ 3 ⌐Ch. ◻ 01/01-31/12
Distance: ⌐200m ⌐1,5km ⊗200m ⌐200m.

8 ⌇€8 ⌐ ⌐WC included. **Surface:** asphalted. ◻ 01/10-30/04
Distance: ⌐100m ⊗100m ⌐100m.

| ⌇S | Serre-Chevalier 🏔❄ | 30C1 |

Parking des Charmettes, Serre Chevalier 1500, D1091, Le Monêtier-les-Bains.
GPS: n44,97602 e6,50933.
40 ⌇€ 4,80/day + tourist tax ⌐ ⌐Ch free. **Surface:** metalled. ◻ 01/01-31/12
Distance: 🎿on the spot.
Remarks: Parking at skipistes.

| ⌇S | Six-Fours-les-Plages | 30B5 |

Promenade Gén. Charles de Gaulle. GPS: n43,10750 e5,81750.
⌐€ 3 ⌐Ch. ◻ 01/01-31/12
Remarks: Behind Office du Tourisme, 8-12, 14-19h.

| ⌇S | Serre-Chevalier 🏔❄ | 30C1 |

Parking de Pontillas, Hameau de Bez. **GPS:** n44,94805 e6,55564. ⬆.
20 ⌇€ 8, tourist tax excl ⌐ ⌐Ch ⌐ included. **Surface:** metalled.
Distance: 🎿20m.

| ⌇S | Sospel 🏔 | 31A4 |

Stade E. Donato, D2566. **GPS:** n43,87876 e7,44213. ⬆.

| ⌇S | Sillans-la-Cascade | 30C4 |

GPS: n43,56837 e6,18196.

4 ⌇free ⌐ ⌐Ch free. **Surface:** asphalted. ◻ 01/01-31/12
Distance: ⌐300m ⊗300m ⌐300m.

| ⌇S | St.André-les-Alpes | 30C3 |

GPS: n43,96535 e6,50639. ⬆➡.

⌇free ⌐. ◻ 01/01-31/12
Distance: ⌐on the spot ⊗50m.
Remarks: Park along river, water falls 800m. D560 Dir Salernes.

| ⌇S | Sisteron 🌿🏔 | 30C3 |

Aire de Saint Jaume, D951. **GPS:** n44,20028 e5,94389.

30 ⌇free ⌐€ 3/10minutes ⌐Ch⌐. S
urface: asphalted. ◻ 01/01-31/12
Distance: ⌐250m ⊗100m ⌐250m.
Remarks: On entering the village from southern dir.

| ⌇S | St.Etienne-de-Tinée | 30D3 |

Camping du Plan d'Eau, Boulevard de la Digue. **GPS:** n44,25620 e6,92350.
6 ⌇€8,50 ⌐ 2,50 ⌐Ch€ 2,50.
Remarks: In village, by lake.

| ⌇S | St.Laurent-du-Var | 30D4 |

Route des Pugets. GPS: n43,68550 e7,18522. ⬆.

⌇⌐€ 2 ⌐Ch⌐ 2. ◻ 01/01-31/12
Distance: ⌐4,5km.
Remarks: On entering city from dir Gap, before tunnel.

Tourist information Sisteron:
🛈 Office de Tourisme, Place de la République, www.sisteron.fr.Small fortress town.

| ⌇S | Six-Fours-les-Plages | 30B5 |

Port de la Coudoulière. GPS: n43,09750 e5,81194.

7 ⌇free ⌐ ⌐Ch free. **Surface:** asphalted.
Distance: ⌐1,2km ⌐4,5km ⊗1,2km ⌐1,2km.
Remarks: Max. 7 days.

FR

St.Mandrier 30C5

Pin Roland, Impasse de la Mer. **GPS:** n43,07771 e5,90444.⬆.

6 🚐free ⚡🔌 Ch free. **Surface:** asphalted. 🅾 01/01-31/12
Distance: ⚓500m ⊗500m.
Remarks: At tennis-courts, max. 48h.

St.Martin-de-Crau 30A4

Place François Miterrand. **GPS:** n43,63859 e4,81454.
3 🚐free ⚡🔌free. **Surface:** metalled. 🅾 01/01-31/12
Remarks: Max. 48h, parking in front of town hall.

St.Michel-l'Observatoire 30B3

GPS: n43,91611 e5,71667.⬆➡.

6 🚐free ⚡€ 2 🔌Ch. **Surface:** grassy/sand. 🅾 01/03-15/11
Distance: ⚓800m ⊗800m 🚰800m.
Remarks: At tennis-courts.

St.Paul-lez-Durance 30B4

Rue du Camping le Retour. **GPS:** n43,68694 e5,70611.⬆➡.

6 🚐free ⚡🔌 Ch free. **Surface:** metalled. 🅾 01/01-31/12
Distance: ⚓300m 🛢4km ⊗500m 🚰700m.
Remarks: Max. 48h.

St.Tropez 30D5

Aire camping-car, Chemin Fontaine du pin, Chemin de la Moutte. **GPS:** n43,26468 e6,67227.⬆.

15 🚐€ 11 ⚡€ 2 🔌Ch 🛢€ 2,50 WC ⚡€ 1. **Location:** Comfortable, isolated, quit. **Surface:** grassy/sand. 🅾 01/01-31/12
Distance: ⚓3km ⚓800m.

Remarks: Route les Salins, dir Les Salins, to the left chemin de la Fontaine du pin, to the left chemin de la Moutte, near Château de la Moutte.
Tourist information St.Tropez:
ℹ Office de Tourisme, Quai Jean Jaurès, www.saint-tropez.st.Small tourist town.
✖ La Citadelle, musée de la Marine.Navy museum.
🎡 Place des Lices.Week market. ⬛ Wed + Sa morning.

St.Véran 🌿🏖❄❅ 30D2

D5. **GPS:** n44,70447 e6,86091.
20 🚐€ 2/day, € 5/night ⚡🔌 Ch WC free. **Surface:** metalled. 🅾 01/01-31/12
Distance: ⚓100m ⊗100m 🚰200m 🛵on the spot ⚓200m.

Ste.Cécile-les-Vignes 30A3

Cave des Vignerons Reunis, D976. **GPS:** n44,25099 e4,89020.⬆.

🚐free ⚡🔌 Ch free. **Surface:** asphalted. 🅾 01/01-31/12

Ste.Croix-de-Verdon 30C4

Route du Lac. **GPS:** n43,75944 e6,15194.

20 🚐€ 6 ⚡🔌Ch 🛢 WC included.
Remarks: Max. 3 nights, service closed during wintertime.

Ste.Maxime 30D5

D25, le Muy dir Ste.Maxime. **GPS:** n43,31730 e6,62999.⬆.

50 🚐€ 10/24h ⚡🔌 Ch free. 🅿 **Surface:** metalled. 🅾 01/01-31/12
Distance: ⚓city centre 1km ⚓1,2km ⊗McDonalds 50m 🚰Lidl 200m.
Remarks: Max. 48h. Parking at roundabout, near McDonalds.
Tourist information Ste.Maxime:
🎡 🅾 Thu-morning.
🎡 Les Greniers du Golfe, Aire des Magnoti.Bric-a-brac. 🅾 Wed 08-18h.

Stes.Maries-de-la-Mer 🏖🌊 30A4

Avenue d'Arles, D570. **GPS:** n43,45535 e4,42750.⬆➡.

FR

60 🛏€ 9,50 🚰🔌 Ch 🚿 WC included. **Surface:** asphalted. 🅾 01/01-31/12
Distance: 🚶200m 🏊beach 400m ⊗100m 🛒50m 💊100m.
Remarks: Max. 48h.

Stes.Maries-de-la-Mer 30A4
Valée des Lys, Avenue Cousteau. **GPS:** n43,45364 e4,43695. ⬆➡

150 🛏€ 9,50 🚰🔌 Ch WC. **Surface:** metalled. 🅾 01/01-31/12
Distance: 🚶250m 🏊beach 50m ⊗100m 💊250m.

Thorenc 30D4
Lac de Thorenc, D2. **GPS:** n43,79930 e6,80838. ⬆

10 🛏free 🚰🔌 Ch free. 🅾 01/01-31/12
Distance: 🚶750m ⊗100m 💊epicerie 750m.

Trigance 30C4
Quartier Saint Roch. GPS: n43,76018 e6,44159.

10 🛏€ 5 🚰🔌 Ch free. **Surface:** asphalted. 🅾 01/01-31/12
Remarks: Max. 2 days.

Uvernet-Fours 30D3
Losissement Le Bachelard, D902. **GPS:** n44,36816 e6,62783. ⬆

6 🛏free 🚰€ 2 🔌Ch€ 2. **Surface:** gravel/sand. 🅾 01/01-31/12

Vaison-la-Romaine 30A3
Aire camping-car, Avenue André Coudray. **GPS:** n44,24650 e5,07392. ⬆

25 🛏€ 6 🚰🔌 Ch free.
🅾 01/01-31/12 Tue-morning.
Distance: 🚶800m.

Tourist information Vaison-la-Romaine:
ℹ Office de Tourisme, Place du Chanoine-Sautel, www.vaison-la-romaine.com.
City from the Roman time, archaeological findings. 🅾 city daily.
👁 Le Pont Romain.Bridge from the Roman Empire.
⌂ Le Château.Ruins of the castle of the Counts of Toulouse.
⌂ 🅾 Tue.

Valberg 30D3
Le Lagopède, Route de Rouya. **GPS:** n44,09615 e6,93675. ⬆➡

21 🛏€ 10 + € 0,20/pp tourist tax 🚰🔌 Ch 🚿 (21x)included WC. **Surface:** asphalted. 🅾 01/01-31/12
Distance: 🚶500m on the spot ⊗on the spot 💊on the spot 🥖600m.

Tourist information Valberg:
ℹ Office de Tourisme, Centre Administratif, www.valberg.com.Ski station, alpine and cross country skiing. In the summer large open-air swimming pool.

Valréas 30A3
Domaine du Lumian, Route de Montélimar, D941. **GPS:** n44,39028 e4,96421. ⬆

6 🛏free 🚰🔌 Ch 🚿 free. **Surface:** gravel. 🅾 01/01-31/12
Distance: 🚶2,5km.

🏕️ S | **Veynes** | 30B2

Base de Loisirs Les Iscles, Les Graviers, D994. **GPS**: n44,51830 e5,79860. ⬆️.
🏕️ €5 📶. **Surface:** gravel.
Distance: 🏊on the spot ⊗on the spot.
Remarks: Wifi at restaurant.

🏕️ S | **Veynes** | 30B2

Place du 19 Mars, D994. **GPS**: n44,53332 e5,82346. ⬆️.

🏕️free 🚰 ♨️Chfree. **Surface:** asphalted. ⬛ 01/03-30/11

🏕️ S | **Villeneuve** | 30C4

GPS: n43,89611 e5,86167. ⬆️.

8 🏕️free 🚰 ♨️Chfree. **Surface:** unpaved. ⬛ 01/01-31/12, service: 01/03-30/11
Distance: 🚰200m 🛒5,5km.

🏕️ S | **Visan** | 30A3

Domaine des Lauribert, D976. **GPS**: n44,34833 e4,97276. ⬆️.

20 🏕️free 🚰♨️Ch ⚡(8x)€ 2 WC. **Surface:** unpaved. ⬛ 01/01-31/12
Remarks: At wine-grower, max. 72h.

SPAIN

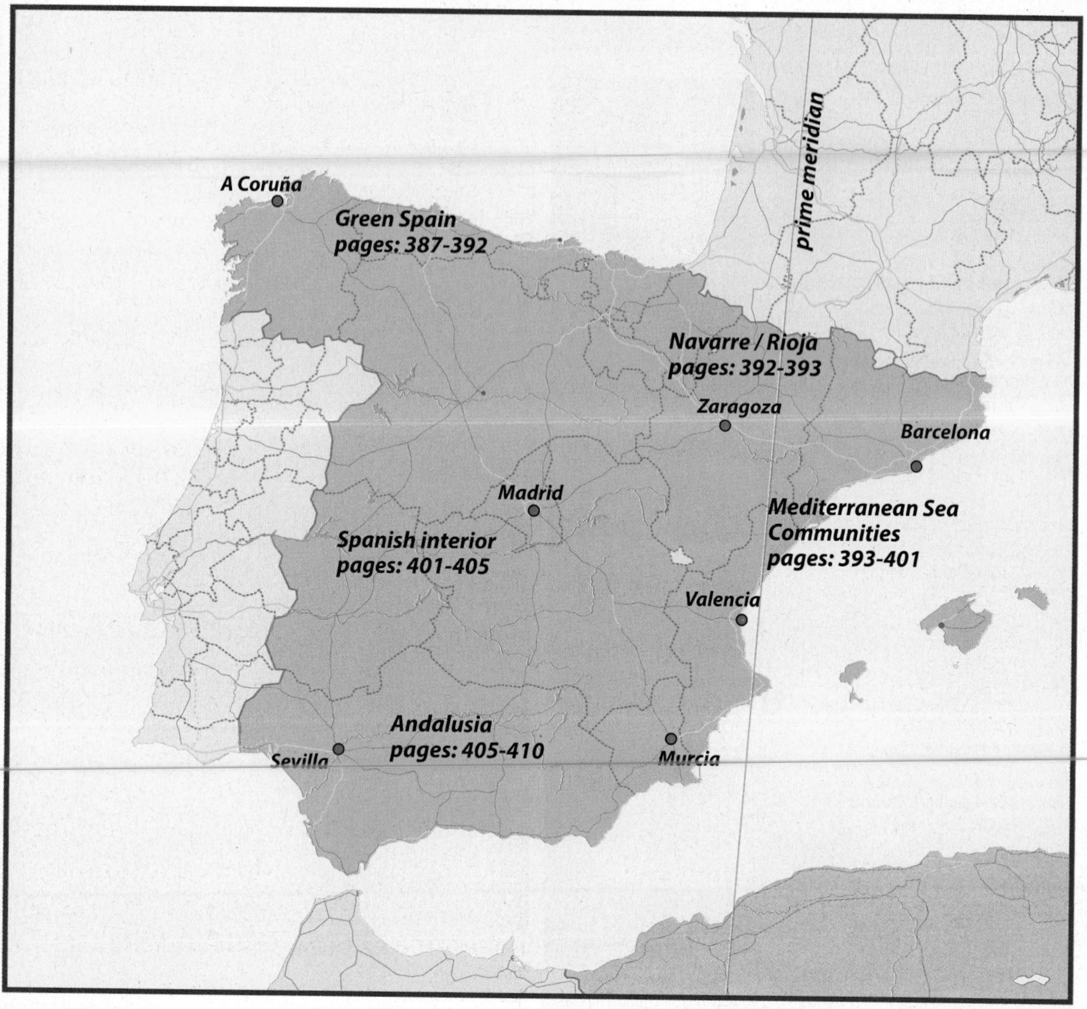

A Coruña

Green Spain
pages: 387-392

prime meridian

Navarre / Rioja
pages: 392-393

Zaragoza

Barcelona

Madrid

Spanish interior
pages: 401-405

Mediterranean Sea Communities
pages: 393-401

Valencia

Andalusia
pages: 405-410

Sevilla

Murcia

Capital: Madrid
Government: Constitutional monarchy
Official Language: Spanish
Population: 46,952,000 (2010)
Area: 505,782 km²

General information
Dialling code: 0034
Currency: Euro

Regulations for overnight stays
Wild camping is allowed having gained permission from the municipality, olice or property owner. Along the Mediterranean coast wild camping is almost always forbidden. Parking places (P) mentioned here can be considered as tolerated places to stay overnight.

Opening hours
Shops: Monday-Saturday 9.30am-1.30pm and 4.30pm-8pm. Shopping centres 10am-21/22pm, sometimes also on Sundays.
Banks: Monday-Saturday 8.30am-2pm, June till August closed on Saturday.
Restaurants: lunch 1pm-3.30pm, dinner 8.30pm-11pm.

Spain

Green Spain

A Coruña 🌿⚓🍵 36C3
Puerto de San Pedro de Visma, Zona de O Portiño. **GPS:** n43,37167 w8,44472.⬆️

12 🅿️free ⛽🚽Ch free. **Surface:** metalled.
Distance: 🚶3km ⛱️on the spot ⊗50m 🛒1km Carrefour 🚆1km.
Remarks: Max. 48h.

A Coruña 🌿⚓🍵 36C3
Tore de Hercules. **GPS:** n43,38378 w8,40228.
🅿️free. **Surface:** asphalted.
Distance: 🚶on the spot ⊗50m 🛒50m.

A Guarda 36B5
GPS: n41,89892 w8,87825.
🅿️.
Remarks: Parking in harbour.

A Pontenova 36D3
Rua de la Estación. **GPS:** n43,34739 w7,19171.⬆️➡️

8 🅿️free ⛽🚽Ch free. **Surface:** asphalted.
Distance: ⊗200m 🛒100m.
Remarks: Max. 48h.

A Rúa 36D4
Área Recreativa O Aguillón. **GPS:** n42,38800 w7,11459.⬆️
10 🅿️free ⛽🚽Ch free. **Surface:** asphalted/grassy. 🅾️ 01/01-31/12
Distance: 🚶500m ⛱️on the spot ⊗500m 🛒500m.
Remarks: Next to football ground.

Arcade 🍴 36B4
Rúa do Peirao. **GPS:** n42,33946 w8,61329.
5 🅿️free ⛽🚽Ch. **Surface:** metalled. 🅾️ 01/01-31/12
Distance: ⊗nearby 🛒nearby.

Arrigorriaga 37C4
Carretera Buia Etorbidea. **GPS:** n43,23772 w2,91938.
8 🅿️.
Remarks: Tolerated place.

As Neves 36C5
Camino del Emenjeric. **GPS:** n42,08726 w8,41374.⬆️➡️
8 🅿️free ⛽🚽Ch free. 🅾️ 01/01-31/12
Distance: ⊗200m 🛒200m.
Remarks: Max. 48h.

Avilés 🍴 37A3
Restaurante Rias Baixas, Camino Heros, 3. **GPS:** n43,55120 w5,93451.
7 🅿️€ 6/24h ⛽🚽Ch.
Distance: ⊗on the spot 🛒500m.

Bakio 37C4
Parking, BI 3101. **GPS:** n43,42783 w2,80442.
🅿️free. **Surface:** asphalted.
Remarks: Tolerated place.

Behobia 37D4
N10, Calle de Aria Juncal. **GPS:** n43,34310 w1,7598.

6 🅿️day time € 2,25, overnight stay free. **Surface:** asphalted.
Distance: 🚲500m.
Remarks: Tolerated place.

Bermeo 37D4
Área de la Pérgola, Itsasoan Galdurakoen Lamera. **GPS:** n43,42306 w2,72556.⬆️

10 🅿️free ⛽🚽Ch free. **Surface:** asphalted.
Remarks: Nearby football ground, max. 48h.

Bertamirans 🍵 36C4
Paseo Fluvial. **GPS:** n42,86009 w8,64838.⬆️

15 🅿️free ⛽🚽Ch free. **Surface:** asphalted. 🅾️ 01/01-31/12
Distance: ⊗100m 🛒50m Carrefour 🚆dir. Santiago every 30 min.
Remarks: Max. 48h.

Bilbao 37C4
Kobetamendi, Monte Kobeta, 31. **GPS:** n43,25961 w2,96355.
72 🅿️€ 15/day ⛽🚽Ch 🚿. **Surface:** asphalted.
Distance: 🚶centre 4,5km 🚲2,8km 🚆Bilbao-bus 58.
Remarks: Max. 72h.

Boiro 🍴 36B4
Playa Jardín de Barraña. **GPS:** n42,64183 w8,89481.⬆️➡️

10 🅿️€ 3-6 ⛽🚽Ch free. **Surface:** asphalted. 🅾️ 01/01-31/12
Distance: 🚶500m ⛱️20m ⊗200m Bistro Prima 🛒400m.
Remarks: Max. 48h.

Boiro 🍴 36B4
Playa Mañons, S/n 15930 Chancelas–Abanqueiro. **GPS:** n42,63138 w8,85311.
⬆️➡️

10 🍽€3-6 🚐🍽Ch.
Distance: 🚶on the spot.

| 🛏 | Bueu | 36B4 |

PO315 dir Cabo Udra. **GPS:** n42,33460 w8,8248.
🍽free. **Surface:** sand.
Remarks: Max. 48h.

| 🛏 | Bueu | 36B4 |

Puerto, Avda. de Montero Rios. **GPS:** n42,32732 w8,7838.
🍽.

| 🛏S | Burela | 36D3 |

Área de Burela, Parque de O Campón, parking Hospital de Burela. **GPS:** n43,65216 w7,35891.⬆

5 🍽free 🚐🍽Chfree. **Surface:** asphalted.
Distance: 🚶200m ⊗300m 🏖200m.
Remarks: Max. 48h.

| 🛏S | Cabárceno | 37C4 |

Área Lago del Acebo, N634> dir Parque de la naturaleze de Cabárceno. **GPS:** n43,35802 w3,81959.⬆
30 🍽free 🚐🍽Chfree. **Surface:** asphalted.
Distance: 🚶100m 🚶50m 🚶50m ⊗on the spot.
Remarks: Max. 48h.

| 🛏 | Camariñas | 36B3 |

Jachthaven. GPS: n43,12694 w9,18333.
5 🍽free. **Surface:** asphalted.

| 🛏S | Cangas de Onís | 37B4 |

Parking Lanzadera Picos de Europa, Calle del Llreau. **GPS:** n43,35211 w5,12536.⬆

15 🍽free 🚐🍽Chfree. **Surface:** asphalted.
Distance: ⊗100m.
Remarks: Max. 48h.

| 🛏 | Carnota | 36B4 |

Portocubelo. **GPS:** n42,80145 w9,14492.

4 🍽free. **Surface:** asphalted.
Distance: 🚶Carnota 5km 🏖10m.
Remarks: Parking next to hatchery.

| 🛏 | Carreno | 37A3 |

Puerto Perlora. GPS: n43,58342 w5,75713.
5 🍽.
Remarks: Tolerated place.

| 🛏S | Cartelle | 36C5 |

Camperpark O Mundil, Antigua Carretera OU-659. **GPS:** n42,21444 w8,03306.

24 🍽€10 🚐🍽Ch 🔧WC🍽🛒📶free.
Surface: gravel. 📅 01/01-31/12
Distance: 🚶1km zona fluvial Río Arnoia ⊗10m.

| 🛏 | Castro Urdiales | 37C4 |

Parking Parco Cotolino. GPS: n43,37364 w3,20899.
🍽€2/3h (10.00-20.00). **Surface:** asphalted.
Remarks: Tolerated place.

| 🛏S | Chantada | 36C4 |

Champ de Sangoñedo. GPS: n42,60598 w7,77989.⬆
3 🍽free 🚐🍽Chfree.
Remarks: At footballstadium.

| 🛏 | Comillas | 37B4 |

Parking, Calle de Manuel Noriega. **GPS:** n43,38821 w4,28319.
🍽free. **Surface:** asphalted.
Remarks: Tolerated place.

| 🛏S | Cospeito | 36D3 |

Camino de la Laguna. **GPS:** n43,23984 w7,55579.
5 🍽free 🚐🍽Ch 🔧free. **Surface:** asphalted. 📅 01/01-31/12
Distance: ⊗300m.

| 🛏 | Cudillero | 37A3 |

Puerto. GPS: n43,56568 w6,1517.
5 🍽.
Remarks: Parking in harbour.

| 🛏S | Ferrol | 36C3 |

Ctra. de la Malata. **GPS:** n43,49333 w8,23972.⬆

15 🍽free 🚐🍽Chfree. **Surface:** asphalted.
Distance: 🚶700m ⊗300m.

| 🛏S | Finisterre | 36B4 |

Praia de Langosteira. GPS: n42,92320 w9,26149.

5 🍽free 🚐.

Distance: ☈on the spot ⊗1km 🛒1km.
Remarks: Parking on beach, max. 48h.

| 🅿 | Finisterre ⛴ 🌊 | 36B4 |

Cabo de Finisterre. GPS: n42,88651 w9,2724.
10 🅿free.

| 🅿 | Fuente Dé | 37B4 |

Picos de Europa, C621. **GPS:** n43,14433 w4,81274.
🅿free. **Surface:** sand.
Remarks: Parking funicular railway.

| 🅿 | Gijón | 37A3 |

Camino de las Mimosas, El Rinconin. **GPS:** n43,54708 w5,63648.
20 🅿free. **Surface:** asphalted.
Distance: ☈300m.
Remarks: In front of instituto de Salut Mental Pérez-Espinez Oria.

| 🅿 | Gorliz 🌿 | 37C4 |

Paseo de Astondo. **GPS:** n43,41220 w2,94194.
🅿free.
Location: Very simple.
Surface: asphalted.
Distance: 🚶500m ☈50m 🚌20m.
Remarks: Parking on beach.

Tourist information Gorliz:

ℹ Bilbao.Capital of the Basque Country and previously centre of the iron industry.
Ⓜ Museo Guggenheim, Avenida Abandoibarra, 2, Bilbao.Collection of modern art. ⏰ Tue-Su 10-20h, 01/07-31/08 10-21h.
✝ Basilica de Begoña, Virgen de Begoña, 38, Bilbao-Vizcaya.Basilica.

| 🅿 | Gozon | 37A3 |

Parking El Penoso. GPS: n43,60341 w5,77325.
3 🅿.
Distance: ☈150m.
Remarks: Tolerated place.

| 🅿 | Guetaria | 37D4 |

N634. **GPS:** n43,30388 w2,2075.
🅿free. **Surface:** asphalted.
Remarks: Parking on beach.

| 🅿 S | Guitiriz | 36C3 |

Rua do Voluntariado. **GPS:** n43,17727 w7,88062.⬆
5 🅿free 🚰 🔌 Ch 🔧 free. **Surface:** gravel. ⏰ 01/01-31/12
Distance: 🚶800m ☈100m.

| 🅿 S | Hermandad De Campoo De Suso | 37B4 |

Estación Invernal Alto Campoo, C 628 Reinosa - Espinilla, dir: Alto Campoo. **GPS:** n43,03839 w4,37036.
20 🅿 🚰 🔌 Ch.
Distance: 🎿on the spot.
Remarks: Tolerated place.

| 🅿 | Hondaribbia | 37D4 |

Ramón Iribarren Pasalekua. **GPS:** n43,37929 w1,79768.

20 🅿€ 1,24/h. **Surface:** asphalted. ⏰ 01/03-31/12
Remarks: Parking on beach.

| 🅿 | La Vega | 37B3 |

GPS: n43,48009 w5,13416.
10 🅿€ 7.
Remarks: Parking on beach.

| 🅿 | Laredo | 37C4 |

Avda. de la Victoria. **GPS:** n43,43227 w3,45024.
5 🅿.
Remarks: Tolerated place.

| 🅿 S | Legazpi | 37D4 |

Parque Mirandaola de Legazpi, Carretera Legazpia, GI 2630. **GPS:** n43,03678 w2,33758.⬆
8 🅿free 🚰 Chfree. **Surface:** asphalted.
Distance: ⊗on the spot.
Remarks: Max. 48h.

| 🅿 S | Liérganes | 37C4 |

Calle de Puente Romano. **GPS:** n43,34479 w3,74183.
10 🅿free 🚰 🔌 Chfree.
Remarks: Parking nearby station, max. 48h.

| 🅿 | Llanes | 37B4 |

Playa de Toró. GPS: n43,41605 w4,7451.
10 🅿.
Remarks: Parking areas along the beach, max. 48h.

| 🅿 | Luarca | 36D3 |

Avda. de la Argentina, AS219. **GPS:** n43,53658 w6,53255.
10 🅿.
Remarks: At sports park.

| 🅿 S | Lugo 🪣 | 36C4 |

Pabellón Municipal de Deportes, Avda. de Santiago. **GPS:** n43,00452 w7,56144.
⬆

10 🅿free 🚰 🔌 Chfree. **Surface:** asphalted.
Distance: 🚶10min ✈5,2km.
Remarks: Parking gymnasium, max. 48h.

| P S | Lugo 🪣 | 36C4 |

Plaza de Asturias, Rúa Ánxel Fole. **GPS:** n43,00972 w7,55805.
15 🅿€ 12/24h 🚰 free. **Surface:** asphalted.

| 🅿 S | Milladoiro | 36C4 |

Traversia do Porto. **GPS:** n42,84512 w8,58079.⬆

20 🅿free 🚰 🔌 Chfree. **Surface:** asphalted.
Distance: ⊗200m 🛒200m 🚌dir. Santiago every 15 min.
Remarks: Max. 48h. A9 exit Santiago de Compostello zouth, N550 dir Pontevedre, near swimming pool.

| 🅿 S | Miño | 36C3 |

AP-9 Coruña-Ferrol >< km 15,5. **GPS:** n43,37404 w8,18736.⬆
12 🅿free 🚰 🔌 Ch WC free. **Surface:** asphalted.
Distance: ⊗on the spot 🛒on the spot.
Remarks: Parking nearby motorway.

| 🅿 S | Miranda de Ebro 🌊 | 37C5 |

Calle de Burgos. **GPS:** n42,68880 w2,95403.⬆

ES

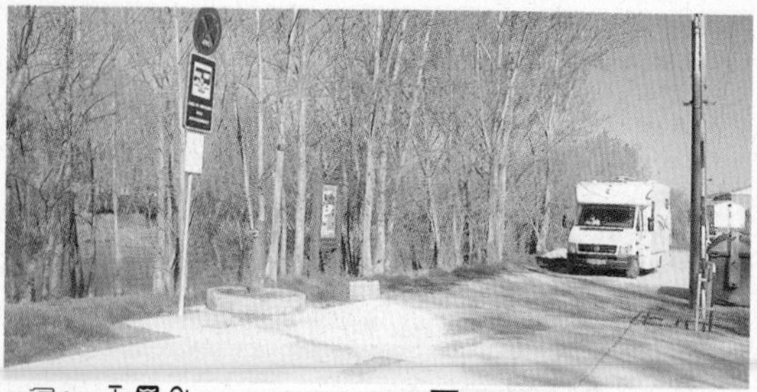

10 🚐free 🚰 🗑 Chfree. **Surface:** metalled. 📅 01/01-31/12
Distance: 🛤3km.
Remarks: Max. 48h.

Tourist information Miranda de Ebro:
ℹ Oficina de Turismo, Parque Antonio Machado, 4.
🏪 Medieval annual fair. 📅 around May 1.
🏪 Week market. 📅 Sa.

🚐 [S] **Mondoñedo** **36D3**
Calle de Vicedo. **GPS**: n43,42778 w7,37028.↑.
10 🚐free 🚰 🗑 Chfree. **Surface:** metalled.

🚐 [S] **Monforte de Lemos** **36C4**
Auditorio Multiusos de Monforte, Calle de la Circuvalación / Calle de Santa Clara.
GPS: n42,52750 w7,5119.↑.

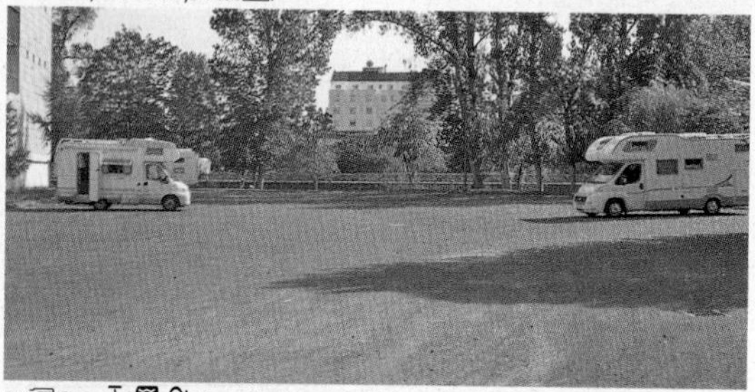

30 🚐free 🚰 🗑 Chfree. **Surface:** asphalted.
Distance: 🍴500m 🛒550m 🚌300m.
Remarks: Max. 48h.

🚐 **Muros** **36B4**
C 550. **GPS**: n42,77516 w9,0573.
🚐free. **Surface:** asphalted.
Remarks: Parking harbour.

🚐 [S] **Muxia** **36B3**
Calle de la Rua Marina. **GPS**: n43,10593 w9,21682.
10 🚐free 🚰. **Surface:** asphalted.
Distance: 🏙on the spot ⛱on the spot 🍴on the spot 🛒on the spot 🚌50m.
Remarks: Parking in harbour.

🚐 **Noia** **36B4**
Rúa de Pedra Marques. **GPS**: n42,78783 w8,8906.

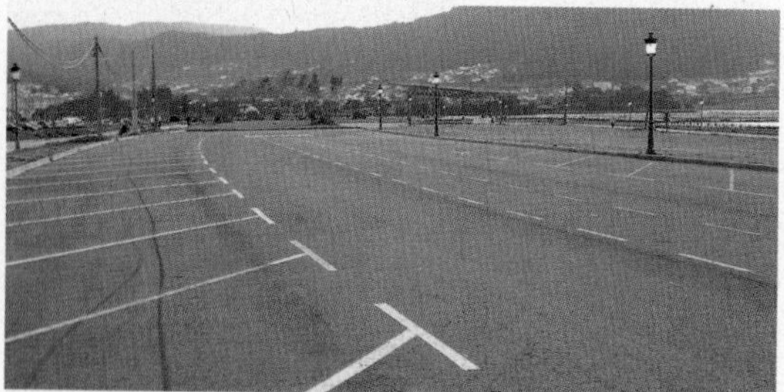

🚐free. **Surface:** asphalted.
Distance: 🏙on the spot 🍴50m 🛒50m 🚌Bus 20m.
Remarks: Tolerated place.

Tourist information Noia:
👁 El Pendo, 5km S. Santander.Cave with petroglyphs.

🚐 [S] **O Barco** **36D4**
Malecón Campiño. **GPS**: n42,41063 w6,97493.↑→.

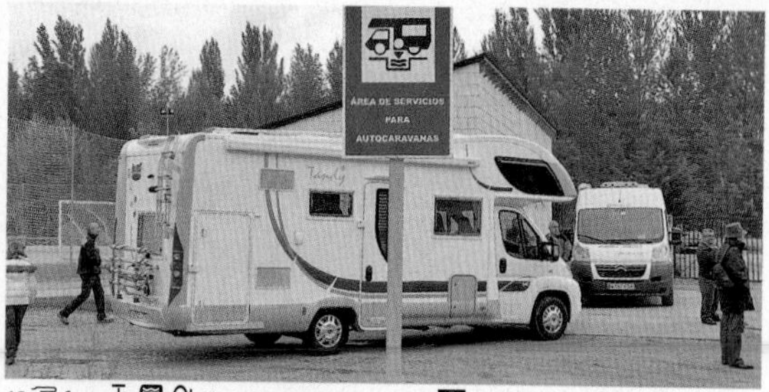

12 🚐free 🚰 🗑 Chfree. **Surface:** unpaved. 📅 01/01-31/12
Distance: 🏙400m 🍴250m 🛒250m.

🚐 [S] **Oia** **36B5**
O Muino. **GPS**: n42,06361 w8,89194.↑.
20 🚐€ 6,30 🚰 🗑 Ch ⚡ included. **Surface:** metalled. 📅 01/01-31/12

🍴 [S] **Parada do Sil** **36C4**
Rural Pepe, Campo da Feira 17. **GPS**: n42,38287 w7,57106.
4 🚐guests free 🚰 🗑 Ch. 📅 01/01-31/12
Distance: 🍴on the spot 🛒on the spot.

🚐 [S] **Pobra do Brollòn** **36D4**
Campo Municipal de Fut. **GPS**: n42,56944 w7,39417.↑.
8 🚐free 🚰 🗑 Chfree. **Surface:** metalled.

🚐 **Porto de Rinlo** **36D3**
GPS: n43,55703 w7,10352.
🚐.
Remarks: Several parking along the coast till Cabo Burela.

🚐 [S] **Potes** **37B4**
Santo Toribio de Liébana, CA885. **GPS**: n43,15028 w4,65389.
🚐free 🚰 🗑 free.
Surface: asphalted.
Distance: 🏙Potes 3km.
Remarks: Parking monastery.

Tourist information Potes:
🏪 Local products. 📅 Mo.
✳ Historical cattle market, since 1379. 📅 01/08-15/08.

🚐 [S] **Redondela** **36B4**
Avda. de Mendiño. **GPS**: n42,28972 w8,61055.↑.
15 🚐free 🚰 🗑 Ch.
Distance: 🏙600m ⛱500m 🍴600m 🛒600m.

🚐 [S] **Rentería** **37D4**
Área Rural de Listorreta-Barrengoloia. **GPS**: n43,26800 w1,90135.

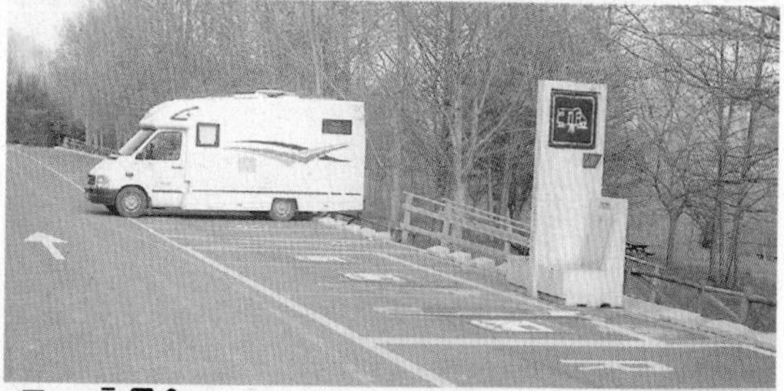

5 🚐free 🚰 🗑 Chfree. **Surface:** asphalted. 📅 01/01-31/12
Distance: 🏙Renteria 7km.
Remarks: Max. 48h. A8 exit Renteria, GI 2132 dir Zamalbide > 5km left then follow this road for 3km.

🚐 **Ribadeo** **36D3**
Rua Daniel Cortezón. **GPS**: n43,53553 w7,04614.
7 🚐free. **Surface:** asphalted. 📅 01/01-31/12
Distance: 🏙300m 🛤2km.

🚐 [S] **Ribamontán al Monte** **37C4**
A8 Bilbao > Santander. **GPS**: n43,40282 w3,62877.
10 🚐free 🚰 🗑 Chfree.

🚐 [S] **Ribamontán al Monte** **37C4**
A8 Santander > Bilbao. **GPS**: n43,40446 w3,62476.
10 🚐free 🚰 🗑 Chfree. **Location:** Highway. **Surface:** asphalted.

🚐 [S] **San Clodio** **36D4**
Parque de Pena da Mula, Calle del Troque. **GPS**: n42,46750 w7,28583.↑.

3 🏕free ⌐ 🔧 Ch free. **Surface:** asphalted. 🅾 01/01-31/12
Distance: 🚶200m ⌐Playa Fluvial 25m ⊗cafetaria.

| 🔧S | San Martín del Rey Aurelio | 37A4 |

Área del Pozo Entrego, Avda. de la Vega, AS17. **GPS:** n43,28639 w5,63889.⬆.
3 🏕free ⌐ 🔧 Ch free. **Surface:** asphalted.
Distance: ⊗on the spot 🔧Alcampo 1km.
Remarks: Max. 48h.

| 🔧S | San Sebastian 🌿🔧 | 37D4 |

Paseo de Berio nº 2. **GPS:** n43,30797 w2,01426.⬆.
44 🏕€ 3,10-6,20 ⌐ 🔧 Ch.
Surface: metalled.
🅾 01/01-31/12
Distance: ✈2km.
Remarks: Max. 48h, marked pitches.

Tourist information San Sebastian:
ℹ️ Centro de Atracción y Turismo (CAT), Reina Regente, www.donostia.org.Old city with, Parte Vieja, historical city centre with numerous cafés, restaurants and tapa bars.
Ⓜ Museo de San Telmo.Basque collections.
Ⓜ Palacio del Mar.Museum for oceanografics. 🅾 10-19h, Sa-Su 10-21h, 15/06-15/09 10-21h.
⚔ Castillo de la Mota.War museum.
🌲 🅾 Su-morning.

| 🔧 | San Vicente de la Barquera 🌿🔧 | 37B4 |

Barrio Rupuente, C6316. **GPS:** n43,39372 w4,36166.
🏕free.
Remarks: Tolerated place. Along coast road, next to Playa Merón.

Tourist information San Vicente de la Barquera:
ℹ️ Oficina de Turismo, Avenida del Generalísimo, nº 20.Old fortress city.

| 🔧 | Santiago de Compostela 🌿🔧 | 36C4 |

Rua das Casas Novas, Santo Agnacio Dumonte. **GPS:** n42,89357 w8,55935.

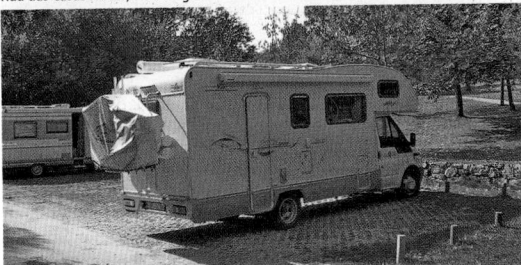

4 🏕free. **Surface:** metalled.
Distance: 🚶cathedral 2km.
Remarks: Tolerated place.

| P | Santiago de Compostela 🌿🔧 | 36C4 |

GPS: n42,88054 w8,54512.
🏕.

Remarks: Parking areas.

| P | Santiago de Compostela 🌿🔧 | 36C4 |

Auditorio de Galicia, Avda. Burgo das Nacións. **GPS:** n42,89043 w8,54331.
🏕.

Tourist information Santiago de Compostela:
ℹ️ Oficina de Turismo, Rúa del Villar, 43, www.santiagoturismo.com.City known for the termination of the pilgrime route.
👁 Plaza de la Quintana.Impressive square.
🎆 Fiesta del Apóstol Santiago.Most important festival of Galicia. 🅾 15/07-31/07.

| 🔧 | Santillana del Mar 🌿🔧 | 37B4 |

Ctra. C6316. **GPS:** n43,38845 w4,10803.

🏕€ 2/24h. **Surface:** asphalted.
Remarks: Tolerated place.

Tourist information Santillana del Mar:
ℹ️ Small medieval town.

| 🔧S | Sanxenxo 🔧 | 36B4 |

Área de Cachadelos, PO-308. **GPS:** n42,41652 w8,86833.⬆→.
65 🏕€ 6 ⌐ 🔧 Ch 🔧 ⊙. **Surface:** grassy.
Distance: ⌐200m ⊗2km 🔧on the spot.

| 🔧S | Sarria | 36D4 |

Calle de Castelo. **GPS:** n42,77194 w7,41028.⬆.
12 🏕free ⌐ 🔧 Ch free. **Surface:** asphalted.
Distance: 🚶800m ⌐on the spot ⊗800m.

| 🔧S | Saturrarán | 37D4 |

GPS: n43,31968 w2,41165.
5 🏕free ⌐free.
Remarks: Parking on beach.

| 🔧 | Suances | 37B4 |

Playa de los Locos. **GPS:** n43,44300 w4,0465.
🏕free.
Remarks: Parking at lighthouse.

| 🔧S | Teverga | 37A4 |

Parking Senda del Oso, Entrago. **GPS:** n43,17178 w6,09562.
20 🏕free ⌐ 🔧 Ch free. **Surface:** asphalted.
Distance: ⊗on the spot.
Remarks: Max. 48h.

| 🔧S | Tui | 36B5 |

Puente Tripes, Avenida de Portual. **GPS:** n42,04333 w8,64656.⬆.
6 🏕free ⌐ 🔧 Ch free. **Surface:** asphalted.
Distance: ✈1,3km ⊗500m.
Remarks: Max. 48h.

| 🔧S | Tui | 36B5 |

Parking Rio Mino. GPS: n42,04751 w8,64388.
🏕free.
Distance: ✈1,5km.

| 🔧S | Valdoviño | 36C3 |

Playa da Frouxeira, Estrada da Lagoa. **GPS:** n43,61389 w8,1515.
5 🏕free ⌐free.
Distance: ⌐on the spot ⊗on the spot.
Remarks: Parking on beach, max. 48h.

| 🔧S | Vares/Bares | 36D3 |

Porto de Bares. GPS: n43,77142 w7,66811.
25 🏕against payment ⌐ 🔧. **Surface:** asphalted.

| 🔧S | Vilalba | 36C3 |

Rua da Feira. **GPS:** n43,29556 w7,67694.⬆.
15 🏕free ⌐ 🔧 Ch free. **Surface:** asphalted.
Distance: ⊗300m 🔧300m.

| 🔧S | Vilanova de Arousa | 36B4 |

Avda. Mola. **GPS:** n42,56293 w8,82833.
🏕⌐.

ES

Villagarcia de Arosa   36B4
Area Camping Rio Ulla, Bamio , Campanario Nº 65. **GPS**: n42,63417 w8,76028.

6 ⌂ € 15 ⌂ ⌂ Ch ✦ included. **Surface**: grassy.
Distance: ⌂10m.
Remarks: >20h <10h.

Vitoria Gasteiz   37D4
Área de Lakua, Forondako Atea. **GPS**: n42,86583 w2,68527. ⬆
10 ⌂free ⌂ ⌂ Chfree. **Surface**: asphalted.

Vitoria Gasteiz   37D4
Portal de Foronde. **GPS**: n42,86684 w2,68539. ⬆ ➡
10 ⌂free ⌂ ⌂ Chfree. **Location**: Urban, comfortable, central, quit. **Surface**: asphalted. ⬛ 01/01-31/12
Distance: ⌂2km ⌂5km ⊗100m ⌂ bakery 50m ⌂50m.
Remarks: Wed, market.

Zumaia   37D4
Calle de la Estación. **GPS**: n43,29302 w2,24701. ⬆

25 ⌂free ⌂ ⌂ Chfree. **Surface**: asphalted.
Distance: ⌂4,4km.

Navarre and Rioja

Aínsa   28C6
Plaza del Castillo. **GPS**: n42,41916 e0,13515.
⌂free.
Surface: sand.

Tourist information Aínsa:
ℹ The capital of a medieval kingdom by surrounded fortress walls.
Ⓜ✕ Castillo de Aínsa.Castle, 11-13th century, with Eco museum.
⌂ ⬛ Tue.

Alquézar   40B1
Alquézar, Ctra.Barbastro,. **GPS**: n42,17097 e0,02382.
⌂. ⬛ 01/01-31/12

Tourist information Alquézar:
ℹ Historical city.

Ansó   28A5
Ctra. de Ansó a Fago. **GPS**: n42,75648 w0,83102.
2 ⌂ ⌂.

Aoiz   28A5
Hotel Ekai. **GPS**: n42,77624 w1,38536.
10 ⌂free ⌂ ⌂.

Ariza   37D6
Area de Servicios La Cadiera, A2 Madrid > Zaragoza. **GPS**: n41,31210 w2,00329.
5 ⌂ ⌂.
Remarks: Tolerated place.

Bielsa   28C6
Calle Mayor. **GPS**: n42,63437 e0,21893.
3 ⌂.

Remarks: Tolerated place.

Botaya   28B6
Parking Monasterio de San Juan la Peña. **GPS**: n42,50699 w0,66414.

3 ⌂free.
Remarks: Tolerated place.

Estelle   37D5
Calle St. Barbara Calea. **GPS**: n42,67306 w2,03972.

3 ⌂free. **Surface**: asphalted. ⬛ 01/01-31/12
Remarks: Tolerated place.

Tourist information Estelle:
⌂ Puebte la Reine. ⬛ Sa.

Haro   37C5
LR111. **GPS**: n42,57296 w2,86423.

4 ⌂free ⌂free. ⬛ 01/01-31/12

Haro   37C5
Parking centro deportivo, Av de los Ingenieros del Ministerio Obras Públicas, LR-111. **GPS**: n42,57677 w2,85222.

4 ⌂free ⌂free. ⬛ 01/01-31/12
Remarks: At sports park.

Tourist information Haro:
ℹ Capital of Rioja wine.

ES

| | Jaca | 28B6 |

Calle De Burnao. **GPS:** n42,57448 w0,55155.

6 🛏free 🚰free.
Remarks: Tolerated place.

| | Jaca | 28B6 |

Calle de Archén. **GPS:** n42,57113 w0,54421.
4 🛏free.
Remarks: Tolerated place.

| | Logroño | 37D5 |

Parking Camino del Pantano. GPS: n42,44913 w2,50142.

20 🛏free. 🅾 01/01-31/12
Remarks: Parking at artificial lake.

| | Navarrete 🌿 | 37D5 |

Calle de la Carretera. **GPS:** n42,42458 w2,55584.

4 🛏free. **Surface:** asphalted. 🅾 01/01-31/12
Remarks: Parking at swimming pool.

| | Pamplona | 37D5 |

Parque de la Tejería, Calle Playa de Capparoso. **GPS:** n42,81908 w1,63766.

4 🛏<6m. **Surface:** asphalted.
Remarks: Tolerated place.

| | Pamplona | 37D5 |

Plaza Errotozar, Calle del Rio Arga. **GPS:** n42,82057 w1,64932.

10 🛏free. **Surface:** metalled.
Remarks: Tolerated place.

| | Roncesvalles | 28A5 |

Paseo Ibaneta. **GPS:** n43,02018 w1,32401.
5 🛏.

| P | Torla | 28B6 |

Torla, Ordesa National Park, A135. **GPS:** n42,62582 w0,11196.
🛏. **Surface:** asphalted.
Remarks: Large parking.

| | Torremontalbo | 37C5 |

LR318. **GPS:** n42,51079 w2,6915.

2 🛏free. **Surface:** grassy/gravel. 🅾 01/01-31/12
Remarks: Picnic area.

| | Zaragoza | 40A1 |

Parque de Atracciones de Zaragoza. GPS: n41,61994 w0,90122.
10 🛏.
Distance: 🚲4,5km.
Remarks: Tolerated place.

Mediterranean Sea Communities

| | Altafulla | 40C2 |

Área de Servicio Mèdol, AP-7 km 237, Barcelona > Taragona. **GPS:** n41,14157 e1,34590.
2 🛏free 🚰 🍽 Chfree. **Surface:** asphalted. 🅾 01/01-31/12
Distance: ⊗on the spot ⚓on the spot.

| | Altafulla | 40C2 |

Área de Servicio Mèdol, AP-7 km 237, Tarragona > Barcelona. **GPS:** n41,14054 e1,34746.
2 🛏free 🚰 🍽 Chfree. **Surface:** asphalted. 🅾 01/01-31/12
Distance: ⊗on the spot ⚓on the spot.

| | Amposta | 40B2 |

Masia Vora Riu, Calle Zamora, 8. **GPS:** n40,75006 e0,56069.
5 🛏€ 10 🚰 Ch 🔌 included. **Surface:** sand. 🅾 01/01-31/12

| | Amposta | 40B2 |

Casa de Fusta, Partida L'Encanyissada. **GPS:** n40,65851 e0,67475. ⬆.

ES

15 ⌧€3 ⌐⌐Ch⌐.
Location: Rural, comfortable. **Surface:** unpaved.
Distance: ⊗on the spot ⚒on the spot.

| ⌧S | Ascó | 40B2 |

C/ Alcalde Tomas Biarnes Radua. **GPS:** n41,18673 e0,56802.⬆️

25 ⌧free ⌐⌐Chfree. **Surface:** asphalted.

| ⌧S | Ayora | 40A4 |

Ayora, N330. **GPS:** n39,04382 w1,04126.

5 ⌧€10 ⌐€ 1 ⌐Ch⚒€ 2 WC⌐included ⌐€ 5 ⌐. **Surface:** gravel.
⏺ 01/01-31/12
Distance: ⚒2,5km.

| ⌧S | Barcelona | 40D2 |

Park & Ride del Besòs, Carrer del Taulat, B10 > salida 24 / 25, Sant Adrià del Besos. **GPS:** n41,41333 e2,22222.⬆️

20 ⌧€30/24h, €3/h ⌐⌐Ch⚒ WC⌐ ⌐included ⚒. **Location:** Urban.
Surface: metalled. ⏺ 01/01-31/12
Distance: ⚒1km ⊗300m ⚒300m ⌐Tram 100m, metro 500m.
Remarks: Max. 72h, guarded parking.

| ⌧S | Benicarló | 40B3 |

Parking La Mercera, Carretera Vieja de Peñiscola. **GPS:** n40,39763 e0,41324.⬆️

+50 ⌧€12 ⌐⌐Ch⚒(18x)included WC⌐ cold shower. **Location:**
Central. **Surface:** metalled.
Distance: ⚒150m.

| S | Benicasim 🌿 | 40B3 |

Calle de Ausias March. **GPS:** n40,05527 e0,05916.⬆️

⌐⌐Chfree.

Tourist information Benicasim:
ℹ️ Oficina de Turismo, Médico Segarra, 4, www.benicassim.org.Bathing resort.

| ⌧S | Benidorm ⛱️⛵ | 40A5 |

Camperpark Los Limbos, Sendero de la Barrina, Benidorm-Albir. **GPS:** n38,56207 w0,08597.⬆️
70 ⌧€9 ⌐€ ⌐Ch⚒(50x)€ 2 WCincluded ⌐€ 0,50 ⌐€ 2,50 ⌐.
Surface: asphalted/gravel. ⏺ 01/01-31/12
Distance: ⚒1,5km ⚒2km ⚒beach 2km ⊗100m ⚒1,5km.

| ⌧S | Benidorm ⛱️⛵ | 40A5 |

Pista Central Tenis y Autocaravaning Club, Sendero de la Barrina, Benidorm-Albir. **GPS:** n38,56000 w0,08361.⬆️
30 ⌧€12 ⌐⌐Ch⚒ ⌐included.
Surface: asphalted/metalled.
Distance: ⚒1,8km ⚒1,8km.

Tourist information Benidorm:
ℹ️ Oficina de Turismo, Avenida de Europa, Avenida Martínez Alejos, nº 6,
benidorm.comunitatvalenciana.com/.Large bathing resort.
🎡 Aqualandia, Sierra Helada s/n.Leisure pool park. ⏺ 01/05-31/05, 01/09-30/09 10-18h, summer 10-20h.
🐬 Mundomar.Zoo, shows with dolphins and seals. ⏺ 01/01-31/12 10-18h.
🎢 Terra Mítica, Ctra. de Benidorm a Finestrat, Partida de Moralet s/n.Attractions and themepark. ⏺ 10-20h, 15/07-31/08 10-22h.

| S | Cadaqués | 40D1 |

Parking, Riera de Sant Vicenç. **GPS:** n42,28964 e3,27260.

⌧€ 20,20/24h WC. ⌐ ⚒ **Surface:** asphalted.
Distance: ⚒100m ⚒1km ⚒1,5km ⊗100m ⚒100m.
Remarks: Tolerated place.

Tourist information Cadaqués:
⛩️ La Riera.Week market. ⏺ Mo 8-14h.

| ⌧S | Calaf | 40C1 |

Calle de Leida-Girona. **GPS:** n41,73306 e1,52667.⬆️

5 ⌧free ⌐⌐Chfree. **Location:** Comfortable. **Surface:** asphalted.
Remarks: At petrol station.

| ⌧S | Calaf | 40C1 |

Carrer Berlin. **GPS:** n41,73500 e1,51389.⬆️

ES

4 free Ch free. **Surface:** gravel/metalled.
Remarks: Max. 24h, Saturday market.

S Calnegre 39D5

Puntas Calnegre, Ctra. Puntas de Calnegre, nº 42. **GPS**: n37,51179 w1,41198.

17 € 10,50 Ch included. **Surface:** metalled. 15/09-01/04
Distance: 600m.

Calnegre 39D5

Cala de Calnegre, Cabo Cope Puntas. **GPS**: n37,50701 w1,41731.

10 free. **Surface:** sand.
Distance: on the spot on the spot.
Remarks: Parking on beach.

S Calpe 40A5

Odissea Camper Area Calpe, Avda. Bulgaria. **GPS**: n38,64893 e0,06665.

58 € 12, 01/07-31/08 € 15 Ch WC included € 2/day.
Location: Comfortable, central.
Surface: gravel. 01/01-31/12
Distance: on the spot 1km 100m.

S Calpe 40A5

Euro Nautica, Ctra. N233. **GPS**: n38,65578 e0,03660.
10 Ch. **Surface:** metalled.

Cañada de Callego 39D5

Loma de St.Antonio, Camino de Perchèles. **GPS**: n37,53542 w1,37226.

free. **Surface:** sand.
Remarks: Parking to sea.

Canet d'En Berenguer 40A3

Puerto Canet, Paseo Maritimo 9 de Octobre. **GPS**: n39,67443 w0,20338.
5.
Remarks: At marina.

S Carcaixent 40A4

Hort de Soriano. **GPS**: n39,07045 w0,40918.

15 free Ch free.
Surface: sand.
Distance: 7km on the spot.
Remarks: Max. 48h, picnic area present. At recreation area, first drive into Carrer Julián Ribera (39°7'19'N 00°27'04'W) ± 5km, than follow Hort de Soriano.

S Cartagena 39D5

Área Belmonte Plus, Ctra. de Tentegorra, 1. **GPS**: n37,61500 w1,00555.
5 € 10 Ch included. **Surface:** asphalted.
Distance: 500m.

S Dénia 40A4

Odissea Camper Area, Ctra. Marines km11.6/Riu de Vernissa. **GPS**: n38,87027 w0,015.

63 € 12, 01/07-31/08 € 15 Ch WC included € 1 € 3 € 2/day.
Surface: sand. 01/01-31/12
Distance: 2km 100m 50m 1km 20m.

Tourist information Dénia:

Oficina de Turismo, Plaza Oculista Buigues, 9.Seaside resort with fishing port.

S El Campello 40A5

Bar-Restaurant, N332 km124. **GPS**: n38,45746 w0,36129.

ES

2-3 ⬛free ⬛ ✚ WC ⬛ ⬛included. **Surface:** sand.
Distance: ⊗on the spot.
Remarks: 3 days free.

| ⬛⬛S | El Pinós | 39D4 |

Bonnie's Bar. GPS: n38,40917 w1,08639.

5 ⬛€ 10-12 ⬛⬛Ch ✚ WC ⬛included. **Surface:** metalled. ⬛ 01/01-31/12

| ⬛S | Elche | 40A5 |

Camperpark Illice, Camino de Alboraya. **GPS:** n38,28226 w0,69232.⬆

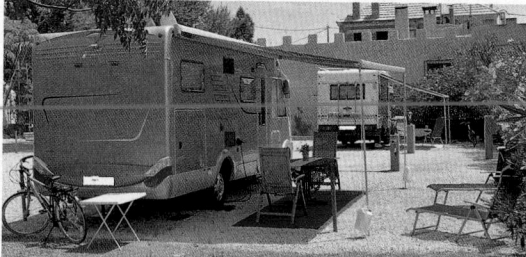

9 ⬛€ 9-12 ⬛⬛Ch ⬛ ⬛included. **Surface:** gravel. ⬛ 01/01-31/12
Distance: ⬛2,5km ✦4,5km ⊗2km ⬛2km ⬛50m.
Remarks: Bread-service, swimming pool incl.

| ⬛S | Elche | 40A5 |

MH VICKY, Partida de Pusol 153, Deramador. **GPS:** n38,19711 w0,7314.⬆➡

10 ⬛€8 ⬛⬛Ch ✚ € 2/day WC⬛ 1 ⬛€ 2 ⬛€ 2/day. **Surface:** gravel. ⬛ 01/01-31/12
Distance: ⬛Elche 6km ⊗2km ✦4km ⬛1,5km.
Remarks: 2 bicylcles available, bread-service, jacuzzi € 1.

| ⬛S | Els Muntells | 40B2 |

Carrer Major. **GPS:** n40,66869 e0,75929.⬆

10 ⬛€6 ⬛⬛Ch ✚ WCincluded. **Location:** Rural, isolated. **Surface:** asphalted/gravel.
Distance: ⬛1,2km.

| ⬛ | Figueres | 40D1 |

Parking Supermercado Esclat, Avda. de los Paisos Catalans, N260. **GPS:** n42,26042 e2,95096.

5 ⬛free. **Surface:** asphalted.
Distance: ⬛on the spot ⊗500m ⬛on the spot ⬛50m.
Remarks: Max. 48h.

Tourist information Figueres:
⬛ Rambla.Antiques market. ⬛ 3rd Sa of the month.
⬛ Plaza Catalunya en Plaza del Gra. ⬛ Tue, Thu, Sa.

| ⬛S | Garrigàs | 40D1 |

Area del Empordà Norte, A7 km-35. **GPS:** n42,17333 e2,93194.⬆
10 ⬛free ⬛ WCfree. **Surface:** metalled. ⬛ 01/01-31/12

| ⬛S | Garrigàs | 40D1 |

Área del Empordà Sur, A7 km-35. **GPS:** n42,17456 e2,93074.⬆

10 ⬛free ⬛⬛WCfree. **Surface:** metalled. ⬛ 01/01-31/12

| ⬛S | Ibi | 40A5 |

Área Chambit, Calle Pedro Valdivia. **GPS:** n38,62222 w0,56694.⬆
25 ⬛free ⬛⬛Chfree. **Surface:** sand. ⬛ 01/01-31/12
Distance: ✦2,3km.

| ⬛S | Jalance | 39D3 |

N330. **GPS:** n39,18740 w1,0761.⬆

ES

10 ⬛free 🚰🔧Chfree. **Surface:** asphalted.
Remarks: Parking next to swimming pool, max. 48h.

	Jávea	40B5

Avda.de Tamarits. **GPS:** n38,76982 e0,19097.

5 ⬛. **Surface:** unpaved.
Remarks: Tolerated place.

	Jérica	40A3

Carre del Rio. **GPS:** n39,91116 w0,57385.

5 ⬛. ⭕ 01/01-31/12
Distance: 🚲2,2km 🏊on the spot.
Remarks: Parking beside river.

S	La Marina	40A5

Finca La Escuera, Escuera 300. **GPS:** n38,14360 w0,66939.

6 ⬛€10 🚰🔧Ch 🔌€ 0,20/kWh WC🚿⬛. **Surface:** sand. ⭕ 01/01-31/12
Distance: 🏖300m 🏊3km ⊗300m 🛒300m 🚶300m 🏃on the spot.

S	La Marina	40A5

La Marina Elche, Cami del Molar o Pinet. **GPS:** n38,15628 w0,63791.

20 ⬛€5, 7 nights €25 🚰🔧Chincluded 🔌€ 0,50/kWh, 16Amp. ⭕ winter

	La Marina	40A5

Camino del Pinet, La Marina nord. **GPS:** n38,15347 w0,62797.

⬛free. **Surface:** sand.
Remarks: Parking on beach.

	La Marina	40A5

Camino del Pinet, La Marina nord. **GPS:** n38,15151 w0,63171.

⬛free. **Surface:** asphalted.
Remarks: Tolerated place.

	La Marina	40A5

La Marina-sud. **GPS:** n38,14031 w0,63653.

⬛free. **Surface:** sand.
Remarks: Parking on beach.

S	La Romana	40A5

Camperpark EuroPeCa, Cuevas de San Anton 2. **GPS:** n38,35662 w0,90378.

7 ⬛€7,50 🚰🔧Ch 🔌€ 2 WC🚿€ 1 📶included. 📡 **Location:** Rural, comfortable. **Surface:** gravel. ⭕ 01/01-31/12
Distance: 🏖1,5km ⊗1,5km 🛒1,5km 🏃on the spot.
Remarks: Possibility for reservation: 0034638278693.

S	La Salzadella	40B3

Av. Tomas Molins. **GPS:** n40,41611 e0,17305. ⬆️➡️

5 ⬛free 🚰🔧Chfree. **Surface:** asphalted.
Distance: 🏖250m.
Remarks: Village of cherries: cherry soap, cherry jam.

	La Seu dÚrgell	28D6

Portal de cerdanya. **GPS:** n42,35888 e1,46447.
8 ⬛.
Remarks: Tolerated place.

S	Lleida	40B1

AP-2 Zaragoze > Barcelona km 143. **GPS:** n41,54111 e0,63917.

10 🛏 🚰 🔧 Ch.
Distance: 🚲 on the spot.

🏕 S | **L'Alfàs del Pi** | 40A5

Camper Park Costa Blanca - l'Alfàz del Pi

info@camperparkcostablanca.com - www.camperparkcostablanca.com

Paved and flat motorhome pitches
Convenient for longer stays
Free wifi access

Camper Park Costa Blanca, Cami des Alguers, 79. **GPS:** n38,58389 w0,08139. ⬆⬆➡

42 🛏 € 12, 01/05-30/09 € 10 🚰 🔧 Ch 💧 (42x)€ 2 WC 🚽 € 0,50 💡 € 4, dryer € 4 📶 included. **Location:** Rural, comfortable, quit. **Surface:** metalled. 🗓 01/01-31/12

Distance: 🚶L'Alfas del Pi 1km, Playa Albir 1km 🚲 5km 🏊 sandy beach 2km 🚌 2km ⊗500m 🚉 1km 🚋 Tram 600m.

🏕 S | **L'Alfàs del Pi** | 40A5
Camper Park Orange Grove, Cami d`Alguers 65. **GPS:** n38,58526 w0,08405. ⬆
30 🛏 € 12 🚰 🔧 Ch 💧 € 3 WC 🚽 💡. **Surface:** gravel. 🗓 01/01-31/12

🏕 S | **L'Arboç** | 40C2
Área del Penedés Norte, AP7 dir Barcelona. **GPS:** n41,28794 e1,59117.
10 🛏 🚰 🔧 Ch free. **Surface:** metalled. 🗓 01/01-31/12
Distance: ⊗ on the spot 🚲 on the spot.

🏕 S | **L'Arboç** | 40C2
Área del Penedés Sur, AP7 dir Taragona. **GPS:** n41,29029 e1,59235.

10 🛏 🚰 🔧 Ch free. **Surface:** asphalted. 🗓 01/01-31/12
Distance: ⊗ on the spot 🚲 on the spot.

🏕 S | **Mataro** | 40D1
Autocaravanas del Sol, Calle de Torrent de Madá, El Cros. **GPS:** n41,53564 e2,41790. ⬆

20 🛏 free 🚰 🔧 free. **Surface:** metalled. 🗓 01/01-31/12
Distance: ⊗ on the spot 🚲 on the spot.

🏕 S | **Montseny** | 40D1
Área de Montseny, AP7-Sur>Barcelona. **GPS:** n41,65000 e2,44222. ⬆

20 🛏 free 🚰 🔧 free. **Surface:** metalled. 🗓 01/01-31/12
Distance: ⊗ on the spot 🚲 on the spot.

🏕 S | **Morella** | 40A2
N232. **GPS:** n40,62398 w0,09141. ⬆

30 🛏 free 🚰 🔧 Ch free. **Surface:** metalled. 🗓 01/01-31/12
Distance: 🚶2km ⊗2km.
Remarks: Max. 72h.

🏕 S | **Mula** | 39D4
Camino de las Curtis. **GPS:** n38,03972 w1,48139. ⬆
5 🛏 free 🚰 🔧 Ch free. **Surface:** asphalted. 🗓 01/01-31/12
Distance: 🚶500m 🚲500m.

🏕 S | **Murcia** | 39D4
Camperpark Huerta de Murcia, Carril los Cánovas, Rincón de Almodóvar, Los Ramos. **GPS:** n38,00722 w1,04361.

32 🛏 € 12 🚰 🔧 Ch 💧 WC 🚽 included 💡 € 3 📶 free. **Surface:** gravel. 🗓 01/01-31/12
Distance: 🚶Alquerías 1,7km ⊗500m 🚲500m 🚌on the spot.
Remarks: Bread-service.

🏕 S | **Navarcles** | 40C1
Calle de la Font de la Cura. **GPS:** n41,75661 e1,90833. ⬆

4 🛏 € 10 🚰 🔧 Ch 💧 WC 📶 included. 🗓 01/01-31/12
Distance: 🚲300m 🚌> Barcelona 100m.
Remarks: Motorhome dealer, max. 7 nights.

🏕 S | **Montseny** | 40D1
Área de Montseny, AP7-Nord km-117 > Francia. **GPS:** n41,64700 e2,42586. ⬆

ES

5 ⌛free ⚡🍴Ch✂free.
Location: Isolated, quit. **Surface:** gravel.
Distance: 🚶500m 🏊on the spot.

⛰S Navata 40D1
Restaurante Can Janot, Ctra. de Olot nº 2. **GPS:** n42,22600 e2,86325.⬆.

40 ⌛€4 ⚡🍴 2 🍴🌊. **Location:** Quit. **Surface:** grassy.
Distance: ⊗on the spot 🍷100m.
Remarks: Free with a meal.

⛰S Olimar 40A4
Area de Ocio Nostrum Caravaning. GPS: n39,47051 w0,64056.⬆.
100 ⌛€15 ⚡🍴Ch✂ included. **Surface:** metalled/sand.
Distance: 🚗300m.
Remarks: 100m from camper/caravan Ocio Nostrum.

🏔 Oliva 40A4
GPS: n38,91448 w0,07703.

⌛free. **Surface:** gravel/sand.
Distance: ⊗150m.
Remarks: Parking on beach.

🏔 Pals 40D1
Plaza Catalunya, Avda. Paul Companyó. **GPS:** n41,96859 e3,14688.

5 ⌛free. **Surface:** metalled. 🅿 01/01-31/12
Distance: 🚶on the spot ⊗on the spot 🍷300m 🚌200m.
Remarks: Max. 24h. Follow 'Policiá Local'.

Tourist information Pals:
🎪 Pg Europa.Week market. 🅿 Tue morning.

⛰S Platja d'Aro 🏖🌊 40D1
Calle Roma. **GPS:** n41,81028 e3,05767.⬆.

30 ⌛€8 ⚡🍴Ch✂ included. **Location:** Comfortable, quit. **Surface:** asphalted.
Distance: 🏖750m..
Remarks: Max. 2 days.

⛰S Ramonete 39D5
Wo-Mo Puerto Villa Brisa, Los Curas, D21, Puntas de Calnegre. **GPS:** n37,52589 w1,4336.⬆➡.

50 ⌛€6 ⚡€ 0,10/10liter 🍴Ch✂€ 0,50 🍴 2 ⊙ washing machine/dryer € 4 🌊. **Surface:** gravel. 🅿 19/09-30/05
Distance: 🚶5km 🏖5km 🏊5km 🍷5km.
Remarks: Bread-service. At D21, Ramonete dir Puntas de Calnegre.

🏔 Ripoll 40D1
Raval de Barcelona. **GPS:** n42,20008 e2,18695.⬆.

5 ⌛free. **Surface:** asphalted.
Distance: 🚶300m ⊗500m 🍷500m.
Remarks: Max. 24h, no camping activities.

Tourist information Ripoll:
🎪 Centrum.Week market. 🅿 Sa-morning.

⛰S San Feliu de Guixols 🏖🌊 40D1
Parking Narcis Massanas, Ronda Narcis Massanas. **GPS:** n41,78045 e3,02190.⬆.

15 ⌛free ⚡🍴Chfree. **Location:** Quit. **Surface:** unpaved.

ES

S San Fulgencio 40A5

Camper Park San Fulgencio, Mar Cartabrico 7, Centro Comercial las Dunas. **GPS**: n38,12080 w0,66005.

38 first day € 14, then € 12 Ch WC 3 included.
Location: Comfortable. **Surface:** gravel. 01/01-31/12
Distance: 1,5km 200m 150m 150m.

S San Raphael del Río 40B2

Restaurante Spätzle-Fritz, Planes del Reine, San Jorge, CV-11. **GPS**: n40,57507 e0,39333.

50 free with a meal, € 6 Ch WC 3. **Location:** Quit. **Surface:** gravel. 01/01-31/12
Distance: 3,5km 9km on the spot.

ES

Santa Cristina d'Aro 40D1

Costa Brava Park, Carretera Platje d'Aro. **GPS**: n41,81306 e3,01119.
46 € 15 € 3 Ch included € 6. **Surface:** metalled/sand.
Distance: 6km 100m.

S Segorbe 40A3

Area de Segorbe, Escalera de la Estación. **GPS**: n39,84805 w0,48166.
12 free Ch free. **Surface:** asphalted/metalled.
Remarks: Max. 48h.

S Sitges 40C2

Avda. del Cami Pla. **GPS**: n41,25083 e1,81838.

10 € 5 1/11-31/3, € 8 1/4-31/10. **Surface:** asphalted. 01/01-31/12
Distance: Boulevard/beach Sitges 2,5km 50m.
Remarks: Max. 7 days, industrial area, Barcelona 40km.

S Sta.Pola 40A5

Europa-Area, Carrer dels Electricistas. **GPS**: n38,20805 w0,57416.

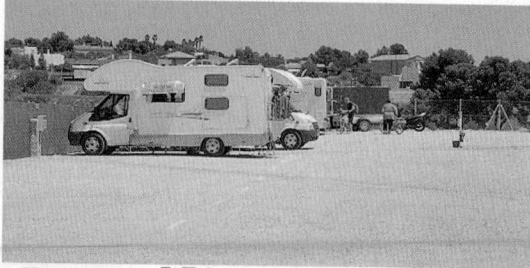

38 € 8, Jul/Aug € 12 Ch € 2. **Surface:** gravel/metalled.
01/01-31/12
Distance: 1,7km 1,8km 1,7km.

S Sta.Pola 40A5

Avenida Granada. **GPS**: n38,19091 w0,5649.

free.
Remarks: Parking at harbour.

S Tortosa 40B2

Área de Tortosa, Cami de la Toia. **GPS**: n40,80277 e0,51388.

30 € 5/24h € 1 Ch. **Surface:** asphalted. 01/01-31/12
Distance: 1,1km 10km 900m 1km.

S Tossa de Mar 40D1

Area Can Marti, Avinguda de Pau Casals 44. **GPS**: n41,72889 e2,92583.
30 € 10 Ch. **Surface:** gravel. 01/01-31/12
Distance: 800m 1,2km.

S Tremp 40B1

Passeig de Conca de Tremp. **GPS**: n42,16312 e0,89043.

5 free free € 1/2h. **Surface:** asphalted.
Remarks: Max. 48h.

S Turis 40A4

Carretera de Silla Tunis. **GPS**: n39,38944 w0,69777.
10 free Ch free. **Surface:** unpaved. 01/01-31/12

S Valencia 40A4

Parking Ficoval, Avda. Peris y Valero, 27. **GPS**: n39,45627 w0,37806.
12 € 25 Ch. **Surface:** gravel/sand.

Distance: ⚿on the spot ⚓2,5km 🚌200m.
Remarks: Monitored parking.

🅱S	Vic	40D1

Carrer de la Fura. **GPS:** n41,93444 e2,24000.⬆️➡️

10 🅱free ⛽€ 2/100liter 🅲Ch 💧€ 6/3h. **Surface:** grassy.
Distance: ⚿1,8km 🚌400m.
Remarks: Max. 48h.

🍽️S	Yelca	39D4

Portichuelo, Paraje el Portichuelo. **GPS:** n38,52833 w1,03944.

3 🅱€ 10 ⛽🅲Ch 💧included. **Surface:** grassy. 🔲 01/01-31/12
Distance: ⚿Yelca 10km ⊗on the spot.
Remarks: Check in at B&B <22h.

Spanish interior

🅱S	Aguilar de Campoo	37B4

N611, Ctra Palencia-Aguillar de Campoo. **GPS:** n42,78631 w4,25757.⬆️➡️

10 🅱free ⛽🅲Chfree. **Surface:** asphalted.
Distance: ⚿on the spot ⚓3,1km ⊗200m 🍴200m.
Remarks: Max. 48h.

🅱S	Aldeadávila de la Ribera	36D6

GPS: n41,22028 w6,61333.⬆️

4 🅱free ⛽🅲Chfree. **Surface:** asphalted. 🔲 01/01-31/12
Distance: ⊗on the spot 🍴200m.
Remarks: Max. 48h.

🅱S	Almazán	37C6

Camino Viejo del Cubo de la Solana. **GPS:** n41,49259 w2,53385.
🅱.
Remarks: Parking at swimming pool.

🅱S	Aranda de Duero	37C6

Dª Ruperta Baraya/Manzane M1. **GPS:** n41,66833 w3,69583.⬆️

10 🅱free ⛽🅲Chfree. **Surface:** asphalted. 🔲 01/01-31/12
Distance: ⊗150m 🍴on the spot.
Remarks: Max. 48h.

🅱S	Astorga 🌿	37A5

Parking plaza de Toros. GPS: n42,45138 w6,06593.⬆️➡️

15 🅱free ⛽🅲Chfree. **Surface:** metalled.
Distance: ⚿500m ⚓1,4km ⊗500m 🍴500m.
Remarks: Max. 48h.

🅱	Avila 🌿🏔️	39A1

Parking del Palacio de Congresos, Calle Molino dell Carril. **GPS:** n40,66111 w4,70472.

10 🅱free.
Surface: asphalted.
Distance: ⚓2,2km.

Tourist information Avila:
ℹ️ Small medieval town surround by ramparts.
✝️ The San Vicenta basilica is a Roman building.

🅱S	Burgo de Osma 🌿	37C6

Calle de Santos Iruela. **GPS:** n41,58662 w3,07338.⬆️.

ES

10 ⌁free ⌁. **Location:** Rural, very simple. **Surface:** metalled. ◻ 01/01-31/12
Distance: ▲500m ✕200m ⬤500m.

10 ⌁free ⌁ᵃCh free. **Surface:** metalled.
Distance: ▲200m ✕200m ⬤200m.
Remarks: Max. 48h.

🅑	Burgos	37C5

N120, Calle de Cartuja de Miraflores. **GPS:** n42,34037 w3,69361.

🅑S	Cervera de Pisuerga	37B4

C/ El Maderao. **GPS:** n42,87139 w4,49972.⬆.
10 ⌁free ⌁ᵃCh free. **Surface:** sand.
Distance: ▲200m ✕200m ⬤200m.
Remarks: Along the river, max. 48h.

🅑	Coca	37B6

GPS: n41,21348 w4,52733.

5 ⌁€ 0,60/h, max. € 2,50, 20.00-10.00 free. **Surface:** asphalted.
Distance: ◢2,6km.
Remarks: Parking beside river.

Tourist information Burgos:
ℹ City, 8th century, with a lot of curiosities such as the cathedral, the castle and Monasterio de las Huelgas.

⚠S	Cabrerizos	37A6

Don Quijote, Ctra. Aldealengua km 4. **GPS:** n40,97500 w5,60306.
⌁€ 16 ⌁ᵃCh. ◻ 01/03-31/10
Remarks: Formula camper.

5 ⌁free. **Surface:** metalled.
Remarks: Parking castle.

🅑	Consuegra	39B2

GPS: n39,45339 w3,6106.
⌁free. **Surface:** sand.
Remarks: Isolated parking at foot of hill with windmills.

🅑S	Cáceres ✿	38D2

Avda. Lope de Vega. **GPS:** n39,48041 w6,36649.⬆➡.

🅑S	Cuellar	37B6

Área El Castillo, Calle del Alamillo, 40. **GPS:** n41,40083 w4,32028.⬆.
15 ⌁free ⌁ᵃfree.
Distance: ◢2km.
Remarks: At castle.

🅑S	Don Benito	38D3

Avda. de los Deportes. **GPS:** n38,96250 w5,86305.⬆➡.
3 ⌁free ⌁ᵃCh free. **Surface:** metalled. ◻ 01/01-31/12
Distance: ✕on the spot ⬤on the spot ▬on the spot.

🅑S	Espinosa de los Monteros	37C4

Parking Las Cocinas, BU-570 > Bárcenas. **GPS:** n43,08556 w3,5575.⬆.
10 ⌁free ⌁ᵃCh free. **Surface:** asphalted.
Remarks: Max. 48h.

🅑S	Foncastín	37A6

A6, salida 175. **GPS:** n41,44131 w4,97957.⬆.
10 ⌁free ⌁ᵃCh free. **Surface:** asphalted. ◻ 01/01-31/12
Distance: ◢250m ✕on the spot.

15 ⌁free ⌁ᵃCh ◫ free. **Surface:** asphalted.
Distance: ◢6,7km.
Remarks: Monitored parking.

Tourist information Cáceres:
ℹ Oficina de Turismo, Plaza Mayor, nº 3, www.inedito.com/caceres/.City with historical centre.
Ⓜ Museo Arqueologico Provincial, Casa de las Veletas.
✶ PeroPalo.Traditional celebration. ◻ 21/02-24/02.

🅑S	Frómista ✿	37B5

Paseo de Julio Senador, P-980. **GPS:** n42,26494 w4,41198.⬆➡.
10 ⌁free ⌁ᵃCh free. **Surface:** metalled. ◻ 01/01-31/12
Distance: ▲600m ◢200m.
Remarks: Max. 48h, at sports grounds, weigh bridge nearby € 0,50.

🅑S	Carrión de los Condes ✿〰	37B5

C/ Las Huertas. **GPS:** n42,33875 w4,60808.⬆.

🅑S	La Alberca	38D1

Casa del Parque. **GPS:** n40,48833 w6,11583.⬆.
10 ⌁free ⌁ᵃCh free. **Surface:** metalled.
Distance: ▲300m.
Remarks: Max. 48h.

⚠S	La Fresneda, Teruel	40B2

La Fresneda, Partida Vall del Pi. **GPS:** n40,90694 e0,06167.
⌁€ 22,47/night/2pers ⚡ included. ◻ 01/04-01/10

ES

🅂 **La Joyosa** 40A1
Área de Marlofa, Calle Sobradiel. **GPS**: n41,73744 w1,06664. ⬆➡.
21 ⬜free ⟍ 🔲Ch ⟍ € 3 WC 🔲. **Surface:** asphalted/grassy.
Distance: ◢9km.

Lagartera 39A2
Camino de la Estacion. **GPS**: n39,91151 w5,19978. ⬆.

3 ⬜free ⟍🔲free. **Surface:** asphalted. ⬛ 01/01-31/12
Distance: ⬛on the spot ◢1,4km 🔲100m.
Remarks: Max. 48h.

🅂 **León** 37A4
Avda. De los Peregrinos, 5. **GPS**: n42,60471 w5,58525. ⬆.

10 ⬜free ⟍🔲Chfree. **Surface:** metalled.
Distance: ⊗300m.
Remarks: Max. 48h.

🅂 **Logrosán** 39A2
El Palomar, Calle Palomar. **GPS**: n39,33305 w5,47888. ⬆➡.
10 ⬜free ⟍🔲free. ⬛ 01/01-31/12
Remarks: Max. 48h.

🅂 **Mérida** ☘ 38D3
P Hernan Cortez, Calle Cabo Verde. **GPS**: n38,91861 w6,33611. ⬆.
20 ⬜€ 13,25/24h ⟍🔲Ch.
Surface: metalled.
Distance: ◢4km.

Tourist information Mérida:
ℹ Oficina de Turismo, Calle Santa Eulalia, 64. Also called Spanish Rome. Former baiting place on the old silver trail.
Ⓜ Museo Arquelogio, Santa Clara. Roman findings.

🅂 **Olmedo** 37B6
Parque del Mudejar, N601, km 148,1. **GPS**: n41,29167 w4,68194. ⬆.

10 ⬜free ⟍🔲Chfree. **Surface:** metalled. ⬛ 01/01-31/12
Distance: ⊗100m 🔲200m.
Remarks: Max. 48h.

🅂 **Osorno** 37B5
Los Chopos, N611 Osorno > Herrera de Pisuerga. **GPS**: n42,41694 w4,35111. ⬆.

30 ⬜free ⟍🔲Chfree. **Surface:** asphalted.
Distance: ⬛700m ◢2,2km ⊗on the spot.
Remarks: Max. 48h, guarded parking.

Palazuelos de Eresma 39B1
Calle Cordel. **GPS**: n40,92848 w4,05529. ⬆.
30 ⬜free. **Surface:** metalled. ⬛ 01/01-31/12
Distance: ◢4km.

🅂 **Palencia** 37B5
Parque Isla Dos Aguas, Avda. Ponce de León, 12. **GPS**: n42,00389 w4,53333. ⬆➡.

10 ⬜free ⟍🔲Chfree. **Surface:** asphalted.
Distance: ⬛on the spot ◢4km ⊗on the spot 🔲El Arbol 50m �cart100m.
Remarks: Max. 48h.

Tourist information Palencia:
ℹ Oficina de Turismo, Plaza San Pablo s/n.

Peñafiel 37B6
GPS: n41,59440 w4,11582.

5 ⬜free. **Surface:** asphalted. ⬛ 01/01-31/12
Remarks: Parking castle.

🅂 **Peñaflor** 40A1
Parking Surrecreo, Urbanizacion Los Rosales Peñaflor. **GPS**: n41,72777 w0,79194. ⬆➡.
150 ⬜€ 15 ⟍🔲Ch ⟍ WCincluded.
Distance: ⬛8 km.

Pesquera de Duero 37B6
Parking Ermita. GPS: n41,64571 w4,16636.

2 🛏free. **Surface:** grassy.
Distance: 🚶Pesquera de Duero 3km.
Remarks: Near church.

| P | Piedrasluengas | 37B4 |

C627. **GPS:** n43,03674 w4,45705.
🛏.
Remarks: Flat parking on the col Piedrasluengas.

| 🛏S | Pollos | 37A6 |

Estación de Servicios La Loba 2000, A62, salida 169. **GPS:** n41,41004 w5,13396.

10 🛏free 🚰🗑Chfree. **Surface:** asphalted.
Distance: ⛽200m ⊗on the spot 🍴on the spot.
Remarks: Petrol station.

| 🛏 | Salamanca 🌺🍴 | 37A6 |

Paring de Buenaventura, Avenida del Padre Ignacio Ellacuria. **GPS:** n40,95758 w5,67646.
50 🛏free. **Surface:** asphalted.
Distance: 🚶city centre 1km 🍴on the spot 🚌on the spot.

| 🛏S | Saldaña | 37B5 |

Calle Polideportivo. **GPS:** n42,51750 w4,74139.🔼
6 🛏free 🚰🗑Ch. **Surface:** metalled. 🅾 01/01-31/12
Remarks: Max. 48h.

| 🍴🍴S | Sancti-Spiritus | 36D6 |

Hostal-Restaurante La Ponderosa, Carretera nacional 620 km303. **GPS:** n40,73481 w6,36093.

🛏customers free 🚰🗑.
Distance: ⛽3km.
Remarks: Day ticket € 8.

| 🛏 | Sepúlveda 🌺 | 37B6 |

Calle de el Postiguillo. **GPS:** n41,29897 w3,74479.

10 🛏free. **Surface:** asphalted.
Distance: 🚶300m ⛽12km ⊗100m.

| 🛏 | Soria | 37D6 |

Monte de las Animas. **GPS:** n41,76769 w2,45391.

🛏free. **Surface:** gravel.

| 🛏 | Toledo 🌺 | 39B2 |

Parking de la Estación, Avda. de Castilla la Mancha. **GPS:** n39,86472 w4,01944.
50 🛏free.
Surface: asphalted.
Distance: ⛽1,3km.

Tourist information Toledo:
🛈 Oficina de Turismo, Puerta de Bisagra, s/n.Old city with historical centre, World Heritage Site.
⚔ Iglesia del Christo de la Vega.Medieval citadel, built for protection of the Puente de Alcantara, the bridge.
✝ Catedral.Cathedral known for its richness.
✝ Iglesia del Christo de la Vega,.Former mosque, catholic church since 12th century.
⌂ El Alcázar.Roman castle ruins, 16th century.

| 🛏 | Turégano | 37B6 |

CL603. **GPS:** n41,15194 w4,00806.🔼
10 🛏free 🚰🗑Chfree. **Surface:** asphalted. 🅾 01/01-31/12
Distance: ⊗200m.
Remarks: Max. 48h.

| 🛏S | Valladolid 🌺🍴 | 37B6 |

San Lorenzo, Avda. Ramon Pradera, 6. **GPS:** n41,65583 w4,73722.🔼
10 🛏€ 2,50/24h 🚰🗑 included.
Distance: 🚶on the spot ⛽3,2km.
Remarks: Max. 48h.

| 🛏S | Villada | 37B5 |

C/ San Fructuoso, Calle del Ferial Nuevo. **GPS:** n42,25389 w4,96667.

6 🛏free 🚰🗑Ch WC 🗑free. **Surface:** gravel.
Distance: 🚶200m ⊗200m 🍴200m.
Remarks: Max. 48h.

🅂 Villalpando 37A5

Area de Servicios Villalpando, A6, salida 236. **GPS**: n41,85906 w5,41993.⬆️
10 🅂free 🚰🍴Chfree. **Surface:** asphalted.
Distance: 🚏200m ⊗on the spot 🛒on the spot.
Remarks: Petrol station.

🅂 Zafra 38D3

Ctra. de los Santos de Maimona, Ex101. **GPS**: n38,42527 w6,41083.⬆️

30 🅂free 🚰🍴Chfree. **Surface:** asphalted. 🚻 01/01-31/12

🅂 Zafra 38D3

Restaurante La Cabaña, N435. **GPS**: n38,42580 w6,41008.
50 🅂 🚰🍴Ch.

🅂 Zamora 37A6

Estadio Barrio 3 Arboles, Calle de los Pisones. **GPS**: n41,50337 w5,75585.

30 🅂free. **Surface:** asphalted.

Andalusia

🅂 Agua Amarga 39C5

GPS: n36,93883 w1,93657.

20 🅂free. **Surface:** gravel/sand. 🚻 01/01-31/12
Distance: 🚏on the spot ⛱100m ⊗50m 🛒500m 🛒2km.
Remarks: Riverbed.

🅂 Alcalá de Guadaíra 38D5

Autocaravanas Hidalgo, A92 Sevilla><Malaga km 7. **GPS**: n37,32856 w5,8056.

18 🅂 🚰€ 0,50 🍴Ch✏️.
Distance: 🚏170m exit 15.

Remarks: Motorhome dealer, max. 2 nights.

🅂 Alcalá de los Gazules 38D6

Los Gazules, Ctra. Patrite, km.4. **GPS**: n36,46392 w5,66479.
7 🅂€ 13 🚰🍴Ch.
🚻 01/01-31/12
Remarks: Formula Camper € 16, 01/10-28/02, >18h <10h.

🅂 Alcaudete 39B4

Plaza del Castillo de Alcaudete, Calle de Paco del Arriero. **GPS**: n37,58972 w4,08916.⬆️
6 🅂free 🚰🍴Chfree. **Surface:** sand. 🚻 01/01-31/12
Distance: 🚏300m ⊗300m.

🅂 Alhaurín del la Torr 39A5

Área de Autocaravanas Sol, Camino de las Curtis. **GPS**: n36,68083 w4,53611.⬆️
150 🅂€ 10 🚰🍴Ch ✏️ included.
Distance: 🚏9 km 🚌100m.
Remarks: Guarded parking.

🅂 Alicún de las Torres 39B5

GR6104. **GPS**: n37,50836 w3,10802.

3 🅂free. **Surface:** metalled. 🚻 01/01-31/12
Distance: 🚏100m ⊗100m.
Remarks: Next to the spa resort.

🅂 Almensilla 38D4

San Diego, A-8054. **GPS**: n37,31361 w6,09333.
15 🅂free 🚰🍴Chfree.
Remarks: At petrol station BP,
restaurant visit appreciated.

🅂 Archidona 39A5

A7200. **GPS**: n37,09097 w4,38879.⬆️

12 🅂free 🚰🍴Chfree. **Surface:** concrete. 🚻 01/01-31/12
Distance: 🚏250m ⊗1km 🛒500m 🛒1km.

🅂 Cabo de Gata 39C6

Cabo de Gata, Ctra. Cabo de Gata s/n, Cortijo Ferrón. **GPS**: n36,80083 w2,24611.
40 🅂€ 16 🚰🍴Ch. 🚻 01/01-31/12
Remarks: Formula Camper, summertime > 20h < 10h, wintertime >18h,
period excluded: 15/07-31/08.

🅂 Cabra 39A5

Auditorio Municipal Alcalde Juan Muños, Juanita la Larga. **GPS**: n37,46608 w4,42361.⬆️

ES

10 🅢free 🚰🗑Chfree. **Surface:** asphalted. ⬛ 01/01-31/12
Distance: 🚶300m ✕300m 🅿300m.
Remarks: Max. 48h.

20 🅢free. **Surface:** asphalted. ⬛ 01/01-31/12
Distance: ⚓on the spot ✕500m 🅿500m.
Remarks: Parking along coast road.

🔺🅢 **Carchuna** 39B6
Don Cactus, Ctra. N 340 km 343 Playa Carchuna. **GPS:** n36,69566 w3,4435.
🅢€ 16 🚰🗑. ⬛ 01/01-31/12
Remarks: Formula Camper, summertime > 20h < 10h, wintertime >18h, period excluded: 01/07-31/08.

🅢 **Córdoba** 39A4
Avda. de los Custodios. **GPS:** n37,87528 w4,78778.
30 🅢against payment. **Surface:** asphalted. ⬛ 01/01-31/12
Distance: 🚶centro histórico 300m 🚲2,3km.
Remarks: In opposite of police station.

🔸 **Castell de Ferro** 〽 39B6
Playa de la Rijana, N340. **GPS:** n36,71009 w3,39277.
🅢free. **Surface:** asphalted/gravel. ⬛ 01/01-31/12
Distance: 🚶3,5km.
Remarks: Parking on beach.

🅿 **Córdoba** 39A4
Avda. del Campo de la Verdad/Calle del Compositor Rafael Castro. **GPS:** n37,87515 w4,76626.
🅢free. **Surface:** asphalted.
⬛ 01/01-31/12
Distance: 🚶1km.

🔺🅢 **Castell de Ferro** 〽 39B6
Huerta Romero, Paseo Maritimo 18. **GPS:** n36,71864 w3,36322.
5 🅢€ 15 🚰🗑Ch.
⬛ 01/01-31/12
Remarks: Formula Camper, summertime > 20h < 10h, wintertime >18h, period excluded: 01/07-31/08.

Tourist information Córdoba:
👁 Puerta de Almodovar.Entrance gate to the old Jewish district, Barrio de la Juderia.
Ⓜ Museo Municipal Taurino, Plaza de las Bulas.Museum about bull-fighting.
Ⓜ Torre de la Calahorra.Urban museum.
✖ Oficina de Turismo, Torrijos, 10 (Palacio de Congresos), www.ayuncordoba.es.Historical and culturally rich city, city of the flamenco and bull-fighting.
✖ Palacio del Marqués de Viana.Palace with collections of leather, silverware, porcelain etc.
✝ Mezquita.World-famous Moorish mosque.

Tourist information Castell de Ferro:
ℹ Coastal town with former Arab fortress in the centre.
🎪 Week market. ⬛ Sa.

🔺🅢 **Castillo de Baños** 39B6
Castillo de Baños, Ctra.N-340, km.360 Playa. **GPS:** n36,74093 w3,30117.
100 🅢€ 14 🚰🗑Ch. ⬛ 01/01-31/12
Remarks: Formula Camper, summertime > 20h < 10h, wintertime >18h, period 01/09-30/06.

🅢 **Cuevas de San Marcos** 〽 39A5
GPS: n37,26059 w4,40237.⬆

🔸 **Chipiona** 38C5
Carretera de la Playa. **GPS:** n36,70442 w6,42915.

10 🅢free 🚰🗑Chfree. **Surface:** asphalted.
Distance: 🚶1km ✕500m 🅿1km.
Remarks: Parking at swimming pool.

8 🅢free. **Surface:** asphalted. ⬛ 01/01-31/12
Distance: 🚶4km ⚓on the spot ✕on the spot 🅿1,5km.
Remarks: Tolerated place.

🅢 **Cullar** 39C5
Venta de Peral2, A-92. **GPS:** n37,55336 w2,6144.

🔺🅢 **Conil de la Frontera** 38D6
La Rosaleda, Ctra. del Pradillo, km 1,3. **GPS:** n36,29305 w6,09555.
20 🅢€ 15 🚰🗑. ⬛ 01/01-31/12
Remarks: Formula Camper, summertime > 20h < 10h, wintertime >18h, July/August € 30.

🔺🅢 **Conil de la Frontera** 38D6
Roche, Carril de Pilahito. **GPS:** n36,31138 w6,11333.
30 🅢€ 15 🗑.
⬛ 01/01-31/12
Remarks: Formula Camper, summertime > 20h < 10h, wintertime >18h.

🅿 **Conil de la Frontera** 38D6
Avda. del Rio. **GPS:** n36,27282 w6,08994.

20 🅢free 🚰WC🗑free. **Surface:** asphalted. ⬛ 01/01-31/12
Distance: 🚶3km ✕10m 🅿10m.

🅢 **El Bosque** 38D5
Calle de Juan Ramón Jiménez. **GPS:** n36,75670 w5,51056.

5 ⌻free ⚡🔧Chfree. **Surface:** metalled. ⬛ 01/01-31/12
Distance: 🚶on the spot ⊗100m 🍽300m.

| △S | El Puerto de Santa Maria | 38C5 |

Playa Dunas de San Anton, Paseo Maritimo Puntilla. **GPS**: n36,58722 w6,2405.
10 ⌻€15 ⚡🔧Ch. ⬛ 01/01-31/12
Remarks: Formula Camper, summertime > 20h < 10h, wintertime >18h,
period 01/10-31/05.

| P | El Puerto de Santa Maria | 38C5 |

Plaza de Toros. GPS: n36,59692 w6,23191.

5 ⌻free. **Surface:** asphalted. ⬛ 01/01-31/12
Distance: 🚶on the spot ⊗100m 🍽300m.
Remarks: Parking arena for bullfighting.

| △S | El Rocío | 38C5 |

La Aldea, Ctra.El Rocío Km.25. **GPS**: n37,14141 w6,49093.
10 ⌻€ 15 ⚡🔧Ch. ⬛ 01/01-31/12
Remarks: Formula Camper, summertime > 20h < 10h, wintertime >18h,
period excluded: pilgrimage.

| ⌻S | Gelves | 38D4 |

Puerto Gelves, Calle de Puerto Gelves. **GPS**: n37,33934 w6,02405.

20 ⌻€ 11,80 ⚡🔧Ch ⚡€ 2,73 WC▯▢🔊💳.
Surface: asphalted.
⬛ 01/01-31/12
Distance: 🚶on the spot ⚓4,3km ⊗on the spot 🍽on the spot 🚌on the spot.
Remarks: Sevilla 10km, Good bus connection.

| ⌻S | Granada 🌿 | 39B5 |

Área de Geysepark-Cármenes, Torre de Comares. **GPS**: n37,15136 w3,59533.⬆

30 ⌻€ 1,15/h, € 12/day ⚡🔧Ch 🔧 included. **Surface:** asphalted. ⬛
01/01-31/12
Distance: 🚶200m ⚓2km ⊗200m 🍽200m 🚌200m.
Remarks: Parking, entrance motorhomes 2nd ramp.

| P | Granada 🌿 | 39B5 |

Alhambra, P5. **GPS**: n37,17168 w3,57974.⬆

50 ⌻€ 46,65/24h, 01/10-31/05 € 26,60/24h.
Surface: gravel.
⬛ 01/01-31/12
Distance: 🚶1,5km ⊗200m 🍽200m 🚌100m.

Tourist information Granada:
ℹ Oficina de Turismo, C/Mariana Pineda, s/n.Former capital of Moorish
Andalusia at the foot of the Sierra Nevada.
👁 Alhambra.Most important curiosity of the city, the best kept Arab palace. ⬛
9-20h, winter, Sa 20-22h, Su 9-18h, summer Tue,Thu, Sa 22-24h.
👁 Cuevas del Sacromonte.Caves in Sacromonte mountain, gypsies previously
lived here. Now important tourist attraction and stage of flamenco shows.
👁 El Albaicín.Moorish district facing the Alhambra.

| 📷 | Grazalema | 38D5 |

Calle Juan de la Rosa. **GPS**: n36,75807 w5,36365.

4 ⌻free. **Surface:** asphalted. ⬛ 01/01-31/12
Distance: 🚶300m ⊗200m 🍽500m.
Remarks: Tolerated place.

| △S | Güejar Sierra | 39B5 |

Las Lomas, Ctra. de Güejar Sierra, Km. 6. **GPS**: n37,15972 w3,45388.
5 ⌻€ 16 ⚡🔧Ch.
⬛ 01/01-31/12
Remarks: Formula Camper, summertime > 20h < 10h, wintertime >18h.

| 📷 | Huelva ⛵ | 38C4 |

Monumento a Colón, Avenida Francesco Montenegro. **GPS**: n37,21333 w6,93972.

ES

14 🛏free ⛲€ 1/100liter ♨Ch. **Surface:** asphalted. ◻ 01/01-31/12
Distance: 🚶500m ⛱500m ⊗500m ☗300m.

△S | Marbella 〰 | 39A6
Cabopino, Ctra. N340 km 194,7. **GPS:** n36,48861 w4,74277.
50 🛏€ 15 ⛲♨Ch. ◻ 01/01-31/12
Remarks: Formula Camper, summertime > 20h < 10h, wintertime >18h, periods excluded: Easter, July/August.

Tourist information Marbella:
ℹ Oficina de Turismo, Glorieta de la Fontanilla, s/n, www.andalucia.org.
☀ Conmemoración de la Conquista de los Cristianos.Traditional celebration. ◻ 11/06.

△S | Marchena | 38D5
Ctra. de las Paradas. **GPS:** n37,33083 w5,42416.⬆.
20 🛏free ⛲♨Chfree. **Surface:** metalled.

🖼 | Motril | 39B6
Marineo Caparros, Camino del Pelailo. **GPS:** n36,72790 w3,53363.

20 🛏free. **Surface:** metalled.
Distance: 🚶200m ⛱100m ⊗100m.
Remarks: Parking beach, next to harbour.

△S | Motril | 39B6
Playa de Poniente, Motril-Puerto. **GPS:** n36,71805 w3,54638.
100 🛏€ 14 ⛲♨Ch. ◻ 01/01-31/12
Remarks: Formula Camper, summertime > 20h < 10h, wintertime >18h, period excluded: 01/07-31/08.

🖼S | Olvera | 38D5
Vía Verde de la Sierra. **GPS:** n36,94138 w5,25305.⬆.
48 🛏€ 5 ⛲♨Ch ⚷ included. ◻ 01/01-31/12
Distance: 🚶1km.

△S | Orgiva | 39B5
Orgiva, Carretera A-348. **GPS:** n36,88708 w3,41754.
7 🛏€ 15,50 ⛲♨Ch.
◻ 01/01-31/12
Remarks: Formula Camper € 16, 01/10-28/02, >18h <10h.

🖼S | Priego de Córdoba | 39A5
Avda. Niceto Alcalá Zamora. **GPS:** n37,44194 w4,21194.⬆.

9 🛏free ⛲♨Ch WC free. **Surface:** concrete. ◻ 01/01-31/12
Distance: 🚶500m ⊗500m ☗500m.

Tourist information Priego de Córdoba:
☀ Iglesia de la Aurora.

🖼S | Rute | 39A5
Calle de Jésus Obrero. **GPS:** n37,33113 w4,37323.⬆➡.

---

15 🛏free. **Surface:** asphalted. ◻ 01/01-31/12
Distance: 🚶6km ⛱50m ⊗on the spot ☗6km �e500m.
Remarks: Parking at monument of Columbus, dir Al Rocio.

△S | Isla Cristina | 38C4
Giralda, Ctra. Provincial 4117, km 1,5. **GPS:** n37,20000 w7,301.
10 🛏€ 16 ⛲♨Ch. ◻ 01/01-31/12
Remarks: Formula Camper, summertime > 20h < 10h, wintertime >18h, period excluded: 15/07-31/08.

△S | La Garrofa | 39C5
La Garrofa, Ctra.N-340, km 435,5. **GPS:** n36,82638 w2,51722.
40 🛏€ 15 ⛲♨Ch. ◻ 01/01-31/12
Remarks: Formula Camper, summertime > 20h < 10h, wintertime >18h, period excluded: 15/07-31/08.

🖼 | La Isleta | 39C6
Playa del Pénom blanca, Carreta Noria. **GPS:** n36,81670 w2,05146.

15 🛏free. **Surface:** gravel.
Distance: 🚶500m ⛱50m ⊗500m ☗500m.
Remarks: Parking to sea.

🖼 | La Línea de Concepción | 38D6
Avda. Principe de Asturias. **GPS:** n36,15583 w5,34553.

50 🛏€ 1/h, € 15/24h. **Surface:** metalled. ◻ 01/01-31/12
Distance: 🚶500m ⛱1km ⊗200m ☗1km.
Remarks: Wed, market.

🖼S | Lekeitio 〰 | 37D4
Iñigo Artieta Etorbidea. **GPS:** n43,35849 w2,50743.⬆➡.

ES

6 🛏free 🚮Chfree. **Surface:** asphalted.
Distance: 🛒500m ⊗500m ⚓300m.
Remarks: Parking next to police station, max. 48h.

| 🏕S | **San Juan de los Terreros** 🏔🌊 | 39D5 |

Playa de Entrevista, A332. **GPS:** n37,35083 w1,67972.

>20 🛏free 🚰. **Surface:** gravel/sand. 🅾 01/01-31/12
Distance: 🛒500m ⚓100m ⊗2km ⚓2,5km.
Remarks: Parking on beach.

| 🏕 | **Sancti Petri La Barrosa** | 38C6 |

Carretera de la Barossa. **GPS:** n36,38612 w6,2053.

20 🛏free. **Surface:** metalled. 🅾 01/01-31/12
Distance: 🛒2km ⚓200m ⊗1km ⚓5km.
Remarks: Parking on beach.

| △S | **Santaella** | 39A4 |

La Campiña, Ctra. Aldea de Quintana.
GPS: n37,62277 w4,85944.
3🛏 🚰🚮. 🅾 01/01-31/12
Remarks: Formula Camper € 14, 01/10-01/04, >18h <10h.

| 🏕 | **Sevilla** 🌊⛪🏖🌊 | 38D4 |

Parking PublicoTorneo, Calle Marqués de Paradas, Seville (Sevilla). **GPS:** n37,39180 w6,00172.
🛏€ 15/night. **Surface:** asphalted. 🅾 01/01-31/12. **Distance:** ⊗150m.
Remarks: Parking nearby station.

| P | **Sevilla** 🌊⛪🏖🌊 | 38D4 |

Parking Kansas City, Avda. de Kansas City, Seville (Sevilla). **GPS:** n37,39194 w5,97333.
🛏€ 18/24h.
Surface: asphalted.

Tourist information Seville (Sevilla):
ℹ️ Oficina de Turismo, Avda. de la Constitución, 21B, www.andalucia.org.Capital of Andalusia with a lot of curiosities.
👁 Barrio de Santa Cruz.Former Moorish and Jewish district in the city centre.
👁 Casa Pilatos.Copy of the house of Pilate in Jerusalem. 🅾 9-18h.
⚔ Alcazar, Plaza del Triumfo.
⌂ Italica.Roman ruins, 9 km at north of Sevilla on N630.
🎋 Almeda de Hercules. 🅾 Su-morning.

🎡 Parque de los Descubrimientos.Theme park science, in pavilion of Expo 1992.
🅾 Fri-Su, summer Tue-Thu from 18h 🅾 10/01-28/02.
⚓ Calle de las Sierpes.Famous shopping street.

| 🏕S | **Sierra Nevada** 🏔❄ | 39B5 |

Los Peñones de San Francisco. GPS: n37,09859 w3,39059.⬆➡

60 🛏€ 15/day 🚰🚮Ch🛏 included. **Surface:** asphalted.
Distance: 🛒3km ⊗1km 🚌300m.
Remarks: Free shuttle to centre. Ring-road Granada, Ronda Sur, exit 5b, carretera de Sierra Nevada.

| 🏕 | **Tarifa** 🌊 | 38D6 |

GPS: n36,06804 w5,6856.

20 🛏free. **Surface:** sand. 🅾 01/01-31/12
Distance: 🛒10km ⚓on the spot ⊗50m ⚓100m.
Remarks: Parking on beach.

Tourist information Tarifa:
ℹ️ Tourist Office, Duke of Kent House, Cathedral Square, Gibraltar, www.gibraltar.gi.British crown colony, island on a high rock.
👁 Siege Tunnels, Gibraltar.Labyrinth of tunnels, ingenious defence system.

| 🏕 | **Torreguadiaro** 🌊 | 38D6 |

Barrio Torreguadiaro. GPS: n36,29818 w5,27151.
🛏free. **Surface:** asphalted.
Distance: ⚓100m ⊗100m ⚓100m.

| 🏕S | **Valverde del Camino** | 38C4 |

Ctra. de Zalamea. **GPS:** n37,58111 w6,75138.⬆

10 🛏free 🚰🚮Chfree. **Surface:** asphalted/sand. 🅾 01/01-31/12
Distance: 🛒500m.

| 🏕S | **Vélez-Rubio** | 39C5 |

Área Puerta Oriental de Andalucía, Calle Granada. **GPS:** n37,65194 w2,07555.⬆➡

10 ⌘free ⌨☕Chfree. **Surface:** metalled. ◘ 01/01-31/12 ◉ 1st week Aug.

Distance: ⚓500m ⚓2,2km ⊗500m ⚓500m.

| ⌘S | Villanueva de Algaidas | 39A5 |

Calle de la Archidona, A-7201. **GPS:** n37,17824 w4,44858. ⬆.

20 ⌘free ⌨☕Chfree. **Surface:** asphalted.

Remarks: Max. 48h.

| ⌘ | Zahara de los Atunes ⚜ | 38D6 |

GPS: n36,13720 w5,84363.

☕.

Distance: ⚓100m ⚓1km ⚓100m ⊗100m ⚓100m.

Remarks: Parking beside river.

Tourist information Zahara de los Atunes:

⌒ Castillo de las Amabradas.Ruins of the castle. ◘ 01/01-31/12.

✳ Fiesta locale.Summer festival. ◘ 1st week Aug.

PORTUGAL

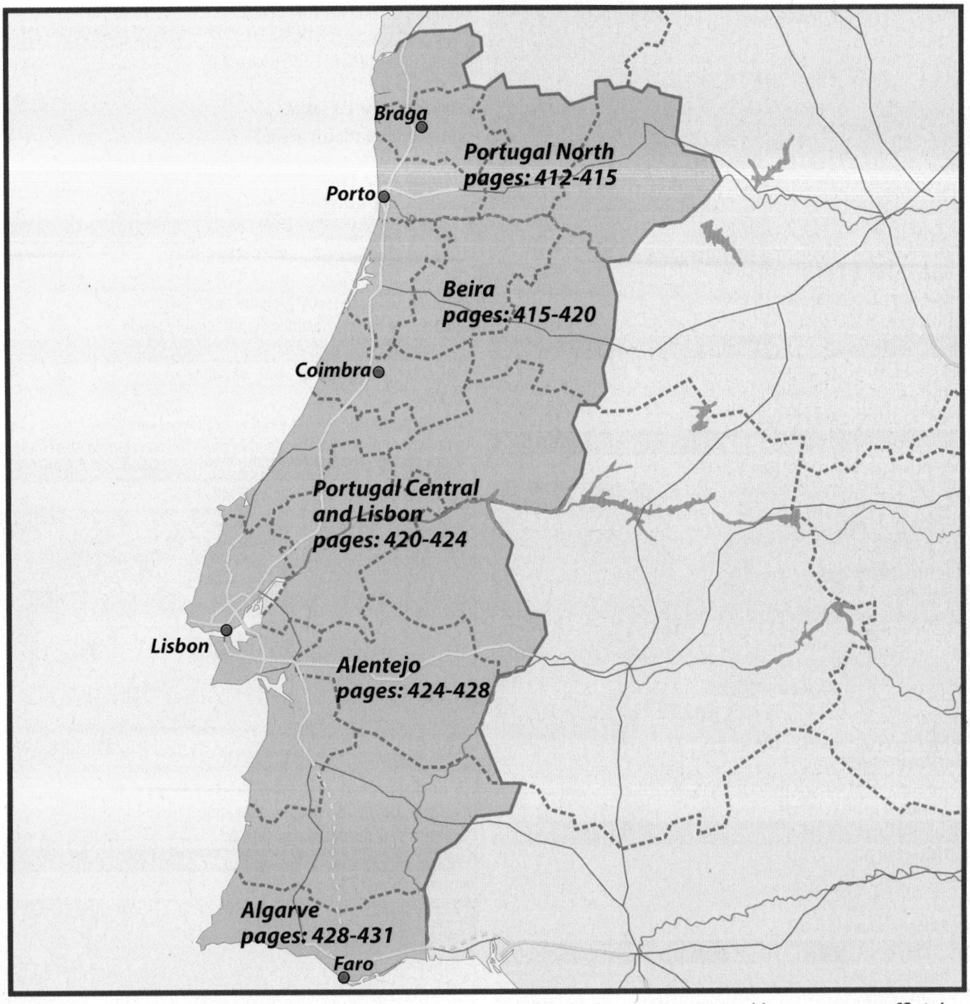

Braga

Portugal North
pages: 412-415

Porto

Beira
pages: 415-420

Coimbra

Portugal Central
and Lisbon
pages: 420-424

Lisbon

Alentejo
pages: 424-428

Algarve
pages: 428-431
Faro

Capital: Lisbon
Government: Parliamentary democracy
Official Language: Portuguese
Population: 10,800,00 (2010)
Area: 91,642 km^2

General information
Dialling code: 00351.
Currency: Euro
Payments by credit card are accepted almost
everywhere.

Regulations for overnight stays
Wild camping is not officially allowed. Overnight

parking places mentioned here are not official
motorhome stopovers but tolerated areas. You will
not find any official motorhome sign.

Opening hours
Shops: Monday-Friday 9am-1pm and 3pm-7pm,
Saturday 9am-1pm.
Supermarket, department stores Monday-Saturday
9am-9/11pm
Bank: Monday-Friday 8.30am-3.30pm.
Restaurants: lunch 12noon-3pm, dinner 7pm-10pm.

Portugal

Portugal North

Aguçadoura 36B5
Aguaçadoura Futebol Clube. GPS: n41,44389 w8,77722.

🛁free. **Surface:** sand. 📅 01/01-31/12
Distance: 🏖500m 🏊50m ⊗500m 🍴500m.
Remarks: At the beach, dir Estela.

Alto de Espinho 36C6
GPS: n41,25191 w7,89744.
🛁.
Remarks: On top of mount Marão on altitude of 900m.

Amarante 36C6
Av. Alexandre Herculano. **GPS:** n41,27286 w8,07178.

🛁 🚰. **Surface:** metalled.
Distance: 🏖800m 🏊on the spot 🚶on the spot 🍴50m.
Remarks: Parking at sports complex.

Amarante 36C6
GPS: n41,27863 w8,06768.
🛁.
Distance: ⊗200m 🍴200m.
Remarks: Parking swimming pool.

Amarante 36C6
GPS: n41,27020 w8,07708.

🛁. **Surface:** metalled.
Distance: ⊗on the spot 🍴on the spot.
Remarks: Market square along the river.

Amarante 36C6
Penedo da Rainha, São Gonçalo. **GPS:** n41,28031 w8,06925.
🛁 🚰 🛒 Ch ✂. 📅 01/02-30/11
Distance: 🏊1km ⊗on the spot 🍴on the spot 🚌1km.

Tourist information Amarante:
Ⓜ ♦ Museu Municipal Amadeu de Souza Cardoso, Alameda Teixeira Pascoaes. Modern art.

Avintes 36B6
Parque Biológico de Gaia, Av. Vasco da Gama. **GPS:** n41,09667 w8,55583. ⬆➡
11 🛁€4 🚰 🛒 Ch ✂ included. **Surface:** grasstiles. 📅 01/01-31/12

Barcelos 36B5
R.Rosa Ramalho. **GPS:** n41,52873 w8,61578.
12 🛁. **Surface:** metalled.
Distance: ✈3,5km.
Remarks: Parking swimming pool.

Barcelos 36B5
Parc da Cidade. **GPS:** n41,53276 w8,61616.
🛁 🚰. 📅 01/01-31/12
Remarks: Park in the centre.

Tourist information Barcelos:
ⓘ Posto de Turismo, Largo da Porta Nova (Torre de Menagem).
Ⓜ Museu de Olaria de Barcelos, R. Cónego Joaquim Gaiolas.Ceramics and archeology. 📅 Tue-Su 10-12.30h, 14-18h, Thu 10-18h.

Barragem do Azibo 36D5
Macedo de Cavaleiros. **GPS:** n41,58333 w6,89944.
🛁.
Distance: 🏊on the spot ⊗on the spot.
Remarks: At barrage, guarded during summer period.

Bico 36B6
R. Vasco da Gama. **GPS:** n40,73016 w8,64747.
🛁 🚰.
Surface: metalled.
Remarks: In fishing port, north of Aveiro N109 dir Estarreja, then Murtosa-Bico.

Braga 36B5
Bom Jesus do Monte. **GPS:** n41,55278 w8,38137.

🛁. **Surface:** gravel/sand. 📅 01/01-31/12
Distance: 🏖6km ⊗20m 🚐on the spot.
Remarks: Parking at funicular railway.

Braga 36B5
Sameiro. **GPS:** n41,53928 w8,36743.

🛁.
Remarks: Parking at place of pilgrimage.

Tourist information Braga:
ⓘ Old city centre.
🎭 Semana Santa.Procession. 📅 week before Easter.
🌿 Parque Nacional da Peneda-Gerês.Hiking routes.

Parque de Merendas, Rue Miguel Torga. **GPS:** n41,80417 w6,74611.

Bragança 🌿 36D5

10 ⌁free ⌁⌁Ch WC free. **Surface:** metalled. ◘ 01/01-31/12
Distance: ⌁200m ⊗200m ⌁200m.
Remarks: P below the castle.

| ⌂ | Bragança ❀ | 36D5 |

Cepo Verde, Gondesende. **GPS:** n41,84598 w6,86043.
⌁.
◘ 01/04-30/09

Tourist information Bragança:
ℹ Medival upper city and castle.
Ⓜ Museu Militar. ◘ 9-11.45h, 14-18.15h.
❀ Parque Natural de Montesinho.Nature reserve.

| ⌁ | Cabedelo | 38B1 |

R.do Cabedelo. **GPS:** n40,14403 w8,86395.
⌁. **Surface:** sand.
Remarks: Beach parking.

| ⌁S | Carrazeda de Ansiães | 36C6 |

GPS: n41,24498 w7,30386.
⌁⌁Ch. ◘ 01/01-31/12
Remarks: Parking swimming pool.

| ⌁ | Castelo do Neiva | 36B5 |

Av. de Santoinho. **GPS:** n41,67501 w8,78243.
⌁.
Remarks: At N13, 8km south of Viana do Castelo.

| ⌁ | Chaves | 36C5 |

Alameda do Trajano. **GPS:** n41,73694 w7,46917.
⌁free. **Surface:** metalled. ◘ 01/01-31/12
Distance: ⌁8,6km.

| ⌂S | Chaves | 36C5 |

Quinta do Rebentão, Vila Nova de Veiga. **GPS:** n41,70127 w7,50013.
⌁⌁Ch⌁. ◘ 01/01-30/11
Distance: ⌁4km ⊗400m ⌁1km ⌁800m.

Tourist information Chaves:
Ⓜ✚ Torre de Mengem.Military museum.

| ⌂S | Covas | 36B5 |

Parque Campismo de Covas, Lugar de Pereiras. **GPS:** n41,88758 w8,69497.
⌁⌁Ch⌁. ◘ 01/01-31/12

| ⌁S | Entre-os-Rios | 36B6 |

GPS: n41,08357 w8,29322.
⌁⌁. ◘ 01/01-31/12
Remarks: South-east of Porto, N108, parking along the Douro river.

| ⌁S | Espinho ⌁⌁ | 36B6 |

GPS: n40,98889 w8,64306.

4 ⌁free ⌁⌁free. ◘ 01/01-31/12
Distance: ⌁25m.
Remarks: N109, parking at beach, south of the city.

| ⌂ | Espinho ⌁⌁ | 36B6 |

Municipal de Espinho, Zona da Ribeira dos Mochos. **GPS:** n41,01402 w8,63743.

⌁. ◘ 01/01-31/12

Tourist information Espinho:
ℹ Posto de Turismo, Rua 23, n° 271, www.cm-espinho.pt.Bathing resort.

| ⌁S | Esposende ⌁⌁ | 36B5 |

Forte de S.João Baptiste, Rue do Farol. **GPS:** n41,54222 w8,79111.

⌁free ⌁⌁⌁free.
Surface: asphalted. ◘ 01/01-31/12
Distance: ⌁1,5km ⌁on the spot ⊗on the spot ⌁1,5km.
Remarks: Free wifi for clients restaurant. Parking next to lighthouse.

| ⌂S | Esposende ⌁ | 36B5 |

Parque de Campismo de Fão, Lírios - Fão. **GPS:** n41,50778 w8,77833.
⌁⌁Ch⌁. ◘ 01/01-31/12
Distance: ⌁500m ⊗500m ⌁on the spot ⌁500m.

Tourist information Esposende:
ℹ Posto de Turismo, Avenida Marginal.Seaside resort at the mouth of the river Rio Cavado.

| ⌁ | França | 36D5 |

N103. **GPS:** n41,90301 w6,73455.
⌁.
Remarks: Parking sports complex.

Tourist information França:
❀ Starting point hiking trails nature reserve Monteshino.

| ⌁S | Freixo de Espada a Cinta | 36D6 |

Espaço Multiusos, R. do Samiteiro de Cima. **GPS:** n41,08826 w6,81751.⬆
12 ⌁free ⌁⌁Ch⌁ (12x)free. **Surface:** metalled. ◘ 01/01-31/12
Distance: ⊗900m ⌁900m.
Remarks: Arrival <18h.

| ⌁S | Freixo de Numão | 36C6 |

Area de autocaravanas Jean Pierre Rossi, Sebarigos. **GPS:** n41,06000 w7,22111.⬆

30 ⌁€ 5/night ⌁⌁Ch ⌁ WC ⌁included. **Surface:** metalled.
Distance: ⌁900m ⊗500m ⌁500m.

| ⌁S | Gerês | 36C5 |

Vila do Gerês. GPS: n41,73538 w8,15969.
⌁⌁. **Surface:** asphalted.
Distance: ⊗on the spot.

| ⌂S | Gondomar | 36B6 |

Medas, Gavinho - Medas. **GPS:** n41,03917 w8,42694.
⌁⌁Ch. ◘ 01/01-31/12

| ⌁S | Izeda | 36D5 |

GPS: n41,56750 w6,72333.⬆
30 ⌁free ⌁⌁Ch free. **Surface:** metalled. ◘ 01/01-31/12

| ⌁S | Lamego | 36C6 |

GPS: n41,09501 w7,80372.

PT

🛒 ⛽free. **Surface:** metalled. 🅾 01/01-31/12
Distance: 🚰on the spot ⊗on the spot 🚽on the spot.
Remarks: At the foot of monumental stairs of the Santuari.

Tourist information Lamego:
ℹ️ www.cm-lamego.pt.Known for its Raposeira white wine.
👁 Bodega Raposeira. 🆃 free.
🌸 Nossa Senhora dos Remédios.Pilgrimage of Portugal, most important festivity of the country. 🅾 end Aug-beginning Sep.

| 📷 | Lindoso | 36C5 |

GPS: n41,86834 w8,19851.
🛒.

Remarks: At the edge of village.

| 📷S | Macedo de Cavaleiros | 36D5 |

Rua das Piscinas. **GPS:** n41,53756 w6,95715.⬆️.
🛒free ⛽€ 2/100liter ⚓Ch➕€ 2/1h. **Surface:** metalled. 🅾 01/01-31/12

| 📷S | Marco de Canaveses | 36C6 |

Quinta dos Agros, Rua dos Agros 169, Sande. **GPS:** n41,10944 w8,18389.⬆️.
🛒€7,50 ⛽⚓Ch ⚒included. **Surface:** grassy. 🅾 01/01-31/12
Distance: 🚽1km.

| 📷 | Matosinhos | 36B6 |

Av. de Praia. **GPS:** n41,26044 w8,72434.
🛒. **Surface:** metalled/sand.
Remarks: Parking to beach.

| △S | Matosinhos | 36B6 |

Municipal de Angeiras. **GPS:** n41,26722 w8,71972.
🛒⛽⚓Ch. 🅾 01/01-31/12

| 📷 | Melgaço | 36C5 |

Porta de Lamas de Mouro, Lamas de Mouro. **GPS:** n42,05202 w8,19413.
🛒free. **Surface:** metalled.

| 📷 | Miranda do Douro 🌀🏞🍽 | 36D6 |

Av. Eduardo Quero. **GPS:** n41,49167 w6,27333.

🛒free. **Surface:** metalled.
Distance: 🚰25m ⊗200m.
Remarks: Parking at city wall, south-east.

| 📷 | Miranda do Douro 🌀🏞🍽 | 36D6 |

Largo do Cestelo. **GPS:** n41,49611 w6,275.

🛒free. **Surface:** metalled.
Distance: 🚰on the spot ⊗50m 🚽50m.
Remarks: Parking near ruins of castle.

| 📷 | Mirandela 🌀 | 36C6 |

GPS: n41,48672 w7,18781.
🛒.

Remarks: At the lake, a the right side of bridge coming from northern dir.

| △S | Mirandela 🌀 | 36C6 |

Três Rios-Maravilha. **GPS:** n41,50683 w7,19716.
🛒⛽⚓Ch.
🅾 15/05-31/09

Tourist information Mirandela:
ℹ️ www.mirandela-online.net.Old city.
Ⓜ️ Museu municipal.Modern Portuguese painting art. 🆃 free.
Ⓜ️ Villa Flôr.Village museum. 🆃 free.

| △S | Mogadouro | 36D6 |

Mogadouro, Complexo Desportivo Municipal. **GPS:** n41,33528 w6,71861.
🛒⛽⚓Ch⚒. 🅾 01/04-30/09
Distance: ⊗500m 🚽on the spot 🚰500m.

| △S | Mondim de Basto | 36C5 |

Mondim de Basto, Montão. **GPS:** n41,40277 w7,95183.
🛒⛽⚓Ch. 🅾 01/02-30/11
Distance: 🏊on the spot 🚽1km 🚰500m.
Remarks: North of Rio Cabril.

| 📷 | Montalegre | 36C5 |

GPS: n41,82606 w7,79027.
🛒. 🅾 01/01-31/12
Remarks: Parking castle.

| 📷 | Parada | 36C5 |

Santuàrio. **GPS:** n41,68806 w8,20167.

| 📷S | Peso da Régua | 36C6 |

Parque Ovar, Av. de Ovar. **GPS:** n41,16278 w7,79222.⬆️.
4 🛒free ⚒WCfree. **Surface:** asphalted.
Distance: 🚤4km.

| 📷 | Pinhao | 36C6 |

GPS: n41,36798 w7,60228.
🛒.

Remarks: Parking beside river.

| 📷 | Ponte de Lima | 36B5 |

Alameda de São João. **GPS:** n41,77052 w8,5847.
🛒.

Remarks: Parking beside river.

| △S | Póvoa de Varzim | 36B5 |

Rio Alto, Estela. **GPS:** n41,46277 w8,77369.
🛒⛽⚓Ch. 🅾 01/01-31/12

| △S | Queimadela | 36C5 |

Parque de Campismo do Baragem. **GPS:** n41,50379 w8,16216.
🛒€5 ⛽⚓Ch ⚒⚓. **Surface:** grassy/metalled.
Distance: 🏊100m 🚰100m 🚽on the spot.

| 📷 | Santa Maria da Feira | 36B6 |

GPS: n40,91972 w8,54306.

PT

5 ⌁free.
Remarks: Parking at castle.

| ⚠S | São Salvador de Lordelo | 36B6 |

R. da Igreja. **GPS:** n41,23472 w8,41139. ⬆➡.
20 ⌁free ⛽⚡Chfree. **Surface:** asphalted. ◯ 01/01-31/12

| ⚠S | Silva | 36B5 |

Lugar de Campelo. **GPS:** n41,96262 w8,66622.
39 ⌁€6 ⛽€ 3 ⚡Ch⚡€ 3 ≋free. **Surface:** gravel.
Distance: 🚲4km.

| ⚠S | Torre de Moncorvo | 36D6 |

GPS: n41,18083 w7,04167.⬆.
9 ⌁free ⛽⚡Chfree. **Surface:** metalled. ◯ 01/01-31/12
Remarks: At sports park.

| 🅿 | Valadares | 36B6 |

GPS: n41,09232 w8,65703.
⌁.
Remarks: Parking at beach.

| ⚠S | Valpaços | 36C5 |

Do Rabaçal, Rua Gago Coutinho. **GPS:** n41,63222 w7,24778.
⌁ ⛽⚡Ch. ◯ 01/01-31/12

| 🅿 | Viana do Castelo 〰 | 36B5 |

GPS: n41,68995 w8,82964.
⌁against payment.
Remarks: Parking at harbour.

| 🅿 | Viana do Castelo 〰 | 36B5 |

Av. do Cabedelo. **GPS:** n41,68310 w8,83226.
⌁.
Remarks: Beach parking.

| 🅿 | Viana do Castelo 〰 | 36B5 |

Estr. de Santa Luzia. **GPS:** n41,70164 w8,83408.
4⌁. ◯ 01/01-31/12
Remarks: West side of the city on mount Santa Luzia.

| ⚠S | Viana do Castelo 〰 | 36B5 |

Cabedelo/Orbitur, Cabedelo - Darque. **GPS:** n41,67862 w8,82611.
⌁ ⛽€ 5,40 ⚡Ch.
◯ 16/01-15/11

Tourist information Viana do Castelo:
ℹ⌒ Posto de Turismo, Praça da Erva, www.cm-viana-castelo.pt.Bathing resort.
⛺ Campo do Costelo.Market. ◯ Fri.
🌸 Romaria da Nossa Senhora da Agonia.Procession with Gigantes (giants). ◯
3rd week Aug.

| ⚠S | Vila Chã | 36B5 |

Sol de Vila Chã, Rua do Sol, Facho. **GPS:** n41,29825 w8,73263.
⌁ ⛽⚡Ch ♨. ◯ 01/01-31/12
Distance: ⚓300m ⊙10m ⛽on the spot 🛒100m.

| 🅿 | Vila do Conde | 36B5 |

Av. Marques de Sa Bandeira. **GPS:** n41,34270 w8,74587.
20 ⌁. **Surface:** gravel/sand.

| 🅿 | Vila Nova de Foz Côa | 36C6 |

Rua Engenheiro Eugénio Nobre. **GPS:** n41,08028 w7,14806.⬆➡.
+50 ⌁free. **Location:** Rural. **Surface:** . ◯ 01/01-31/12
Distance: 🏊500m ⊙500m.

| S | Vila Nova de Foz Côa | 36C6 |

Autocross, N102. **GPS:** n41,06727 w7,15496.⬆➡.
⛽⚡Ch ✂free.

| ⚠S | Vila Nova de Gaia | 36B6 |

Madalena, Rua de Cerro, Praia de Madalena. **GPS:** n41,10750 w8,65556.
⌁ ⛽⚡Ch. ◯ 01/01-31/12

Remarks: Service only € 3,15-5,40.

Tourist information Vila Nova de Gaia:
ℹ City of the port wine, at the left bank of the river Douro, Port houses can be visited daily.
ℹ Caves A. A. Ferreira, Avenida Ramos Pinto, 70.The only real Portuguese company of port wine, Guided tour in english. ◯ 01/03-31/10 10-12.30h, 14-18h 01/11-28/02 Tue-Sa 10.30-12.30h, 14-18h. 🅃 € 2,50.

| ⚠S | Vila Real 〰 | 36C6 |

Municipal de Vila Real, Rua Dr. Manuel Cardona, Quinta da Carreira. **GPS:** n41,30333 w7,73667.
⌁ ⛽Ch.
◯ 01/01-31/12

Tourist information Vila Real:
👁 Solar de Mateus.Baroque country house, 18th century, known from label of the Matheus wine.

Beira

| 🅿 | Almeida 〰 | 36D6 |

GPS: n40,72295 w6,90489.

⌁free. **Surface:** metalled. ◯ 01/01-31/12
Remarks: Parking and at fort-castle.

| 🅿 | Anadia | 38B1 |

GPS: n40,44056 w8,4375.
⌁free. **Surface:** asphalted.
Distance: ⊗100m 🍽100m.
Remarks: At restaurants.

| ⚠S | Aveiro 〰 | 36B6 |

Galitos. **GPS:** n40,63722 w8,63889.⬆.
⌁free ⛽⚡Chfree. **Surface:** asphalted.
Distance: 🚶800m.
Remarks: At petrol station BP and Galitos Club Paviljon.

| ⚠S | Aveiro 〰 | 36B6 |

Parcue de S João, Canal São Roque. **GPS:** n40,64328 w8,65859.

10 ⌁free ⛽free. **Surface:** metalled. ◯ 01/01-31/12
Distance: 🚶200m ⚓25m ⊗200m 🍽200m.
Remarks: Parking at the Canal and A25.

Tourist information Aveiro:
ℹ Região de Turismo Rota da Luz, Rua João Mendonça, 8.
Ⓜ Ecomuseu da Troncalhada, Canal das Pirâmides.Salt-making. ◯ summer.
Ⓜ Museu de Aveiro, Av. Sta. Joana Princesa.Collection baroque art. ◯ Tue-Su 10-17.30h.

| ⚠S | Barril de Alva 🔆🍴 | 38C1 |

EM517-1. **GPS:** n40,28611 w7,96167.⬆.

PT

50 🛏free ⚓🔌 Ch free. **Location:** Rural, quit. **Surface:** unpaved. 🅿 01/01-31/12
Distance: 🚶500m ⚓river-beach ⊗on the spot.

10 🛏. **Surface:** metalled.
Remarks: Parking sports complex.

🛏S	Belmonte	38C1

Parque de Santiago. GPS: n40,36396 w7,34099.⬆.

	Cinfães	36C6

GPS: n41,07167 w8,08719.

6 🛏free ⚓🔌 Ch WC 🍴free. **Surface:** metalled. 🅿 01/01-31/12
Distance: 🚶500m 🛒150m.

🛏. **Surface:** metalled. 🅿 01/01-31/12
Distance: 🚶100m ⊗100m 🚰100m.
Remarks: Parking on entering village.

△S	Castelo Branco ⚜	38C1

Municipal de Castel Branco, N18. **GPS:** n39,85815 w7,49351.
🛏⚓🔌Ch free. 🅿 01/05-31/10

🛏S	Coimbra ⚜🍴	38B1

Av. Inês de Castro. GPS: n40,19970 w8,42905.⬆.

Tourist information Castelo Branco:
⌒ Castelo.Ruins of castle of the Templars.
🌳 Alameda da Liberdade. 🅿 Mo.

🛏S	Castelo de Paiva	36B6

R. Emidio Navarro. GPS: n41,03955 w8,27406.⬆.
50 🛏free ⚓🔌Ch WC free. **Surface:** metalled.
Remarks: Market square.

🛏S	Castelo Mendo	38D1

GPS: n40,59444 w6,94833.
3 🛏free ⚓free.
Distance: 📍6,8km.
Remarks: From Vilar Fornoso, P5, on entering the village.

🛏	Castelo Rodrigo ⚜	36D6

GPS: n40,87778 w6,96611.

20 🛏free ⚓🔌Ch 🍴free.
Surface: metalled. 🅿 01/01-31/12
Remarks: Max. 24h.
Tourist information Coimbra:
ℹ Posto de Turismo, Largo da Portagem.University town.
👁 Portugal dos Pequeninos.Miniature Portugal. 🅿 9-19h.

△S	Coimbrão	38B1

Praia do Pedrógão. GPS: n39,91500 w8,95.
🛏⚓🔌Ch against payment 💰. 🅿 16/02-15/12
Distance: 🚶50m ⊗on the spot 🚰on the spot 🚗10m.

🛏S	Condeixa	38B1

Rua Santo António. GPS: n40,11291 w8,49336.⬆.
15 🛏free ⚓🔌 Ch free. **Surface:** asphalted.

🛏	Condeixa	38B1

Conimbriga. GPS: n40,09895 w8,4894.⬆.
5 🛏free. **Surface:** grassy/metalled. 🅿 01/01-31/12
Remarks: Parking next to archaeological site.

🛏free. **Surface:** sand.
Remarks: At the entrance of fort.

🛏	Celorico da Beira	36C6

GPS: n40,63389 w7,40472.

🛏S	Escalos de Baixo	38C1

Hanmar, Estrada National 352. **GPS:** n39,89917 w7,40028.

PT

20 🛏️€ 8, May-Aug € 10 🚰🗑️Ch 💧 WC ⬜included. **Surface:** grassy. 🅿️ 01/01-31/12

Distance: ⊗1km. 🚉1km.

| | Estarreja | 36B6 |

R. Dr.Antonio Madureira. **GPS:** n40,75417 w8,56611.⬆️

6 🛏️€ 2/48h 🗑️Ch 💧included. **Surface:** asphalted. 🅿️ 01/01-31/12

Remarks: Max. 48h, check in Cafe Piscina, Ag. Seguros Rebelo.

| | Estarreja | 36B6 |

Ribeira do Maurão. **GPS:** n40,81328 w8,61588.⬆️

6 🛏️free 🚰🗑️Chfree. **Surface:** metalled. 🅿️ 01/01-31/12

| | Figueira da Foz | 38B1 |

Av. de Espanha. **GPS:** n40,14856 w8,86791.

🛏️. 🅿️ 01/01-31/12

Remarks: Beach parking.

| △S | Figueira da Foz | 38B1 |

Gala/Orbitur, Matas Nacias, Gala. **GPS:** n40,11861 w8,85639.

🛏️🚰🗑️Ch. 🅿️ 16/01-15/11

Remarks: Service only € 3,15-5,40.

| △S | Figueira da Foz | 38B1 |

Praia de Quiaios. **GPS:** n40,22083 w8,885.

🛏️🚰🗑️Ch 🛒. 🅿️ 01/07-30/09

Distance: 🏖️500m 🚉on the spot 🚉on the spot 🚌500m.

Remarks: Service only € 2,60-4,40.

Tourist information Figueira da Foz:

ℹ️ Posto de Turismo, Av. 25 de Abril.

| | Fratel | 38C2 |

Vila Velha de Ródão. **GPS:** n39,63250 w7,74694.⬆️➡️

10 🛏️free 🚰🗑️Chfree. **Surface:** unpaved. 🅿️ 01/01-31/12

Distance: 🚣200m 🚲1km ⊗300m 🚉300m.

| △S | Fundão | 38C1 |

Quinta do Convento. **GPS:** n40,13276 w7,51205.

🛏️🚰🗑️Ch 💧 WC ⬜📶. 🅿️ 01/01-31/12

| | Furadouro | 36B6 |

Praia do Furadouro. **GPS:** n40,87645 w8,67381.

30 🛏️free. **Surface:** asphalted.

Distance: 🏖️on the spot.

Remarks: Beach parking.

| | Guarda 🌿🍴 | 38C1 |

Av. Dr. Afonso Costa. **GPS:** n40,53694 w7,27639.

🛏️free. **Surface:** metalled. 🅿️ 01/01-31/12

Remarks: Parking at sports complex.

| | Guarda 🌿🍴 | 38C1 |

R. da Direccao Geral di Viacao. **GPS:** n40,54935 w7,24508.

🛏️. **Surface:** metalled.

Distance: ⊗50m.

| | Guarda 🌿🍴 | 38C1 |

Rua Dom Nuno de Álvarez Pereira. **GPS:** n40,53469 w7,26383.

🛏️free. **Surface:** asphalted.

| △S | Guarda 🌿🍴 | 38C1 |

Rossio de Valhelhas. **GPS:** n40,40333 w7,40528.

🛏️🚰🗑️Ch. 🅿️ 01/05-30/09

Distance: 🏖️50m ⊗300m 🚉150m 🚌100m.

Tourist information Guarda:

🏛️ Medieval city.

| △S | Idanha-a-Nova | 38C1 |

Municipal de Idanha-a-Nova, Albufeira da Barragem Marechel Carmona. **GPS:** n39,95056 w7,18722.

🛏️🚰🗑️Ch 🛒. 🅿️ 01/01-31/12

Distance: 🏖️50m ⊗on the spot 🚉on the spot 🚌8km.

Remarks: Service only € 2,60-4,40.

| | Idanha-a-Velha | 38C1 |

N332. **GPS:** n39,99830 w7,1445.

🛏️.

Remarks: In village.

Tourist information Idanha-a-Velha:

🌙 Archeological tour.

| | Ilhavo | 36B6 |

Costa Nova do Prado. **GPS:** n40,61222 w8,74917.

7 🛏️free. **Surface:** metalled.

Distance: ⊗on the spot 🚉on the spot.

Remarks: Beach parking.

| S | Ilhavo | 36B6 |

Av Ns.da Saude, Costa Nova do Prado. **GPS:** n40,61417 w8,75222.

15 🛏️free 🚰Ch WC. **Surface:** metalled.

Distance: 🏖️on the spot.

PT

Ilhavo   36B6
Av. Dr. Rocha Madahill. **GPS:** n40,60472 w8,66583.

3 free. **Surface:** asphalted.
Distance: 500m 500m.
Remarks: South of Aveiro, in the village, next to Maritime museum.

Ilhavo   36B6
Av. Infante Dom Henrique, Praia da Barra. **GPS:** n40,64375 w8,74456.
free. **Surface:** metalled.
Distance: 300m 300m.

Tourist information Ilhavo:
Posto de Turismo de Ilhavo, Praça do Município.
Museu Histórico da Vista Alegre, Fábrica de Porcelanas da Vista Alegre. Collection of porcelain. Tue-Fri 9-18h, Sa-Su 9-12.30h, 14-17h.
Museu Marítimo de Ílhavo, Av. Dr. Rocha Madahil. Shipping museum. Tue-Fri 10-12.30h, 14.30-18h, Sa-Su 14.30-17.30h.

Linhares   38C1
Misericordia. GPS: n40,54028 w7,46333.

.

Lorvão   38B1
Rua do Malhao. **GPS:** n40,25896 w8,31468.

10 free Ch free. **Surface:** metalled.

Luso   38B1
GPS: n40,38639 w8,38139.

10 free. **Surface:** metalled. 01/01-31/12
Remarks: Parking next to Hotel de Terme.

Tourist information Luso:
Health resort.
Mata Nacional do Buçaco. Nature reserve.

Melo-Gouveia   38C1
Quinta das Cegonhas, Nabainhos. **GPS:** n40,52057 w7,54169.
50 € 12,40-13,70 Ch .
Remarks: N17 - the road between Celorico da Beira and Coimbra, milestone 114.

Mira   36B6
Praia de Mira. GPS: n40,44472 w8,79806.
Ch. 16/01-15/11
Remarks: Service only € 3,15-5,40.

Miranda do Corvo   38B1
GPS: n40,08803 w8,33232.
20 free Ch free. **Surface:** asphalted.
Distance: 700m.

Murtosa   36B6
Praia da Torreira, R. do São Pato. **GPS:** n40,76532 w8,70231.
free Ch WC free. **Surface:** metalled.
Distance: 300m.

Oleiros   38C1
R. Dr. Barata Relvas. **GPS:** n39,92056 w7,91389.
free Ch free. **Surface:** metalled. 01/01-31/12

Pardilhó   36B6
Ribeira da Aldeia, R. Joaquim Maria Resende. **GPS:** n40,80111 w8,63472.
15 € 2/48h Ch included.
Surface: metalled. 01/01-31/12
Remarks: Max. 48h.

Penacova   38B1
Bairro de Carrazedos. **GPS:** n40,26722 w8,28306.

10 free Ch WC free. **Surface:** metalled. 01/01-31/12
Distance: 400m 3km 400m.

Penamacor   38C1
Benquerença. GPS: n40,22938 w7,22136.
4 free Ch free. **Surface:** gravel/sand.
Distance: on the spot on the spot.

Pinhel   36C6
GPS: n40,77389 w7,06194.

.
Distance: on the spot on the spot.
Remarks: At town hall.

Praia de Mira   36B6
GPS: n40,45800 w8,8025.
free. 01/01-31/12
Remarks: Parking on beach.

Praia de Quiaos   38B1
GPS: n40,22034 w8,89116.
free. 01/01-31/12

PT

Remarks: Parking at beach north of village.

⬛S Sangalhos 36B6
R. do Mercado. **GPS:** n40,48639 w8,47528. ⬆ ➡.
20 ⬛free ⬛Chfree. **Surface:** gravel/sand. ⬛ 01/01-31/12

△S Santa Ovaia 38C1
Ponte das Três Entradas, Avô. **GPS:** n40,30667 w7,87139.
⬛€ 11 ⬛ **Surface:** grassy. ⬛ 01/01-31/10
Distance: ⬛10m ⬛on the spot ⊗on the spot ⬛on the spot ⬛10m.

🍴S São João da Pesqueira 36C6
Restaurant Carocha, N222. **GPS:** n41,15120 w7,42378.
⬛free ⬛Chfree. ⬛ 01/01-31/12
Distance: ⊗on the spot.
Remarks: Next to restaurant and Port wine cellar Cave Cadão.

⬛S Sao Joao de Areias 38C1
Terra de Iguanas, Estrada principal 76, Vila Dianteira. **GPS:** n40,39045 w8,08574.
⬆.
4 ⬛€ 7,50, 01/06,50-31/08 € 10 ⬛Ch⬛included.
⬛ 01/01-31/12
Remarks: Max. 3 nights, swimming pool incl..

♨S São Pedro do Sul 36C6
Termas São Pedro do Sul. **GPS:** n40,74056 w8,08639. ⬆.
⬛free ⬛Chfree. **Surface:** asphalted.

⬛S Sertã 〰 38B1
Palácio da Justiça, R. Baden Powell. **GPS:** n39,80028 w8,09944. ⬆ .

⬛free ⬛WC free. **Surface:** metalled.
Distance: ⬛100m ⬛3km ⊗50m ⬛100m.

⬛S Sertã 〰 38B1
R. Amaro Vicente Martins. **GPS:** n39,79729 w8,09588. ⬆.

4 ⬛free ⬛Ch⬛free. **Surface:** asphalted. ⬛ 01/01-31/12
Distance: ⬛500m ⬛3km ⬛50m.
Remarks: At sports park.

⬛S Sertã 〰 38B1
Albergue do Bonjardim, Nesperal, Sertã. **GPS:** n39,81306 w8,16278.

2 ⬛€6 ⬛⬛€ 4 WC⬛. **Location:** Luxurious, isolated. **Surface:**
unpaved. ⬛ 01/04-31/10
Distance: ⬛200m ⊗2,5km ⬛1k ⬛50m.

Remarks: Sauna, steam bath and covered pool € 7,50, breakfast € 7,50.

⬛S Tabua 38C1
Piscina. **GPS:** n40,36306 w8,03.

3 ⬛free. **Surface:** metalled.

⬛S Tabua 38C1
Rua Aurora Jesus Goncalves. **GPS:** n40,36306 w8,02278.

10 ⬛free. **Surface:** metalled.

⬛S Trancoso 36C6
Parque Sportivo. GPS: n40,77139 w7,36222.

3 ⬛free. **Surface:** metalled.

⬛S Trancoso 36C6
Av. Heróis de São Marcos. **GPS:** n40,77583 w7,35056.

10 ⬛. **Surface:** metalled.
Distance: ⊗50m.
Remarks: Note: Friday market day. Parking on entering the village.

⬛S Vagos 36B6
Praia da Vagueira. GPS: n40,54944 w8,77056. ⬆.
20 ⬛€ 7,50, Oct-May € 5 ⬛Ch⬛€ 2.
Surface: sand. ⬛ 01/01-31/12
Remarks: Passerby € 2,50.

⬛S Vagos 36B6
EPADRV, Gafanha da Boa Hora. **GPS:** n40,54568 w8,7515.
⬛free.
Remarks: Near school.

⚠S Vagos   36B6

Vagueira, Gafanha da Boa Hora. **GPS:** n40,55806 w8,74528.

🚿🚰🔌Ch♻. ⭕ 01/01-31/12

Distance: 🏊1km ⊗on the spot 🏪1km 🚌500m.

Remarks: Service only € 2,60-4,40.

🏕S Vila Nova de Oliveirinha 🌿🏕⛱🚶🏇 38C1

Quinta do Tapadinho, Rua da Quinta dos Brandões. **GPS:** n40,36520 w7,92195.

5 🍴€10 🚰€ 3 🔌Ch🔧€ 3,50 ⓌⒸincluded ⊙€ 2,50. **Surface:** grassy/sand. ⭕ 01/01-31/12

Distance: 🏊1km ⊗6km 🏪6km.

🏕S Vila Pouca da Beira   38C1

Despinheiro, Avenida Principal. **GPS:** n40,30159 w7,9257.

4 🍴€8 🚰🔧Ⓦ€ 1 ⊙€ 4. **Location:** Rural, isolated, quit. **Surface:** grassy ⭕ 01/01-31/12

Distance: 🏊500m 🏊2km 🚣2km ⊗800m 🚲on the spot 🚶on the spot.

🏕S Vilar Formoso   38D1

Zaza, N332. **GPS:** n40,61528 w6,83833.⬆

🍴€5/24h 🚰€ 2 🔌Ch🔧included. **Surface:** asphalted/grassy.

Distance: 🏪on the spot.

🏊S Viseu 🌿🏔 36C6

R. Cap. Silva Pereira. **GPS:** n40,65944 w7,90833.

🍴🚰free.

⭕ 01/01-31/12

Remarks: Parking in east part of the city.

Tourist information Viseu:

ℹ Centre of Vinho do Dão.

Ⓜ Museu municipal, Castre Daire.Etnographical collection.

Portugal Central

🏕S A-dos-Cunhados   38A2

R. Monsenhor José Fialho. **GPS:** n39,15222 w9,30083.⬆

🍴free 🚰🔌Chfree. **Surface:** asphalted. ⭕ 01/01-31/12

Distance: 🏊100m 🚣6km 🏖beach 7km ⊗200m.

🏕S Abrantes   38B2

Aquapolis, São Joao. **GPS:** n39,45489 w8,18977.⬆

🍴free 🚰🔌Ch🚿free. **Surface:** metalled. ⭕ 01/01-31/12

Distance: 🏊3km 🚣4,7km ⊗100m 🏪6km.

🏕S Abrantes   38B2

Aquapolis, São Joao. **GPS:** n39,45333 w8,19056.⬆

10 🍴free. **Surface:** metalled.

Distance: 🏊3km 🚣4,8km 🏖sandy beach.

Remarks: Along the Tagus river.

🏕S Abrantes   38B2

Largo do Pralvo. **GPS:** n39,44956 w8,18968.⬆

10 🍴free. **Surface:** metalled. ⭕ 01/01-31/12

Distance: 🏊1km 🚣6,5km ⊗1km 🏪1km.

Remarks: Along the Tagus river.

🏕S Abrantes   38B2

Parque Urbano de São Lourenço, São Vincente. **GPS:** n39,47530 w8,21541.⬆

10 🍴free. **Surface:** grassy/gravel. ⭕ 01/01-31/12

Distance: 🏊centre ±2,4km 🚣4,4km ⊗50m 🏪3,5km.

Remarks: Max. 48h.

Tourist information Abrantes:

⛰ Posto de Turismo, Esplanada 1º de Maio, www.cm-abrantes.pt.City with historical centre.

⚠S Alenquer   38A2

Alenquer camping, Casal das Pedras. **GPS:** n39,05917 w9,02833.

4 🍴€ 12,50 🚰€ 2,50 🔌Ch. ⭕ 01/01-31/12

Distance: 🛢on the spot 🚽on the spot.

| 📷 | **Almourol** | 38B2 |

Castelo de Almourol, Praia do Ribatejo. **GPS**: n39,46295 w8,38297.

10 🗑free. **Surface:** metalled.
Distance: 🚶2km 🚲4km ⊗on the spot 🛢2km.
Remarks: On the banks of the Tejo river, parking castle.

| 📷 S | **Arruda dos Vinhos** | 38A2 |

Casal da Pevide. GPS: n38,99861 w9,08417.⬆

3 🗑free. 🚰 🚽 Ch free. **Surface:** asphalted. ⬛ 01/01-31/12
Distance: 🚶2km ⊗on the spot 🛢on the spot.
Remarks: Parking Intermarché.

| 📷 | **Baleal** | 38A2 |

Estrada do Baleal. GPS: n39,37240 w9,33702.

🗑free. **Surface:** asphalted. ⬛ 01/01-31/12
Distance: 🚶2km ⚓sandy beach 50m ⊗on the spot 🛢2km.
Remarks: Parking next to bar restaurant in village square, not recommended at the weekend.

| 📷 S | **Batalha** | 38B1 |

Parque Cónego M. Simões Inácio, Rua Cerca Conventual. **GPS**: n39,66134 w8,82516.⬆

15 🗑free. 🚰 🚽 Ch 📷 free. **Surface:** asphalted. ⬛ 01/01-31/12 ◉ Mo.
Distance: 🚶100m ⚓250m 🛢on the spot.
Remarks: At football ground/tennis, max. 48h.

| 📷 | **Cascais** 🔱📷 | 38A2 |

Cap Raso. GPS: n38,71134 w9,48498.

🗑free. **Surface:** sand. ⬛ 01/01-31/12
Distance: 🚶6km ⊗on the spot 🛢6km.
Remarks: Parking near the cliffs Also possibility for overnight stay at restaurant Maremonte.

| 🔺 S | **Cascais** 🔱📷 | 38A2 |

Guincho, Areia, Guincho. **GPS**: n38,72167 w9,46639.

🗑 🚰📷Ch. ⬛ 01/01-31/12
Remarks: Service only € 3,15-5,40.

Tourist information Cascais:
ℹ www.cm-cascais.pt.Bathing resort.

| 📷 S | **Constância** | 38B2 |

Estrada National. **GPS**: n39,47670 w8,34365.⬆

20 🗑free 🚰 🚽 Ch free. **Location:** Comfortable. **Surface:** metalled. ⬛ 01/01-31/12
Distance: 🚶500m 🚲2,3km ⚓on the spot ⊗500m 🛢300m.
Remarks: Along the Zêzere river.

| 📷 S | **Coruche** | 38B2 |

Área autocaravana, Rua 5 de Outubro. **GPS**: n38,96139 w8,51944.

100 🗑free 🚰 🚽 Ch free. **Surface:** metalled. ⬛ 01/01-31/12 ◉ last Sa of the month.
Distance: 🛢on the spot 🚽on the spot.

| 🔺 S | **Costa da Caparica** 🔱📷 | 38A2 |

Caravanismo da Costa da Caparica, Santo António da Caparica. **GPS**: n38,65389 w9,23833.
🗑 🚰📷Ch 🚿 📷
⬛ 01/01-31/12
Distance: ⚓500m ⊗on the spot 🛢on the spot 🚽100m.
Remarks: Service only € 3,15-5,40.

Tourist information Costa da Caparica:
ℹ Popular bathing resort.

| 📷 S | **Dois Portos** | 38A2 |

GPS: n39,03689 w9,18098.

🗑 🚰free. **Surface:** metalled. ⬛ 01/01-31/12
Remarks: Village square.

PT

△S **Ericeira** 🚐 38A2

Municipal de Mil Regos, N247, Casal do Moinho Velho. **GPS:** n38,97778 w9,41861.

🚿🚰Chfree.

❑ 01/01-31/12

Remarks: Service in front of campsite.

Tourist information Ericeira:

ℹ️ Seaside resort with fishing port.

👁 Aldeia Museu de José Franco, Sobreiro.Miniature village. ❑ 9-19h. 🎫 free.

🏕S **Fátima** 38B1

Rua de Sao Vicente de Paulo. **GPS:** n39,63389 w8,67111.⬆️.

10 🚐free 🚰WC free. **Surface:** asphalted. ❑ 01/01-31/12

Distance: 🚶1km 🚲3,2km ⊗100m 🛒1km.

Remarks: May 12-13 festivities.

🏕S **Foz do Arelho** 38A2

Av. do Mar. **GPS:** n39,42888 w9,22201.⬆️.

10 🚐free WC. **Surface:** metalled. ❑ 01/01-31/12

Distance: 🚶1km 🚲50m ⊗on the spot 🛒1,5km.

Remarks: Beach parking.

🏕 **Lisbon** 🌊🚐🛒🍴 38A2

Av. de Brasilia. **GPS:** n38,69463 w9,19966.

50 🚐free. **Surface:** asphalted.

Distance: 🚶city centre 6km ⊗300m 🛒500m 🚌400m bus-tram.

△S **Lisbon** 🌊🚐🛒🍴 38A2

Municipal de Lisboa-Monsanto, Monsanto, Estrada da Circunvalação. **GPS:** n38,72472 w9,20805.

🚿🚰🛁Ch🔧WC 📷🚿

❑ 01/01-31/12

Distance: 🚲3km ⊗on the spot 🛒on the spot 🚌50m.

Tourist information Lisbon:

ℹ️ Lisboa Card.Card gives entrance to museums, public transport, available at: Rua Jardim do Regedor 50 (10-18), Mosteiros do Jeronimos, Museu dos Coches. 🎫 € 18/24h, € 31/48h, € 38/72h.

ℹ️ Posto de Turismo, Rua do Arsenal, 15, www.atl-turismolisboa.pt.Capital of Portugal with a lot of curiosities.

🏪 Market. ❑ Tue, Sa.

🏙 32 Covered markets, most important market: Av. 24 de Julho. ❑ 6-14h ⦿ Su.

🏙 Campo de Sta Clara.Flea market.

🏙 Rua de São Bento.Antiques market.

⦿ Arena near metro Campo Pequeno. ❑ 01/05-30/09 Thu.

⦿ Feira Popular.Fair oppposite metro Entre Campos. ❑ 01/05-30/09.

⦿ Oceanário, Parque das Nações.Aquarium. ❑ 10-19h.

🛍 Chiado.Elegant shopping district. ❑ elevator 7-24h.

🏕S **Mação** 38B2

Campo de Feiras, Av. Vicente Mirrado. **GPS:** n39,55723 w7,99303.⬆️.

10 🚐free 🚰🛁Ch 🔧WC free. **Surface:** metalled. ❑ 01/01-31/12

Distance: 🚶500m 🚲6km ⊗500m 🛒500m.

Remarks: Max. 48h.

🏕S **Mafra** 38A2

Palacio Nacional. GPS: n38,93758 w9,33548.

🚿🚰free. ❑ 01/01-31/12

Tourist information Mafra:

🏢 Posto do turismo, Palácio Nacional de Mafra - Torreão Sul, Terreiro D. João V, www.cm-mafra.pt/turismo.

⦿ Parque Tapada Nacional, Portão do Codeçal.Safaripark. ❑ 10-19h.

🏕 **Marinha Grande** 38B1

São Pedro de Moel. **GPS:** n39,76974 w9,02752.

🚐free. **Location:** Very simple. **Surface:** metalled. ❑ 01/01-31/12

Distance: 🚶10km 🚲100m 🛒50m.

Remarks: Beach parking.

△S **Marinha Grande** 38B1

Parque de Campismo Orbitur, São Pedro de Moel. **GPS:** n39,75806 w9,02583.

🚿🚰🛁Ch. ❑ 01/01-31/12

Remarks: Service only € 3,15-5,40.

🏕 **Montijo** 38A2

GPS: n38,70286 w8,97665.

50 🚐free. **Surface:** metalled.

Distance: 🚶800m 🚲200m ⊗100m 🛒200m 🚌2km.

Remarks: Parking at ferry-boat to Lisbon.

🏕 **Nazaré** 🚐🍴 38B1

Avenue do Municipio. **GPS:** n39,59741 w9,0696.

7 🗺free. **Surface:** asphalted. 🅾 01/01-31/12
Distance: 🚰200m ⛱250m ⊗250m 🛒750m.

🔺S	Nazaré 🎣🌊	38B1

Valado, Mata do Valado. **GPS:** n39,59778 w9,05611.
🚰 🔧Ch.
🅾 01/02-30/12
Remarks: Service only € 2,60-4,40.

Tourist information Nazaré:
ℹ Posto de Turismo, Avenida da República, www.cm-nazare.pt/nazare.htm.
Bathing resort.

🗺S	Obidos 🌀	38A2

Rue do Ginasio. **GPS:** n39,35628 w9,15672.⬆.

20 🗺€ 6/24h 🔧🔌Ch 🔧 WC included. **Surface:** gravel/sand. 🅾 01/01-31/12
Distance: 🚰500m 🚲1km ⊗500m 🛒500m.

🏖S	Odivelas	38A2

Rolarlivre, Rua Alm. Gago Coutinho, Póvoa de Santo Adrião. **GPS:** n38,79605 w9,16384.⬆.
3 🗺€ 5 🔧🔌Ch 🔧 included. **Surface:** metalled. 🅾 01/01-31/12
Distance: 🚲700m ⊗100m.
Remarks: Motorhome dealer, video surveillance, only service € 2,50.

🗺S	Outeiro da Cabeça	38A2

GPS: n39,19306 w9,1825.⬆.

🗺free 🔧🔌Chfree. **Surface:** gravel. 🅾 01/01-31/12
Distance: 🚰300m 🚲2,5km ⊗300m 🛒300m.

🌊	Palmela	38A3

GPS: n38,56664 w8,90032.
🗺.
Remarks: Parking at castle.

🗺	Peniche	38A2

Av. Porto De Pesca. **GPS:** n39,35852 w9,37752.⬆.

🗺. **Surface:** metalled. 🅾 01/01-31/12
Distance: 🚰500m 🚲900m ⛱1km ⊗500m 🛒500m.
Remarks: At fire-station and marina.

🗺	Peniche	38A2

Farol do Cabo Cavoeiro, Caminho do Farol. **GPS:** n39,35989 w9,4082.⬆.

🗺. **Location:** Very simple, isolated.
Surface: metalled. 🅾 01/01-31/12
Distance: 🚲5km ⛱300m ⊗1,5km 🛒3km.
Remarks: At lighthouse.

🗺	Peniche	38A2

Praia de Consolação, Av. do Mar, Consolação. **GPS:** n39,32567 w9,35713.⬆.

🗺free. **Surface:** asphalted.
Distance: 🚰on the spot ⛱sandy beach.
Remarks: Beach parking.

🗺	Peniche	38A2

R. de Liberdade. **GPS:** n39,36577 w9,37417.⬆.

🗺. **Location:** Very simple. **Surface:** sand. 🅾 01/01-31/12
Distance: 🚰1,7km ⛱50m ⊗200m 🛒200m.
Remarks: Nearby Intermarché.

🔲S	Peniche	38A2

Peniche Praia, Estrada Marginal Norte. **GPS:** n39,36959 w9,392.⬆.

PT

23 ⅀€ 15,20, 2 pers.incl ⚡🔌 Ch WC ⚡included 📷📶. **Surface:** grassy. 🅿 01/01-31/12
Distance: At the sea on the spot 1,5km 1,5km.

Tourist information Peniche:

Ⓜ✗ Fortaleza de Peniche.Bathing resort.
Ⓜ✗ Posto de Turismo, Rua Alexandre Herculano, www.cm-peniche.pt.Bathing resort.

⚡S	Praia de Santa Cruz	38A2

GPS: n39,14418 w9,37482.
⅀free WC free. **Location:** Very simple. **Surface:** asphalted. 🅿 01/01-31/12
Distance: 300m 20m on the spot 300m.
Remarks: Parking at the beach or near the cliffs.

⚡	Praia de Santa Cruz	38A2

GPS: n39,13640 w9,38006.
⅀free. **Surface:** metalled.
Distance: on the spot 50m on the spot on the spot.

⚡	Ribamar	38A2

R. do Cacho Longo, São Lourenço. **GPS:** n39,01120 w9,42078.
⅀free. **Location:** Very simple, isolated.
Surface: asphalted. 🅿 01/01-31/12
Distance: sandy beach on the spot 6km.

⚡	São Martinho do Porto	38A1

Av. Marigal. **GPS:** n39,50176 w9,14132. ⬆.

⅀free. **Surface:** metalled. 🅿 01/01-31/12
Distance: 1,4km 5,5km sandy beach 50m 850m.

⚡	Sintra	38A2

R. Guilherme Gomes Fernandes. **GPS:** n38,79701 w9,38854.
4 ⅀free. **Surface:** metalled.
Distance: 200m 200m 400m.

⚡S	Tomar	38B1

Av. Gen. Bernardo Faria. **GPS:** n39,59972 w8,41306.

⅀free WC. **Location:** Very simple.
Surface: gravel. 🅿 01/01-31/12
Distance: 200m 200m 300m.
Remarks: Nearby railway station.

Tourist information Tomar:

Ⓜ Sinagoga de Tomar, Museu Luso-Hebraico, Rua Dr. Joaquim Jacinto, 75.Synagogue and Jewish Portuguese history. Ⓣ free.
✝ Convento de Cristo.Fortified monastery.
✿ Festa dos Tabuleiros. 🅿 Whitsuntide.
⚓ Barragem de Castelo de Bode.Artificial lake, 15km east of the city.

⚠S	Torres Vedras	38A2

Municipal da Praia de Santa Cruz. GPS: n39,13444 w9,37472.
⅀⚡🔌Ch against payment. 🅿 01/01-31/12

⚡S	Vermoil	38B1

R. Vale de Fojo, Pombal. **GPS:** n39,85080 w8,66125.⬆.

5 ⅀free ⚡🔌 Ch free. **Surface:** gravel/sand. 🅿 01/01-31/12
Distance: 200m 300m 300m.
Remarks: At cemetery.

Alentejo

⚡S	Alcácer do Sal	38B3

GPS: n38,37054 w8,5147.

⅀free ⚡ WC. **Surface:** asphalted.
Distance: 200m 6,3km 50m 50m 100m 500m 800m.
Remarks: Parking in centre at river Sado.

⚡S	Alcácer do Sal	38B3

Barragem Pego do Altar, Alcácer do Sal > N253 > Montemoro o Novo > N380.
GPS: n38,42055 w8,39384.
⅀free WC.
Distance: Alcácer do Sal 13km.

⚠S	Alcácer do Sal	38B3

Municipal Alcácer dp Sal. GPS: n38,38028 w8,51556.
⅀⚡🔌 Ch free.
🅿 16/01-14/12
Distance: 2km 50m 50m 300m.

Tourist information Alcácer do Sal:

ℹ Little town on the Rio Sado.

⚡S	Aldeia da Luz	38C3

R. de Mourão. **GPS:** n38,34278 w7,37389.⬆➡.
3 ⅀free ⚡🔌 Ch free. **Surface:** metalled.

⚡S	Almograve	38A4

GPS: n37,65313 w8,8015.

PT

🏕free 🚿free. **Surface:** metalled. 🅿 01/01-31/12
Remarks: From village dir beach, in front of large square go to the left, sandy surface, rather remote parking.
Tourist information Almograve:
ℹ Bathing resort.

Alvito	38B3

Rua de Tapadinha. **GPS:** n38,25917 w7,99222.
🏕free.
Remarks: At swimming pool.

△ S	Avis	38B2

Municipal Albufeira do Maranhão, Barragam Albufeira do Maranhão. **GPS:** n39,05682 w7,91145.
🏕 🚿 🗑 Ch.
Distance: 🏊 on the spot.
Remarks: Service only € 1,90.

🖼	Campo Maior	38C2

Barragem do Caia. GPS: n39,00308 w7,14219.
🏕.

Tourist information Campo Maior:
ℹ Fortified town. 🅿 9-13h, 15-17h.

🖼	Castelo de Vide	38C2

GPS: n39,41583 w7,45778.⬆.
🏕free.
Remarks: At the city walls.

🖼	Castelo de Vide	38C2

Estr. de São Vincente. **GPS:** n39,41028 w7,44917.
🏕.
Remarks: At stadium.

Tourist information Castelo de Vide:
ℹ www.cm-castelo-vide.pt.Historical centre with medieval citadel.

🖼 S	Cavaleiro	38A4

Cabo Sardano. GPS: n37,59806 w8,81806.

🏕free 🚿. **Surface:** gravel/sand. 🅿 01/01-31/12
Remarks: From Cavaleiro dir of sea, at lighthouse to the left, sandy parking at football ground.

🖼 S	Comporta	38A3

GPS: n38,38308 w8,78712.

🏕 🚿free. **Surface:** sand. 🅿 01/01-31/12
Distance: 🏊250m 🛒1km ⊗300m 🚆500m.
Remarks: Near the church.

🖼	Comporta	38A3

GPS: n38,37849 w8,78544.
🏕. **Surface:** sand. 🅿 01/01-31/12
Remarks: Holiday centre of Banco do Espirito Santo.

🖼	Elvas 🌿	38C3

GPS: n38,87766 w7,17763.

🏕. **Surface:** metalled.
Remarks: Parking aqueduct.

Tourist information Elvas:
ℹ Fortified city.

🖼 S	Estremoz	38C2

GPS: n38,84252 w7,5858.

10 🏕 🚿. **Surface:** metalled.
Distance: 🏊on the spot ⊗50m 🚆50m.
Remarks: Parking in the centre.

Tourist information Estremoz:
🎪 Market. 🅿 Sa.

🖼	Evora 🌿	38B3

GPS: n38,57529 w7,90519.

🏕free. **Surface:** gravel/metalled. 🅿 01/01-31/12

Remarks: Parking university, illuminated.

Evora 38B3
Ave Túlio Espanca, N114. **GPS**: n38,56655 w7,91541.

free. **Surface:** gravel/metalled. 01/01-31/12
Distance: 500m 800m 600m 1km.

Evora 38B3
Lago da Porta de Avis. **GPS**: n38,57672 w7,91096.

free.
Surface: gravel/metalled.
 01/01-31/12
Remarks: Parking at aqueduct.

Tourist information Evora:
 Posto de Turismo, Praça do Geraldo, www.cm-evora.pt.City with historical centre.
 Igreja de S. Francisco, Capela dos Ossos.Chapel of the bones.
 8-18h 12-14h.
  Tue.

Ferreira do Alentejo 38B3
GPS: n38,05675 w8,11955.

free. **Surface:** asphalted.
Distance: 500m 100m 1km 1,5km.
Remarks: Parking sports park.

Lousal 38B3
Azinheira Dos Barros E São Mamede do Sádão. **GPS**: n38,03591 w8,42908.
6 free Ch free.
Surface: gravel. 01/01-31/12
Distance: 15km.

Marvão 38C2
GPS: n39,39556 w7,37667.

12 free free. **Surface:** metalled.
Distance: on the spot 500m.

Mértola 38B4
N122/IC27. **GPS**: n37,64250 w7,65833.

.
Distance: 200m 200m.

Mértola 38B4
Rua dos Bombeiros Voluntários. **GPS**: n37,64114 w7,66326.
10 free. **Surface:** gravel/sand.
Remarks: At fire-station.

Mértola 38B4
GPS: n37,64103 w7,6574.
.
Remarks: Along river.

Tourist information Mértola:
 Convento São Francisco.Former convent, exposition room and atelier. 10-17h.

Mina de São Domingos 38C4
Praia Fluvial, R265. **GPS**: n37,67228 w7,50418.
20 free. **Surface:** metalled/sand.
Distance: 50m.
Remarks: At recreation area, marked pitches.

Mina de São Domingos 38C4
GPS: n37,67052 w7,50194.
 € 2 Ch.

Monsaraz 38C3
GPS: n38,44250 w7,37944.

4 free free.
Surface: metalled.
 01/01-31/12
Remarks: Near old remparts.
Tourist information Monsaraz:
 www.monsaraz.com.pt/.Small medieval town.

⛺ⓢ Montargil 38B2
Ponte de Sôr. **GPS:** n39,09972 w8,145.
📡⛽🚰💧Ch. ⬛ 01/01-31/12
Remarks: Service only € 3-5.

📡ⓢ Montemor-o-Novo 38B3
A6-IP7. **GPS:** n38,61791 w8,08014.
📡free 🚰free.
Surface: gravel/sand.
Remarks: Note: toll ticket is valid for 12 hours!. Parking motorway.

📷 Odeceixe 38A4
GPS: n37,43750 w8,79833.

📡free. **Surface:** sand. ⬛ 01/01-31/12
Distance: 🖥️laundry service.
Remarks: Parking at beach, west of the village.

📷 Odemira 38A4
GPS: n37,59839 w8,64615.

📡free. **Surface:** asphalted. ⬛ 01/01-31/12 **Remarks:** Parking beside river, northern part of village, after roundabout to the left.

📡ⓢ Pedrogão do Alentejo 🌿🏖️🌊 38B3
Alqueva Camping-Car Park, Estrada nacional 258, Km38,5. **GPS:** n38,11560 w7,63228.⬆️
11 📡 € 7,50 🚰💧Ch.
Location: Rural. **Surface:** gravel. ⬛ 01/01-31/12
Distance: 🚾1km 🏊1km 🛒1km ⊗1km 💧on the spot 🚲500m 🚶500m.

📡 Ponte de Sôr 38B2
Avenida da Liberdade. **GPS:** n39,24996 w8,00824.
📡free. **Surface:** asphalted. ⬛ 01/01-31/12
Distance: ⊗100m 💧100m.

📷 Porto Covo 38A3
GPS: n37,85040 w8,7943.
📡.
Remarks: At the sea.

📷 Porto Covo 38A3
Ilha do Pessegueiro. **GPS:** n37,82742 w8,79084.
📡.
Remarks: Parking at castle, south.

📷 Porto Covo 38A3
Praia Grande. **GPS:** n37,85590 w8,79325.

20 📡. **Surface:** gravel.
Distance: 🚾1km 🏊100m ⊗100m 💧1km.
Remarks: Parking to beach.

📡 Santa Clara-e-Velha 38B4
Barragem de Santa Clara. **GPS:** n37,51303 w8,44024.
📡free. **Surface:** metalled/sand.
Distance: 🏊on the spot ⊗on the spot.

📡ⓢ Santiago do Cacém 🌿🍽️🏖️🍴 38B3
R. do Parque. **GPS:** n38,01731 w8,69536.

10 📡free Ch. **Surface:** asphalted. ⬛ 01/01-31/12
Distance: 🚾on the spot ⊗500m 💧500m 🚾800m.
Remarks: Parking in the centre.

📡ⓢ Santiago do Cacém 🌿🍽️🏖️🍴 38B3
Rua das Nogueiras. **GPS:** n38,01245 w8,69448.⬆️
📡free 🚰💧Chfree. **Surface:** metalled.
Distance: 🚾600m ⊗100m.
Remarks: At swimming pool.

📷ⓢ Santo André 38A3
Praia de Santo André. **GPS:** n38,11494 w8,79664.

📡🚰.
Distance: 🚾5km.
Remarks: Parking to beach.

⛺ⓢ Santo André 38A3
Lagoa de Santa André. **GPS:** n38,10972 w8,78722.
📡🚰💧Ch🧺. ⬛ 17/01-14/11
Distance: 🏊1km ⊗500m 💧on the spot 🚐500m.
Remarks: Service only € 2,50.

⛺ⓢ Santo António das Areias 🌿🏖️ 38C2
Camping Asseiceira, Asseiceira. **GPS:** n39,41012 w7,34062.
10 📡 € 12-20 🚰💧Ch 🧺 WC 🖥️📶. **Surface:** grassy. ⬛ 01/01-31/12

📡 São Martinho das Amoreiras 38B4
N503. **GPS:** n37,56250 w8,34139.

▧free. **Surface:** metalled.
Remarks: At barrage.

| 🛏S | Terrugem | 38C3 |

Largo Joaquim Codero Vinaigre. **GPS:** n38,84556 w7,34861.⬆️.
25 ▧free 🚰🔌Chfree. **Surface:** asphalted/metalled.

| 🛏S | Vendas Novas | 38B3 |

GPS: n38,67795 w8,45609.
🛏🚰free. ⭕ 01/01-31/12
Remarks: Parking at Caserma.

| | Vila Viçosa | 38C3 |

Largo Gago Coutinho. **GPS:** n38,77661 w7,42034.

10 ▧free. **Surface:** metalled.
Distance: 🏊250m ⊗25m 🛒100m.

| 🛏S | Zambujeira do Mar | 38A4 |

GPS: n37,52500 w8,78667.

▧free 🚰🔌Ch.
Surface: metalled. ⭕ 01/01-31/12
Remarks: Service at tourist office. Next to the church, service at tourist office.

Algarve

| 🛏S | Albufeira 🏖 | 38B4 |

Parque da Galé, Rua do Barranco Vale Rabelo. **GPS:** n37,09347 w8,31125.

28 ▧🛏€6,50 🚰🔌Ch 🔌 (28x) 📶included. **Location:** Comfortable. **Surface:** unpaved.
Distance: 🏊1,8km ⊗200m 🛒500m.

Tourist information Albufeira:
😊 Posto de Turismo, R. 5 de Outubro,, www.cm-albufeira.pt. ⭕ 10-20h.
😊 ZooMarine, N125.Attractions park, dolphinarium, aquarium. ⭕ 10-20h.

| 🛏S | Alcoutim | 38B4 |

Estrada da Pousada da Juventude. **GPS:** n37,47500 w7,47472.⬆️.
▧free 🚰🔌Chfree.
Surface: sand. ⭕ 01/01-31/12
Remarks: Next to 'Centro de Saude'.

Tourist information Alcoutim:
ℹ️ Fortified city. ⭕ 9-17.30h.

| 🛏S | Aljezur 🌿 | 38A4 |

Largo do Mercado. **GPS:** n37,31611 w8,80278.

▧free 🚰🔌Ch WC free. **Location:** Very simple. **Surface:** asphalted. ⭕
01/01-31/12
Distance: 🏊on the spot ⊗200m 🛒200m.

| 🛏 | Altura 🏖 | 38B4 |

Rua de Alagoa. **GPS:** n37,17138 w7,49952.
+10 ▧free. **Surface:** sand.
Distance: 🏊100m 🏊on the spot ⊗100m.
Remarks: Beach parking.

| 🔺S | Alvor | 38A4 |

Dourada, Estrada Monte de Alvor. **GPS:** n37,13500 w8,59056.
🛏🚰🔌Ch🔌. ⭕ 01/01-31/12
Distance: 🏊1km ⊗on the spot 🛒on the spot 🚆50m.

| | Cabo de São Vicente | 38A4 |

N268. **GPS:** n37,02361 w8,995.

▧free. **Surface:** metalled. ⭕ 01/01-31/12
Distance: 🏊Sagres 6km.
Remarks: Parking at lighthouse.

| 🛏S | Caldas de Monchique | 38A4 |

Parque Rural Autocaravanas Vale da Carrasqueira, Barracão 190. **GPS:**
n37,27667 w8,54333.⬆️.

15 ▧€12,50/24h 🚰🔌Ch 🔌 WC ⬛included. **Surface:** gravel.

| | Carrapateira | 38A4 |

Praia de Amado. GPS: n37,19623 w8,90156.

🛏free. **Surface:** metalled.
Distance: 🏖Carrapateira 2km.
Remarks: Beach parking.

| 🅿 | Carrapateira | 38A4 |

Praia de Bordeira. GPS: n37,19735 w8,90726.

🛏free. **Surface:** metalled.
Distance: 🏖Carrapateira 2,5km.
Remarks: Parking near the cliffs, from the village dir of sea.

| 🅿 | Carvoeiro | 38B4 |

Estr. do Farol. **GPS:** n37,08774 w8,44285.
4🛏. **Surface:** sand.
Remarks: Parking at lighthouse.

| 🅿S | Castro Marim | 38B4 |

Av. Dr. José Afonso Gomes. **GPS:** n37,22024 w7,44457.⬆

25🛏free 🚰🗑Chfree. **Surface:** gravel. 🅾 01/01-31/12 ⏺ 2rd Sa of the month.
Distance: 🛒1,3km ⊗on the spot.

| 🅿 | Faro | 38B5 |

Parking Largo de São Francisco. GPS: n37,01194 w7,9325.

50🛏free. **Surface:** metalled.
Tourist information Faro:
ℹ Posto de Turismo, Rua da Misericórdia, 8-12.Capital of the Algarve with historical centre.

| 🅿S | Ferragudo | 38A4 |

Camping Ferragudo, Estr. EM530. **GPS:** n37,11305 w8,51083.
🛏🚰🗑 Ch 💧. **Surface:** gravel.

| 🅿S | Lagos 🌿🏖🏊 | 38A4 |

GPS: n37,11563 w8,678.⬆

10🛏free 🚰€ 2 🗑Chfree.
Location: Comfortable.
Surface: gravel.
Distance: 🏖city centre 2km 🏊2,3km ⊗McDonalds 450m.
Remarks: At sports park.
Tourist information Lagos:
ℹ Posto de Turismo, Rua Vasco da Gama.Lively port with historical centre.
Ⓜ Museu Municipal, Rua General Alberto da Silveira.Regional museum. 🅾
9.30-12.30h, 14-17h ⏺ holiday-Feiertag-jours de fête-giorni di festa.

| 🅿S | Manta Rota 🏖 | 38B4 |

Quinta Manta Rota 15. **GPS:** n37,16445 w7,52175.

80🛏€4 🚰🗑Chincluded 🔌€ 2/8h. **Surface:** metalled.
Distance: 🏖on the spot 🚲6,5km 🏊100m ⊗100m 🚉500m.

| 🅿S | Moncarapacho | 38B4 |

Caravanas Algarve. GPS: n37,09785 w7,78618.
20🛏€ 11 🚰 Ch 💧. **Surface:** gravel. 🅾 01/01-31/12
Distance: 🏖1km 🏊beach 6km ⊗1km.

| 🅿 | Olhão 🌿🏖🏊 | 38B5 |

Avenida das Forças Armadas. **GPS:** n37,02585 w7,83608.

15🛏free.
Surface: metalled.
🅾 01/01-31/12
Distance: 🏖200m 🏊50m ⊗200m 🚉100m.
Remarks: Follow 'porto' (harbour).
Tourist information Olhão:
ℹ Posto de Turismo, Largo Sebastião Martins Mestre n.º 6A, www.cm-olhao.pt.Port with car-free centre.

| 🅿 | Portimão 🏖🏊 | 38A4 |

Avenida Rio Arade, Praia da Rocha. **GPS:** n37,11952 w8,53021.⬆

PT

+100 ⌇€ 2,50 ⏚€ 1,50/100liter 🔧Ch.
Surface: metalled.
Distance: 🚶on the spot ⚓100m ⊗on the spot ⛴200m.
Tourist information Portimão:
ℹ Posto de Turismo, Avenida de Zeca Afonso.
Port city.

50 ⌇free. **Surface:** asphalted. ◻ 01/01-31/12
Distance: 🚶1km.
Remarks: Parking at fort.

Salema   38A4
Praia Boca do Rio. GPS: n37,06716 w8,81035.

Quarteira   38B4
Urbanizacan Quintado Roman. **GPS:** n37,07215 w8,108.

30 ⌇free. **Location:** Central. **Surface:** metalled.
Distance: 🚶on the spot ⊗on the spot ⛴on the spot.
Tourist information Quarteira:
ℹ Bathing resort.

20 ⌇free. **Surface:** sand.
Distance: 🚶2,2km ⚓50m.
Remarks: Forbidden during Summer period.

Salema   38A4
GPS: n37,06680 w8,82552.

Raposeira   38A4
Praia do Barranco. GPS: n37,04700 w8,8785.

⌇free. **Surface:** sand.
Distance: 🚶5km ⚓on the spot.

⌇free. **Surface:** sand. ◻ 01/01-31/12
Distance: ⚓100m.

Sagres   38A4
GPS: n37,00641 w8,93943.

Silves   38B4
N124. **GPS:** n37,18528 w8,44222.

10 ⌇free ⏚🔧Chfree. **Surface:** gravel/sand. ◻ 01/01-31/12
Distance: 🚶400m ⚓on the spot.
Remarks: Service at the left-hand dir harbor. Parking behind tourist office.

+10 ⌇free ⏚〰free.
Surface: metalled. ◻ 01/01-31/12
Distance: 🚶on the spot ⚓on the spot ⊗on the spot ⛴200m 🚌on the spot.
Remarks: Parking near the river and swimming pool.

Sagres   38A4
Fortaleze de Sagres. GPS: n37,00523 w8,94545.

Silves   38B4
Barregem do Arade, N124-3. **GPS:** n37,23905 w8,37778.
10 ⌇free. **Surface:** sand.
Distance: 🚶Silves 10km.
Remarks: At barrage and restaurant.

Silves   38B4
Campismo Silves. GPS: n37,18452 e8,44223.

🏞S Vila Real de Santo António 🚤 38B4
Avenida de República. **GPS**: n37,19955 w7,4153.
30 🗺€4 ⚱🍴Ch 🔌 📶included. **Surface:** metalled/sand.
Distance: 🚶500m ⊗on the spot.

13 🗺€ 5, peak season € 8,50 ⚱🍴Ch 🔌 WC 🗑▣€ 3. **Surface:** grassy.
Distance: 🚶Silves 2km ⊗300m 🚰2km.
Remarks: Free fruits of the trees.

Tourist information Silves:
Ⓜ Museu Municipal de Arqueologia.Archeological findings.
🏰 Castello. 🕐 9-18h.
☀ Festival da cerveja.Beer festival. 🕐 July.

🏞S Tavira 38B4
Parque de Autocaravanes. GPS: n37,13637 w7,64013.⬆
20 🗺€ 8,50 ⚱🍴Ch 🔌 WC 🗑▣€ 2 📶included. **Surface:** unpaved. 🕐
15/09-15/06 🕐 summer.
Distance: 🚶1km.

Tourist information Tavira:
🏰 Castello. 🕐 Mo-Fri 8-17.30h.

🏞 Vila do Bispo 38A4
Praia do Castelejo. GPS: n37,04694 w8,88028.

3 🗺free.
Surface: gravel/sand. 🕐 01/01-31/12
Distance: 🏊100m ⊗200m.
Remarks: Small parking, from Vila do Bispo keep following dir beach.

🏞S Vila do Bispo 38A4
Estr. EM1265. **GPS**: n37,08333 w8,91361.
🗺free ⚱. **Surface:** sand.
Distance: 🚶on the spot.
Remarks: At football ground.

🏞 Vila do Bispo 38A4
Praia da Barriga, N1265. **GPS**: n37,09970 w8,94445.

🗺free. **Surface:** asphalted.
Distance: 🚶Vila do Bispo 3,8km 🏊on the spot.
Remarks: Beach parking, from Vila do Bispo dir beaches Castelejo and Cordama,
take most northern road at T-junction, 6km.

🏔S Vila do Bispo 38A4
Sagres, Cerro da Moita. **GPS**: n37,02278 w8,94583.
🗺 ⚱Ch ♻. 🕐 01/01-30/11
Distance: 🏊2km ⊗on the spot 🚰on the spot 🚌500m.

DENMARK

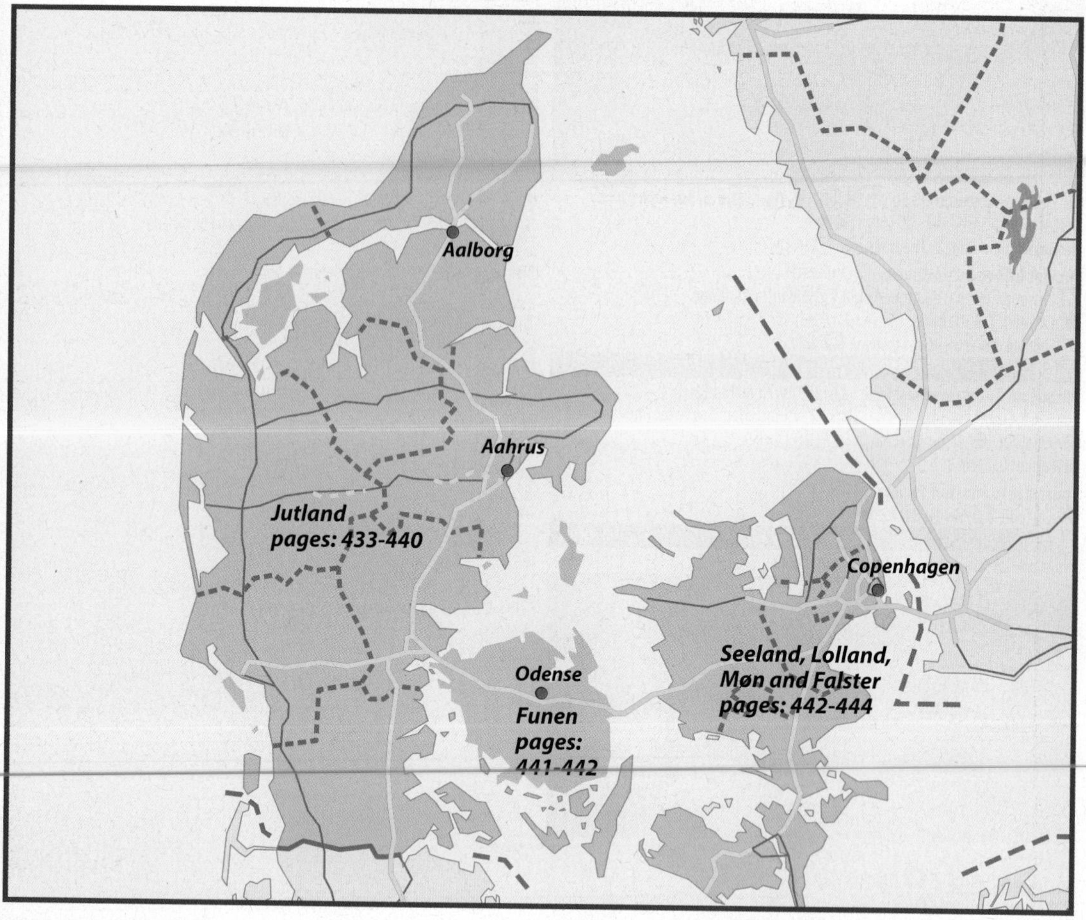

Map of Denmark showing:
- Aalborg
- Aahrus
- **Jutland** pages: 433-440
- **Funen** pages: 441-442
- Odense
- Copenhagen
- **Seeland, Lolland, Møn and Falster** pages: 442-444

Capital: Copenhagen
Government: Constitutional monarchy
Official Language: Danish
Population: 5,535,000 (2010)
Area: 44,000m²

General information
Dialling code: 0045.
Currency: Danish Krone (DKK), 1 DKK= 100 øre, DKK 1 = € 0,13, € 1 = DKK 7,46 (October 2012)
Payments by credit card are accepted at almost every shop and restaurant.

Regulations for overnight stays/campsites
Overnight parking is allowed: for 1 night, if there is no local prohibition, but no "camping" activities are allowed.

Camping cards are obligatory when using Danish campsites: Camping Card International (CCI) or Camping Card Scandinavia is accepted. A card can be purchased at any campsite for DKK 100 (± € 13,40), valid for one year.

Opening hours
Shops: no standard opening hours, most shops are open from: Monday-Thursday 9/10am-5.30/6pm, Friday 9/10am-7/8pm, Saturday 9/10am-12noon/2pm.
Shopping centres, department stores Monday-Saturday 9/10am-7/8pm
Bank: Monday-Friday 9.30am-4pm, Thursday 9.30am-6pm.

Jutland

| C S | Aalborg | 2B3 |

Aalborg, Skydebanevej 50. **GPS**: n57,05379 e9,87233.
DKK 105 Ch against payment. 01/01-31/12
Remarks: QuickStop: >20 - <10h.

| △ S | Aalborg | 2B3 |

Strandparken, Skydebanevej 20. **GPS**: n57,05502 e9,88499.
DKK 140 Ch against payment. 01/02-15/12
Remarks: QuickStop: >20 - <10h.

Tourist information Aalborg:
Aalborg Tourist & Convention Bureau, østeraagade 8, www.visitaalborg.com.
Søfarts - og Marinemuseum, Vestre Fjordvej 81.Maritime museum.
01/05-31/12.
Aalborg Zoo, Mølleparkvej 63.Zoo. 01/05-30/12.
Tivoliland, Karolinelundsvej 40.Amusement park. 12-19h.

| S | Aalbæk | 2B2 |

Aalbæk Havn, Sdr. Havnevej 56. **GPS**: n57,59194 e10,42639.

6 DKK 140 WC . **Surface:** gravel. 01/01-31/12
Distance: 250m on the spot on the spot on the spot on the spot 250m.

| Aalbæk | 2B2 |

Galleri & Selskabslokal Gyllegaard, Hirtshalsvej 48. **GPS**: n57,60639 e10,41631.
5 DKK 100. **Surface:** grassy.

| S | Åbenrå | 2B6 |

Camperstop Aabenraa, Sønderskovvej 104. **GPS**: n55,02513 e9,41471.

34 € 14 Ch WC . **Surface:** grassy/gravel. 01/01-31/12
Distance: 2km 8km 400m.
Remarks: Chip-card available at campsite.

| S | Åbenrå | 2B6 |

Lystbådehavn, Kystvej 55. **GPS**: n55,03434 e9,42352.

48 DKK 125 Ch WC against payment. . **Location:**
Comfortable. **Surface:** gravel. 01/04-31/10
Distance: 1km on the spot on the spot on the spot 50m
200m on the spot on the spot.
Remarks: Harbour Åbenrå.

Tourist information Åbenrå:
ÅbenråTuristbureau, H. P. Hanssens Gade 5, www.visitaabenraa.dk.Old city
with a lot of curiosities and restored city centre.
Den Gamle Smedie, Skibbrogade 13.Forge from 1845. Mo,Tue, Thu 9-12h.
free.
Sønderjysk Spejdermuseum, Bjerggade 4 H.Scouting museum. Tue
10-15h. free.

| △ S | Allingåbro | 2C4 |

Dalgård, Nordkystvejen 65. **GPS**: n56,50895 e10,54593.
DKK 140 Ch against payment. 04/04-20/09
Remarks: QuickStop: >20 - <10h.

| S | Århus | 2B5 |

Gammle Lystbådehavn, Kystpromenaden 17. **GPS**: n56,16833 e10,22536.
10 DKK 100 WC included. **Surface:** metalled.
01/01-31/12
Distance: 750m on the spot on the spot.

| S | Århus | 2B5 |

Pier 1, Nordhavnsgade 8A. **GPS**: n56,15572 e10,21578.
50 free. **Surface:** asphalted.
Distance: 250m on the spot on the spot.

| C S | Århus | 2B5 |

Aarhus Nord, Randersvej 400. **GPS**: n56,22672 e10,16335.
DKK 90 Ch against payment. 01/01-31/12
Remarks: QuickStop: >20 - <10h.

| △ S | Aså | 2B3 |

Asaa, Vodbindervej 13. **GPS**: n57,14635 e10,40249.
DKK 125 Ch against payment. 04/04-28/09
Remarks: QuickStop: >20 - <10h.

| S | Aså | 2B3 |

østkystvej 409a. **GPS**: n57,17806 e10,44111.

10 free Ch WC free. **Surface:** grassy. 01/04-31/10
Distance: 5km.

| S | Augustenborg | 2B6 |

Augustenborg Slot, Palævej. **GPS**: n54,94694 e9,85389.

70 DKK 100 Ch WC . **Location:** Rural, comfortable.
Surface: grassy. 01/01-31/12
Distance: 1,5km on the spot on the spot.

| C S | Augustenborg | 2B6 |

Hertugbyens, Ny Stavenbøl 1. **GPS**: n54,94639 e9,85951.
DKK 100 Ch against payment. 01/04-30/09
Remarks: QuickStop: >20 - <10h.

| S | Augustenborg | 2B6 |

Yachthavn Peder Dahl, Langdel 6. **GPS**: n54,94074 e9,86942.

DK

19 ⌇DKK 130 ⌁🍴Ch ⌁ DKK 25 WC ⌁. 🚿 **Location:** Luxurious, central.
Surface: gravel. ⬤ 01/04-15/10
Distance: ⛵1km ⟿1km 🏪 on the spot.

| ⬚⬚ | Bjert | 2B6 |

Stensager Strand, Oluf Ravnsvej 16. **GPS:** n55,42076 e9,58785.
⌇DKK 180 ⌁🍴Ch ⌁against payment. ⬤ 03/04-14/09
Remarks: QuickStop: >20 - <10h.

| ⬚⬚ | **Bonnerup Strand** | 2C4 |

Lystbådehavnen, Vestre mole 1. **GPS:** n56,53139 e10,71139.⬆.

20 ⌇DKK 130 ⌁ ⌁ ⌁included. **Surface:** gravel. ⬤ 01/01-31/12
Distance: ⛵500m ⟿on the spot ⟿on the spot ⊗250m 🏪400m.
Remarks: Parking at marina.

| △⬚ | Bredebro | 2A6 |

Bredebro Kig-Nai, Borgvej 13. **GPS:** n55,05247 e8,82554.
⌇DKK 100 ⌁🍴Ch ⌁against payment. ⬤ 15/05-15/09
Remarks: QuickStop: >20 - <10h.

| ⬚⬚ | Bredebro | 2A6 |

Claus Cornelsen, Galgemark 9. **GPS:** n55,04853 e8,83270. ⬆.

50 ⌇free ⌁🍴Ch ⌁against payment ⌁. **Location:** Rural, quit. **Surface:**
gravel. ⬤ 01/01-31/12
Distance: ⛵1km.

| △⬚ | Brædstrup | 2B5 |

Gudenå, Bolundvej 4. **GPS:** n55,93507 e9,65283.
⌇DKK 125 ⌁🍴Ch ⌁against payment. ⬤ 04/04-27/09
Remarks: QuickStop: >20 - <10h.

| △⬚ | Brørup | 2A6 |

Foldingbro, Kongeåvej 110. **GPS:** n55,44113 e8,99978.
⌇DKK 150 ⌁🍴Ch ⌁against payment. ⬤ 01/01-31/12
Remarks: QuickStop: >20 - <10h.

| △⬚ | Bylderup-Bov | 2B6 |

Kristianshåb Autocamper Park, Kristianshåbvej 5. **GPS:** n54,96189 e9,06950.
➡.

50 ⌇DKK 100 incl. 2 pers ⌁🍴Ch ⌁ DKK 4/24h WC ⌁⌁.🚿 ⌁
Location: Rural, comfortable, isolated. **Surface:** grassy.
⬤ 01/01-31/12
Distance: ⛵6km ⊿1km ⊗5km.

| ⬚⬚ | Bylderup-Bov | 2B6 |

Boskov, Kvænholtvej 15. **GPS:** n54,94488 e9,06078. ⬆.
10 ⌇DKK 60 ⌁🍴Ch ⌁ included. 🚿 **Location:** Rural, isolated. **Surface:**
grassy/gravel.
Distance: 🏪200m.

| ⬚⬚ | Bylderup-Bov | 2B6 |

B&B Bredevad, Bredevadvej 5. **GPS:** n54,96885 e9,12138.⬆.

2 ⌇€ 13 incl. 2 pers ⌁🍴Ch ⌁ WC ⌁included. 🚿 **Location:** Rural.
Surface: .
Distance: 🏪4km.

Tourist information Bylderup-Bov:
🏰 Schackenborg Slot, Schackenborg 2, Tønder.Visit the castle garden.
🎡 Sommerland Syd, Terkelsbøl, Tinglev.Amusement park. ⬤ 01/05-30/06,
01/09-30/09 Sa-Su, 01/07-31/08 daily. ⌁ DKK 150.

| △⬚ | Børkop | 2B5 |

Mørkholt, Hagenvej 105 B. **GPS:** n55,65146 e9,72250.
⌇DKK 140 ⌁🍴Ch ⌁against payment. ⬤ 01/01-31/12
Remarks: QuickStop: >20 - <10h.

| ⬚⬚ | Ebeltoft | 2C5 |

Blushøj, Elsegårdevej 53. **GPS:** n56,16795 e10,72943.
⌇DKK 125 ⌁🍴Ch ⌁against payment. ⬤ 01/04-14/09
Remarks: QuickStop: >20 - <10h.

| ⬚⬚ | Ebeltoft | 2C5 |

Dråby Strand, Dråby Strandvej 13. **GPS:** n56,22172 e10,73778.
⌇DKK 150 ⌁🍴Ch ⌁against payment. ⬤ 04/04-14/09
Remarks: QuickStop: >20 - <10h.

| ⬚⬚ | Ebeltoft | 2C5 |

Elsegårde, Kristoffenvejen 1. **GPS:** n56,16843 e10,72278.
⌇DKK 140 ⌁🍴Ch ⌁against payment. ⬤ 01/01-31/12
Remarks: QuickStop: >20 - <10h.

| ⬚⬚ | Ebeltoft | 2C5 |

Krakær, Gl. Kærvej 18. **GPS:** n56,19730 e10,67426.
⌇DKK 125 ⌁🍴Ch ⌁against payment. ⬤ 17/04-23/10
Remarks: QuickStop: >20 - <10h.

| ⬚⬚ | Egtved | 2B6 |

Egtved, Verstvej 9. **GPS:** n55,60680 e9,27870.
⌇DKK 145 ⌁🍴Ch ⌁against payment. ⬤ 01/01-31/12
Remarks: QuickStop: >20 - <10h.

| ⬚⬚ | Engesvan | 2B5 |

Pårup Autocamperplads, Silkeborgvej 8. **GPS:** n56,13694 e9,35028.⬆.
4 ⌇against payment ⌁🍴Ch ⌁ against payment. **Surface:** gravel. ⬤
01/04-01/11

DK

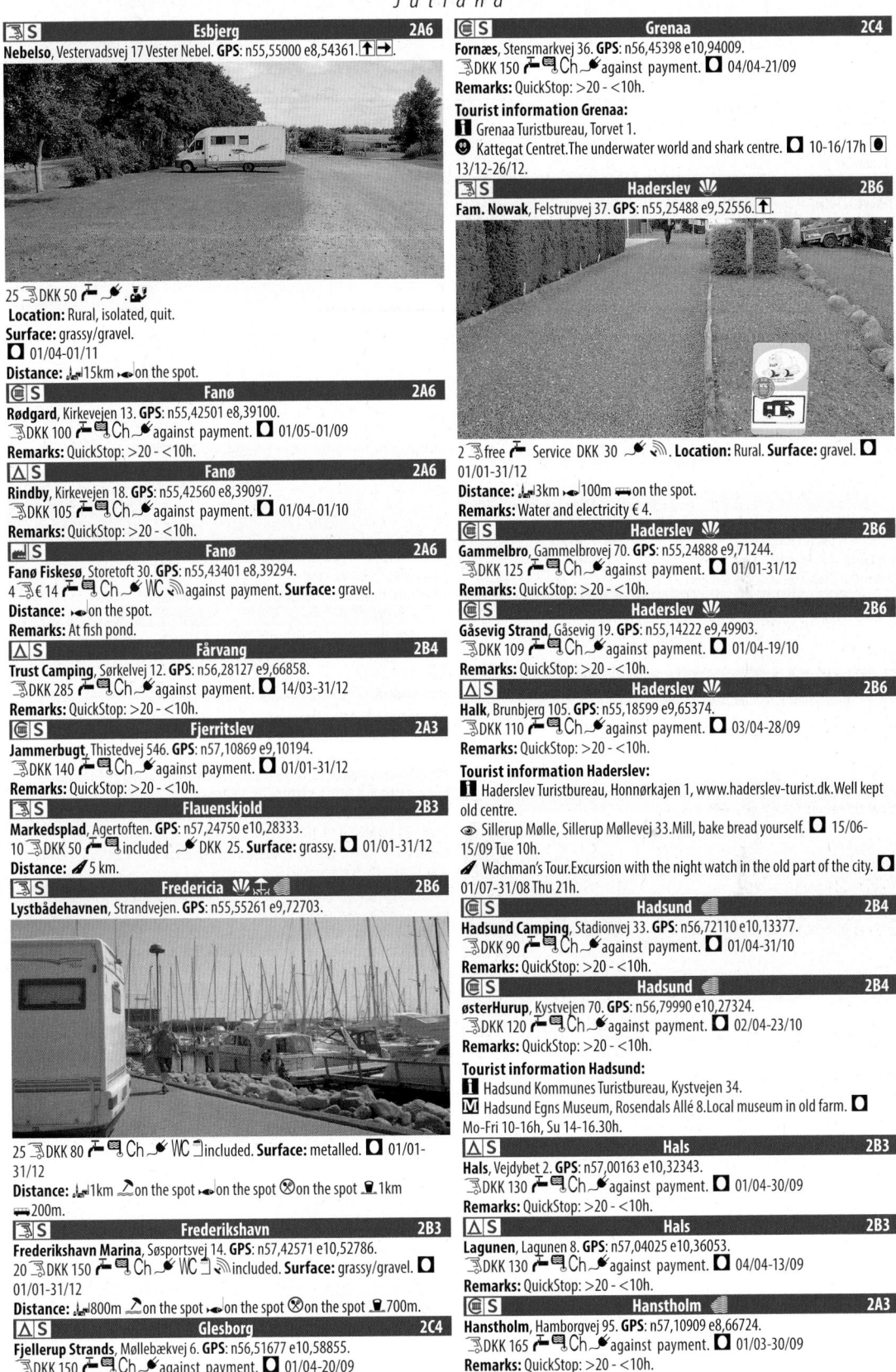

Esbjerg   2A6
Nebelso, Vestervadsvej 17 Vester Nebel. **GPS**: n55,55000 e8,54361. ⬆➡.

25 DKK 50
Location: Rural, isolated, quit.
Surface: grassy/gravel.
◉ 01/04-01/11
Distance: 15km on the spot.

Fanø   2A6
Rødgard, Kirkevejen 13. **GPS**: n55,42501 e8,39100.
DKK 100 Ch against payment. ◉ 01/05-01/09
Remarks: QuickStop: >20 - <10h.

Fanø   2A6
Rindby, Kirkevejen 18. **GPS**: n55,42560 e8,39097.
DKK 105 Ch against payment. ◉ 01/04-01/10
Remarks: QuickStop: >20 - <10h.

Fanø   2A6
Fanø Fiskesø, Storetoft 30. **GPS**: n55,43401 e8,39294.
4 € 14 Ch WC against payment. **Surface:** gravel.
Distance: on the spot.
Remarks: At fish pond.

Fårvang   2B4
Trust Camping, Sørkelvej 12. **GPS**: n56,28127 e9,66858.
DKK 285 Ch against payment. ◉ 14/03-31/12
Remarks: QuickStop: >20 - <10h.

Fjerritslev   2A3
Jammerbugt, Thistedvej 546. **GPS**: n57,10869 e9,10194.
DKK 140 Ch against payment. ◉ 01/01-31/12
Remarks: QuickStop: >20 - <10h.

Flauenskjold   2B3
Markedsplad, Agertoften. **GPS**: n57,24750 e10,28333.
10 DKK 50 included DKK 25. **Surface:** grassy. ◉ 01/01-31/12
Distance: 5 km.

Fredericia   2B6
Lystbådehavnen, Strandvejen. **GPS**: n55,55261 e9,72703.

25 DKK 80 Ch WC included. **Surface:** metalled. ◉ 01/01-31/12
Distance: 1km on the spot on the spot on the spot 1km 200m.

Frederikshavn   2B3
Frederikshavn Marina, Søsportsvej 14. **GPS**: n57,42571 e10,52786.
20 DKK 150 Ch WC included. **Surface:** grassy/gravel. ◉ 01/01-31/12
Distance: 800m on the spot on the spot on the spot 700m.

Glesborg   2C4
Fjellerup Strands, Møllebækvej 6. **GPS**: n56,51677 e10,58855.
DKK 150 Ch against payment. ◉ 01/04-20/09
Remarks: QuickStop: >20 - <10h.

Grenaa   2C4
Fornæs, Stensmarkvej 36. **GPS**: n56,45398 e10,94009.
DKK 150 Ch against payment. ◉ 04/04-21/09
Remarks: QuickStop: >20 - <10h.

Tourist information Grenaa:
🛈 Grenaa Turistbureau, Torvet 1.
☻ Kattegat Centret. The underwater world and shark centre. ◉ 10-16/17h ◉ 13/12-26/12.

Haderslev   2B6
Fam. Nowak, Felstrupvej 37. **GPS**: n55,25488 e9,52556. ⬆.

2 free Service DKK 30 . **Location:** Rural. **Surface:** gravel. ◉ 01/01-31/12
Distance: 3km 100m on the spot.
Remarks: Water and electricity € 4.

Haderslev   2B6
Gammelbro, Gammelbrovej 70. **GPS**: n55,24888 e9,71244.
DKK 125 Ch against payment. ◉ 01/01-31/12
Remarks: QuickStop: >20 - <10h.

Haderslev   2B6
Gåsevig Strand, Gåsevig 19. **GPS**: n55,14222 e9,49903.
DKK 109 Ch against payment. ◉ 01/04-19/10
Remarks: QuickStop: >20 - <10h.

Haderslev   2B6
Halk, Brunbjerg 105. **GPS**: n55,18599 e9,65374.
DKK 110 Ch against payment. ◉ 03/04-28/09
Remarks: QuickStop: >20 - <10h.

Tourist information Haderslev:
🛈 Haderslev Turistbureau, Honnørkajen 1, www.haderslev-turist.dk. Well kept old centre.
👁 Sillerup Mølle, Sillerup Møllevej 33. Mill, bake bread yourself. ◉ 15/06-15/09 Tue 10h.
✎ Wachman's Tour. Excursion with the night watch in the old part of the city. ◉ 01/07-31/08 Thu 21h.

Hadsund   2B4
Hadsund Camping, Stadionvej 33. **GPS**: n56,72110 e10,13377.
DKK 90 Ch against payment. ◉ 01/04-31/10
Remarks: QuickStop: >20 - <10h.

Hadsund   2B4
østerHurup, Kystvejen 70. **GPS**: n56,79990 e10,27324.
DKK 120 Ch against payment. ◉ 02/04-23/10
Remarks: QuickStop: >20 - <10h.

Tourist information Hadsund:
🛈 Hadsund Kommunes Turistbureau, Kystvejen 34.
Ⓜ Hadsund Egns Museum, Rosendals Allé 8. Local museum in old farm. ◉ Mo-Fri 10-16h, Su 14-16.30h.

Hals   2B3
Hals, Vejdybet 2. **GPS**: n57,00163 e10,32343.
DKK 130 Ch against payment. ◉ 01/04-30/09
Remarks: QuickStop: >20 - <10h.

Hals   2B3
Lagunen, Lagunen 8. **GPS**: n57,04025 e10,36053.
DKK 130 Ch against payment. ◉ 04/04-13/09
Remarks: QuickStop: >20 - <10h.

Hanstholm   2A3
Hanstholm, Hamborgvej 95. **GPS**: n57,10909 e8,66724.
DKK 165 Ch against payment. ◉ 01/03-30/09
Remarks: QuickStop: >20 - <10h.

Tourist information Hanstholm:

DK

ℹ️ Hanstholm Turistbureau, Bytorvet 9, www.hanstholmturist.dk.Biggest commercial fishing-port in Denmark.
👁 Frøstrup mini-village, Søndergade 36, Frøstrup.Miniature village. ◘ 01/05-15/10 Wed-Thu 10-13h, 01/07-31/08 daily 13-16h.

△ S	Harboøre	2A4

Vesterhavs, Flyvholmvej 36. GPS: n56,62841 e8,15773.
🏕 DKK 115 ⛽🔌 Ch.✂against payment. ◘ 04/04-16/09
Remarks: QuickStop: >20 - <10h.

🏕 S	Havndal	2B4

Udbyhøj Havn, Havnevej 5. GPS: n56,61111 e10,30583.
10 🏕 DKK 95 ⛽🔌 Ch ✂ WC ⬜included. ◘ 01/01-31/12
Distance: ⚓on the spot 🚌on the spot 🚆500m.

ⓒ S	Havndal	2B4

Randers Fjord, Midtvasen 21. GPS: n56,60997 e10,29334.
🏕 DKK 130 ⛽🔌Ch✂against payment. ◘ 01/04-15/09
Remarks: QuickStop: >20 - <10h.

ⓒ S	Hejls	2B6

Hejlsminde Strand, Gendarmvej 3. GPS: n55,36851 e9,60095.
🏕 DKK 150 ⛽🔌Ch✂against payment. ◘ 04/04-14/09
Remarks: QuickStop: >20 - <10h.

ⓒ S	Hemmet	2A5

Bork Havn, Kirkehøjvej 9A. GPS: n55,84850 e8,28257.
🏕 DKK 112 ⛽🔌Ch✂against payment. ◘ 01/04-01/11
Remarks: QuickStop: >20 - <10h.

🏕	Hirtshals	2B3

Banegårdspladse, Banegårdspladsen 1. GPS: n57,59148 e9,96311.
10 🏕free. Surface: metalled.
Distance: ⚓600m ⚓4,8km.
Remarks: At station and ferry terminal.

△ S	Hirtshals	2B3

Tornby Strand, Strandvejen 13. GPS: n57,55540 e9,93264.
🏕 DKK 125 ⛽🔌Ch✂against payment. ◘ 01/04-01/10
Remarks: QuickStop: >20 - <10h.

S	Hirtshals	2B3

Q8, østergade 59. GPS: n57,58750 e9,97766.
⛽🔌Ch.

Tourist information Hirtshals:
Ⓜ Nordsømuseet, Willemoesvej 2.Oceanarium, large aquarium. ◘ 15/06-15/08 10-20h, 16/08-14/06 10-17h.

P S	Hjallerup	2B3

E45. GPS: n57,15333 e10,15750.

10 🏕free ⛽🔌 Ch WCfree. Surface: asphalted. ◘ 01/01-31/12

ⓒ S	Hobro	2B4

Hobro Camping Gattenborg, Skivevej 35. GPS: n56,64015 e9,78265.
🏕 DKK 120 ⛽🔌Ch✂against payment. ◘ 01/04-02/10
Remarks: QuickStop: >20 - <10h.

🏕 S	Holsted	2A6

Holsted Golfbanen, Bergardsvej 4, Vejen-Esberg. GPS: n55,52353 e8,93228.

15 🏕€ 10 ⛽ ✂ WC. Surface: gravel. ◘ 01/04-30/10
Distance: ⚓1km.

🏕 S	Horsens	2B5

Lystbådehavn, Jens Hjernøes Vej 29. GPS: n55,85764 e9,87417.

7 🏕DKK 120 ⛽🔌 Ch ✂. ◘ 01/04-17/09
Distance: ⊗on the spot.
Remarks: Harbour Horsen, special part for motorhomes.

ⓒ S	Horsens	2B5

Husodde, Husoddevej 85. GPS: n55,86035 e9,91537.
🏕DKK 130 ⛽🔌Ch✂against payment.
◘ 17/04-18/10
Remarks: QuickStop: >20 - <10h.

Tourist information Horsens:
ℹ️ Horsens Turistbureau, Søndergade 26, www.visitendelave.dk.
👁 Dolmen "Jættestuen", åbjerg Skov.Dolmen. ◘ 01/01-31/12.
Ⓜ Danmarks Nimbus Tourings Motorcykle-Museum, Gasvej 21.Collection of motorcycles. ◘ 01/04-31/10 Sa-Su 11-16h.
Ⓜ Horsens Museum, Sundvej 1A.City museum. ◘ 01/09-30/06 Tue-Su 11-17h, 01/07-31/08 Mo-Su 10-16h.
Ⓜ Industrimuseet, Gasvej 17.Industry museum. ◘ 01/09-30/06 Tue-Su 11-16h, 01/07-31/08 Mo-Su 10-16h.

🏕	Hoven	2A5

GPS: n55,85059 e8,76119.
🏕free. Surface: asphalted/gravel. ◘ 01/01-31/12
Remarks: Motorhome friendly town, parking and stay overnight possible at several places; Brugsen 2/3 campers; sport hall.

🔌 S	Hurup	2A4

Nordisk Folkecente, Kammersgaardsvej 16. GPS: n56,69358 e8,41306.
5 🏕DKK 60 ✂ included. Surface: gravel. ◘ 01/01-31/12

ⓒ S	Hvidbjerg	2A6

Hvidbjerg Strand Camping, Hvidbjerg Strandvej. GPS: n55,54415 e8,13385.
4 🏕DKK 95 ⛽🔌Ch ✂ included. Surface: gravel. ◘ 01/04-31/10
Distance: ⚓1,2km.

	Hvide Sande	2A5

P Tungevej. GPS: n55,99722 e8,12222.
40 🏕. Surface: gravel/metalled.
Distance: ⚓200m ⚓on the spot.

ⓒ S	Hvide Sande	2A5

Bjerregaard, Sdr. Klitvej 185. GPS: n55,90620 e8,16565.
🏕DKK 120 ⛽🔌Ch✂against payment. ◘ 15/04-01/10
Remarks: QuickStop: >20 - <10h.

ⓒ S	Hvide Sande	2A5

Hvide Sande (Beltana), Karen Brands Vej 70. GPS: n55,98689 e8,13478.
🏕DKK 110 ⛽🔌Ch✂against payment. ◘ 03/04-26/10
Remarks: QuickStop: >20 - <10h.

△ S	Højslev	2B4

Virksund, Sundvej 14. GPS: n56,60785 e9,28917.

DK

🏕S DKK 220 ⛽🚿Ch 🛁against payment. 🅿 04/04-20/09
Remarks: QuickStop: >20 - <10h.

| 🏕S | Ikast | 2B5 |

Tony Bülow, Bangsvej 50, Tulstrup. **GPS:** n56,15500 e9,16167.
5 🏕against payment ⛽🚿Ch 🛁against payment. **Surface:** grassy.

| 🏕S | Juelsminde | 2B5 |

Havn & Marina, Havnegade 15. **GPS:** n55,71528 e10,01556.
5 🏕DKK 115 ⛽🚿Ch 🛁included. **Surface:** metalled.
Distance: ⚓on the spot ⛵on the spot.

| ©S | Karup | 2A4 |

Hessellund Sø, Hessellundvej 12. **GPS:** n56,32308 e9,11501.
🏕DKK 150 🚿Ch 🛁against payment. 🅿 27/03-29/09
Remarks: QuickStop: >20 - <10h.

| 🚲S | Karup | 2A4 |

2B Pack, Ulvedalsvej 43. **GPS:** n56,31528 e9,27361. 🔼.
4 🏕€ 14 ⛽🚿Ch 🛁. 🅿 23/03-29/10

| 🏕S | Kolding 🍺🌊 | 2B6 |

Lystbådehavn, Skamlingvejen 5. **GPS:** n55,48746 e9,50051. 🔼.

6 🏕DKK 110 ⛽🚿Ch 🛁🌊.📶 **Location:** Urban, isolated. **Surface:** grassy/gravel. 🅿 01/05-01/10
Distance: 🏖2,6km ⚓on the spot.

| 🚲S | Kvissel | 2B3 |

Bondegård Hansen, Mejlingvej 65. **GPS:** n57,46753 e10,39556.
19 🏕DKK 75 🚿Ch 🛁WCincluded 🏕DKK 10. 🅿 01/01-31/12

| ©S | Langå | 2B4 |

Langå, Skov Alle 16. **GPS:** n56,38780 e9,90439.
🏕DKK 120 ⛽🚿Ch 🛁against payment. 🅿 01/01-31/12
Remarks: QuickStop: >20 - <10h.

| 🏕S | Lemvig | 2A4 |

Hofte, Kjeldjergvej. **GPS:** n56,47583 e8,12472. 🔼.

10 🏕free ⛽WC 🚻. **Surface:** metalled.
Remarks: Beach parking.

| △S | Lemvig | 2A4 |

Lemvig Strandcamping, Vinkelhagevej 6. **GPS:** n56,57061 e8,29054.
🏕DKK 125 ⛽🚿Ch 🛁against payment. 🅿 03/04-14/09
Remarks: QuickStop: >20 - <10h.

Tourist information Lemvig:
ℹ Lemvig Turistbureau, Toldbodgade 4, www.visitlemvig.dk.
👁 Bovbjerg Fyr, Fyrvej 27.Lighthouse.

| 🏕S | Løgstør | 2B3 |

Kanalvejen 1. **GPS:** n56,96728 e9,24528.
5 🏕DKK 110 ⛽🚿🛁included. **Surface:** grassy/metalled. 🅿 01/01-31/12
Distance: 🏖200m ⚓on the spot ⛵on the spot ⚓200m.

| 🏕S | Løgstør | 2B3 |

Løgstør Golfklub, Viborgvej 13. **GPS:** n56,94689 e9,25390.
3 🏕against payment 🛁.
Distance: 🏖2km.

| △S | Løgstør | 2B3 |

Løgstør, Skovbrynet 1. **GPS:** n56,96233 e9,24873.
🏕DKK 100 ⛽🚿Ch 🛁against payment. 🅿 01/01-31/12
Remarks: QuickStop: >20 - <10h.

| ©S | Løkken 🍺🌊 | 2B3 |

Gl.Klitgaard, Lyngbyvej 331. **GPS:** n57,41784 e9,76017.
🏕DKK 148 ⛽🚿Ch 🛁against payment. 🅿 15/04-23/10
Remarks: QuickStop: >20 - <10h.

| ©S | Løkken 🍺🌊 | 2B3 |

Grønhøj Strand, Kettrupvej 125. **GPS:** n57,32127 e9,67293.
🏕DKK 100 ⛽🚿Ch 🛁against payment. 🅿 15/04-18/09
Remarks: QuickStop: >20 - <10h.

| ©S | Løkken 🍺🌊 | 2B3 |

Løkken Strand, Furreby Kirkevej 97. **GPS:** n57,38533 e9,72571.
🏕DKK 125 ⛽🚿Ch 🛁against payment. 🅿 05/05-04/09
Remarks: QuickStop: >20 - <10h.

| ©S | Løkken 🍺🌊 | 2B3 |

Rolighed, Grønhøj Strandvej 35. **GPS:** n57,32143 e9,67818.
🏕DKK 120 ⛽🚿Ch 🛁against payment.
🅿 04/04-18/10
Remarks: QuickStop: >20 - <10h.

Tourist information Løkken:
ℹ Løkken Turistbureau, Harald Fischers Vej 8, www.loekken.dk.Bathing resort.
🅼 Kystfiskerimuseum, Løkkennordstrand.Fishery museum.
🅼 Vendsyssel historiske museum "Jens Thomsens Gård", Strandfogedgården i Rubjerg, Langelinie 2.Cultural past of the coast area. Hiking-trails. 🅿 16/06-15/09 Mo, Wed-Fri, Su 11-17h. 🎫 free.
🎡 Familiy Farm Fun Park, Lyngbyvej 86, Vittrup.Animal park. 🅿 01/05-30/09.

| △S | Malling | 2B5 |

Ajstrup strand, Ajstrup Strandvej 81. **GPS:** n56,04131 e10,26472.
🏕DKK 150 ⛽🚿Ch 🛁against payment. 🅿 03/04-20/09
Remarks: QuickStop: >20 - <10h.

| ©S | Mariager | 2B4 |

Mariager, Ny Havnevej 5A. **GPS:** n56,65399 e9,97640.
🏕DKK 145 ⛽🚿Ch 🛁against payment. 🅿 08/04-25/09
Remarks: QuickStop: >20 - <10h.

| △S | Nibe | 2B3 |

Sølyst, Løgstørvej 2. **GPS:** n56,97248 e9,62460.
🏕DKK 140 ⛽🚿Ch 🛁against payment. 🅿 01/01-31/12
Remarks: QuickStop: >20 - <10h.

| ©S | Nordborg 🌊 | 2B6 |

Lavensby Strand, Arnbjergvej 49. **GPS:** n55,07119 e9,79600.
🏕DKK 109 ⛽🚿Ch 🛁against payment. 🅿 27/03-31/10
Remarks: QuickStop: >20 - <10h.

| △S | Nordborg 🌊 | 2B6 |

Købingsmark, Købingsmarksvej 53. **GPS:** n55,07887 e9,72912.
🏕DKK 120 ⛽🚿Ch 🛁against payment. 🅿 01/04-25/10
Remarks: QuickStop: >20 - <10h.

| 🚲S | Nordborg 🌊 | 2B6 |

Lone & Henning Carlsson, Kådnervej 7. **GPS:** n55,03194 e9,73111. 🔼.

5 🏕DKK 100 🔌 WC 🌊. 🚿 **Location:** Rural, comfortable, quit. **Surface:** gravel. 🅿 01/01-31/12
Distance: 🏖5km.
Remarks: Narrow entrance road.

| 🏕S | Nykøbing Mors | 2A4 |

Morsø Sejlklub & Marin, Jernbanevej. **GPS:** n56,79282 e8,86370.
10 🏕DKK 120 ⛽🚿Ch 🛁WC 🚻against payment. **Surface:** gravel. 🅿 01/01-31/12
Distance: 🏖150m ⚓on the spot ⛵on the spot ⊗on the spot ⚓200m.

DK

DK

| Ⓒ S | Nørre Nebel | 2A5 |

Nymindegab, Lyngtoften 12. **GPS**: n55,81368 e8,19992.
🔲DKK 160 ⛽🔌Ch 🚿against payment. 🅾 01/04-27/09
Remarks: QuickStop: >20 - <10h.

| Ⓒ S | Odder | 2B5 |

Odder strand Camping, Toldvejen 50. **GPS**: n55,93891 e10,25054.
🔲DKK 110 ⛽🔌Ch 🚿against payment. 🅾 01/04-21/09
Remarks: QuickStop: >20 - <10h.

| △ S | Odder | 2B5 |

Saksild Strand, Kystvejen 5. **GPS**: n55,98002 e10,24904.
🔲DKK 160 ⛽🔌Ch 🚿against payment. 🅾 01/04-18/10
Remarks: QuickStop: >20 - <10h.

| Ⓒ S | Pandrup | 2B3 |

Rødhus Klit, Rødhusmindevej 25. **GPS**: n57,20195 e9,58138.
🔲DKK 110 ⛽🔌Ch 🚿against payment. 🅾 01/04-25/09
Remarks: QuickStop: >20 - <10h.

| S | Randers | 2B4 |

Randers havn, Toldbodgade 14. **GPS**: n56,46229 e10,05122.⬆
10 🔲free. **Surface:** gravel. 🅾 01/01-31/12
Remarks: Max. 24h.

| S | Ribe | 2A6 |

Fabelbo, Hølleskovvej 48. **GPS**: n55,24076 e8,86077.
🔲free ⛽free. **Location:** Isolated, quit.
Surface: grassy. 🅾 01/01-31/12

| S | Ribe | 2A6 |

Stampemøllevej. **GPS**: n55,32480 e8,75740.⬆

25 🔲free ⛽🔌 WCfree. **Location:** Urban. **Surface:** asphalted. 🅾 01/01-31/12
Distance: 🚏500m ✕100m 🗑400m.
Remarks: Max. 48h, parking south of centre.

| S | Ribe | 2A6 |

Storkesøen, Haulundvej 164. **GPS**: n55,31703 e8,76022.⬆➡

24 🔲DKK 140 ⛽🔌 Ch 🚿included. **Location:** Rural, comfortable, quit.
Surface: grassy. 🅾 01/01-31/12
Distance: 🚏1km 🚌on the spot.
Remarks: At fish pond.

| S | Ribe | 2A6 |

Maglegaard, Toftlundvej 6. **GPS**: n55,31067 e8,79151.

3 🔲DKK 100 ⛽ 🚿DKK 20. 🐕
Location: Rural, quit.
Surface: grassy.
Distance: 🚏3km.

Tourist information Ribe:
ℹ Ribe Tourism Office, Torvet 3, www.ribetourist.dk.Oldest city of Denmark to Ribeå River.
👁 Vadehavscentret, Okholmvej 5.Wadden Sea centre. 🅾 10-16/17h 🅾 01/12-31/01.
Ⓜ Museet Ribes Vikinger, Odins Plads.Viking period in Denmark. 🅾 daily 10-16h, summer 10-18h 🅾 01/11-31/03 Mo.
Ⓜ Ribe Vikingecenter.Open air museum. 🅾 01/05-30/06, 01/09-15/10 Mo-Fri 10-15.30h, 01/07-31/08 daily 11-17h.
⊗ Weis Stue, Torvet 2.Oldest inn of Denmark with traditional Danish kitchen.

| | Ringkøbing | 2A5 |

Lystbadenhavn, Fiskerstraede 60. **GPS**: n56,08611 e8,24056.⬆

10 🔲DKK 75 ⛽ 🚿included. **Surface:** asphalted/grassy. 🅾 01/01-31/12
Distance: 🚏on the spot 🚢on the spot 🚌on the spot ✕500m 🗑500m.
Remarks: Parking at pier.

| | Ringkøbing | 2A5 |

Vesterled 11. **GPS**: n56,09338 e8,23740.
20 🔲€ 9,50. **Surface:** gravel. 🅾 01/01-31/12

| Ⓒ S | Ringkøbing | 2A5 |

Søndervig, Solvej 2. **GPS**: n55,11198 e8,11854.
🔲DKK 115 ⛽🔌Ch 🚿against payment. 🅾 04/04-25/10
Remarks: QuickStop: >20 - <10h.

| | Ringkøbing | 2A5 |

æblehavens, Herningverj 105. **GPS**: n56,08699 e8,31642.
🔲DKK 125 ⛽🔌Ch 🚿against payment. 🅾 01/04-30/09
Remarks: QuickStop: >20 - <10h.

Tourist information Ringkøbing:
ℹ Ringkøbing Tourist Office, Vestergade 2, www.ringkobingfjord.dk.Bathing resort with old centre, several cycle and hiking trails available.
🎣 Fishing and Family Park West, Hovervej 56.Recreation park with swimming pool. 🅾 10h-sunset.

| Ⓒ S | Roslev | 2A4 |

Glyngøre, Sundhøj 20A. **GPS**: n56,74401 e8,86259.
🔲DKK 125 ⛽🔌Ch 🚿against payment. 🅾 01/04-12/10
Remarks: QuickStop: >20 - <10h.

| Ⓒ S | Roslev | 2A4 |

Junget Strand, Jungetgårdvej 3. **GPS**: n56,76269 e9,10111.
🔲DKK 120 ⛽🔌Ch 🚿against payment. 🅾 01/04-01/10
Remarks: QuickStop: >20 - <10h.

| Ⓒ S | Ry | 2B5 |

Birkhede, Lyngvej 14. **GPS**: n56,10428 e9,74089.
🔲DKK 168 ⛽🔌Ch 🚿against payment. 🅾 20/04-15/09

Remarks: QuickStop: >20 - <10h.

△S	Ry	2B5

Holmens, Klostervej 148. **GPS:** n56,07753 e9,76971.
DKK 130 🚐🍽Ch ⚡against payment. ⏺ 04/04-27/09
Remarks: QuickStop: >20 - <10h.

Tourist information Ry:
ℹ️ Ry Turistbureau, Klostervej 3, www.visitry.com,.
👁 Himmelbjergtårnet, Himmelbjergvej 20.Observation tower. ⏺ 01/05-15/09 10-17h, 16/09-31/10 Sa-Su 10-16h. 🇹 DKK 7,50.
👁 Labyrinthia, Ryvej 2.Wooden labyrinth,. ⏺ summer 10-18h.

🏭S	Rødding	2B6

Brændekilde, Haderslevvej 59. **GPS:** n55,35750 e9,18833.⬆️

10 free 🚐DKK 25 Ch ⚡DKK 25 WC. **Location:** Rural, noisy. **Surface:** metalled. ⏺ 01/01-31/12
Distance: 🚶1km.
Remarks: Max. 1 week.

Tourist information Rødding:
ℹ️ Midtsønderjyllands Turistbureau, Jels Møllegade 5, www.visitmidt.com.

🏭S	Rødekro	2B6

Rødekro Fiskepark, Østermarkvej 3-7. **GPS:** n55,08806 e9,30889.➡️

50 DKK 100 🚐🍽 Ch ⚡DKK 2/kWh WC DKK 5 🗑DKK 25.♨
Location: Rural, quit. **Surface:** grassy. ⏺ 01/01-31/12
Distance: 🚶2km 🏊on the spot 🍴on the spot 🛒on the spot 🚌100m.
Remarks: At fish lake.

Tourist information Rødekro:
👁M Damgaard Mill, Foldingbrovej 6.Mill and agriculture museum. ⏺ 01/05-30/09 Tue-Su 10-17h.

△S	Rømø	2A6

Lakolk, Lakolk 2. **GPS:** n55,14465 e8,49361.
DKK 124 🚐🍽Ch ⚡against payment. ⏺ 15/04-18/10
Remarks: QuickStop: >20 - <10h.

©S	Saltum	2B3

Saltum Strand, Saltum Strandvej 141. **GPS:** n57,28560 e9,65228.
DKK 110 🚐🍽Ch ⚡against payment. ⏺ 15/04-18/09
Remarks: QuickStop: >20 - <10h.

△S	Saltum	2B3

Guldager, Bondagervej 67. **GPS:** n57,29355 e9,65322.
DKK 122 🚐🍽Ch ⚡against payment. ⏺ 05/04-25/09
Remarks: QuickStop: >20 - <10h.

△S	Sdr. Omme	2A5

Omme Å camping, Sønderbro 2. **GPS:** n55,83859 e8,88883.
DKK 130 🚐🍽Ch ⚡against payment. ⏺ 01/04-30/09
Remarks: QuickStop: >20 - <10h.

△S	Silkeborg 🏕🍴⛴	2B5

Gudenåens, Vejlsøvej 7. **GPS:** n56,15414 e9,56004.
DKK 160 🚐🍽Ch ⚡against payment. ⏺ 03/04-19/10
Remarks: QuickStop: >20 - <10h.

△S	Silkeborg 🏕🍴⛴	2B5

Sejs Bakker, Borgdalsvej 15-17. **GPS:** n56,14052 e9,62111.
DKK 125 🚐🍽Ch ⚡against payment. ⏺ 08/04-11/09
Remarks: QuickStop: >20 - <10h.

△S	Silkeborg 🏕🍴⛴	2B5

Skyttehusets, Svejbækvej 3. **GPS:** n56,12050 e9,64440.
DKK 140 🚐🍽Ch ⚡against payment. ⏺ 04/04-13/09
Remarks: QuickStop: >20 - <10h.

△S	Silkeborg 🏕🍴⛴	2B5

Sø-Camping, Århusvej 51. **GPS:** n56,16984 e9,57657.
DKK 170 🚐🍽Ch ⚡against payment.
⏺ 15/04-18/10
Remarks: QuickStop: >20 - <10h.

Tourist information Silkeborg:
ℹ️ Silkeborg Turistbureau, åhavevej 2A, www.silkeborg.com.
👁 AQUA, Vejlsøvej 55.Aquarium. ⏺ 01/09-31/05 Mo-Fri 10-16h, Sa-Su 10-17h, 01/06-31/08 10-18h.
M⊗ Hotel- og Restaurantmuseet "Ludvigslyst", Julsøvej 248.Original café/restaurant from 1906, demonstrations. ⏺ 01/05-31/10 Tue-Su 10-22h. 🇹 free.
M KunstCentret Silkeborg Bad, Gjessøvej 40.Art museum. ⏺ 01/10-30/04 Tue-Fri 12-16h, Sa-Su 11-17h, 01/05-30/09 Tue-Su 10-17h.

©S	Sindal	2B3

Sindal, Hjørringvej 125. **GPS:** n57,46849 e10,17945.
DKK 110 🚐🍽Ch ⚡against payment. ⏺ 01/04-20/09
Remarks: QuickStop: >20 - <10h.

©S	Sjølund	2B6

Grønninghoved strand, Mosvigvej 21. **GPS:** n55,41105 e9,59220.
DKK 125 🚐🍽Ch ⚡against payment. ⏺ 04/04-15/09
Remarks: QuickStop: >20 - <10h.

©S	Skagen	2B2

Råbjerg Mile, Kandestedvej 55. **GPS:** n57,65636 e10,45081.
DKK 110 🚐🍽Ch ⚡against payment. ⏺ 17/04-23/10
Remarks: QuickStop: >20 - <10h.

©S	Skals	2B4

Ulbjerg, Skråhedevej 6. **GPS:** n56,64495 e9,33915.
DKK 125 🚐🍽Ch ⚡against payment. ⏺ 01/01-31/12
Remarks: QuickStop: >20 - <10h.

©S	Skjern	2A5

Skjern å Camping, Birkvej 37. **GPS:** n55,93316 e8,49291.
DKK 100 🚐🍽Ch ⚡against payment. ⏺ 01/04-01/10
Remarks: QuickStop: >20 - <10h.

©S	Skærbæk	2A6

Skærbæk, Ullerupvej 76. **GPS:** n55,16584 e8,77909.
DKK 120 🚐🍽Ch ⚡against payment. ⏺ 01/01-31/12
Remarks: QuickStop: >20 - <10h.

©S	Spøttrup	2A4

Gyldendal hav, Vester Hærup Strandvej 34. **GPS:** n56,58107 e8,71066.
15 DKK 100 🚐🍽Chincluded ⚡against payment 🔌. **Surface:** gravel/sand. ⏺ 01/01-31/12
Distance: 🏊on the spot 🛒on the spot ⊗on the spot.

©S	Storvorde	2B3

Egense Lystbådehavan, Kystvej 1. **GPS:** n56,98270 e10,30451.
5 DKK 100 🚐⚡. **Surface:** metalled. ⏺ 01/01-31/12
Distance: 🏊on the spot 🛒on the spot.

©S	Storvorde	2B3

Dokkedal, Kystvej 118. **GPS:** n56,93305 e10,26225.
DKK 110 🚐🍽Ch ⚡against payment. ⏺ 01/01-31/12
Remarks: QuickStop: >20 - <10h.

©S	Storvorde	2B3

Egense, Kystvej 6. **GPS:** n56,98071 e10,30086.
DKK 130 🚐🍽Ch ⚡against payment. ⏺ 15/04-20/09
Remarks: QuickStop: >20 - <10h.

🏭S	Strandby	2B3

Strandby havn, Søndre Havnevej 27. **GPS:** n57,49249 e10,50245.
6 DKK 120 🚐⚡against payment WCincluded. **Surface:** metalled.
Remarks: Pay at harbourmasters.

△S	Struer ⛴	2A4

Toftum Brjerge, Gl. Landevej 4. **GPS:** n56,45530 e8,41190.
DKK 100 🚐🍽Ch ⚡against payment.

DK

⬛ 01/01-31/12
Remarks: QuickStop: >20 - <10h.
Tourist information Struer:
👁 Gimsinghoved, Gimsinghoved 1.Former large Danish farm.
Ⓜ Det gamle klubhus, V/Struer Lystbådehavn.Old Club building of the sailing club, mini museum. ⬛ 01/04-15/11 10-22h. Ⓣ free.

△S	Sunds	2A5

Sunds Sø, Søgårdvej 2. **GPS**: n56,20846 e9,02335.
🛏DKK 175 ⚡🔌Ch⚡against payment. ⬛ 28/03-28/09
Remarks: QuickStop: >20 - <10h.

©S	Sydals	5A1

Lysabildskov, Skovforten 4. **GPS**: n54,89159 e10,05268.
🛏DKK 105 ⚡🔌Ch⚡against payment. ⬛ 01/04-30/09
Remarks: QuickStop: >20 - <10h.
Tourist information Sydals:
ℹ Sydals Turistbureau, Kegnæsvej 52, www.visitsydals.com.
👁 Kegnæs Fyr, Nørre Landevej 7.Lighthouse. ⬛ 01/06-30/09 Mo-Su 9-19h.

△S	Tarm	2A5

Skaven Strand, Skavenvej 32. **GPS**: n55,89181 e8,36780.
🛏DKK 120 ⚡🔌Ch⚡against payment. ⬛ 04/04-01/11
Remarks: QuickStop: >20 - <10h.

⛰S	Tårs (Hjørring)	2B3

Vendelbo Vans Autocampere, Damhusvej 23. **GPS**: n57,38972 e10,11500.

8 🛏free ⚡🔌Ch⚡ WC 🔌. **Surface:** grassy/gravel. ⬛ 01/01-31/12
Distance: 🚲100m 🏊500m 🛒500m ⊗300m 🍴300m 🚂200m.
Remarks: Max. 24h, sanitary 9-17.

©S	Thisted	2A4

Vildsund, Parkvej 33A. **GPS**: n56,88017 e8,62477.
🛏DKK 125 ⚡🔌Ch⚡against payment. ⬛ 01/04-25/09
Remarks: QuickStop: >20 - <10h.

△S	Thisted	2A4

Thisted, Iversensvej 3. **GPS**: n56,95309 e8,71249.
🛏DKK 150 ⚡🔌Ch⚡against payment. ⬛ 01/04-01/10
Remarks: QuickStop: >20 - <10h.
Tourist information Thisted:
ℹ Thisted Turistforening, Store Torv 6, www.thisted-turist.dk.Bathing resort.
👁 Thisted Bryghus, Bryggerivej 10.Brewery, information at Turistbureau. ⬛ summer Wed 11-13h. Ⓣ DKK 25.

△S	Tim	2A5

Thorager, Søgårdvej 7. **GPS**: n56,20649 e8,25451.
🛏DKK 90 ⚡🔌Ch⚡against payment. ⬛ 01/04-30/09
Remarks: QuickStop: >20 - <10h.

⛰S	Toftlund	2B6

Dahl, Lebækvej 2. **GPS**: n55,17839 e9,07768.
5 🛏DKK 35 ⚡🔌Ch⚡ included.

©S	Ulfborg	2A5

Rejkjær, Holstebrovej 151. **GPS**: n56,23319 e8,30966.
🛏DKK 98 ⚡🔌Ch⚡against payment. ⬛ 03/04-18/10
Remarks: QuickStop: >20 - <10h.

©S	Ulfborg	2A5

Thorsminde, Klitrosevej 4. **GPS**: n56,25870 e8,13770.
🛏DKK 150 ⚡🔌Ch⚡against payment. ⬛ 03/04-18/10
Remarks: QuickStop: >20 - <10h.

©S	Ulfborg	2A5

Vedersø Klit, øhusevej 23. **GPS**: n56,25829 e8,14130.
🛏DKK 150 ⚡🔌Ch⚡against payment. ⬛ 04/04-18/10
Remarks: QuickStop: >20 - <10h.

DK

⛰	Ulfborg	2A5

Tvind Skolecenter, Skorkærvej 8. **GPS**: n56,25611 e8,27722.
4 🛏free.
Tourist information Ulfborg:
ℹ Ulfborg-Vemb Turistbureau, Bredgade 9, www.ulfborg-turist.dk.Situated between sea, heathland, forest and fjord.

©S	Vejers Strand	2A6

Stjerne, Vejers Havvej 7. **GPS**: n55,61915 e8,14090.
🛏DKK 110 ⚡🔌Ch⚡against payment. ⬛ 01/01-31/12
Remarks: QuickStop: >20 - <10h.

©S	Vejers Strand	2A6

Vejers Familiecamping, Vejers Havvej 15. **GPS**: n55,61950 e8,13594.
🛏DKK 110 ⚡🔌Ch⚡against payment.
⬛ 01/04-18/09
Remarks: QuickStop: >20 - <10h.
Tourist information Vejers Strand:
ℹ Vejers Turistinformation - Dan Turist, Vejers Havvej 81, www.bte.dk.Bathing resort, dunes and white beaches.
👁 Tirpitz.German bunker.

⛰S	Vesløs	2A3

Amtoft Havn, Gårdbækvej 1. **GPS**: n57,00647 e8,94068.
5 🛏DKK 100 ⚡🔌Ch⚡ WC 🔌included ⬛. **Surface:** gravel/sand. ⬛ 01/01-31/12
Distance: 🚲on the spot 🛒on the spot.

©S	Vesløs	2A3

Bygholm, Bygholmvej 27. **GPS**: n57,02603 e9,03733.
🛏DKK 130 ⚡🔌Ch⚡against payment. ⬛ 01/01-31/12
Remarks: QuickStop: >20 - <10h.

🍴	Vesløs	2A3

Cafe Bondstuen, Aalborgvej 219B. **GPS**: n57,02501 e9,01517.
🛏free. **Surface:** gravel. ⬛ 01/01-31/12
Distance: 🏊250m.

🍴	Vesløs	2A3

Vejlernes Grill & Kiosk, Aalborgvej 219B. **GPS**: n57,02518 e9,01585.
🛏free. **Surface:** gravel. ⬛ 01/01-31/12

△S	Vestervig	2A4

Krik-Vig, Krikvej 112. **GPS**: n56,77800 e8,26210.
🛏DKK 100 ⚡🔌Ch⚡against payment. ⬛ 04/04-27/09
Remarks: QuickStop: >20 - <10h.

©S	Vinderup	2A4

Vinderup, Sevelvej 75. **GPS**: n56,47488 e8,81184.
🛏DKK 110 ⚡🔌Ch⚡against payment.
⬛ 01/04-23/10
Remarks: QuickStop: >20 - <10h.
Tourist information Vinderup:
Ⓜ Hjerl Hedes Frilandsmuseum, Hjerl Hedevej 14.Open air museum. ⬛ 01/04-31/10 10-17h.
🏠 Stubber Kloster, Stubbergård sø.Ruins of former Benedictine monastery. ⬛ 01/01-31/12. Ⓣ free.

⛰S	Voerså	2B3

Parking Havn, Havstokken 4. **GPS**: n57,20389 e10,49389.

10 🛏DKK 100 ⚡🔌Ch⚡ WC 🔌included. **Surface:** gravel.
⬛ 01/04-30/10
Distance: 🚲3km 🏊on the spot 🛒on the spot ⊗3km 🍴3km.

△S	Østbirk	2B5

Elite Camp Vestbirk, Møllehøjvej 4. **GPS**: n55,96840 e9,75000.
🛏DKK 140 ⚡🔌Ch⚡against payment. ⬛ 04/04-28/09
Remarks: QuickStop: >20 - <10h.

Funen

| △S | Asperup | 2B6 |

Skovlund, Kystvejen 1. **GPS**: n55,50628 e9,89932.
DKK 140 ⛺🔌Ch✂against payment. 🅾 08/04-20/09
Remarks: QuickStop: >20 - <10h.

| △S | Assens 🌿🚣⛵ | 2B6 |

Sandager Næs, Strandgårdsvej 12. **GPS**: n55,33399 e9,88964.
DKK 135 ⛺🔌Ch✂against payment. 🅾 05/04-14/09
Remarks: QuickStop: >20 - <10h.

| △S | Assens 🌿🚣⛵ | 2B6 |

Willemoes, Næsvej 15. **GPS**: n55,26521 e9,88428.
DKK 140 ⛺🔌Ch✂against payment. 🅾 09/04-14/09
Remarks: QuickStop: >20 - <10h.

Tourist information Assens:

ℹ Assens Turistbureau, Damgade 22, www.visit-vestfyn.dk.Historical city centre and harbour.

Ⓜ Ernst s Samlinger, østergade 57.Collection of art and antiques of the silversmith. 🅾 01/05-30/09 Sa 14h. 🎫 DKK 50.

Ⓜ Vestfyns Hjemstavnsgård, Klaregade 23.,Gummerup, Glamsbjerg.Open air museum. 🅾 01/04-31/10 10-16h 🔴 Mo.

| 👁 | Bagenkop | 5B1 |

Koldkrigsmuseum Langelandsfor, Vognsbjergvej 4A. **GPS**: n54,75306 e10,71583.
DKK 85. **Surface:** metalled. 🅾 01/04-31/10
Remarks: Check in at museum.

Tourist information Bagenkop:

Ⓜ Koldkrigsmuseum Langelandsfort, Vognsbjergvej 4A.War museum. 🅾 1/4-30/10.

| △S | Ebberup | 2B6 |

Aa Strand Camping, Aa Strandvej 61. **GPS**: n55,21698 e9,97442.
DKK 150 ⛺🔌Ch✂against payment. 🅾 09/04-14/09
Remarks: QuickStop: >20 - <10h.

| △S | Ebberup | 2B6 |

Helnæs, Strandbakken 21. **GPS**: n55,13326 e10,03869.
DKK 125 ⛺🔌Ch✂against payment. 🅾 01/04-01/10
Remarks: QuickStop: >20 - <10h.

| ☕S | Faaborg | 2B6 |

Faaborg Havn, Kanalvej 19. **GPS**: n55,09368 e10,29524.
10 DKK 110 ⛺🔌Ch✂included WC🗑. **Surface:** asphalted. 🅾 01/01-31/12
Distance: 🛒200m ⚓on the spot 🍴on the spot ⊗on the spot 🍺500m 🚌200m.
Remarks: Check in at harbourmaster.

| △S | Faaborg | 2B6 |

Faaborg Camping, Odensevej 140. **GPS**: n55,11667 e10,24477.
DKK 140 ⛺🔌Ch✂against payment. 🅾 01/01-31/12
Remarks: QuickStop: >20 - <10h.

| 🚐S | Gram | 2A6 |

Anholm Fiskesø, Folevej 11. **GPS**: n55,30564 e8,99888.⬆.

15 DKK €6,75 ⛺🔌Ch✂included. 🚻 **Location:** Rural, isolated, quit.
Surface: . 🅾 01/04-01/11
Distance: 🛒5km 🍴on the spot ⊗1km 🍺5km.
Remarks: At fish pond.

| | Gram | 2A6 |

Annemettes, Ribelandevej 18. **GPS**: n55,28647 e9,00098.⬆.

3 DKK €14 ⛺🔌Ch✂. 🚻 **Location:** Rural, isolated, quit. **Surface:** grassy/gravel.

| △S | Haarby | 2B6 |

Løgismosestrand, Løgismoseskov 7. **GPS**: n55,18156 e10,07001.
DKK 120 ⛺🔌Ch✂against payment. 🅾 08/04-19/10
Remarks: QuickStop: >20 - <10h.

| △S | Hesselager | 2C6 |

Bøsøre strand, Bøsørevej 16. **GPS**: n55,19742 e10,80626.
DKK 150 ⛺🔌Ch✂against payment. 🅾 04/04-18/10
Remarks: QuickStop: >20 - <10h.

| △S | Hesselager | 2C6 |

Lundeborg Strand-Camping, Gl. Lundeborgvej 46. **GPS**: n55,14625 e10,78138.
DKK 120 ⛺🔌Ch✂against payment. 🅾 09/04-14/09
Remarks: QuickStop: >20 - <10h.

| ☕S | Humble | 5B1 |

Ristinge, Ristingevej 104. **GPS**: n54,81944 e10,63988.
DKK 140 ⛺🔌Ch✂against payment. 🅾 09/04-06/09
Remarks: QuickStop: >20 - <10h.

| △S | Martofte | 2C5 |

Fyns Hoved Camping, Fynshovedvej 748. **GPS**: n55,60764 e10,61905.
DKK 135 ⛺🔌Ch✂against payment. 🅾 01/01-31/12
Remarks: QuickStop: >20 - <10h.

| 🚐S | Middelfart 🚣⛵ | 2B6 |

Lystbådehavn, østre Hougvej 124. **GPS**: n55,49250 e9,73028.

7 DKK 100 ⛺🔌Ch✂DKK 25 WC🗑. **Surface:** metalled. 🅾 01/01-31/12
Distance: 🛒2km.
Remarks: Harbour Middelfart.

| ☕S | Middelfart 🚣⛵ | 2B6 |

Vejlby Fed Camping, Rigelvej 1. **GPS**: n55,51949 e9,84975.
DKK 150 ⛺🔌Ch✂against payment. 🅾 09/04-11/09
Remarks: QuickStop: >20 - <10h.

| △S | Middelfart 🚣 | 2B6 |

Røjle Klint Natur Camping, Røjle Klintvej 29. **GPS**: n55,55039 e9,81876.
DKK 120 ⛺🔌Ch✂against payment. 🅾 01/01-31/12
Remarks: QuickStop: >20 - <10h.

Tourist information Middelfart:

ℹ Turistbureauet, Havnegade 21, middelfartturist.dk.

| △S | Nr. Åby | 2B6 |

Ronæs strand, Ronæsvej 10. **GPS**: n55,43975 e9,82692.
DKK 110 ⛺🔌Ch✂against payment. 🅾 01/04-13/09
Remarks: QuickStop: >20 - <10h.

| 🚐S | Nyborg | 2C6 |

GPS: n55,29734 e10,83963.

DK

🗎DKK 95 ⌐🔲Ch ⮑against payment. 🅾 01/01-31/12
Remarks: QuickStop: >20 - <10h.

| 🔲S | Tranekær | 2C6 |

Lohals, Birkevej 11. **GPS:** n55,13390 e10,90501.
🗎DKK 150 ⌐🔲Ch ⮑against payment. 🅾 01/01-31/12
Remarks: QuickStop: >20 - <10h.

| 🔲S | Varde | 2A6 |

Fritidscenter, Lerpøtvej 55. **GPS:** n55,63294 e8,47447.
20🗎against payment ⌐🔲 ⮑against payment. **Surface:** grassy. 🅾
01/05-31/10
Remarks: At sports centre.

| 🔲S | Varde | 2A6 |

Jensen, Ringkøbingvej 143. **GPS:** n55,65762 e8,48942.⬆.

4 🗎DKK 75 ⌐🔲 ⮑WC. 🚐 **Location:** Rural, comfortable, isolated, quit.
Surface: grassy/metalled.
Distance: 🚶5km.

| 🔲S | Varde | 2A6 |

Joan & Preben Christensen, Ringkøbingvej 259, Hindsig. **GPS:** n55,72077
e8,49345.⬆.

5 🗎DKK 50 ⌐🔲 Ch. 🚐 **Location:** Rural, comfortable, quit. **Surface:** grassy.
🅾 01/01-31/12
Distance: 🚶12km 🚢3km.

🗎free ⌐🔲Chfree. **Surface:** metalled.

| ⚠S | Nyborg | 2C6 |

Grønnehave strand, Rejstrupvej 83. **GPS:** n55,35646 e10,78767.
🗎DKK 120 ⌐🔲Ch ⮑against payment. 🅾 09/04-21/09
Remarks: QuickStop: >20 - <10h.

| ⚠S | Nyborg | 2C6 |

Nyborg strandcamping, Hjejlevej 99. **GPS:** n55,30543 e10,82236.
🗎DKK 140 ⌐🔲Ch ⮑against payment. 🅾 09/04-21/09
Remarks: QuickStop: >20 - <10h.

Tourist information Nyborg:
ℹ Nyborg Turistbureau, Torvet 9, www.nyborgturist.dk.Old reinforced city.
Ⓜ Mads Lerches Gård, Slotsgade 11.Local history. 🅾 01/04-31/10 10-15/17h.
✖ Nyborg Fæstning, Slotsgade 1.Fortress.
✖ Nyborg Slot / Danehofslottet, Slotsgade 34.Castle, end 12th century. 🅾
01/04-31/10 10-15/17h.

| 🔲 | Odense | 2C6 |

Tarup Campingcenter, Agerhatten 31. **GPS:** n55,36110 e10,46722.
20 🗎free. **Surface:** grassy.
Distance: 🚶6km ⚓2 km.

| 🔲S | Otterup | 2C6 |

Hasmark Strand, Strandvejen 205. **GPS:** n55,53692 e10,42248.
🗎DKK 100 ⌐🔲Ch ⮑against payment. 🅾 04/04-01/10
Remarks: QuickStop: >20 - <10h.

| 🔲S | Rudkøbing | 2C6 |

Billevænge, Spodsbjergvej 182. **GPS:** n54,92382 e10,81606.
🗎DKK 125 ⌐🔲Ch ⮑against payment. 🅾 04/04-18/10
Remarks: QuickStop: >20 - <10h.

| 🔲S | Rudkøbing | 2C6 |

Færgegårdens, Spodsbjergvej 335. **GPS:** n54,93219 e10,82945.
🗎DKK 130 ⌐🔲Ch ⮑against payment. 🅾 04/04-04/10
Remarks: QuickStop: >20 - <10h.

| ⚠S | Skårup | 2C6 |

Skårupøre, Skårupøre Strandvej 56 A. **GPS:** n55,06317 e10,69735.
🗎DKK 100 ⌐🔲Ch ⮑against payment. 🅾 01/05-01/09
Remarks: QuickStop: >20 - <10h.

| 🔲S | Stenstrup | 2C6 |

Tronbjerggård Strandhave, Rårudvej 8, Kirkeby. **GPS:** n55,11820 e10,57840.
2 🗎DKK 50 ⌐🔲 ⮑WC.

| ⚠S | Svendborg | 2C6 |

Carlsberg, Sundbrovej 19. **GPS:** n55,03344 e10,61332.
🗎DKK 115 ⌐🔲Ch ⮑against payment. 🅾 04/04-28/09
Remarks: QuickStop: >20 - <10h.

| ⚠S | Svendborg | 2C6 |

Vindebyøre Camping, Vindbyørevej 52. **GPS:** n55,05416 e10,63019.
🗎DKK 140 ⌐🔲Ch ⮑against payment. 🅾 03/04-27/09
Remarks: QuickStop: >20 - <10h.

| S | Svendborg | 2C6 |

Idrætshallen, Ryttervej 70. **GPS:** n55,05668 e10,57613. ⌐🔲Ch.

Tourist information Svendborg:
ℹ Sydfyns Turistbureau, Centrumpladsen 4, www.visitsydfyn.dk.Old city centre,
many bars and restaurants at the harbour.
Ⓜ✖ Egeskov Slot, Kværndrup.Citadel with park and 6 museums. 🅾 01/05-
31/10 10-17/20h.
✖ Valdemars Slot, Slotsalléen 100, Troense, Tåsinge.Castle on the island Tåsinge,
fully furnished. 🅾 Easter, 01/04-30/04, 01/10-31/10 Sa-Su 10-17h, 01/05-
30/09 10-17/18h.

| ⚠S | Søby, ærø | 2C6 |

Søby, Vitsø 10. **GPS:** n54,93628 e10,24358.

Seeland, Møn, Lolland and Falster

| ⚠S | Boeslunde | 2C6 |

Campinggaarden Boelunde, Rennebjergvej 110. **GPS:** n55,28463 e11,26837.
🗎DKK 150 ⌐🔲Ch ⮑against payment. 🅾 01/04-30/09
Remarks: QuickStop: >20 - <10h.

| 🗎S | Copenhagen | 2D5 |

Copenhagen City Camp, Fisketorvet, Kalvebod Pladsvej. **GPS:** n55,65889
e12,55778.

100 🗎DKK 35, DKK 75/pp ⌐🔲Ch ⮑DKK 35. 🅾 01/06-31/08
Distance: 🚶within walking distance ⊗on the spot 🚢on the spot.
Remarks: Motorhome parking next to harbour and new shopping center
Fisketorv.

Tourist information Copenhagen:

ℹ️ Copenhagen Card.Card gives free entrance to public transport, 60 museums and attractions. Available at Tourist Offices, hotels, camp-sites.

ℹ️ Tourist Information Center, Copenhagen Right Now, Vesterbrogade 4A, København V, www.visitcopenhagen.com.Capital of Denmark, design city, lot of curiosities and museums.

☻ Dyrehavsbakken, Dyrehavevej 62, Klampenborg (ten n. van Kopenhagen). Popular amusement park, oldest park of Denmark, with among other things 100 attractions and 35 restaurants. T free.

☻ Tivoli, Vesterbrogade 3.Large amusement park in the centre of the city with among other things 32 restaurants, 26 attractions, shows, concerts etc. ⏰ 11-21/1h.

| ©S | Dannemare | 5C1 |

Hummingen, Pumpehusvej 1. **GPS**: n54,71317 e11,24606.
⌂DKK 140 🚰🔌Ch✎against payment. ⏰ 04/04-17/10
Remarks: QuickStop: >20 - <10h.

| △S | Fakse | 2D6 |

Feddet, Feddet 12. **GPS**: n55,17366 e12,10118.
⌂DKK 126 🚰🔌Ch✎against payment. ⏰ 01/01-31/12
Remarks: QuickStop: >20 - <10h.

| △S | Fakse | 2D6 |

Vemmetofte, Ny Strandskov 1. **GPS**: n55,23919 e12,23994.
⌂DKK 110 🚰🔌Chagainst payment. ⏰ 01/01-31/12
Remarks: QuickStop: >20 - <10h.

Tourist information Fakse:

ℹ️ Faksekystens Turistinformation, Hovedgaden 29, Fakse Ladeplads, www. faksekysten.dk.The municipality Fakse has 30 kilometres coast-line, marked cycle and hiking routes.

⚐ Fortællerfestival, Fakse Lime Beach.Festival for story tellers. ⏰ last weekend Jun.

⚐ Rivierafest, Fakse Ladeplads.Festival with free herring-table on Sunday. ⏰ Thu-Su of week 29.

| ⌂S | Farø | 2D6 |

Farø, Grøsundvej. **GPS**: n54,94876 e11,98696.
20 ⌂free 🚰🔌ChWCfree. **Surface**: asphalted.
Remarks: Exit 42 from E47.

| △S | Føllenslev | 2C5 |

Vesterlyng, Ravnholtvej 3. **GPS**: n55,74278 e11,30883.
⌂DKK 110 🚰🔌Ch✎against payment. ⏰ 03/04-18/10
Remarks: QuickStop: >20 - <10h.

| △S | Guldborg | 2D6 |

Guldborg, Guldborgvej 147. **GPS**: n54,85985 e11,73014.
⌂DKK 110 🚰🔌Ch✎against payment. ⏰ 01/04-01/10
Remarks: QuickStop: >20 - <10h.

| △S | Horbelev | 5D1 |

Falster, Tværmosevej 2. **GPS**: n54,81358 e12,07409.
⌂DKK 175 🚰🔌Ch✎against payment. ⏰ 01/01-31/12
Remarks: QuickStop: >20 - <10h.

| △S | Hundested 🚤🍦🍺 | 2D5 |

Rosenholm, Torpmaglevejen 37. **GPS**: n55,96260 e11,86152.
⌂DKK 90 🚰🔌Ch✎against payment. ⏰ 01/01-31/12
Remarks: QuickStop: >20 - <10h.

| S | Hundested 🚤🍦🍺 | 2D5 |

Sølager, Kulhusvej 2. **GPS**: n55,94669 e11,89909.
DKK 200 🚰🔌Ch✎against payment. ⏰ 01/01-31/12
Remarks: QuickStop: >20 - <10h.

| ©S | Hørve | 2C5 |

Teglværksgårdens, Teglværksvej 9A. **GPS**: n55,75794 e11,36568.
⌂DKK 120 🚰🔌Ch✎against payment. ⏰ 01/01-31/12
Remarks: QuickStop: >20 - <10h.

| ©S | Jyderup | 2C5 |

Skarresø, Slagelsevej 40. **GPS**: n55,61179 e11,38698.
⌂DKK 125 🚰🔌Ch✎against payment. ⏰ 25/03-25/09
Remarks: QuickStop: >20 - <10h.

| ©S | Karrebæksminde | 2D6 |

De Hvide Svaner Camping, KarrebæKvej 741. **GPS**: n55,20160 e11,66371.
⌂DKK 100 🚰🔌Ch✎against payment. ⏰ 03/04-18/10
Remarks: QuickStop: >20 - <10h.

| ⌂S | Korsør 🚤🍺 | 2C6 |

Lystbådehavn, Sylowsvej 10. **GPS**: n55,32664 e11,13190.

⌂DKK 120 🚰WC⌐against payment.

| ©S | Korsør 🚤🍺 | 2C6 |

Lystskov, Korsør Lystskov 2. **GPS**: n55,32219 e11,18505.
⌂DKK 90 🚰🔌Ch✎against payment. ⏰ 01/04-01/10
Remarks: QuickStop: >20 - <10h.

| △S | Korsør 🚤🍺 | 2C6 |

Storebælt, Storebæltsvej 85. **GPS**: n55,34866 e11,10281.
⌂DKK 140 🚰🔌Ch✎against payment. ⏰ 01/01-31/12
Remarks: QuickStop: >20 - <10h.

Tourist information Korsør:

ℹ️ Korsør Tourist Information Office, Nygade 7, www.korsoer-turistbureau.dk.

Ⓜ The Great Belt Bridge and Nature Centre, Storebæltsvej 88.Exhibition about the construction of the bridge over the Grote Belt. ⏰ 01/03-31/12 10-17/19h.

✖ Korsør Fæstning, Korsør Coastal Battery, The Fortress, Søbatteriet 7.Fortress. ⏰ 01/04-30/11 Tue-Su 11-16h.

| ⌂S | Maribo | 5C1 |

Skelstrupgåren Bed and Breakfas, Skelstupvej 3. **GPS**: n54,78774 e11,52095.
5 ⌂DKK 50 🚰✎ against payment. **Surface**: grassy.
Distance: 🚶2,2km 🚲4 km.

| △S | Nakskov | 5C1 |

Albuen Strand, Vesternæsvej 70. **GPS**: n54,78058 e10,99481.
⌂DKK 100 🚰🔌Ch✎against payment. ⏰ 05/04-20/09
Remarks: QuickStop: >20 - <10h.

| ⌂S | Nykøbing | 2D5 |

Nykøbing Havn, Korvetvej 10. **GPS**: n55,91610 e11,67287.⬆️
⌂DKK 85 🚰Ch✎ WC⌐. **Surface**: metalled.

| ©S | Nykøbing F. | 5D1 |

Falster City Camping, østre Allé 112. **GPS**: n54,76243 e11,89479.
⌂DKK 120 🚰✎against payment. ⏰ 01/04-01/12
Remarks: QuickStop: >20 - <10h.

| 🏞S | Ringsted | 2D6 |

Mogens Madsen, Vibevej 34. **GPS**: n55,44222 e11,80667.
3 ⌂free ✎ against payment. **Surface**: metalled. ⏰ 01/01-31/12
Distance: 🚲4 km 🚉800m.

| △S | Rude | 2D6 |

Bisserup, Skafterupvej 182. **GPS**: n55,21065 e11,49812.
⌂DKK 140 🚰🔌Ch✎against payment. ⏰ 01/04-18/10
Remarks: QuickStop: >20 - <10h.

| △S | Rødby | 5C1 |

Rødby Lystskov, Strandvej 3. **GPS**: n54,69850 e11,39163.
⌂DKK 120 🚰🔌Ch✎against payment. ⏰ 01/01-31/12
Remarks: QuickStop: >20 - <10h.

| © | Rødvig | 2D6 |

Rødvig Camping, Højstrupvej 2 A. **GPS**: n55,24346 e12,34999.
⌂DKK 120. ⏰ 01/04-28/09
Remarks: QuickStop: >20 - <10h.

| © | Stege | 2D6 |

Keldby Camping Møn, Pollerupvej 3. **GPS**: n54,99114 e12,35678.
⌂DKK 130 🚰Ch✎against payment. ⏰ 01/04-18/10
Remarks: QuickStop: >20 - <10h.

| △S | Strøby | 2D6 |

Stevns, Strandvejen 29. **GPS**: n55,40009 e12,29067.
⌂DKK 115 🚰🔌Ch✎against payment. ⏰ 01/01-31/12
Remarks: QuickStop: >20 - <10h.

| 🍴S | Taastrup | 2D5 |

Park Hotel, Brorsonvej 3. **GPS**: n55,65389 e12,30000.⬆️
10 ⌂DKK 125 ✎ DKK 25 WC⌐. **Surface**: metalled. ⏰ 01/01-31/12
Distance: 🚶300m 🚲1,5 km ⊗on the spot 🚉300m.

DK

| ©S | Tårs (Harpelunde) | 2C6 |

Fiskeri & lystbådehavn, Tårsvej. **GPS**: n54,87841 e11,02355.
DKK 85 ⌐WC⌐.
Remarks: Harbour Tårs.

| ©S | Torrig | 2C6 |

Kragenæs Havn, Kragenæsvej 84. **GPS**: n54,91565 e11,35730.
DKK 125 ⌐ Ch against payment. ◘ 03/04-27/09
Remarks: QuickStop: >20 - <10h.

| ©S | Vallensbæk | 2D5 |

Lystbådehavn, Vallensbæk Havnevej, Vallensbæk Strand. **GPS**: n55,62455
e12,38888.
15 DKK 100 ⌐ Ch included.
Distance: 7km on the spot.
Remarks: Harbour Vallensbæk, nearby harbour office.

| △S | Vejby | 2D5 |

Vejby Strand, Rågelejevej 37. **GPS**: n56,07538 e12,14100.
DKK 180 ⌐ Ch against payment. ◘ 09/04-06/09
Remarks: QuickStop: >20 - <10h.

| ©S | Vipperød | 2D5 |

Tempelkrogens, Krogvejen 2. **GPS**: n55,66213 e11,76246.
DKK 100 ⌐ Ch against payment. ◘ 01/01-31/12
Remarks: QuickStop: >20 - <10h.

DK

GERMANY

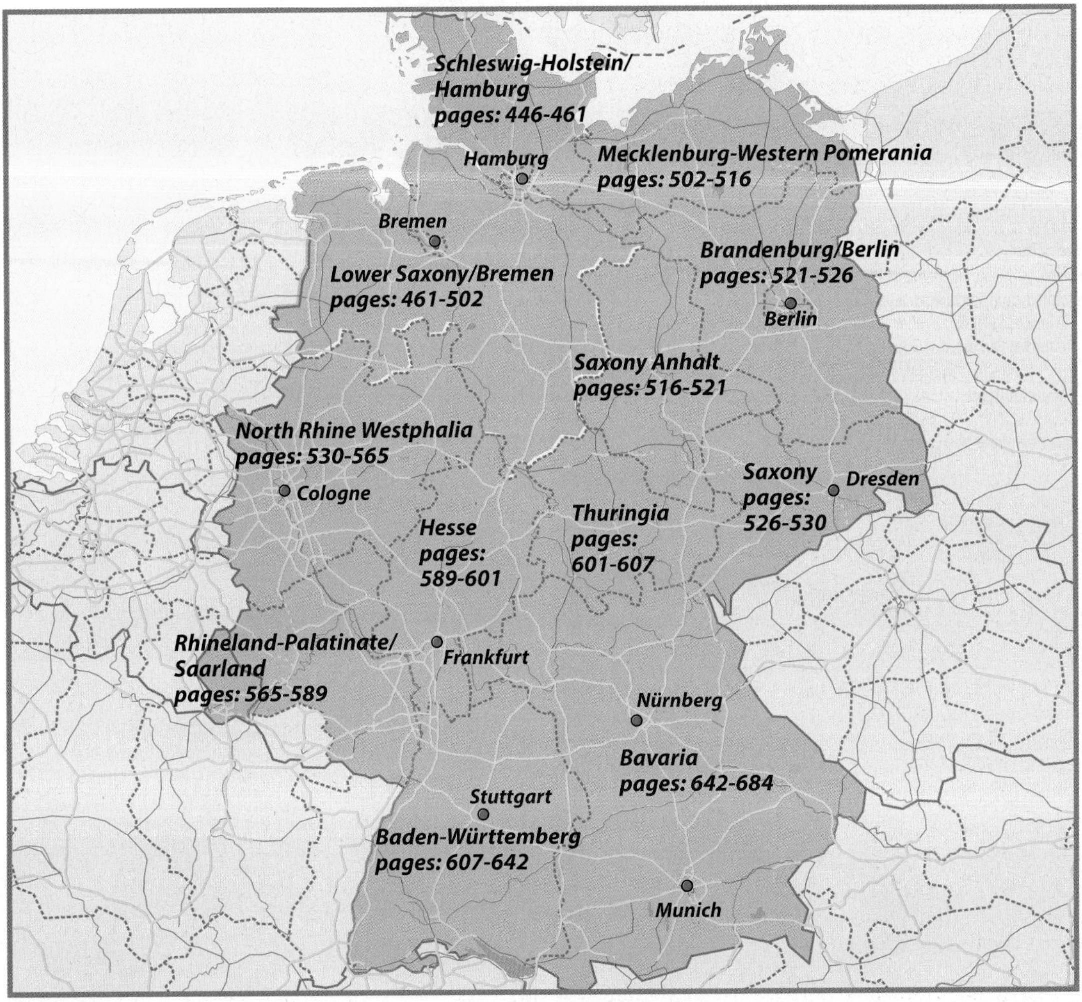

Schleswig-Holstein/
Hamburg
pages: 446-461

Hamburg

Mecklenburg-Western Pomerania
pages: 502-516

Bremen

Lower Saxony/Bremen
pages: 461-502

Brandenburg/Berlin
pages: 521-526

Berlin

Saxony Anhalt
pages: 516-521

North Rhine Westphalia
pages: 530-565

Cologne

Saxony
pages:
526-530

Dresden

Hesse
pages:
589-601

Thuringia
pages:
601-607

Rhineland-Palatinate/
Saarland
pages: 565-589

Frankfurt

Nürnberg

Bavaria
pages: 642-684

Stuttgart

Baden-Württemberg
pages: 607-642

Munich

Capital: Berlin
Government: Federal republic
Official Language: Germany
Population: 83,250,000
Area: 356,970 km².

General information
Dialling code: 0049.
Currency: Euro

Regulations for overnight stays
Overnight stays on the public highway are allowed,
if there is no local prohibition, but no "camping"
activities are allowed.

Opening hours
Shops: Monday-Friday 9am-6.30pm, Thursdays often
till 8.30pm, Saturday 9am-4pm, in smaller towns till
12noon
Bank: Monday-Friday 8.30am-1pm and 2.30pm-4pm.

Schleswig-Holstein

🏊S | Albersdorf | 4D2

Freitzeitbad Albersdorf, Weg zur Badeanstalt 18. **GPS:** n54,15350 e9,28055.

6 ⌁€15 swimming pool incl 🚰🗑Ch✂(6x)included. **Location:** Rural, isolated, quit. **Surface:** grassy. 🕐 01/05-31/08
Distance: 🚶1km ⊗100m 🛒300m 🚲on the spot 🎣on the spot.
Remarks: Parking at swimming pool, max. 3 days.

🏊S | Altenhof | 5A2

Wohnmobilpark Ostsee, Grünen Jäger. **GPS:** n54,46170 e9,82584. ⬆➡

80 ⌁€8 🚰🗑Ch✂€3 WC🚽€1🚿.
Surface: grassy. 🕐 01/01-31/12
Distance: ⊗on the spot.

🏊S | Aukrug | 5A3

Zum Sportplatz 1. **GPS:** n54,07441 e9,79160. ⬆➡

8 ⌁€10 🚰🗑Ch✂included. **Surface:** grassy/metalled. 🕐 01/01-31/12
Distance: 🚶1km ⊗800m 🛒1km.
Remarks: Max. 3 days, check in at Chandlers' Sportclub.

🏊S | Aventoft | 4C1

Bauernhof Clausen, Gotteskoogstrasse 5. **GPS:** n54,88250 e8,80722. ⬆➡

5 ⌁€6 🚰✂€2 WC🚽€2.🚿 **Location:** Rural, very simple, isolated, quit.
Surface: grassy. 🕐 01/01-31/12
Distance: 🚶5km 🛒5km.
Remarks: <3000kg.

🏊S | Aventoft | 4C1

Wohnmobillstellplatz Zu den Fuchswiesen, Revtoftweg 1. **GPS:** n54,87661 e8,84562. ⬆

15 ⌁€5, dog €1 🚰🗑Ch✂€1,50. 🚿 **Location:** Rural, very simple, isolated, quit. **Surface:** asphalted/grassy. 🕐 01/01-31/12
Distance: 🚶3km ⊗3km 🛒3km 🚲on the spot.
Remarks: Bread-service.

🏊S | Bad Bramstedt | 5A3

Parkplatz P7, Christian Königstrasse. **GPS:** n53,92167 e9,88967. ⬆➡

5 ⌁free. **Surface:** metalled. 🕐 01/01-31/12
Remarks: At station, max. 1 night.

Tourist information Bad Bramstedt:
ℹ Tourismusbüro Bad Bramstedt im Rathaus, Bleeck 17-19, www.bad-bramstedt.de.

🏊S | Bad Malente | 5B2

Parkplatz Krützen, Sebastian Kneipp strasse. **GPS:** n54,17198 e10,54919. ⬆

8 ⌁€2/pp 🚰€1 🗑€1 Ch.🚐 **Location:** Rural. **Surface:** metalled. 🕐 01/01-31/12
Distance: 🚶on the spot ⊗500m 🛒1km.

🏊S | Bad Oldesloe | 5B3

Wohnmobilplatz Exer, Am Bürgerpark. **GPS:** n53,81101 e10,36915. ⬆➡

8 ⌁free 🚰€1/10minutes 🗑Ch✂(8x)€2/10h WC🚽. **Location:** Urban, quit. **Surface:** metalled. 🕐 01/01-31/12
Distance: 🚶on the spot 🚲3km ⊗on the spot 🛒400m.

DE

Barmstedt   5A3

Am Rantzauer See, Seestrasse 12. **GPS:** n53,78640 e9,76420.⬆️.

5 ◳€ 5 🚰🔌Ch ✈️ WC▯included. **Surface:** metalled. ▯ 01/01-31/12
Distance: 🛶on the spot ⊗on the spot 🚮500m.

Behrensdorf   5B2

Campingpark Waldesruh, Neuland. **GPS:** n54,35754 e10,60216.⬆️.

18 ◳€ 10-12 2 pers.incl, dog € 1,50 🚰🔌Ch ✈️€ 1/24h WC▯📶.
Location: Rural, comfortable. **Surface:** grassy. ▯ 01/04-31/10
Distance: 🛶2km ⛵on the spot 🛒on the spot ⊗on the spot 🚮on the spot.

Bistensee   5A2

Ferienplatz bei Matz, Mühlenweg. **GPS:** n54,39538 e9,71386.

5 ◳€ 3 + € 3/pp 🚰🔌Ch ✈️€ 0,30/kWh WC▯.
Surface: grassy.
Distance: 🛶500m ⊗2km 🚮1km.

Tourist information Bistensee:
ℹ️ www.bistensee.de.Village on lake of the same name.

Blekendorf   5B2

Am Sehlendorfer Strand, Strandstrasse 24. **GPS:** n54,30571 e10,69358.⬆️.

40 ◳€ 13,50 🚰€ 1 🔌Ch ✈️included WC▯.🚻 **Location:** Rural, comfortable. **Surface:** grassy. ▯ 01/01-31/12
Distance: 🛶1km ⛵on the spot 🛒on the spot ⊗on the spot 🚮5km.

Bosau   5B3

Dat Gröne Huus, Stadtbeker Strasse 97. **GPS:** n54,09198 e10,42886.⬆️.

---

3 ◳€ 5, guests free ✈️€ 3 📶.🚻
Location: Rural, quit.
Surface: gravel. ▯ 01/04-30/11
Distance: 🛶100m ⛵Großer Plöner See 🛒on the spot ⊗on the spot 🚮1km.
Remarks: Bread-service.

Bösdorf   5B2

Wohnmobilcamp Augustfelde, Vierer See, Augustfelde. **GPS:** n54,12898 e10,45506.⬆️➡️.

16 ◳€ 11,50-13,50 🚰🔌Ch ✈️(16x) WCincluded ▯€ 0,75.🚻 **Surface:** grassy. ▯ 01/04-25/10
Distance: ⛵on the spot 🛒on the spot ⊗on the spot 🚮on the spot.

Bösdorf   5B2

Campingpark Gut Ruhleben, Missionsweg 2, Ruhleben. **GPS:** n54,14308 e10,45021.

10 ◳€ 10,50-13,50 🚰🔌Ch ✈️📶included.🚻 **Location:** Rural. **Surface:** grassy/gravel. ▯ 01/04-30/09
Remarks: Max. 3 nights.

Bredstedt   4D1

Süderstraße. **GPS:** n54,61307 e8,97082.⬆️➡️.

5 ◳free. **Location:** Rural. **Surface:** asphalted. ▯ 01/01-31/12
Distance: 🛶900m 🚮Aldi 650m.
Remarks: Nearby swimming pool.

Brodersby   5A1

Camping Am Mussinder Fährhaus, Missunder Fahrstrasse 33. **GPS:** n54,52500 e9,71583.

20 ⌧ € 12 ⊏━ 🔌 Ch 💧 WC 🚻. **Surface:** grassy. ⬛ 01/04-31/10

100 ⌧ 1/11-28/2 € 10, 1/3-31/10 € 13 ⊏━ € 0,50/50liter 🔌 Ch 💧 WC 🚻 📶. **Location:** Rural, comfortable, isolated, quit.
Surface: grassy. ⬛ 01/01-31/12
Distance: 🚶1km ⛱500m ⛽300m.

🔌S **Brodersby** 5A1
Ferienhof Lassen, Grossbrodersbyer weg 5. **GPS:** n54,53829 e9,71443.
1 ⌧ € 10 ⊏━ 🔌 Ch 💧 included. **Surface:** grassy.
Distance: 🚶500m ⊗2km ⛽500m.

Ⓟ **Büsum** 4D3
Deichmuseum P2, Westereck 2. **GPS:** n54,14210 e8,84212. ⬆.

🔌S **Brokdorf** 4D3
Parkplatz, Dorfstrasse. **GPS:** n53,86417 e9,31667. ⬆.

30 ⌧ free ⊏━ € 1/5minutes 🔌 € 1 Ch 💧 (30x)€ 0,50/kWh WC 🚻 € 0,50.
Location: Rural, comfortable. **Surface:** metalled. ⬛ 01/01-31/12
Distance: 🚶800m ⛱400m ⊗on the spot ⛽500m 🚲on the spot 🥾on the spot.

50 ⌧ free. **Location:** Isolated, quit. **Surface:** .
Distance: 🚶500m ⛱500m.

🔌S **Dagebüll** 4C1
Am Nordseedeich, Am Badedeich 15. **GPS:** n54,72666 e8,69527. ⬆.

🔌S **Brunsbüttel** 4D3
An der Braake, Am Freizeitbad. **GPS:** n53,89832 e9,13138. ⬆.

12 ⌧ free ⊏━ € 1 🔌 Ch. **Location:** Rural, comfortable, central, quit. **Surface:** grassy/metalled. ⬛ 01/01-31/12
Distance: 🚶500m ⊗500m ⛽500m 🚲on the spot.

10 ⌧ € 6 ⊏━ 💧 € 2.🚽
Location: Rural. **Surface:** grassy. ⬛ 01/01-31/12
Distance: 🚶5km ⛱100m ⊗100m ⊗on the spot ⛽bakery 300m.

🔌S **Bünsdorf** 5A2
Wohnmobilplatz Steinrade, Steinrade 17. **GPS:** n54,36265 e9,77463. ⬆➡.

⍟S **Drelsdorf** 4D1
Drelsdörper Krog, Dorfstrasse 23. **GPS:** n54,60555 e9,03555. ⬆.

5 ⌧ € 5 ⊏━ 🔌 💧 € 1. **Surface:** grassy.
Distance: 🚶3km.

15 ⌧ € 5, guests free ⊏━ € 2 WC. **Location:** Very simple, central, noisy.
Surface: grassy. ⬛ 01/01-31/12
Distance: 🚶200m ⛱2km.
Remarks: Along through road.

🔌S **Büsum** 4D3
Wohnmobilstellplatz Nordsee, Dr. Martin Bahr Strasse. **GPS:** n54,12889 e8,86889. ⬆➡.

🔌S **Eckernförde** 5A2
Parkplatz P1, Grüner Weg, B76. **GPS:** n54,46549 e9,83574. ⬆➡.

DE

45 🛏€ 4,50 ⛽€ 0,50/120liter 🔌€ 0,50 Ch ⚡€ 0,50/kWh. **Surface:** metalled. ☐ 01/01-31/12

Distance: 🚶within walking distance ⊗300m 🛒300m.

Remarks: Parking nearby centre and beach, along busy through road.

Tourist information Eckernförde:

🏠 Eckernförde Touristik GmbH, Am Exer 1, www.ostseebad-eckernfoerde.de.

| | Elmshorn 🍴 | 5A3 |

Stellplatz Elmshorn, Nordufer. **GPS:** n53,75157 e9,65268. ⬆.

6 🛏free ⛽€ 1/80liter 🔌Ch WC. **Location:** Urban, central, quit. **Surface:** metalled. ☐ 01/01-31/12

Distance: 🚶800m 🏊on the spot 🚤on the spot.

Remarks: Northern bank of the harbour, in front of centre.

| | Eutin | 5B2 |

Elisabethstrasse. **GPS:** n54,13507 e10,60935. ⬆.

5+3 🛏free. **Location:** Urban. **Surface:** metalled. ☐ 01/01-31/12

Distance: 🚶on the spot.

Remarks: Parking at station.

| | Eutin | 5B2 |

Schloss-Parkplatz P11, Schlossstraße. **GPS:** n54,13828 e10,61990. ⬆.

5 🛏free. **Surface:** metalled. ☐ 01/01-31/12

Distance: 🏊Großer Eutiner See.

| | Falshöft | 5A1 |

Campingplatz Seehof, Falshöft 12. **GPS:** n54,77083 e9,96166.

5 🛏€ 7,50 ⛽🔌Ch ⚡€ 0,40/kWh WC. **Surface:** grassy/gravel. ☐ 01/04-31/10

Distance: 🏊on the spot.

| | Fehmarn | 5C2 |

Wohnmobilpark Wulfener Hals, Wulfener-Hals-Weg 16, Wulfen. **GPS:** n54,40687 e11,17489. ⬆.

100 🛏from € 11,80-27,40 ⛽🔌Ch ⚡€ 2,10 WC 🚿€ 0,90 📺 📶 🚗. **Location:** Rural, luxurious. **Surface:** grassy. ☐ 01/01-31/12

Distance: 🏊on the spot.

| | Fehmarn | 5C2 |

Hintz-Heizungsbau, Landkirchenerweg 1b, Burg. **GPS:** n54,44228 e11,18967. ⬆.

16 🛏€ 10 ⛽€ 1 🔌Ch ⚡ (16x)€ 5. **Location:** Very simple, quit. **Surface:** metalled. ☐ 01/01-31/12

Distance: 🚶on the spot.

| | Fehmarn | 5C2 |

Kommunal- und Yachthafen Burgstaaken, Burgstaaken/am Binnensee, Burgstaaken. **GPS:** n54,42028 e11,19224. ⬆.

15 🛏€ 10 21-08h. 🚗 **Location:** Rural. **Surface:** metalled. ☐ 01/01-31/12

Distance: ⊗100m 🛒100m.

| | Fehmarn | 5C2 |

Parkplatz Ost, Osterstrasse, Burg. **GPS:** n54,43754 e11,19990. ⬆.

30 🛏€ 8 (21-8h). 🚗 **Location:** Urban, very simple. **Surface:** metalled. ☐ 01/01-31/12

Distance: 🚶100m.

| | Fehmarn | 5C2 |

Camping Strukkamphuk, Strukkamp. **GPS:** n54,41239 e11,10223. ⬆.

21 🚐€ 14,50-31 🚰 Ch ⚡ WC included. Location: Rural. **Surface:** grassy. □ 01/01-31/12
Distance: 🍴10m.

[🚐] Flensburg 4D1

Am Industriehafen, dir Flensburg Mürwick. **GPS**: n54,80444 e9,44388.[↑].

20 🚐free. **Surface:** gravel.
Distance: 🏙1,5km ⛱on the spot 🐟on the spot.

[🚐] [S] Fockbek 5A2

Grosse Rheie 17. **GPS**: n54,30190 e9,60331.[↑].

3 🚐free 🚰 Ch. **Surface:** grassy. □ 01/01-31/12
Remarks: Parking swimming pool, max. 24h.

[🍴] [S] Fockbek 5A2

Gaststätte Paulsen, Rendsburgerstrasse 58. **GPS**: n54,30581 e9,60177.

3 🚐guests free 🚰 ⚡ WC. **Surface:** metalled. □ 01/01-31/12

[🚐] Friedrichskoog 4D3

P2, Nordseestrasse. **GPS**: n54,03272 e8,84833.[↑][→].

30 🚐€ 2, overnight stay free. **Location:** Rural, comfortable, isolated, quit.
Surface: asphalted/grassy. □ 01/03-31/10
Distance: 🏙1km ⛱550m 🍴800m.
Remarks: Bread-service.

[🚐] [S] Gelting 5A1

Hafen Wackerballig, Strandweg, Wackerballig. **GPS**: n54,75564 e9,87842.

18 🚐€ 8 🚰€ 0,50/40liter Ch ⚡€ 1,50 WC € 0,50. **Surface:** asphalted. □ 01/04-31/10
Distance: 🏙1,5km 🛒2km.

[🚐] Glückstadt 4D3

Am Außenhafen, Am Hafen. **GPS**: n53,78560 e9,41088.[↑][→].

16 🚐€ 5. **Location:** Rural, comfortable. **Surface:** metalled. □ 01/01-31/12 ■ high water.
Distance: 🏙1km ⛱on the spot 🐟on the spot 🍴on the spot 🚲on the spot 🚶on the spot.
Remarks: Along the river Elbe.

[🚐] Glückstadt 4D3

Park & Ride platz, Bahnhofstrasse. **GPS**: n53,78776 e9,43145.

10 🚐free. **Location:** Urban, very simple.
Surface: asphalted. □ 01/01-31/12
Distance: 🏙900m 🛒200m 🚲on the spot 🚶on the spot.

[🚐] [S] Grömitz 5C2

Wohnmobilstellplatz am Lensterstrand, Blankwasserweg. **GPS**: n54,15650 e10,99134.[↑].

DE

50 🛏 winter free, summer € 7,50 ⚡ WC . 🚐 **Location:** Rural. **Surface:** grassy. ⬛ 01/01-31/12 ⬛ water disconnected in winter.
Distance: 🏊 on the spot 🛒 on the spot.

50 🛏 € 8 ⚡ 🍽 Ch 🧺 (8x)€ 2. **Surface:** grassy. ⬛ 01/01-31/12

🅂 Hamburg 🌊🏖🧁 5A4

Wohnmobilhafen Hamburg, Grüner Deich 8, Hammerbrook. **GPS:** n53,54303 e10,02814. ⬆➡.

🅂 **Grömitz** 5C2

Wohnmobilstellplatz, Gildestraße 14. **GPS:** n54,14490 e10,95262. ⬆➡.

60 🛏 € 19 ⚡ 🍽 Ch 🧺 WC 🍴. 🚲 **Location:** Urban, very simple, central, noisy. **Surface:** gravel. ⬛ 01/01-31/12
Distance: 🚆 4km 🛒 200m.

🅂 Hamburg 🌊🏖🧁 5A4

Wohnmobilplatz Hamburg Süd, Finkenrieker Hauptdeich 5. **GPS:** n53,47440 e10,00134. ⬆➡.

60 🛏 winter € 6, summer € 12 ⚡ € 0,50 🍽 Ch 🧺 (20x)€ 1/kWh. 🚐
Location: Rural, comfortable. **Surface:** metalled. ⬛ 01/01-31/12
Distance: 🏊 200m 🛒 on the spot 🛑 200m.

🅂 **Großenbrode** 5C2

Wassersportzentrum, Am Kai 29. **GPS:** n54,35583 e11,07798. ⬆➡.

80 🛏 € 12 ⚡ € 1 🍽 € 1 Ch € 1 🧺 (10x)€ 1/2kWh WC 🍴 € 1 🚲. 🚐
Location: Urban, noisy. **Surface:** metalled. ⬛ 01/01-31/12
Distance: 🚆 14km 🛒 100m 🛑 100m 🛑 5 min.

🅂 Hamburg 🌊🏖🧁 5A4

Am Strand Pauli, St. Pauli Hafenstraße. **GPS:** n53,54598 e9,96099.
20 🛏 € 8,50, weekend € 13.
Surface: asphalted.
⬛ 01/01-31/12
Distance: 🚆 Hamburg Altstadt 2,4km 🏊 on the spot 🍴 many restaurant 100m 🛑 600m.

50 🛏 € 8-10 ⚡ € 0,50/100liter 🍽 Ch 🧺 € 1/1kWh WC 🍴 € 0,50 🚲. 🚐
Location: Rural. **Surface:** grassy/metalled. ⬛ 01/01-31/12
Distance: 🏊 300m 🛒 on the spot 🛑 2km.

🅂 **Großenbrode** 5C2

Wohnmobilhafen Reise, Südstrand 1. **GPS:** n54,36170 e11,08567. ⬆➡.

Tourist information Hamburg:
ℹ️ www.hamburg-tourismus.de.City-state on the mouth of the river Elbe, Hanseatic town and most important port city of Germany.
ℹ️ Hamburg-card.Card offers free entrance to public transport and museums, discounts on boat trips, zoo etc. Available at Tourist Information. 🎫 € 8 1 day, € 18/3 days, 1 adult max. 3 childeren.
ℹ️ Tourist Information am Hafen, St. Pauli Landungsbrücken, zwischen Brücke 4 und 5.
ℹ️ Tourist Information im Hauptbahnhof, Hauptausgang Kirchenallee.
👁 Sankt Pauli.City district with well-known Reeperbahn.
⛩ Flohmarkt Barmbek, Hellbrookstrasse.Flea market. ⬛ Fri 7-13h, Sa 7-16h.

36 🛏 € 10-12 ⚡ € 0,50 🍽 Ch WC 🍴 € 0,50 🚲 € 5/24h. **Location:** Rural, comfortable. **Surface:** gravel. ⬛ 01/01-31/12
Distance: 🏊 on the spot 🛑 500m 🛑 on the spot.

🅂 **Großsolt** 4D1

Stellplatz Mühlenbrück, Flensburger strasse, Mühlenbrück. **GPS:** n54,70853 e9,52243.

⛩ Flohmarkt St. Pauli, Budapesterstrasse.Antiques and flea market. ⬛ Sa 10-16h.
⛩ Flohschanze, Rinderschlachthalle St Pauli.Antiques and flea market. ⬛ Sa 8-16h.
😊 Tierpark Hagenbeck, Stellingen.Zoo. ⬛ 01/01-31/12 9.h.

DE

⊕ Antikpassage, Klosterwall 9-21.Arcade with 39 antique stores. ⬛ Tue-Fri 12-18h, Sa 10-16h.

Hanerau-Hademarschen · 4D3
Ferienhof Sievers, Wilhelmsburg. **GPS:** n54,12360 e9,38627.⬆.

6 🚐€ 10 🚰🔌 Ch ✂ (6x) WC 🚽. 🛁 **Location:** Rural, comfortable, isolated, quit. **Surface:** grassy. ⬛ 01/01-31/12
Distance: 🏊2km.

Harrislee · 4D1
Skandic Camping, Am Oxer 17a. **GPS:** n54,79800 e9,36960.
5 🚐🚰🔌Ch✂. **Surface:** metalled. ⬛ 01/01-31/12
Remarks: Motorhome dealer, accessory shop.

Hasselberg · 5A1
Camping Oehe-Draecht, Drecht. **GPS:** n54,71590 e9,99030.
10 🚐€11 🚰🔌 Ch ✂€ 2,80 WC 🚽included. **Surface:** grassy. ⬛ 01/04-30/09
Distance: 🏊3km 🛒on the spot ⊗on the spot.

Heide · 4D2
Wohnmobilplatz Heide, Langvogt-Johannsen-strasse. **GPS:** n54,20181 e9,11319. ⬆.

16 🚐free 🚰€ 1/100liter 🔌€ 1 Ch ✂€ 1/2kWh. **Surface:** grasstiles/metalled. ⬛ 01/01-31/12
Distance: 🏊800m 🚲5,5km ⊗100m 🛒300m.

Heiligenhafen · 5C2
Parkplatz Steinwarder, B207 Abfahrt Heiligenhafen. **GPS:** n54,37896 e10,97875. ⬆➡.

90 🚐€ 7,50, peak season € 12/24h 🚰€ 0,50 🔌Ch ✂(42x)€ 2 WC. 🚮
Surface: asphalted. ⬛ 01/01-31/12
Distance: 🏊400m 🛒on the spot ⊗on the spot.
Remarks: Direct access to the beach.

Heiligenhafen · 5C2
Reisemobilstellplatz Binnensee, Eichholzweg. **GPS:** n54,37721 e10,95548. ⬆.

20 🚐€ 7,50-10 ✂(21x)€ 2. 🚮
Location: Urban.
Surface: metalled. ⬛ 01/01-31/12
Distance: 🏊1km 🛒on the spot.
Remarks: Max. 24h.

Tourist information Heiligenhafen:
ℹ Bicycles for hire at Ostsee-Ferienpark.
ℹ Tourist-Information, Bergstrasse 43, www.heiligenhafen.de.Fishing-port and modern marina.
☀ Hafenfest.Festival with events. ⬛ July.

Hohenfelde · 5B2
Campingpark Ostseestrand, Strandstraße. **GPS:** n54,38588 e10,49152. ⬆➡.

25 🚐€ 15 🚰🔌 Ch ✂ WC 🚽included 📷. **Location:** Rural, luxurious.
Surface: grassy. ⬛ 01/04-15/10
Distance: 🏊1km 🏖beach 150m 🛒150m ⊗on the spot 🍽on the spot.

Hohenfelde · 5B2
Wohnmobilplatz Radeland, Strandstraße 18. **GPS:** n54,38278 e10,49295. ⬆➡.

20 🚐€ 5 🚰🔌 Ch ✂€ 0,60/kWh WC 🚽€ 3/day. **Location:** Rural. **Surface:** grassy/sand. ⬛ 01/04-30/09
Distance: 🏖300m.

Hohwacht · 5B2
Parkplatz Alt-Hohwacht, Strandstrasse. **GPS:** n54,31902 e10,67529. ⬆➡.

20 🚐€ 10 🚰€ 1/80liter 🔌€ 1 Ch ✂(20x)€ 1/kWh. 🚮 **Location:** Urban.
Surface: metalled. ⬛ 01/01-31/12
Distance: 🏖on the spot 🛒on the spot.

DE

Husum 4D2

Loof's Wohnmobilhafen, Dockoogstrasse 7. **GPS:** n54,47451 e9,04249.

30 € 12 € 1 € 2 Ch€ 2 (30x)€ 3 WC € 0,50.
Location: Rural, very simple, central, quit.
Surface: gravel. 01/01-31/12
Distance: 200m 200m 200m 200m on the spot on the spot.

Husum 4D2

Wohnmobilplatz Am Dockkoog, Dockoogstrasse 17. **GPS:** n54,47888 e9,01138.

40 € 12 2 pers.incl, dog € 1 Ch WC included € 1. **Location:** Rural, very simple, quit. **Surface:** grassy. Easter-31/10
Distance: 500m 200m 200m on the spot on the spot on the spot.
Remarks: Max. 3 nights.

Itzehoe 5A3

Malzmüllerwiesen, Schuhmacherallee. **GPS:** n53,91970 e9,51815.

5 free € 1/100liter € 1 Ch € 1.
Location: Rural, central, quit. **Surface:** metalled/sand. 01/01-31/12 during event.
Distance: 600m 20m on the spot on the spot.

Jagel 5A2

Wohnmobilhafen Jagel, Bundesstrasse 13. **GPS:** n54,45388 e9,53416.

31 € 10 Ch (25x) WC . **Surface:** grassy. 01/01-31/12
Distance: 4,5km.

Kaltenkirchen 5A3

Reisemobilstellplatz Holstentherme, Norderstrasse 8. **GPS:** n53,84056 e9,94650.

20 free € 3 Ch. **Surface:** grassy/metalled. 01/01-31/12
Distance: 1,5km on the spot.
Remarks: Coins available at pay-desk of theTherme.

Kellinghusen 5A3

Am Freibad. GPS: n53,94715 e9,71035.

10 free € 0,50 Ch (4x)€ 1/kWh. **Surface:** gravel. 01/01-31/12
Remarks: Check in at swimming pool.

Kiel 5A2

Parkplatz Soling, Solling. **GPS:** n54,43033 e10,16634.

€ 10 € 0,50 Ch WC . **Surface:** metalled.
Distance: 13km 400m 400m.

Kiel 5A2

Wohnmobilstellplatz Kiel, Förde und Kanalblick, Mecklenburgstrasse. Kiel-Wik. **GPS:** n54,36362 e10,14705.

33 € 10-13 Ch € 2,50 WC € 1.
Surface: metalled.
Distance: 6,5km on the spot 1,5km.

Tourist information Kiel:
Tourist Information Kiel e.V, Andreas-Gayk-Str. 31.City on the mouth of fiord.
Schleswig-Holsteinisches Freilichtmuseum, Molfsee.Open air museum.

DE

01/04-31/10 daily 9-18h, 01/11-31/03 Su 11-16h. ⊤ € 4,50, family card € 11.

Krempe 5A3
Am Schul- und Sportzentrum, Am Freibad. **GPS:** n53,83356 e9,49447. ⬆

3 ﬡ free. **Location:** Rural, quit. **Surface:** gravel. ⬛ 01/01-31/12
Distance: ⬥200m.

Kremperheide 5A3
Heidekrug, Dorfstraße. **GPS:** n53,88006 e9,47967.
4 ﬡ € 5, guests free. ⬛ 01/01-31/12
Distance: ⊗on the spot.
Remarks: In front of restaurant.

Kropp 5A2
Hotel Wikingerhof, Tetenhusener Chaussee 1. **GPS:** n54,40638 e9,51055.

8 ﬡ € 5, guests free ⊐ ⚲ WC ⊐ ⟫.
Surface: metalled. ⬛ 01/01-31/12

Kropp 5A2
Restaurant Rosengarten, Rheiderweg 7. **GPS:** n54,41388 e9,50138.

5 ﬡ € 5. **Surface:** metalled.

Kropp 5A2
Garage Audi-VW Thomsen, Werkstrasse 2. **GPS:** n54,41361 e9,52833.

5 ﬡ € 5 ⊐ ⊑ Ch. **Surface:** metalled. ⬛ 01/01-31/12

Laboe 5B2
Ostseebad Laboe Ehrenmal, Steinerweg/Prof. Munzerring. **GPS:** n54,41029 e10,23289. ⬆

18 ﬡ € 12 ⇥ € 1/5minutes ⊑ € 1 Ch. 🚌 **Location:** Urban. **Surface:** metalled. ⬛ 01/01-31/12
Distance: ⬥1km ⚊400m ⬥400m ⊗on the spot ⚋1km.

Ladelund 4D1
Am Naturbad, Stato. **GPS:** n54,84919 e9,03629. ⬆

4 ﬡ € 5, € 10 swimming pool incl ⊐ ⊑ Ch ⚲ WC ⊐included. ⚴
Location: Rural, comfortable, isolated, quit.
Surface: grassy. ⬛ 01/01-31/12
Distance: ⬥1km ⚊on the spot.

Langballig 5A1
Campingplatz Langballigau, Strandweg 3, Langballigau. **GPS:** n54,82234 e9,65969.
50 ﬡ € 8, dogs € 1 ⊐ ⊑ Ch ⚲ € 2 WC ⊐ € 0,50. **Surface:** grassy/gravel. ⬛ 01/01-31/12
Distance: ⚊100m.

Langwedel 5A2
Caravanpark am Brahmsee, Mühlenstraße 30a. **GPS:** n54,21462 e9,91943. ⬆ ➡

20 ﬡ € 10 ⊐ ⊑ Ch ⚲ € 2. **Surface:** grassy/gravel. ⬛ 01/01-31/12
Remarks: Bread-service.

Lauenburg/Elbe 5B4
Marina Lauenburg/Yachthafen, Hafenstrasse 14. **GPS:** n53,37156 e10,56527. ⬆

10 ﬡ € 7 ⊐ € 1/100liter ⚲ € 4 WC ⊐.
Surface: metalled. ⬛ 01/01-31/12
Distance: ⬥10 min walking ⊗on the spot.

Lensahn 5C2
Reisemobilplatz Lensahn, Dr. Julius-Stinde strasse. **GPS:** n54,21446 e10,87745. ⬆ ➡

15 🛏 € 8 ⟊ € 1/80liter 🗑 Ch 💧 (4x)€ 2. 🚽 **Location:** Rural. **Surface:** grasstiles. ⬛ 01/01-31/12
Distance: 🚶1,5km 🏊 on the spot ⊗200m ⛟2,5km.

| 🚲S | Lübeck 🌱⚓⛵ | 5B3 |

Wohnmobil Treff Lübeck, An der Hülshorst 11. **GPS:** n53,89510 e10,71088. ⬆.

40 🛏 € 9/day ⟊ 🗑 Ch 💧 WC 🍽 € 1/5minutes 🔌 € 1,50. 🚽 **Location:** Urban, luxurious, quit. **Surface:** gravel. ⬛ 02/01-31/10
Distance: 🚶4,5km 🚗 5km ⊗ on the spot 🚌50m.

| 🚲 | Lübeck 🌱⚓ | 5B3 |

Wohnmobilstellplatz Lübeck Marienbrücke P4, Lastadie. **GPS:** n53,87147 e10,67904. ⬆➡.

16 🛏 free, 18-10h.
Location: Urban.
Surface: asphalted. ⬛ 01/01-31/12
Distance: 🚶500m 🚗2km 🏊 on the spot 🎣 on the spot.
Remarks: Follow 'Media Docks'.

Tourist information Lübeck:
ℹ www.luebeck-tourismus.de.Old Hanseatic town, birth place of the Mann brothers.
🅜 Buddenbrookhaus, Mengstrasse 4.Literature museum with work of the Mann family. ⬛ 01/04-31/10 10-18h, 01/11-31/03 10-17h. 🎫 € 4,10, family card € 12,50.
🅜 Günter-Grass-Haus Kulturstiftung Hansestadt Lübeck, Glockengiesserstr. 21.Literature museum.
🅜 Museum Holstentor, Holstentorplatz.Historical museum. ⬛ 10-16/17h. 🎫 € 4 (incl. 3 children).
🅜 Niederegger Einkaufserlebnis, Café und Marzipan-Museum, Breite strasse 89.Marzipan, Lübecker speciality, museum, café and shop.

| 🚲S | Maasholm | 5A1 |

Stellplatz am Yachthafen, Uleweg 31. **GPS:** n54,68334 e9,99436.
80 🛏 € 9 ⟊ 🗑 Ch 💧 € 2 WC 🍽 € 0,50 ⊗ € 2 🔌. **Surface:** grassy/gravel.
⬛ 01/01-31/12
Remarks: Parking marina.

| 🚲S | Meldorf | 4D3 |

Reisemobil-Stellplatz am Deich, Deichstraße 2. **GPS:** n54,09409 e8,95070. ⬆.

80 🛏 € 7, only overnight stay € 3,50 ⟊ 🗑 Ch 💧 (18x)€ 3 WC 🍽 € 2. 🚽
Location: Rural, comfortable, isolated, quit. **Surface:** grassy/metalled. ⬛ Easter-31/10
Distance: 🚶7km 🏊 on the spot ⊗Imbiss 10-18 uur 🚴 on the spot 🚶 on the spot.

| 🍴 | Molfsee | 5A2 |

Restaurant Dratenhof, Hamburger Landstrasse. **GPS:** n54,27779 e10,08589.

20 🛏 free. ⬛ 01/01-31/12
Remarks: At open air museum.

| 🚲S | Mölln | 5B4 |

Alt Möllner strasse. **GPS:** n53,62564 e10,68314.

24 🛏 € 7/24h 💧 (20x)included. **Surface:** gravel. ⬛ 01/01-31/12
Distance: 🚶1km.

Tourist information Mölln:
ℹ Small town to the old Salzstrasse, salttrail.

| 🚲S | Neumünster | 5A3 |

Bad am Stadtwald, Hansaring 177. **GPS:** n54,08078 e9,96064. ⬆➡.

22 🛏 € 6 ⟊ € 0,50 🗑 € 0,50 Ch 💧 € 0,50/kWh WC 🍽 € 0,50 🔌.
Surface: metalled. ⬛ 01/01-31/12
Distance: 🚶2km ⊗ on the spot ⛟300m.
Remarks: Check in at swimming pool.

| 🚲S | Neustadt in Holstein ⚓ | 5C2 |

Wohnmobilstellplatz Ostsee, Auf der Pelzer Wiese 45, Pelzerhaken. **GPS:** n54,08889 e10,87250. ⬆➡.

DE

90 🅿 € 12 + tourist tax (summer) 🚰 € 1 🔽 € 1 Ch 🔌 (90x) € 1/2kWh WC 🚿 🧺 € 2. 🚌 🔑 **Location:** Rural, luxurious, noisy. **Surface:** grassy. ☐ 01/01-31/12
Distance: 🏙 900m 🏖 150m 🍴 900m 🛒 400m 🚌 on the spot.

[S] Neustadt in Holstein 5C2

P5, Am Binnenwasser. **GPS**: n54,11096 e10,81496. ⬆➡.

10 🅿 Mo-Fr € 5/24h, Sa-Su free 🔌 (2x) € 0,50/kWh. 🚌 **Location:** Urban, very simple. **Surface:** metalled. ☐ 01/01-31/12
Distance: 🏙 on the spot.

[S] Niebüll 4C1

Parkplatz, Lornsenstrasse 19. **GPS**: n54,78901 e8,82546. ⬆.

25 🅿 € 5 🚰 € 1 🔽 € 1 Ch 🔌 (12x) € 1. **Location:** Urban, central, quit. **Surface:** grassy. ☐ 01/01-31/12
Distance: 🏙 on the spot 🍴 200m.
Remarks: Parking swimming pool, max. 24h.

[S] Nordstrand 4D2

Wohnmobilplatz Margarethenruh, Süderhafen 8. **GPS**: n54,46944 e8,91000. ⬆.

21 🅿 € 14,80-17,50, 2 pers.incl. 🚰 🔽 Ch 🔌 € 2,60 WC 🚿 🧺 € 3 📶 🔑
Location: Rural, comfortable, central, quit.
Surface: gravel. ☐ 01/01-31/12
Distance: 🏙 3km 🏖 300m 🍴 150m 🛒 3km.

[S] Nordstrand 4D2

Womoland, Norderquerweg 2. **GPS**: n54,51736 e8,93012.

38 🅿 € 7 + € 3,50/pp 🚰 🔽 Ch 🔌 € 2,50 WC 🚿. **Surface:** grassy/gravel. ☐ 01/01-31/12

🍴 [S] Nordstrand 4D2

Landgasthof Pohnshallig, Pohnshalligkoogstrasse 17. **GPS**: n54,49772 e8,92906. ⬆.

4 🅿 € 5, guests free 🚰 € 2,50. 🔑 **Location:** Rural, very simple. **Surface:** metalled. ☐ 01/07-31/10 ■ Thu.
Distance: 🏙 3km 🍴 on the spot 🛒 3km.
Remarks: Along through road.

Tourist information Nordstrand:
ℹ Former Wadden island.

[S] Ockholm 4C1

Wohnmobilstellplätze Altes Pastorat Ockholm, Baderstrasse 5/6. **GPS**: n54,66517 e8,82940. ⬆.

5 🅿 € 8 🚰 🔽 Ch 🔌 (5x) € 1,60 WC 🚿 🧺 € 5, dryer € 5. 🔑 **Location:** Rural, isolated, quit. **Surface:** grassy. ☐ 01/01-31/12
Remarks: Bread-service, along through road.

[S] Oeversee 4D1

Kranzbinderei Schnell, Frörupsand 2. **GPS**: n54,69134 e9,43602.
9 🅿 € 5 🚰 🔽 Ch 🔌 € 1. **Surface:** grassy. ☐ 01/01-31/12
Distance: 🍴 500m.

[S] Osterhever 4C2

Stellplatz Norderheverkoog, Norderheverkoogstraße 12, Norderheverkoog. **GPS**: n54,39656 e8,76163. ⬆.

10 🅿 € 6 🚰 🔽 € 1 Ch 🔌 (10x) € 3 WC 🚿 € 1. 🔑 **Location:** Rural.

DE

Surface: grassy. 🅾 01/04-31/10
Distance: 🚶1km 🚲2km 🛒1km 🛝 on the spot 🎿 on the spot.
Remarks: Bread-service.

| | | Pahlen | | 4D2 |

Fischerstrasse. **GPS:** n54,27101 e9,30015. ⬆️➡️.

6 🅿️€6 ⚡(6x) 🔲€ 1. **Location:** Rural, quit.
Surface: grassy. 🅾 01/01-31/12
Distance: 🚶200m 🏊50m 🚲50m 🛒200m 🍴200m.

| | | Plön | | 5B2 |

Wohnmobilhafen Plön, Ascheberger straße 76. **GPS:** n54,14709 e10,39841. ⬆️➡️.

14 🅿️€15 🔌 Ch ⚡WC 🔲📶 included. **Location:** Comfortable, noisy.
Surface: grassy/gravel. 🅾 01/04-15/12
Distance: 🚶1,5km 🛒 on the spot.

| | | Plön | | 5B2 |

Womo-Stop Kleinen Plöner See, Hamburgerstrasse/Aschenberg strasse, B430.
GPS: n54,15278 e10,40417. ⬆️➡️.

16 🅿️€5 🔌€ 0,50 🔲€ 0,50 Ch. 🚽 **Surface:** metalled. 🅾 01/01-31/12
Distance: 🏊 on the spot.
Remarks: Max. 24h, in front of passage to beach. Driving ou village dir Neumünster.

Tourist information Plön:
ℹ️ Tourist Info Plön, Am Lübschen Tor 1, www.touristinfo-ploen.de.Small town around 17th century Schloss Plön. Many watersports.

Wohnmobilpark Kirchsee, Kahlbrook 25a. **GPS:** n54,22811 e10,28616. ⬆️➡️.

| | | Preetz | | 5B2 |

10 🅿️€ 5, 01/04-30/10 € 15 🔌 🔲 ⚡ included WC 🔲. 🚿 **Surface:** gravel.
🅾 01/01-31/12 🅿️ service 01/11-31/03.
Distance: 🚶10min 🏊 on the spot ⊗ on the spot.
Remarks: Bread-service, canoe and bicycle rental.

| | | Puttgarden | | 5C1 |

Wohnmobilplatz Johannisberg, Johannisbergstrasse. **GPS:** n54,50208
e11,18000. ⬆️➡️.

50 🅿️€6 + € 4/pp, dog € 2 🔌€ 2,50 🔲Ch ⚡€ 2,50 WC 🔲. 🚿
Location: Rural, quit. **Surface:** grassy/metalled. 🅾 01/01-31/12
Distance: 🚶2,5km 🏊800m 🚲800m ⊗ on the spot.
Remarks: In nature reserve Am Grüner Brink, bread-service.

| | | Puttgarden | | 5C1 |

Bade- und Surfstrand Grüner Brink, Krögenweg. **GPS:** n54,51174 e11,18285.
30 🅿️€8 🔌€ 2,50 🔲Ch. **Surface:** gravel. 🅾 01/01-31/12
Distance: 🏊 on the spot.

| | | Quickborn bei Burg | | 4D3 |

Am Helmschen-Bach, Hauptstraße 2. **GPS:** n54,01165 e9,21648. ⬆️➡️.

6 🅿️€5 🔌. 🚿 **Location:** Rural, comfortable, quit. **Surface:** grassy. 🅾
01/04-30/09
Distance: 🚶300m 🛝 on the spot.

| | | Ratzeburg | | 5B3 |

Hallenbad Aqua Siwa, Fischerstrasse 43. **GPS:** n53,69567 e10,77598. ⬆️➡️.

12 🅿️€7 🔌€ 1/80liter 🔲Ch. **Surface:** gravel. 🅾 01/01-31/12
Remarks: On the island, at swimming pool.

DE

Ratzeburg 5B3

Stellplatz Reeperbahn, Reeperbahn. **GPS**: n53,70124 e10,77151. ⬆

10 € 4. **Surface**: gravel. 01/01-31/12
Distance: 500m on the spot.

Ratzeburg 5B3

Stellplatz Zum Gildehaus, Mechower strasse 56. **GPS**: n53,70189 e10,79094. ⬆

50 free € 1 Ch (10x)€ 1. **Surface**: grassy. 01/01-31/12
Distance: 2,5km on the spot.

Reinfeld 5B3

Am Herrenteich, Klosterstraße. **GPS**: n53,83024 e10,48362. ⬆

5 free € 0,50/70liter € 0,50 Ch € 0,50/kWh. **Location**: Urban, quit. **Surface**: metalled. 01/01-31/12
Distance: 500m.

Rendsburg 5A2

Wohnmobilpark Eiderblick, An der Untereider 9. **GPS**: n54,29977 e9,64840. ⬆ ➡

44 € 11 € 1/100liter € 0,50/kWh WC € 0,50 01/01-31/12
Distance: 5 min walking on the spot.
Remarks: Internetcafé, bread-service.

Tourist information Rendsburg:
ℹ Tourist-Information Nord-Ostsee-kanal, Altstädter Markt 1, www.rendsburg.de.Small town on canal.
👁 Eiserne Lady.Train-bridge North Sea-Baltic Canal, 42m high.
Blue Line.City walk 3 km.

Hausbrauerei Niewarker, Paradeplatz.Guided tour and tastery.

Reußenköge 4D1

Amsinck Haus, Sönke Nissenkoog 36a. **GPS**: n54,61666 e8,87027. ⬆ ➡

9 € 7 (6x)€ 2/day WC € 3. **Location**: Rural, comfortable, isolated, quit. **Surface**: asphalted. 01/01-31/12

Scharbeutz 5B3

Reisemobilplatz Hamburger Ring, Hamburgerring/Trelleborg Strasse. **GPS**: n54,03028 e10,75222. ⬆

70 € 10/24h, 01/04-31/10 beach tax € 3,50 € 1/100liter Ch (2x)€ 1. **Location**: Rural. **Surface**: sand. 01/01-31/12
Distance: 300m 300m, dog friendly beach 1km 400m.

Schashagen 5C2

Wohnmobilpark Ostseeblick, Biesdorf. **GPS**: n54,11934 e10,92108. ⬆ ➡

30 01/04-30/09 € 10-13, 2 pers.incl., dog € 1,50-2,50 Ch € 2,50 WC. **Location**: Rural, comfortable, quit. **Surface**: grasstiles. 01/01-31/12 Service facilities.
Distance: 300m.
Remarks: If campsite is closed free, (6x) electricity € 1/5h.

Schleswig 5A2

Am Stadthafen, Am Hafen. **GPS**: n54,51167 e9,56917.

30 € 14 Ch WC € 1 included.
Surface: asphalted.
01/01-31/12
Distance: nearby.
Remarks: Max 48h, check in at harbourmaster.

Dir Altstadt and Stadhaven.

Tourist information Schleswig:

Tourist Information Schleswig, Plessenstrasse 7.Historical city, founded by the Vikings, Haithabu.

Schloß Gottorf.Regional museum, archeological museum and museum for art and culture.

M Museum am Danewerk, Ochsenweg 5, Dannewerk.Defences, 650-1200. winter 10-16h, 01/04-31/10 Tue-Fri 9-17h, Sa-Su 10-18h.

M Outsidermuseum, Stadweg 54.Creativity/art from psychiatry. Wed-Thu 14.30-17.30h.

M Stadtmuseum, Friedrichstr 9.City museum. Tue-Su 10-17h.

M Wikinger Museum Haithabu, Haddeby-Busdorf.All about the life of the Vikings. 01/04-31/10 9-17h, 01/11-31/03 Tue-Su 10-16h.

Tolk-Schau, Tolk.Family park. 01/04-30/09 10-18h.

Schönberg/Ostsee 5B2

Brasilien, Seesternweg. **GPS**: n54,42408 e10,39116.

40 € 9, 15/05-15/09 € 11 Ch included. **Location**: Rural. **Surface**: grassy. 01/01-31/12 **Distance**: 200m 200m.

Schönberg/Ostsee 5B2

Stellplatz Mittelstrand, Mittelstrand. **GPS**: n54,42233 e10,39573.

50 € 9, 15/05-15/09 € 11 Ch € 2 WC. **Location**: Rural. **Surface**: grassy. 01/01-31/12 **Distance**: 200m 200m on the spot. **Remarks**: Bread-service in sommer period.

Seestermühe 5A4

Achtern Diek. **GPS**: n53,70333 e9,56232. 4 free. **Surface**: metalled. 01/01-31/12 **Distance**: 200m.

Sehestedt 5A2

Wohnmobilstellplatz Sehestedt, Fährstrasse 1. **GPS**: n54,36922 e9,81973.

13 € 7/24h € 1/100liter Ch. **Surface**: gravel. 01/01-31/12 **Remarks**: Directly at North Sea-Baltic canal.

Sierksdorf 5B3

Wohnmobilstellplatz Hof Sierksdorf, Altonaer Straße. **GPS**: n54,06013 e10,75737. 15 € 11 € 1 € 1 Ch € 0,50/kWh WC . **Surface**: gravel. 01/04-15/10 **Distance**: beach 100m.

Simonsberg 4D2

Nordsee Camping Zum Seehund, Lundenbergweg 4. **GPS**: n54,45515 e8,96958.

30 € 15 Ch WC included € 5. **Location**: Rural, comfortable, isolated, quit. **Surface**: gravel. Easter-31/10 **Distance**: 2km 500m on the spot on the spot. **Remarks**: Use steam bath, sauna, fitness-studio incl.

Sörup 5A1

Südsee, Seeblick. **GPS**: n54,71216 e9,66611. 5 € 4 . **Surface**: grassy. **Remarks**: Parking at small lake.

St.Peter Ording 4C2

Reisemobilhafen St.Peter-Ording, Am Ketelskoog. **GPS**: n54,30881 e8,63522.

70 € 12 € 1/50liter Ch € (70x)€ 0,60/kWh WC € 0,20 € 1 € 1. **Location**: Rural, comfortable. **Surface**: gravel. 01/01-31/12 **Distance**: 300m 1km 300m 300m. **Remarks**: Wed, market.

Tourist information St.Peter Ording:

www.st.peter-ording.de.Seaside resort on the Wadden coast. Westküstenpark, Wohldweg 6.Animal park. summer 9.30-19h, winter 10.30h-sunset.

Süderlügum 4D1

Wohnmobilplatz Mehrzweckhalle, Jahnstrasse. **GPS**: n54,87472 e8,90306.

5 free. **Location**: Rural, central, quit. **Surface**: metalled. 01/01-31/12 **Distance**: 500m 300m.

Timmendorfer Strand 5B3

Am Vogelpark, P4, Bäderrandstraße, B76. **GPS**: n53,99136 e10,81439.

DE

50 🚐 € 7,50 + tourist tax 🚰 € 0,50/120liter 🚽 Ch 🔌. 🚌 **Location:** Rural. **Surface:** grassy/sand. 📅 01/01-31/12
Distance: 🍴 180m.
Remarks: Max. 1 night.

[S] Tönning — 4D2

Wohnmobilplatz Eiderblick - Kapitänshaus, Am Strandweg. **GPS**: n54,30920 e8,93684. ↑.

33+15 🚐 € 11 2p incl., excl. tourist tax 🚰 € 1/100liter 🚽 Ch 🔌 € 0,50/kWh 🚿 included 🧺 € 3,50, dryer € 3. ♿ **Location:** Rural, luxurious, isolated, quit.
Surface: grassy. 📅 01/01-31/12
Distance: 🏘 500m 🏊 on the spot 🚲 on the spot 🚶 on the spot.
Remarks: Along the Eider river.

[S] Travemünde — 5C3

Wohnmobilparkplatz Kowitzberg, Kowitzberg. **GPS**: n53,97598 e10,87830. ↑ →.

49 🚐 15/5-14/9 € 10, 15/9-14/5 € 6 🚰 € 1/100liter 🚽 Ch 🔌 (48x)€ 1/5kWh. **Location:** Urban. **Surface:** grassy. 📅 01/01-31/12
Distance: 🏘 2,5km 🏊 800m 🐟 800m 🍴 300m 🥖 250m 🚌 50m.
Remarks: Near golfcourse and Brodtener Ufer.

[S] Travemünde — 5C3

Parkplatz am Fischerreihafen, Auf dem Baggersand 15. **GPS**: n53,95556 e10,86139. ↑.

120 🚐 € 12-14 🚰 € 1/50liter 🚽 Ch 🔌 (5x)€ 3/kWh WC 🚿 € 2. ♿
Location: Urban. **Surface:** gravel. 📅 01/01-31/12
Distance: 🏊 beach 1,8km 🥖 max. 250m 🚌 express bus Altstadt Lubeck.

Remarks: Parking fishing port, no camping activities.

Tourist information Travemünde:

[i] Lübeck und Travemünde Tourist-Service, Strandpromenade 1b, www.travemuende.de.

Uetersen — 5A4

Am Stichhafen, Ziegelei. **GPS**: n53,67977 e9,66861. ↑.
4 🚐 free. **Surface:** metalled. 📅 01/01-31/12
Distance: 🏘 400m ⛽ 7,4km 🍴 300m.

[S] Wedel — 5A4

Am Freibad. **GPS**: n53,57860 e9,69520. ↑.

20 🚐 € 6 🚰 € 1/10minutes 🚽 Ch 🔌 (14x)€ 1/8h WC 🚿. ♿
Location: Rural, quit. **Surface:** grassy/metalled. 📅 01/01-31/12 ⛔ during event.
Distance: 🏘 800m.
Remarks: Max. 3 days.

[S] Westerholz — 5A1

Campingplatz Fördeblick, Haffstraße. **GPS**: n54,81998 e9,66686.
45 🚐 € 7 🚰 € 1 🚽 Ch 🔌 € 2,50 WC 🚿.
Surface: grassy. 📅 01/03-15/10
Distance: 🏊 150m.
Remarks: At Flensborg Fjord, max. 24h.

[S] Wilster — 4D3

Colosseumplatz, Etatsrätin-doos-strasse 14-17. **GPS**: n53,92419 e9,37449. ↑ →.

15 🚐 free 🚰 🚽 Ch 🔌 € 0,50. **Location:** Urban, central, quit. **Surface:** grassy/gravel. 📅 01/01-31/12 ⛔ fair.
Distance: 🏘 200m 🥖 100m 🚲 on the spot.

Tourist information Wilster:

[i] Wilstermarsch Service GmbH, Mühlenstrasse 13, www.wilstermarsch-service.de.

[S] Wischhafen — 4D3

Hafenstrasse 6. **GPS**: n53,77278 e9,32278. ↑ →.

15 🚐 € 3 🔌 (6x)€ 1/kWh. ♿ **Location:** Rural. **Surface:** grassy/gravel. 📅 01/01-31/12
Distance: 🍴 500m 🥖 1km.

[S] Wischhafen — 4D3

Ziegelstraße, Gewerbegebiet Wischhafen. **GPS**: n53,76417 e9,32111. ↑ →.

DE

8 ⌕ € 3 🚰 🔧 Ch free. 🚿 **Location:** Rural, very simple. **Surface:** gravel. ⬛
01/01-31/12
Distance: 🚶1km 🛒200m.

Wischhafen 4D3

Süder-Elbe, Glückstädter Straße. **GPS:** n53,78678 e9,34017. ⬆➡.

15 ⌕ € 3. 🚿 **Location:** Rural, very simple, isolated. **Surface:** sand. ⬛ 01/01-31/12
Distance: 🚶3km ⊗150m.
Remarks: Parking at ferry-boat.

Wischhafen 4D3

Unterm Deich 7. **GPS:** n53,77528 e9,32111. ⬆➡.

6 ⌕ € 3. 🚿 **Location:** Rural. **Surface:** grassy. ⬛ 01/01-31/12
Distance: 🚶300m ⊗on the spot 🛒1km.

Tourist information Wischhafen:
Ⓜ Kehdinger Küstenschifffahrtsmuseum, Unterm Deich 7. Shipping museum.
⬛ Easter-16/11. 🎫 € 3.

Lower Saxony/Bremen

Adendorf 5B5

Freizeitzentrum, Scharnebecker Weg. **GPS:** n53,28947 e10,45891.
10 ⌕ free. ⬛ 01/01-31/12
Remarks: Parking sports centre, max. 3 days.

Aerzen 10A2

Restaurant Waldquelle, Waldquelle 1. **GPS:** n52,05952 e9,26146. ⬆➡.

3 ⌕ € 4 🚰 🔧 € 1. **Surface:** metalled. ⬛ 01/01-31/12 ⬛ Tue.

Distance: 🚶2km 🛒1km 🚰500m.

Ahlerstedt 5A4

Ahlerstedt Ottendorf, Rickstücken 2. **GPS:** n53,38908 e9,41017. ⬆➡.

25 ⌕ € 8 🚰 🔧 Ch 🔧 included. 🚿 **Location:** Rural. **Surface:** metalled. ⬛
01/01-31/12
Distance: 🚶3km 🛒3km.

Alfeld/Leine 10A2

Bornstrasse. GPS: n51,98586 e9,82769. ⬆.

4 ⌕ free. **Surface:** metalled. ⬛ 01/01-31/12
Distance: 🚶on the spot ⊗nearby 🛒200m.
Remarks: Parking in city centre behind the evangelical church.

Altenau 10B2

Restaurant Alter Bahnhof, Rothenbergerstrasse 52. **GPS:** n51,79879 e10,43320.
⬆.

20 ⌕ € 5 🚰 € 1 🔧 € 1 Ch 🔧 € 2 WC. **Surface:** gravel.
Distance: 🚶2km ⊗2km 🛒2km.

Altenau 10B2

Kristall-Saunatherme Heißer Brocken, Karl-Reinecke-Weg 35. **GPS:** n51,79836
e10,44408.
20 ⌕ € 10 excl. tourist tax 🚰 🔧 Ch 🔧.
Surface: metalled. ⬛ 01/01-31/12
Distance: ⊗on the spot 🛒on the spot.

Amelinghausen 5B5

Lopausee, Auf der Kalten Hude. **GPS:** n53,13324 e10,23441. ⬆➡.

50 ⌕ € 5, 1/9-1/7 € 3,50 🚰 🔧 Ch included. **Location:** Very simple, isolated,

DE

quit.
Surface: gravel/sand. ◻ 01/01-31/12
Distance: 🚉1 km 〰100m ⛽100m ⊗1km 🛒1km 🏍on the spot 🚶on the spot.
Remarks: Ticket at station, kiosk Lopausee, pay desk Waldbad and tourist office.

🅂 Amelinghausen 🌿⛺🏕🌾 5B5
Waldbad, Zum Lopautal. **GPS:** n53,12402 e10,23018. ⬆

40 ⬛€ 8, 1/9 - 1/7 € 5 ⛽💬Ch 🔧 included. 🚰 **Location:** Comfortable.
Surface: . ◻ 01/01-31/12
Distance: 🚉1km 〰500m ⊗1km 🛒1km 🏍on the spot 🚶on the spot.
Remarks: Including access to swimming pool, bread-service.

🅂 Amelinghausen 🌿⛺🏕🌾 5B5
Kronsbergheide, Hochseilgarten. **GPS:** n53,13500 e10,23389. ⬆➡

10 ⬛€ 5, 1/9-1/7 € 3,50.
Location: Rural, very simple, isolated, quit.
Surface: . ◻ 01/01-31/12
Distance: 🚉1km 〰500m ⛽on the spot ⊗1km 🛒1km 🏍on the spot 🚶on the spot.
Remarks: Ticket at station, kiosk Lopausee, pay desk Waldbad and tourist office.

🅂 Amelinghausen 🌿⛺🏕🌾 5B5
Schwindbeckerheide, Steinbeckerstrasse, Soderstorf. **GPS:** n53,12247 e10,09934. ⬆

15 ⬛€ 5.
Location: Rural, very simple. **Surface:** metalled/sand. ◻ 01/01-31/12 🏍on the spot 🚶on the spot.
Remarks: Ticket at station, kiosk Lopausee, pay desk Waldbad and tourist office.

🍴🅂 Amelinghausen 🌿⛺🏕🌾 5B5
Gasthaus Eichenkrug, Unter den Eichen 10, Dehnsen. **GPS:** n53,12804 e10,16817.

4 ⬛€ 5 ⛽🔧 included. 🚰🧺 **Location:** Isolated. **Surface:** metalled. ◻ 01/01-31/12
Distance: 🚉4km ⊗on the spot 🛒4km 🏍on the spot 🚶on the spot.
Remarks: Max. 3 nights.

🍴🅂 Amelinghausen 🌿⛺🏕🌾 5B5
Gasthaus Schenck, Lüneburgerstrasse 48. **GPS:** n53,12568 e10,21426. ⬆

15 ⬛€ 5 ⛽🔧 WC included. 🚰🧺 **Location:** Central. **Surface:** metalled.
Distance: 🚉on the spot ⊗on the spot 🛒on the spot 🏍on the spot 🚶on the spot.

Tourist information Amelinghausen:
ℹ Touristikcenter Amelinghausen, Lüneburger strasse 55.Signposted cycle and hiking routes.
👁 Oldendorfer Totenstatt.Hunebed cinerarium from the ice-age. ◻ guided tour 01/05-30/09.
Ⓜ Jachtmuseum Wulff, Hässelmühler WegOerrel. ◻ Wed-Sa 14-18h, Su 11-17h.

🅂 Ankum 9B1
Ferienhof Buse-Glass, Tütingen 5. **GPS:** n52,51431 e7,86842. ⬆

5 ⬛€ 14 ⛽🔧 WC included 🗑. **Location:** Quit. **Surface:** grassy. ◻ 01/01-31/12
Distance: 🚉2,5km ⊗500m 🛒2,5km.

🅂 Apen 4B5
Am Freibad, Hauptstraße, Hengstforde. **GPS:** n53,21795 e7,78706. ⬆
10 ⬛free.
Location: Rural, very simple. **Surface:** metalled. ◻ 01/05-15/09
Distance: 🚲5,8km ⊗50 m.
Remarks: Swimming pool Hengstforde, along railwayline.

🅂 Apen 4B5
Viehmarktplatz, Hauptstraße. **GPS:** n53,21820 e7,80221.
10 ⬛free. **Surface:** metalled. ◻ 01/01-31/12
Distance: 🚉400m 🚲5km.

🅂 Artlenburg 5B4
Am Sportboothafen, Am Deich 9. **GPS:** n53,37680 e10,48550.
40 ⬛€ 10 ⛽💬Ch 🔧 WC 🗑. **Surface:** grassy. ◻ 15/04-15/10
Distance: 🛒on the spot.
Remarks: Along the river Elbe.

Aurich 4B4

Alter Bahnhof, Emderstrasse. **GPS:** n53,47031 e7,47356.

12 free. **Surface:** metalled. 01/03-31/12
Distance: 200m on the spot.
Remarks: Max. 3 nights.

Aurich 4B4

An den Kiesgruben, Tannenhausen. **GPS:** n53,52173 e7,47834.

40 free. **Surface:** unpaved.
Distance: 10m on the spot.
Remarks: At the lake of Tannenhausen.

Aurich 4B4

Landgasthof Alte Post, Essenerstrasse. **GPS:** n53,54573 e7,60736.

6 € 6, guests € 3 1 Ch WC. **Surface:** metalled. 01/01-31/12
Distance: on the spot.
Remarks: Caution key service € 10.

Bad Bentheim 9A1

Am Mühlenberg, Mühlenberg. **GPS:** n52,29360 e7,10095.

10 € 7 € 1/80liter Ch € 0,50/kWh WC. **Location:** Rural.
Surface: metalled. 01/01-31/12
Distance: 200m 50m on the spot on the spot.

Bad Bentheim 9A1

Am Schloßpark, Funkenstiege. **GPS:** n52,30328 e7,15448.

30 € 7 € 1/80liter Ch € 0,50/kWh WC. **Surface:** metalled.
01/01-31/12
Distance: 200m 100m.

Bad Bevensen 5B5

Reisemobilplatz, Am Waagekai. **GPS:** n53,07417 e10,60139.

30 € 10, 2 pers.incl Ch included. **Surface:** grassy. 01/01-31/12
Distance: on the spot 1km 600m.

Bad Essen 9C1

Wohnmobilstellplatz Falkenburg, Falkenburg 3. **GPS:** n52,32352 e8,36384.

50 € 6, 3 pers.incl € 1/100liter Ch € 2/4kWh WC € 0,50.
Location: Rural, comfortable, quit.
Surface: grassy/metalled. 01/03-30/10
Distance: 1,2km 900m 300m.
Remarks: Along the Mittelland canal, near marina.

Tourist information Bad Essen:
Tourist-Information Bad Essen, Lindenstr. 39, www.badessen.info.Small town with historical city centre.

Bad Gandersheim 10B2

Wohnmobil-Stellplatz Rio Gande, An der Wiek. **GPS:** n51,87191 e10,01881.

24 € 5/24h € 1/30liter Ch (14x)€ 0,50/kWh. **Surface:** gravel.
01/01-31/12
Distance: 400m 100m 200m.
Remarks: Bread-service in sommer period. Follow 'P Stadtmitte' then

'Wohnmobilstellplatz'.

Tourist information Bad Gandersheim:

ℹ️ Tourist- Information, Stiftsfreiheit 12.Historical town with half-timbered houses.

Bad Lauterberg — 10B3

Erlebnisbad Vitamar, Mast Tal 1. **GPS:** n51,63358 e10,48661. ⬆️.

5 free ⚡€ 1 💧€ 1 Ch. **Surface:** metalled. ⏰ 01/01-31/12
Distance: 🛒1,5km ⊗1,5km 🚿1,5km 🚂on the spot.

Bad Lauterberg — 10B3

Wiesenbeker Teich. GPS: n51,61719 e10,49074. ⬆️➡️.

4 ⚡€ 13 ⚡💧 Ch 🔧 included. **Surface:** gravel. ⏰ 01/01-31/12
Distance: ⊗on the spot.

Bad Lauterberg — 10B3

Hotel-Restaurant Zur Post, Osterhagener Strasse 6. **GPS:** n51,59090 e10,48993.

3 guests free ⚡🔧 WC included. **Surface:** grassy/metalled. ⏰ 01/01-31/12
Distance: 🛒on the spot ⊗on the spot 🚿200m.

Bad Münder — 10A1

Wermuthstrasse. **GPS:** n52,19837 e9,46067. ⬆️.

2 free. **Surface:** metalled. ⏰ 01/01-31/12
Distance: 🛒200m ⊗200m 🚿on the spot 🚂on the spot.
Remarks: 19-9h.

Bad Münder — 10A1

Rhomelbad, Lindenallee. **GPS:** n52,19305 e9,47111.

10 free. **Surface:** metalled. ⏰ 01/01-31/12
Distance: 🛒400m on the spot 🚿400m 🚂200m.

Bad Nenndorf — 10A1

Wohnmobilstellplatz am Schulzentrum, Bahnhofstrasse 77. **GPS:** n52,34294 e9,37666.

8 free ⚡€ 2/45liter 💧Ch 🔧 (8x)€ 1/6h WC 🚰. **Surface:** metalled. ⏰ 01/01-31/12
Distance: 🛒700m 🏖️3,4km ⊗on the spot 🚿on the spot.

Bad Pyrmont — 10A2

Reisemobilplatz am Gondelteich, Südstrasse/Milchweg. **GPS:** n51,98073 e9,24828. ⬆️➡️.

22 ⚡€ 7/24h 2 pers incl ⚡€ 1/100liter 💧€ 1 Ch 🔧€ 0,50/kWh.
Surface: asphalted.
⏰ 01/01-31/12
Distance: 🛒400m ⊗500m 🚿500m.
Remarks: To pay at swimming pool, free access Kurpark and palm tree garden, and several discounts.

Tourist information Bad Pyrmont:

ℹ️ Bad Pyrmont Tourismus GmbH, Europa-Platz 1, www.badpyrmont.de.Health resort.

Bad Sachsa ❄️ — 10C3

Wohnmobilplatz auf dem Schützenplatz, Im Osteral. **GPS:** n51,60361 e10,54939. ⬆️➡️.

72 ⚡€7 ⚡€ 0,50 💧€ 0,50 Ch 🔧€ 0,50/kWh WC 🚰.
Surface: gravel. ⏰ 01/01-31/12
🔴 3rd weekend July.
Distance: 🛒on the spot 🚿800m.

Bad Sachsa ❄️ — 10C3

Gasthof Alter Grenzkrug, Nüxei 5. **GPS:** n51,56838 e10,52133.

20 🗑️ € 5, guests free 🚰 ✇ WC 🗑️. **Surface:** asphalted/gravel. ⬛ 01/01-31/12
Distance: 🚶2km ✇on the spot 🛒2km.
Remarks: Arrival <21h.

| 🍴 | Bad Sachsa ❄ | 10C3 |

Zum Kachelofen, Schützenstrasse 13. **GPS:** n51,59778 e10,55056.

2 🗑️ guests free. ⬛ 01/01-31/12
Distance: 🚶on the spot ✇on the spot 🛒100m.
Remarks: Max. 2 days.

| 🍴S | Bad Zwischenahn | 4B5 |

Wohnmobilstellplatz Am Badepark, Am Badepark. **GPS:** n53,18722 e8,00021. ⬆➡.

35 🗑️ € 8,50 🚰 € 0,50/70liter 🔌 Ch ✇ (35x)€ 1/2kWh WC 🗑️ € 3, (spa resort). 🏪
Location: Urban. **Surface:** metalled. ⬛ 01/01-31/12
Distance: 🚶on the spot ⚓6,8km ⛱on the spot ⛴on the spot ✇100m 🛒500m 🚗on the spot.

| 🗑️S | Balge | 4D6 |

Blenhorster Bauernhof, Klünderberg 1. **GPS:** n52,71361 e9,13011. ⬆.

20 🗑️ € 5 🚰 ✇ included. **Surface:** grassy. ⬛ 01/01-31/12
Distance: ✇on the spot.

| 🗑️ | Balje | 4D3 |

Naturkundemuseum Niederelbe, Neuenhof, Neuhaus. **GPS:** n53,81958 e9,03867. ⬆.

---

6 🗑️ free.
Location: Rural, very simple, isolated. **Surface:** . ⬛ 01/01-31/12
Distance: 🚶4km ⚓on the spot ✇4km 🛒4km.

| 🗑️S | Barsinghausen | 10A1 |

Wohnmobilstellplatz am Besucherbergwerk Klosterstollen, Conrad-Bühreweg. **GPS:** n52,29858 e9,46943. ⬆➡.

5 🗑️ € 6,50 🚰 ✇ included. **Surface:** metalled. ⬛ 01/01-31/12
Distance: 🚶300m ✇nearby 🛒300m.
Remarks: Max. 3 days.

| 🗑️S | Barßel | 4B5 |

Am Bootshafen, Deichstrasse. **GPS:** n53,16754 e7,73441. ⬆➡.

14 + 20 🗑️ € 6 🚰 🔌 Ch ✇ (34x)€ 2/24h WC 🗑️ included 📺 € 1. 🚿
Location: Urban. **Surface:** grasstiles. ⬛ 01/01-31/12
Distance: 🚶500m ⛴on the spot ✇on the spot 🛒500m.

| 🗑️S | Berge | 4B6 |

Stift Börstel, Börstel 5. **GPS:** n52,64957 e7,69438.
€ 5, in envelope in mail box 🚰 ✇ On demand. **Surface:** metalled. ⬛ 01/01-31/12
Remarks: Near abbey, max. 2 nights.

| 🗑️ | Berge | 4B6 |

Dorfteich Berge, Schienenweg 19. **GPS:** n52,62011 e7,75099.
2 🗑️ free. ⬛ 01/01-31/12

| 🗑️S | Bergen | 5A6 |

Ziegeleiweg. **GPS:** n52,81273 e9,96457. ⬆.

6 🗑️ € 3,50 🚰 € 1 🔌 Ch ✇.

DE

Surface: gravel. ◻ 01/01-31/12
Distance: 🚿nearby ⊗on the spot.
Remarks: Caution key € 20 at town hall.
Tourist information Bergen:
④ Wildpark Lüneburger Heide, Nindorf.Game preserve. ◻ 01/03-31/10 8-19h,
01/11-28/02 9-16.30h.

🏕S	Berne	4C5

Fähranleger Motzen, Motzener Strasse. **GPS**: n53,17972 e8,55778.⬆️

4 🏕free 🔌€ 1 ⚡Ch 🔧(4x)€ 1. **Surface:** metalled. ◻ 01/01-31/12
Distance: 🚿3,5km 🛒on the spot ⊗1km 🛒100m.
Remarks: Parking at ferry-boat at river Weser.

🏕	Bevern	10A2

Schwimm- und Freizeitzentrum, Jahnstrasse. **GPS**: n51,85750 e9,50805.➡️

5 🏕free. **Surface:** asphalted. ◻ 01/01-31/12
Distance: 🚿1,2km 🛒500m 🚌500m.

🏕S	Bienenbüttel	5B5

Wohnmobilstellplatz Ilmenauwiese, Niendorfer strasse, K42. **GPS**: n53,14514
e10,49051.⬆️
12 🏕€6 🔌€ 1 ⚡Ch 🔧(14x)€ 1/8h WC ⊇€ 0,50. **Surface:** metalled.
◻ 01/01-31/12
Distance: 🚿500m ⊗on the spot.
Remarks: Follow 'Ilmenauhalle'.

🏕S	Bippen 🌲 🎡	9B1

Ferienhof Neyenhuis, Hallweg. **GPS**: n52,59360 e7,73005.➡️

20 🏕€ 10 🔌 🔧 WC ⊇€ 2. 🏇 **Location:** Rural, quit. **Surface:** grassy. ◻
01/01-31/12
Distance: 🚿1km.
Remarks: Follow 'Neyenhuis'.

🏕S	Bispingen 🏕	5A5

Parkplatz Oberhaverbeck, Oberhaverbeck. **GPS**: n53,14281 e9,91998.

100 🏕€ 3/day, € 6/night 🔌€ 1/10minutes ⚡Ch 🔧(8x)€ 1/10h. 🛒
Location: Rural, very simple, isolated. **Surface:** grassy/gravel. ◻ 01/01-31/12
◻ Service: winter.
Distance: ⊗on the spot 🏇on the spot 🚶on the spot.
Remarks: In nature reserve the the Lüneburg Heide (heath).

🏕S	Bispingen 🏕	5A5

Parking Rathaus, Borsteler Straße 4-6. **GPS**: n53,08499 e9,99789.

5 🏕free. **Location:** Central. **Surface:** metalled. ◻ 01/01-31/12
Distance: 🚿on the spot 🚲1km ⊗100m 🛒100m 🏇on the spot 🚶on the
spot.

🏕S	Bispingen 🏕	5A5

Reiter- und Ferienhof Cohrs, Volkwardingen 1, Moorweg. **GPS**: n53,13409
e10,00047.

10 🏕€ 14 🔌 ⚡Ch 🔧included WC ⊇◻€ 3. 🏇 **Location:** Comfortable,
isolated, quit. **Surface:** grassy. ◻ 01/01-31/12
Distance: 🚿3km 🚲5,5km ⊗500m 🛒5km 🏇on the spot.
Remarks: Bread-service.

🏕S	Bissendorf	9C1

Reisemobil-Center Veregge & Welz, Gewerbepark 14, A30 Abfahrt Bissendorf.
GPS: n52,24026 e8,13977.⬆️

5 🏕free 🔌€ 1/5minutes ⚡Ch 🔧(4x)€ 1/6h. **Location:** Urban, quit.
Surface: metalled. ◻ 01/01-31/12
Distance: 🚿1km 🚲650m ⊗800m 🛒800m.

🏕S	Bleckede	5C5

Reisemobilplatz Alt Garge, Am Waldbad 23. **GPS**: n53,25606 e10,81047.⬆️➡️

DE

15 🛏 € 9, 2 pers.incl ⚓ 1 🍽 Ch ⚡ € 0,50/kWh WC ⊐. **Surface:** grassy. ◘ 01/01-31/12

Distance: 🚶on the spot ⊗800m 🚲6km.

| �Ⓢ | Blomberg | 4B4 |

Dorfplatz Blomberg, Hauptstrasse. **GPS:** n53,57718 e7,55815. ⬆➡.

20 🛏 free ⚓ 🍽 Ch € 1 🍽 € 0,50/30minutes WC. **Surface:** grassy/metalled. ◘ 01/01-31/12

Distance: 🚶on the spot ⊗200m 🚲200m 🚐50m.

| �Ⓢ | Bockenem | 10B2 |

Am Freibad, In den Reesen. **GPS:** n52,00787 e10,13610. ⬆➡.

5 🛏 free. **Surface:** grassy. ◘ 01/01-31/12

Distance: 🚶800m ⊗200m 🚐300m.

| 🍽Ⓢ | Bockenem | 10B2 |

Hotel Sauer am Aral Autohof, Allensteiner strasse 7. **GPS:** n52,00224 e10,13379. ⬆.

20 🛏 guests free ⚓ € 1,50 🍽 Ch ⚡ € 1,50 WC ⊐. **Surface:** metalled. ◘ 01/01-31/12

Distance: 🚶300m ⊗on the spot 🚲500m.

| �Ⓢ | Bockhorn | 4B5 |

Reisemobilplatz Germer, Am Geeschendamm 1. **GPS:** n53,38399 e8,01369.
30 🛏 € 6 ⚓ 1 🍽 Ch ⚡ € 1,50 WC ⊐ € 1. ◘ 01/01-31/12

| | Bockhorn | 4B5 |

Urwaldstrasse 35a. **GPS:** n53,38988 e7,95686.
3 🛏 free. **Surface:** gravel. ◘ 01/01-31/12

Remarks: Parking swimming pool, max. 1 day.

| 🍽Ⓢ | Bockhorn | 4B5 |

Die Kleine Moorkneipe, Grenzweg 3, Bockhornerfeld. **GPS:** n53,31564 e8,03121.
2 🛏 free ⚓. **Surface:** gravel. ◘ 01/01-31/12

| 🍽Ⓢ | Bockhorn | 4B5 |

Gaststätte Altdeutsche Diele, Landesstrasse 11, Steinhausen. **GPS:** n53,41539 e8,03622.
3 🛏 free ⚓ against payment. **Surface:** metalled. ◘ 01/01-31/12

| 🍽Ⓢ | Bockhorn | 4B5 |

Gaststätte Zum Sandkrug, Sandkrugsweg 21,Grabstede. **GPS:** n53,34965 e7,99336.
4 🛏 free ⚓ free. **Surface:** grassy. ◘ 01/01-31/12

Distance: ⊗on the spot.

| �Ⓢ | Bodenwerder | 10A2 |

Parkplatz Am Mühlentor. GPS: n51,98109 e9,51733. ⬆➡.

15 🛏 € 6 ⚓ € 1/10minutes 🍽 € 1 Ch WC ⊐ € 1. **Surface:** grassy/metalled. ◘ 01/01-31/12

Distance: 🚶2,5km ⊗500m 🚲500m 🚐500m.

| �Ⓢ | Bohmte | 9C1 |

Golfclub Arenshorst, Arenshorster Kirchweg 2. **GPS:** n52,35651 e8,28450. ➡.

3 🛏 guests free.
Location: Rural. **Surface:** grassy/metalled. ◘ 01/01-31/12
Distance: 🚶3km ⊗on the spot 🚲3km.

| 🍽Ⓢ | Bohmte | 9C1 |

Landgasthaus Gieseke-Asshorn, Bremer strasse 55. **GPS:** n52,36674 e8,31261.

4 🛏 guests free ⚓ ⚡ free. **Location:** Urban, quit. **Surface:** metalled. ◘ 01/01-31/12

Distance: 🚶on the spot ⊗on the spot 🚲200m.

| �Ⓢ | Bohmte | 9C1 |

VARIOmobil Fahrzeugbau GmbH, Bremer strasse. **GPS:** n52,38623 e8,30761. ➡.

DE

Remarks: Next to campsite Waldwinkel.

🛏 Bramsche 9C1
Hasebad, Malgartener strasse 49. **GPS:** n52,41493 e7,99423.⬆.

2 🍴free 🚰 🗑 Ch free. **Location:** Rural, quit. **Surface:** metalled. 🔘 01/01-31/12
Distance: 🚶500m ⊗1km 🚊1km.
Remarks: Service only during opening hours.

😊 Bomlitz 5A6
Am Weltvogelpark, Am Vogelpark. **GPS:** n52,88425 e9,59720.⬆.

10 🍴free. **Location:** Urban, quit. **Surface:** metalled. 🔘 01/01-31/12
Distance: 🚶500m.

🛏S Bramsche 9C1
Reisemobile Lewandowsky, Am Kanal 1b. **GPS:** n52,38524 e7,92958.⬆➡.

50 🍴free. **Location:** Rural, very simple, central. **Surface:** grassy. 🔘 01/01-31/12
Distance: 🚶2,5km ⊗on the spot 🚊2,5km.
Remarks: Max. 1 night.

🛏S Brake ☕ 4C5
Am Binnenhafen, Hafenstrasse. **GPS:** n53,32802 e8,48296.⬆.

2 🍴free 🚰 🗑 Ch free 🚿€ 2/day.
Location: Rural.
Surface: gravel. 🔘 01/01-31/12
Distance: 🚶1km ⊗1km 🚊1km.
Remarks: Also repairs possible, walking and bicycle area.

Tourist information Bramsche:
ℹ Stadtmarketing Bramsche GmbH, Maschstrasse 9, www.bramsche.de.
Ⓜ Tuchmacher museum.History of the textile industry. 🔘 Tue-Fri, Su 10-18h, Sa 14-18h. 🎫 € 3.
Ⓜ Varusschlacht im Osnabrücker Land.Battle of the Teutons against the Roman. 🔘 10-18h. 🎫 € 5.

🛏S Braunlage ❄ 10C2
Schützenplatz, Schützenstrasse 21. **GPS:** n51,71658 e10,60847.

4 🍴free 🚰€ 1 🗑Ch 🚿€ 1. **Surface:** metalled. 🔘 01/01-31/12
Distance: 🚶on the spot ⊗100m 🚊200m.

🛏S Brake 4C5
City-Parkplatz, Breite Strasse. **GPS:** n53,32583 e8,47944.⬆➡.
2 🍴free 🚿. **Surface:** metalled. 🔘 01/01-31/12
Distance: 🚶on the spot ⊗on the spot 🚊100m.
Remarks: Key at touristoffice: An der Kaje ± 1km.

🛏S Bramsche 9C1
Wohnmobilstellplatz Waldwinkel, Zum Dreschhaus 4. **GPS:** n52,39591 e8,10244. ⬆➡.

85 🍴€ 9,50, tourist tax € 2,20/pp/day 🚰🗑Ch 🚿 WC included. 🔘 01/01-31/12
Distance: ⊗Café Restaurant Hubertushöhe.
Remarks: Exit Braunlage-Mitte via Lauterberger Strasse and Bahnhofstrasse.

🛏S Braunschweig 10B1
Theodor Heussstrasse. **GPS:** n52,24971 e10,52004.⬆.

60 🍴€ 6 🚰€ 1,50/70liter 🗑Ch 🚿(80x)€ 2 WC €1. **Location:** Rural, comfortable, quit. **Surface:** grassy. 🔘 01/01-31/12
Distance: 🚶3,5km ⊗100m 🚊3,5km 🚲on the spot 🚶on the spot.

🎋 Antik- und Trödelmarkt, Weserpromenade Schlachte.Antiques and flea market. ⬛ Sa 8-14h.

🎪 Bremer Freimarkt, Marktplatz.Large folk festival. ⬛ 15/10-31/10.

15 free 🔌 (16x)€ 1/h. **Surface:** asphalted. ⬛ 01/01-31/12
Distance: 🚶2km 🚌on the spot.
Remarks: Parking exhibition ground.

Bremen 4D5
Wohnmobil Oase Bremen, Schoster born, via Emil von Behringstrasse. **GPS:** n53,06778 e8,86333.⬆

10 € 13 🔌 2 Ch 🔌 WC included, use luxurious bathroom € 5, sauna € 5 € 6 **Surface:** grasstiles. ⬛ 01/01-31/12
Distance: 🚶3km on the spot 🚊50m 🚋Tram.

Bremen 4D5
Am Kuhhirten, Kurhirtenweg. **GPS:** n53,06500 e8,81871.⬆➡

30/45 € 10 🔌 1/100liter Ch (30x)€ 0,50/kWh WC Use sanitary € 1. **Surface:** grasstiles.
Distance: 🚶Old city centre 1,3km 🚗500m on the spot 🚊800m 🚋Tram 700m.

Bremen 4D5
Bremer Schweiz, Im Pohl, Lesum. **GPS:** n53,16765 e8,69560.⬆➡

7 € 3/24h 🔌 1/10minutes Ch 🔌(8x)€ 1.
Surface: gravel.

Tourist information Bremen:
ℹ Tourist Information, Obernstrasse en Hauptbahnhof, www.bremen-tourism.de.Hanseatic city and second harbour of Germany.
👁 Böttcherstrasse.Pedestrian passage.
👁 Bremer Ratskeller.Winery, 650 German wines. ⬛ 11-24h.

Bremerhaven 4C4
Reisemobil-Parkplatz Doppelschleuse, An der Neuen Schleuse. **GPS:** n53,53230 e8,57607.⬆➡

63 € 6,50 🔌 1 Ch 🔌€ 0,50/kWh WC. **Surface:** asphalted. ⬛ 01/01-31/12
Distance: 🚶1,5km 🚗1,5km 🚊1,2km.
Remarks: Bread-service.

Bremerhaven 4C4
Wohnmobil-Parkplatz Fischereihafen, Hoebelstrasse, Fischereihafen 1. **GPS:** n53,52664 e8,57586.⬆

47 € 6,50 🔌 1/80liter Ch 🔌(36x)€ 0,50/kWh WC € 0,50.
Surface: asphalted/metalled. ⬛ 01/01-31/12
Distance: 🚶3km 🚗500m 🚊500m.
Remarks: Parking in harbour.

Bremervörde 4D4
Wohnmobilstation - Bremervörde

touristik@bremervoerde.de - www.bremervoerde.de
Located directly at lake
Excellent location for city visit
Ideal base for walking and cycling

Wohnmobilstation Bremervörde, Kiebitzweg 1. **GPS:** n53,49453 e9,15576.⬆➡
40 € 9,50 Ch 🔌(21x)€ 3/day WCincluded € 1.
Location: Rural, comfortable, quit.
Surface: metalled. ⬛ 01/01-31/12
Distance: 🚶2km 🚲3km 🏊100m 🚏100m 🚗300m 🚊1km on the spot 🎣on the spot.

DE

🗑S **Brietlingen** 5B4
Reihersee. GPS: n53,34344 e10,45844.
50 🗑€8 ⌁Ch ✎€ 2,50 WC. ▢ 01/03-31/10

🍴 **Brietlingen** 5B4
Hotel Franck, Bundesstrasse 31b. **GPS:** n53,33221 e10,44735.
🗑.

🗑S **Bruchhausen-Vilsen** 4D6
Reisemobilstellplatz Bruchhausen-Vilsen, Bollenstrasse. **GPS:** n52,82671
e8,99536. ⬆➡.

20 🗑€4 incl. electricity ⌁€ 1/100liter ⌁Ch ✎(6x)included WC.
Surface: gravel. ▢ 01/01-31/12
Distance: 🚶200m ⊗200m ⛽200m.

🍴S **Bruchhausen-Vilsen** 4D6
Forsthaus Heiligenberg, Heiligenberg 3. **GPS:** n52,80377 e8,99204. ⬆.

2 🗑guests free ⌁✎€ 1/8h WC 🎧 📹. **Surface:** gravel. ▢ 01/01-31/12
Distance: 🚶4km ⊗on the spot ⛽4km.
Remarks: Arrival <22h.

Tourist information Bruchhausen-Vilsen:
Ⓜ Niedersächsisches Kleinbahn-Museum, Am Bahnhof 1.Railway museum.

©S **Buchholz/Nordheide** 5A5
Buchholz/Nordheide, Weg zum Badeteich 20. **GPS:** n53,28202 e9,87495. ⬆.

12 🗑€12-15 ⌁Ch ✎(6x) 2 WCincluded 🍴. Location: Rural,
comfortable. **Surface:** metalled/sand. ▢ 01/01-31/12
Distance: 🚶200m ⊗on the spot ⊗on the spot ⛽200m.

🗑S **Bückeburg** 9D1
Neumarktplatz, Unterwallweg 5c. **GPS:** n52,26326 e9,05040. ⬆.

15 🗑⌁€ 1/80liter ⌁Ch ✎(6x)€ 0,50/kWh. **Surface:** metalled. ▢
01/01-31/12
Distance: 🚶250m ⊗250m ⛽250m 🚌250m.

🗑S **Bückeburg** 9D1
Wohnmobilstellplatz am Schloss, Georgstrasse/Liebesallee. **GPS:** n52,25777
e9,04583. ⬆➡.

30 🗑€5 ⌁€ 1 ⌁Ch ✎(24x)€ 1/12h ♨. **Surface:** asphalted. ▢
01/01-31/12
Distance: 🚶500m ⊗500m ⛽500m 🚌200m.

🗑 **Büddenstedt** 10C1
Am Sportplatz. GPS: n52,17567 e11,01843. ⬆.

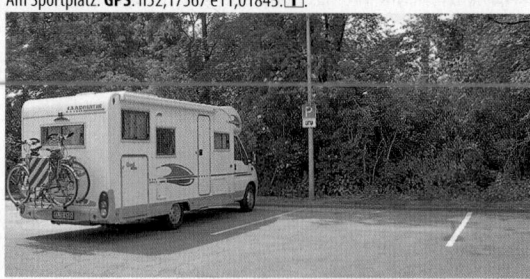

3 🗑free. **Surface:** asphalted. ▢ 01/01-31/12
Distance: ⊗on the spot.
Remarks: Parking swimming pool.

🗑S **Bunde (Nieder-Sachsen)** 4A5
Am Friedhofsweg. GPS: n53,18500 e7,26639. ⬆➡.

10 🗑€3 ⌁€ 0,50 ⌁Ch ✎€ 1. **Surface:** grasstiles. ▢ 01/01-31/12
Distance: 🚶100m 🚲2,3km ⊗350m ⛽200m.
Remarks: At townhall, max. 3 days.

🗑S **Butjadingen** 4C4
Henken's Stellplatz, Am Hafen 6, Fedderwardersiel. **GPS:** n53,59581 e8,35669.

100 🛏free, Kurtaxe € 1,10/pp, € 2,20/pp (peak season) 🚰€ 1 🍳Ch€ 1 🚿€ 2,50. **Surface:** grassy. 🅾 01/01-31/12
Distance: 🚶1km 🏊on the spot 🛒on the spot 🛒on the spot 🍴on the spot.
Remarks: Bread-service.

Butjadingen   4C4
©S
Knaus Campingpark Burhave, Strand Allee, Burhave. **GPS:** n53,58306 e8,37000. ⬆➡.

70 🛏€ 15, peak season € 17, Kurtaxe incl 🚰 🍳 Ch 🚿. **Surface:** grassy. 🅾 15/04-15/10
Distance: 🚶1km 🏊on the spot 🛒200m 🍴1km.
Remarks: Next to campsite.

Butjadingen   4C4
©S
Knaus Campingpark Eckwarderhörne, Butjadinger Strasse 116, Eckwarderhörne. **GPS:** n53,52107 e8,23670. ⬆➡.

15 🛏€ 7, € 2,20/pp tourist tax 🚰 🍳 Ch included 🚿 🍴€ 3, on camp site.
Surface: grassy. 🅾 01/01-31/12
Distance: 🚶200m 🏊on the spot 🛒200m 🍴200m.

Buxtehude   5A4
S
Pfingstmarktplatz, Cuxhavenerstrasse, Neukloster, B73. **GPS:** n53,47974 e9,63528. ⬆.

40 🛏free 🚰€ 0,50/90liter 🍳Ch 🍴 2. **Location:** Rural. **Surface:** asphalted. 🅾 01/01-31/12 ⏺ week before/after Whitsuntide.
Distance: 🚶3km 🛒Imbiss 🍴bakery 200m.
Remarks: Key shower at Imbiss.

Buxtehude   5A4
S
Schützenplatz, Genslerweg. **GPS:** n53,47139 e9,69528. ⬆➡.

30 🛏free 🚰€ 1/90liter 🍳Ch 🚿(36x)€ 1/kWh. **Location:** Urban, central.
Surface: gravel. 🅾 01/01-31/12
Distance: 🚶nearby Old city centre 🛒50m 🍴bakery 50m.

Tourist information Buxtehude:
ℹ City with historical half-timbered houses.
👁 Das Fleth.Old inland-port.

Cadenberge   4D3
S
Reisemobilvermietung Hennig, Alter Postweg 1. **GPS:** n53,76686 e9,05681. ⬆.

4 🛏€ 5 🚰€ 0,50/100liter 🚿€ 1,50/24h. **Location:** Rural, very simple.
Surface: grassy. 🅾 01/01-31/12
Distance: 🚶on the spot 🛒on the spot 🍴50m.

Celle   5B6
S
Schützenplatz, Hafenstraße. **GPS:** n52,62794 e10,07348. ⬆.

35 🛏free 🚰€ 1 🍳Ch WC. **Surface:** grassy/metalled. 🅾 01/01-31/12
Distance: 🚶150m 🍴100m.

Celle   5B6
S
Langensalzaplatz. GPS: n52,61842 e10,08052. ➡.

3 🛏free. **Surface:** metalled. 🅾 01/01-31/12
Distance: 🚶on the spot.

Clenze   5C5
S
Regenbogen-Hof, Mützen. **GPS:** n52,94056 e10,93889. ⬆➡.

DE

5 ⬛ € 5/pp ⬛ Ch ⬛ WC ⬛ included. **Surface:** grassy. ◯ 01/01-31/12
Distance: ⬛3km ⊗on the spot ⬛3km.
Remarks: Arrival <22h.

60 ⬛ € 10, 1/9-1/7 € 6 ⬛ Ch ⬛ € 2/day WC € 0,50 ⬛ € 1. ⬛ **Surface:** asphalted. ◯ 01/01-31/12
Remarks: Beach parking, in front of campsite am Bäderring.

⬛ S | **Cloppenburg** | 4C6
Am Stadtpark, Hagenweg. **GPS:** n52,84649 e8,04687. ⬛.

⬛ S | **Cuxhaven** ⬛ | 4C3
Elbe-Ferry, Am Fährhafen. **GPS:** n53,87508 e8,70315. ⬛ ⬛.

3 ⬛ free ⬛ € 0,50/80liter ⬛ Ch. **Location:** Urban. **Surface:** metalled. ◯ 01/01-31/12
Distance: ⬛100m ⬛2km.
Remarks: Max. 3 days.

100 ⬛ € 10-13, tourist tax incl ⬛ Ch. ⬛ **Location:** Urban. **Surface:** asphalted. ◯ 01/01-31/12
Distance: ⬛1km ⊗500m.
Remarks: Bread-service. Harbour area, follow Fährhafen.

⬛ S | **Cloppenburg** | 4C6
Museumsdorf Cloppenburg, Bether Straße. **GPS:** n52,85197 e8,05335. ⬛.

⬛ S | **Cuxhaven** ⬛ | 4C3
Privatparkplatz Kugelbake Halle, Nordfeldstraße. **GPS:** n53,89033 e8,67703. ⬛.

20 ⬛ free.
Location: Rural, very simple. **Surface:** metalled. ◯ 01/01-31/12
Distance: ⬛900m ⬛1km.
Remarks: Parking in front of museum village, max. 24h.

80 ⬛ € 8 ⬛ Ch WC. ⬛ **Location:** Urban. **Surface:** metalled. ◯ 01/01-31/12
Distance: ⬛200m ⊗100m.

⬛ S | **Coppenbrügge** | 10A2
Parkplatz am Frei- und Hallenbad, Felsenkellerweg. **GPS:** n52,11562 e9,53579. ⬛ ⬛.

⬛ S | **Cuxhaven** ⬛ | 4C3
Campingplatz Finck, Am Sahlburger Strand 25. **GPS:** n53,86039 e8,59167. ⬛ ⬛.

50 ⬛ € 3,50 ⬛ Ch ⬛ included. **Surface:** metalled. ◯ 01/01-31/12
Distance: ⬛on the spot ⊗500m ⬛500m.
Remarks: Parking at swimming pool.

⬛ S | **Cuxhaven** ⬛ | 4C3
Duhner Allee, Duhnen. **GPS:** n53,88284 e8,64814. ⬛.

12 ⬛ € 15,00 ⬛ Ch ⬛ (12x) WC. ⬛ ⬛
Location: Comfortable. **Surface:** .
◯ 01/01-31/12
Distance: ⬛3km ⬛on the spot ⊗on the spot ⬛on camp site ⬛100m.
Tourist information Cuxhaven:
⬛ Nordseeheilbad Cuxhaven, Cuxhavener strasse 92, www.cuxhaven.de.Health resort in the Wadden region.

✤ Neptuntaufe.Baptism of Neptune: beach of Duhne, Döse, Sahlenburg and Grimmershörn. ⬛ 30/05-03/09.

| 📷S | **Damme** | 9C1 |

Am Flugplatz 8. **GPS:** n52,49055 e8,17925. ⬆️➡️.

25 📷 € 5 🚰 € 0,50/80liter 🔲 Ch ⚡(12x)€ 0,50/kWh WC 🚻 € 1. **Location:** Luxurious. **Surface:** grassy/gravel. ⬛ 01/01-31/12
Distance: ⊗on the spot.
Remarks: Parking airport Damme.

| 📷S | **Damme** | 9C1 |

Olgahafen, Dümmerstrasse, Dümmerlohausen. **GPS:** n52,52917 e8,31098. ⬆️.

12 📷free 🚰€ 1 🔲Ch ⚡€ 1. **Location:** Rural, quit. **Surface:** gravel. ⬛ 01/01-31/12
Distance: ⊿100m ⊿100m ⊗on the spot 🛒bakery.
Remarks: At lake Dummen, max. 3 days.

| 📷S | **Damme** | 9C1 |

Parkplatz Altes Amtsgericht, Große Straße. **GPS:** n52,52381 e8,19486. ⬆️.
5 📷free. **Surface:** metalled. ⬛ 01/01-31/12
Distance: ⊿300m.

| 📷S | **Delmenhorst** | 4C5 |

Reisemobilhafen Delmenhorst, An den Graften. **GPS:** n53,04722 e8,62278. ⬆️➡️.

8 📷free 🚰🔲Ch ⚡against payment.
Surface: metalled. ⬛ 01/01-31/12
Distance: ⊿on the spot ⊿2,8km ⊗on the spot 🛒200m.
Remarks: Max. 2 days.

| 📷S | **Detern** | 4B5 |

Reisemobilhafen Detern, Alte Heerstrasse 6, Stickhausen. **GPS:** n53,21560 e7,64743. ⬆️➡️.

40 📷 € 5 🚰€ 1/100liter 🔲Ch ⚡(44x)€ 2/24h WC 🚻€ 1 🔲€ 0,50. 🎣
🅿️ **Location:** Urban, luxurious. **Surface:** asphalted/gravel. ⬛ 01/01-31/12
Distance: ⊿on the spot ⊿6km ⊿on the spot ⊿on the spot ⊗on the spot ⊿on the spot ⅄on the spot.
Remarks: Behind Tourist-Info, bread-service.

| 📷S | **Diepenau** | 9D1 |

Am Bahnhof. **GPS:** n52,42470 e8,74106. ⬆️.

6 📷free 🚰€ 1 🔲Ch ⚡€ 1/8h.
Surface: metalled. ⬛ 01/01-31/12
Distance: ⊿500m ⊗500m 🛒500m.

| 📷S | **Diepholz** | 4C6 |

Parkplatz Am Heldenhain, Am Heldenhaim (B69). **GPS:** n52,61250 e8,37056. ⬆️➡️.

12 📷free 🚰€ 1 🔲Ch ⚡(12x)€ 0,50/kWh. **Location:** Urban. **Surface:** grassy. ⬛ 01/01-31/12
Distance: ⊿500m ⊗500m 🛒500m.

| 📷 | **Ditzum** | 4A5 |

Reisemobil-platz Ditzum, Am Deich. **GPS:** n53,31555 e7,28666. ⬆️.

20 📷€ 5/night. **Surface:** metalled. ⬛ 01/01-31/12
Distance: ⊿100m ⊿100m ⊿100m ⊗100m 🛒300m.
Remarks: Waste dump € 1, shower € 1.

| 📷S | **Ditzum** | 4A5 |

Aktiv-Markt, Molkereistrasse. **GPS:** n53,31489 e7,27619. ⬆️.

DE

4 ⌧ € 5/24h ⚲ € 1 🏳Ch ⚡ € 1/kWh.
Surface: metalled. 🚻 01/01-31/12
Distance: 🚶100m ⚓300m 🚌300m ⊗100m 🛒on the spot.

| ♨ S | **Dollart** | 4A5 |

Freizeitgelände, Denkmalstrasse 11, Ditzumerverlaat. **GPS:** n53,26028 e7,26861. ⬆➡.

10 ⌧ € 3/24h ⚲ € 0,50 🏳Ch ⚡ (8x)€ 1/8h. **Surface:** metalled. 🚻 01/01-31/12 ⊙ during event.
Distance: 🚶250m ⚓on the spot 🚌on the spot ⊗350m 🛒250m.
Remarks: Max. 3 days.

| ♨ S | **Dornum** | 4B4 |

P3, Schützenplatz. **GPS:** n53,64850 e7,42365. ⬆.

15 ⌧ € 9 ⚲ 🏳Chincluded ⚡ € 1/8h. **Surface:** grassy.
Distance: ⊗300m 🛒50m.
Remarks: Max. 1 night.

| ♨ | **Dörpen** (📻) | 4A6 |

Festplatz, Veeneweg. **GPS:** n52,97115 e7,33425. ⬆➡.

10 ⌧ free. **Location:** Very simple. **Surface:** grassy/metalled. 🚻 01/01-31/12 ⊙ 1st week in June: fair.
Distance: 🚶500m ⊗on the spot 🛒500m 🎣 on the spot.

| ♨ S | **Dorum** ⛵ | 4C4 |

Wohnmobilhafen Wurster-Land, Am Neuen Deich 2a. **GPS:** n53,73838 e8,51966. ⬆➡.

24 ⌧ € 10 + € 1,50/pp tourist tax ⚲ € 1/100liter 🏳Ch ⚡24h WC 📷 🚰
Surface: metalled. 🚻 01/01-31/12
Distance: ⚓on the spot 🚌on the spot ⊗on the spot.
Remarks: Check in at Deichhotel.

| ♨ S | **Drage/Elbe** ⛵ | 5B4 |

Reisemobilplatz Stover Strand, Stover Strand 10. **GPS:** n53,42460 e10,29514.
100 ⌧ € 11 ⚲ 🏳Ch ⚡ € 0,50/kWh WC 🚾 € 0,50 📶 📡.
Surface: grassy.
Distance: ⚓on the spot ⊗on the spot 🛒on the spot.
Remarks: Next to campsite.

| ♨ S | **Drochtersen** ⚓ | 4D4 |

Krautsand, Deichverteitigungsweg. **GPS:** n53,75167 e9,39028. ⬆➡.

12 ⌧ € 10 ⚡ (12x)included. 🚐 **Location:** Rural. **Surface:** metalled. 🚻 01/01-31/12
Distance: ⚓Elbestrand 🛒300m.

| ♨ | **Drochtersen** ⚓ | 4D4 |

Am Alten Hafen, Asseler Sand. **GPS:** n53,69418 e9,43928. ⬆.

6 ⌧ free. **Location:** Rural, very simple.
Surface: gravel. 🚻 01/01-31/12
Distance: ⊗500m 🛒1km.

| ♨ | **Drochtersen** ⚓ | 4D4 |

Hallenbad Drochtersen, Am Sportplatz. **GPS:** n53,70548 e9,38215. ⬆.

6 ⌧ free. **Location:** Very simple. **Surface:** metalled. 🚻 01/01-31/12
Distance: 🚶1km 🛒1km.
Remarks: Parking at swimming pool.

DE

🔲S | **Duderstadt** | 10B3
Parkplatz, Adenauerring. **GPS:** n51,51346 e10,27144. ⬆️.

🔳free 🚰€ 1 🔋€ 1 Ch 💧against payment. **Surface:** gravel. ⭕ 01/01-31/12
Distance: 🚶800m ⊗800m 🚊200m 🚌200m.
Remarks: Max. 1 night. East edge of the Altstadt.

🔲 | **Duderstadt** | 10B3
Eichsfeldhalle, August Werner Allee. **GPS:** n51,50662 e10,25890.

10 🔳free.
Surface: gravel. ⭕ 01/01-31/12
Distance: 🚶900m ⊗900m 🚊900m 🚌700m.
Remarks: Max. 1 night.

Tourist information Duderstadt:
ℹ️ Gästeinformation der Stadt Duderstadt, Marktstrasse 66, www.duderstadt.de.Old part of town with half-timbered houses.

🔲S | **Edewecht** | 4B5
Rathhausstrasse. **GPS:** n53,12834 e7,98201. ⬆️.

8 🔳free 🚰€ 1 🔋Ch 💧(8x)€ 1/6h. **Location:** Urban. **Surface:** grasstiles.
⭕ 01/01-31/12
Distance: 🚶on the spot ⊗400m 🛒Aldi 50m.

🔲S | **Egestorf** | 5A5
Naturerlebnisbad Acquadies, Ahornweg 5. **GPS:** n53,19796 e10,05455. ⬆️➡️.

40 🔳€7 🚰€ 1 🔋Ch 💧(30x)€ 2/10h WC 🗑️. 🚿 **Location:** Quit.
Surface: gravel/metalled. ⭕ 01/01-31/12
Distance: 🚶1km 🚴2,2km 🏊on the spot ⊗700m 🚊1km.

Remarks: At swimming pool.

🔲S | **Eggermühlen** | 9B1
Reiterhotel Vox, OT Bockraden 1. **GPS:** n52,57278 e7,79553. ⬆️➡️.

8 🔳€ 25, clients € 7,50 🚰🔋Ch 💧 WC 🗑️included. **Location:** Rural.
Surface: grassy. ⭕ 01/01-31/12
Distance: 🚶3km 🚊3km.

🔲 | **Eggestedt** | 4C5
Eggestedt, Betonstrasse/Habichthorsterweg. **GPS:** n53,22819 e8,63902. ⬆️➡️.

8 🔳free. **Location:** Very simple, isolated, noisy. **Surface:** metalled/sand. ⭕ 01/01-31/12
Distance: 🚶4km 🚴400m.

🔲S | **Einbeck** 🌿🎣⛩ | 10A2
Am Schwimmbad, Ochsenhofweg. **GPS:** n51,82433 e9,86464. ⬆️➡️.

30 🔳free 🚰€ 1/5minutes 🔋€ 1 Ch. **Surface:** gravel. ⭕ 01/01-31/12
Distance: 🚶800m ⊗500m 🚊500m.
Remarks: Parking swimming pool, max. 1 night.

Tourist information Einbeck:
ℹ️ Tourist Information, Altes Rathaus, Marktplatz 6.Motorhome friendly beer town with half-timbered houses and city walls.
👁 Blaudruckerei Wittram.350 years printing of fabrics. Information at Tourist Information.
👁 Einbecker Bierdiplom.Guided tour and tastery, information at Tourist Information.
⛱ Alte Marktplatz. ⭕ Wed + Sa morning.

🔲S | **Elsfleth** | 4C5
Im Hafen, An der Kaje. **GPS:** n53,23771 e8,46545. ⬆️➡️.

20 �free ⌁€ 1 ⌁Ch ⌁ (8x)€ 1/8h.
Surface: gravel. ◻ 01/01-31/12
Distance: ⌁on the spot ⌁on the spot ⊗on the spot ⌁on the spot ⌁on the spot.

Emden | 4A5

Am Hafentor, Am Eisenbahndock. **GPS:** n53,36306 e7,20778.↑.

45 ⌁€ 7 ⌁€ 0,50/100liter ⌁€ 0,50 Ch ⌁ (36x)€ 0,50/kWh WC€ 0,50
⌁€ 1 ⌁€ 3. **Surface:** metalled. ◻ 01/01-31/12
Distance: ⌁500m ⊗500m ⌁500m.
Remarks: Pay at harbourmasters.

Emden | 4A5

Ostmole Ostufer, An der Nesserlander Schleuse. **GPS:** n53,36354 e7,20844.↑.
⌁free. **Surface:** metalled. ◻ 01/01-31/12
Distance: ⌁on the spot ⌁on the spot.

Emden | 4A5

Wohnmobilstellplatz Knock, Jannes Ohling Strasse. **GPS:** n53,35559 e7,00367.
↑.

25 ⌁€ 4,50. **Surface:** metalled. ◻ 01/01-31/12
Distance: ⌁13km ⌁500m ⊗on the spot ⌁13km.
Remarks: Parking harbour.

Emmerthal | 10A2

Gasthaus Zur Post, Grohnder Strasse 25. **GPS:** n52,02185 e9,41865.

20 ⌁guests free. **Surface:** asphalted. ◻ 01/01-31/12
Distance: ⌁400m ⊗on the spot ⌁500m.
Remarks: Arrival <17h.

Emsbüren | 9B1

Landgasthof Elberger Schlipse, Elbergen 1, Elbergen. **GPS:** n52,46825 e7,30103.

40 ⌁€ 3 ⌁Ch ⌁ (15x)€ 2,50/24h WC ⌁. **Location:** Rural, quit.
Surface: grassy. ◻ 01/01-31/12
Distance: ⌁2km ⌁100m ⌁2km ⌁on the spot ⌁on the spot.

Eschershausen | 10A2

Reisemobil-Stellplatz am Angerplatz, Angerweg. **GPS:** n51,92965 e9,62806.
10 ⌁free ⌁Ch ⌁ free. **Surface:** metalled. ◻ 01/01-31/12
Distance: ⌁1km.

Esens | 4B4

Schützenplatz. GPS: n53,63921 e7,61077.↑.

20 ⌁€ 4 + tourist tax € 2,50/pp ⌁ ⌁Ch ⌁ included. **Surface:** grassy. ◻
01/01-31/12
Distance: ⊗50m ⌁200m.

Essel | 5A6

Hotel Heide-Kröpke, Esseler Damm 1. **GPS:** n52,73240 e9,69419.↑.

5 ⌁free ⌁ ⌁ ⌁. **Surface:** grassy. ◻ 01/01-31/12
Distance: ⊗on the spot ⌁9km.
Remarks: Use of a meal desired, bird reserve Ostenholzer-Moor.

Esterwegen | 4B6

Am Erikasee. GPS: n52,99366 e7,66768.↑.

6 ⌁free ⌁€ 1/100liter ⌁Ch ⌁(6x)€ 1/2kWh WC ⌁. **Location:** Rural,
isolated. **Surface:** gravel/metalled. ◻ 01/01-31/12
Distance: ⌁2km ⌁100m ⊗Imbiss 80m.

Remarks: Walking and bicycle area.

🏕 S | **Eystrup** | 4D6

Bahnhofstrasse 21. **GPS**: n52,78004 e9,21840. ⬆️➡️.

5 free. **Surface:** grassy. ⭕ 01/01-31/12
Remarks: Max. 5 days.

🏕 S | **Fassberg** | 5B6

Am Schützenplatz, Moorweg. **GPS**: n52,90518 e10,16991. ⬆️.

50 €2 € 1 Ch WC. **Surface:** grassy. ⭕ 01/01-31/12
Distance: 700m.

🏕 S | **Fassberg** | 5B6

Parkplatz Heidesee, Unterlüsserstrasse, L280, Müden. **GPS**: n52,87889 e10,12472. ⬆️.

20 €2 € 1 Ch € 1. **Surface:** grassy. ⭕ 01/01-31/12 ⭕ end Sep.
Distance: 500m 1km.

🏕 | **Fassberg** | 5B6

Parkplatz am Wildpark, Willinghäuser Kirchweg, Müden. **GPS**: n52,87222 e10,10861. ⬆️.

20 € 2. **Surface:** grassy. ⭕ 01/01-31/12
Distance: 1km 1km.

🏕 S | **Freiburg/Elbe** | 4D3

Am Bassin. **GPS**: n53,82285 e9,29305. ⬆️➡️.

50 8 Ch WC included € 1. **Location:** Rural. **Surface:** metalled. ⭕ 01/01-31/12
Distance: 200m 50m 300m 400m.
Remarks: Find more possibilities on the city plan.

🏕 S | **Friedeburg** | 4B4

Schützenplatz. **GPS**: n53,45488 e7,83349. ⬆️.
20 free Ch free against payment. **Surface:** metalled. ⭕ 01/01-31/12
Remarks: Max. 3 days.

🏕 S | **Fürstenau** | 9B1

Schlossinsel Fürstenau, Schlossplatz 1. **GPS**: n52,51638 e7,67333. ⬆️.

2 free € 3 Ch € 2/day. **Location:** Quit. **Surface:** metalled. ⭕ 01/01-31/12
Distance: 100m 100m 100m on the spot on the spot.
Remarks: Next to the castle.

Tourist information Fürstenau:
ℹ️ Touristisches Informationsbüro, im Alten Rathaus, Grosse strasse 27, www.fuerstenau.de.Small town around a medieval castle farm.

🏕 S | **Geeste** | 9A1

Am Speicherbecken, Biener Straße. **GPS**: n52,59407 e7,27417. ⬆️.

50 free. **Location:** Quit. **Surface:** metalled. ⭕ 01/01-31/12
Distance: 2km 100m.
Remarks: Max. 1 night.

🏕 | **Geeste** | 9A1

P Biotop/Ausblick, Osterbrocker Strasse. **GPS**: n52,59840 e7,29279. ⬆️.

DE

4 ⬛free. **Surface:** metalled. ⚫ 01/01-31/12
Distance: 🚶1,5km 🏊1,5km 🚴 on the spot 🏃 on the spot.
Remarks: Max. 1 night, hiking area.

| 🏞️S | Gifhorn | 5B6 |

Fischer Camping + Gas, Schmiedeweg 4. **GPS:** n52,50863 e10,48462.
8 ⬛free 🔌🍽️Ch🧹. **Surface:** grassy. ⚫ 01/01-31/12
Distance: ⊗500m.
Remarks: Accessory shop.

| 🏞️S | Gnarrenburg | 4B5 |

Parkplatz Brillit, Alte Strasse, Brillit. **GPS:** n53,41390 e9,00007.⬆️➡️.

15 ⬛free 🔌🍽️Ch free. **Location:** Rural, very simple. **Surface:** gravel. ⚫ 01/01-31/12
Distance: 🚶1km ⊗3km 🏊1km.
Remarks: At community centre.

| 🏞️S | Gnarrenburg | 4B5 |

Schulzentrum, Brilliterweg. **GPS:** n53,39000 e8,00028.⬆️➡️.

15 ⬛free 🔌🍽️Ch free. **Surface:** metalled. ⚫ 01/01-31/12
Distance: ⊗1km 🏊500m.
Remarks: Sports centre.

| 🏞️S | Göttingen 🚴🛁 | 10B3 |

Reisemobilhafen Eiswiese, Badeparadies Eiswiese, Windausweg 6. **GPS:** n51,52320 e9,92965.➡️.

28 ⬛€9 🔌€ 1 🍽️Ch🧹€ 1 WC 🚿€ 1/15h. **Surface:** gravel. ⚫ 01/01-31/12
Distance: 🚶500m 🏊5,2km 🏖️100m 🚲20-400m ⊗100m 🏊500m 🚌100m.
Remarks: Follow Reisemobilplatz/Badeparadies Eiswiese/Stadion.

| 🏞️S | Göttingen 🚴🛁 | 10B3 |

VW-garage Südhannover, Kasseler-Landstrasse 53-69. **GPS:** n51,53053 e9,89780.

2 ⬛free 🔌🍽️Ch free. **Surface:** asphalted. ⚫ 01/01-31/12
Distance: 🚶2,5km 🚌200m.

Tourist information Göttingen:
ℹ️ Gö-card.Card offers free access to public transport and discounts at museums, bathe etc. Available at Tourist Information. 🎫 € 5/day.
ℹ️ Tourist-Information, Altes Rathaus, Markt 9, www.goettingen-tourismus. de.University town with old university buildings.
👁️ Bismarckhäuschen.Student appartment of the Reichskansler Otto von Bismarck. ⚫ Tue 10-13h, Wed, Thu, Sa 13-17h.

| 🏞️S | Grasberg | 4D5 |

P&R, Wörpedorfer Straße. **GPS:** n53,18411 e8,98433.⬆️.

10 ⬛free 🔌€ 1 🍽️Ch🧹(8x)€ 1/6h.
Surface: gravel. ⚫ 01/01-31/12
Distance: 🚶on the spot ⊗on the spot 🏊on the spot 🚌> Bremen.

| 🏞️S | Gronau (Nieder-Sachsen) | 10A2 |

Kuhmasch. **GPS:** n52,08265 e9,77034.⬆️➡️.

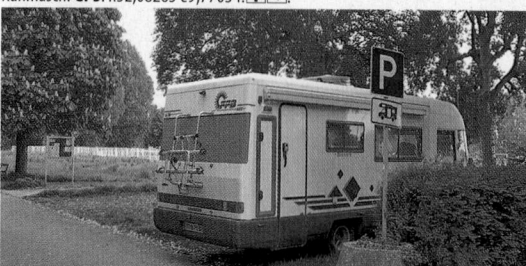

4 ⬛free. **Surface:** grassy. ⚫ 01/01-31/12
Distance: 🚶200m ⊗300m 🏊300m.

| 🍴S | Grossefehn | 4B5 |

Ostfriesen-Bräu Bagband, Voerstad 8, Badband. **GPS:** n53,35034 e7,61060.⬆️.

4 ⬛€ 5,70, free with 3 beer 🔌🍽️🧹 included, 16Amp WC. **Surface:** metalled. ⚫ 01/01-31/12
Distance: 🚶10km 🚲4km ⊗on the spot 🏊600m.

| 🏞️S | Grossheide | 4A4 |

Kirchweg, Berumerfehn. **GPS:** n53,56040 e7,34713.⬆️.

4 ⛺free. **Surface:** asphalted. 🅾 01/01-31/12
Distance: 🔌on the spot ⊗on the spot 🛒2km.
Remarks: Max. 1 night.

| Großenkneten | 4C6 |

Dorfplatz, Bahnhofstrasse, Huntlosen. **GPS:** n52,99139 e8,28611.⬆️.

6 ⛺free.
Location: Rural, very simple. **Surface:** grasstiles. 🅾 01/01-31/12
Distance: 🔌on the spot ⊗50m 🛒1km.

| Großenkneten | 4C6 |

Wilhelm-Wellman-Platz, Ahlhorner Strasse. **GPS:** n52,94274 e8,25751.⬆️.

15 ⛺free.
Location: Rural, very simple. **Surface:** grasstiles. 🅾 01/01-31/12
Distance: 🔌200m ⊗200m 🛒on the spot.

| Großenwieden | 9D1 |

Am Steinbrink. **GPS:** n52,17191 e9,18982.⬆️➡️.

5 ⛺free.
Location: Rural. **Surface:** gravel.
Distance: 🔌on the spot ⊗🚴 Weserradweg 🚶on the spot.

| Hambergen | 4D5 |

Festplatz, Kirchweg/Am Langenend. **GPS:** n53,31050 e8,82389.⬆️➡️.

20 ⛺€ 3,50 🔌🍽Ch🚿.
Location: Urban, very simple.
Surface: gravel/sand. 🅾 01/01-31/12
Distance: 🔌on the spot ⊗50m 🛒50m 🚆1km 🚴on the spot 🚶on the spot.
Remarks: Caution key service € 25.

| Hameln | 10A2 |

Hannes Weserblick, Ruthenstrasse 14. **GPS:** n52,09623 e9,35853.⬆️➡️.

27 ⛺€ 8/24h 🔌€ 1/100liter 🍽Ch🚿€ 1/8h.
Surface: metalled. 🅾 01/01-31/12
Distance: 🔌1km ⊗600m 🛒600m 🚆800m 🚴 Weser-Radweg.

| Hankensbüttel | 5B6 |

Parkplatz Am Boldhamm. **GPS:** n52,73111 e10,61417.⬆️➡️.

20 ⛺€ 6 🔌🍽Ch🚿WC included. **Surface:** grassy. 🅾 01/01-31/12
Remarks: Service: Mo/Fri 8 - 11h, Sa/Su 8-10h. Over railway passage,
Emmerdorfstraße, Isenhagersee.

Tourist information Hankensbüttel:
☺ Otter-Zentrum.Zoo. 🅾 15/03-31/10 9.30-18h, 01/11-14/03 9.30-17h ⏹
15/12-15/01.

| Hannoversch Münden | 10A3 |

Parkplatz Tanzwerder. **GPS:** n51,42000 e9,64888.⬆️➡️.

30 ⛺€ 5,10 🔌€ 1 🍽Ch🚿 (8x)€ 1/8h. **Surface:** metalled. 🅾 01/01-
31/12
Distance: 🔌900m ⊗100m.
Remarks: 01/11/- 31/03 no service. Follow centre.

Hannoversch Münden — 10A3

Am Hochbad, Rattwerder. **GPS:** n51,40595 e9,64643.

15 🛏free. **Surface:** asphalted. ◐ 01/01-31/12
Distance: 🚶1,7km.

Hannoversch Münden — 10A3

Am Werraweg. **GPS:** n51,41701 e9,66176.➡.

5 🛏free. **Surface:** metalled. ◐ 01/01-31/12
Distance: 🚶1,5km.

Hannoversch Münden — 10A3

Camping Grüne Insel, Tanzwerder 1. **GPS:** n51,41694 e9,64751.

20 🛏€7 ⚡€ 1 🚰Ch 💧€ 0,50/kWh WC 🚽.
Surface: grassy.
◐ 01/01-31/12
Distance: 🚶100m ⊗150m 🛒150m.
Remarks: Max. 3t.

Tourist information Hannoversch Münden:
ℹ Touristik Naturpark Münden e.V, Rathaus, www.hann-muenden.net/spontan. Old city centre with 430 half-timbered houses.
👁 Boat trip with steamer from Unterer Tanzwerder, close to the motorhome parking. ◐ 01/05-30/09 Tue-Su 10h-11.30h-13h-14.30h-16h, Wed 10-11.30h.

Hardegsen — 10A3

Wohnmobilhafen Steinbreite, Alte Uslarer Straße 1. **GPS:** n51,65093 e9,82267.
⬆.
15 🛏€6 ⚡ 🚰Ch 💧 WC 🚽 🌊. **Surface:** grasstiles. ◐ 01/01-31/12
Distance: 🚶500m.

Haren/Ems — 4A6

Freizeitzentrum Schloss Danken, Rentmeisterstrasse. **GPS:** n52,79724 e7,20530.⬆.

17 🛏€ 10/24h ⚡🚰Ch 💧 (18x) WC 🚽€ 1. **Location:** Rural. **Surface:** grassy/gravel. ◐ 21/03-25/10
Distance: 🚶1km ⚓2,8km 🛒on the spot ⊗on the spot 🛒on the spot 🚲on the spot.

Haren/Ems — 4A6

Schleusenstraße. **GPS:** n52,78873 e7,24705.
15 🛏free. **Surface:** grasstiles. ◐ 01/01-31/12
Distance: 🚶500m🛒550m.

Harsefeld — 5A4

Klosterpark, Kirchenstrasse. **GPS:** n53,45384 e9,50344.⬆➡.

5 🛏free.
Location: Rural, very simple. **Surface:** . ◐ 01/01-31/12
Distance: 🚶100m ⊗100m 🛒100m 🛒100m 🚲on the spot 🏃on the spot.
Remarks: Parking park of monastery, max. 5 days.

Haselünne — 4B6

Plesseparkplatz, Plessestrasse. **GPS:** n52,67210 e7,48865.⬆.

3 🛏free ⚡€ 2/10minutes 🚰Ch WC. **Location:** Urban, noisy. **Surface:** metalled. ◐ 01/01-31/12
Distance: 🚶400m ⊗300m 🛒300m.
Remarks: Parking behind town hall.

Haselünne — 4B6

Lingener Strasse. **GPS:** n52,66778 e7,48222.⬆.

4 🛏free. **Location:** Quit. **Surface:** metalled. ◐ 01/01-31/12
Distance: 🚶400m ⊗400m 🛒400m 🛒100m 🏃on the spot.
Remarks: Parking swimming pool.

Haselünne 4B6

Restaurant Esders-Ab der Hasebrücke, Lingenerstrasse 1. **GPS**: n52,66992 e7,48638.

10 € 10, guests free. **Location:** Urban. **Surface:** metalled.
Distance: 200m on the spot.

Helmstedt 10C1

Am Maschweg. GPS: n52,23535 e11,01128.

25 free. **Surface:** grassy.
Distance: 100m 50m.

Helmstedt 10C1

Brunnentheater, Brunnenweg 6A. **GPS**: n52,23676 e11,06411.

5 free. **Surface:** asphalted. 01/01-31/12

Helmstedt 10C1

Wallplatz. GPS: n52,22833 e11,01417.

3 free. **Surface:** asphalted. 01/01-31/12
Distance: on the spot on the spot.
Remarks: Parking in the centre.

Hermannsburg 5B6

Parkplatz Waldschwimmbad, Lotharstrasse 66. **GPS**: n52,82718 e10,10807.

6 free € 0,50 Ch . **Surface:** metalled. 01/01-31/12
Distance: 500m.
Remarks: Parking at swimming pool.

Hermannsburg 5B6

Schützenplatz, Lotharstraße 75. **GPS**: n52,82787 e10,10963.

40 € 2 Ch. **Surface:** grassy. 01/01-31/12
Distance: 500m.
Remarks: Max. 1 night, service at Waldbad (50m).

Hermannsburg 5B6

Grillplatz Bonstorf, Schulstrasse. **GPS**: n52,86492 e10,05134.

4 free. **Surface:** grassy. 01/01-31/12
Distance: 5km.
Remarks: Parking sports park.

Hermannsburg 5B6

Parkplatz am Feuerwehrhaus, Weesenerstrasse, Weesen. **GPS**: n52,83645 e10,13692.

3 free. **Surface:** grassy. 01/01-31/12
Distance: 500m.
Remarks: Parking fire-station.

Hermannsburg 5B6

Parkplatz Örtzetal- Halle, Lutterweg. **GPS**: n52,83363 e10,09579.

DE

5 ⌇free. **Surface:** metalled. 01/01-31/12
Distance: 100m.

10 ⌇free € 0,50/5minutes € 0,50. Ch. **Surface:** metalled. 01/01-31/12
Distance: 650m 500m 500m.

Hermannsburg 5B6
Lutter Hof, Waldstrasse, Lutter. **GPS:** n52,84188 e10,09894.

Hitzacker 5C5
Bleichwiesen, K36, Elbufferstrasse. **GPS:** n53,15074 e11,04941.

5 ⌇€5 included. **Surface:** grassy. 01/01-31/12

70 ⌇€6 € 1,50/70liter Ch WC.
Surface: metalled. 01/01-31/12
Distance: 200m.
Remarks: Max. 2 nights.

Herzlake 4B6
Hasetal, Im Mersch. **GPS:** n52,68211 e7,60780.

Hohne 5B6
Am Waldbad, Am Schwimmbad 23. **GPS:** n52,59340 e10,37398.
4 ⌇€5 Ch WC included. **Surface:** gravel. 01/01-31/12
Distance: 1km.
Remarks: Use sanitary only during opening hours swimming pool.

Hohnstorf/Elbe 5B4
Wohnmobilstellplatz Hohnstorf, Schulstraße 1. **GPS:** n53,36234 e10,56223.
8 ⌇€8 Ch. **Surface:** metalled. 01/01-31/12
Distance: 500m 500m.
Remarks: Along the river Elbe.

30 ⌇free Ch WC free. **Surface:** grassy. 01/03-30/11
Remarks: Parking sports centre.

Holdorf 9C1
Erholungszentrum Heidesee, Zum Heidesee 53. **GPS:** n52,57696 e8,11533.

Hesel 4B5
Marktplatz, Kirchstrasse. **GPS:** n53,30497 e7,59174.

12 ⌇free Ch free. **Surface:** asphalted. 01/01-31/12
Distance: on the spot 1km.

60 ⌇€4/pp Ch € 2. **Surface:** grasstiles. 01/03-15/10
Distance: 1,5km 3,4km sandy beach on the spot 1,5km.

Hessisch Oldendorf 10A1
Südwall P1, Weserstrasse. **GPS:** n52,16693 e9,25049.

Hollern 5A4
Am Deich, Twielenfleth. **GPS:** n53,60417 e9,55917.

15 ⛽€ 5/0-24h. 🏠 **Location:** Rural.
Surface: metalled. 📅 01/01-31/12
Distance: 🚶200m ✕Imbiss 300m.
Remarks: Along the river Elbe.

⛽S	Holzminden	10A2

Mobilcamping, Stahler Ufer 16. **GPS:** n51,82681 e9,43909. ⬆️.

70 ⛽€ 6,50 🚰€ 1/100liter 🚽Ch 🔌€ 0,60/kWh WC 🚿€ 0,50. **Surface:** grassy. 📅 01/01-31/12
Distance: 🚶1,5km 🏊100m 🚉100m 🚌200m.
Remarks: Bread-service.

⛽S	Hoya/Weser	4D6

Reisemobilstellplatz Weserblick, Stettiner Straße. **GPS:** n52,80106 e9,13987. ⬆️➡️.

10 ⛽voluntary contribution 🚰€ 1/150liter 🚽Ch. **Surface:** grassy/gravel.
📅 01/01-31/12
Distance: 🚶5 min walking 🏊100m 🚉5 min walking.

⛽S	Hude	4C5

Wohnmobilstellplatz Hude, Schützenstrasse. **GPS:** n53,10758 e8,45867. ⬆️➡️.

10 ⛽free 🔌 consumption. **Surface:** gravel. 📅 01/01-31/12
Distance: 🚶on the spot ✕on the spot 🚉400m.
Remarks: Parking swimming pool.

Tourist information Hude:
Ⓜ️ Zisterzienserkloster, Klosterhude.Monastery, 13th century.
⛳ Golf court; the 9 holes-court is accessoe for everyone.

⛽S	Hüde (49448)	9C1

Freizeitarena Dümmer See, Rohrdommelweg 33. **GPS:** n52,50176 e8,35425. ⬆️.

50 ⛽€ 10 🚰🚽Ch 🔌€ 2,50 WC 🚿. **Location:** Rural, quit. **Surface:** grassy.
📅 15/04-15/10
Distance: 🏊150m ✕on the spot.

⛽S	Jade	4C5

Quittenweg, Süderschweiburg. **GPS:** n53,39139 e8,26639. ⬆️.

8 ⛽free 🚰€ 1 🚽Ch 🔌(8x)€ 1/8h. **Surface:** gravel.
Distance: 🚶on the spot ✕1km 🚉800m.

🚲S	Jade	4C5

Melkhus Drei Eichen, Kreuzmoorstrasse 28. **GPS:** n53,31531 e8,23084.

10 ⛽€ 10 🚰🚽Ch 🔌WC included 🚿against payment. **Surface:** gravel/metalled. 📅 01/01-31/12
Distance: 🚉4km.

🍴S	Jade	4C5

Schützenhof, Am Schützenplatz, Vareler Strasse. **GPS:** n53,34111 e8,18667.

30 ⛽guests free 🚰🚽Chfree 🔌€ 1.
Surface: metalled. 📅 01/01-31/12
Distance: 🚶on the spot ✕on the spot 🚉on the spot.

🕐	Jade	4C5

Jaderberg, Tiergartenstrasse 69, Jaderberg. **GPS:** n53,32679 e8,18521.

DE

20 🛏free. **Surface:** gravel. ⬛ 01/01-31/12
Distance: 🛒on the spot ⊗on the spot.
Remarks: Parking Jarderpark, zoo and adventure park.

🛏S   **Jever** 🅿️   4B4
Jahnstrasse, Jever-Nord. **GPS:** n53,57733 e7,89074.⬆️➡️

20 🛏€7 🛒🍽Ch🔌(20x)included.
Surface: metalled. ⬛ 01/01-31/12
Distance: 🚰100m.
Remarks: Sports centre, max. 3 days, coins at petrol station Henn.

Tourist information Jever:
ℹ️ Jever Marketing und Tourismus GmbH, Alter Markt 18, www.stadt-jever.de.
Ⓜ️🍴 Schloßmuseum.Castle, English gardens and museum. ⬛ Tue-Su 10-18h, 01/07-31/08 Mo-Su 10-18h.
Ⓜ️ Frisiesches Brauhaus.Brewery with museum. Guided tour 2 hours, 2 drinks included. ⬛ Mo-Fri 9.30-16.30h, Sa 9.30-12.30h.

🛏S   **Jork** ⚓   5A4
Am Yachthafen, Neuenschleuse. **GPS:** n53,55375 e9,66858.⬆️➡️

18 🛏free 🛒€ 1/90liter 🍽Ch🔌(18x)€ 0,50/kWh WC🚽€ 2. **Location:** Urban. **Surface:** unpaved. ⬛ 01/01-31/12
Distance: 🛒Jork 3km ⊗on the spot 🚲on the spot 🏊on the spot.
Remarks: Along the river Elbe.

🛏S   **Jork** 🅿️   5A4
Festplatz, Schützenhofstrasse/Festplatzweg. **GPS:** n53,53100 e9,68336.⬆️➡️

80 🛏free 🛒€ 1/100liter 🍽Ch WC🚽€ 0,50. **Location:** Rural. **Surface:** metalled. ⬛ 01/01-31/12

Distance: 🛒200m ⊗200m 🚰200m.
Remarks: Parking event ground, max. 24h.

🛏S   **Jork** 🅿️   5A4
Stellplatz Lühe-Anleger, Fährstraße, Grünendeich. **GPS:** n53,57271 e9,63129.⬆️

10 🛏€ 10/24h. **Surface:** gravel. ⬛ 01/01-31/12

🍴S   **Jork** 🅿️   5A4
Stubbe's Gasthaus, Lühe 46. **GPS:** n53,56861 e9,63333.⬆️.

7 🛏€8 🛒€ 2 📶🚿. **Location:** Rural, comfortable. **Surface:** grasstiles. ⬛ 01/01-31/12
Distance: ⊗on the spot.
Remarks: Picnic area Am Gartenteich, bread-service.

🛏S   **Kirchlinteln** 🛝   4D6
Auf dem Kleberhof, Scharnhorster Weg 1. **GPS:** n52,95562 e9,30651.

7 🛏€ 10 🛒🔌(4x) WC🚽included 🚽€ 3.🛒 **Location:** Rural, comfortable, quit. **Surface:** grassy. ⬛ 01/01-31/12
Distance: 🛒3,5km 🍴6km ⊗3,5km 🚰3,5 km.
Remarks: Bread-service.

🛏S   **Königslutter am Elm**   10C1
P1 Niedernhof, Amtsgarten. **GPS:** n52,25009 e10,81996.⬆️.
5 🛏free 🛒🔌free. **Surface:** grasstiles. ⬛ 01/01-31/12

🛏S   **Krummendeich**   4D3
Stellplatz Krummendeich, Schulweg 107. **GPS:** n53,83145 e9,20231.⬆️➡️

5 🛏free WC€ 0,50 🚽€ 0,50. **Location:** Rural. **Surface:** gravel. ⬛ 01/01-31/12
Distance: 🏊100m 🚰300m.

🛏S   **Krummhörn** 🌼🛝   4A4
Parkplatz Greetsieler Zwillingsmühlen, Mühlenstrasse 3, Greetsiel. **GPS:** n53,49711 e7,10181.

DE

50 🛏€ 10 🚰€ 2 🗑Ch 🚿 (40x)€ 1/8h.
Surface: gravel. 🅿 01/01-31/12
Distance: 🚶250m.

Lamspringe		10B2

Am Bahnhof. **GPS:** n51,95404 e10,00656. ⬆➡.

3 🛏free. **Surface:** gravel. 🅿 01/01-31/12
Distance: 🚶750m 🚊400m 🚏250m.

S	Lautenthal	10B2

Kaspar Bitter Strasse 7b. **GPS:** n51,87020 e10,28729.

25 🛏€ 4 + € 2 Kurtaxe 🚰€ 1 🗑Ch€ 1 🚿 (10x)€ 1/6h. **Surface:** gravel.
🅿 01/01-31/12
Distance: 🚶300m 🚊300m 🚏500m 🚌50m.

S	Leer	4B5

Am Hafen, Nessestrasse. **GPS:** n53,22527 e7,45472. ⬆➡.

10 🛏free WC€ 0,50 🗑€ 1. **Location:** Urban, very simple. **Surface:** asphalted/
gravel. 🅿 01/01-31/12
Distance: 🚶500m 🚊300m 🚏2km.
Remarks: Sanitary at offices Bruchbrücke, caution sanitary € 30.

S	Leer	4B5

P9, Grosse Bleiche. **GPS:** n53,22577 e7,44686. ⬆.

6 🛏free 🚰€ 1/100liter 🗑€ 1 Ch 🚿 (6x)€ 1/24h WC€ 0,50 🗑€ 1.
Location: Urban. **Surface:** metalled. 🅿 01/01-31/12
Distance: 🚶200m 🚫on the spot 🚏2km.
Remarks: Sanitary at offices Bruchbrücke, caution sanitary € 30.

	Leer	4B5

Hallen- und Freibad, Burfehnerweg 32. **GPS:** n53,23927 e7,44998. ⬆.

10 🛏free.
Location: Urban, very simple. **Surface:** metalled. 🅿 01/01-31/12
Distance: 🚶on the spot 🚫on the spot 🚏1km.

S	Leer	4B5

Windmühlenhof Eiklenborg, Logabirumer Straße, Logabirum. **GPS:** n53,24745
e7,51582. ⬆.
5 🛏€ 11 🚰🗑Ch 🚿WC🗑€ 2. **Surface:** grassy/metalled. 🅿 01/01-31/12
Remarks: Near old Dutch windmill.

	Leese	9D1

Loccumer straße. **GPS:** n52,50272 e9,11733. ⬆.

4 🛏free. **Surface:** metalled. 🅿 01/01-31/12
Distance: 🚶200m 🚫on the spot 🚏200m.

S	Leese	9D1

Rasthaus Leeser Tanger, Bahlweg. **GPS:** n52,49372 e9,12055. ⬆.

8 🛏€ 15, discount for clients 🚰 🚿 🗑included. **Surface:** metalled. 🅿
01/01-31/12
Distance: 🚶800m 🚫on the spot.

	Lembruch	9C1

Stellplatz Dümmer-See Lembruch, Seestraße. **GPS:** n52,52439 e8,36703. ⬆.

DE

20 ⚑free. **Location:** Rural. **Surface:** grassy. ◙ 01/01-31/12
Distance: ⛴300m ⊗100m.

| ⒸⓈ | Lembruch 🏕〰 | 9C1 |

Campingplatz Seeblick, Birkenallee. **GPS:** n52,52583 e8,36056.⬆.

16 ⚑free 🚰€ 1 🔌Ch 💧(16x)€ 0,50/kWh. **Location:** Rural. **Surface:** gravel. ◙ 01/01-31/12
Distance: 🚶1km on the spot 🚲on the spot.
Remarks: Max. 3 days.

| ⚑Ⓢ | Lüdersfeld | 9D1 |

Heinrichs'Reisemobil Stellplatz, Am Hülsebrink 10+11. **GPS:** n52,35972 e9,25512.⬆.
30+15⚑€6 🚰🔌Ch💧. **Surface:** metalled.
Remarks: Bread-service.

| ⚑Ⓢ | Lüneburg | 5B5 |

Am Sülzwiesen, Pieperweg. **GPS:** n53,24556 e10,39694.⬆.

20 ⚑€9 🚰🔌Ch on camp site. **Location:** Rural. **Surface:** grassy. ◙ 01/01-31/12
Distance: ⛴50m ⊗50m.
Remarks: Max. 1 night.

| ⚑Ⓢ | Lemwerder | 4C5 |

Reisemobilhafen Peter-Baxmann-Platz, Schulstrasse 44. **GPS:** n53,15784 e8,61783.⬆➡.

50 ⚑€8/24h 🚰€ 1 🔌Ch💧€ 1/8h. ◙ 01/01-31/12
Distance: ⚑300m.
Remarks: Max. 1 night.

| ⚑Ⓢ | Mardorf | 10A1 |

Wohnmobilstellplatz Steinhuder Meer, Rote-Kreuz-Strasse 16. **GPS:** n52,48704 e9,30065.⬆➡.

50 ⚑€3 🚰🔌Ch💧(50x)free. **Surface:** gravel.
Distance: 🚶on the spot ⊗on the spot ⚑500m.

| ⚑ | Lemwerder | 4C5 |

Vulkanparkplatz, Uferweg. **GPS:** n53,17000 e8,60028.⬆.

60 ⚑€6 🚰€ 1/100liter 🔌Ch💧(60x)€ 3. **Surface:** grassy. ◙ 01/01-31/12
Distance: 🚶1km ⛴300m ⊗1km.
Remarks: Bread-service.

| ⚑ | Melle | 9C1 |

Am Wellenbad 43. GPS: n52,20497 e8,32368.⬆.

5 ⚑free. **Surface:** metalled. ◙ 01/01-31/12
Distance: 🚶1km 🚶on the spot ⊗1km ⚑1km.

| ⚑Ⓢ | Lingen/Ems | 9B1 |

Linus Bad, Teichstrasse. **GPS:** n52,51863 e7,30606.⬆➡.

10 ⚑free.
Location: Very simple, quit. **Surface:** metalled. ◙ 01/01-31/12

DE

Distance: 🚶on the spot 🚲1,2km ⊗nearby 🛒300m.
Remarks: Parking swimming pool.

📷S | **Meppen** | **4A6**

Reisemobilplatz am Hallenbad, An der Bleiche. **GPS:** n52,69107 e7,28399.⬆️.

10 🚐€ 6 2 pers, swimming pool incl ⛽€ 2/100liter 🗑Ch 🚿 (4x)€ 1/12h.
Surface: metalled. 🅿 01/01-31/12
Distance: 🚶200m ⊗on the spot 🛒300m.
Remarks: Parking swimming pool, max. 2 nights.

Tourist information Meppen:
⛺ 🕐 Tue-Sa morning.

📷S | **Moormerland** | **4B5**

Am Rathausplatz, Theodor Heussstrasse 12, Warsingsfehn. **GPS:** n53,31062 e7,48618.⬆️➡️.

5 🚐free. **Surface:** metalled. 🅿 01/01-31/12
Distance: 🚶50m ⊗250m 🛒50m 🚰50m.
Remarks: Parking townhall, max. 3 nights.

🍴S | **Moormerland** | **4B5**

Bei Cassi, Deichlandstraße 10, Rorinchem. **GPS:** n53,32010 e7,35473.⬆️➡️.

17 🚐guests free ⛽🗑Ch 🚿free.
Surface: gravel. 🅿 01/01-31/12
Distance: ⊗on the spot.
Remarks: Restaurant is closed on Monday.

📷S | **Neuharlingersiel** | **4B4**

Wohnmobilstellplatz am Ostanleger, Am Hafen Ost. **GPS:** n53,70173 e7,70741. ⬆️.
23 🚐€ 12 ⛽🗑Ch 🚿included. 🚻 **Surface:** metalled. 🅿 01/01-31/12
Distance: 🚶500m 🏖800m.
Remarks: Max. 3 nights.

📷S | **Neuharlingersiel** | **4B4**

Neuharlingersiel, Alt Addenhausen 4. **GPS:** n53,69580 e7,69021.⬆️.

8 🚐€ 10-12, tourist tax incl ⛽🗑Ch 🚿 included. **Surface:** metalled. 🅿 01/01-31/12
Distance: 🚶800m 🏖sandy beach 1km.
Remarks: Max. 1 night.

📷S | **Nienburg** | **4D6**

Reisemobilstellplatz Nienburg/Weser, Oyler Straße. **GPS:** n52,64094 e9,20137. ⬆️➡️.

18 🚐€ 5 ⛽€ 1/120liter 🗑Ch 🚿 (12x)€ 1/8h.
Surface: gravel. 🅿 01/01-31/12
Distance: 🚶10 min walking 🏖on the spot 🚲on the spot ⊗300m 🛒500m.
Remarks: Along the river Weser.

📷S | **Norddeich** 🌿⛳🏄 | **4A4**

Reisemobilhafen Ocean Wave, Itzendorferstrasse/Dörperweg. **GPS:** n53,61073 e7,15649.⬆️➡️.

50 🚐€ 13/24h, 2 pers., incl. 50% discount Erlebnisbad Ocean Wave ⛽🗑Ch 🚿 (47x) WC🔲. **Surface:** metalled. 🅿 01/01-31/12
Distance: 🚶100m 🏖100m 🚲100m 🛒500m 🚰100m.

📷S | **Norddeich** 🌿⛳🏄 | **4A4**

Womo Park Norddeich, Deichstraße 24. **GPS:** n53,60166 e7,13527.⬆️.

48 🚐€ 9,50, tourist tax excl ⛽€ 1/100liter 🗑Ch 🚿€ 1/2kWh WC🔲.
Surface: gravel. 🅿 01/01-31/12
Distance: 🚶2km 🏖beach 1,5km, beach (dogs allowed) 1km ⊗on the spot 🛒500m 🚰100m.
Remarks: Bread-service.

Tourist information Norddeich:
ℹ️ Tourist Information Norddeich, Dörper Weg 22, www.norddeich.de.

Norden 🍲 4A4
Am Hafen. **GPS:** n53,59055 e7,21176.⬆️.

3 🚐 parking paid, free overnight stay. **Surface:** metalled. ⬛ 01/01-31/12
Distance: 🚶100m ⊗100m 🚆100m.

🚐S Nordenham 4C4
Freizeitbad Störtebeker, Atenser Allee. **GPS:** n53,49472 e8,47444.⬆️➡️.

10 🚐 free 🚰🗑️Ch 💧(8x)free 🗑️€ 2, at sauna.
Surface: grasstiles.
Distance: 🚶on the spot ⊗on the spot 🚆on the spot.
Remarks: Bread-service.

🚐S Nordholz 4C4
Wuster Strasse 12, Spieka. **GPS:** n53,75772 e8,59409.⬆️.

5 🚐free 🚰€ 1/100liter 🗑️€ 1 Ch 💧(5x)€ 1/2kWh. **Location:** Rural.
Surface: metalled.
Distance: 🚶on the spot ⊗100m.

🚐S Nordhorn 🍲 9A1
Vechtesee, Heseperweg. **GPS:** n52,43683 e7,08190.⬆️.

35 🚐€5 🚰€ 1/100liter 🗑️Ch 💧€ 1/5h. 🏠 **Location:** Rural. **Surface:** grassy. ⬛ 01/01-31/12
Distance: 🚶400m ⊗300m 🚆300m 🚲on the spot 🚶on the spot.

🚐S Northeim 10B3
In der Fluth. **GPS:** n51,70766 e10,00597.⬆️.

20 🚐free. **Surface:** gravel. ⬛ 01/01-31/12
Distance: 🚶300m.
Remarks: Max. 24h.

🍽️ Northeim 10B3
Grosser Freizeitsee, Am Nordhafen. **GPS:** n51,72920 e9,96286.

30 🚐free. **Surface:** gravel. ⬛ 01/01-31/12
Distance: 🚶5km ⊗on the spot 🚆2km.

🚐S Oberndorf/Oste 4D4
Wohnmobilplatz Bentwisch, Hoffmann-von-Fallersleben-Straße 10. **GPS:** n53,75398 e9,15054.⬆️➡️.

8 🚐€5 🚰€ 2/100liter 🗑️Ch 💧(6x)€ 2/8h WC€ 0,50 🗑️€ 0,50.
Location: Rural, comfortable. **Surface:** grassy/gravel. ⬛ 01/01-31/12
Distance: 🚶2km 🏖️100m 🚆100m 🚲on the spot.

🚐 Oldenburg 🍲 4C5
Am Küstenkanal, Westfalendamm. **GPS:** n53,12927 e8,21465.⬆️.

3 🚐free.
Location: Rural, very simple. **Surface:** gravel. ⬛ 01/01-31/12
Distance: 🚶on the spot ⛵1km 🏖️on the spot ⊗100m 🚆400m.
Remarks: Alternative: in front of campsite Am Flötenteich, 53,166944 8,235, 2 pitches free.

Tourist information Oldenburg:
ℹ️ Oldenburg Tourismus und Marketing GmbH, Wallstrasse 14, www.oldenburg-tourist.de.Historical city centre.
Ⓜ️ Horst-Janssen-Museum.Modern museum concerning living and working Horst Janssen, 1929-1995, drawer and graphic artist. ⬛ Tue-Su 10-18h. 🎫 €

3,50, family card € 7.

🅂 **Osnabrück** 🌿🏕🍴 **9C1**

Schlosswallhalle, Heinrichstrasse. **GPS:** n52,27074 e8,03953.⬆️

8 📷€5 🚰€ 1/100liter 🗑Ch.🚻 **Location:** Urban. **Surface:** asphalted. ◻ 01/01-31/12
Distance: 🚶on the spot ⊗300m 🚊300m.

🅂 **Osnabrück** 🌿🏕🍴 **9C1**

Wohnmobilplatz Netebad, Im Haseesch 6. **GPS:** n52,30470 e8,05413.⬆️

5 📷€5 🚰€ 1/100liter 🗑Ch.🧹€ 1/10h. 🚻 **Location:** Urban, quit.
Surface: grassy/metalled. ◻ 01/01-31/12
Distance: 🚃on the spot.
Remarks: Max. 48h.

🅂 **Osnabrück** 🌿🏕🍴 **9C1**

Natruper Straße / Nobbenburger Straße. **GPS:** n52,28116 e8,03651.
📷€5. **Surface:** metalled. ◻ 01/01-31/12
Distance: 🚶1,5km.

Tourist information Osnabrück:
ℹ️ Tourist Information, Bierstrasse 22-23, www.osnabrueck.de.

🅂 **Osten** **4D4**

Festhalle, Altendorf 13. **GPS:** n53,69602 e9,18813.⬆️➡️

5 📷€5 🗑Ch.🧹(2x)included.🚿 **Location:** Rural, very simple. **Surface:**
metalled. ◻ 01/01-31/12
Distance: 🚶on the spot ⊗on the spot 🚊500m.
Remarks: Pay at Hotel Fährkrug.

🅂 **Osterholz-Scharmbeck** **4D5**

August Schlüter Turnhalle, Lange Strasse. **GPS:** n53,22562 e8,79000.⬆️➡️

4 📷free 🚰€ 1 🗑. **Location:** Urban, very simple, central. **Surface:** metalled.
◻ 01/01-31/12

🅲🅂 **Osterode** **10B2**

Waldcampingplatz Eulenburg, Scheerenberger Straße 100. **GPS:** n51,72868
e10,28638.
13 📷€8 🚰🗑Ch.🧹 WC 🗑 🛜. ◻ 01/01-31/12
Distance: 🚶2km.

🅂 **Ostrhauderfehn** **4B5**

Reisemobilhafen Ostrhauderfehn, Hauptstrasse 115. **GPS:** n53,13872
e7,62318.⬆️

20 📷€5 🚰🗑Ch.🧹(12x)€ 1/2kWh WC 🗑€ 0,50 🔲.🚿
Surface: asphalted.
◻ 01/01-31/12 ⚫ during fair in June.
Distance: 🚶100m ⊗100m 🚊100m.
Remarks: Sanitary at bar, caution sanitary € 10.

🅂 **Otterndorf** **4D3**

Parking Mitte, Jahnstrasse. **GPS:** n53,80861 e8,89444.⬆️➡️

8 📷free. **Location:** Rural. **Surface:** metalled. ◻ 01/01-31/12
Distance: 🚶on the spot ⊗200m.

🍴🅂 **Otterndorf** **4D3**

Seglertreff, Schleuse 5. **GPS:** n53,82250 e8,89472.⬆️

12 📷free, 01/04-31/10 € 7,00 🚰🗑Ch.🧹€ 2,50/24h WC 🗑.🚿
Location: Rural, comfortable. **Surface:** metalled. ◻ 01/01-31/12
Distance: 🚶2km 🏊50m 🚣on the spot ⊗on the spot 🚊2km 🚲on the spot
🚶on the spot.

🅂 **Ottersberg** 4D5

Am Sportzentrum, Fährwisch. **GPS**: n53,10721 e9,13558.⬆️
8 🏕free 🚰€ 1 Ch 🔌€ 1/8h.
Surface: gravel/sand. ⬛ 01/01-31/12
Distance: 🚶500m ⊗200m.

🅂 **Ovelgönne** ⚓ 4C5

Burgdorf Ovelgönne, Am Sportplatz. **GPS**: n53,34333 e8,42750.⬆️

5 🏕free 🚰🔌Ch 🔌free. **Surface**: gravel. ⬛ 01/01-31/12
Distance: 🚶700m ⊗700m 🍴700m.

🅲🅂 **Oyten** ⚓🚣 4D5

KNAUS Reisemobilpark, Oyter See 1. **GPS**: n53,04645 e9,00396.

20 🏕€ 12-15 🚰€ 2,20 🍴Ch 🔌€ 0,70/kWh WC ⊋included 🔲 📶€ 1 ♨🚿🚮
Location: Rural, comfortable. **Surface**: metalled. ⬛ 01/04-01/11
Distance: 🚶2,5km 🚲3km 🏊Oyter See 150m.
Remarks: Caution key € 10.

🅂 **Papenburg** 4B5

Roten Kreuz, Rathausstraße. **GPS**: n53,07646 e7,39266.
30 🏕free. **Surface**: gravel. ⬛ 01/01-31/12
Distance: 🚶on the spot ⊗300m.

🅲🅂 **Papenburg** 4B5

Poggenpoel, Zum Poggenpoel. **GPS**: n53,06526 e7,42630.⬆️➡️

20 🏕€ 8 🚰€ 3/100liter 🔌€ 3 Ch 🔌(8x)€ 2/24h WC ⊋€ 2 ♨🚿
Location: Rural. **Surface**: gravel. ⬛ 01/01-31/12
Distance: 🚶3,5km 🏊Badesee.
Remarks: At lake, max. 3 nights.

🅂 **Rehburg-Loccum** 9D1

Wohnmobilstellplatz Rehburg, Auf der Bleiche. **GPS**: n52,47370 e9,23227.⬆️
➡️

8 🏕€ 5 🔌€ 1/12h. **Surface**: gravel. ⬛ 01/01-31/12
Distance: 🚶400m.
Tourist information Rehburg-Loccum:
👀 Dinosaurierpark Münchehagen.Attractions park around the dinosaur. ⬛ 28/02-30/11 10h, summers 9h.

🅂 **Remels** 4B5

Remelser Paddel- & Pedalstation, Raiffeissenstrasse/Uferstrasse. **GPS**: n53,30123 e7,75151.⬆️

5 🏕€ 5 🚰🔌Ch 🔌(4x)€ 2. **Surface**: metalled. ⬛ 01/01-31/12
Distance: 🚶500m 🚲50m 🏊500m.
Remarks: Max. 3 days, canoe and bicycle rental.

🅂 **Remels** 4B5

Schützenplatz, Schützenstraße. **GPS**: n53,30719 e7,74708.⬆️➡️

10 🏕€ 5 🚰🔌Ch 🔌€ 1/12h. **Surface**: grasstiles. ⬛ 01/01-31/12 🔘
10/06-15/06.
Distance: 🚶500m.
Remarks: Max. 3 nights.

🅂 **Rhauderfehn** 🚣 4B5

Paddel- und Pedalstation, Am Siel 8. **GPS**: n53,13878 e7,58689.⬆️➡️

16 🏕€ 5 🚰€ 1/100liter 🍴Ch 🔌(16x)€ 1/8h WC ⊋€ 2. 🚐 **Location**: Rural, luxurious, quit. **Surface**: grassy. ⬛ 01/01-31/12
Distance: 🚶500m 🏊on the spot 🚲on the spot ⊗50m.
Remarks: Caution sanitary € 10, canoe and bicycle rental.

🅂 **Rhede/Ems** 4A5

Emspark, Am Sportplatz 6. **GPS**: n53,05853 e7,27621.⬆️

DE

5 🛏 free. **Location:** Very simple. **Surface:** metalled. ⬛ 01/01-31/12
Distance: 🚶500m ⊗500m 🛒500m.
Remarks: Parking in front of sports park.

🛏 S **Rinteln** 9D1
Reisemobilplatz am Weseranger, Dankerser strasse. **GPS:** n52,19226 e9,07842.
⬆➡.

50 🛏 free ⛽€ 2/100liter 🚻€ 2 Ch🚽 2 ⚡(36x)€ 0,50/kWh. **Location:**
Rural. **Surface:** asphalted/gravel. ⬛ 01/01-31/12
Distance: 🚶1km 🏊on the spot 🚿on the spot ⊗100m 🛒400m 🚌400m
🚲Weserradweg 🎣on the spot.

🛏 S **Rodewald** 5A6
Am Freibad, Im Zentrum. **GPS:** n52,66369 e9,48020.⬆.

10 🛏 free ⚡(10x)€ 0,50/kWh. **Surface:** grasstiles. ⬛ 01/01-31/12
Distance: 🛒200m 🚌on the spot.

🛏 S **Rotenburg (Wümme)** 5A5
Am Weichelsee, Bremer Straße. **GPS:** n53,11960 e9,38230.⬆➡.

20 🛏 € 2,50 ⛽€ 2 🚻Ch ⚡(20x)€ 2.🚿🚲 **Location:** Rural. **Surface:**
metalled. ⬛ 01/01-31/12
Distance: 🚶2km 🏊on the spot ⊗Strandhaus 🚌2km 🎣on the spot.
Remarks: Check in at StrandHouse.

🛏 S **Salzgitter** 10B1
Reisemobilstellplatz am Salzgittersee, Zum Salzgittersee. **GPS:** n52,15222
e10,31306.
12 🛏 free ⛽€ 2/100liter 🚻Ch ⚡€ 1/6h. **Surface:** grassy/metalled.
Distance: 🚶1km 🏊on the spot ⊗nearby 🚌200m.

Remarks: Max. 4 days.
🛏 S **Salzhausen** 5B5
Am Waldbad. **GPS:** n53,22199 e10,17841.
6 🛏 free ⛽🚻Ch ⚡free. **Surface:** gravel.
Distance: 🚶1km.

Salzhemmendorf 10A2
Naturerlebnisbad Lauenstein, Landstrasse, Hemmendorfer. **GPS:** n52,07952
e9,57124.⬆.
3 🛏 € 5. **Surface:** asphalted. ⬛ 01/01-31/12
Distance: 🚶500m.

🛏 S **Salzhemmendorf** 10A2
Ith-Sole-Therme, In der Saale-Aue. **GPS:** n52,07093 e9,58564.⬆.

20 🛏 € 5 ⛽€ 0,20/20liter 🚻€ 1 Ch ⚡€ 0,50/kWh. **Surface:** metalled.
⬛ 01/01-31/12
Distance: 🚶400m.

Salzhemmendorf 10A2
Rasti-land, Quanthofer strasse 9. **GPS:** n52,09706 e9,66451.

5 🛏 free. **Surface:** metalled.
Distance: 🚶1km.
Remarks: Bus parking amusement park.
Tourist information Salzhemmendorf:
🎡 Rasti-Land, Quanthofer strasse 9.Amusement park. ⬛ 01/04-31/10 10-
17/18h, Apr, Sep: Mo, Sa, Su.

🛏 **Sande (Nieder-Sachsen)** 4B4
Am Markt. **GPS:** n53,50251 e8,01113.⬆.

4 🛏 free. **Surface:** metalled. ⬛ 01/01-31/12
Distance: 🚶100m ⊗100m 🛒100m.

🛏 **Sande (Nieder-Sachsen)** 4B4
Sander See. **GPS:** n53,51162 e8,00206.⬆.

DE

4 🛏free. **Surface:** metalled. ⬛ 01/01-31/12
Distance: 🚶2km.

| | S | Sande (Nieder-Sachsen) | 4B4 |

Fa. Freizeitmobile von der Kammer, Huntestraße 1. **GPS:** n53,49076 e8,02292.
⬆.

5 🛏free ⬛Ch 🔌On demand. **Surface:** gravel.

| | S | Sandstedt | 4C5 |

Wohnmobilstellplatz Sandstedt - Sandstedt

info@hagen-cux.de - www.hagen-cux.de

Beautiful view
Paved and flat motorhome pitches
Located near marina

Wohnmobilstellplatz Sandstedt, Am Radarturm 5. **GPS:** n53,36317 e8,51231.
10 🛏free ⬛€ 1/100liter ⬛€ 1 Ch€ 1 ⬛€ 1. **Surface:** metalled. ⬛
01/04-30/09
Distance: 🚶500m ⬛ 3km ⬛100m ⬛950m ⊗100m.

| | S | Saterland | 4B5 |

Reisemobilhafen am Maiglöckchensee, Am Sportplatz, Scharrel. **GPS:**
n53,07060 e7,70116. ⬆➡.

28+7 🛏€4 ⬛€ 1/100liter ⬛€ 1 Ch€ 1 ⬛(28x)€ 2/24h WC⬛€ 0,50
⬛€ 2.⬛ **Location:** Rural, luxurious, quit. **Surface:** grassy. ⬛ 01/01-31/12
Distance: 🚶300m ⬛50m ⬛50m ⊗1km ⬛500m ⬛500m.

| | S | Saterland | 4B5 |

Reisemobilplatz Am Bootshafen, Hauptstrasse 640, Strücklingen. **GPS:**
n53,12819 e7,66762. ⬆.

15 🛏€ 3 ⬛€ 1/100liter ⬛€ 1 Ch⬛€ 1,50/24h WC⬛€ 1 ⬛€ 0,50. ⬛
Location: Rural. **Surface:** grassy/gravel. ⬛ 01/01-31/12
Distance: 🚶100m ⬛on the spot ⬛on the spot ⊗on the spot ⬛on the spot
⬛100m.

| | S | Scharnebeck | 5B5 |

Wohnmobilstellplatz Am Schiffshebewerk, Adendorfer Straße 40. **GPS:**
n53,29196 e10,49320. ⬆.

15 🛏€ 6/24h ⬛€ 1 ⬛Ch⬛ (8x)€ 1/8h. **Location:** Urban. **Surface:**
metalled.
Distance: 🚶1km ⊗200m ⬛Aldi 400m.
Remarks: Boat lift Scharnebeck, climbing wall 100m.

| | S | Schneverdingen | 5A5 |

Am Quellenbad, Inseler Straße. **GPS:** n53,13110 e9,77280. ⬆➡.

20 🛏free ⬛€ 2 ⬛Ch WC⬛€ 1. **Location:** Urban. **Surface:** grassy. ⬛
01/01-31/12
Distance: 🚶2km ⬛on the spot ⬛on the spot 🧍on the spot.
Remarks: Use sanitary only during opening hours swimming pool.

| | S | Schneverdingen | 5A5 |

Wohnmobilhafen Lüneburger Heide, Badeweg 3, Heber. **GPS:** n53,07104
e9,86481. ⬆.

38 🛏€ 12 ⬛€ 1 ⬛Ch ⬛ (38x)included WC⬛ Use sanitary € 2/pp ⬛.
⬛ ⬛

Location: Rural, comfortable. **Surface:** grassy. ☐ 01/04-31/10
Distance: 🚿on camp site 🚰 on the spot 🎣 on the spot.
Remarks: Use sanitary facilities at campsite.

| 🛁 S | Schneverdingen 🏕 🛶 🌳 | 5A5 |

Parkplatz Festhalle, Im Osterwald. **GPS:** n53,11893 e9,80681. ⬆.

4 🚐 free. **Location:** Very simple. **Surface:** metalled. ☐ 01/01-31/12
Distance: 🚲2km 🚿2km.
Remarks: Entrance via Festhalle.

| 🅿 S | Schneverdingen 🌳 🛶 🌲 | 5A5 |

Reisemobilhafen Lüneburgheide, Badeweg 3, Heber. **GPS:** n53,07108 e9,86464. ⬆.

5 🚐 €12 🔌 🗑 Ch 🚿(5x) WC 🧺 🗑€ 2,50. 🛒 🧺 **Location:** Rural,
luxurious, quit. **Surface:** grasstiles/metalled. ☐ 01/04-31/10
Distance: 🚲5km 🚿on camp site.
Remarks: Sanitary at campsite.

| 🅿 S | Schneverdingen 🌳 🛶 🌲 | 5A5 |

Mariechens Hoff, Voßbarg 15, Reinsehlen. **GPS:** n53,17122 e9,83316. ⬆ ➡.

8 🚐 €8 🔌 🗑 Ch included 🚿(8x)€ 0,40/kWh. 🛒 **Location:** Rural, isolated,
quit. **Surface:** grassy. ☐ 01/01-31/12
Distance: 🚲7km 🚴15km ⊗3km 🚿4 km on the spot 🎣 on the spot.

| 🅿 S | Schöppenstedt | 10C1 |

Elm-Asse-Platz, Schützenplatz am Berge. **GPS:** n52,14756 e10,77737. ⬆.

15 🚐 free. **Surface:** asphalted. ☐ 01/01-31/12
Remarks: Parking next to sports ground and swimming pool.

Tourist information Schöppenstedt:

ℹ The region of Till Eulenspiegel. Tills-Tauf-Tour: cycle and hiking routes in the
country of Jester Till, start at the Till Eulenspiegel museum. ☐ Tue-Fri 14-17h,
Sa-Su 11-17h.
Ⓜ Till Eulenspiegelmuseum, Nordstrasse 4a. ☐ Tue-Fri 14-17h, Sa-Su 11-17h
☐ Mo.

| 🅿 | Schortens | 4B4 |

Aqua-toll, Beethovenstrasse. **GPS:** n53,53961 e7,93780. ⬆ .

2 🚐 free. **Surface:** metalled. ☐ 01/01-31/12
Distance: 🚿200m 🚰25m.
Remarks: Parking swimming pool.

| 🍴 | Schortens | 4B4 |

Reisemobilstellplatz Fair-Cafe, Accumer Strasse 5. **GPS:** n53,55226 e7,97624.

3 🚐 guests free. **Surface:** unpaved. ☐ 01/01-31/12
Distance: 🚲3km 🏊100m.

| 🅿 S | Schulenberg | 10B2 |

Wiesenbergstrasse. **GPS:** n51,83535 e10,43464. ⬆.

30 🚐 €5 + €1,20/pp 🔌 1 🗑 Ch 🚿(6x)€ 0,60/kWh. WC ☐ 01/01-
31/12
Distance: ⊗on the spot.
Remarks: Parking centre, view on Okerstausee.

| 🅿 S | Schüttorf | 9A1 |

Am Kuhmplatz, Graf-Egbert-Straße. **GPS:** n52,32123 e7,22642. ⬆.

10 🚐 free 🔌 🗑 Ch free.
Location: Rural. **Surface:** gravel. ☐ 01/01-31/12
Distance: 🚴2,4km 🚿100m.

DE

Remarks: Parking swimming pool.

🏊 **Schwanewede** 4C5
Am Markt, Am Markt. **GPS:** n53,22412 e8,59644. ⬆.

3 🅿free.
Location: Very simple, central. **Surface:** metalled. ⬛ 01/01-31/12
Distance: 🚶on the spot ⊗on the spot 🛒on the spot.

🏊 **Schwanewede** 4C5
Brücke zu Harriersand, Inselstraße. **GPS:** n53,26489 e8,49762. ⬆.

5 🅿free. **Location:** Rural, very simple, isolated. **Surface:** grassy. ⬛ 01/01-31/12
Distance: 🚶7km.

🏊 **Schwanewede** 4C5
Löhnhorst, Hammersbeckerweg/Am Fosshall. **GPS:** n53,20355 e8,62453. ⬆.

2 🅿free. **Location:** Rural, very simple, isolated, quit. **Surface:** metalled. ⬛ 01/01-31/12
Distance: 🚶6km ⊗6km 🛒6km.

🏊 **Schwanewede** 4C5
Wohnmobilstellplatz, Klint, Neuenkirchen. **GPS:** n53,23670 e8,50919. ⬆.

5 🅿free. **Location:** Rural, very simple, quit. **Surface:** unpaved. ⬛ 01/01-31/12
Distance: 🚶500m.
Remarks: Dead end street.

🏁S **Selsingen** 5A4
Wohnmobilstation, Im Sick. **GPS:** n53,42764 e9,50764. ⬆➡.

25 🅿free 🚰 Chfree. **Location:** Rural, very simple, quit. **Surface:** metalled. ⬛ 01/01-31/12
Distance: 🚶500m 🛒100m.

🏁S **Sittensen** 5A5
Parkplatz, Mühlenstrasse. **GPS:** n53,27652 e9,50750. ⬆.

5 🅿free 🚰 Ch WC free. **Location:** Central. **Surface:** metalled. ⬛ 01/01-31/12
Distance: 🚶centre ⊗200m 🚲on the spot 🚶on the spot.

Soltau 5A5
Soltau Therme, Stubbendorffweg. **GPS:** n52,99301 e9,84443.

10 🅿free.
Location: Central, quit. **Surface:** metalled. ⬛ 01/01-31/12
Distance: 🚶1km ⊗on the spot 🚲on the spot 🚶on the spot.
Remarks: Max. 1 night.

Soltau 5A5
Heidepark, Parking bij pretpark. **GPS:** n53,02166 e9,87370.

100 🅿€5. 🚻
Location: Rural, very simple, isolated.
Surface: grasstiles. ⬛ 01/01-31/12
Remarks: Parking amusement park.

Tourist information Soltau:
ℹ Small town at the border of the Lüneburg Heath.
Heidepark. Amusement park. ⬛ 01/04-31/10 9-18h, 01/07-15/08 Sa 9-21h.

🏁S **Spieka-Neufeld** 4C3
Wohnmobilhafen, Deichweg. **GPS:** n53,78899 e8,55060. ⬆.

40 ⌂ € 8 ⌂ € 1/100liter ⚡Ch ⚡ (18x)€ 1/2kWh. **Location:** Rural.
Surface: gravel/metalled. ◻ 01/01-31/12
Distance: ⌂300m ⊗on the spot ⌂on the spot ⊗200m.
Remarks: Bread-service.

| 🚐S | St.Andreasberg | 10C2 |

Panoramabad, Braunlagerstrasse. **GPS:** n51,71683 e10,52891.⬆.

20 ⌂ € 8 ⌂ ⚡Ch ⚡ (20x) WC ⬜included. **Surface:** asphalted. ◻ 01/01-31/12
Distance: ⌂750m ⊗50m ⌂750m ⚡2km.

| 🚐S | St.Andreasberg | 10C2 |

Silbererzgrube Samson, Am Samson 4. **GPS:** n51,71398 e10,51625.
20 ⌂ € 10 ⌂ ⚡Ch ⚡ included. **Surface:** gravel. ◻ 01/01-31/12

| 🚐S | Stade 🛒 | 5A4 |

Wohnmobilstellplatz Am Schiffertor, Schiffertorsstrasse 21. **GPS:** n53,60278 e9,46667.⬆➡.

79 ⌂ € 8,50/24h ⌂ € 1/80liter ⚡Ch ⚡ € 0,50/kWh.🚐
Location: Urban, central.
Surface: gravel. ◻ 01/01-31/12
Distance: ⌂500m ⊗700m.
Tourist information Stade:
ℹ Tourist Information am Hafen, Hansestrasse 16.Renovated Hanseatic harbour.

| 🚐S | Stadland 🛒 | 4C4 |

Am Sportplatz, Hauptstrasse, Seefeld. **GPS:** n53,45639 e8,35778.

5 ⌂free ⌂ € 1/10minutes ⚡ (4x)€ 1/8h. **Surface:** asphalted. ◻ 01/01-31/12

Distance: ⌂on the spot ⊗on the spot ⌂on the spot.

| 🚐S | Stadland 🛒 | 4C4 |

Birkenweg, Kleinensiel. **GPS:** n53,44194 e8,47444.

4 ⌂free ⌂ ⚡Chfree. **Surface:** metalled. ◻ 01/01-31/12
Distance: ⌂on the spot.
Remarks: At community centre.

| 🚐S | Stadland 🛒 | 4C4 |

Deichparkplatz, Fährstrasse, Kleinensiel. **GPS:** n53,44250 e8,47833.⬆.

5 ⌂free ⌂ € 1 ⚡. **Surface:** gravel. ◻ 01/01-31/12
Distance: ⚓200m Weserstrand.

| 🚐S | Stadland 🛒 | 4C4 |

Rathausplatz, Am Markt, Rodenkirchen. **GPS:** n53,39944 e8,45444.⬆.

10 ⌂free ⌂ € 1/10minutes ⚡Ch ⚡ (4x)€ 1/8h. **Surface:** metalled. ◻ 01/01-31/12 🅿 Thu 5-13h.
Distance: ⌂on the spot ⊗on the spot ⌂on the spot 🚐on the spot.

| 🚐S | Stadthagen | 9D1 |

Reisemobilplatz am Tropicana, Jahnstraße 2. **GPS:** n52,32236 e9,18896.⬆.
⌂free ⌂ ⚡Ch ⚡ WC ⬜ 📶against payment. **Surface:** metalled. ◻ 01/01-31/12

| 🚐S | Stadtoldendorf | 10A2 |

Mobilcamping unter dem Homburg, Linnenkämper Strasse 33. **GPS:** n51,87777 e9,63500.⬆➡.

30 ⌂ € 5/day ⌂ € 1 ⚡. **Surface:** grassy. ◻ 01/01-31/12
Distance: ⌂1km ⊗50m ⌂1km.

DE

Steinfeld 9C1

Zur Schemder Bergmark, Dammer Strasse. **GPS:** n52,58308 e8,21476. ↑ →

20 ⌁ free ⌁ € 1/100liter Ch. **Location:** Rural, quit. **Surface:** metalled. ⬤ 01/01-31/12
Distance: 500m 500m.
Remarks: Parking swimming pool.

Steinhude 10A1

Wohnmobilstellplatz Steinhude, Am Bruchdamm. **GPS:** n52,44874 e9,35478. ↑

180 ⌁ € 7,50 ⌁ € 1 Ch (60x)€ 3/day WC ⌁ € 1 ⬤ washing machine/dryer € 2,50.
Surface: grassy. ⬤ 01/01-31/12
Distance: 500m 500m ⊗500m 500m ⬤ on the spot.
Remarks: Max. 3 nights, bread-service. Altenhagen > Steinude.

Tourist information Steinhude:
ℹ Marina on lake of the same name.

Steyerberg 4D6

Waldferienpark Steyerberg, Zum Ferienpark 37. **GPS:** n52,57395 e9,01096. ↑

40 ⌁ € 5 ⌁ € 1 Ch € 2 WC ⌁ € 2. **Surface:** metalled. ⬤ 01/01-31/12
Distance: 1km ⊗1km 1km.

Steyerberg 4D6

Gasthaus Zur Eiche, Sarninghausen 2. **GPS:** n52,56944 e8,99444. ↑ .

15 ⌁ guests free ⌁. **Surface:** grassy. ⬤ 01/01-31/12

Stolzenau 9D1

Reisemobilstellplatz Stolzenau, Weserstrasse. **GPS:** n52,51021 e9,08104. ↑ →

33 ⌁ € 4 ⌁ € 1 Ch (24x)€ 2/12h. **Surface:** grasstiles. ⬤ 01/03-30/09
Distance: 250m on the spot on the spot ⊗300m 300m.
Remarks: Along the Weser river.

Sulingen 4D6

Am Stadtsee, Kornstraße. **GPS:** n52,67653 e8,80127. ↑

10 ⌁ free ⌁ € 1/5minutes ⌁ € 1 Ch € 1. **Surface:** metalled. ⬤ 01/01-31/12
Distance: 600m 300m.

Surwold 4B5

Erholungsgebiet Surwolds Wald, Waldstrasse. **GPS:** n52,96743 e7,51535. ↑

20 ⌁ € 5 ⌁ € 1/100liter Ch € 2 WC ⌁ € 0,50. **Surface:** grassy. ⬤ 01/01-31/12
Distance: 800m ⊗250m.

Surwold 4B5

Privatplatz Klapper, Papenburgerstrasse 57. **GPS:** n53,01774 e7,48470. ↑

10 ⌁ € 10 ⌁ Ch (4x)€ 1/24h WC ⌁ € 2. **Location:** Rural. **Surface:** grassy. ⬤ 01/01-31/12
Distance: 1km 1,5km ⊗1km 1km.
Remarks: Swimming pool and picnic area available.

Tarmstedt 4D5

Landtechniek Grabau, Bahnhofstraße. **GPS:** n53,22421 e9,08728. ↑ →

15 ⑤ € 6 ⚡🔧 Ch 💧 included. 🚲 **Surface:** metalled. 🚰 01/01-31/12
Distance: 🚉on the spot ⊗500m 🍴on the spot.

Thedinghausen 4D6
Reisemobilstellplatz Thedinghausen, Braunschweiger Straße. **GPS:** n52,96188 e9,03020.🔼.

8 ⑤free ⚡€ 1 🔧Ch 💧€ 1/6h WC.
Surface: metalled. 🚰 01/01-31/12
Distance: 🚉500m 🏄on the spot 🍴on the spot.

Twist 4A6
Am Hallenbad. **GPS:** n52,64719 e7,08918.🔼.
6 ⑤free ⚡€ 1/100liter 🔧Ch 💧(8x)€ 1/2kWh. **Surface:** metalled. 🚰 01/01-31/12
Distance: 🚉on the spot 🏊on the spot.
Remarks: Barefoot path.

Uchte 9D1
Balkenkamp. **GPS:** n52,49761 e8,90618.🔼.

3 ⑤free ⚡€ 1 🔧Ch. **Surface:** metalled. 🚰 01/01-31/12
Distance: 🚉100m ⊗500m 🍴100m.

Uelsen 9A1
Festplatz, Hardinghauserstrasse. **GPS:** n52,49575 e6,88840.🔼➡.

10 ⑤free ⚡€ 2 🔧Ch WC. **Surface:** asphalted. 🚰 01/01-31/12

Uelzen 5B5
Im Sportboothafen, Riedweg 7. **GPS:** n52,95722 e10,59444.🔼.
8 ⑤ € 8 + € 0,50/pp ⚡€ 1/90liter 🔧Ch 💧€ 1/12h WC 🚿 washing
machine/dryer € 2,50. **Surface:** metalled. 🚰 01/01-31/12

Distance: 🍴1,9km.
Remarks: Playground, free bicycles available, max. 3 nights.

Undeloh 🏕🌳👥 5A5
Am Naturschutzpark, Wilseder Straße. **GPS:** n53,19253 e9,97709.

30 ⑤ € 3/day, € 6/night. 🏠 **Location:** Rural, very simple. **Surface:** unpaved. 🚰 01/01-31/12
Distance: 🚉500m ⊗100m 🚶on the spot.
Remarks: In nature reserve the the Lüneburg Heide (heath).

Uslar 10A3
Reisemobilpark am Badeland, Zur Schwarzen Erde. **GPS:** n51,66715 e9,62824. 🔼➡.

20 ⑤€ 6 + reduction swimming pool ⚡€ 1/10minutes 🔧Ch 💧€ 1/8h WC 🚽. **Surface:** metalled. 🚰 01/01-31/12
Distance: 🚉1km 🏊on the spot.

Uslar 10A3
Am Lindenhof, Lindenhof 1. **GPS:** n51,67213 e9,62952.
5 ⑤first night € 8, € 2 each additional night ⚡🔧Ch 💧€ 0,30/kWh. 🚰 01/01-31/12

Tourist information Uslar:
ℹ Touristik Information, Mühlentor 1,, www.uslarer-land.de.Historical little
town with half-timbered houses.
🛍 Market, city centre. 🚰 Fri 9-13h.
🦋 Alaris Schmetterlingspark.Butterfly park in tropical rain forest. 🚰 01/04-
31/10 Tue-Su 9.30-17.30h.
🌲 Erlebniswald.Educational park, discovering nature. 🚰 01/01-31/12.
🏊 Uslarer Badeland.Swimming pool complex. 🚰 Sa/Su 10-18h, Tue-Fri 10-
20h, Mo 10-13h.

Vechta 4C6
Am Hallenwellen- und Freibad, Dornbusch. **GPS:** n52,74000 e8,29639.🔼.

10 ⑤free. **Location:** Urban, very simple. **Surface:** grassy/metalled. 🚰 01/01-31/12
Distance: 🚉1km ⊗1km 🍴1km.
Remarks: Parking swimming pool, max. 3 days, service Bokenerddamm 40.

Vechta 4C6
Oldenburgerstraße. **GPS:** n52,73245 e8,28833.🔼.

5 🛏free.
Location: Urban, very simple. **Surface:** metalled. 🅾 01/01-31/12
Distance: 🚶on the spot ⊗on the spot 🍴on the spot.

22 🛏 € 15,80 🚰 ⚡Ch 🚿 WC 🚮included. **Surface:** concrete. 🅾 01/04-30/10
Distance: 🚶600m 🏊on the spot.

🏕🅂 **Visselhövede** 5A5

🅂 **Wangerland** 4B4

Zu den Visselwiesen, Wüstenhof 1. **GPS:** n52,98530 e9,57772. ⬆➡.

An der Ostdüne, Bäderstrasse, Hooksiel. **GPS:** n53,64103 e8,03514. ⬆➡.

8 🛏free.
Location: Urban, very simple. **Surface:** metalled. 🅾 01/01-31/12
Distance: ⊗100m 🍴200m.

75 🛏€ 10 + € 2,90/pp Kurtaxe, dogs € 3,10 🚰 ⚡Ch 🚿 WC 🚮 📶included. **Surface:** gravel. 🅾 01/04-30/10
Distance: 🚶1,7km 🏊beach ±250m.

🅒🅂 **Walchum** 👪 4A6

🅂 **Wangerland** 4B4

Marinapark Emstal, Steinbilder Straße. **GPS:** n52,92680 e7,29624.

Nordsee-Camping-Schillig, Jadestraße, Schillig. **GPS:** n53,69986 e8,02338. ⬆➡.

10 🛏€ 10 🚰 ⚡Ch 🚿(6x) WC 🚮€ 1,50. ♿ **Location:** Rural. **Surface:** grassy. 🅾 01/01-31/12
Distance: 🎣fishing permit obligatory ⊗300m 🍴on the spot 🐎 on the spot 🚶on the spot.

60+150 🛏€ 10 + € 2,90/pp Kurtaxe, dogs € 3,10 🚰 ⚡ Ch 🚿 WC 🚮 📶included. **Surface:** grassy. 🅾 01/04-31/10
Distance: 🚶200m.

🏕🅂 **Walsrode** 5A6

🅂 **Wardenburg** 4C5

Forellenhof, Hünzingen 3. **GPS:** n52,89855 e9,59122.

Keilstrasse, Astrup. **GPS:** n53,04770 e8,21197. ⬆.

10 🛏€ 10 🚰 🚿 (2x). ♿ 🏪 **Location:** Rural, isolated, quit. **Surface:** grasstiles/grassy.
Distance: 🚶3km ⊗on the spot 🍴3km.
Remarks: Free with a meal.

Tourist information Walsrode:
🌐 Vogelpark Walsrode.Bird park and botanical garden. 🅾 01/03-31/10 8-19h.

5 🛏free 🚿 (3x). **Location:** Urban, very simple. **Surface:** gravel. 🅾 01/01-31/12
Distance: ✈2,5km.

🅂 **Wardenburg** 4C5

🅂 **Wangerland** 4B4

Marktplatz, Huntestraße. **GPS:** n53,06401 e8,19832. ⬆➡.

Am Yachthafen, Zum Hafen, Horumersiel. **GPS:** n53,68293 e8,02091. ⬆➡.

3 ⌂free.
Location: Urban, very simple. **Surface:** metalled. ⬛ 01/01-31/12
Distance: ⬇on the spot ➹3,6km.

🖥🅂 **Weener** ⚓🌊 4B5
Am Alten Hafen, Panneborgstrasse. **GPS:** n53,16953 e7,36167.⬆.

45 ⌂€ 7,50/24h ⛲€ 1/100liter 🚽Ch ➹(45x)€ 2,50/24h WC⬚€ 1.🚐
Location: Urban, comfortable. **Surface:** asphalted. ⬛ 01/01-31/12 ⬤ during harbor festival 3rd week of June.
Distance: ⬇on the spot ⊗on the spot ⬛on the spot.
Remarks: Max. 3 days.

🖥 **Weener** ⚓🌊 4B5
Am Yachthafen, Am Marina-Park. **GPS:** n53,16570 e7,36480.⬆➡.
24 ⌂€ 7,50 ➹€ 2,50 ⬚€ 2. **Surface:** metalled. ⬛ 01/04-30/09
Distance: ⬇centre ±1,2km ⊗50m.

🖥🅂 **Werlte** 4B6
Kreutzmanns Mühle, Kirchstraße. **GPS:** n52,85463 e7,68155.⬆.

6 ⌂free ⛲€ 1/100liter 🚽Ch ➹(8x)€ 1/2kWh. **Location:** Urban, comfortable. **Surface:** metalled. ⬛ 01/01-31/12
Distance: ⬇200m ⊗200m ⬛200m.

🖥🅂 **Westergellersen** 5B5
Turniergelände Luhmühlen, Westergellerser Heide. **GPS:** n53,23306 e10,21623. ⬆➡.

35 ⌂€ 8 ⛲€ 1 🚽Ch ➹(35x)€ 1/8h WC⬚.🚿 **Location:** Rural, comfortable, isolated, quit. **Surface:** grassy. ⬛ 01/01-31/12
Distance: ⬇4km ⤓1,5km ⊗4km ⬛4km 🚃2km.

🖥🅂 **Westerholt** 4B4
Am Schul- und Sportzentrum, Ewigsweg. **GPS:** n53,59089 e7,44907.
5 ⌂free ⛲🚽Chfree. **Surface:** metalled. ⬛ 01/01-31/12
Distance: ⬇500m ⬛600m.

🖥 **Westerstede** 4B5
Albert-Post-Platz, Auf der Lohe. **GPS:** n53,25883 e7,92685.
5 ⌂free. **Surface:** metalled. ⬛ 01/01-31/12
Distance: ⬇100m ➹2km ⊗250m.

🖥 **Westerstede** 4B5
Badesee Karlshof, Bekassinenweg. **GPS:** n53,18708 e7,87529.⬆.
5 ⌂free. **Surface:** gravel. ⬛ 01/01-31/12
Distance: ⤓Badesee.
Remarks: Max. 3 days.

🅲🅂 **Westerstede** 4B5
Wohnmobilhafen Westerstede, Süderstraße 2. **GPS:** n53,24968 e7,93438.⬆.
50 ⌂€ 5 ⛲🚽Ch ➹€ 2 WC⬚ Use sanitary ⛲euro ➹ 2,50. **Surface:** grassy/gravel. ⬛ 01/01-31/12
Distance: ⬇800m ➹1,4km ⊗McDonalds 200m.

🖥🅂 **Westoverledingen** 4B5
Rathausplatz, Bahnhofstrasse 18, Ihrhove. **GPS:** n53,16634 e7,45173.⬆➡.

3 ⌂free ⛲€ 1/100liter 🚽Ch. **Location:** Urban. **Surface:** grassy. ⬛ 01/01-31/12 ⬤ last week Jun.
Distance: ⬇on the spot ⊗50m.
Remarks: At townhall.

🍴🅂 **Westoverledingen** 4B5
Reisemobilhafen zur Mühle, Mühlenstrasse 214, Steenfelderfehn. **GPS:** n53,12944 e7,44051.⬆➡.

30 ⌂€ 5 ⛲🚽Ch ➹(18x)included. 🚿 **Location:** Rural. **Surface:** grassy/metalled. ⬛ 01/01-31/12
Distance: ⊗on the spot ⬛1km.

🍴🅂 **Westoverledingen** 4B5
Schützenplatz Flachsmeer, Papenburger strasse 74, Flachsmeer. **GPS:** n53,12700 e7,46367.⬆➡.

10 ⌂€ 5 ⛲🚽 ➹(10x)included. 🚿 **Location:** Rural. **Surface:** grassy. ⬛ 01/01-31/12
Distance: ⊗on the spot 🚃100m.

S Wiefelstede 4C5
Wohnmobilstellplatz am Bernsteinsee, Dorfstrasse 11, Conneforde. **GPS**: n53,32657 e8,06362.⬆➡.

25 €6 € 0,50 Ch € 0,50 WC € 0,50 . **Surface:** grassy. 01/01-31/12
Distance: on the spot on the spot.
Remarks: In front of campsite.

S Wiefelstede 4C5
Freibad Wiefelstede, Alter Damm 11. **GPS**: n53,26146 e8,10713.
10 free. **Surface:** metalled. 01/01-31/12
Distance: 500m on the spot 1,5km.

S Wiesmoor 4B4
Bootshafen Ottermeer, Am Stadion. **GPS**: n53,40951 e7,71841.⬆➡.

14 €5,50 Ch € included. **Surface:** grassy/metalled. 01/01-31/12
Distance: 1,5km.
Remarks: Key service at Gastätte (12-19h).

S Wietzendorf 5A6
Übernachtungsoase Südsee Camp, Südsee camp 1. **GPS**: n52,93120 e9,96474.⬆.

40 €12 € 1/100liter € 0,50/kWh WC€ 0,50.
Surface: metalled.
Distance: nearby on the spot.

S Wildeshausen 4C6
Am Krandel, Krandelstrasse. **GPS**: n52,90042 e8,42728.⬆➡.

16 €5 € 1/80liter Ch (15x)included. **Location:** Rural.
Surface: grassy/metalled. 01/01-31/12
Distance: 500m 4,4km 400m 700m.
Remarks: Parking at swimming pool.

S Wilhelmshaven 4C4
Wohnmobilhafen Nautimo, Friedenstrasse 99. **GPS**: n53,53546 e8,10104.⬆➡.

25 €7 € 1 Ch (16x)€ 1/8h € 1. **Surface:** metalled. 01/01-31/12
Distance: 2km on the spot 800m.
Remarks: Max. 7 days.

S Wilhelmshaven 4C4
Wohnmobilstellplatz Schleuseninsel, Schleussenstrasse 37. **GPS**: n53,51478 e8,15218.⬆.

28 €8, trailer €5 € 0,50/50liter Ch (28x)€ 3/24h WC.
Surface: gravel. 01/01-31/12
Distance: 250m Jadebus.

S Wilhelmshaven 4C4
Am Freibad Nord, Möwenstraße 30. **GPS**: n53,57032 e8,10368.⬆➡.

6 €3,50, free with use of swimming pool Ch € 1/6h WC.
Surface: gravel. 01/05-31/08
Distance: 1,5km.
Remarks: Use sanitary only during opening hours swimming pool.

S Wilhelmshaven 4C4
Reisemobilstellplatz Wilhelmshaven Südstadt, Banterweg 12. **GPS**: n53,51559 e8,09072.⬆.

15 ⅀ € 8 ⌇ ⬛ Ch ⚓ 🔊. **Surface:** gravel. ⬛ 01/01-31/12

🛏 Wilhelmshaven ⚘⛵🌊 **4C4**

Fliegerdeich. GPS: n53,50996 e8,12718.⬆.

40 ⅀ € 5.
Surface: asphalted. ⬛ 01/01-31/12
Distance: 🚶2,5km ⛱sea ⊗nearby.
Remarks: No camping activities.

Tourist information Wilhelmshaven:

ℹ Wilhelmshaven Touristik & Freizeit GmbH, Südstrand 108, www.whv-touristik.de.Large port city with the touristic centre Südstrand.
👁 Aquarium Wilhelmshaven, Südstrand.Sea aquarium. ⬛ 10-18h.
👁 Oceanis, Am Bontekai.Virtual under water station; museum and aquarium. ⬛ 10-18h.
Ⓜ Deutsches Marinemuseum, Südstrand 125. ⬛ 10-19h, 01/10-31/03 10-17h. Ⓣ € 7,50, family card € 18.
Ⓜ Piratenmuseum, Eberstrasse 88 A.History of the piracy. ⬛ 01/04-31/10 11-17h.

🛏 Winsen/Luhe **5B4**

Festplatz Bleiche, Tönnhäuserweg. **GPS:** n53,36600 e10,21200.

10 ⅀free. **Surface:** asphalted. ⬛ 01/01-31/12
Distance: 🚶100m ⊗100m 🛒100m.

🛏S Winsen/Luhe **5B4**

Freizeit Center Albrecht, Porchestrasse 15, Gewerbegebiet Lühdorf. **GPS:** n53,33750 e10,21947.⬆.
11 ⅀free ⌇ € 2 ⬛Ch ⚓ (11x) WC. **Location:** Rural. **Surface:** metalled. ⬛ 01/01-31/12
Distance: 🚶4,5km ♨on the spot.

🛏S Wittmund **4B4**

Hafen Harlesiel, Am Harlesiel. **GPS:** n53,70853 e7,80888.⬆➡.

54 ⅀ € 10-13 + € 2 Kurtaxe ⌇ ⬛ Ch ⚓ € 3 WC ⅃. **Surface:** metalled. ⬛ 15/03-31/10
Distance: ⛱on the spot.
Remarks: Caution key electricity € 10.

🛏 Wittmund **4B4**

Schützenplatz, Auricherstrasse. **GPS:** n53,55763 e7,69156.
30 ⅀free. **Surface:** grassy. ⬛ 01/01-31/12
Distance: 🚶800m 🛒bakery 200m.

⊙S Wolfsburg **10C1**

Autostadt, Berliner Brücke. **GPS:** n52,43436 e10,79947.
20 ⅀ € 10 ⌇ ⬛Ch ⚓ included. **Surface:** asphalted. ⬛ 01/01-31/12

Tourist information Wolfsburg:

☺ Autostadt.Of the Volkswagen-concern; with pavilion of several car makes, car tower of 20 floors, test driving. ⬛ 9-20h.

🛏S Zetel ⛵🌊 **4B4**

Johann Quathamer, Fuhrenkampstrasse 60. **GPS:** n53,40366 e7,92032.
15 ⅀ € 7 ⌇ ⬛ Ch ⚓ WC included ⅃ € 0,50. **Surface:** grassy. ⬛ 01/01-31/12
Distance: 🚶4km.

🛏S Zetel ⛵🌊 **4B4**

Markthamm, Neuenburger Strasse. **GPS:** n53,41706 e7,97000.⬆.
40 ⅀free ⌇ ⬛Ch free. **Surface:** grasstiles. ⬛ 01/01-31/12
Distance: ⊗Imbiss.
Remarks: Parking centre, max. 2 days, service open: Mo/Tue 11-23h, Thu/Sa 11-23h, Su 16-23h.

🛏S Zetel ⛵🌊 **4B4**

Driefeler Esch. GPS: n53,42128 e7,99554.
10 ⅀free. ⬛ 01/01-31/12
Remarks: Parking swimming pool, max. 48h.

🛏S Zetel ⛵🌊 **4B4**

Schulmuseum Bohlenbergerfeld, Wehdestrasse. **GPS:** n53,41322 e7,92143.⬆.
25 ⅀free. **Surface:** grassy/gravel. ⬛ 01/01-31/12

🛏S Zetel ⛵🌊 **4B4**

Urwald, Urwaldstrasse, Neuenburg. **GPS:** n53,39326 e7,99006.
20 ⅀free. ⬛ 01/01-31/12
Remarks: Max. 1 day.

S Zetel ⛵🌊 **4B4**

Kläranlage, Mohrstrasse. **GPS:** n53,42302 e7,97937.
⌇⬛Ch free. ⬛ 01/01-31/12
Remarks: Mo/Thu 7-16h, Fri 7-13h, Sa/Su 9-9.30h.

🛏 Zeven **4D5**

Viehmarkt, Meyerstrasse/Godenstedterstrasse. **GPS:** n53,29764 e9,27514.⬆➡.

4 ⅀free. **Location:** Very simple. **Surface:** metalled. ⬛ 01/01-31/12
Distance: 🚶500m.

🛏S Zeven **4D5**

Mobile Freizeit, Zum Hochkamp 2. **GPS:** n53,27735 e9,29388.⬆.

DE

30 € 5 € 1/100liter Ch (30x) WC included € 2
Location: Rural, comfortable. **Surface:** grassy/gravel. 01/01-31/12**Distance:** 1,5km 10km 1,5km 100m on the spot.**Remarks:** Caution key shower € 2,50.

Mecklenburg-Western Pomerania

Ahlbeck 6C2

Caravanplatz Am Wiesenrand, Gothenweg 5a. **GPS**: n53,94100 e14,17600.

24 € 10, peak season € 12,50 Ch € 2 WC € 1 € 3, dryer € 3. **Surface:** grassy. 01/03-31/10
Distance: 10min 10min 500m 200m.
Remarks: Bread-service.

DE

Ahlbeck 6C2

Wohnmobilstellplatz Rauthe, Waldstrasse 7. **GPS**: n53,93660 e14,18660.

30 € 15 Ch WC € 2 € 4.
Surface: grassy. 01/01-31/12
Distance: on the spot 5 min 200m 200m.

Ahlbeck 6C2

Parkplatz an der Grenze, Swinemüdestrasse. **GPS**: n53,92380 e14,21280.

30 € 5. **Surface:** metalled. 01/01-31/12
Distance: 3km.
Remarks: Max. 24h.

Ahrenshoop 6A2

Dorfstraße. **GPS**: n54,39155 e12,43914.

€ 7,50 day/€ 7,50 night. **Surface:** gravel. 01/01-31/12
Distance: 2km beach 50m.

Alt Schwerin 6A4

Insel Camping Werder, Wendorf 8. **GPS**: n53,48696 e12,31833.

13 € 9,80 Ch € 2 washing machine/dryer € 3. **Surface:** grassy. 01/01-31/12
Distance: 4km on the spot on the spot on the spot.

Altwarp 6D3

Hafen, Seestrasse. **GPS**: n53,73905 e14,27147.

40 € 11 Ch WC included . 01/01-31/12
Distance: on the spot 300m on the spot 300m 400m.

Anklam 6C3

Wasserwanderrastplatz, Demminer strasse. **GPS**: n53,85610 e13,67870.

5 € 5. **Surface:** metalled. 01/01-31/12
Distance: 500m on the spot.

Bansin 6C2

Waldparkplatz Bansin. **GPS**: n53,99800 e14,11260.

80 ⬛€ 4/5 + € 2,50/pp 🚰🚿Ch 🔌€ 2 WC ⬛€ 1. **Surface:** metalled. ⬛ 01/05-31/09

Distance: 🚶3km 🏖400m ⊗300m 🚊on the spot.

| ⬛S | **Bansin** | 6C2 |

Caravanstellplatz Jürgen Wille, Seestrasse 30. **GPS:** n53,96560 e14,13670.➡

9 ⬛€ 9 + € 4/pp 🚰🚿Ch 🔌€ 0,40/kWh WC ⬛€ 1 🔲 washing machine/dryer € 3 📶€ 2,50/h. **Surface:** grassy. ⬛ 01/01-31/12

Distance: 🚶200m 🏖800m.

| ⬛S | **Bansin** | 6C2 |

Udo Labahn, Seestrasse 35. **GPS:** n53,96520 e14,13510.⬆

5 ⬛€ 5 🚰 🔌€ 0,40/kWh. ⬛ 01/01-31/12

Distance: 🚶300m 🚊300m.

| 🍴 | **Banzkow** | 5D4 |

Lewitz Mühle, An der Lewitzmühle 40. **GPS:** n53,52094 e11,50496.⬆

10 ⬛€ 20. **Surface:** asphalted. ⬛ 01/01-31/12

Distance: ⊗on the spot 🚊2km 🚶5 min.

| ⬛S | **Bargeshagen** | 5D2 |

Firma Caravaning Nord, Rabenhorster Damm 3. **GPS:** n54,11198 e11,97174.➡

10 ⬛€ 10 🚰🚿Ch 🔌included. **Surface:** grassy. ⬛ 01/01-31/12

Distance: 🚶3km 🚊2km.

Remarks: Arrival < 18h, Sa < 13h.

| ⬛S | **Barth** | 6A2 |

Segelverein, Am Westhafen. **GPS:** n54,37130 e12,72510.

20 ⬛€ 10 🚰🚿Ch 🔌€ 2 WC ⬛€ 1. **Surface:** grassy. ⬛ 01/05-01/10

Distance: 🚶on the spot 🏖on the spot 🚊on the spot.

| ⬛ | **Barth** | 6A2 |

Wohnmobilparkplatz Barth, Am Osthafen. **GPS:** n54,36870 e12,77770.⬆

30 ⬛€ 7. **Surface:** metalled. ⬛ 01/01-31/12

Distance: 🚶on the spot.

| CS | **Beckerwitz** | 5C3 |

Ostseecamping Beckerwitzer Strand, Haus 2a. **GPS:** n53,94137 e11,31682.⬆➡

16 ⬛€ 12, Jul-Aug € 16 🚰🚿Ch 🔌 WC ⬛included 🔲. **Surface:** grassy. ⬛ 01/04-15/10

Distance: 🏖on the spot.

Bergen/Rügen — 6B1

Wohnmobilstellplatz Rügen - Bergen auf Rügen

info@ruegen-mobile.de - www.wohnmobil-stellplatz-ruegen.de

Paved and flat motorhome pitches
Ideal base for walking and cycling
Open all year

Wohnmobilstellplatz Rügen, Tilzower Weg 32A. **GPS:** n54,40757 e13,42949.

16 € 12 € 1/60liter Ch (16x), WC included € 2/6minutes
€ 4. **Surface:** metalled. 01/01-31/12
Distance: 1,5km 400m 500m 100m.
Remarks: Bread-service.

Binz — 6B1
Wohnmobil-Oase Rügen, Proraer Chaussee 60. GPS: n54,44819 e13,56181.

150 € 10, Jul/Aug € 13 € 1 € 1 Ch € 1/1kWh WC € 0,50 €
0,50 washing machine/dryer € 4. **Location:** Luxurious, isolated, quit.
Surface: grassy/gravel. 01/04-31/10
Distance: Binz 5km 10 min 700m on the spot.
Remarks: Bread-service.

Binz — 6B1
Parkplatz Zentrum, Proraer Chaussee 8. **GPS:** n54,40278 e13,60194.

60 € 14/24h, € 3/2h € 1/50liter Ch included WC € 1. **Surface:**
grassy/metalled. 01/01-31/12
Distance: on the spot 50m on the spot.
Remarks: In the centre, parking next to Elf petrol station.

Bobitz — 5C3
Wohnmobilpark Rastplatz No. 6, Wismarsche strasse 6. **GPS:** n53,79451 e11,34458.

40 € 6, 2 pers.incl € 1 Ch € 2.
Surface: grassy. 01/01-31/12
Distance: 2km 2km 2km.

Boiensdorf — 5D3
Am Strand, Werder. **GPS:** n54,02412 e11,54744.

€ 7 Ch WC € 0,30. **Surface:** grassy. 01/01-31/12
Distance: on the spot on the spot 50m.

Boltenhagen — 5C3
Krämer's Wohnmobilhafen, Ostsee-allee 58b. **GPS:** n53,98122 e11,21908.

45 Apr/Oct € 12 Nov/Mar € 10/2 pers incl. Ch € 2,50 WC .
01/01-31/12
Distance: 800m 200m 200m on the spot 700m on the spot.
Remarks: Bread-service in sommer period.

Boltenhagen — 5C3
Wohnmobilpark Boltenhagen, Ostsee-allee 58. **GPS:** n53,98133 e11,21854.

50 € 13 + € 2,10/pp Ch € 2 WC included € 1 .
Surface: grassy. 01/01-31/12
Distance: 700m 200m 200m on the spot 700m.

Boltenhagen — 5C3
Regenbogen Boltenhagen, Ostseeallee 54. **GPS:** n53,98196 e11,21714.

DE

20 ⌱ € 20 🛠 ⚡ WC ⎈ included 🔲.
Surface: grassy/metalled.
🅾 01/01-31/12
Distance: 🚶600m ⚓200m ⛵200m ⊗on the spot ⛽700m 🚂on the spot.
Remarks: Max. 1 night.

⊙S Boltenhagen 🏖️🚤 5C3
Swin Golf Boltenhagen, Ausbau 15, Redewisch. **GPS:** n54,00851 e11,17180.⬆️

10 ⌱ € 10 🛠 ⚡ € 2. **Surface:** grassy. 🅾 01/04-31/10
Distance: ⚓on the spot.

Tourist information Boltenhagen:
ℹ️ Kurverwaltung, Ostseeallee 4, www.boltenhagen.de. Bathing resort in holiday region. Many biking possibilities.

⊔ Brenz 5D4
Landhaus Böttcher, Parchimer strasse 11. **GPS:** n53,38364 e11,66271.
5 ⌱ € 10, guests free.
Distance: 🚶on the spot 🏊3km ⊗on the spot ⛽5km.

⊔S Broock 5D4
Hotel-Restaurant Am Worns-Berg, Am Worns-Berg 1. **GPS:** n53,46734 e12,10698.⬆️

6 ⌱ € 5/pppn, guests free 🛠 ⛽Ch ⚡ € 2 WC ⎈ € 1,50. **Surface:** gravel.
🅾 01/01-31/12
Distance: 🚶5km ⚓1,5km ⛵1,5km ⊗on the spot ⛽5km 🚂500m.

⊔S Buchholz 6A4
Gasthof Zum Storchennest, Dorfstrasse 7. **GPS:** n53,27814 e12,64035.⬆️
15 ⌱ € 10 🛠 ⛽Ch ⚡ WC included. **Surface:** grassy. 🅾 01/01-31/12
Distance: 🚶5km ⚓300m ⛵300m on the spot ⛽10km.

⊔S Carpin 6B4
Landgasthof Am Schlesersee, Hauptstrasse 25. **GPS:** n53,35424 e13,24028.⬆️

---

10 ⌱ € 5, guests free 🛠 ⚡ WC included.
Surface: metalled. 🅾 01/01-31/12
Distance: 🚶500m ⚓on the spot ⛵on the spot ⊗on the spot ⛽4km.

⊗ Dabitz 🚤 6A2
Hafen Dabitz, Boddenstraße. **GPS:** n54,36217 e12,80610.

⌱ € 6/night. **Surface:** gravel.
Distance: 🚶500m ⚓on the spot.

⊔S Dalwitz 6A3
Ferien Gut Dalwitz, Dalwitz 46. **GPS:** n53,93484 e12,53830.⬆️

2 ⌱ € 10 🛠 € 1 ⚡ WC ⎈🔲 washing machine/dryer € 3 📶. **Surface:** grassy. 🅾 01/01-31/12
Distance: 🚶15km ⊗on the spot ⛽on the spot.
Remarks: Parking estate.

⊔S Dassow 5C3
Reisemobilplatz Ostseestrand, Straße des Friedens 14, Rosenhagen. **GPS:** n53,96195 e10,93944.⬆️

5 ⌱ € 10 🛠 ⛽Ch ⚡ € 3 WC ⎈ € 3. 📍 **Location:** Rural, comfortable, quit.
Surface: grassy. 🅾 01/01-31/12
Distance: ⚓500m ⊗on the spot.
Remarks: At Café Strandgut.

⊙S Dobbertin 5D4
Campingplatz Am Dobbertiner See, Am Zeltplatz 1. **GPS:** n53,61868 e12,06440.⬆️

DE

10 ⌁ € 10, 2 pers.incl ⌐⌐🔲 Ch ⚡€ 0,50/kWh.
Surface: grassy.
🅾 01/04-31/10
Distance: 🏊500m ⚓on the spot ⛟on the spot ⊗500m 🛒500m 🚏500m.

Dömitz 5C5
Campingpark Marina Dömitz, An der Schleuse 1. **GPS**: n53,14078 e11,25908.

26 ⌁ € 10 ⌐⌐🔲 Ch ⚡ WC ⊒included. **Surface:** grassy/metalled. 🅾
01/01-31/12
Distance: 🏊400m ⚓20m 🛒20m ⊗100m 🛒800m.

Dömitz 5C5
Dömitzer Hafen, Hafenplatz 3. **GPS**: n53,13805 e11,26015.

22 ⌁ € 5 ⌐⌐🔲 Ch ⚡ WC ⊒against payment.
Surface: grassy. 🅾 01/01-31/12
Distance: 🏊1km ⚓10m 🛒10m ⊗200m 🛒800m 🚏600m.

Dranske/Bakenberg 6B1
Küstencamp, Nonnevitz 23. **GPS**: n54,66288 e13,26929. ➡️

18 ⌁ € 15 ⌐⌐🔲 Ch ⚡ WC ⊒🅾.
Distance: ⚓400m 🛒400m ⊗100m 🛒800m.
Remarks: Bread-service.

Eldena 5D5
Bootshafen und Campingplatz Eldena, Am Bootshafen 1. **GPS**: n53,23163 e11,42422.

12 ⌁ € 10,50 ⌐⌐🔲 Ch ⚡ WC ⊒🅾against payment. **Surface:** grassy. 🅾
01/01-31/12
Distance: 🏊400m ⚓10m 🛒10m ⊗50m 🛒400m.

Fresenbrügge 5D4
Womo & Caravan Stelplatz Eldekrug, Eldeufer 1. **GPS**: n53,26355 e11,54243.

18 ⌁ € 7 ⌐⌐🔲 Ch ⚡ WCincluded. **Surface:** grassy. 🅾 01/01-31/12
Distance: ⚓on the spot 🛒on the spot ⊗on the spot.

Graal-Müritz 5D2
Strandmitte, Buchenkampweg. **GPS**: n54,25663 e12,25005.

15 ⌁ € 8. **Surface:** grassy/metalled. 🅾 01/01-31/12
Distance: 🏊500m ⚓on the spot 🛒on the spot ⊗500m 🛒500m.

Grabow 5D4
Stadthafen, Canalstrasse. **GPS**: n53,27738 e11,55949.

18 ⌁ free ⌐⌐🔲 Ch ⚡ WCagainst payment.
🅾 01/01-31/12
Distance: 🏊200m ⚓10m 🛒10m ⊗100m 🛒50m.
Remarks: Parking harbour, in the centre, max. 20h, parking disk required.

Greifswald 6B2
Caravanstellplatz Wöller, Chausseestraße 12. **GPS**: n54,07450 e13,35230. ⬆️

40 🗊 € 10 ⛽ 🔌 Ch ✎ included WC 🗑 Use sanitary € 5/day. **Surface:** metalled. 🅾 01/01-31/12
Distance: 🚶1km ⊗800m 🛒1km.

🗊Ⓢ | **Greifswald** | 6B2
Marktkauf, Dorfstrasse, Neuenkirchen. **GPS:** n54,11810 e13,36390.

10 🗊free ⛽€ 1 🔌Ch ✎(5x)€ 1. **Surface:** metalled. 🅾 01/01-31/12

🗊Ⓢ | **Greifswald** | 6B2
Am Museumhafen, Marienstraße 10. **GPS:** n54,09887 e13,38945.⬆

20 🗊€11 ⛽€ 2 🔌Ch€ 2 ✎€ 1 WC 🗑.
Surface: metalled.
🅾 01/04-30/11
Distance: 🚶8 min walking ⊗300m.

Tourist information Greifswald:
🛈 Greifswald-Information, Rathausarkaden, Domstrasse, www.greifswald.
de.Hanseatic city, with historical city centre.
👁 Fischerdorf Greifswald-Wieck.Fishermen's village worth seeing.

🗊Ⓢ | **Güstrow** | 6A3
Gleviner Platz. GPS: n53,79117 e12,18054.⬆

3 🗊free ⛽€ 0,50 🔌 Ch WC. **Surface:** asphalted. 🅾 01/01-31/12
Distance: 🚶400m ⛱5km ⛽5km ⊗100m 🛒100m.

🍴Ⓢ | **Güstrow** | 6A3
Am Tierpark, Verbindungschaussee 7. **GPS:** n53,79159 e12,21577.
30 🗊€ 15, 2 pers.incl ⛽🔌Ch ✎€ 2,50.
Surface: grassy. 🅾 01/01-31/12

Distance: 🚶5km ⊗on the spot 🛒5km.

🗊Ⓢ | **Gützkow** | 6B3
Rittergut Schloss Pentin, Zum Bollwerk 11. **GPS:** n53,91824 e13,46763.➡

40+10 🗊€ 8 ⛽€ 0,50/80liter 🔌Ch ✎€ 0,50/kWh WC 🗑€ 1. **Surface:** grassy/gravel. 🅾 01/01-31/12
Distance: ⊗1km 🛒400m.
Remarks: Bread-service.

🗊Ⓢ | **Heiligendamm** | 5D2
Wohnmobilparkplatz, Kühlungsborner Strasse. **GPS:** n54,13927 e11,85281.➡

4 🗊€ 10. **Surface:** metalled. 🅾 01/01-31/12
Distance: 🚶1,5km 🛒1,5km.

🗊Ⓢ | **Heringsdorf** | 6C2
Pension Ariane, Bülowstrasse 13. **GPS:** n53,95240 e14,16600.⬆

6 🗊€ 12 ⛽€ 1/40liter 🔌Ch ✎€ 2 WC 🗑€ 2. **Surface:** grassy. 🅾 01/04-30/09
Distance: 🚶on the spot ⛱300m ⊗on the spot 🛒on the spot.

🗊Ⓢ | **Hornstorf** | 5D3
Gartencenter Offermann, Dorfstraße 1. **GPS:** n53,89473 e11,54159.⬆

20 🗊€ 10 ⛽🔌Ch ✎ included. **Surface:** concrete. 🅾 01/01-31/12

🗊 | **Kägsdorf** | 5D2
Strandparkplatz Kägsdorf, Zum Strande. **GPS:** n54,14231 e11,66541.⬆

DE

20 🛌 15. **Surface:** grassy. 🅾 01/01-31/12
Distance: ⛱20m. 🚶20m.

| 🛁 | Kamminke | 6C3 |

Stettinerhaff. GPS: n53,86750 e14,20480. 🔼 .

10 🛌 5 🚰 1 🗑 Ch 🖊 € 2 WC 🚿. **Surface:** grassy/metalled. 🅾
01/01-31/12
Distance: 🏊1,5km ⊗1km 🚲3km.

| 🛁 | Kühlungsborn | 5D2 |

Am Hafen, Hafenstrasse. **GPS:** n54,15063 e11,77150.

15 🛌 8. **Surface:** grassy. 🅾 01/01-31/12
Distance: 🏊on the spot ⊗on the spot.

| 🛁🅂 | Karenz | 5C5 |

Reiterhof am Steinberg, Grebserstrasse 1. **GPS:** n53,23638 e11,34836.

50 🛌 € 10/night. **Surface:** gravel. 🅾 01/01-31/12
Distance: 🏊800m ⊗on the spot 🚲600m.

| 🍴🅂 | Langen Brütz | 5D3 |

3 🛌 6 🚰 🗑 Ch 🖊 WC against payment. **Surface:** grassy. 🅾 01/01-31/12
Distance: 🏊1km ⊗1km 🚲1km.
Remarks: Parking at manege. Karenz dir Eldena.

| 🛁🅂 | Kargow | 6A4 |

Reisemobilstellplatz Ziegenwiese, Schwarzenhof 7. **GPS:** n53,46433
e12,79925. 🔼 .

Landhaus Bondzio, Hauptstrasse 21a. **GPS:** n53,65722 e11,55737. 🔼 .

10 🛌 € 7,50 🚰 € 3 🗑 Ch 🖊 € 3. **Surface:** grassy. 🅾 01/01-31/12
Distance: ⛱1km 🚶1km 🚲200m 🚲4km.

| 🛁🅂 | Karnin | 6C3 |

Hafen, Karnin 14a. **GPS:** n53,84450 e13,85860. 🔼 .

6 🛌 € 10 🚰 🖊 WC included 🗑 € 2. **Surface:** asphalted/grassy. 🅾 01/01-31/12
Distance: 🏊150m ⊗on the spot 🚲50m.

| 🍴🅂 | Lassahn | 5C4 |

Pension Seeblick, Dorfstrasse 59. **GPS:** n53,60271 e10,95342.

3 🛌 € 10 🚰 € 0,50/100liter 🗑 Ch € 1 🖊 € 0,50/1kWh WC 🗑 € 1 🚿.
Surface: metalled. 🅾 01/01-31/12
Distance: ⊗500m.

| 🛁🅂 | Krassow | 5D3 |

Caravan Krassow, Kastanienalle 56. **GPS:** n53,87379 e11,56618. 🔼 .

5 🛌 € 10, guests free 🖊 included. **Surface:** grassy. 🅾 01/01-31/12

| 🛁🅂 | Lauterbach | 6B1 |

Im-Jaich Wasserferienwelt, Am Yachthafen 1, Putbus. **GPS:** n54,34278
e13,50167. 🔼 ➡ .

20 🅢 € 7-8, € 1,20/pppd tourist tax ⛽ 🔌 ⚡ WC included 🚰 € 1 🚽 € 4, dryer € 3 📶. **Surface:** gravel. 🅿 01/01-31/12
Distance: 🏊500m 🏖on the spot 🛒on the spot 🍴800m.
Remarks: Seaview, bead kiosk.

Lenzer Hafen, Zum Hafen 1. **GPS:** n53,46793 e12,34929. ⬆.

25 🅢 € 8,30- €12,40 ⛽ 🔌 Ch ⚡ WC 🚰 € 1,30 🚽 € 2. **Surface:** grassy. 🅿
01/03-31/10
Distance: 🏊6km 🏖on the spot 🛒on the spot 🍴6km.
Remarks: Parking eastern bank Plauersee.

Knöpfle Dorfladen, Arkonastrasse 4. **GPS:** n54,58300 e13,61150.

14 🅢 € 12 ⛽ € 1/90liter 🔌 Ch ⚡ WC € 0,50 🚰 € 2 🚽.
Surface: grassy/metalled.
🅿 01/01-31/12
Distance: 🏊on the spot 🏖200m 🛒on the spot 🍴on the spot 🚌on the spot.

Königsstuhl P&R, Hagen. **GPS:** n54,56220 e13,62590. ⬆.

60 🅢 € 8 ⛽ € 2 🔌 Ch € 2 ⚡ € 2,50/day WC 🚰 € 1 📶. **Surface:**
metalled. 🅿 01/01-31/12
Distance: 🛒on the spot 🍴600m 🚐on the spot.

Tourist information Lohme:
ℹ Tourismusverein Gemeinde Lohme, Dorfstrasse 23.Holiday resort on the island Rügen, accessed by a bridge.

Am Schloss, Friedrich-Naumann-Allee. **GPS:** n53,32735 e11,49080. ⬆.

20 🅢 free. **Surface:** sand. 🅿 01/01-31/12
Distance: 🏊600m 🛒500m 🍴600m.

Yachtlieger Achterwasser, Netzelkow. **GPS:** n54,02690 e13,90950. ➡.

22 🅢 € 1/meter + € 1/pp ⛽ 🔌 Ch ⚡ € 2 WC 🚰 € 2. **Surface:** grassy. 🅿
01/01-31/12
Distance: 🏖on the spot 🛒on the spot 🍴on the spot.
Remarks: Marina, peninsula Gormitz.

Malchiner Kanu-club, Am Kanal 2. **GPS:** n53,74417 e12,76611.

7 🅢 € 9 ⛽ 🔌 ⚡ WC 🚰 € 0,50 🚽 washing machine/dryer € 1. **Surface:**
grassy. 🅿 01/01-31/12
Distance: 🏊500m 🏖on the spot 🛒on the spot 🍴500m 🍴500m.

Marina Malchow, Ziegeleiweg 5. **GPS:** n53,46432 e12,42417. ⬆.

20 🅢 € 10 ⛽ 🔌 Ch ⚡ WC 🚰. **Surface:** grassy. 🅿 01/01-31/12
Distance: 🏊2km 🏖on the spot 🛒on the spot 🍴100m 🍴4km 🍴250m.

Altstad Ost, Klosterstrasse. **GPS:** n53,47199 e12,43796. ⬆.
15 🅢 free. **Surface:** asphalted. 🅿 01/01-31/12
Distance: 🏊200m 🏖200m 🍴200m.

DE

DE

Malchow — 6A4

Wohnmobilstellplatz Am Plauer See, Zum Plauer See 1. **GPS**: n53,49192 e12,37268. ⬆ .

6 ⬛€ 8-10, 2 pers.incl ⟿ Ch€ 1,50 ✎ WC€ 1 ⬛€ 5 ⬛ ⬛. **Surface:** gravel. ◔ 01/01-31/12
Distance: ⬛4km ⬛on the spot ⟿on the spot ⬛on the spot.

Mistorf — 5D3

Wohnmobilpark Mistorf, Dorfstraße 50. **GPS**: n53,88152 e12,14325. ⬆
10 ⬛€ 8 ⟿ Ch ✎€ 2,50 WC ⬛€ 2,50.
Surface: grassy.
◔ 01/01-31/10
Remarks: Check in at Imbiss, bread-service, grill and picknic area.

Mönkebude — 6C3

Stettinger Haff, Am Hafen. **GPS**: n53,77174 e13,96868. ⬆

25+15 ⬛€ 8,50/€ 10 ⟿€ 0,50/100liter ⬛Ch ✎€ 2/24h WC ⬛€ 1 ⬛€
3,50, dryer € 3 ⬛€ 1,50/h. **Surface:** grassy. ◔ 01/03-30/11
Distance: ⬛50m ⬛nearby ⬛50m.
Remarks: Excl. Tourist tax € 0,75, nov/apr service only on demand, peak season: sanitary installation.

Mönkebude — 6C3

Gastätte Kregelin's Bistro, Hauptstrasse. **GPS**: n53,76663 e13,97614. ⬆

4 ⬛guests free. **Surface:** metalled.

Muess — 5D4

Awo Feriendorf Muess, Alte Crivitzer Landstrasse 6. **GPS**: n53,59995 e11,47940. ⬆

6 ⬛€ 10 31/10-01/03, € 20 01/03-31/10 ⟿ ⬛ Ch ✎ WC ⬛included, winter fee no shower. **Surface:** grassy. ◔ 01/01-31/12
Distance: ⬛100m ⬛100m.
Remarks: At open air museum.

Neu Kaliss — 5C5

Find 's Hier, An der Elde 2. **GPS**: n53,17810 e11,29720. ⬆

22 ⬛€ 4 + € 2/pp ⟿ ✎€ 1,50 WC ⬛€ 1.
Surface: grassy. ◔ 01/01-31/12
Distance: ⬛on the spot ⟿on the spot ⬛on the spot.

Neubrandenburg — 6B4

Wassersportzentrum Tollensesee, Augustastrasse 7. **GPS**: n53,53861 e13,25665. ➡

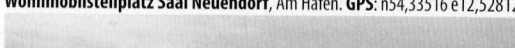

30 ⬛€ 10 ⟿€ 1 ⬛Ch ✎€ 0,50/kWh WC ⬛ ⬛ 2/day. **Surface:** grassy/ metalled. ◔ 15/03-31/10
Distance: ⬛2km ⬛on the spot ⟿on the spot ⬛on the spot ⬛1km.
Remarks: Water sports centre.

Neuendorf — 6A2

Wohnmobilstellplatz Saal Neuendorf, Am Hafen. **GPS**: n54,33516 e12,52812.

20 ⬛€ 10 ⟿ ✎ WC€ 0,20 ⬛€ 1. **Surface:** grassy. ◔ 01/04-31/10
Distance: ⬛on the spot ⬛Imbiss ⬛kiosk.

Neuhof — 6C2

Blasendorff, Labahnstrasse 10. **GPS**: n53,95940 e14,15680. ⬆

3 ⬛€ 10 ⟿€ 0,50/40liter ⬛ ✎€ 1,70. **Surface:** grassy. ◔ 01/01-31/12
Distance: ⬛10min ⬛300m ⬛300m.

Neukloster 5D3

Wohnmobilpark Neuklostersee, Alte Gärtnerei 3. **GPS:** n53,86121 e11,69536.

69 16/3-15/10 € 9,50, 16/10-15/3 € 8 Ch € 1/2kWh WC € 1.
Surface: gravel. 01/01-31/12, toilets/showers 8-21h
Distance: 500m on the spot 50m 500m 1200m 500m.

Neustrelitz 6B4

Stellplatz am Stadthafen - Neustrelitz

touristinformation@neustrelitz.de - www.neustrelitz.de

Comfortable motorhome stopover
Excellent location for city visit
Ideal base for walking and cycling

Parkplatz Am Stadthafen, Zierker Nebenstrasse 6. **GPS:** n53,36568 e13,05551.

25 8 € 0,50/80liter € 1 Ch € 1 (25x)€ 0,50/kWh WC € 0,20
€ 0,50 washing machine/dryer € 2.
Location: Comfortable, quit.
Surface: metalled.
Distance: on the spot 100m, swimming 1km 200m 100m 200m
200m on the spot on the spot.
Remarks: Coins available at harbourmaster (200m), historical centre.

Niendorf 5C3

Poeler Forellenhof, Niendorf 13. **GPS:** n53,99454 e11,44714.

16 10 WC included. **Surface:** asphalted. 01/01-31/12
Distance: 1,5km on the spot on the spot on the spot 1,5km.
Remarks: Check in at restaurant.

Nossentin 6A4

Am Fleesensee, Am Park 33. **GPS:** n53,51866 e12,46766.

4 8 WC included . **Surface:** grassy. 01/04-31/10
5km 100m 100m on the spot 5km.

Ostseebad Sellin/Rügen 6C1

Reisemobilhafen Sellin, Kiefernweg 4b. **GPS:** n54,37170 e13,70165.

50 12 € 0,50/50liter Ch € 1 € 0,50/kWh WC € 0,50
2/day. **Surface:** grassy/metalled.
Distance: 300m 1km 1km 200m 300m 300m.

Ostseebad Wustrow 6A2

Surfcenter Wustrow, An der Nebelstation 2. **GPS:** n54,34080 e12,38040.

30 8 + € 3/pp Ch € 2,50 WC . **Surface:** asphalted.
01/04-31/10
Distance: 1km 50m.

Ostseebad Wustrow 6A2

Hafenstraße. **GPS:** n54,34363 e12,40053.

30 € 3/day, € 7/night. **Surface:** gravel.
Distance: 400m 1,5km on the spot.
Remarks: Max. 1 night.

Parchim 5D4

Jachthafen, Am Fischerdamm. **GPS:** n53,42594 e11,84494.

DE

8 ⌂ € 5 ⛽ € 0,50 🚽Ch 💧 WC 🚿. **Surface:** asphalted. 🅿 01/01-31/12
Distance: 🛒100m 🏊on the spot 🍴on the spot ⊗100m 🚉100m.

🛏️S | Passin | 5D3
Hauptstrasse 20. **GPS:** n53,90274 e12,00091.⬆.

3 ⌂ free. **Surface:** asphalted. 🅿 01/01-31/12
Remarks: Next to cemetery.

©S | Pepelow | 5D3
Wohnmobilpark Pepelow, Strandweg 1. **GPS:** n54,03805 e11,58441.

12 ⌂ € 10-12 ⛽ 🚽Ch 💧 € 2,50 WC 🚿 sanitary € 2/pp 🔲 washing
machine/dryer € 2,50. **Surface:** grassy. 🅿 01/01-31/12
Distance: 🛒700m 🏊on the spot 🍴on the spot ⊗200m 🚉200m.

🍴S | Petersdorf | 6A4
Hotel Haus Waldesruh, Lenzerstrasse 19. **GPS:** n53,45892 e12,36060.⬆.

10 ⌂ € 7,50 ⛽ € 1 🚽Ch 💧 € 2 WC 🚿 € 1,50 🔲 washing machine/dryer
€ 1,50. **Surface:** grassy. 🅿 01/01-31/12
Distance: 🛒7km 🏊600m 🍴600m on the spot 🚉7km.

🍴S | Poseritz | 6B2
Lindenkrug, Lindenstrasse 27+28. **GPS:** n54,30130 e13,27610.⬆.

4 ⌂ guests free 💧 WC. **Surface:** metalled. 🅿 01/01-31/12
Distance: ⊗on the spot.

🛏️S | Priepert | 6B4
Wohnmobilpark Am Großen Priepertsee, An der Freiheit 8. **GPS:** n53,22043
e13,04201.⬆.

22 ⌂ € 7 ⛽ 🚽Ch 💧 € 2 WC 🚿 € 1,50 🔲 washing machine/dryer € 5.
Surface: grassy. 🅿 01/01-31/12
Distance: 🏊1,5km 🍴1,5km.

🛏️S | Putgarten | 6B1
Kaparkona Bahn, Am Sportplatz 2. **GPS:** n54,67190 e13,40800.⬆.

26 ⌂ € 5. **Surface:** asphalted. 🅿 01/01-31/12
Remarks: Parking on entering the village.

🍴S | Rerik | 5D2
Dünenstrasse. **GPS:** n54,10520 e11,60843.⬆.

10 ⌂ € 10/08-18h. **Surface:** sand. 🅿 01/01-31/12
Distance: 🛒500m 🏊on the spot 🍴on the spot ⊗500m 🚉500m.

🛏️S | Röbel | 6A4
Am Seglerhafen, Müritzpromenade 20. **GPS:** n53,38734 e12,61755.
45 ⌂ € 12 ⛽ 🚽Ch 💧 € 1 WC 🚿. **Surface:** grasstiles/metalled. 🅿 01/04-
31/10
Distance: 🏊on the spot ⊗300m.

🍴S | Roggendorf | 5C3
Landhotel Hänsel, Kneeser strasse18. **GPS:** n53,69228 e11,01538.⬆.

DE

8 🛏 € 6 🚰🗑Ch ⚓ WC included. **Surface:** asphalted. 🅾 01/01-31/12
Distance: 🚶200m ⊗on the spot 🍽200m 🚌200m.

🛏 Rostock 🏄🎣🏖 5D2
Parkplatz Stadtmitte, Am Bahnhof, Warnmünde. **GPS:** n54,17841 e12,09185.

100 🛏 € 6/3h, € 12/12h, € 16/24h. 🚐
Surface: metalled. 🅾 01/01-31/12

Tourist information Rostock:
ℹ️ www.rostock.de.Hanseatic city with historical centre.

🛏 S Rüterberg 5C5
Wohmobilparkplatz Dorfrepublik Rüterberg, Ringstraße 2. **GPS:** n53,15294 e11,18511.

10 🛏 € 5/24h 🚰🗑Ch ⚓ WC 🅾against payment. **Surface:** grassy. 🅾 01/01-31/12
Distance: 🚶10m ⊗50m.

🛏 S Schwerin 5C4
Am Hauptbahnhof, Wismarsche Straße. **GPS:** n53,63692 e11,40893.⬆️.
4 🛏 € 8/24h 🚰€ 1/80liter 🗑Ch ⚓ (4x)€ 1/2kWh. 🚌 **Location:** Central.
Surface: metalled.
Distance: 🚶on the spot.

🛏 S Schwerin 5C4
Marina-Nord Schwerin, Buchenweg 19. **GPS:** n53,64584 e11,43264.⬆️.

20 🛏 € 10 + € 1/pp 🚰🗑Ch ⚓ (14x)€ 0,50/kWh WC 🅾 € 1,50. **Surface:** grassy. 🅾 15/04-15/10
Distance: 🚶4km ⊗on the spot 🍽1km.

🛏 Schwerin 5C4
Altstadt, Schliemannstraße-Werderstraße. **GPS:** n53,62978 e11,41975.
🛏€ 8/24h. 🚌 **Location:** Central. **Surface:** metalled.
Distance: 🚶on the spot.

🛏 Schwerin 5C4
Sport- und Kongresshalle, Wittenburgerstrasse 118. **GPS:** n53,62802 e11,39005.
🤸.

50 🛏free. **Surface:** grasstiles/metalled. 🅾 01/01-31/10
Distance: 🚶500m ⊗500m 🍽100m.

⚏S Seehof 5C3
Campingplatz Seehof, Am Zeltplatz 1. **GPS:** n53,69676 e11,43658.⬆️.

10 🛏 € 10 🚰🗑Ch ⚓ WC included 🅾€ 0,80 🔌. **Surface:** grassy. 🅾 01/01-31/10
Distance: 🚶1,2km 🏊on the spot 🚣on the spot ⊗on the spot 🍽on the spot.

🍴S Sehlen 6B1
Zur Kastanie, Dorfstrasse 24. **GPS:** n54,37820 e13,38870.

5 🛏 € 15 🚰🗑 ⚓ WC 🅾included. **Surface:** grassy/metalled. 🅾 01/04-31/10
Distance: 🚶on the spot ⊗on the spot.

🛏 S Sembzin 6A4
Rasthof Sembzin, Dorfstrasse 2. **GPS:** n53,46445 e12,60386.

16 🛏 € 8, guests free 🚰🗑Ch ⚓ WC€ 1 🅾€ 2 🚿€ 2/24h. **Surface:** grassy/gravel. 🅾 01/01-31/12
Distance: 🚶5km ⊗on the spot.

DE

Remarks: Swimming pool.

⌁S **Sievershagen** 5D2

Ferienhof Dubberke, Alt Sievershagen 16. GPS: n54,11480 e12,03481.⬆.

5 ⌁€ 10 🔌 ⌁Ch 💧 WC ⊐included. **Surface:** grassy. ⬛ 01/01-31/10
Distance: 🚶500m ⊗800m.

ⓒS **Sommersdorf** 6B3

Wohnmobilpark Sommersdorf, Am Kummerower See. GPS: n53,79824 e12,87576.

23 ⌁€ 8-10, 2 pers.incl 🔌€ 3 ⌁Ch 💧€ 2,50/night WC€ 2 ⊐€ 2,50
📶. **Surface:** grassy. ⬛ 01/01-31/12
Distance: ⊅on the spot ⏚on the spot ⏚on the spot.

ⓒS **Sternberg** 5D3

Sternberger, Maikamp 11. GPS: n53,71318 e11,81236.➡.

15 ⌁€ 12-€ 16 🔌 ⌁Ch 💧€ 2,70/day WC ⊐ 📶. **Surface:** grasstiles. ⬛
Easter-31/10
Distance: 🚶1km ⊅on the spot ⏚on the spot ⊗on the spot ⏚500m
🚮500m.

⌁S **Stralsund** 🌿 6B2

Caravan Center Dhanke, Werftstrasse 16. GPS: n54,30190 e13,10110.⬆➡.

60 ⌁€ 12 🔌€ 1/5minutes ⌁Ch€ 1 💧. **Surface:** grassy/gravel. ⬛
01/01-31/12
Distance: 🚶1,5km 🚮on the spot.

⌁S **Timmendorf** 5C3

Strandparkplatz Timmendorf, Timmendorf Strand, Insel Poel. GPS: n53,99287 e11,38058.⬆.

60 ⌁€ 4/day, € 3/night 🔌€ 2,50 ⌁Ch 💧€ 1/2kWh ⊐€ 1.
Surface: grassy. ⬛ 01/01-31/12
Distance: 🚶150m ⊗250m ⊗200m ⏚300m.

⌁S **Ückeritz** 6C2

Am Achterwasser, Mühlenstrasse. GPS: n54,01390 e14,04170.⬆.

30 ⌁€ 10. **Surface:** metalled. ⬛ 01/01-31/12
Distance: 🚶700m ⊅on the spot.

⌁S **Ueckermünde** 6C3

An der Uecker, Ueckerstrasse 127. GPS: n53,73470 e14,04930.⬆.

13 ⌁€ 7 🔌 ⌁ 💧 included. **Surface:** grassy/metalled. ⬛ 01/01-31/12
Distance: 🚶200m ⊗200m.

ⓒS **Ueckermünde** 6C3

Kron Bellin, Dorfstrasse 8b. GPS: n53,73760 e14,11400.

10 ⌁€ 10, 2 pers.incl 🔌 ⌁Ch 💧€ 2 WC ⊐ ▣.
Surface: grassy. ⬛ 01/04-31/10
Distance: ⊅on the spot ⏚on the spot ⊗on the spot.

⌁S **Usedom** 6C3

Am Hafen Usedom, Peenestraße. GPS: n53,87099 e13,92679.⬆.

DE

20 🔲€5 ⛽🔌Ch🚿€ 5 WC€ 0,50 🚽€ 2.
Surface: metalled. 🔳 01/01-31/12
Distance: 🛒600m 🏊on the spot ⊗on the spot.
Remarks: At former fishing-port.

🍴S | **Usedom** | 6C3
Gaststätte Haffschänke, Dorfstraße 19, Karnin. **GPS:** n53,84348 e13,86537. ⬆️

20 🔲€7 ⛽🔌Ch🚿€ 3 WC🚽€ 2,50.
Surface: grassy. 🔳 01/01-31/12
Distance: 🏊on the spot 🛒on the spot ⊗on the spot.

🍴S | **Vielank** | 5C5
Vielanker Brauhaus, Lindenplatz 1. **GPS:** n53,23443 e11,14023.

12 🔲free 🚿€ 3 WC. **Surface:** grassy. 🔳 01/01-31/12
Distance: 🛒20m ⊗20m.
Remarks: Check in at reception.

🍴S | **Waren** | 6A4
Gärtnerei Steindorf-Sabath, Mecklenburgerstrasse. **GPS:** n53,51363 e12,69431. ⬆️ .

50 🔲€ 8,50 ⛽🔌Chfree 🚿€ 0,50/kWh WC🚽€ 1.
Surface: grassy/gravel. 🔳 01/01-31/12
Distance: 🛒100m 🏊1km 🛒1km ⊗1km 🍴1km 🚌on the spot.
🍴S | **Waren** | 6A4
Wohnmobilpark Kamerun, Zur stillen Bucht 3, Müritz. **GPS:** n53,51175 e12,65174. ⬆️

35 🔲€ 8-12 ⛽🔌Ch🚿€ 2,50 WC🚽 sanitary € 2/pp ▣ 📶. **Surface:** grassy. 🔳 01/01-31/12
Distance: 🛒3km 🏊on the spot 🛒on the spot ⊗on the spot 🍴on the spot 🚌500m.

🍴S | **Waren** | 6A4
Wohnmobilpark, Teterower Straße 35, Waren-Müritz. **GPS:** n53,52611 e12,67194. ⬆️➡️

22 🔲€ 8/24h ⛽🔌Ch🚿€ 2 WC🚽€ 1,50. **Surface:** grasstiles/grassy. 🔳 01/01-31/12
Distance: 🛒4km 🏊4km 🛒4km ⊗4km 🍴Edeka 10m.

🍴S | **Waren** | 6A4
Womo-Stellplatz Waren, Strandstrasse 3b. **GPS:** n53,51194 e12,68583. ⬆️➡️

20 🔲€ 10 ⛽🔌Ch🚿included. **Surface:** metalled. 🔳 01/01-31/12
Distance: 🛒on the spot 🏊on the spot 🛒on the spot ⊗on the spot 🍴on the spot.

🍴S | **Waren** | 6A4
Campingplatz Ecktannen, Fontanestraße 66. **GPS:** n53,49944 e12,66361. ⬆️➡️

16 🔲€ 16 ⛽🔌Ch🚿WC🚽included ▣ washing machine/dryer € 2,60 📶. **Surface:** grasstiles/metalled. 🔳 01/01-31/12
Distance: 🛒3,5km 🏊500m 🛒500m ⊗Bistro 🍴3km 🚌on the spot.
🍴S | **Wesenberg** | 6B4
Womo Stellplatz & Marina Wesenberg, Ahrensberger weg 11. **GPS:** n53,27666 e12,98694. ⬆️

DE

34 🛏€ 14, 2 pers.incl ⚡🗑Ch ✦ WC ⬛included.
Surface: grassy/gravel. ⬛ 01/01-31/12
Distance: 1km ⚓on the spot ⚓on the spot ⚓on the spot 🚲2,5km
🚌1km.

Wismar 5C3
Wohnmobilpark Westhafen Wismar, Schiffbauerdamm 12. **GPS**: n53,89430 e11,45151.⬆.

50 🛏€ 7/12 uur € 9/24 uur ⚡€ 1/100liter 🗑Ch ✦€ 1/8h WC ⬛€ 1.
Surface: gravel.
⬛ 01/01-31/12
Distance: 800m ⚓300m, Burger King 400m 🚲300m ⬛800m 🚌100m.
Tourist information Wismar:
ℹ Tourist Information, Am Markt 11.Hanseatic city a number of curiosities.

Wittenbeck 5D2
Parkplatz, Bäderweg. **GPS**: n54,14513 e11,79277.

40 🛏€ 5 day/€ 5 night ⚡€ 3 🗑Ch WC.
Surface: grassy. ⬛ 01/01-31/12
Distance: 1,5km ⚓on the spot.

Wittenbeck 5D2
Parkplatz, Bäderweg. **GPS**: n54,14437 e11,79268.➡.

60 🛏€ 5 day/€ 5 night ⚡€ 3 🗑Ch WC. **Surface:** metalled. ⬛ 01/01-31/12.
Distance: 1,4km 🚲1,4km.
Remarks: Follow signs Parkplatz.

Wittenburg 5C4
Snow parkfun, Zur Winterwelt 1. **GPS**: n53,51123 e11,08795.

50 🛏free. **Surface:** metalled. ⬛ 01/01-31/12 ⬛ Mon, Tue.
Distance: 1,2km ✎1,3km ⚓on the spot.

Wittenburg 5C4
Caravan Schiemann, Lehsener Chaussee 4. **GPS**: n53,50118 e11,07393.

⚡🗑Chagainst payment.

Zingst 6A1
Wohnmobilhafen Am Freesenbruch. **GPS**: n54,44060 e12,66058.
40 🛏€ 18-24, 2 pers.incl ⚡🗑Ch ✦€ 2 WC ⬛included. ⬛ 01/01-31/12

Zingst 6A1
Straminke, Seestrasse. **GPS**: n54,44070 e12,70750.

40 🛏€ 15 ⚡WC ⬛. **Surface:** grassy. ⬛ 01/01-31/12
Remarks: Parking beach passage 6, max. 1 day.
Tourist information Zingst:
ℹ Kur- und Tourismus GmbH, Seestrasse 56, www.zingst.de.Large bathing resort to the Baltic Sea.

Saxony Anhalt

Ahlum 5C6
Fischreihütte Ahlumer See, Am Mühlenberg 63. **GPS**: n52,69541 e11,00583.⬆.

100 🛏€ 8 ⚡🗑Ch ✦€ 0,50/kWh WC ⬛included. ⬛ 01/01-31/12
Distance: ⚓on the spot ⚓on the spot.
Remarks: Bread-service.

🚿S | **Aken/Elbe** 〰️☂️🦢 | **11A2**

Elbe Bootscenter, Am Russendamm. **GPS:** n51,85901 e12,03799.➡️
10 🚐 € 10 + € 2/pp 🚰🔌Ch✎€ 2 WC🚻. **Surface:** grassy. 🔌 01/04-31/10
Remarks: At marina.

🚿 | **Altenbrak** | **10C2**

Am Bielstein. **GPS:** n51,72569 e10,94196.⬆️

8 🚐 € 5, overnight stay free. 🏚️ **Location:** Rural, very simple. **Surface:** metalled. 🔌 01/01-31/12
Distance: 🚶100m 🛒on the spot ⊗100m.

🚿 | **Altenbrak** | **10C2**

Parkplatz Rappbodetalsperre, Hasselfelderstrasse, L96. **GPS:** n51,74298 e10,88770.⬆️

20 🚐free. **Surface:** asphalted.

🍴🚿S | **Altenbrak** | **10C2**

Hotel Zur Talsperre, Oberbecken 1. **GPS:** n51,73434 e10,90690.⬆️

50 🚐 € 10 🚰🔌Ch✎(20x)€ 0,40/kWh WC🚻included. 🔌 01/01-31/12
Distance: ⊗on the spot.

🚿S | **Arendsee** | **5D5**

Im kleinen Elsebusch, Lüchower strasse 6a. **GPS:** n52,87656 e11,46121.⬆️➡️

20 🚐 € 10 🚰€ 1 🔌€ 1 Ch✎. **Surface:** grassy. 🔌 01/01-31/12
Distance: 🚶2,5km ⊗on the spot 🚮2,5km.

🚿S | **Bad Kösen** | **10D4**

Am Saalebogen, Stendorfhaus 14. **GPS:** n51,11356 e11,69609.⬆️➡️

11 🚐 € 5 🚰🔌Ch🚻€ 2 WC🚻 sanitary € 1,50.
Surface: grasstiles/metalled. 🔌 01/01-31/12
Distance: 🚶3km ⊗800m 🚮800m.

🚿S | **Ballenstedt** | **10D2**

Verkehrslandeplatz Ballenstedt/Quedlinburg, Asmusstedt 13. **GPS:** n51,74190 e11,23427.⬆️

32 🚐 € 4/pppn 🚰🔌Ch✎WC🚻included. **Surface:** grasstiles/metalled. 🔌 01/01-31/12
Distance: 🚶2km ⊗on the spot 🚮2km 🚌200m.

🍴 | **Berssel** | **10C2**

Gasthof Zum Schloß, Am Schloß 1. **GPS:** n51,95266 e10,76027.🅿️.
5 🚐free. **Surface:** metalled.

🚿S | **Bertingen** | **10D1**

Freizeitgelände, Im Wald 2. **GPS:** n52,35994 e11,82264.⬆️➡️

60 🚐 € 7,50 🚰🔌Ch✎included. **Surface:** grassy. 🔌 01/01-31/12
Distance: ⊗on the spot 🚮5km.
Remarks: Bread-service.

🚿S | **Blankenburg** | **10C2**

Am Schnappelberg, Schnappelberg 2. **GPS:** n51,78870 e10,96002.⬆️

15 🚐 € 4 🚰€ 1 🔌Ch✎€ 1 🚻 2 WC. **Surface:** metalled. 🔌 01/01-31/12
Distance: 🚶on the spot ⊗300m 🚮on the spot.
Remarks: Waste dump € 0,50.

🚿S | **Brachwitz** | **11A3**

Marina Saale-Ufer, An der Fähre. **GPS:** n51,53441 e11,87083.⬆️

DE

14 🛁€5 🔌€ 1 ⛲ Ch 🚿 (4x)€ 0,50/kWh WC.
Surface: grassy. 🅾 01/01-31/12
Distance: 🛒500m ⊗500m 🍴500m.

15 🛁€5 🔌 (2x). **Surface:** grassy. 🅾 01/01-31/12

| 🛁S | **Burg bei Magdeburg** | 10D1 |

Wassersportfreunde Burg, Am Kanal 20a. **GPS:** n52,28329 e11,84808. ⬆

| 🛁S | **Harzgerode** | 10C3 |

Parkplatz Wallgarten, Wallstrasse. **GPS:** n51,64210 e11,14060. ⬆

6 🛁€10 🔌€ 1/100liter 🚿 WC ⬜included.
Surface: grassy. 🅾 01/05-30/09
Distance: on the spot.

5 🛁free. **Surface:** metalled. 🅾 01/01-31/12
Distance: 🛒100m ⚓1km ⛽3km ⊗100m 🍴100m 🚌100m 🚂1km.

| 🍴S | **Burg bei Magdeburg** | 10D1 |

Eschenhof, Parchauer Chaussee 5. **GPS:** n52,28718 e11,86583. ⬆➡

| 🛁S | **Ilsenburg** | 10C2 |

Wohnmobilstellplatz Ilsetal, Ilsetal. **GPS:** n51,85386 e10,67013. ⬆

15 🛁€10 🔌⛲Ch 🚿€ 2 WC ⬜included.
Surface: grassy. 🅾 01/01-31/12
Distance: on the spot ⊗on the spot 🍴1km.

40 🛁€ 6, tourist tax € 1/pp 🔌€ 2 ⛲Ch 🚿(24x)€ 2.
Surface: metalled. 🅾 01/01-31/12
Distance: 🛒700m ⚓500m ⛽2km ⊗300m 🍴800m 🚌50m 🚲15km 🚂15km.

| 🛁S | **Darlingerode** | 10C2 |

Wohnmobilpark Harzblick, Hinter den Gärten 11. **GPS:** n51,85278 e10,73667.
⬆➡

| 🛁S | **Magdeburg** | 10D1 |

Stellplatz Petriförde, Petriförder 1. **GPS:** n52,13289 e11,64714.

15 🛁€8 🔌⛲Ch 🚿(12x)€ 0,50/kWh WC.
Surface: grasstiles. 🅾 01/01-31/12
Distance: ⊗500m 🍴500m.

| 🛁S | **Elend** | 10C2 |

Waldbad Schenke, Am Waldbad 1. **GPS:** n51,74612 e10,69531. ⬆

50 🛁€ 5. **Surface:** metalled. 🅾 01/01-31/12
Distance: on the spot.
Remarks: Along the river Elbe.

| 🍴S | **Magdeburg** | 10D1 |

Zum Anker, Schiffshebewerk. **GPS:** n52,22441 e11,67342.
3 🛁€5 🔌🚿.
Distance: ⊗on the spot.
Remarks: Max. 3 nights.

| 🛁S | **Naumburg(Saale)** | 11A4 |

Altstadtparkplatz Vogelwiese, Luisenstraße. **GPS:** n51,14861 e11,81391. ⬆

10 🛏️ € 5/night ⛽ € 0,50/80liter 🚰 Ch 🔌 € 0,50/kWh WC.
Surface: metalled. 🅾️ 01/01-31/12
Distance: 🚶500m ⊗50m 🏪500m 🚌50m.
Remarks: Max. 3 days.

| 📷 S | **Naumburg(Saale)** | 11A4 |

Caravan Rossol, Kroppentalstrasse 1. **GPS:** n51,15188 e11,82679. ⬆️
10 🛏️ € 5 ⛽ € 3 🚰 € 3 🔌 € 3/night. **Surface:** grassy.
Distance: 🚶1,2km.
Remarks: Waste dump € 1.

| 📷 S | **Quedlinburg** | 10C2 |

An den Fischteichen. GPS: n51,79308 e11,14863. ⬆️➡️

10 🛏️ free ⛽ € 1 🚰 🔌 € 1/6h. **Surface:** grasstiles/metalled. 🅾️ 01/01-31/12
Distance: 🚶350m ⊗300m 🏪250m 🚌150m.

| 📷 S | **Quedlinburg** | 10C2 |

Marschlinger hof. GPS: n51,79138 e11,13965. ⬆️➡️

6 🛏️ € 5/24h ⛽ 🚰 Ch 🔌 (4x)€ 1/6h WC. **Surface:** metalled. 🅾️ 01/01-31/12
Distance: 🚶100m ⊗50m 🏪400m 🚌200m.
Remarks: Max. 7m.

| 📷 S | **Quedlinburg** | 10C2 |

Schloßparkplatz, Schenkgasse. **GPS:** n51,78725 e11,13494. ⬆️➡️

6 🛏️ € 3/24h ⛽ 🚰 Ch 🔌 (4x)€ 1/6h.
Surface: metalled. 🅾️ 01/01-31/12

| 📷 S | **Sangerhausen** | 10D3 |

An der Walkmühle, Taubenberg. **GPS:** n51,49056 e11,31127. ⬆️

50 🛏️ free. **Surface:** sand. 🅾️ 01/01-31/12
Distance: 🚶2km ⊗on the spot.

| 📷 S | **Sangerhausen** | 10D3 |

P7, An der Probstmühle. **GPS:** n51,47707 e11,30798. ⬆️

20 🛏️ free. **Surface:** sand. 🅾️ 01/01-31/12
Distance: 🚶500m ⊗200m 🚌100m.

| S | **Sangerhausen** | 10D3 |

Rosarium, Sotterhäuser Weg. **GPS:** n51,47245 e11,31798. ⬆️
⛽ € 2 🚰Ch. 🅾️ 15/04-15/10
Remarks: Check in at shop.

| 📷 S | **Seehausen** | 5D5 |

Stellplatz Seehausen, Schulstrasse 6. **GPS:** n52,89068 e11,75119. ⬆️

50 🛏️ € 5 ⛽ 🚰 Ch 🔌 included. **Surface:** metalled. 🅾️ 01/01-31/12
Distance: 🚶100m 🏪200m.
Remarks: At tourist office.

| 📷 S | **Stendal** | 5D6 |

Nordwall-Schützenplatz. GPS: n52,61116 e11,86121. ⬆️

20 🛏️ free ⛽ € 1/80liter 🚰 € 1 Ch.
Surface: grassy/metalled.
🅾️ 01/01-31/12
Distance: 🚶on the spot 🏪bakery 50m.

Tourist information Stendal:
ℹ️ Stendal Information, Kornmarkt 8.Hanseatic city with historical centre, city of

the Brick Gothic.

Ⓜ Wickelmanmuseum.Founder of the modern archeology. ⬤ Wed-Mo 10-17h.

Tangermünde 5D6

Tangerplatz, Klosterberg. **GPS:** n52,53774 e11,96803.⬆.

30 ⬧€ 4 ⌁⬧Ch⬧ included. **Surface:** metalled. ⬤ 01/01-31/12

Wahrenberg 5D5

Stellplatz Storchenwiese, Eichenwinkel 34. **GPS:** n52,98342 e11,67362.⬆.

3 ⬧€ 5 ⌁⬧ (3x)included. **Surface:** grassy. ⬤ 01/01-31/12

Weddersleben 10C2

Lebenshilfe Harzkreis-Quedlinburg, Quedlinburgerstrasse 2. **GPS:** n51,76569 e11,09061.⬆.

12 ⬧€ 15 ⌁⬧Ch⬧WC⬧included ⬧against payment. **Surface:** metalled. ⬤ 01/01-31/12

Remarks: Commune for mentally disableds, special metalled part for motorhomes.

Weissenfels 11A4

Caravan- und Freizeitmarkt Gerth, Selauer Strasse. **GPS:** n51,19783 e11,99824.⬆.

7 ⬧free ⌁€ 1/80liter ⬧Ch⬧ (4x)€ 0,50/kWh. **Surface:** asphalted. ⬤ 01/01-31/12

Distance: ⊗on the spot ⬧on the spot.
Remarks: Industrial area Borau.

Wernigerode 10C2

Am Katzenteich. GPS: n51,83889 e10,78148.⬆➡.

20 ⬧€ 5 ⌁€ 1/40liter ⬧Ch⬧(20x)€ 1/kWh. **Surface:** grasstiles. ⬤ 01/01-31/12

Distance: ⬧500m.

Wernigerode 10C2

Schlossparkplatz am Anger, Halberstädler strasse 1. **GPS:** n51,83807 e10,79535.⬆.

24 ⬧€ 2,50, overnight stay free ⌁€ 2 ⬧Ch. **Surface:** metalled. ⬤ 01/01-31/12

Distance: ⬧300m.

Wernigerode 10C2

Gästehaus Familie Mann, Mühlental 76, B244. **GPS:** n51,81688 e10,81519.⬆.

5 ⬧€ 10 ⌁⬧Chincluded ⬧€ 0,45/kWh ⬧€ 0,50. **Surface:** gravel. ⬤ 01/04-10/11

Distance: ⊗on the spot.
Remarks: Check in at restaurant, arrival before 22h.

Wörlitz 11A2

Seeparke, Seespitze, K2376. **GPS:** n51,84820 e12,41277.⬆➡.

24 ⬧€ 5 day/€ 5 night ⬧€ 2 WC⬧ Use sanitary ⌁euro⬧ 0,50. **Surface:** asphalted. ⬤ 01/01-31/12

Remarks: Parking at the edge the Wörlitzer park, max. 24h.

Wörlitz 11A2

Hotel Coswiger Elbterrasse, Elbterrasse 1. **GPS:** n51,87750 e12,45097.⬆.

10 🛁 € 5 ⚡ 💧 included.
Surface: grassy.
🔵 01/01-31/12
Distance: ⊗on the spot.
Remarks: Free with a meal.
Tourist information Wörlitz:
🛈 Wörlitz-Information, Förstergasse 26, www.woerlitz-information.de.Park city; "Hier ists jetzt unendlich schön" according Goethe in 1778.

Brandenburg/Berlin

| 🍴 S | Abbendorf | 5D5 |

Gasthaus Dörpkrog an Diek, Am Deich 7. **GPS:** n52,89663 e11,90975. ⬆️.

6 🛁 € 5, guests free ⚡🔲Ch 💧 WC included. 🔵 01/01-31/12
Remarks: Bread-service.

| 🐴 S | Alt-Zeschdorf | 6D6 |

Reiterhof Blumrich, Falkenhagerweg 11. **GPS:** n52,42649 e14,42328. ⬆️.

30 🛁 € 8,50 ⚡🔲Ch 💧 included. **Surface:** grassy. 🔵 01/01-31/12 🔘 winter Mo.
Distance: 🚶1,5km.
Remarks: At manege, bread-service.

| 🔵 S | Altdöbern | 11D2 |

Kfz Dienstleistungcenter, Senftenberger strasse 11. **GPS:** n51,64523 e14,03544.

20 🛁 € 10 ⚡🔲 💧 WC included. **Surface:** metalled.
Distance: 🚶500m ⊗on the spot 🛒500m.

| 🔵 | Angermünde | 6C5 |

NABU-Erlebniszentrum Blumberger Mühle. GPS: n53,03572 e13,96806. ⬆️.

10 🛁 free. **Surface:** metalled. 🔵 01/01-31/12

| 🔵 | Bad Saarow ♨ | 11D1 |

Parkplatz Strolin, Silberbergerstrasse. **GPS:** n52,28726 e14,03895. ⬆️.

4 🛁 free. **Surface:** metalled. 🔵 01/01-31/12
Distance: 🏊100m ⊗100m.

| 🔵 | Bad Saarow ♨ | 11D1 |

Ringstrasse. **GPS:** n52,29399 e14,06243. ⬆️.

6 🛁 free. **Surface:** metalled.
Distance: 🚶on the spot ⊗300m 🛒400m.

| 🍴 S | Bad Wilsnack | 5D5 |

Zur gemütlichen Einkehr, Am Park 3. **GPS:** n52,95800 e11,95873. ⬆️.

15 🛁 € 5, free with a meal ⚡ 💧 € 2,50 WC included. **Surface:** grassy. 🔵 01/01-31/12
Distance: 🚶on the spot ⊗on the spot 🛒1km.

| 🔵 S | Bad Wilsnack | 5D5 |

Kur- und Gradier-Therme Bad Wilsnack, Am Kähling. **GPS:** n52,96316 e11,95007. ➡️.

DE

18 ⏚€ 10 + € 1 Kurtaxe pppd ⛽€ 1/80liter 🅲h ⚡(8x)€ 1/kWh.
Surface: sand.
Distance: 🚶500m ⊗200m 🍴500m.
Remarks: Check in at pay-desk of theTherme, bread-service.

Märkischer Waidmann - Baumgarten Sonnenberg

info@maerkischer-waidmann.de - www.maerkischer-waidmann.de

Located in a quit location
BBQ area
Good fishing spot

Märkischer Waidmann, Heidestrasse 33, OT Baumgarten Sonnenberg. **GPS:** n52,98028 e13,07444.⬆.
5 ⏚€ 10 ⛽€ 2 🅲h ⚡(5x)€ 2/day WC€ 0,50 🚿. **Location:** Rural, comfortable. **Surface:** grassy/gravel. ⬛ 01/01-31/12
Distance: 25km 600m 200m ⊗on the spot 6km 50m.
Remarks: € 10 reduction for guests, , fishing permit available at restaurant € 10/day.

Springbach Mühle, Mühlenweg 2. **GPS:** n52,16523 e12,61078.⬆➡.

info@reisemobilstellplatz-berlin.de - www.reisemobilstellplatz-berlin.de

Located near marina
Comfortable motorhome stopover
Ideal base for walking and cycling

Historisches Fährhaus Berlin, Muggelbergallee 1, Berlin-Köpenick. **GPS:** n52,41851 e13,58734.⬆.
15 ⏚01/03-01/11 € 18, 02/11-28/02 € 14 ⛽🅲hincluded ⚡(15x)€ 2 WC€ 1 🚿€ 5/stay. **Location:** Urban, luxurious, quit. **Surface:** grassy/gravel. ⬛ 01/01-31/12
Distance: 🚶on the spot 🚲8km 🏊on the spot 🛒on the spot ⊗on the spot 🍴100m, supermarket 750m 1km 🚃100m tram.
Remarks: At old harbour.

Wohnmobilpark Berlin, Waidmannsluster Damm 12-14. **GPS:** n52,59311 e13,28697.⬆➡.

90 ⏚€ 9-21, dog € 2 ⛽🅲h ⚡€ 3/24h WC€ 1 🚿€ 3, dryer € 3 🚿.
Location: Central. **Surface:** grassy/metalled. ⬛ 01/01-31/12
Distance: ⊗on the spot 🍴on the spot 🚃few minutes.
Remarks: Hotline-Nr.: 0176 – 99 55 25 00.

Reisemobilhafen Berlin Spandau, Askanierring 70. **GPS:** n52,55324 e13,20164.⬆.

130 ⏚€ 15, 2 pers.incl ⛽€ 1/100liter 🅲h ⚡included 🚿€ 1 🚿€ 2/day. **Location:** Central, noisy. **Surface:** . ⬛ 01/01-31/12
Distance: ⊗100m 🚃300m.
Remarks: Near approach route of airport, 23-5h quiet. In area of the former English barracks 'Alexander Barracks', A10 exit Berlin-Spandau, follow road till cross roads Heerstraße/Gatowerstraße,here to the left, at Flakenseerplatz straight on, Neuendorferstraße, before Hohenzollernring to the left.

50 ⏚€ 15 ⛽🅲h ⚡. ⬛ 01/01-31/12

S Berlin 🌿⛵🍵 6B6
Int. Reisemobilstation Berlin-Mitte, Chausseestrase 82. **GPS:** n52,53817 e13,37304.

45 € 18, > 9m € 20, summer € 20-22,50, incl. 2 pers Ch WC included. **Location:** Urban, comfortable, central, noisy.
Surface: grassy/metalled. 01/01-31/12
Distance: on the spot 500m 500m 200m.
Remarks: A100 exit Wedding/Seestrasse after ca. 2km to the right Mütterstrasse, this street becomes Chausseestrasse.

S Berlin 🌿⛵🍵 6B6
Köpenicker Hof, Stellingdamm 15, Berlin-Köpenick. **GPS:** n52,45929 e13,58532.

40 € 10/24h Ch € 1 WC included. **Surface:** gravel. 01/01-31/12
Distance: Tram (centre 30min).
Remarks: Bread-service.

S Berlin 🌿⛵🍵 6B6
Marina Lanke Berlin, Scharfe Lanke 109-131. **GPS:** n52,50344 e13,18801.
15 € 7,50/5m, €12,50/7,5m + € 3,50/pp Ch WC included € 3, dryer € 2.
Location: Urban.
Surface: metalled.
01/05-15/10
Distance: centre Berlin 16km on the spot on the spot 1km.
Remarks: Marina.

Tourist information Berlin:
ℹ️ Tourist Info, Europacenter, Eingang Budapester strasse 3; Brandenburgertor, Südflügel; Fernsehturm, Alexanderplatz, www.btm.de.Documentation available, via Internet.
👁🅼 Zeughaus.German historical museum.
👁 Alexanderplatz.The old historical centre of Berlin.
👁 Brandenburger Tor.Built in 1791 as a triumphal arch after the construction of the Berlin Wall the arch remained as a symbol of the German separation. 🆃 free.
👁 Fernsehturm.Television tower. 9-01h, 01/11-28/02 10-24h.
👁 Haus am Checkpoint Charly, Friedrichstrasse 44.At the former border crossing. History of the Wall is told with photographs. 9-22h.
👁 Holländische Viertel.Dutch district many cafés, luxurious boutiques and art galeries.
👁 Reichstag, Platz der Republik.Old parliament building. daily till 20h. 🆃 free.
🅼 Funkturm en radiomuseum, Messedamm, Charlottenburg.Radio and television museum. Tue-Su 10-23h.
🅼 Museum-Insel.Complex of musea.
✖ Schloß Charlottenburg, Luisenplatz.Summer residence of the Prussian kings. Tue-Fri 9-17h, Sa-Su 10-17h.
✖ Sloss Glienicke.Original country-house developed to castle. 15/05-15/10

Sa-Su 10-17h.
🎪 Antik- und Trödelmarkt, Ostbahnhof. Sa 9-15h, Su 10-17h.
🎪 Kunst- und Flohmarkt, strasse des 17. Juni.Arts and fleamarket. Sa-Su 11-17h.
🎪 Nollendorf rommelmarkt, Altes S-Bahnstation. Wed-Mo 8-13h.
🎪 Trödelmarkt, Arkonaplatz.Flea market. Su 10-16h.
🎪 Türkische Markt, MaybachuferNeuköln.Turkish market. Tue + Fri afternoon.
😊 Zoologischer Garten, Hardenbergplatz 8.City-zoo. 01/04-30/09 9-18.30h, 01/10-31/10 9-18h, 01/11-28/02 9-17h.

S Brandenburg 🌿⛵🍵 11A1
Am Brandenburger Dom, Grillendamm. **GPS:** n52,41724 e12,56576.⬆

60 € 10 € 1/100liter Ch € 1 WC € 1. 01/01-31/12
Distance: Neustadt 15min, Altstadt 15min.

S Brandenburg 🌿⛵🍵 11A1
Wassersportzentrum Alte Feuerwache, Franz Zieglerstrasse 27. **GPS:** n52,40485 e12,54868.⬆➡

25 € 8 Ch WC included € 1 📶.
Surface: metalled.
01/01-31/12
Distance: 500m 500m.

Tourist information Brandenburg:
ℹ️ Tourist Information, Steinstrasse 66-67, www.stadt-brb.de.Hanseatic city with historical centre.
🅼🆁 Dom St. Peter und Paul.Cathedral.
⌒ Stadtmauer mit Tortürmen.City wall and towers.

S Brieske 11D3
Reimann, Brieske Dorf 27. **GPS:** n51,49203 e13,94743.➡

20 € 5 Ch WC included. **Surface:** grassy. 01/01-31/12
Distance: 200m 9,3km 2km.

DE

⌂S | Burg/Spreewald | 11D2

Hagens Insel - Wasserwanderrastplatz, Weidenweg 4. **GPS**: n51,86138 e14,11527.

10 �€10 ⊨ 🗑Ch 🖌WC ⛶included. **Surface**: grassy.

⎰⎱S | Burg/Spreewald | 11D2

Hotel Kurhaus zum Spreewald, An der Haupstspree 1. **GPS**: n51,84388 e14,10972.⬆.

18 �€17/24h ⊨ 🗑Ch ✔included. **Surface**: grassy. ◑ 01/01-31/12

⎰⎱S | Burg/Spreewald | 11D2

Landgasthof zur Wildbahn, Wildbahnweg 20. **GPS**: n51,85104 e14,09384.

9 �€13, 2 pers.incl, tourist tax €1,50/pp, dog €2 ⊨ 🗑 ✔WC included. **Surface**: metalled. ◑ 01/03-30/10

⎰⎱S | Dollenchen | 11D2

Gasthaus Stuckatz, Hauptstrasse 29. **GPS**: n51,60745 e13,86226.➡.

20 �€8 ⊨ 🗑Ch ✔WC ⛶included. **Surface**: grassy. ◑ 01/01-31/12
Distance: 🚶on the spot ⊗on the spot 🚂3km.

⌂S | Dreetz | 6A6

Reiterhof Müller, Schulstrasse 61. **GPS**: n52,79322 e12,46698.

5 ⌱€10 ⊨ 🗑Ch 🖌WC included ⛶€ 1.
Surface: grassy. ◑ 01/04-31/10
Distance: 🚶800m ⊗300m 🛒500m. 🚂500m.

⌂S | Fürstenberg (Havel) | 6B4

Marina Fürstenberg, Ravensbrücker Dorfstrasse 26. **GPS**: n53,19489 e13,14895. ⬆.

50 ⌱€6 ⊨€ 2 🗑Ch 🖌€ 3 WC ⛶€ 1,50.
Surface: grassy.
◑ 01/01-31/12
Distance: 🚶1km ⊗on the spot 🚂1km.
Remarks: At marina, boat rental.

⎰⎱S | Kienitz | 6D6

Ferienhaus Marth, Kienitzeroderstrasse 20. **GPS**: n52,67616 e14,39890.⬆.

8 ⌱€6 ⊨ 🗑Ch 🖌€ 1,50 WC ⛶€ 1,50.
Surface: grassy. ◑ 01/04-30/09
Distance: 🚶3km 🚂3km.

⎘S | Klein-Ossnig | 11D2

Caravan-Krokor, Hauptstrasse 12/a, B169. **GPS**: n51,69962 e14,27917.➡.

8 ⌱€6 ⊨ 🗑Ch 🖌included. **Surface**: grassy. ◑ 01/01-31/12
Distance: 🚶on the spot 🚂2km.
Remarks: Arrival only during opening hours: Mo-Fr 8-19, Sa 8-13.

⌂S | Kolkwitz | 11D2

Papitzerstrasse 48. **GPS**: n51,76676 e14,22410.⬆.

DE

3 ⬛ € 10 ⚡ 🔌 Ch 🔧 WC included. **Surface:** grassy. ⭕ 01/01-31/12
Distance: 🚶2,5km.

| ⬛ S | Lübbenau | 11D2 |

Autocamping im Spreewald, Chausseestrasse 17a, Lübbenau-Zerkwitz. **GPS:** n51,86559 e13,93324. ⬆️➡️.

6 ⬛ € 13/24h, tourist tax € 1/pp, dog € 1 ⚡ € 1,50 Ch 🔧 WC included.
Surface: grasstiles. ⭕ Easter-31/10
Distance: 🚴2,5km 🚋500m.

| ⬛ | Lübbenau | 11D2 |

Am Bahnhof, Bahnhofstraße (B115). **GPS:** n51,86139 e13,96361.

10 ⬛ € 10 ⚡ € 1 Ch 🔧 consumption. **Surface:** asphalted. ⭕ 01/01-31/12
Distance: 🚶800m 🚴3,3km ⊗350m 🚋50m.
Remarks: Max. 48h.

| ⬛ | Lübbenau | 11D2 |

Kahnfährhafen Leipe, Dorfstrasse 34, Leipe. **GPS:** n51,85301 e14,05023. ⬆️.

4 ⬛ € 5. **Surface:** metalled. ⭕ 01/01-31/12
Distance: 🚴11,6km.

| ⬛ S | Lübbenau | 11D2 |

Spreewaldhof Leipe, Leiper Dorfstraße 2, Leipe. **GPS:** n51,85161 e14,03912. ⬆️.

4 ⬛ € 6 + € 1,50/pp tourist tax ⚡ 🔧 € 2/day WC included. **Surface:** grassy.
Distance: ⊗on the spot.
Remarks: Bread-service.

| ⬛ S | Luckenwalde | 11B1 |

Restaurant Elsthal, Teichwiesenweg, Elsthal. **GPS:** n52,07428 e13,16744. ⬆️.
10 ⬛ € 10 ⚡ Ch 🔧 included. **Surface:** sand. ⭕ 01/01-31/12
Remarks: Max. <>2.35m.

| ⬛ S | Lychen | 6B4 |

Marina-Yachthafen Lychensee, Schlüsssstrasse 7. **GPS:** n53,21187 e13,29686. ⬆️.

6 ⬛ € 1/meter ⚡ Ch 🔧 € 2 WC € 1.
Surface: grassy. ⭕ 15/04-15/10
Distance: 🚋650m.
Remarks: Information at harbourmaster, boat rental.

| ⬛ S | Nackel | 6A5 |

Gaststätte Birkenhof, Segeletzerstrasse 2. **GPS:** n52,82503 e12,56528.

3 ⬛ € 3 ⚡ Ch 🔧 € 3 WC. **Surface:** metalled.

| ⬛ | Potsdam | 6B6 |

Georg-Hermans Allee/Esplanade. GPS: n52,41946 e13,05130. ⬆️.

20 ⬛ € 4/24h. **Surface:** asphalted. ⭕ 01/01-31/12
Distance: 🚶3km ⊗500m 🚋500m 🚊tram BUGA-Park.

Tourist information Potsdam:
☺ Filmpark Babelsberg, August-Bebel-Str. 26-53. Attractions park concerning the film. ⭕ 23/03-31/10 10-18h.

⚌S   **Schmergow**   **6B6**

Zum fröhlichen Landmann, Ziegeleiweg 17. **GPS**: n52,45416 e12,80553.⬆️

30 🏕️ € 5, guests free 🚰€ 2,50 ♻️Ch 💧€ 2,50. **Surface:** grassy. ◻️ 01/01-31/12

⚌S   **Schwedt-Oder**   **6D5**

Wassersportzentrum Schwedt, Wasserplatz 4. **GPS**: n53,05759 e14,29861.⬆️

30 🏕️ € 10 🚰♻️ Ch 💧WC ⬜included. **Surface:** grassy. ◻️ 01/01-31/12
Distance: 🚶1km 🏊on the spot ⊗on the spot 🍺500m.
Remarks: Check in at harbourmaster or bar.

⚌S   **Stolzenhagen**   **6D5**

Am Kiez, Hohensaalenstrasse. **GPS**: n52,94916 e14,10833.

20 🏕️ € 7,50 🚰♻️Ch 💧€ 2 WC⬜ Use sanitary 🚰euro ♻️ 2,50.
Distance: 🏊on the spot.
Remarks: Directly beside canal, bread-service.

⚌S   **Templin**   **6C5**

Alter Knehdenerstrasse. **GPS**: n53,12359 e13,49423.➡️

40 🏕️free 🚰€ 1 ♻️Ch. **Surface:** asphalted/metalled. ◻️ 01/01-31/12
Distance: 🚶300m ⊗300m 🍺300m.

⚌S   **Tiefensee**   **6C6**

Reisemobilplatz, Country Camping Tiefensee, Schmiedeweg 1. **GPS**: n52,68302 e13,84292.

30 🏕️€ 12 🚰♻️Ch 💧WCincluded ⬜€ 0,50 🧼. ◻️ 01/01-31/12
Distance: 🚶on the spot 🏊on the spot ➤on the spot ⊗on the spot 🍺on the spot 🚌on the spot.

⚌S   **Weisen**   **5D5**

Wohnmobilstellplatz Am Biotop, Heinrich-Heine-Strasse 4. **GPS**: n53,02062 e11,78086.⬆️➡️

5 🏕️free 🚰♻️. **Surface:** gravel. ◻️ 01/01-31/12

⚌S   **Werder-Havel**   **11B1**

An der Föhse. **GPS**: n52,37807 e12,93704.⬆️

20 🏕️€ 5 🚰♻️Chincluded 💧(8x)€ 2,50/day, WC€ 0,30.
Surface: gravel.
◻️ 01/01-31/12
Distance: 🚶on the spot 🏊on the spot ⊗on the spot 🍺on the spot 🚌100m.
Remarks: Check in at harbourmaster.

Saxony

⚌   **Adorf**   **11A6**

Waldbad, Waldbadstrasse 5. **GPS**: n50,30778 e12,25056.

🏕️free. **Surface:** metalled. ◻️ 01/01-31/12
Distance: 🚶1km 🍺500m.
Remarks: Max. 24h.

⚠S   **Amtsberg**   **11C5**

Waldcamping Erzgebirge, B174, An der Dittersdorfer Höhe, Dittersdorf. **GPS**: n50,76583 e13,01444.

DE

60 ⌇€ 13-15 ⊨ ᴄʜ ⚡€ 2 WC ᴵincluded. **Surface:** grassy/metalled.
◯ 01/01-31/12

Bad Elster 11A6

Forsthausschänke, Heissenstein 19. **GPS:** n50,27194 e12,24639.

4 ⌇€ 4 ⊨ ᴄʜincluded ⚡€ 2. ◯ 01/01-31/12
Distance: 1,5km ⊗campsite 1,5km.

Tourist information Bad Elster:
ℹ Traditional health resort.

Bad Lausick 11B4

Campingplatz Landidyll, Beuchaer Oberweg 7. **GPS:** n51,15200 e12,62663.
35 ⌇€ 7,50 ⊨ ᴄʜ ⚡ WC included ᴵ€ 0,50. ◯ 01/01-31/12
Distance: on the spot ⊗1km 2km.

Bad Lausick 11B4

Am Riff 3. **GPS:** n51,14321 e12,65383.
10 ⌇free. **Surface:** asphalted.
Remarks: At swimming pool.

Bad Muskau 11aA1

Am Fürst-Pückler-Park, Heideweg 2. **GPS:** n51,53365 e14,71727.
20 ⌇€ 8 ⊨ ᴄʜ ⚡€ 2 WC included.
Distance: on the spot ⊗4km 2km.

Biehain 11aA1

Erholungsgebiet Biehainer See'n, Am Waldsee. **GPS:** n51,28662 e14,92490.
10 ⌇€ 5 ⊨ ᴄʜ ⚡ WC ᴵincluded.
Distance: 1km on the spot ⊗on the spot 2km.
Remarks: Max. 48h.

Breitenbrunn 11B5

Sportpark Rabenberg, Rabenbergweg. **GPS:** n50,45556 e12,74417.

15 ⌇€ 5 + €5/pp ⊨ ᴄʜ ⚡€ 2/day WC ᴵ€ 0,50. **Surface:** metalled.
◯ 01/01-31/12
Distance: 5km ⊗5km 5km.
Remarks: Arrival <22h, dog € 2/day.

Crottendorf 11B5

Pension Kalkberg, Joachimsthaller strasse 294. **GPS:** n50,46378 e12,92238.
16 ⌇€ 15 ⊨ ᴄʜincluded ⚡€ 2. ◯ 01/01-31/12 ◯ Mo.
Distance: 4km ⊗on the spot 1,5km.

Diesbar-Seusslitz 11C3

Restaurant Zum Rosengarten, S88, Meissnerstrasse 4, Nünchritz. **GPS:** n51,23333 e13,42667.

4 ⌇guests free ⊨ ᴄʜ ⚡ WC. **Surface:** metalled.
Distance: ⊗on the spot.
Remarks: Along the river Elbe.

Dresden 11D4

Parkplatz Grosse Meissner, Wiesentor Strasse. **GPS:** n51,05639 e13,74306.

30 ⌇€ 14 <6,8m, € 16 6,8m-8m, € 20 >8m ⊨ ⚡ 2/100liter ᴄʜ€ 2 ⚡
(14x)€ 4/day. **Surface:** asphalted. ◯ 01/01-31/12
Distance: 100m.

Dresden 11D4

Werner Knopf, B6, Meissner Landstrasse. **GPS:** n51,08131 e13,65563.
⚡€ 5 ⚡€ 2.
Distance: 500m.

Dresden 11D4

Fritz-Berger-Freizeit-Markt, Sachsenallee, Kesseldorf. **GPS:** n51,03567 e13,58962.

⌇⊨ € 1/80liter ᴄʜ. ◯ opening hours shop

Dresden 11D4

Schaffer-mobil, Wohnmobile GmbH, Kötzschenbroderstrasse 125. **GPS:** n51,08639 e13,68222.

45 ⌇€ 11 ⊨ € 0,50 ⚡€ 0,50 ᴄʜ€ 0,50 ⚡€ 0,50/kWh WC ᴵ€ 0,50.
◯ 01/01-31/12
Distance: Dresden 5km 2km ⊗200m 500m 200m.

Remarks: Repair possibilities motorhome, access <19h, bread service.

Tourist information Dresden:

ℹ️ Dresden-City-Card.Card gives among other things for free public transport, entrance to many museums, discounts on boat trips, restaurants etc. ⭘ 01/01-31/12. 🎫 € 18/48h.

ℹ️ Tourist Information, Prager strasse; Schinkelwache/Theaterplatz, www. dresden.de.Former residence city with many curiosities.

👁 Frauenkiche.Protestant church.

👁 Zwinger.Baroque complex in the old city center with important museums. ⭘ Tue-Su.

Ⓜ Albertinum Museum.Art collection.

🎄 Striezelmarkt, Altstadt.Christmas fair. ⭘ Dec.

DE

🏕 S	Ebersbach/Sachsen 🎿	11aA2

Fest- und Parkplatz am Freibad, Kottmarsdorfer Strasse. **GPS:** n51,00972 e14,59806.

7 🏕 € 5, € 10 service incl ⛽🍽 Ch 🔌 📷. **Surface:** metalled. ⭘ 01/04-30/10
Distance: 🚶1km ⊗500m 🏊1km.

🍴 S	Eichigt	11A6

Landgasthof Süssebach, Hauptstrasse 9. **GPS:** n50,36278 e12,15583.

2 🏕 € 10 ⛽🍽 Ch 🔌 WC 🗑 included. ⭘ 01/01-31/12
Distance: 🏊3km.

🏕 S	Elsterheide	11D3

Wohnmobilstellplatz Lothar Meusel, Am Hochwald 27, Tätzschwitz. **GPS:** n51,48304 e14,10750.

8 🏕 € 6,50-7,50 ⛽🍽 Ch 🔌 WC included 🗑€ 2,25. ⭘ 01/04-31/10
Distance: ⊗3km 🏊8-10km.

🏕 S	Freiberg	11C4

Messeplatz, Winklerstrasse. **GPS:** n50,92375 e13,34261.⬆.

3 🏕 free ⛽ WC. **Surface:** grasstiles. ⭘ 01/01-31/12
Distance: 🚶300m ⊗300m 🏊300m 🚌50m.

🏕 S	Geierswalde	11D3

Ferien- und Freizeitpark Geierswalde See, Promenadeweg. **GPS:** n51,49547 e14,13146.

🏕 € 6 ⛽ 🔌 2 Ch 🔌 WC 🗑. **Surface:** grassy. ⭘ 01/04-01/10
Distance: 🚶500m ⟋Geierswaldesee 300m 🏊5km.

🏕 S	Grünhain	11B5

Freizeitpark, Auer Strasse 82, Haus des Gastes, Grünhain-Beierfeld. **GPS:** n50,58139 e12,79167.

6 🏕 € 5 ⛽ € 1 🍽 € 1, customers free Ch 🔌 € 1,50/day WC 🗑 € 1. **Surface:** metalled. ⭘ 01/01-31/12
Distance: 🚶1km 🏊3km.

🏕 S	Heidenau	11D4

Wohnmobilplatz Heidenau, Rudolf Breischeidstrasse 23. **GPS:** n50,98417 e13,85028.

20 🏕 € 9 ⛽ € 1,50 🍽 Ch 🔌 € 1,50 🗑 € 1,50. **Surface:** gravel. ⭘ 01/04-31/10
Distance: 🚶Heidenau 4km ⊗1,5km, Imbiss 50m 🏊2km 🚌1,5km.
Remarks: A17 exit Heidenau, dir Pirna (B172), in Heidenau follow signs.

🍴 S	Hermsdorf	11D5

Ski- & Sporthotel SWF, Bahnhofstraße 7. **GPS:** n50,73241 e13,66400.
8 🏕 € 4, tourist tax € 0,50/pp ⛽ € 2 🍽 € 2 Ch 🔌 € 1/day. ⭘ 01/01-31/12

🏕 S	Hermsdorf	11D5

Autofhof Kanzfei, Kraftsdorferstrasse. **GPS:** n50,88902 e11,87206.⬆.
10 🏕 € 2,50 ⛽ € 1/80liter 🍽 Ch WC. **Surface:** metalled. ⭘ 01/01-31/12
Distance: 🚶2km ⟋500m ⊗on the spot 🏊Shell-shop.

🏕 S	Königsfeld-Stollsdorf	11B4

Spreer's Ferienhaus, Hauptstrasse 28. **GPS:** n51,04861 e12,74500.

4 ⌁8 ⌁ ᴄh ⌁€ 2. ◘ 01/01-31/12
Distance: ⌁4km ⌁4km.

3 ⌁€4/night ⌁ ᴄhfree ⌁€ 1.
Surface: metalled. ◘ 01/01-31/12
Distance: ⌁2,1km.

| ⌁S | **Königstein** | 11D4 |

Panoramhotel Lilienstein, Ebenheit 7. **GPS:** n50,92527 e14,07527.
10 ⌁€10 ⌁ ⌁.
Distance: ⌁on the spot.
Remarks: Bread-service and breakfast buffet.

| ⌁S | **Leipzig** | 11A3 |

Campinghof Bartl, Bornaer Chaussee 36, Markkleeberg. **GPS:** n51,27000 e12,43194.

26 ⌁15 ⌁€ 2 ᴄh ⌁€ 2 WC ⌁. **Surface:** grassy/metalled. ◘
01/01-31/12
Distance: ⌁Leipzig 5km ⌁2km ⌁1,5km.

| ⌁S | **Leipzig** | 11A3 |

Querstraße 14. **GPS:** n51,34020 e12,38595.⌁.
20 ⌁10-15/24h ⌁€ 3.
Distance: ⌁8,5km.

Tourist information Leipzig:
ℹ Leipzig Information, Richard-Wagner-strasse 1, Leipzig, www.leipzig.de.

| ⌁S | **Marienberg** ⌁❄ | 11C5 |

Rätzteich, Gelobtland 27c. **GPS:** n50,62417 e13,17861.

3 ⌁€3 ⌁€ 1 ⌁€ 1 ᴄh€ 1 ⌁€ 1.
Surface: metalled. ◘ 01/01-31/12
Distance: ⌁5km ⌁500m ⌁5km ⌁3km.
Remarks: Recreation area.

| ⌁S | **Oberschindmaas** | 11B5 |

Caravan Service Bressler, Zwickauerstrasse 78. **GPS:** n50,80889 e12,48667.

| ⌁S | **Oberwiesental** ⌁⌁❄ | 11C5 |

OTG Tennishalle, Vieren Strasse 1a. **GPS:** n50,42722 e12,96944.

20 ⌁€ 11, 01/12-31/03 € 17 ⌁ ᴄh ⌁ WC ⌁included. **Surface:** metalled.
◘ 01/01-31/12
Distance: ⌁on the spot ⌁250m.
Remarks: Parking tennishall, check in at reception tennishall < 22h, bread-
service.

| ⌁ | **Rothersdorf** | 11B3 |

Zur-Tabak-Baude. GPS: n51,30647 e12,73830.

20 ⌁€ 6, guests free. **Surface:** grassy. ◘ 01/01-31/12
Distance: ⌁2km ⌁on the spot ⌁1,5km.

| ⌁S | **Sebnitz** | 11D4 |

Touristik zentrum Sebnitz, Albert Kunzeweg 30-36. **GPS:** n50,96156 e14,27735.

30 ⌁€ 6/pppd ⌁ ᴄh ⌁ WCincluded.
Surface: metalled.
◘ 01/04-31/10
Distance: ⌁2km ⌁1-2km ⌁500m ⌁2km Sebnitz.
Remarks: Swimming pool, tourist tax € 0,75/pppd.

Tourist information Sebnitz:
ℹ Touristinformation Sebnitz, Schillerstrasse 3.Silk flower city.

| ⌁S | **Thräna** | 11aA2 |

Freizeitcamp, Zum Wildgehege, Hohendubrau. **GPS:** n51,23528 e14,69972.

DE

10 🛏 € 5, campsite € 14,50 🚰 🔌Ch 🚿 € 0,45/kWh. **Surface:** grassy/ metalled. ⬛ 01/05-30/09
Distance: ⊗Gaststätte ⚓2,5km Gebelzig.

🛏S **Zittau** 11aA2
Zittau Am Dreiländereck, Brückenstrasse 23. **GPS:** n50,89405 e14,82176.⬆⬆➡
40 🛏 € 7 🚰 € 1 🔌Ch 🚿 (16x)€ 1/8h WC🚽. **Surface:** metalled. ⬛
01/01-31/12
Distance: ⚓1,5km ⚓200m.
Remarks: Three Countries' Corner Germany-Czech Republic-Poland.

🛏S **Zwota** 11B6
Alte Scheune Camping, Merkneukirchner Strasse 79. **GPS:** n50,35111 e12,38111.

70 🛏 € 5 🚰 € 1 🔌Ch 🚿 € 2 WC🚽€ 1. **Surface:** metalled. ⬛ 01/01-31/12. **Distance:** ⚓Klingenthal 6km ⚓6km.

North Rhine Westphalia
🛏S **Aachen** 8D5
Aachen-Camping, Branderhofer Weg 11. **GPS:** n50,76111 e6,10306.

46 🛏 € 10/night 🚰 🔌Ch 🚿 WC included 🚽€ 1. ⬛ 01/01-31/12
Distance: ⚓1,7km ⊗700m ⚓700m ⚓300m.
Tourist information Aachen:
ℹ Informationsbüro Elisenbrunnen, www.aachen.de.

🛏S **Ahaus** 9A2
Krimesplatz, Schlossstrasse. **GPS:** n52,07450 e7,00299.⬆

8 🛏free 🚰€ 0,50/80liter 🔌Ch 🚿(6x)€ 0,50/kWh WC. **Surface:** metalled. ⬛ 01/01-31/12 ⬛ during event.
Distance: ⚓on the spot.
Remarks: Parking in the centre, max. 3 nights.

🛏S **Ahlen** 9C3
Freizeitbad Berliner Park, Dolbergerstrasse 66. **GPS:** n51,75559 e7,89694.⬆

2 🛏 € 8/24h 🚰 🔌 🚿.
Distance: ⚓Nearby centre.
Remarks: Max. 3 nights.

🛏S **Alpen** 8D3
An der Motte, Burgstrasse 66. **GPS:** n51,57985 e6,51846.⬆

11 🛏 € 7,50 🚰 🔌Ch 🚿 included. 🏠 **Location:** Rural, comfortable. **Surface:** gravel. ⬛ 01/01-31/12
Distance: ⚓500m ⚓2,5km ⚓500m.

🛏S **Altena** 9B4
Sauerlandhalle Pragpaul, Hermann Vossstrasse 14. **GPS:** n51,30861 e7,66056.➡.

12 🛏free 🚰€ 0,50 🔌€ 0,50 Ch 🚿€ 1/2kWh. **Surface:** metalled. ⬛ 01/01-31/12
Distance: ⚓2km ⊗nearby ⚓2km.

🛏 **Altenbeken** 9D3
Landhaus Friedenstal, Hüttenstrasse 42. **GPS:** n51,75992 e8,95111.⬆

5 🛏 € 5. **Surface:** grassy/gravel. ⬛ 01/01-31/12
Distance: ⚓200m ⊗on the spot ⚓200m.

Ⓢ Ⓢ **Altenberge** 👥 **9B2**
Sportpark Grosseberg, Bijlenweg. **GPS**: n52,05528 e7,47056. ⬆️.

20 ⬛free ⚡€ 0,50 🚰Ch. **Surface:** metalled. ⚫ 01/01-31/12
Distance: 🚶on the spot ⊗nearby 🛒1,5km.
Remarks: Parking sports centre.

Ⓢ **Arnsberg** **9C4**
An der Schlacht/Ruhrstrasse. **GPS**: n51,40127 e8,06468. ⬆️.
4 ⬛free. **Location:** Very simple. **Surface:** gravel.
Distance: ⚓3,3km 🛒Lidl 50m.

🍴Ⓢ **Ascheberg** **9B2**
Gasthaus Eickholt, Frieport 22, Davensberg. **GPS**: n51,82619 e7,59391.

6 ⬛guests free ⚡🔌€ 5 WC 📶. **Surface:** grassy. ⚫ 01/01-31/12 ⚫
Wed.
Distance: 🚶800m ⚓5,5km ⊗on the spot 🛒1km 🚂800m.

Ⓢ **Attendorn** **9C4**
Stellplatz Attendorn, Am Zollstock 5. **GPS**: n51,12449 e7,97123. ⬆️.

8 ⬛free. **Surface:** metalled. ⚫ 01/01-31/12
Distance: 🚶500m 🛒500m.

🍴Ⓢ **Attendorn** **9C4**
Haus Schnepper, Talstrasse 19. **GPS**: n51,10530 e7,95744.

15 ⬛guests free ⚡🔌Ch 🔌free.
Surface: metalled. ⚫ 01/01-31/12
Distance: 🚶1km ⊗on the spot 🛒1km.

🍴Ⓢ **Attendorn** **9C4**
Land-Hotel-Struck, Repetalstrasse 245, Niederhelden. **GPS**: n51,12073 e7,97284.

6 ⬛guests free 🔌€ 2,60 WC. ⚫ 01/01-31/12
Distance: 🚶on the spot ⊗on the spot 🛒2km.

Ⓢ **Bad Berleburg** **9C4**
Rothaarbad, Am Stöppel. **GPS**: n51,04229 e8,38151.

3 ⬛free ⚡€ 2 🚰Ch 🔌€ 1/8h. ⚫ 01/01-31/12
Remarks: Parking at the swimming pool.

🍴Ⓢ **Bad Berleburg** **9C4**
Pension-Bauernladen Schmelzhütte, K52 Hoheleye. **GPS**: n51,13969 e8,45868.

6 ⬛€10 🚰🔌Ch 🔌€ 2. ⚫ 01/01-31/12
Distance: 🚶1km ⊗on the spot 🛒1km.
Remarks: Bread-service.

👥 **Bad Berleburg** **9C4**
Hotel-Restaurant Erholung, L717 Wemlighausen. **GPS**: n51,06776 e8,44527.

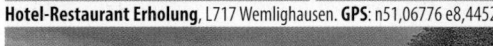

8 ⬛free. ⚫ 01/01-31/12
Distance: ⊗on the spot.

Ⓢ Ⓢ **Bad Driburg** ♨️ **9D3**
P Driburg Therme, Georg-Nave-Strasse 24. **GPS**: n51,74194 e9,02542. ⬆️.

DE

10 🛏 € 5 + tourist tax 🚿 (10x)€ 2,50/day. **Surface:** metalled. ⬛ 01/01-31/12
Distance: 🚶1km 🛒1km.
Remarks: Max. 7m.

| 🚿S | Bad Laasphe | 9C5 |

Mühlenstrasse. **GPS:** n50,92412 e8,41146.➡.

7 🛏 € 6/day 🚰 € 0,50/80liter 🔌Ch🚿 € 0,50/kWh. ⬛ 01/01-31/12
Distance: 🚶500m ⊗500m 🛒500m.
Remarks: Parking at town hall.

| 🍴S | Bad Laasphe | 9C5 |

Hotel Jagdhof Glashütte, Glashütterstrasse 20, Volkholz. **GPS:** n50,92008 e8,28070.

6 🛏 € 10 🚿. **Surface:** grassy. ⬛ 01/01-31/12
Distance: ⊗on the spot.

| 🍴 | Bad Laasphe | 9C5 |

Landhotel Doerr, Sieg-Lahn Strasse 8, Feudingen. **GPS:** n50,94105 e8,32985.

2 🛏 € 5/day. ⬛ 01/01-31/12
Distance: 🚶500m ⊗on the spot 🛒500m.

| 🚿S | Bad Lippspringe | 9D3 |

Arminiuspark, Burgstraße 10. **GPS:** n51,78124 e8,82447.
11 🛏 € 2,80/1p +1p € 2/pp 🚰🔌Ch🚿.
Surface: gravel. ⬛ 01/01-31/12
Distance: 🚶300m ⊗350m.

| 🚿S | Bad Münstereifel | 9A6 |

Wohnmobilpark Eifel, Dr.Grevestraße 16. **GPS:** n50,54600 e6,76514.

30 🛏 € 6,50 + € 1/pp tourist tax 🚰 2 🔌Ch🚿included WC. **Surface:** grassy/metalled. ⬛ 01/01-31/12
Distance: 🚶350m ⊗on the spot 🛒100m.
Remarks: To pay at swimming pool.

| 🚿 | Bad Oeynhausen ♨ | 9D1 |

Südbahnstraße/Detmolder Straße. **GPS:** n52,19680 e8,80038.
3 🛏free. **Surface:** asphalted. ⬛ 01/01-31/12
Remarks: Max. 2 days.

| 🍴 | Bad Oeynhausen ♨ | 9D1 |

Siekmeiers Hof, Volmerdingsener strasse 111. **GPS:** n52,24679 e8,78394.

10 🛏guests free. ⬛ 01/01-31/12 ⬤ Mon, Tue.
Distance: 🚶on the spot ⊗on the spot 🛒1km.

| 🚿S | Bad Salzuflen | 9D2 |

Wohnmobil-Park Flachsheide, Forsthausweg. **GPS:** n52,09868 e8,74569.
25 🛏 € 7/day, tourist tax € 2,90/pp/day 🚰🔌Ch🚿 WC included. ⬛ 01/01-31/12
Distance: 🚶1,5km 🚴5,5km 🏊on the spot ⊗500m 🛒1,5km 🚌free.
Remarks: Follow 'Vitasol'.

| ♨S | Bad Sassendorf ♨ | 9C3 |

Kurcamping Rumkerhof, Weslarnerstrasse 30. **GPS:** n51,59581 e8,17909.⬆➡.

93 🛏 € 6,50, € 1,30/pp tourist tax 🚰 € 0,50/100liter 🔌Ch🚿 (93x)€ 0,50/kWh. **Surface:** gravel. ⬛ 01/01-31/12
Distance: 🚶1,3km ⊗1,3km.
Remarks: Bread-service, waste dump € 0,50.

| 🚿S | Bad Waldliesborn | 9C3 |

Wohnmobilstellplatz, Quellenstraße. **GPS:** n51,71759 e8,33587.⬆.

8 �€ 4,40, tourist tax € 2,10/pp 🚰 € 2/100liter ⬛Ch ✦ (8x)€ 2/24h, 16Amp. **Surface:** gravel. ◑ 01/01-31/12
Distance: 🚶400m ⊗200m 🛒400m 🚏400m.
Remarks: Discount on access terme.

Bad Westernkotten 9C3
Wohnmobilplatz An den Sole-Thermen, Mühlenweg 1. **GPS:** n51,52028 e8,39770.⬆.

46 ⌐₃€ 6, tourist tax € 2/pp 🚰 € 1/100liter ⬛Ch ✦ € 0,50/kWh. ◑ 01/01-31/12
Distance: 🛒bakery 300m.
Remarks: Bread-service.

Bad Wünnenberg 9D3
Wohnmobilhafen, In den Erlen. **GPS:** n51,52058 e8,70133. ⬆➡.

12 ⌐₃free, tourist tax € 1/pp 🚰 € 1 ⬛€ 1 Ch ✦ € 1/24h. **Surface:** gravel. ◑ 01/01-31/12
Distance: 🚶100m 🚲400m ⊗100m 🛒400m.
Remarks: Walking and bicycle area.

Balve 9B4
Am Hallenbad, In der Murmke 9. **GPS:** n51,32729 e7,86920.⬆.
3 ⌐₃free ✦ € 1/80liter ⬛Ch ✦ € 1/kWh. **Surface:** metalled. ◑ 01/01-31/12
Distance: 🚶600m.

Barntrup 9D2
Ferienpark Teutoburger Wald, Badeanstaltsweg 4. **GPS:** n51,98768 e9,11027.
9 ⌐₃€ 7,50 🚰 € 1 ⬛Ch ✦ € 1.
Surface: grassy/metalled. ◑ 01/04-31/10
Distance: 🚶450m.

Bedburg-Hau 8D3
Womo-Moyland, Moyländer Allee 3a, Moyland. **GPS:** n51,75562 e6,24381.⬆➡.

50 ⌐₃€ 5/24h, € 9/48h, € 12/72h 🚰 € 0,50/100liter ⬛Ch ✦ € 2,50/24h 📶.🏠🧺
Location: Rural, comfortable. **Surface:** grasstiles. ◑ 01/01-31/12
Distance: 🚶Kleve-zentrum 8km ⊗300m.
Remarks: Schloss Moyland 300m, golf court 500m.

Bedburg-Hau 8D3
Landgasthaus Schwanenhof, Mühlenstraße 71, Ortsteil Schneppenbaum. **GPS:** n51,76096 e6,20404.⬆.

25 ⌐₃€ 5 🚰 ⬛Ch ✦ (18x). 🛁 **Location:** Rural, comfortable. **Surface:** grassy. ◑ 01/01-31/12
Distance: 🚶500m ⊗on the spot 🛒1km.
Remarks: Bread-service.
Tourist information Bedburg-Hau:
Ⓜ✖ Schloß Moyland, Am Schloss 4.Castle. ◑ Tue-Fri 11-18h, sa-su 10-18h, 1/4-31/3 tue-so 11-17h ◉ Mon.

Bergheim 9A5
Stellplatz Paffendorf, Königsstrasse/Kastanienallee. **GPS:** n50,96389 e6,61194. ⬆➡.

8 ⌐₃free. **Surface:** asphalted. ◑ 01/01-31/12
Distance: 🚶Bergheim 2km 🚲2,3km ⊗300m 🛒500m.
Remarks: Max. 2 days, castle Paffendorf 100m.

Bergkamen 9B3
Wohnmobilhafen Marina Rünthe, Hafenweg, Rünthe. **GPS:** n51,64106 e7,64309.
18 ⌐₃€ 7/24h 🚰 € 1/80liter ⬛Ch ✦ (12x)€ 0,50/kWh. **Surface:** grassy/gravel. ◑ 01/01-31/12
Distance: 🚶500m 🚲3,8km.
Remarks: Only exact change, max. 3 days.

Bergkamen 9B3
Freizeitzentrum Im Häupen, Häupenweg 29. **GPS:** n51,61300 e7,63075.⬆➡.

DE

5 ⛺free. **Surface:** metalled. 🚻 01/01-31/12
Distance: ⚓on the spot ⛵3,4km ⊗on the spot 🛒on the spot.

4 ⛺free 🚰 Ch ✂ (4x)€ 1. **Surface:** gravel. 🚻 01/01-31/12
Distance: ⚓500m 🛒500m.
Remarks: At swimming pool, service Kläranlage.

🏕S **Beverungen** 🍨🏤🌊 **10A3**
Wohnmobilhafen Weser, Am Hakel. **GPS:** n51,66167 e9,37639. ⬆➡

🏕S **Blankenheim** **9A6**
Weiherhalle, Koblenzerstrasse. **GPS:** n50,43499 e6,65439. ⬆

10 ⛺free 🚰free. **Surface:** grassy. 🚻 01/01-31/12
Distance: ⚓on the spot ⛵on the spot 🎣on the spot ⊗on the spot 🛒on the spot.
Remarks: Next to Festplatz.

15 ⛺€ 5/24h 🚰€ 1/80liter 🗑Ch ✂ (12x)€ 2/10h WC. **Surface:** metalled. 🚻 01/01-31/12
Distance: ⚓150m.

🍴S **Beverungen** 🍨🏤🌊 **10A3**
Fährklause Wehrden, Weredunstrasse, Wehrden. **GPS:** n51,71278 e9,39028. ⬆

🏕S **Bocholt** 🏤 **4C4**
WoMo Park am Aasee, Uhlandstraße 39. **GPS:** n51,83496 e6,63146. ⬆

30 ⛺free 🚰WCfree. 🚻 01/01-31/12
Distance: ⚓on the spot ⛵on the spot 🎣on the spot ⊗on the spot 🛒on the spot.

37 ⛺€ 5 🚰€ 0,50/50liter 🗑Ch ✂ (20x)€ 0,50/kWh WC🧺€ 3,50, dryer € 2,50 📶.🚲 **Location:** Urban, central, noisy. **Surface:** metalled. 🚻 01/01-31/12
Distance: ⊗300m 🛒300m.

🏕S **Bielefeld** 〰🏤 **9C2**
Am Johannisberg, Dornbergerstrasse. **GPS:** n52,02270 e8,51155. ⬆➡

🏕S **Bocholt** 🏤 **4C4**
Inselbad Bahia, Hemdenerweg 169. **GPS:** n51,86265 e6,61002. ⬆➡

10 ⛺01/03-01/12 € 5/24h 🚰€ 1 🗑Ch ✂€ 1/8h. 🚌 **Location:**
Comfortable, quit. **Surface:** metalled. 🚻 01/01-31/12
Distance: ⚓2km ⊗Imbiss 🛒2km 🚮2km.

10 ⛺free 🚰 🗑Ch.
Location: Rural.
Surface: grasstiles. 🚻 01/01-31/12
Distance: ⚓2,5km ⊗450m 🛒1km 🚮on the spot.
Remarks: Max. 48h, coins available at swimming pool.

🏕S **Billerbeck** **9B2**
Am Freibad, Osterwickerstrasse. **GPS:** n51,97928 e7,28190. ⬆➡

🏕 **Bocholt** 🏤 **4C4**
Euregio-Gymnasium, Unter den Eichen, Blücherstrasse. **GPS:** n51,84884 e6,63700. ⬆

DE

10 🛏free.
Location: Urban, very simple.
Surface: metalled.
🅿 01/01-31/12
Distance: 🚶1km ⊗700m 🚐on the spot.
Remarks: Parking 'Stadtswald', max. 3 nights.

Tourist information Bocholt:

ℹ Tourist-Info Bocholt, Europaplatz 26-28, www.bocholt.de.Motorhome friendly town, former center of textile industry, modern city centre.
Ⓜ Textilmuseum, Uhlandstrasse 50.Industry museum. 🅿 Tue-Su 10-18h.
🛖 Rathaus - Gasthausplatz. 🅿 Thu-evening.
🛹 Vier Räder und acht Rollen.Skating routes, available at Tourist-Info and on Internet.

🛏 S	Bonn	9A5

An den Museen, Baunscheidtstrasse 17. **GPS:** n50,71193 e7,12191.⬆.

8 🛏€ 5/24h 🚐€ 3/24h WC 🚻.
Surface: asphalted. 🅿 01/01-31/12
Distance: 🚐800m.

🛏	Bonn	9A5

Wohnmobilplatz An der Josefhöhe, An der Josefhöhe. **GPS:** n50,75273 e7,08072.⬆➡.

10 🛏free. 🅿 01/01-31/12
Distance: 🚶on the spot ⊗1km 🚰300m.

🛏 S	Borken	9A2

Aquarius-Bad, Feldmark. **GPS:** n51,83644 e6,86479.⬆➡.

20 🛏free 🚰🍽 Chfree.
Location: Rural. **Surface:** grassy. 🅿 01/01-31/12
Distance: 🚶1km ⊗1km 🚰1km.
Remarks: Parking swimming pool, max. 3 nights, service: Kläranlage Borken Mo-Thu 7-16h. Fri 7-11.30h.

🛏	Borken	9A2

Festplatz Weseke, Borkenwirther strasse, Weseke. **GPS:** n51,90529 e6,85210.⬆.

5 🛏free.
Location: Rural, very simple. **Surface:** metalled. 🅿 01/01-31/12
Distance: 🚶500m ⊗500m 🚰500m.
Remarks: Max. 3 nights.

🛏	Borken	9A2

Schlossklinik Pröbsting, Pröbstaller Allee. **GPS:** n51,83861 e6,80556.⬆.
10 🛏free. **Surface:** metalled. 🅿 01/01-31/12
Distance: 🏊Badesee 150m.

🛏	Borken	9A2

Wasserburg Gemen, Coesfelderstrasse, Gemen. **GPS:** n51,86172 e6,86909.⬆➡.

5 🛏free. **Location:** Rural. **Surface:** metalled. 🅿 01/01-31/12
Distance: 🚶1km 🏊500m 🚰500m ⊗1km 🚰1km.
Remarks: Parking sports park, max. 3 nights.

🛏 S	Borken	9A2

Camping Pröbstingersee, Dirkshof 11, Hoxfeld. **GPS:** n51,83237 e6,78764.

10 🛏free 🚰🍽 Ch.
Surface: metalled. 🅿 01/01-31/12
Distance: 🚶6,5km 🏊100m ⊗100m.
Remarks: Max. 3 nights, service agains payment on campsite.

🛏 S	Borken	9A2

Gestüt Forellenhof Wolter, Zum Hombron 9. **GPS:** n51,86245 e6,89797.⬆.
15 🛏€ 11 🚰🍽 Ch 🛠 (7x)included. **Surface:** gravel. 🅿 01/01-31/12
Distance: 🚶Borken 3,5km 🎣fish pond ⊗on the spot.
Remarks: Check in at Gaststätte, € 5 euro discount coupon.

Tourist information Borken:

ℹ Tourist Info, Im Bahnhof, www.borken.de.

🛏	Bottrop	9A3

Warner Bros Movie World, Kirchhellen, Warner Allee 1. **GPS:** n51,62400 e6,97096.⬆.

DE

100 ⌶ free.
Surface: asphalted. ⬛ visiting hours park
Distance: 2,7km 100m 2,7km.

Tourist information Bottrop:
⬤ Alpincenter, Prosperstrasse.Indoor ski centre. ⬛ 9-24h. day ticket € 25, <18h € 18.
⬤ Freizeitpark Schloß Beck.Amusement park. ⬛ 01/03-31/10 9-18h.
⬤ Warner Bros Movie World, Kirchhellen.Attractions park concerning the film.
⬛ 01/04-31/10 10-18h, summer, weekend 9-21/22h.

| | Brakel/Bellersen | 9D2 |

Wohnmobilhafen Mühlengrund, Meinolfussstrasse 6. **GPS:** n51,77217 e9,18804.

23 ⌶ € 8,50 € 0,50 Ch included.
Surface: grasstiles.
⬛ 01/01-31/12
Distance: 800m 400m 800m 800m.

Tourist information Brakel/Bellersen:
www.bellersen.de.Health resort.

| | Bruchhausen | 10A3 |

Bruchhäuserstrasse. **GPS:** n51,70714 e9,29192.

4 ⌶ free. **Surface:** gravel. ⬛ 01/01-31/12
Distance: 200m 200m 200m.

| | Brüggen | 8D4 |

Freizeitplatz Brachter Wald, St.-Barbara-Straße 40–42, Bracht. **GPS:** n51,25713 e6,17022.
14 ⌶ € 7,50, 2 pers.incl. Ch € 2/day WC 1. **Surface:** grasstiles.
⬛ 01/01-31/12
Distance: 2km on the spot on the spot.

| | Brüggen | 8D4 |

Wohnmobilhafen Brüggen, Bornerstraße 48. **GPS:** n51,24264 e6,18955.

30 ⌶ € 4 Ch included. € 2. **Surface:** metalled. ⬛ 01/01-31/12
Distance: 50m 100m 50m 50m.
Remarks: Behind Aldi-süd.

| | Brühl | 9A5 |

Phantasialand P1, Berggeiststrasse 31-41. **GPS:** n50,79919 e6,87875.

7 ⌶ € 12,50/night WC 1.
Surface: metalled. ⬛ 04/04-31/10
Distance: 100m.

Tourist information Brühl:
⬤ Phantasialand.Large amusement park. ⬛ 01/04-31/10 9-18h, winter changing visiting hours.

| | Bünde | 9D1 |

Stadtgarten, Steinmeisterstrasse/Viktoriastrasse. **GPS:** n52,19869 e8,58986.
10 ⌶ free. **Surface:** metalled. ⬛ 01/01-31/12
Distance: 50m 50m 50m.
Remarks: Max. 72h.

| | Burbach | 9C5 |

Hotel Zollhaus, Zollhaus 1, Lippe. **GPS:** n50,70417 e8,06730.

100 ⌶ € 3. **Surface:** metalled. ⬛ 01/01-31/12
Distance: on the spot.

| | Büren | 9D3 |

Parkplatz an der Afte, Fürstenberger Strasse. **GPS:** n51,54897 e8,56381.
8 ⌶ free Ch . ⬛ 01/01-31/12
Distance: on the spot 500m 200m.
Remarks: Parking nearby swimming pool.

| | Coesfeld | 9A2 |

Brauhaus Stephanus, Overhagenweg 1. **GPS:** n51,93719 e7,15617.
4 ⌶ customers free . **Surface:** metalled. ⬛ 01/01-31/12
Distance: on the spot.

| | Dahlem | 8D6 |

Flugplatz Dahlemer Binz, Dahlemer Binz. **GPS:** n50,40663 e6,53700.

DE

6 🗇free 🔧 ⬛Ch 🧹against payment. **Surface:** asphalted. ⬤ 01/01-31/12
Distance: ⊗on the spot.
Remarks: Airport Dahlemer Binz.

🗇S | **Dahlem** | 8D6
Wohnmobilstellplatz Kronenburger See, Seeuferstrasse 6. **GPS:** n50,35785 e6,46989.⬆.

16 🗇€ 6/24h 🔧€ 2 ⬛Ch 🧹included.
Surface: grassy. ⬤ 01/01-31/12

🍴🗇S | **Delbrück** | 9C3
Landgasthaus Roseneck, Haselhorster Strasse 3. **GPS:** n51,75770 e8,43441.

10 🗇€ 5, free with a meal 🧹(10x)included. **Surface:** metalled. ⬤ 01/01-31/12
Distance: ⬇2km ⊗on the spot 🚰2km.

🗇S | **Detmold** 🌿🍴🎨 | 9D2
Detmolder City Camp, Bahnhofstrasse 8. **GPS:** n51,94055 e8,87123.⬆➡.

14 🗇€ 8 🔧€ 1/100liter ⬛Ch 🧹(14x)€ 2, 16Amp WC 🗇. **Surface:** asphalted. ⬤ 01/01-31/12
Distance: ⬇500m ⊗500m 🚰200m kiosk 🚗50m.

🗇S | **Dinslaken** | 9A3
Am Rotbachsee, Am Freibad. **GPS:** n51,56707 e6,77807.⬆➡.

10 🗇free. **Surface:** sand. ⬤ 01/01-31/12
Distance: ⬇100m ⊗100m 🚰100m.

🗇S | **Dormagen** | 9A4
Parkplatz Flügeldeich, Herrenweg, Feste Zons. **GPS:** n51,12553 e6,85001.⬆.

3 🗇€ 5. **Surface:** metalled. ⬤ 01/01-31/12
Distance: ⬇400m 🚿on the spot 🛒on the spot ⊗100m 🚰500m.
Remarks: Max. 3 days, near the Rhine river.

🗇S | **Dorsten** | 9A3
Reisemobilhafen An der Lippe, Zur Lippe. **GPS:** n51,66550 e6,96744.⬆➡.

38 🗇€ 5 🔧 ⬛Ch 🧹(34x)€ 1/8h. **Surface:** metalled/sand. ⬤ 01/01-31/12
Distance: ⬇300m ⊗300m 🚰300m.

Tourist information Dorsten:
ℹ Verkehrsverein Dorsten, Ursulastrasse 24.Former Hanseatic town on the Lippe.
🎪 Antikmarkt.Antiques market. ⬤ 1st Su of the month.
🎪 Pferdemarkt.Horse market. ⬤ 1st Su May.

🗇S | **Dortmund** 🌿🍴🎨 | 9B3
Mobil-Camp Wischlingen, Wischlinger Weg 50-61, Wischlingen. **GPS:** n51,52001 e7,39868.⬆➡.

50 🗇€ 8, 2 pers.incl 🔧€ 1/80liter ⬛Ch 🧹(30x)€ 0,50/kWh WC 🗇€ 1.
Surface: asphalted. ⬤ 01/01-31/12
Distance: ⬇1km 🚰Rewe 1km 🚗200m.
Remarks: Former tennis-court in recreation area. A45 exit DO-Marten, then follow signs.

Remarks: Parking sports centre south.

⫟⫠S **Drolshagen** **9B4**
Gasthof Pension Zur Bauernschänke, Am Kleefeld 1, Lüdespert. **GPS:** n51,06807 e7,70787.

4 ⛺€ 5, guests free ⟗🔱Ch. **Surface:** asphalted. ◻ 01/01-31/12
Distance: 🚲2km ⊗on the spot 🍴8km.

⫟⫠S **Drolshagen** **9B4**
Gasthof Zum Hobel, Biggeseestrasse 4. **GPS:** n51,03832 e7,81483.
3 ⛺guests free ⟗🔱.

⫟⫠S **Drolshagen** **9B4**
Haus Dumicketal, Dumicker strasse 11, Dumicke. **GPS:** n51,05936 e7,82180.⬆

3 ⛺free ⟗🔱 WCagainst payment.
Distance: ⊗on the spot 🍴10km.

⫟⫠ **Drolshagen** **9B4**
Haus Wigger, Vorm Bahnhof 4, Hützemert. **GPS:** n51,03846 e7,75099.➡

4 ⛺guests free. **Surface:** metalled. ◻ 01/01-31/12
Distance: 🚲200m ⊗on the spot.

⫟⫠S **Duisburg** **9A3**
Landschaftspark Duisburg-Nord, Emscherstraße 71, Meiderich. **GPS:** n51,48413 e6,78077.
5 ⛺free ⟗🔱Ch. **Surface:** asphalted. ◻ 01/01-31/12
Distance: ⚓1,6km.

⫟⫠S **Dülmen** **9B2**
Kapellenweg. GPS: n51,82331 e7,27945.⬆

7 ⛺free ⟗🔱free. **Surface:** metalled. ◻ 01/01-31/12
Distance: 🚲500m.

⫟⫠S **Dülmen** **9B2**
P6, Hüttendyk/Ecke Halterner Strasse. **GPS:** n51,82606 e7,27228.➡

6 ⛺free ⟗€ 1/80liter 🔱Ch 🔌€ 1/8h. **Surface:** metalled. ◻ 01/01-31/12
Distance: 🚲500m 🍴50m 🚏100m.
Remarks: Max. 1 night.

⫟⫠ **Dülmen** **9B2**
Reisemobilstellplatz Hausdulmen, Sandstrasse. **GPS:** n51,80707 e7,24746. ⬆➡

12 ⛺free. **Surface:** grassy. ◻ 01/01-31/12
Distance: 🚲2,5km ⊗500m 🍴400m 🚏on the spot.

⫟⫠S **Düren** **8D5**
IG Reisemobilhafen Düren, Rurstrasse 170. **GPS:** n50,80861 e6,46556.

20 ⛺€8 ⟗🔱Ch 🔌€ 2. **Surface:** gravel.
Distance: 🚲900m ⊗Bistro 100m 🍴Lidl 500m.

⫟⫠S **Düsseldorf** 🌿🏛🍦🌊 **9A4**
P Rheinterasse/Tonhalle, Joseph Beuys Ufer. **GPS:** n51,23710 e6,77029.⬆⬆

10 ⛺€12/day. **Surface:** metalled. ◻ 01/01-31/12
Distance: 🚲3km ⊗50m 🍴1,3km.
Remarks: Parking at the Rhine River, follow city centre.

⫟⫠S **Düsseldorf** 🌿🏛🍦🌊 **9A4**
Wohnmobilstellplatz Düsseldorf/Erkrath, Heinrich-Hertz-Straße 18, Unterfeldhaus, Düsseldorf/Erkrath. **GPS:** n51,19825 e6,91679.
6 ⛺€6 ⟗€ 1/100liter 🔱Ch 🔌included. **Surface:** metalled. ◻ 01/01-

31/12
Distance: ⊗300m 🚃50m.

| S | Düsseldorf ⚜🏊🍽 | 9A4 |

Großmarkt/Daimler Chrysler, Ulmenstraße. **GPS**: n51,25920 e6,77854. ↑→.

🚰 Ch free.

Tourist information Düsseldorf:

ℹ️ Tourist Info, Immermannstrasse, Gegenüber Station; Kö-Galerie/Finanzhaus, Berliner Alee; Burgplatz, Berliner Allee, www.duesseldorf-tourismus.de.Historical centre, important city of fashion, all large marks established in the Königsallee. 🎥 During the Caravan Salon (by the end of August/beginning September) there is a large area for motorhomes available. Free shuttlebus to the exhibition and Old city centre. Also several events on the exhibition grounds.

| S | Emmerich ⚓🎪🛶 | 8D3 |

Yachthafen, Fackeldeystrasse 15-65. **GPS**: n51,83693 e6,21948. ↑.

75 🅿€8 🚰€ 0,50 Ch ✎ (80x)€ 2,50 WC ⬛€ 0,50 📶€ 1. 🚿
Location: Rural, comfortable. **Surface:** grassy/metalled. ⬛ 01/01-31/12
Distance: 🚶2,5km ◿on the spot ⊗on the spot 🚰on the spot 🚲on the spot ⅄on the spot.

| S | Emmerich ⚓🎪🛶 | 8D3 |

Auf dem Eltenberg, Luitgardisstraße. **GPS**: n51,86559 e6,17265. ↑→.

25 🅿 free. **Location:** Rural. **Surface:** grasstiles. ⬛ 01/01-31/12
Distance: 🚶1km ⊗1km 🚰on the spot.

| S | Emmerich ⚓🎪🛶 | 8D3 |

P6, Kleiner Wall, Rheinpromenade. **GPS**: n51,83229 e6,23594. ↑.

6 🅿 free. **Location:** Urban, very simple, noisy. **Surface:** unpaved. ⬛ 01/01-31/12
Distance: 🚶on the spot.

| S | Ennepetal | 9B4 |

Firma Möller-Elektronic, Königstrasse 17, Oelkinghausen. **GPS**: n51,29086 e7,32050.

5 🅿 against payment 🚰€ 3 Ch ✎€ 3.
Surface: metalled. ⬛ 01/01-31/12
Distance: 🚶2km ⊗on the spot 🚰200m.

| S | Ennigerloh | 9C2 |

Am Freibad 3. **GPS**: n51,83304 e8,01629. ↑.
2 🅿 free 🚰€ 0,50/50liter ⬛ Ch ✎€ 0,50/kWh. **Surface:** metalled. ⬛ 01/01-31/12
Distance: 🚶600m.

| S | Ennigerloh | 9C2 |

Ferienhof Bettmann, Beesen 4. **GPS**: n51,84366 e7,99567.

4 🅿€6/pp 🚰 Ch ✎ WC⬛.
Distance: 🚶2km ⊗on the spot 🚰3km.

| S | Erftstadt | 9A5 |

Mobilcamp am Ville-Express, Carl-Schurz-strasse 1a, Liblar. **GPS**: n50,81781 e6,81986. ↑→.

11 🅿€6 🚰€ 1/80liter ⬛Ch ✎€ 0,50/kWh. 🚿 **Location:** Urban.
Surface: metalled. ⬛ 01/01-31/12
Distance: 🚶1km ⚓4,4km ⊗200m 🚰1km.

| S | Erndtebrück | 9C5 |

Pension Hofius, Hilchenbacherweg 2, Zinse. **GPS**: n51,00599 e8,21224. ↑.

DE

3 🛏 € 7/24h 🚰 🗑 Ch 🚿 WC 🚽. ⬛ 01/01-31/12

🛏 S **Everswinkel** 9B2

Vitus-Bad, Alverkirchenerstrasse 29. **GPS**: n51,92309 e7,83776. ⬆️

30 🛏 € 7/24h 🚰 🗑 Ch 🚿 € 0,50/kWh.
Surface: grassy/sand. ⬛ 01/01-31/12
Distance: 🚶 city centre Walbeck 1km, city centre Geldern 6km ⊗1km 🛒1km.
Remarks: At swimming pool.

🛏 S **Geldern** 8D3

Reisemobilstellplatz Am Sportplatz, Hülspassweg 20, Veert. **GPS**: n51,52960 e6,30347. ⬆️➡️

3 🛏 free 🚰 🗑 Ch. **Surface:** metalled. ⬛ 01/01-31/12
Distance: 🚶 500m ⊗on the spot 🚌on the spot.
Remarks: Parking swimming pool, Kläranlage Everswinkel, mo-thu 7.30-17 fr 7.30-12.15.

🛏 S **Gangelt** 8D5

Rodebachtal, Am Freibad 13. **GPS**: n50,98583 e5,99806.

30 🛏 free. **Surface:** gravel. ⬛ 01/01-31/12
Distance: 🚶 city centre Veert 200m, city centre Geldern 2km 🛒500m.
Remarks: Parking at sports park.

🍴 🛏 S **Geldern** 8D3

Restaurant Zum Lünebörger, Venloerstrasse 120, Pont. **GPS**: n51,49021 e6,29822.

40 🛏 € 7, weekend € 10 🚰 🗑 Ch 🚿 WC 🚽 € 0,50/4minutes. **Surface:** metalled. ⬛ 01/01-31/12
Distance: 🚶 on the spot ⊗on the spot 🛒on the spot.

🛏 S **Geldern** 8D3

Am Holländer See, Am Holländer See 19. **GPS**: n51,51131 e6,32867. ⬆️➡️

5 🛏 guests free. **Surface:** gravel. ⬛ 01/01-31/12
Distance: ⊗on the spot 🛒on the spot.
Remarks: Only for guest.

S **Geldern** 8D3

Freizeit-Store Diepers, Lieblgstrasse 33. **GPS**: n51,52971 e6,35456.
🚰€ 1 🗑€ 1 Ch. ⬛ 01/01-31/12
Remarks: Industrial area, north-east of the city.

Tourist information Geldern:
✴ Internationaler Wettbewerb der strassenmaler und strassenmusikanten und -theatergruppen, Centrum.International street painting competition, street musicians and theater groups. ⬛ beginning Sep.
✴ Internationales Reisemobilfest.International festival for motorcaravanners with vast tourist program. Not necessary to book in advance,. ⬛ last weekend April. 🚻 free.

50 🛏 € 5/24h, 3 days € 12 🚰 🗑 Ch 🚿 € 0,50/kWh. **Surface:** grassy/ metalled. ⬛ 01/01-31/12
Distance: 🚶 1km ⊗1km 🛒1km.
Remarks: Parking in the centre.

🛏 S **Geldern** 8D3

Reisemobilhafen Am Freibad, Am Freibad 6, Walbeck. **GPS**: n51,49461 e6,22666. ⬆️➡️.

🛏 S **Gelsenkirchen** 9A3

Revierpark Nienhausen, Feldmarkstraße 201. **GPS**: n51,50167 e7,06333. ⬆️.

DE

20 ⌇€7, 2 pers.incl. ⛽€ 1/80liter ☕Ch ⚡€ 1/2kWh. **Surface:** metalled. ⏰ 01/01-31/12
Distance: 🚶2,8km ✈3,2km ⊗100m 🚉2km 🚋Tram 700m.
Remarks: Bread-service.

⌇S Gladbeck 9A3
Freizeitstätte Witringer Wald, Bohmertstrasse 277. **GPS:** n51,55912 e6,98403. ⬆➡

20 ⌇voluntary contribution ☕Ch. **Surface:** grasstiles/grassy. ⏰ 01/01-31/12
Distance: 🚶2km ✈1km ⊗200m 🚉1km.
Remarks: Service at petrol station nearby.

⌇S Goch 8D3
Friedensplatz, Thielenstrasse. **GPS:** n51,67556 e6,16639. ⬆➡

80 ⌇€ 4/24h ⛽€ 1/100liter ☕Ch ⚡(60x)€ 0,50/kWh. **Surface:** grassy. ⏰ 01/01-31/12
Distance: 🚶700m 🏊on the spot ⊗700m 🚉700m 🚌100m.
Remarks: Along the Niers river.

⌇ Goch 8D3
Freizeitbad GochNess, Kranenburger Strasse 20, Kessel. **GPS:** n51,70291 e6,08915. ⬆

6 ⌇free.
Surface: grassy. ⏰ 01/01-31/12
Distance: 🚶1km ⊗1km 🚉1km.

Tourist information Goch:
ℹ KulTOURbühne Goch, Markt 15, www.goch.de.Motorhome friendly town on

the Lower Rhine river.
Ⓜ Museum Goch, Kastellstrasse.Art and culture history. ⏰ Tue-Fri 10-17h, Sa-Su 11-17h.
☀ Pilgrimage for motorhomes. ⏰ last weekend Jun.
☀ Museumscafé Edison, Museum Goch.Collection of gramophones. ⏰ Su 15-17h.
🚲 Herrensitz-Route.Cycle route along the Meuse and the Niers, available at Kultourbühne Goch. 🎫 € 5.

⌇ Grefrath 8D4
Eissportzentrum Grefrath, Stadionstrasse. **GPS:** n51,34889 e6,33972.
50 ⌇free. **Surface:** grasstiles.
Distance: 🚶2km ⊗300m 🚉2km.
Remarks: Niederrheinisches Freilichtmuseum, Open air museum 650m.

⌇ Grefrath 8D4
Niers-Perle-Oedt, Mühlengasse 6. **GPS:** n51,32306 e6,37667. ⬆
7 ⌇free. **Surface:** asphalted.
Distance: 🚶350m ⊗450m 🚉350m.

⌇S Greven 9B2
Wohnmobilcamp Marina, Alten Fahrt Fuestrup,, Fuestruperstrasse 37, Fuestrup. **GPS:** n52,04449 e7,68328. ⬆

90 ⌇€ 9 ⛽ ☕Ch ⚡€ 1,50 WC ∫€ 0,50 📷. ⏰ 01/01-31/12
Distance: ⊗Restaurant/Biergarten 🚉3km.
Remarks: Marina at canal.

⌇S Gronau (Nordrhein-Westfalen) 9A1
Erholungsgebiet Dreiländersee, Brechter Weg. **GPS:** n52,23716 e7,08006. ⬆➡

90 ⌇free, 01/04-30/09 € 5/24h ⛽€ 0,50/130liter ☕Ch ⚡€ 1/4h WC ∫.
Surface: grassy/metalled. ⏰ 01/01-31/12
Distance: 🚶2km 🏊100m 🎣on the spot ⊗200m 🚉50m (camping) 🚌on the spot.
Remarks: Parking nearby small lake.

⌇S Haltern am See 9A3
Reisemobilstellplatz Silbersee II, Münsterstraße/Zum Vogelsberg. **GPS:** n51,79764 e7,21008. ⬆➡

15 ⌇€ 10 ⛽€ 1/80liter ☕Ch ⚡€ 1/8h. **Surface:** grassy. ⏰ 01/04-31/10

Distance: Haltern 6km on the spot on the spot.
Remarks: At Silbersee.

Haltern am See 9A3
Reisemobilstellplatz, Hullerner Straße/West, Lippspieker. **GPS:** n51,74278 e7,19525.

40 free 1 Ch € 1/8h.
Surface: metalled. 01/01-31/12
Distance: Old city centre 1km 1km 100m.

Haltern am See 9A3
Reisemobilstellplatz Hellweg, RMS ReisemobileSpezialist, Hellweg 252.
GPS: n51,75589 e7,20127.

4 €6 1 Ch € 3,50. **Surface:** grassy/gravel. 01/01-31/12
Distance: Old city centre 1km 800m 800m.

Harsewinkel 9C2
Frei- und Hallenbad, Prozessionsweg 8. **GPS:** n51,96556 e8,21935.

15 free. **Surface:** grassy. 01/01-31/12
Distance: 200m 100m 200m.
Remarks: Parking next to swimming pool.

Hattingen 9A4
Wohnmobilstellplatz Ruhrtal, Ruhrdeich 24. **GPS:** n51,40839 e7,18091.

15 €7 1/90liter Ch € 1/2kWh free. **Surface:** metalled.
01/01-31/12
Distance: 2km on the spot.
Remarks: Along ther Ruhr, next to midget golf, bread-service.

Hattingen 9A4
Isenbergstrasse. **GPS:** n51,38969 e7,15340.

2 free. **Surface:** gravel. 01/01-31/12
Distance: 2km 300m 1km on the spot.
Remarks: Parking along the Ruhr, max. 2 days.

Hattingen 9A4
Ruhrgasse, Bahnhofstrasse. **GPS:** n51,40127 e7,17700.

3 free. **Surface:** gravel. 01/01-31/12
Distance: 500m 500m 500m.
Remarks: Parking behind the Amtshäusern, only on Sa and Su.

Hattingen 9A4
Wassersportverein, Ruhrdeich 16. **GPS:** n51,40815 e7,18111.

15 free. **Surface:** metalled. 01/01-31/12
Distance: 2,5km on the spot 500m 1km.

Hattingen 9A4
Hotel Landhaus Siebe, Am Stuten 29. **GPS:** n51,35762 e7,19583.

2 guests free. **Surface:** asphalted. 01/01-31/12
Distance: on the spot.

Hattingen 9A4
Hotel-Restaurant zum Hackstück, Zum Hackstückstrasse 123. **GPS:** n51,36247 e7,22630.

5 🏕free. **Surface:** metalled. 🅾 01/01-31/12
Distance: ⊗on the spot.

| 📷S | Havixbeck � | 9B2 |

Freibad, Kardinal von Hartmann strasse. **GPS**: n51,97507 e7,42092.⬆➡.

4 🏕free 🚰🗑ChOn demand WC. **Surface:** metalled. 🅾 01/01-31/12
Remarks: Parking swimming pool, small pitches.

| ⑂S | Havixbeck 🌿 | 9B2 |

Klute's Historischem Brauhaus, Poppenbeck 28. **GPS**: n51,98938 e7,39291.⬆.

15 🏕free 🚰 ⚡(8x)€ 5 🔊 🗑. **Surface:** metalled. 🅾 01/01-31/12
Distance: ⚓2km ⊗on the spot 💧2km.

| 🏞 | Havixbeck 🌿 | 9B2 |

EDEKA, Blickallee 44. **GPS**: n51,97480 e7,41168.⬆.

4 🏕free. **Surface:** metalled. 🅾 01/01-31/12
Distance: ⚓100m ⊗100m 💧on the spot 🚐100m.
Remarks: At supermarket, small pitches.

| 📷S | Heimbach | 8D6 |

Womohafen Heimbach, An der Laag 4. **GPS**: n50,63683 e6,47265.⬆.

19 🏕€ 6,50/24h 🚰€ 1/100liter 🗑Ch ⚡(20x)€ 0,50/kWh. **Surface:**
gravel. 🅾 01/01-31/12
Distance: ⚓200m ⊗100m.

| 📷S | Heinsberg | 8D4 |

Heinsberg am Lago, Fritz-Bauer-Strasse 3. **GPS**: n51,07333 e6,09278.
44 🏕€ 10 🚰 Ch ⚡€ 0,50/kWh. **Surface:** grasstiles.
Distance: ⚓600m ⚓Bagger See ⊗on the spot 💧800m.

| 📷S | Heinsberg | 8D4 |

3H-Camping-Center, Von-Liebig-strasse 6. **GPS**: n51,06780 e6,11203.

5 🏕voluntary contribution 🚰🗑Ch ⚡WC free. **Surface:** metalled. 🅾
01/01-31/12
Distance: ⊗on the spot 💧on the spot.
Remarks: Special motorhome washing place, also small repairs possible.

| 📷S | Hellenthal 🏔🌼❄ | 8D6 |

Grenzlandhalle Hellenthal, Aachenerstrasse. **GPS**: n50,49083 e6,43639.⬆.

15 🏕free 🚰🗑Ch against payment. **Surface:** asphalted. 🅾 01/01-31/12
Distance: ⚓500m 💧on the spot.
Remarks: Service on campsite.

| 📷S | Hellenthal 🏔🌼❄ | 8D6 |

Wohnmobilhafen Weißer Stein, Am Weissen Stein, Udenbreth, B265. **GPS**:
n50,40896 e6,37220.⬆➡.

16 🏕€ 7 🚰€ 1/80liter 🗑Ch ⚡(16x). **Surface:** metalled. 🅾 01/01-31/12
Distance: ⚡on the spot.
Remarks: Winter sports area Hellenthal am Wald, service on campsite.

Hellenthal 🅂 8D6

Breuerhof, Zum Wilsamtal 39, Udenbreth. **GPS**: n50,41081 e6,38992.

2 ₃ € 5/pppn 🚰 🔌 Ch ⚡. **Surface:** metalled.

Tourist information Hellenthal:
ℹ️ www.hellenthal.de.Small town the vulcany Eifel region.
👁 Greifvogelstation.Predatory bird station. ⭕ 01/11-31/03 9-17h, 01/04-31/10 9-18h.
👁 Grube Wohlfahrt.Visit to the mine shaft and museum. ⭕ 11h, 14h and 15.30h.

Hemer 🅂 9B4

Wohnmobilstellplatz Hemer, Hönnetalstraße. **GPS**: n51,37841 e7,77151.
20 ₃free 🚰 1/100liter 🔌 Ch ⚡ € 0,50/kWh. **Surface:** asphalted/grassy.
⭕ 01/01-31/12
Distance: 🚶1km ⊗300m 🛒bakery 500m.

Herford 9D2

Am Stadion, Dennewitzstrasse 15. **GPS**: n52,10474 e8,68931. ⬆➡

10 ₃free. ⭕ 01/01-31/12
Distance: 🚶2,5km 🚴1,8km 🏊100m 🚆100m ⊗2,5km 🛒2,5km.

Herscheid 🅂 9B4

Am Warmwasserfreibad, Unterdorfstraße. **GPS**: n51,17567 e7,74368. ⬆.
2 ₃free 🚰 🔌 Ch ⚡ against payment. **Surface:** gravel. ⭕ 01/01-31/12
Distance: 🚶on the spot ⊗400m 🛒650m.

Hilchenbach 🅂 9C5

Hallenbad Dahlbruch, Bernhard-Weiss-Platz, Dahlbruch. **GPS**: n50,97778 e8,05333. ⬆.

3 ₃free 🚰 € 1 🔌. **Surface:** asphalted/metalled.
Distance: 🚶400m 🛒400m.
Remarks: Parking behind swimming pool.

Hilchenbach 9C5

Bürgenhaus, Merklinghäuser weg, Müsen. **GPS**: n50,99267 e8,04497. ⬆.

3 ₃free. **Surface:** asphalted. ⭕ 01/01-31/12
Remarks: Max. 48h.

Hilchenbach 9C5

Parkplatz P4, Rothenberger strasse, L728. **GPS**: n50,99702 e8,11103. ⬆➡.

3 ₃free. **Surface:** metalled. ⭕ 01/01-31/12
Distance: 🚶100m ⊗200m 🛒100m.
Remarks: Parking in front of shopping centre Gerberpark, max. 48h.

Hilchenbach 9C5

Landhotel Steubers Siebelnhof, Siebelnhoferstrasse, Vormwald. **GPS**: n50,98658 e8,13173.

4 ₃free. **Surface:** metalled. ⭕ 01/01-31/12

Hille 🅂 9D1

Am Marktplatz, Sportplatzweg 31. **GPS**: n52,34205 e8,73017. ⬆.
8 ₃free 🚰 € 1 🔌 Ch ⚡ € 1. **Surface:** gravel. ⭕ 01/01-31/12
Distance: 🚶1km ⊗500m.

Hopsten 9B1

Dreifachturnhalle, Rüschendorfer strasse 4. **GPS**: n52,38900 e7,60230.

3 ₃free 🚰 Ch ⚡ free. **Surface:** grassy. ⭕ 01/01-31/12
Distance: 🚶100m ⊗100m 🛒100m.
Remarks: Parking at gymnasium, max. 2 nights.

Horn 🅂 9D2

Wohnmobilhafen Mein Bad, Wällenweg, Bad Meinberg. **GPS**: n51,89818 e8,99249. ⬆➡.

35 ⌷€5 + € 2,60/pp tourist tax ⛽€ 1/100liter ⚡Ch ⚡€ 0,50/kWh.
Surface: grassy/metalled. 🅿 01/01-31/12
Distance: 🚶200m ⊗on the spot 🚰200m.
Remarks: Behind spa, discount at swimming pool.

🛁S	Hörstel	9B1

Wohnmobilhafen Riesenbeck, Postdamm-Lazarusbrücke. **GPS:** n52,25574
e7,63387.⬆➡.

50 ⌷€6, only overnight stay € 4 ⛽€ 1/80liter ⚡Ch ⚡(18x)€ 0,50/kWh.
Surface: gravel. 🅿 01/01-31/12
Distance: 🚶300m ⊗on the spot 🎣fishing permit available ⊗100m
🚰300m 🛒500m on camp site 🚮50m.
Remarks: Parking beside river Weser.

🏞S	Hückelhoven	8D4

Hückelhovener Ruraue, Rheinstraße 4b. **GPS:** n51,05111 e6,21306.
6 ⌷€ 4,50 ⛽ ⚡Ch ⚡€ 0,50/kWh. **Surface:** metalled. 🅿 01/01-31/12
Distance: 🚶500m.

🛁S	Hürtgenwald	8D5

Einmünding Kall-Rur, Zerkall. **GPS:** n50,69156 e6,45212.⬆

13 ⌷free ⚡. 🅿 01/01-31/12
Distance: 🏊on the spot 🚮on the spot 🚰on the spot 🚮on the spot.
Remarks: Max. 3 nights.

🛁S	Hövelhof 🌳	9D2

P Bahnhof, Westfalenstrasse. **GPS:** n51,82417 e8,66099.⬆

10 ⌷free ⛽⚡Ch ⚡WC. 🅿 01/01-31/12
Distance: 🚶100m 🏊on the spot 🚮200m.
Remarks: Along the river Kall/Rur.

🛁	Hürtgenwald	8D5

Parkplatz Burgstrasse, Burgstrasse, Bergstein. **GPS:** n50,69582 e6,43848.

6 ⌷free ⛽free ⚡(6x)€ 0,50/kWh, 6Amp.
Surface: gravel. 🅿 01/01-31/12
Distance: 🚶500m 🚲4,2km ⊗500m 🚰500m 🚮50m.

🛁S	Höxter 🌿🍴🌳	10A2

Freizeitanlage Godelheimer See, Godelheimer Strasse, Höxter-Godelheim. **GPS:**
n51,75787 e9,37557.⬆

5 ⌷free. **Surface:** metalled. 🅿 01/01-31/12

🛁	Hürtgenwald	8D5

Soldatenfriedhof, Höhenstrasse, Hürtgen. **GPS:** n50,70552 e6,36063.⬆

50 ⌷€6 ⛽Ch ⚡WC ⌷included. **Surface:** grasstiles. 🅿 01/01-31/12 ◗
service: 01/10-01/04.
Distance: 🚶2km 🏊on the spot 🚮river 500m ⊗on the spot 🚰2km.
Remarks: Recreation area, bread-service + breakfast-service.

🛁S	Höxter 🌿🍴🌳	10A2

Wohnmobilhafen Flossplatz, Milchweg. **GPS:** n51,77325 e9,38781.⬆➡.

9 ⌷free. **Surface:** asphalted. 🅿 01/01-31/12

🛁S	Hürtgenwald	8D5

Simonskall 20, Kallweg. **GPS:** n50,66716 e6,35395.

DE

5 free ⚡ € 2 Ch . **Surface:** metalled. ☐ 01/01-31/12
Distance: 200m ⊗on the spot.

Hüsten 9C3

Parkplatz Große Wiese. GPS: n51,43151 e8,00475.⬆.
4 free. **Surface:** asphalted.
Distance: 2km.
Remarks: Next to the Sole-Bad.

Ibbenbüren 9B1

Aseebad, An der Umfluth 99. **GPS:** n52,26181 e7,73171.

20 € 3. **Surface:** grassy/metalled.
Distance: 2,3km.
Remarks: Parking next to swimming pool, max. 4 nights.

Ibbenbüren 9B1

Sommerrodelbahn, Münsterstrasse 265. **GPS:** n52,24977 e7,70292.

10 free. **Surface:** metalled.
Distance: 1,2km.

Ibbenbüren 9B1

Gasthof Dickenberg, Rheinerstrasse 324. **GPS:** n52,31314 e7,66988.
20 free.
Surface: metalled.
Distance: ⊗on the spot on the spot.

Tourist information Ibbenbüren:

ℹ Tourist-Information Ibbenbüren, Bachstrasse 14, www.ibbenbueren.de.
Ⓜ Ibbenbürener Bergbaumuseum.Mining museum. ☐ 01/05-30/09 2nd Sa of
the month. ⊤ free.
Ⓜ Motorrad-Museum, Lengericher strasse.Exhibition of motor cycles. ☐
01/04-31/10 Sa 14-18, Su 10-18h.
Flea market. ☐ 1st Sa May, last Sa Oct.
Tollen Knollen, Neumarkt.Potato festival. ☐ weekend, beginning Oct.
Sommerrodelbahn, Münsterstrasse 265.Toboggan slide of 120 m.

Iserlohn 9B4

Parkplatz Seilerblick, Friesenstraße. **GPS:** n51,38456 e7,71128.
5 free ⚡ Ch. **Surface:** metalled. ☐ 01/01-31/12
Remarks: Next to tennis-court.

Isselburg 8D3

Hotel Restaurant Brüggenhütte, Hahnerfeld 23, Anholt. **GPS:** n51,85301
e6,47187.⬆.

5 free.
Location: Rural, very simple. **Surface:** grassy. ☐ 01/01-31/12
Distance: 200m ⊗on the spot.
Remarks: Behind restaurant, along through road.

Isselburg 8D3

Parkplatz Zentrum, Münsterdeich. **GPS:** n51,83452 e6,46477.⬆.

3 free. **Surface:** grassy. ☐ 01/01-31/12
Distance: on the spot on the spot ⊗300m 100m.
Remarks: Parking centre, at the Issel, max. 72h.

Isselburg 8D3

Spargelhof Mäteling, Buchenallee 4, Anholt. **GPS:** n51,84120 e6,41597.⬆.

5 free. **Location:** Rural. **Surface:** asphalted. ☐ 01/01-31/12
Distance: ⊗on the spot.
Remarks: Max. 72h.

Isselburg 8D3

Bürgerhaus, Anholter strasse, Vehlingen. **GPS:** n51,83089 e6,42297.⬆.

3 free. **Location:** Rural. **Surface:** gravel. ☐ 01/01-31/12 May.
Distance: ⊗on the spot.
Remarks: Max. 2 nights.

Isselburg 8D3

Ponyhof Leiting, Alte Bundesstrasse 3, Werth. **GPS:** n51,81332 e6,49258.⬆➡.

DE

10 🛏free.
Surface: grassy.
⬛ 01/01-31/12
Distance: ⊗on the spot.
Remarks: Max. 72h.
Tourist information Isselburg:
ℹ️ Isselburger Verkehrsverein e.V, Markt 9, www.isselburg-online.
de.Motorhome friendly town.
👁 Anholter Schweiz.Game preserve.
👁 Wasserburg Anholt.Castle with English gardens. ⬛ 01/05-30/09 Tue-Su
11-17h, 01/10-30/04 Su 13-17h.

🏕S Issum-Sevelen 8D3
Wohnmobilpark Hexenland-Sevelen, Koetherdyck 18. **GPS:** n51,49926
e6,43676.⬆️➡️.

20 🛏€8 ⚡🔌Ch🔋€ 2/24h WC. **Surface:** gravel. ⬛ 01/01-31/12
Distance: 🚂Sevelen 1km 🏊200m ⊗100m 🛒1km.

🏕S Jülich 8D5
Brückenkopf-Park, Rurauenstrasse. **GPS:** n50,92345 e6,34029.

22 🛏€6,50 ⚡€1 🔌Ch🔋WC⬛. ⬛ 01/01-31/12 ⬛ sanitary building:
1/11-31/3.
Remarks: Parking at bank of the Rur.

🅿 Jülich 8D5
Parkplatz Ruraue, Rurauenstrasse. **GPS:** n50,92424 e6,34931.
10 🛏free. **Surface:** asphalted. ⬛ 01/01-31/12
Remarks: Parking behind Ruhrstadium.
Tourist information Jülich:
ℹ️ Old fortress city.
⛺ Marktplatz. ⬛ Tue, Thu, Sa 7-13h.

🏕S Kalkar 8D3
Reisemobilstellplatz Kalkar, Waysche strasse. **GPS:** n51,74008 e6,30101.⬆️➡️.

35-40 🛏€4/24h ⚡€ 2/100liter 🔌Ch🔋€ 1/5kWh. 🚐 **Location:** Rural,
comfortable. **Surface:** grassy. ⬛ 01/01-31/12
Distance: 🚂500m ⊗400m 🛒700m.
Remarks: Max. 3 nights.
Tourist information Kalkar:
ℹ️ Touristik-Informationen Kalkar, Markt 20, www.kalkar.de.Attractive medieval
centre.
👁 KernWasser Wunderland.Amusement park.

🏕S Kall 8D6
Im Kallbachtal, Kapellenstrasse 25, Golbach. **GPS:** n50,52784 e6,53681.⬆️➡️.

6 🛏€8 ⚡🔌Ch🔋 against payment. **Surface:** metalled. ⬛ 01/01-31/12

🏕 Kamp-Lintfort 8D3
Pappelsee, Berthastraße 74. **GPS:** n51,50026 e6,53861.⬆️➡️.

20 🛏free.
Surface: asphalted. ⬛ 01/01-31/12
Distance: 🚂1,5km ⊗1km 🛒1,5km.
Remarks: Caution € 2,50 to pay-desk of the park.
Tourist information Kamp-Lintfort:
⛺ Marktplatz, Eberstrasse. ⬛ Thu, Sa.
⛺ Rathausplatz. ⬛ Tue 7.30-13h.
⚔ Mittelalterlicher Markt, Abteiplatz.Medieval market. ⬛ 3rd weekend Sep.

🏕S Kempen 8D4
Reisemobilpark Kempen am Aqua-sol, Berliner Allee. **GPS:** n51,36719
e6,40910.⬆️.

29 €7 € 1/80liter Ch € 0,50/kWh. **Surface:** metalled. 01/01-31/12
Distance: 1,5km on the spot 1,5km.

S Kerken 8D4

Wohnmobilpark Aldekerker Platte, Kempener Straße 9, Aldekerk. **GPS:** n51,43551 e6,41902.

30 €8 Ch € 2. **Surface:** grassy/gravel. 01/01-31/12
Distance: 600m 600m 600m.

S Kevelaer 8D3

Den Heyberg, Im Auwelt 45, Twisteden. **GPS:** n51,56345 e6,19418.

150 €8 Ch (150x)included. **Surface:** asphalted/metalled. 01/01-31/12
Distance: 2km 100m 2km 100m.
Remarks: Bread-service (weekend), barbecue place.

DE

S Kevelaer 8D3

Sporthotel Schravelsche Heide, Grotendonkerstrasse 54-58. **GPS:** n51,59556 e6,25306.

80 €7,50 Ch WC included. **Surface:** grassy. 01/01-31/12
Distance: 1,5km 100m 1km.
Remarks: To pay at sanitary building tennis-courts.

Kevelaer 8D3

Europaplatz, Bahnhof/Geldernstrasse, B9. **GPS:** n51,57904 e6,25192.

3 free. **Surface:** asphalted.
Distance: 500m 500m on the spot.

Remarks: Follow 'Zweckplatz'.

Tourist information Kevelaer:
- Traberpark Den Heyberg, Twisteden.Hippodrome.
- Plantaria.Adventurepark with parrots, kangaroos, play garden etc. 10-18h.

S Kirchhundem 9C4

Restaurant Rhein-Wester-Turm, Alfons Kleffmann, Rhein-Weser-Turm. **GPS:** n51,07109 e8,19791.

40 €5 € 5. 01/01-31/12
Distance: on the spot.

S Kleve 8D3

Van-den-Bergh-Straße. **GPS:** n51,78917 e6,14836.

60 €4 Ch (30x)€ 0,50/kWh. **Location:** Urban. **Surface:** metalled. 01/01-31/12
Distance: 500m.

S Kleve 8D3

Reisemobilpark Kleve, Landwehr/Spyckstraße. **GPS:** n51,80083 e6,13222.

75 €6,50, 2 pers.incl € 1 Ch (45x)€ 1,50 WC € 1 .
Location: Comfortable. **Surface:** grassy/metalled. 01/01-31/12
Distance: Kleve-zentrum 1,5km 300m 400m.

Kleve 8D3

Parkplatz Bürgerhaus, Drususdeich, Rindern. **GPS:** n51,81212 e6,12884.

5 free. **Surface:** asphalted. 01/01-31/12
Distance: Kleve-zentrum 2,3km 450m 400m.
Remarks: Behind church.

Kleve 8D3

Parkplatz Sporthalle Kleve-Kellen, Postdeich, Kellen. **GPS**: n51,80463 e6,16378.

20 free. **Location**: Rural. **Surface**: metalled.
Distance: 2,5km Steakhaus 350m on the spot.

Kleve 8D3

Parkplatz Sportplatz Reichswalde, Dorfanger, Reichswalde. **GPS**: n51,75985 e6,10243.

10 free. **Location**: Urban, very simple. **Surface**: metalled.
Distance: 5km 500m.

Kleve 8D3

Schenkenschanz. **GPS**: n51,83526 e6,11205.

5 free. **Surface**: metalled. 01/01-31/12
Distance: 2,5km.

Kleve 8D3

Tiergarten, Tiergartenstrasse, B9 dir Nijmegen. **GPS**: n51,79784 e6,12059.

5 free. **Location**: Highway. **Surface**: metalled. 01/01-31/12
Distance: 800m 250m.

Kleve 8D3

Wehrpöhl, Griethausen. **GPS**: n51,82476 e6,16448.

5 free. **Location**: Rural. **Surface**: asphalted. 01/01-31/12
Distance: 2,5km 300m 300m.
Remarks: Access via Brienen.

Tourist information Kleve:

Kleve Marketing GmbH, Werftstraße 1, www.kleve.de.Area with many possibilities for hiking and biking.
Klever Stadtfest.City celebration. end Sep.
Tiergarten Kleve, Tiergartenstrasse.Animal park.

Köln 9A5

P+R-Terminals Haus Vorst, Emmy-Noether-Straße, Marsdorf, Cologne (Köln).
GPS: n50,91777 e6,84987.
21 free € 0,50/100liter Ch € 1/12h. **Surface**: concrete.
01/01-31/12
Distance: Old city centre 8km 450m 250m on the spot Tram centre 50m.
Remarks: Max. 24h.

Köln 9A5

Reisemobilhafen Köln, An der Schanz, Cologne (Köln). **GPS**: n50,96265 e6,98254.

40 € 8/24h € 1 Ch € 1/8h.
Distance: metro 10 min walking.

Königswinter 9A5

Hauptstrasse, Niederdollendorf. **GPS**: n50,69697 e7,17641.

30 free. **Surface**: asphalted. 01/01-31/12
Distance: 400m 800m.

Kranenburg 8D3

Am Hallenbad, Großen Haag. **GPS**: n51,79242 e6,01033.

DE

30 ⬛€ 4 🚰 € 0,20/liter 💧Ch ♨ (12x)€ 0,50/kWh. 🚌 **Location:** Rural, very simple. **Surface:** grassy. 🅾 01/01-31/12
Distance: 🏊500m ⛵1km 🛒1km ⊗500m 🍴500m.
Remarks: Service 100m.

🚐S	**Kürten**	9B4

Wohnmobil Park - Kürten, Broch 8. **GPS:** n51,05586 e7,28943.⬆.
20 ⬛€ 8 🚰♨ Ch included ♨ € 3. **Surface:** gravel. 🅾 01/01-31/12
Distance: 🏊2km ⊗on the spot.
Remarks: Behind Sauna-/Badeland Splash.

🚐S	**Ladbergen**	9B2

Rathauspark, Jahnstrasse. **GPS:** n52,13652 e7,74009.⬆.

10 ⬛free. **Surface:** grassy. 🅾 01/01-31/12
Distance: 🏊200m ⊗200m 🚐200m.
Remarks: Parking behind town hall.

🍽S	**Ladbergen**	9B2

Rest.-Cafe Zur Waldschänke, Erpenbecker Siedlung 63. **GPS:** n52,13474 e7,79422.
8 ⬛guests free 🚰 ♨ WC. **Surface:** grassy.
Distance: 🏊4km ⊗on the spot.

🚐S	**Lennestadt**	9C4

Parkplatz P4, An der Sauerlandhalle. **GPS:** n51,10557 e8,08017.⬆.

4 ⬛free ♨ € 0,50/4h. **Surface:** asphalted. 🅾 01/01-31/12
Distance: 🏊700m ⊗700m 🍴100m.

📊S	**Leverkusen**	9A4

Camping-Caravaning Meier, Adolf-Kaschny-Straße 9, Küppersteg. **GPS:** n51,05211 e7,00003.
10 ⬛free 🚰💧Ch. **Surface:** metalled. 🅾 01/01-31/12
Remarks: Motorhome dealer, accessory shop, repairs.

🚐S	**Lienen**	9C2

Hallenfreibad, Holperdorperstrasse 37/39. **GPS:** n52,15575 e7,97392.⬆➡.

3 ⬛free 🚰💧Ch WC 🍴.
Surface: metalled. 🅾 01/01-31/12
Distance: 🏊1km.
Remarks: Parking next to swimming pool, max. 3 nights, to be paid at swimming pool.

Tourist information Lienen:
ℹ City centre with restored half-timbered houses.
👁 Voss Hof, Baggerien 4.Biological dynamic farm products. 🅾 Fri 15-18h, Sa 9-12h.

🚐S	**Lindlar**	9B5

Am Freizeitpark, Brionner Straße. **GPS:** n51,01550 e7,36645.⬆.
2 ⬛free 🚰€ 1 💧Ch ♨ (4x)€ 1/6h.
Surface: metalled. 🅾 01/01-31/12

©S	**Lippstadt**	9C3

Campingoase Lange, Dorfstraße 47, Benninghausen. **GPS:** n51,66103 e8,24435.
15 ⬛€ 10, 2 pers.incl 🚰💧Ch ♨ included. **Surface:** metalled. 🅾 01/01-31/12
Distance: 🍴on the spot.

🚐S	**Löhne**	9D1

Reisemobilstellplatz, Albert-Schweitzer-strasse 12. **GPS:** n52,20399 e8,71892.
⬆➡.

18 ⬛€ 8 🚰💧Ch included ♨ (18x)€ 1/2kWh. **Surface:** metalled. 🅾 01/01-31/12
Distance: 🏊500m ⛵1km 🛒100m ⊗500m 🍴500m.

🚐S	**Lotte**	9B1

Tennishalle Lotte, Kornweg 3. **GPS:** n52,27192 e7,92275.⬆.
10 ⬛free 🚰💧Ch 🍴On demand. **Surface:** gravel. 🅾 01/01-31/12
Distance: 🏊900m ⛵3,5km 🍴1km.

🚐S	**Lübbecke**	9D1

Stellplatz Lübbecke, Rahdener Straße. **GPS:** n52,31019 e8,61839.
4 ⬛€ 6 🚰€ 3 💧Ch ♨ € 3. **Surface:** metalled. 🅾 01/01-31/12
Distance: 🏊600m 🍴500m.
Remarks: Max. 3 days.

🚐S	**Lüdenscheid**	9B4

Familienbad Nattenberg, Talstraße 59. **GPS:** n51,21042 e7,61803.⬆.
4 ⬛free 🚰€ 1 💧Ch ♨ € 1/6h.
Surface: metalled. 🅾 01/01-31/12
Distance: 🏊city centre 1,6km ⊗Burger King 450m 🍴Aldi 900m.

🚐S	**Lüdinghausen**	9B3

Parkplatz Rosengarten, Am Rosengarten, Seppenrade. **GPS:** n51,76407 e7,39728.⬆.

DE

2 🅿free ⚓. **Surface:** asphalted. ☐ 01/01-31/12
Distance: 🚶200m.

40 🅿free. **Surface:** asphalted. ☐ 01/01-31/12
Distance: 🚶500m.

| 🔵S | **Lüdinghausen** | 9B3 |

Parkplatz Aqua-See, Rohrkamp 23. **GPS:** n51,77229 e7,42731.⬆️

| 🔵 | **Meschede** 🍽️🍴 | 9C4 |

P Hallenbad, Arnsberger Strasse. **GPS:** n51,34897 e8,27356.⬆️➡️

2 🅿free. **Surface:** metalled. ☐ 01/01-31/12
Distance: 🚶1,5km 🚌on the spot.
Remarks: Parking swimming pool.

3 🅿free. **Surface:** metalled. ☐ 18.30-9.30h
Distance: 🚶500m ⛱on the spot ⛽500m 🔧500m.

| 🔵 | **Marsberg** 🍴 | 9D3 |

Wohnmobilhafen, Am Sportplatz. **GPS:** n51,45974 e8,84864.⬆️➡️

| ©S | **Meschede** 🍽️🍴 | 9C4 |

Knaus Campingpark Hennesee, Lielinghausen 7. **GPS:** n51,29846 e8,26366.⬆️

4 🅿€5 ⚓🔌Ch ⚡(4x)included, 16Amp. **Surface:** asphalted. ☐ 01/01-31/12
Distance: 🚶100m ⛽200m 🔧200m.
Remarks: Max. 5 days, caution key € 20 (pay-desk of theTherme). Parking next to gymnasium.

16 🅿€7 ⚓🔌Ch ⚡(16x)€ 0,50/kWh, 16Amp WCincluded 🔌€ 2 ⊙ on camp site. **Surface:** metalled. ☐ 01/01-31/12
Distance: 🚶5km ⛱100m 🚌100m ⊗on the spot 🔧on the spot.

| 🔵S | **Mechernich** | 9A6 |

Parkplatz Essensgasse, Am Kirchberg, Kommern. **GPS:** n50,61376 e6,64479.

| 🔵S | **Mettingen** | 9B1 |

Hallenbad, Bahnhofstrasse 18-20. **GPS:** n52,31679 e7,78337.

8 🅿free ⚓🔌Ch ⚡against payment.
Surface: metalled. ☐ 01/01-31/12
Distance: 🚶historical centre 200m.
Remarks: Via B266.

3 🅿free ⚓🔌 ⚡WC. **Surface:** metalled. ☐ 01/01-31/12
Distance: 🚶on the spot ⊗200m 🔧200m.
Remarks: Parking swimming pool, bicycle rent, service: Kläranlage, Neuenkirchenerstrasse 208.

| 🔵 | **Mechernich** | 9A6 |

Mühlental, Elisabethhütte, B477. **GPS:** n50,59686 e6,63207.⬆️

| 🔵S | **Minden** | 9D1 |

Reisemobilstellplatz Kanzlers Weide, Hausbergerstrasse. **GPS:** n52,28750 e8,92551.⬆️

100 🗒free 🚰€ 1/120liter 🔌€ 0,50 Ch ⚡ (18x)€ 0,50/kWh, 6Amp.
Surface: metalled. ◻ 01/01-31/12
Distance: 🚶200m ⛵50m 🚏50m ⊗200m 🛒200m 🍽200m.
Remarks: Max. 3 nights, not during large events.

4 🗒€ 5/19-10h 🚰€ 5 🔌Ch ⚡€ 5/10h. **Surface:** asphalted. ◻ 01/01-31/12
Distance: 🚶600m ⊗600m 🛒600m.
Remarks: Max. 1 night.

| 🏕 | Moers 🍦🍴 | 9A3 |

Freizeitpark Schoßpark, Krefelder straße. **GPS:** n51,44659 e6,61642. ⬆➡

| 🍴 | Monschau | 8D6 |

Haus Vennblick, Hauptstrasse 24, Höfen. **GPS:** n50,53934 e6,25292.
6 🗒free. **Surface:** gravel.
Distance: 🚶300m ⊗on the spot 🍴on the spot.

| 🏕 | Mülheim/Ruhr 🚣🏕 | 9A4 |

Mintarder Straße 4. GPS: n51,41462 e6,86934. ⬆

3 🗒free. **Surface:** grasstiles. ◻ 01/01-31/12
Distance: 🚶700m ⊗700m 🛒500m.

6 🗒free. **Surface:** metalled. ◻ 01/01-31/12
Distance: 🚶2,7km ⊗50m 🛒100m.
Remarks: Max. 72h.

| 🏕 | Mönchengladbach | 8D4 |

Schloß Wickrath, Neukircherweg, Wickrath. **GPS:** n51,12889 e6,42258. ⬆

| S | Mülheim/Ruhr 🚣🏕 | 9A4 |

Hymer Zentrum, Kölner Strasse 35-37. **GPS:** n51,39985 e6,87700.
🚰€ 0,50/80liter 🔌Ch.

| S | Münster | 9B2 |

Campingplatz Münster, Laerer Werseufer. **GPS:** n51,94583 e7,69082. ⬆

10 🗒free. **Surface:** asphalted. ◻ 01/01-31/12
Distance: 🚶2km ⊗2km 🛒500m.
Remarks: Parking behind castle (500m), max. 2 days. Follow 'P Schloß'.

| 🏕 S | Mönchengladbach | 8D4 |

Camping-Center Krings, Monschauerstrasse 12/32. **GPS:** n51,19454 e6,40884. ⬆➡

24 🗒€ 15 🚰🔌Ch ⚡WC 📶 ◻ 01/01-31/12
Distance: 🚶Münster 4,5km ⊗100m 🍴on the spot 🛒100m.

| 🏕 S | Netphen | 9C5 |

Freizeitpark Netphen, P3, Brauersdorferstrasse. **GPS:** n50,91250 e8,12567. ➡

10 🗒free 🚰🔌Chfree. **Surface:** metalled. ◻ 01/01-31/12
Distance: 🚶3km ⊗1km 🛒500m.
Remarks: Max. 2 nights, service during opening hours.

| 🏕 S | Monschau | 8D6 |

Biesweg, B258. **GPS:** n50,55389 e6,23194. ⬆➡

3 🗒€ 3,50/day 🚰€ 0,50/80liter 🔌Ch.
Surface: metalled. ◻ 01/01-31/12
Distance: 🚶2km 🛒2km.

DE

Remarks: Max. 24h.

| 🛁 S | **Nettersheim** | 9A6 |

Wohnmobilhafen Nettersheim, Urftstraße. **GPS**: n50,48591 e6,62597. ⬆.

30 🛏 € 7/24h 🚰 € 1,50 🗑 Ch 🧹 included. **Surface:** metalled. ⬜ 01/01-31/12

| 🛏 | **Nettetal** | 8D4 |

Am Nettebruch, Flothender straße/Flothend. **GPS**: n51,30188 e6,26715. ⬆ ➡.

3 🛏 free. **Surface:** grassy/gravel. ⬜ 01/01-31/12
Distance: 🚶1km 🏊on the spot 🛒on the spot 🛒1km.

| 🍴 | **Nettetal** | 8D4 |

Am Krickenbeck See, Krickenbecker Allee 38. **GPS**: n51,34460 e6,25793.

50 🛏 € 8. **Surface:** asphalted. ⬜ 01/01-31/12
Distance: 🚶2km 🏊on the spot 🛒2km.

| 🛏 | **Neuss** | 9A4 |

Allrounder Winterworld/Skihalle, An der Skihalle 1. **GPS**: n51,17316 e6,64862.

30 🛏 free. **Surface:** metalled. ⬜ 01/01-31/12
Distance: 🏊on the spot 🎿indoor ski.
Remarks: A46, exit Neuss-Holzheim.

| 🛏 | **Nideggen** | 8D5 |

Parkplatz Danzley, Bahnhofstrasse. **GPS**: n50,69247 e6,47952. ⬆.

6 🛏 free. **Surface:** metalled. ⬜ 01/01-31/12
Distance: 🚶500m 🛒500m.

| 🍴 | **Nordkirchen** | 9B3 |

Hotel Plettenberger Hof, Schlossstrasse 28. **GPS**: n51,73659 e7,52819. ⬆.

2 🛏 guests free. **Surface:** asphalted. ⬜ 01/01-31/12
Distance: 🚶200m ⊗on the spot.

| 🍴 | **Nordkirchen** | 9B3 |

Minigolfpark, Am Schlosspark 5. **GPS**: n51,73553 e7,53494. ⬆.

2 🛏 free. **Surface:** metalled. ⬜ 01/03-31/10
Distance: 🚶1km ⊗on the spot 🚌100m.

| 🛏 S | **Nottuln** | 9B2 |

Wellenfreibad/Hallenbad, Rudolf-Harbigstrasse. **GPS**: n51,92410 e7,34514.

5 🛏 free 🚰. **Surface:** metalled. ⬜ 01/01-31/12
Distance: 🚌on the spot.
Remarks: Parking swimming pool, service during opening hours.

| 🛏 S | **Oberhausen** | 9A3 |

Am Kaisergarten. **GPS**: n51,48690 e6,85551. ⬆ ➡.

DE

60 🛏€7 🔌€ 1 🚽Ch ⚡ € 0,50/3h.
Surface: grassy. 🅾 01/01-31/12
Distance: 🚶Oberhausen City 30 min walking ⚓1,6km 🎡1,7km 🛒1,7km.

| 📷 | **Oberhausen** | 9A3 |

Parking 10 - CentrO, Arenastraße. **GPS:** n51,48930 e6,87063. ⬆️➡️.

40 🛏free.
Surface: metalled. 🅾 01/01-31/12
Distance: 🚶100m 🎡on the spot 🛒on the spot.
Remarks: At CentrO.

Tourist information Oberhausen:
😀 CentrO Park, Promenade 10.Amusement park. 🅾 01/04-31/10 11-18/19h.
🍲 CentrO.Large shopping centre, 300 shops, 100 restaurants/bars and a market.
🅾 Mo-Thu 10-20h restaurant 10-22h, Fri-Sa 10-22h restaurant 10-24h.

| 📷 | **Oedt** 👣 | 8D4 |

Wohnmobile-Stellplatz Niers-Perle-Oedt, Mühlengasse. **GPS:** n51,32327 e6,37650. ⬆️.

8 🛏free. **Surface:** asphalted. 🅾 01/01-31/12
Distance: 🚶800m 🎡500m 🛒500m.

| 📷S | **Olpe** | 9B4 |

Freizeitbad Olpe, Seeweg 5. **GPS:** n51,03242 e7,84163.
10 🛏€5 🚽Chfree ⚡€ 2/10h.
Surface: asphalted. 🅾 01/01-31/12
Distance: 🚶500m 🎡250m.
Remarks: Max. 3 days.

| 📷S | **Ostbevern** | 9B2 |

Bever Bad, Am Hanfgarten 22. **GPS:** n52,03673 e7,84392.➡️.

6 🛏€10 🔌🚽Ch ⚡ WC. **Surface:** grassy. 🅾 01/01-31/12
Distance: 🚶400m 🎡300m 🛒300m.
Remarks: Parking swimming pool, incl. entry swimming pool.

| 📷S | **Overhetfeld** | 8D4 |

Camp Graskamp, Graskamp 19. **GPS:** n51,22259 e6,13977. ⬆️.

5 🛏€10 🔌🚽Ch ⚡ WC ⬜included. **Surface:** grassy. 🅾 01/01-31/12
Distance: 🚶200m 🎡200m 🛒on the spot.

| 📷 | **Paderborn** 🌊🍲 | 9D3 |

Liboriberg. **GPS:** n51,71543 e8,75529. ⬆️➡️.
2 🛏€3,50/24h. 🅾 01/01-31/12
Distance: 🚶on the spot 🎡on the spot 🛒on the spot 🚌on the spot.

| 📷 | **Paderborn** 🌊🍲 | 9D3 |

Lippesee-Nordufer, Sennelagerstraße 58, Sande. **GPS:** n51,76087 e8,67756. ⬆️.

20 🛏free. **Surface:** grassy. 🅾 01/01-31/12
Distance: 🚶1km ⛵150m 🚣150m 🎡1km 🛒500m.
Remarks: North bank lake Lippe.

| 📷 | **Paderborn** 🌊🍲 | 9D3 |

Marpernplatz, P4, Hathumarstrasse. **GPS:** n51,72278 e8,75417. ⬆️➡️.

8 🛏€ 2,50/24h. **Surface:** metalled. 🅾 01/01-31/12
Distance: 🚶on the spot ⚓4km 🎡100m 🛒500m 🚌on the spot.

| 📷 | **Petershagen** | 9D1 |

Stellplatz Petershagen, Hohoffstrasse. **GPS:** n52,37532 e8,96875. ⬆️➡️.

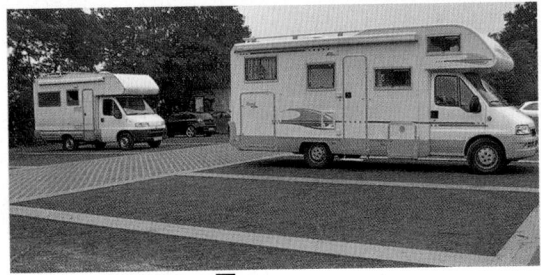

10 🛏free. **Surface:** metalled. ⬛ 01/01-31/12
Distance: 🚶100m ⊗100m 🚰100m.
Remarks: Nearby football ground, max. 3 days.

🚐S | **Plettenberg** | 9B4

Aqua Magis, Albert Schweizerstrasse, Böddinghausen. **GPS:** n51,23220 e7,85308.
⬆➡

10 🛏free 🚰€ 1/40liter 🗑Ch. **Surface:** metalled. ⬛ 01/01-31/12
Distance: 🚶on the spot ⊗on the spot 🚰200m.
Remarks: Max. 48h.

🚐S | **Raesfeld** | 9A3

Wohnmobilstellplatz Graf Alexander, Südring. **GPS:** n51,76523 e6,83035.
8 🛏€8 🚰€ 1 🗑Ch 🔌€ 1/12h WC 🚻.
Surface: gravel. ⬛ 01/01-31/12
Distance: 🚶1km ⊗150m.
Remarks: At historic moated castle, max. 2 nights.

🚐S | **Rahden** | 9D1

Am großen Stein, Hahnenkamp 12, Tonnenheide. **GPS:** n52,42395 e8,70224.
10 🛏 🚰🗑🔌 WC. **Surface:** grassy. ⬛ 01/01-31/12
Distance: 🚶3km.
Remarks: Cheese farm.

🚐S | **Recke** | 9B1

Yackthafen Marina Recke, Auf der Haar 23. **GPS:** n52,35082 e7,71174.⬆

40 🛏€5 🚰🗑Ch 🔌(10x)€ 1,50 WC 🚻. **Surface:** grassy/metalled. ⬛
01/01-31/12
Distance: 🚶1km, Recke 3,5km 🏊on the spot ⊗on the spot 🚰900m
🚗400m.
Remarks: Parking marina to Mittellland canal.

🚐S | **Rees** | 8D3

Wohnmobilstellplatz, Ebentalstrasse. **GPS:** n51,76428 e6,38829.⬆

31 🛏€ 6/day 🚰🗑Ch 🔌included 🚰€ 1. 🏠**Location:** Urban,
comfortable. **Surface:** grassy. ⬛ 01/01-31/12
Distance: 🚶400m.
Remarks: Behind swimming pool.

🚐S | **Reken** 🍴 | 9A2

Wohnmobilstellplatz Reken, Bergen 2a. **GPS:** n51,82864 e7,05895.⬆

25 🛏€6 🚰€ 1/200liter 🗑Ch 🔌(10x)€ 0,50/kWh. **Surface:** grassy. ⬛
01/01-31/12
Distance: 🚶1km ⊗1km 🚰1km.
Remarks: Max. 2 days.

🚐 | **Remscheid** | 9B4

Brückenpark Müngsten, Mügstener Brückenweg. **GPS:** n51,16833 e7,13750.⬆

4 🛏free. **Surface:** metalled. ⬛ 01/01-31/12
Distance: 🚶5km 🏞100m 🚤100m.

🚐 | **Remscheid** | 9B4

Schützenplatz, Hindenburgstrasse. **GPS:** n51,18555 e7,16944.
8 🛏free. **Surface:** metalled. ⬛ 01/01-31/12
Distance: ⊗on the spot.

🏭S | **Remscheid** | 9B4

Garage Pauli GmbH, Lenneperstrasse 152 (Bundesstrasse 229). **GPS:** n51,18020
e7,22591.
3 🛏free 🚰🗑Chfree. ⬛ 01/01-31/12
Distance: 🚶500m ⊗2km 🚰500m.

🚐S | **Rheda-Wiedenbrück** | 9C2

Am Werl, Gütersloherstrasse. **GPS:** n51,85456 e8,29768.

20 ⌂free ⌂⌂Ch⌂WCfree. **Surface:** metalled. ☉ 01/01-31/12
Remarks: Max. 3 days.

| ⌂ | **Rheda-Wiedenbrück** | 9C2 |

P Hallenbad, Ostring/Am Hallenbad, Wiederbrück. **GPS:** n51,83188 e8,32350.
⬆️➡️.

4 ⌂free. **Surface:** metalled. ☉ 01/01-31/12
Distance: ⌂1km ⌂200m ⌂bakery 200m.
Remarks: Parking swimming pool.

| ⌂S | **Rhede** | 9A2 |

Reisemobilstellplatz Kettelplatz, Kettelerstrasse 9. **GPS:** n51,83677
e6,69346.⬆️.

15 ⌂free ⌂€ 1/75liter ⌂Ch⌂(6x)€ 1/2kWh. **Location:** Urban.
Surface: grassy. ☉ 01/01-31/12
Distance: ⌂750m ⌂750m ⌂500m.

| ⌂ | **Rhede** | 9A2 |

Hallen- und Freibad, Heideweg 59. **GPS:** n51,83164 e6,68635.⬆️.

2 ⌂free. **Location:** Urban, very simple.
Surface: metalled. ☉ 01/01-31/12
Distance: ⌂1,5km.
Remarks: Parking swimming pool, max. 3 days.

| ⌂S | **Rheinbach** | 9A6 |

Parkplatz Freizeitpark/Erlebnisbad Monte Mare, Münstereifelerstraße 69.
GPS: n50,61883 e6,93262.⬆️➡️.

4 ⌂free ⌂WC. **Surface:** metalled. ☉ 01/01-31/12
Distance: ⌂1,5km ⌂1,5km.

Remarks: Max. 3 days.

| ⌂ | **Rheine** | 9B1 |

Am Walshagenpark, Liobastrasse/Walshagenstrasse. **GPS:** n52,29562 e7,43580.
2 ⌂free. ☉ 01/01-31/12
Distance: ⌂300m ⌂300m ⌂300m ⌂300m.

| ⌂ | **Rheine** | 9B1 |

Im Stadtpark, Kopernikusstrasse. **GPS:** n52,28137 e7,45478.⬆️.
2 ⌂free. **Surface:** metalled. ☉ 01/01-31/12

| ⌂ | **Rheine** | 9B1 |

Parkplatz Tennishalle, Gertrudenweg/Bentlager Weg, Bentlage. **GPS:** n52,29234
e7,42936.
3 ⌂free.
Distance: ⌂350m.

| ⌂ | **Rheine** | 9B1 |

Parkplatz, Salinenstrasse, Bentlage. **GPS:** n52,29828 e7,41904.
3 ⌂free. **Surface:** metalled.

| ⌂S | **Rheine** | 9B1 |

Hotel Borchert, Russenweg 3. **GPS:** n52,29826 e7,48215.
3 ⌂free ⌂. **Surface:** metalled.
Remarks: Asphalted inner court.

| ⌂S | **Rheurdt** | 8D3 |

Wohnmobilhafen Ökodorf, St. Nikolausweg 15. **GPS:** n51,46382 e6,46780.⬆️
➡️.

21 ⌂8 ⌂⌂Ch⌂€ 2/24h WC.
Surface: metalled. ☉ 01/01-31/12
Distance: ⌂500m ⌂500m ⌂500m.

| ⌂S | **Rietberg** ⌂ | 9C2 |

Jakobistrasse, Mastholte. **GPS:** n51,75667 e8,39111.⬆️.

4 ⌂free ⌂€ 0,50/80liter ⌂Ch. **Surface:** asphalted. ☉ 01/01-31/12
Distance: ⌂100m ⌂100m ⌂100m.

| ⌂ | **Rietberg** ⌂ | 9C2 |

Am Heimathaus, Langenberger Strasse, Mastholte. **GPS:** n51,75765 e8,38945.⬆️.

2 ⌂free. **Surface:** asphalted. ☉ 01/01-31/12
Distance: ⌂100m ⌂100m ⌂100m.

| ⌂ | **Rietberg** ⌂ | 9C2 |

Schulzentrum, Torfweg. **GPS:** n51,80724 e8,43295.⬆️.

DE

2 🅿free. **Surface:** metalled. 🚰 01/01-31/12
Distance: 🚶200m 🚲100m ⊗200m 🚊200m 🚌on the spot.

| 🅿 | Roetgen | 8D5 |

Am Bahnhof, Bahnhofstrasse. **GPS:** n50,64868 e6,18506.

10 🅿free. **Surface:** gravel/metalled. 🚰 01/01-31/12
Distance: 🚶300m 🚊300m.

| 🅿 S | Rosendahl 🏕 | 9B2 |

Wohnmobilplatz Darfeld, Sudetenstrasse, Darfeld. **GPS:** n52,02696 e7,26501. ➡.

20 🅿free 🚰€ 1/100liter 🗑Ch ⚡€ 0,50/kWh. **Surface:** grassy/metalled. 🚰 01/01-31/12
Distance: 🚶500m ⊗on the spot 🚊500m.

| 🅿 | Rüthen | 9C3 |

Am Hachtor, Hachtorstrasse. **GPS:** n51,49405 e8,43119. ⬆➡.

4 🅿free. 🚰 01/01-31/12
Distance: 🚶50m ⊗50m 🚊50m, Aldi 200m.

| 🍴 | Saerbeck | 9B2 |

Hotel-Rest. Stegemann, Westladbergen 71. **GPS:** n52,15169 e7,68343.
8 🅿guests free. **Surface:** metalled. 🚰 01/01-31/12
Distance: 🚶3km ⊗on the spot 🚊3km.

| 🅿 S | Sassenberg | 9C2 |

Parkplatz Feldmark, Feldmark. **GPS:** n52,00172 e8,06546. ⬆.

3 🅿free 🚰€ 1/80liter 🗑Ch.
Distance: 🚶4km ⊗on the spot 🚊on the spot.

| 🅿 | Sassenberg | 9C2 |

Freibad, Telgenkamp. **GPS:** n51,98378 e8,04981.

🅿free.
Remarks: Parking swimming pool.

| 🅿 S | Schieder | 9D2 |

Freizeitzentrum Schiedersee, Kronenbruch. **GPS:** n51,92073 e9,16471. ⬆➡.

300 🅿€ 7 🚰€ 1/100liter 🗑Ch ⚡€ 0,50/kWh WC🚻€ 0,50 🚿€ 2.
Surface: grassy/metalled. 🚰 01/01-31/12
Distance: 🚶1,3km 🏊50m 🚲50m ⊗on the spot 🚊on the spot.

| 🅿 S | Schleiden | 8D6 |

Wohnmobilhafen am Nationalpark-Eifel, Pfarrer-Kneipp-strasse, Gemünd. **GPS:** n50,57855 e6,49107. ⬆.

40 🅿€ 7, tourist tax € 0,50/pp 🚰€ 0,50/50liter 🗑Ch ⚡€ 0,50/kWh.
Surface: gravel/metalled. 🚰 01/01-31/12
Distance: 🚶within walking distance ⊗500m 🚊500m.
Remarks: Bread-service.

| 🅿 | Schleiden | 8D6 |

Am Freibad, Im Wiesengrund. **GPS:** n50,52993 e6,47022.

DE

8 free. **Surface:** asphalted.

10 free ⛺ Ch. **Surface:** grasstiles. 01/01-31/12
Distance: on the spot 200m 300m on the spot.
Remarks: Parking swimming pool.

Schloss Holte/Stukenbrock 9D2

Senden 9B2

Reisemobilstellplatz Am Sennebach, Liemkerstrasse 27, Liemke. **GPS:** n51,86979 e8,61531.

Ponyhof Steinhoff, Gettrup 37. **GPS:** n51,83305 e7,46878.

20 € 5 € 2 € 2 Ch. (18x)included. **Surface:** grasstiles. 01/01-31/12 service: sa/su.
Distance: 1km 1km.
Remarks: Behind Froli Kunstoffwerk Fromme.

10 € 6 ⛺ Ch. € 0,50/kWh. **Surface:** grassy/metalled. 01/01-31/12
Distance: Senden 4km 2,5km 2,5km.

Schmallenberg 9C4

Sendenhorst 9B2

Im Sorpetal, Winkhausen 21. **GPS:** n51,16083 e8,34056.

Westor 31. **GPS:** n51,84286 e7,81849.

13 € 9 € 0,50/80liter € 0,50/kWh. 01/01-31/12
Distance: 100m 2km 500m.

4 free € 0,50/40liter Ch. € 0,50. **Surface:** metalled. 01/01-31/12
Distance: on the spot 300m 1km.

Schmallenberg 9C4

Siegen 9C5

Bauernhofpension Paul Vogt, Obringhausen 7. **GPS:** n51,16976 e8,28105.
3 € 8.
Distance: 2km.

Am Hallenbad, Poststraße. **GPS:** n50,89536 e8,02605.
3 free ⛺ Ch. **Surface:** metalled. 01/01-31/12
Remarks: Max. 3 days.

Schöppingen 9A2

Simmerath 8D6

Schulze Althoff, Heven 48. **GPS:** n52,07361 e7,22361.

Wohnmobilhafen Rurseezentrum, Seeufer 1, Rurberg. **GPS:** n50,60658 e6,38177.

30 € 12/night, 3p incl., +3p € 4/pp ⛺ Ch. WC included sanitary € 2/pp 4. **Surface:** grassy.
Distance: 2,5km on the spot on the spot 2,5km on the spot.

10 € 5/24h ⛺ 2 Ch. 01/01-31/12

Senden 9B2

Simmerath 8D6

Sportpark Senden, Buldenerstrasse. **GPS:** n51,85419 e7,47433.

Ehrenfriedhof Rurberg, L166. **GPS:** n50,60931 e6,36386.

6 🛏️free. **Surface:** asphalted. 📅 01/01-31/12

| 🛁S | Soest | 9C3 |

Georg-Plange Platz, Ostenhellweg. **GPS:** n51,57069 e8,11908.

10 🛏️free 🚰€ 1 🗑️Ch 🧹 (4x)€ 1/10h, 16Amp. **Surface:** gravel.
Distance: 🚶500m 🚲3,6km.
Remarks: May 2009 during inspection service out of order.

| 🛏️ | Solingen | 9A4 |

Am Brandteich, Gräfrath. **GPS:** n51,21151 e7,07217.⬆️

10 🛏️free. 📅 01/01-31/12
Distance: 🚶on the spot 🚲2,7km ⊗on the spot 🚱300m.
Remarks: Parking fire-station.

| 🛁S | Stadtlohn | 9A2 |

Freizeit- und Hallenbad, Uferstrasse 29. **GPS:** n51,99792 e6,93019.⬆️➡️

4 🛏️against payment 🚰€ 0,50/100liter 🗑️Ch 🧹 (4x)€ 1 WC 🧺. **Surface:**
metalled. 📅 01/01-31/12
Distance: 🚶800m.
Remarks: Parking swimming pool.

| 🛁S | Steinfurt 🔧 | 9B2 |

Wohnmobilstellplatz Steinfurt, Liedekerkerstrasse 70, Burgsteinfurt. **GPS:**
n52,14738 e7,34746.⬆️➡️

25 🛏️voluntary contribution 🚰€ 1/100liter 🗑️Ch 🧹€ 1/2kWh. **Surface:**
asphalted. 📅 01/01-31/12
Distance: 🚶300m 🚱200m.
Remarks: Parking behind police station, max. 3 nights.

| 🛏️ | Steinhagen | 9C2 |

Am Cronsbach. **GPS:** n51,99998 e8,42351.⬆️➡️

2 🛏️free. **Surface:** metalled. 📅 01/01-31/12
Distance: 🚶100m ⊗100m 🚱100m.

| 🛏️ | Stemwede | 9C1 |

Fest- und Schiesshalle, Schrottinghauserstrasse, Levern. **GPS:** n52,37217
e8,44552.⬆️➡️

2 🛏️free. **Surface:** metalled. 📅 01/01-31/12
Distance: 🚶1,5km ⊗1,5km 🚱1,4km.

| 🛏️ | Stemwede | 9C1 |

Park Stemwederberg, Stemwederbergstrasse/Freudeneck, Westrup. **GPS:**
n52,43246 e8,43973.⬆️➡️

8 🛏️free. **Surface:** grassy/gravel. 📅 01/01-31/12
Distance: 🚶2km ⊗2km 🚱2km.

| 🍽️S | Stemwede | 9C1 |

Hotel-Gasthof Moorhof, Wagenfelderstrasse 34, Oppenwehe. **GPS:** n52,49979
e8,53507.⬆️

DE

20 ⌂ € 7, free with a meal ⛽ 🔌 included ⚡ € 2, 16Amp. **Surface:** grassy. ⬜ 01/01-31/12
Distance: ⊗on the spot.

⌂free ⛽ Ch ⚡. **Surface:** asphalted. ⬜ 01/01-31/12
Distance: 🚶1km.
Remarks: Parking swimming pool, recreation area.

DE

Rila Feinkost-Importe, Schröttinghauser Strasse/Hinterm Teich 3, Levern. **GPS:** n52,36783 e8,43833.

Altes Gasthaus Lauheide, Lauheide 3, K17. **GPS:** n51,99862 e7,75319.⬆.

50 ⌂ € 15 ⛽ Ch ⚡ WC 🚽. **Surface:** grassy. ⬜ 01/01-31/12
Distance: ⊗on the spot.
Remarks: Incl. voucher € 6 for 'Rila erleben': restaurant, Tapas bar, food, garden, playground.

120 ⌂ ⛽ Ch ⚡ € 6. **Surface:** grassy. ⬜ 01/01-31/12
Distance: 🚶4km ⊗on the spot.

Reisemobilstellplatz Uedem, Bergstraße. **GPS:** n51,66173 e6,28734.⬆.

Fitnessbad Wasserstraelen, Lingsforterstraße 100. **GPS:** n52,45201 e6,25708. ⬆.

10 ⌂free ⛽ € 0,50/80liter Ch ⚡ (8x)€ 0,50/kWh. **Surface:** asphalted. ⬜ 01/01-31/12
Distance: 🚶1,2km ⊗1km 🚂1km.

28 ⌂ € 8 ⛽ Ch ⚡ (24x)€ 2/24h WC. **Surface:** grassy. ⬜ 01/01-31/12
Distance: 🚶1,5km.

Tourist information Straelen:

ℹ Verkehrsverein Straelen e.V, Rathausstrasse 1, www.straelen.de.City with historical center, cycle and skating routes.

Unter der Saubrücke, Parkstraße, Velbert-Mitte. **GPS:** n51,34097 e7,03050.
6 ⌂free ⛽ € 1/100liter Ch ⚡ € 0,50/kWh. **Surface:** gravel. ⬜ 01/01-31/12
Distance: 🚶800m 🚴1,6km ⊗250m.

Parkplatz Bismarckturm, Am Weingarten. **GPS:** n52,22129 e7,99905.⬆→.

Panoramabad Velbert-Neviges, Wiesenweg. **GPS:** n51,30582 e7,08546.⬆.

5 ⌂free. **Surface:** asphalted. ⬜ 01/01-31/12
Distance: 🚶800m.

5 ⌂free ⛽ € 1/80liter Ch. **Surface:** metalled. ⬜ 01/01-31/12
Distance: ⊗nearby 🚂500m.
Remarks: Parking swimming pool, max. 3 nights.

Waldschwimmbad Klatenberge, Waldweg. **GPS:** n51,99459 e7,78328.⬆.

Domparkplatz, Bernsaustrasse Schloss Hardenberg. **GPS:** n51,31565 e7,08724. ⬆.

5 🛏 € 2. **Surface:** metalled. 🔲 01/01-31/12
Distance: ⊗on the spot.

9 🛏 free ⛽ € 0,50/100liter 🔌 Ch ✦ (6x)€ 1/2kWh. **Surface:** metalled. 🔲 01/01-31/12
Distance: 🚶Dülken 400m, Viersen 3km ⊗400m 🚻 2km 🚏100m.
Remarks: Max. 3 days.

| 🛏 | Velbert | 9A4 |

Nizzabad, Kalversiepen, Langenberg. **GPS:** n51,34362 e7,13766.

| 🍴 S | Vreden ⛵ | 9A2 |

Hotel Zum Möwenparadies, Zwillbrockstrasse 39. **GPS:** n52,05305 e6,70733. ⬆️.

4 🛏 free. **Surface:** metalled. 🔲 01/01-31/12
Distance: ⊗on the spot.

10 🛏 € 10 ⛽🔌 Ch ✦ WC ⬜included. **Surface:** grassy. 🔲 01/01-31/12
Distance: 🚿on the spot 🚰on the spot ⊗on the spot 🚏200m.

| 🛏 S | Velen 🍴 | 9A2 |

Erholungsgebiet Waldvelen, ven der Buss, Klyer Damm 8-10. **GPS:** n51,90167 e7,01167. ⬆️➡️.

| 🍴 S | Vreden | 9A2 |

Pension Ostendarp, Wüllenerstrasse 107. **GPS:** n52,03440 e6,84174.

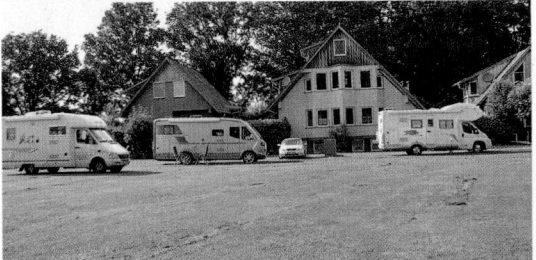

30 🛏 € 15, 2 pers.incl ⛽🔌 Ch ✦ (50x). **Location:** Rural, luxurious. **Surface:** gravel. 🔲 01/01-31/12
Distance: 🚶2km 🏊8,5km.

5 🛏 free ⛽🔌 Ch ✦ WC. **Surface:** grassy. 🔲 01/01-31/12
Distance: 🚶800m ⊗on the spot 🚻300m.

| 🛏 | Velen 🍴 | 9A2 |

Freibad Ramsdorf, Velener Straße, Ramsdorf. **GPS:** n51,88955 e6,92503. ⬆️.

| 🍴 S | Vreden ⛵ | 9A2 |

Wohnmobilpark Vreden, Ottensteiner Strasse 59. **GPS:** n52,03962 e6,84136. ⬆️.

5 🛏 free. **Surface:** asphalted. 🔲 01/01-31/12
Distance: 🚶Ramsdorf 300m.
Remarks: At swimming pool.

30 🛏 € 8 ⛽🔌 Ch ✦ (20x)included WC ⬜€ 2 📶 € 3/h ♻. **Surface:** grassy. 🔲 01/01-31/12
Distance: 🚶500m ⊗on the spot.
Remarks: Guarded parking.

| 🛏 S | Viersen | 8D4 |

Am Familienbad Ransberg, Heesstraße 80, Viersen-Dülken. **GPS:** n51,25083 e6,35291. ⬆️.

| 🛏 S | Wachtendonk | 8D4 |

Bleiche P4, Achter de Stadt. **GPS:** n51,40601 e6,33170. ⬆️➡️.

DE

18 🏕€5 🚰€ 0,50/80liter ⚡€ 0,50 Ch ⚡ (12x)€ 0,50/kWh. **Surface:** gravel. 🅾 01/01-31/12
Distance: 🚶400m ⊗100m ⛽400m.

Schützenplatz, Paderborner Tor. **GPS:** n51,48993 e9,13810.
5 🏕€5 🚰⚡Ch ⚡ included. **Surface:** metalled.
Distance: 🚶500m.

🏕   **Warendorf**   9C2
Beelener Strasse. GPS: n51,94975 e8,00127.⬆➡.

🏕S   **Wadersloh**   9C3
Im Klostergarten 18, Liesborn. **GPS:** n51,71414 e8,25960.⬆➡.

4 🏕free 🚰€ 0,50/80liter ⚡Ch ⚡ (4x)€ 0,50/12h. **Surface:** metalled. 🅾 01/01-31/12
Distance: 🚶400m ⊗100m ⛽400m.
Remarks: Behind gymnasium.

🏕   **Waldbröl**   9B5
Am Hallenbad, Vennstrassse. **GPS:** n50,87511 e7,60987.⬆.
4 🏕free. **Surface:** metalled. 🅾 01/01-31/12
Remarks: Max. 2 days.

🏕S   **Waldfeucht Brüggelchen**   8D4
Reisemobilstellplatz, Tilderweg. **GPS:** n51,07016 e5,99567.⬆.

10 🏕free.
Distance: 🚶1,5km ⛽on the spot.
Remarks: Max. 24h.

🏕   **Warendorf**   9C2
Parkplatz Emssee, Sassenberger Strasse. **GPS:** n51,95514 e7,99797.⬆.

2 🏕free. 🅾 01/01-31/12
Distance: 🚶1km ⊗on the spot.
Remarks: Max. 24h.

18 🏕free 🚰€ 0,50/80liter ⚡Ch ⚡ (8x)€ 0,50/kWh. **Surface:** metalled. 🅾 01/01-31/12
Distance: 🚶1km ⊗on the spot ⛽500m.
Remarks: Max. 4 nights.

🏕   **Warendorf**   9C2
Parkplatz Zwischen den Emsbrücken, Am Emswehr. **GPS:** n51,95426 e7,99164.⬆.

2 🏕free. 🅾 01/01-31/12
Distance: 🚶100m.
Remarks: Max. 24h.

🍴S   **Waltrop** 👥   9B3
Restaurant Zur Lohburg, Lohburgerstrass 105, A2 Ausfahrt henreichenburg, Schiffshebewerk. **GPS:** n51,60613 e7,34882.

🏕S   **Warstein** 〰🍽👥   9C3
Camperpark zum Bayernstadl, Enkerbruch 12a. **GPS:** n51,43041 e8,37432.⬆➡.

20 🏕€5 🚰 ⚡ € 2. **Surface:** grassy. 🅾 01/01-31/12
Distance: 🚶1km ⊗on the spot ⛽1km.

40 🏕€7,50 🚰⚡Ch ⚡ (18x), € 1 summer, € 2 winter. **Surface:** gravel. 🅾 01/01-31/12

Distance: 🛒1,5km ⊗on the spot 💧1,5km 🚮1,5km.
Remarks: Bread-service.

| 🅢 | Warstein 🐾🍽️🍴 | 9C3 |

Vans in Paradise, Zu Hause im Waldpark. **GPS:** n51,42578 e8,35713.⬆️.

60 🚐€ 15 🚰♻️Ch ⚡(76x), 16Amp WC 🍽️included 🔌€ 2, dryer € 2.
Surface: grassy/gravel. 🅞 01/01-31/12
Distance: 🛒2km ⊗small menu 💧2km 🚮2km.
Remarks: At Warstein brewery, bread-service + breakfast-service.

| 🅢 | Warstein 🐾🍽️🍴 | 9C3 |

Wohnmobilstellplatz, Dammweg. **GPS:** n51,45103 e8,34750.⬆️➡️.

5 🚐free.
Surface: grassy. 🅞 01/01-31/12
Distance: 🛒2km ⊗500m 💧1km 🚮1km.
Remarks: At sports park.

Tourist information Warstein:

👁️ Warsteiner Brauerei, Zu Hause im Waldpark.Guided tour 1.45h, 2 drinks included. 🅞 daily 12-17, Su 13-15h.

| 🅢 | Wassenberg | 8D4 |

Parkbad Wassenberg, Auf dem Taubenkamp 2. **GPS:** n51,09833 e6,14364.⬆️.

11 🚐€ 5/day 🚰€ 1 🔌€ 1 Ch ⚡€ 0,50/kWh. **Surface:** metalled. 🅞
01/01-31/12
Distance: 🛒1,5km.
Remarks: To pay at swimming pool.

| 🅢 | Weeze | 8D3 |

Tierpark Fährsteg, L5 Fährsteg. **GPS:** n51,63047 e6,20130.⬆️.

12 🚐€ 5 ⚡€ 0,50/kWh. 🅞 01/01-31/12
Distance: 🛒500m 💧500m.

| 🅢 | Weeze | 8D3 |

Aral, Industriestraße. **GPS:** n51,62029 e6,20972.⬆️.

🚰€ 1 ♻️Ch.

| 🅢 | Wegberg | 8D4 |

Wegberger Reisemobilstellplatz, Schul- und Sportzentrum, Maaseiker
Strasse 67. **GPS:** n51,13389 e6,28266.⬆️➡️.

10 🚐€ 6 🚰♻️Ch ⚡included.
Surface: gravel/sand. 🅞 01/01-31/12
Distance: 🛒400m ⊗400m 💧400m 🚮on the spot.
Remarks: Caution key € 20 at swimming pool.

| 🅢 | Werne 🍴 | 9B3 |

Natur Solebad, Am Hagen. **GPS:** n51,65910 e7,63414.⬆️➡️.

10 🚐free 🚰€ 1/80liter ♻️Ch ⚡€ 0,50. **Surface:** metalled. 🅞 01/01-
31/12
Distance: 🛒400m ⊗200m 💧400m.
Remarks: Parking swimming pool.

| 🅢 | Wiehl | 9B5 |

Freizeitpark Wiehl, Brüchnerstrasse. **GPS:** n50,94716 e7,54585.⬆️➡️.

3 🚐free 🚰€ 1/80liter ♻️Ch. **Surface:** metalled.
Distance: 🛒300m ⛵5,4km 💧400m.
Remarks: Parking next to recreation park and disco, max. 2 days.

| 🅢 | Wiehl | 9B5 |

Eissporthalle, P17. **GPS:** n50,94714 e7,55233.⬆️.

3 ⏚free. **Surface:** metalled. ◻ 01/01-31/12
Distance: ⛟300m ☕150m.
Remarks: Parking skating rink.

| ⏚ S | **Wiehl** | 9B5 |

Sportplatz Eichhardt, Friedhofstrasse. **GPS:** n50,95110 e7,54482.

3 ⏚free.
Surface: metalled. ◻ 01/01-31/12
Remarks: Parking sports park, max. 2 days.

Tourist information Wiehl:
ℹ www.wiehl.de.Small town in the green hills. 180 kilometres marked hiking routes.
👁 Wiehler Dahlienschau.400 varieties of dahlias. ◻ 15/08-15/10 daily 8-18h.
Ⓣ free.
👁 Wiehler Trofsteinhöhle.Caves Temperature is approx. 8ºC. ◻ 15/03-31/10 9-17h, 01/11-14/03 Sa-Su 11-16h.
Ⓜ Schloß Homburg/Museum des Oberbergisches Kreises, Nürnbrecht. ◻ 01/04-31/10 Tue-Sa 10-17h, Su 10-18h.
✐ Bergische Postkutsche, Nümrecht Post.Ride by mail-coach between Wiehl and Nümbrecht. ◻ 01/05-30/09 Fri-Su 10-16h.

| ⏚ S | **Wilnsdorf** | 9C5 |

Wielandshof, Bauhofstraße 5. **GPS:** n50,80692 e8,10896.⬆
5 ⏚€5 ⚡€ 0,50/60liter ⚓Ch ⚓(4x)€ 1/12h. **Surface:** gravel. ◻ 01/01-31/12
Distance: ⛟900m ⊗900m.

| 🍴 | **Wilnsdorf** | 9C5 |

Gästehaus Wilgersdorf, Am Kalkhain 9-23, Wilgersdorf. **GPS:** n50,80751 e8,14782.

3 ⏚free. **Surface:** asphalted. ◻ 01/01-31/12
Distance: ⛟500m ⊗on the spot ☕1km.

| ⏚ S | **Windeck** | 9B5 |

Am Sportplatz, Im Bungert, Herchen. **GPS:** n50,78025 e7,51308.⬆

5 ⏚free ⚡. **Surface:** metalled. ◻ 01/01-31/12
Distance: ⛟200m ⊗200m ☕200m.
Remarks: Parking sports park.

| ⏚ S | **Windeck** | 9B5 |

Heimatmuseum, Im Thal Windeck 17, Alt-Windeck. **GPS:** n50,81276 e7,57554.

4 ⏚free ⚡ ⚓. ◻ 01/01-31/12
Distance: ⛟2km ⊗on the spot ☕2km.
Remarks: Parking museum, max. 2 days.

| ⏚ | **Windeck** | 9B5 |

Brunnenweg, Dattenfeld. **GPS:** n50,80486 e7,56087.⬆

5 ⏚free. **Surface:** metalled. ◻ 01/01-31/12
Distance: ⛟200m ⊗200m ☕150m.
Remarks: Recreation park.

| ⏚ | **Windeck** | 9B5 |

Festplatz Auf dem Greent, Dattenfeld. **GPS:** n50,80697 e7,55495.

50 ⏚free. **Surface:** asphalted/grassy. ◻ 01/01-31/12
Distance: ⛟500m ⊗500m ☕500m.
Remarks: Fair ground.

| S | **Windeck** | 9B5 |

Hallenbad, Bergische strasse 21, Dattenfeld. **GPS:** n50,80754 e7,56105.⬆➡
⚡€ 1 ⚓€ 1,50 Ch. ◻ 01/01-31/12

| ⏚ S | **Winterberg** ❄ | 9D4 |

Parkplatz Stadthalle, Schulstrasse. **GPS:** n51,19163 e8,53810.⬆

150 ⏚€ 8/24h ⚡ ⚓Ch ⚓ 0,50/kWh. ◻ 01/01-31/12

| ⏚ | **Winterberg** ❄ | 9D4 |

GPS: n51,18632 e8,50445.

🅂 € 3 day/€ 3 night.
Remarks: Parking skiruns.

| ⚠️S | **Winterberg** ❄️ | 9D4 |

Park Hochsauerland, Remmeswiese 10. **GPS**: n51,19869 e8,52524.⬆️.

🅂 tariff camp site 🚰🍴Ch🧹WC🗑️. ⬛ 01/01-31/12
Remarks: Parking skilift, reservation recommended in winter peak season: tel. 0049 2981 3249.

| 🍴S | **Winterberg** ❄️ | 9D4 |

Kirchmeier Sporthotel, Renauweg 54, Altastenberg. **GPS**: n51,19391 e8,46844.
10 🅂 € 25 🚰🍴Ch🧹WC🗑️. **Surface:** asphalted. ⬛ 01/01-31/12
Distance: 🚶Winterberg 5km.
Remarks: Free entrance swimming pool, Dampfbad, sauna.

| 🍴 | **Winterberg** ❄️ | 9D4 |

Bergrestaurant Bobhaus, Auf der Kappe 1. **GPS**: n51,18493 e8,50559.⬆️.

8 🅂 € 6, free with a meal.
Remarks: Parking ski-lift.

| 🛏️S | **Witten** | 9B3 |

Reisemobil-Center, Pferdebachstrasse 150. **GPS**: n51,45411 e7,35246.⬆️.

10 🅂 free 🚰€ 1/80liter 🍴Ch. **Surface:** gravel. ⬛ 01/01-31/12
Distance: 🚶3km ⊗3km 🚲3km.

| 🅂 | **Wülfrath** | 9A4 |

Parkplatz, Mettmanner strasse 42. **GPS**: n51,28213 e7,02716.⬆️.

10 🅂 free. ⬛ 01/01-31/12
Distance: 🚶on the spot ⊗500m 🚲800m.

| 🅂S | **Zülpich** | 9A5 |

Wohnmobilhafen am Zülpicher See, Am Wassersportsee. **GPS**: n50,67592 e6,65795.⬆️➡️.

40 🅂 € 5 🚰€ 1/80liter 🍴Ch🧹(4x). **Surface:** grassy/metalled. ⬛ 01/01-31/12

Rhineland-Palatinate/Saarland

| 🅂S | **Alf** | 16D1 |

Freibad Arrastal, Junkergasse 1. **GPS**: n50,05273 e7,11326.

30 🅂 € 6 🚰🍴Ch🧹 included. **Surface:** asphalted/grassy. ⬛ 01/01-31/12
Distance: 🚶800m.

| 🅂 | **Alken** 〰️ | 9B6 |

P2, Grinschelheck. **GPS**: n50,24493 e7,44607.

6 🅂 free. **Surface:** metalled. ⬛ 01/01-31/12
Distance: 🚶500m ⊗on the spot 🚐200m.

| 🅂S | **Altdorf** | 17A3 |

Spelzenhof, Hauptstrasse 77. **GPS**: n49,28869 e8,22028.

6 ⛺6 🚰 🧹 WC. **Surface:** grassy. ⬛ 01/01-31/12
Distance: 🚰nearby ⊗on the spot 🛒nearby 🚌nearby.

🍴S | **Altendiez** | 9C6
Restaurant Bimbes-Stubb, Lahnblick 4. **GPS:** n50,36612 e7,98041. ⬆.

6 ⛺free 🚰 € 1 ♻Ch WC. **Surface:** asphalted. ⬛ 01/01-31/12
Distance: 🚰1km 🛒600m.

⛽S | **Bacharach** 🏖 | 17A1
Reisemobilplatz Bacharach, B9 Leinpfad. **GPS:** n50,05693 e7,77076. ⬆.

6 ⛺5 🚰 🔌 € 5. **Surface:** gravel. ⬛ 01/01-31/12 ⬤ Mo.
Distance: 🚰on the spot ⊗on the spot 🛒500m.

⛽S | **Altenglan** 🍴 | 16D2
Draisine, Austrasse. **GPS:** n49,55001 e7,46465. ⬆.

30 ⛺7 🚰 € 1 ♻Ch 🔌 (12x)€ 2,50/24h. **Surface:** metalled. ⬛ 01/01-31/12 ⬤ high water.
Distance: 🚰on the spot 🏞Rhine river ⊗300m 🛒300m.
Remarks: Check in at reception campsite.

⛽S | **Bad Bergzabern** | 17A3
Schloßgärten, Weinbergstrasse. **GPS:** n49,10322 e7,99737. ⬆➡.

4 ⛺free 🚰 € 1/80liter ♻Ch 🔌 (4x)€ 1/12h. **Surface:** gravel. ⬛ 01/04-31/10
Distance: ⊗100m 🛒100m.

⛽S | **Andernach** | 9B6
Wohnmobilstellplatz Andernach, Scheidsgasse/Uferstrasse. **GPS:** n50,44176 e7,40796. ⬆.

5 ⛺4 🚰 € 1 ♻€ 1 ♻Ch 🔌 € 1. ⬛ 01/01-31/12 ⬤ water disconnected in winter.
Distance: 🚰on the spot ⊗on the spot 🛒200m.

🛒S | **Bad Bergzabern** | 17A3
Weingut Hitziger, Liebrauenbergweg 3. **GPS:** n49,10667 e7,99611.

70 ⛺6 🚰 € 1/80liter ♻Ch 🔌 (40x).
Surface: metalled. ⬛ 01/01-31/12
Distance: 🚰on the spot ⊗200m 🛒400m.
Remarks: Max. 3 nights.

⛽S | **Annweiler** | 17A3
Am Kurpark, Bindersbacherstrasse. **GPS:** n49,19624 e7,96817. ⬆.

⛺5 🚰 ♻Ch 🔌 € 1. **Surface:** grassy. ⬛ 01/01-31/12
Distance: 🚰1km ⊗2km 🛒2km.

⛽S | **Bad Dürkheim** 🏊⚓ | 17A2
In der Silz, Leistadterstrasse. **GPS:** n49,46944 e8,16722. ⬆➡.

DE

50 🚐€6 🚰€ 1/4minutes 🔧Ch 🔌€ 1/kWh. 🚐 **Location:** Urban.
Surface: grassy. ⬛ 01/01-31/12
Distance: 🏊300m ⊗100m 🛒300m 🚌200m.
Remarks: Servicepoint at Knaus Park.

🅒🅢 Bad Dürkheim ⛲ ⛵ 17A2
Knaus park, In den Almen 3. **GPS:** n49,47472 e8,19167.⬆.

8 🚐€7 🚰€ 1/70liter 🔧Ch 🔌€ 0,50 🗑€ 3/pp. **Surface:** gravel/metalled.
⬛ 01/01-31/12

🅢 Bad Ems 9B6
Yachthafen Kutscher's Marina, Nievernerstrasse 20. **GPS:** n50,33278 e7,70167.
⬆.

12 🚐€8 🚰🔧Ch 🔌€ 1/kWh WC🗑€ 1 ◼. **Surface:** gravel. ⬛ 01/03-15/11
Distance: 🏊on the spot ⊗1km 🛒300m.

🍴 Bad Ems 9B6
Restaurant Schöne Aussicht, Bei Kemmenau. **GPS:** n50,34778 e7,74417.
10 🚐.

⛲🅢 Bad Hönningen 9B6
Kristall Rheinpark-Therme, Allée St. Pierre les Nemours 1. **GPS:** n50,51227
e7,30772.⬆➡.

15 🚐€16 🚰🔧Ch 🔌WC🗑€ 0,50 ◼€ 2 🚿. **Surface:** grassy. ⬛
01/01-31/12
Distance: ⊗on the spot 🛒on the spot.

🅢 Bad Kreuznach 17A1
Wohnmobilstellplatz Salinental, Karlhalle 2, Saline. **GPS:** n49,82778
e7,85001.⬆➡.

32 🚐€11 🚰€ 0,50/80liter 🔧Ch 🔌€ 2/night. **Surface:** gravel. ⬛
01/01-31/12
Distance: 🏊2km 🏊on the spot 🛒on the spot ⊗200m 🛒2km 🚌on the spot.

🅢 Bad Marienberg 9C5
Marienbad, Bismarckstrasse 65. **GPS:** n50,64466 e7,93528.⬆.

10 🚐€6,50 🚰€ 1/80liter 🔧Ch 🔌(3x)€ 1/day. **Surface:** metalled. ⬛
01/01-31/12

🅢 Bad Neuenahr ⛵ 9A6
Reisemobilhafen, Kalvarienbergstrasse 1, Ahrweiler. **GPS:** n50,53891 e7,09600.
⬆.

🚐€ 7,50/24h 🚰🔧Ch 🔌€ 2 WC included 🗑€ 1 ◼€ 2.
Surface: grassy.
Distance: 🏊200m.

🅢 Bad Neuenahr ⛵ 9A6
Am Schwimmbad. GPS: n50,53806 e7,10139.
14 🚐€6 🚰🔧Ch 🔌. **Surface:** metalled. ⬛ 01/01-31/12
Distance: 🏊600m ⊗300m 🛒bakery 500m.
Remarks: Along the Ahr river.

🅢 Bad Neuenahr ⛵ 9A6
Apolinaris-Stadion, Kreuzstrasse. **GPS:** n50,54456 e7,15132.

50 🚐€ 5/24h 🚰€ 1/80liter 🔧Ch. **Surface:** asphalted. ⬛ 01/01-31/12

DE

Bad Neuenahr ♨ 9A6

St Piusstrasse. **GPS:** n50,53962 e7,10775.

10 🅿️ € 5/24h. **Surface:** asphalted. ⬜ 01/01-31/12
Remarks: Parking at the Ahr.

Bad Sobernheim 17A2

Reisemobilstellplatz am Nohfels, Felkestraße. **GPS:** n49,77993 e7,65702. ⬆️

39 🅿️ € 7 ⚡€ 1/80liter 🗑️Ch ✂️ (48x)€ 2/day 📶. **Surface:** grassy/gravel. ⬜ 01/01-31/12
Distance: 🚶1km ⊗on the spot.
Remarks: Bread-service.

Baumholder 16D2

Freizeitzentrum Am Weiher, Ringstrasse. **GPS:** n49,61111 e7,33917. ➡️

3 🅿️ free. **Surface:** asphalted. ⬜ 01/01-31/12
Distance: 🚶2km ⚓on the spot ⊗on the spot 🚌250m.

Becheln 9B6

Restaurant Zum Wolfsbusch, Emser strasse 1. **GPS:** n50,29609 e7,71503.

5 🅿️ € 2, guests free ⚡€ 2. **Surface:** gravel/metalled.
Distance: 🚶on the spot ⊗on the spot 🚌300m.

Beckingen 16C3

Brunnenstrasse, Düppenweiler. **GPS:** n49,41414 e6,76973.

10 🅿️ € 2 ⚡€ 1 🗑️Ch. **Surface:** metalled.

Beckingen 16C3

Landgasthaus Wilscheider Hof, Zum Wilscheider Hof, Düppenweiler. **GPS:** n49,42585 e6,76431.

15 🅿️ € 5 ⚡ ✂️ € 1 WC 🗑️ 🚿. **Surface:** grassy. ⬜ 01/01-31/12
Distance: 🚶1,5km ⊗on the spot 🚌1,5km.

Bernkastel 16D1

Weingut Studert-Prüm im Maximin Hof, Hauptstrasse 150, Wehlen. **GPS:** n49,93771 e7,04811. ⬆️

50 🅿️ € 9 ⚡🗑️Ch ✂️.
Surface: grassy. ⬜ 01/01-31/12
Distance: 🚶on the spot ⚓on the spot ⚓on the spot ⊗on the spot 🚌500m.

Bernkastel 16D1

Nikolausufer. **GPS:** n49,91119 e7,06721. ⬆️

40 🅿️ 10-18h ⚡🗑️Ch. 🚻 **Location:** Urban. **Surface:** grasstiles. ⬜ 01/01-31/12
Remarks: Max. 6h.

Bexbach 🌿🌼🌾 16D3

Bexbacher Reisemobilhafen, Im Blumengarten. **GPS:** n49,34161 e7,25698. ⬆️ ➡️

36 �€6 ⌐€ 1/80liter ⌐Ch ⌐(36x)€ 2/night WC. **Surface:** grassy. ⌐
01/01-31/12
Distance: ⌐900m ⌐on the spot ⌐500m ⌐200m.
Remarks: Bread-service.

| ⌐S | **Biebelnheim** | **17A2** |

Wohnmobilpark am Petersberg, Flonheimer Strasse 34. **GPS:** n49,79432 e8,16236.

20 ⌐€5 ⌐€ 2 ⌐Ch ⌐€ 2. **Surface:** metalled. ⌐ 01/01-31/12
Distance: ⌐1km ⌐1,5km ⌐Bistro Am Petersberg ⌐1km.
Remarks: Max. 2 nights.

| ⌐S | **Bingen/Rhein** | **17A1** |

Wohnmobilpark Bingen, Mainzer Straße, Bingen/Kempten. **GPS:** n49,96860 e7,94417.⌐⌐.

39 ⌐€ 6,50/night ⌐⌐Ch ⌐€ 2/24h ⌐€ 3, dryer € 3 ⌐€ 2/h.
Surface: grassy/metalled. ⌐ 01/01-31/12
Distance: ⌐800m ⌐2,7km.
Remarks: Bread-service.

| ⌐S | **Birgel** | **9A6** |

Historische Wassermühle, Bahnhofstrasse 16. **GPS:** n50,31934 e6,61752.⌐.

10 ⌐€ 15, free with a meal > € 15 ⌐⌐Ch ⌐included. **Surface:** gravel.
⌐ 01/01-31/12
Distance: ⌐500m ⌐on the spot ⌐1km.

| ⌐S | **Blieskastel** | **16D3** |

Freizeitanlage Würzbacher Weiher, Marxstraße, Niederwürzbach. **GPS:**
n49,24674 e7,19226.⌐⌐.

10 ⌐€ 4,50 ⌐Ch ⌐.
Surface: grassy/gravel. ⌐ 01/01-31/12
Distance: ⌐500m ⌐on the spot ⌐on the spot ⌐100m ⌐600m ⌐600m.
Remarks: At lake, Würzbacher Weiher.

| ⌐S | **Blieskastel** | **16D3** |

Freizeitzentrum Blieskastel, Bliesaue 1, Webenheim. **GPS:** n49,23527 e7,26946.
5 ⌐free ⌐. **Surface:** metalled. ⌐ 01/01-31/12

| ⌐S | **Blieskastel** | **16D3** |

Hotel Restaurant Hubertushof, Kirschendell 32. **GPS:** n49,24456 e7,21573.⌐
⌐.

8 ⌐€ 5, free with a meal ⌐⌐. **Surface:** asphalted. ⌐ 01/01-31/12
Distance: ⌐on the spot ⌐on the spot ⌐1km.
Remarks: Max. 2 nights, arrival < 19h, bread-service.

| ⌐ | **Bobenthal/Bornich** | **17A3** |

Hotel-Restaurant St. Germanshof, Hauptstrasse 10. **GPS:** n49,04749 e7,89985.

4 ⌐guests free. **Surface:** metalled. ⌐ 01/01-31/12 ⌐ Mo.
Distance: ⌐5km ⌐on the spot ⌐7km.

| ⌐S | **Bockenheim** | **17C2** |

Weingut W. Kohl, Am Sonnenberg 3. **GPS:** n49,59902 e9,17925.⌐.

6 ⌐€ 8/night ⌐⌐WC ⌐included. **Surface:** metalled. ⌐ 01/01-31/12
Distance: ⌐500m ⌐500m ⌐3km.

| ⌐S | **Braubach** | **9B6** |

Braubacher Rheintreff, Rheinuferstrasse, B42. **GPS:** n50,26972 e7,64750.⌐.

DE

30 ⌥ € 7 🚰 🔌 Ch ⚡ WC ⌐included ▣ € 3.
Surface: asphalted.
⬛ 01/01-31/12
Distance: 🚶300m ⛱on the spot 🛒on the spot ⊗300m 🚉300m 🚌300m.

20 ⌥ € 8 🚰 🔌 Ch ⚡ € 2,50 WC ⌐ € 1. ⬛ 01/01-31/12
Distance: 🚶on the spot ⊗on the spot 🚉300m.

DE

🏞 S | **Brauneberg** | **16C1**
Wohnmobilplatz Juffer, Moselweinstrasse. **GPS:** n49,90518 e6,97760. ⬆.

🏞 S | **Burrweiler** | **17A3**
Wein- und Sektgut Hermann-Bruno Eberle, Böchingerstrasse 1a. **GPS:** n49,24649 e8,07989. ⬆.

15 ⌥ € 7 🚰 🔌 Ch ⚡. **Surface:** metalled. ⬛ 01/01-31/12
Distance: 🚶100m ⛱on the spot ⊗300m 🚉300m 🚌100m.

3 ⌥ € 6 🚰 ⚡ WC. **Surface:** metalled. ⬛ 01/01-31/12
Distance: 🚶100m 🚉200m.
Remarks: Arrival <21h.

🏞 S | **Bremm** | **16D1**
Weingut Oster-Franzen, Calmontstrasse 96. **GPS:** n50,09593 e7,12383.

🏞 S | **Burrweiler** | **17A3**
Weingut Diether Bauer, Weinstrasse 52. **GPS:** n49,21982 e8,03059. ⬆.
3 ⌥ € 5 🚰 ⚡ WC. **Surface:** metalled. ⬛ 01/01-31/12
Distance: 🚶on the spot 🚉300m.

🏞 S | **Burrweiler** | **17A3**
Weingut Winzerhof, Am Schlossberg 3. **GPS:** n49,25147 e8,07902. ⬆.

12 ⌥ € 11, 2 pers.incl 🚰 € 0,50/60liter 🔌 Ch ⚡ € 0,60/kWh WC ⌐ € 1 ▣
washing machine/dryer € 3,50. **Surface:** gravel. ⬛ 01/01-31/12

4 ⌥ € 6 🚰 ⚡ WC. **Surface:** metalled. ⬛ 01/01-31/12
Distance: 🚶1km 🚉300m.

🏞 | **Briedern** | **16D1**
Wohnmobilstellplatz Briedern, Birkenweg. **GPS:** n50,11165 e7,20867.

🏞 | **Cochem** | **16D1**
Bergstrasse, K59. **GPS:** n50,15028 e7,17083.

15 ⌥ € 4. **Surface:** grassy.
Distance: 🚶2km ⊗300m 🚉200m.

⌥ € 5 9-19h, overnight stay free.
Surface: grasstiles/metalled.
Distance: 🚶300m ⊗300m.

🏞 S | **Burgen** | **16D1**
Hotel Schmause Mühle, Baybachstrasse 50. **GPS:** n50,20859 e7,39365. ⬆.

🏞 | **Cochem** | **16D1**
Moselpromenade, B49. **GPS:** n50,14108 e7,16936. ⬆.

12 🚐 € 1/h 8-19h, overnight stay free. **Surface:** metalled.

| 🚽 | **Cochem** | 16D1 |

Moselstrasse, B49. **GPS**: n50,15329 e7,16828.⬆️.

6 🚐 € 6-8 🚰🔧 Ch ⚡(6x)€ 2 WC 🚽⊡ € 3,50. **Surface:** grassy/gravel. 🔲
Easter-01/11
Remarks: Incl. swimming pool (summer), bread-service.

| 🍴 S | **Dörrenbach** | 17A3 |

Übergasse. **GPS**: n49,08840 e7,96921.
10 🚐 € 5 🚰🔧 Ch ⚡. **Surface:** unpaved. 🔲 01/01-31/12
Distance: 🛒100m 🍷700m.
Remarks: Next to sports fields.

| 🍴 S | **Edenkoben** | 17A3 |

Wohnmobilstellplatz, Kirchbergpfad. **GPS**: n49,28233 e8,13151.

16 🚐 € 1/h 8-19h, overnight stay free.
Surface: metalled. 🔲 01/01-31/12
Distance: 🚂700m ⊗200m 🍷200m 🚌on the spot.

| 🍴 S | **Dahn/Reichenbach** | 17A3 |

Altes Bahnhöf'l, An der Reichenbahn 6. **GPS**: n49,13890 e7,79908.⬆️.

40 🚐 € 4/24h 🚰 € 0,50 🔧 Ch ⚡ € 1.
Surface: asphalted. 🔲 01/01-31/12

| 🍷 S | **Edenkoben** | 17A3 |

Obstgut & Brennerei Göring, Blücherstrasse 45. **GPS**: n49,27792 e8,13487.

10 🚐 guests free 🚰 ⚡ WC. 🔲 01/01-31/12 ⬤ Mo.
Distance: 🛒on the spot ⊗on the spot 🍷500m.

| 🍴 S | **Dierbach** | 17A3 |

Jahnstrasse. **GPS**: n49,08177 e8,06201.⬆️.
10 🚐 free 🚰🔧 Ch free. **Surface:** asphalted. 🔲 01/01-31/12

| 🍴 S | **Dierbach** | 17A3 |

Weingut-Weinstube Geiger, Hauptstrasse 1. **GPS**: n49,08344 e8,06673.⬆️.

5 🚐 € 5 🚰 € 3 🔧 Ch ⚡ € 3. **Surface:** grassy. 🔲 01/01-31/12

| 🍴 | **Edenkoben** | 17A3 |

Gasthof Ziegelhütte, Luitpoldstrasse. **GPS**: n49,28539 e8,13872.

30 🚐 guests free 🚰 ⚡ WC. **Surface:** grassy. 🔲 01/01-31/12
Distance: 🛒on the spot 🍷500m.

| 🍴 S | **Dohm** | 9A6 |

Am Heidberghof, Heidberghof 1, Dohm-Lammersdorf. **GPS**: n50,26696 e6,67366.

3 🚐 guests free. **Surface:** metalled. 🔲 01/01-31/12
Distance: 🛒on the spot ⊗on the spot 🍷on the spot.

| 🍴 S | **Edesheim** | 17A3 |

Weingut Boos, Ludwigstrasse 150. **GPS**: n49,25785 e8,11673.⬆️.

3 🛌 € 5 🔌 🧹. ☐ 01/01-31/12
Distance: ⊗300m 🍴1km.

| | | Edesheim | 17A3 |

Weingut Erlenmühle, Erlenmühle 1. **GPS:** n49,26111 e8,11389.⬆

3 🛌 € 6 🚰 🧹. **Surface:** gravel. ☐ 01/01-31/12
Distance: 🚶500m 🍴1km.
Remarks: Arrival <22h.

| | | Edesheim | 17A3 |

Weinstube Wolf, Ruprechtstrasse 20. **GPS:** n49,25976 e8,12935.
2 🛌guests free 🚰 🧹 included. ☐ 01/01-31/12
Distance: 🚶on the spot ⊗on the spot 🍴200m.

| | | Ediger/Eller | 16D1 |

Stellplatz Ediger, Moselweinstrasse. **GPS:** n50,09291 e7,16041.

15 🛌 € 4,50, 01/12-31/03 free 🚰 1 🍴Ch.
Surface: grassy/metalled.
☐ 01/01-31/12
Distance: 🚶100m 🏊on the spot 🛒on the spot ⊗on the spot 🚌on the spot.
Remarks: Along the Moselle river in Ediger.

| | Ediger/Eller | 16D1 |

Stellplatz Moselufer, Eller. **GPS:** n50,09915 e7,14370.⬆

15 🛌 € 4,50, 01/12-31/03 free. **Surface:** metalled. ☐ 01/01-31/12
Distance: 🏊on the spot 🛒on the spot 🍴200m.
Remarks: Along the Moselle river in Eller.

| 🍴 | | Eisenschmitt | 16C1 |

Hotel-Restaurant Molitors Mühle, Eichelhütte. **GPS:** n50,03681 e6,73766.

5 🛌guests free 🚰 🧹 WC. ☐ 01/01-31/12
Distance: 🚶1km 🏊on the spot 🛒on the spot ⊗on the spot 🍴1km
🚌300m.
Remarks: Arrival <23h.

| | | Ellenz/Poltersdorf | 16D1 |

Weingut Loosen, Im Goldbäumchen 4. **GPS:** n50,11389 e7,23528.

12 🛌 € 8 🧹 WC 🍴. **Surface:** metalled. ☐ 01/01-31/12
Distance: 🚶on the spot 🏊150m ⊗500m 🍴1km.

Tourist information Ellenz/Poltersdorf:
ℹ Wine- and holiday village on the Moselle river with half-timbered houses and winetasteries.
✳ Strassenweinfest. Wine-growers and - houses open their doors, wine-tastery. ☐ end Sep.
✳ Wein- und Heimatfeste. Traditional wine celebration. ☐ last weekend Jul, 1st weekend Aug.

| | | Enkirch | 16D1 |

Wohnmobilplatz an der Mosel, Moselvorgelände, B53. **GPS:** n49,98396 e7,12157.⬆

200 🛌 € 6 🚰 🍴Ch 🧹 € 1,50/day WC 🍴€ 1. **Surface:** grassy. ☐ Easter-31/10
Remarks: Along the Moselle river.

| | | Ensch | 16C2 |

Reisemobilplatz An den Pappeln, Moselwiesen. **GPS:** n49,82917 e6,83389.⬆ ➡

45 🛌 € 5 🚰 € 1/10minutes 🍴Ch 🧹 € 2. ☐ 01/04-31/10

Distance: 📍200m ⊗300m 🚊500m 🚃100m.
Remarks: Bread-service.

| 🏕 | **Eppenbrunn** | 16D3 |

Im Sportzentrum. **GPS:** n49,11179 e7,56512.
6 🏕free. **Surface:** metalled. ⬛ 01/01-31/12
Distance: 📍500m ⊗on the spot 🚊1km.
Remarks: Parking sports centre in nature reserve Pfälzer Wald.

| 🏕 S | **Ernst** | 16D1 |

Winzergenossenschaft der Kreises Cochem-Zell, Weingartenstrasse. **GPS:** n50,14339 e7,23237. ⬆

30 🏕€8 🚰 ⚡Ch 📶 € 5/10h. **Surface:** gravel. ⬛ 01/01-31/12
Distance: 📍300m ⊗on the spot 🚊200m 🚃100m.

| 🍴 S | **Ernst** | 16D1 |

Mosella Restaurant, Weingatenstrasse. **GPS:** n50,14382 e7,23071. ⬆

18 🏕€8 🚰 ⚡ included. **Surface:** grassy.

| 🍴 S | **Eschbach** | 17A3 |

Weingut Wind, Weinstrasse 3-5. **GPS:** n49,17594 e8,02171. ⬆
3 🏕€5, free for clients 🚰 ⚡ WC included.
Surface: gravel. ⬛ 01/01-31/12
Distance: 📍on the spot ⊗on the spot 🚊250m.

| 🏕 | **Fischbach** | 16D2 |

Wohnmobilpark, Marktstraße 1. **GPS:** n49,74046 e7,40444. ⬆➡

50 🏕€6,50/night 🚰 ⚡Ch ⚡(40x)€ 2.
Surface: grassy. ⬛ 01/01-31/12
Distance: 📍800m 🚶on the spot 🚊1,5km.
Remarks: Bread-service.

| 🏕 S | **Fischbach** | 16D2 |

Historisches Kupferbergwerk, Hosenbachstraße. **GPS:** n49,75398 e7,38287.
10 🏕free 🚰. **Surface:** gravel. ⬛ 01/01-31/12
Distance: 📍1,7km ⊗on the spot.
Remarks: Visitors' center former copper mine.

| 🏕 S | **Gau-Algesheim** | 17A1 |

Reimo Gau-Algesheim, Bingerstrasse 8. **GPS:** n49,96331 e8,01213. ⬆➡

40 🏕€ 4/night 🚰 ⚡Ch ⚡(40x)€ 2.
Surface: metalled. ⬛ 01/01-31/12
Distance: 📍800m 🚲2,5km ⊗500m 🚊200m.

| 🏕 | **Gau-Odernheim** | 17A2 |

Petersberghalle, Mühlstraße. **GPS:** n49,78528 e8,19575. ⬆➡

3 🏕free. **Surface:** metalled. ⬛ 01/01-31/12
Distance: 📍200m 🚊200m.

| 🏕 S | **Germersheim** | 17B3 |

Carnot'sche Mauer, Rüdolf von Habsburgstrasse. **GPS:** n49,22004 e8,37906.

8 🏕€3/24h 🚰 € 1/100liter ⚡Ch ⚡ € 1/kWh. **Surface:** grassy. ⬛
01/01-31/12

| 🏕 S | **Gerolstein** | 16C1 |

Wohnmobilplatz Gerolstein, Raderstrasse 22. **GPS:** n50,22147 e6,65501.

20 🏕€6/24h 🚰 € 1/100liter ⚡Ch ⚡(12x)€ 1/day. 🗑 **Surface:** grassy/metalled. ⬛ 01/01-31/12
Distance: 📍nearby.
Remarks: Parking swimming pool.

| 🏕 S | **Gillenfeld** | 16C1 |

Wohnmobilpark Pulvermaar, K14. **GPS:** n50,13294 e6,93218. ➡

DE

30 ⌇€ 6 🚰€ 1/100liter 🗑Ch ⚡€ 0,50/kWh. **Surface:** gravel. ⬤ 01/01-31/12
Distance: ⊿on the spot 🚰on the spot ⊗200m 🚽200m 🚌300m.

Feriendorf Pulvermaar, Vulkanstrasse. **GPS:** n50,13000 e6,93194.⬆

15 ⌇€ 6, 2 pers.incl. 🚰🗑Ch ⚡€ 1,20/kWh WC ⌐. **Surface:** grassy. ⬤ 01/03-30/11
Distance: 🚿3km ⊿on the spot 🚰on the spot ⊗on the spot 🚽3km.

Schwimbadstrasse. **GPS:** n49,77806 e8,38278.

8 ⌇€ 4/night. **Surface:** asphalted/grassy. ⬤ 15/05-15/09
Distance: 🚿500m 🚽300m.

Weingut Falger-Baier, Alsheimerstrasse 25. **GPS:** n49,77733 e8,36959.
3 ⌇€ 5 🚰🗑⚡. ⬤ 01/01-31/12
Distance: 🚿3km ⊗Pizzeria 50m 🚽500m.

Am Bahnhof, Bahnhofstraße. **GPS:** n49,46935 e7,44420.
3 ⌇free 🚰€ 1 🗑Ch ⚡€ 1/2h.
Surface: metalled. ⬤ 01/01-31/12
Distance: 🚄750m ⊗150m 🚽on the spot.

Wohnmobilpark Sun-Park, Gestade 16a. **GPS:** n49,93267 e7,06035.⬆

350 ⌇€ 6/day 🚰€ 1/100liter 🗑Ch ⚡€ 0,60/kWh WC ⌐. **Surface:** grasstiles.

Distance: 🚿200m 🚰on the spot ⊗200m 🚽2km 🚌on the spot.

Huppert's Wohnmobile Wingert, Untere Grabenstraße 21. **GPS:** n49,69499 e8,20465.⬆➡

12 ⌇€ 5 ⚡€ 2. **Surface:** gravel/sand. ⬤ 01/01-31/12
Distance: ⊗on the spot 🚽300m.
Remarks: Max. 3 nights.

Am Sportanlage, Alsheimerstrasse 85. **GPS:** n49,78974 e8,34373.
12 ⌇€ 5 🚰€ 1/80liter 🗑Ch ⚡€ 0,50/kWh. **Surface:** gravel. ⬤ 01/01-31/12
Distance: 🚿500m ⊗500m 🚽500m.

P4 - Burggarten, Alexanderring. **GPS:** n50,66250 e7,82694.⬆

10 ⌇free 🚰€ 1/70liter 🗑Ch ⚡€ 1/6h WC. **Surface:** metalled. ⬤ 01/01-31/12
Distance: 🚿on the spot ⊗on the spot 🚽300m.

Holiday Park, Holiday Parkstrasse. **GPS:** n49,31667 e8,30528.⬆➡

100 ⌇€ 5,50 🚰€ 0,50 ⚡(12x). **Surface:** grassy. ⬤ 01/04-01/11
Distance: 🚿8km ⊗on the spot 🚽8km.

Tourist information Hassloch:
🌐 Holiday Park.Attractions park with shows. ⬤ 01/04-30/09 10h, summer 9h, Oct weekend. 🎫 € 21.

Stellplatz am Deutschen Schumuseum Hauenstein, Turnstrasse. **GPS:** n49,18896 e7,85669.⬆

10 🛏€7 🚰🗑 Ch. **Surface:** gravel. ⬛ 01/01-31/12
Distance: 🚶on the spot ⊗200m 🚉300m.
Remarks: Pay at museum.

🛏S Herrstein 🌿⛵👣 16D2
Wohnmobilstellplatz Herrstein, Brühlstrasse. **GPS:** n49,77963 e7,33569.⬆.

3 🛏free 🚰€ 1/80liter 🗑 🔌€ 0,50/kWh WC.
Surface: metalled.
⬛ 01/01-31/12
Distance: 🚶300m on the spot.
Remarks: Max. 48h.

Tourist information Herrstein:
ℹ️ Touristinformation Deutsche Edelsteinstraße, Brühlstrasse 16.Renovated mall half-timbered city.

🛏S Herxheim 17A3
Festhalle, Bonifatiusstraße. **GPS:** n49,14463 e8,21656.
8 🛏free 🚰🗑 Ch. **Surface:** grasstiles. ⬛ 01/01-31/12

🛏S Hillesheim 9A6
Markt- und Messeplatz, Am Viehmarkt. **GPS:** n50,28895 e6,67239.⬆➡.

6 🛏€4 🚰🗑 Ch 🔌 WC. **Surface:** gravel. ⬛ 01/01-31/12
Distance: 🚶on the spot ⊗on the spot.

🛏S Hillesheim 9A6
Wohnmobilstellplatz Birkenhof, Birkenhof 1. **GPS:** n50,28639 e6,69083.

4 🛏€5 🚰🔌 water and electricity € 2/night 📶free. **Surface:** gravel.

🛏S Hillesheim 9A6
Wohnmobile Theres, Prümer Straße 20. **GPS:** n50,28957 e6,66310.

15 🛏€5 🚰🗑 Ch 🔌 included. **Surface:** asphalted. ⬛ 01/01/31/12
Distance: 🚶750m ⊗750m 🚉750m.
Remarks: Motorhome dealer, accessory shop, repairs.

🛏S Hornbach 16D3
Wohnmobilpark Hornbach, Bahnhofstraße. **GPS:** n49,18419 e7,36601.⬆.

9 🛏€6 🚰€ 1/60liter 🗑Ch 🔌(12x)€ 2/24h. **Surface:** gravel. ⬛ 01/01-31/12
Distance: 🚶on the spot ⊗on the spot.

🛏S Idar/Oberstein 16D2
Edelsteinbörse, Hauptstrasse 100. **GPS:** n49,71932 e7,30313.⬆.

12 🛏€ 6/day, first 24h free 🚰€ 1/70liter 🗑Ch WC.
Surface: asphalted.
⬛ 01/01-31/12
Distance: 🚶on the spot ⊗on the spot 🚉300m.

Tourist information Idar/Oberstein:
ℹ️ Tourist Information, Georg-Maus-strasse 2, www.idar-oberstein.de.City of the gems.
👁 Edelsteinminen des Steinkaulenberges.Gem mine. ⬛ 15/03-15/11 9-17h.
Ⓜ Deutsches Edelsteinmuseum.Gem museum. ⬛ 01/05-31/10 9-18h, 01/11-30/04 9-17h.

🛏S Jettenbach 👣 16D2
Freizeitgelände Schwimmbad, Austrasse. **GPS:** n49,52919 e7,56453.⬆➡.

6 🛏free 🚰🗑Ch 🔌. **Surface:** asphalted. ⬛ 01/01-31/12

Distance: 500m 800m.

|||S **Kamp-Bornhofen** **16D1**

Bistro Rheinufer, Rheinuferstrasse 66 A. **GPS:** n50,22305 e7,61888. ↑→.
7 7 € 7 € 1 € 1,50 WC.
Surface: metalled. 01/01-31/12
Distance: on the spot on the spot 300m on the spot.
Remarks: Along the Rhine river, toilets only during opening hours restaurant.

|||S **Kandel** **17A3**

Adams Hof, Rheinzaberner Strasse 1. **GPS:** n49,08902 e8,22194. ↑.

30 € 2/night € 2 € 2/12h WC. **Surface:** grassy. 01/01-31/12
Distance: 1,5km on the spot on the spot 1,5km 1,5km.

S **Kempfeld** **16D2**

An der Wildenburg, Wildenburgstraße. **GPS:** n49,77588 e7,25423. ↑→.

3 free. **Surface:** metalled. 01/01-31/12
Distance: 2km.

S **Kesten** **16C1**

Wohnmobilpark Kesten/Mosel, Urmetzgasse. **GPS:** n49,90306 e6,96232.

80 € 5/24h € 0,10/10liter Ch € 1,50/24h WC € 1,50.
Surface: grassy/metalled. 01/04-02/11
Distance: 300m 10m 300m 1km.
Remarks: Parking at the Moselle River, bread-service + breakfast-service.

S **Kinheim** **16D1**

Am Moselufer, Moselweinstraße, B53. **GPS:** n49,97218 e7,05706. ↑.

40 € 6 Ch included. **Surface:** grassy. 01/01-31/12

Distance: 100m 150m.
Remarks: Parking at the Moselle River.

Tourist information Kinheim:

Tourist Information, Moselweinstrasse 14, www.kinheim.de. Wine village with half-timbered houses.
Tag den offenen Weinkeller. Open wine-cellars. 2nd Thu after Whitsuntide.
Wein- und Frülingsfest. Wine and spring celebration. Whitsuntide.
Winzerfest. Wine festival. 2nd weekend Sept.

S **Kirchheimbolanden** **17A2**

Messeplatz, Hitzfeldstrasse. **GPS:** n49,66667 e8,01501. ↑.

20 free € 1/70liter Ch € 0,50. **Surface:** metalled. 01/01-31/12 2nd weekend May-Aug-Oct.
Distance: 300m 300m on the spot.

S **Klüsserath** **16C2**

Reisemobilpark Klüsserath, B53. **GPS:** n49,84316 e6,85437.

400 € 5,50 € 1/90liter Ch € 1,50. **Surface:** grassy. Easter-31/10
Remarks: Along the Moselle river.

S **Kobern** **9B6**

B416, Kobern-Gondorf. **GPS:** n50,30524 e7,46064.

30 € 5 € 1 Ch. **Surface:** metalled.

S **Köwerich** **16C2**

Weingut Hans Klären-Maringer 'Off'm Herrach', Beethovenstrasse 40. **GPS:** n49,84169 e6,86242. ↑.

DE

20 ⬛6 🔌€ 0,50/kWh WC ⬛ 1. **Surface:** grassy. ◖ 01/01-31/12
Distance: 🚂500m 🏊500m 🚶500m ⊗on the spot ⛽2km 🛒100m.
Remarks: Bread-service.

| 🛁 S | **Kusel** ⛲ | 16D2 |

Parkplatz der Tuchfabriken, Trierer Straße 61. **GPS:** n49,54016 e7,39626. ⬆➡.

3 ⬛free 🚰 🔌. **Surface:** asphalted. ◖ 01/04-31/10
Distance: 🚂500m ⛽300m.
Remarks: Max. 3 days, key service at Touristinformation (300m).

| 🛁 S | **Landau** | 17A3 |

Wellnessoase La Ola, Horstring 2. **GPS:** n49,20230 e8,14270. ⬆.
5 ⬛€ 10/24h 🚰€ 4 Ch 🔌 included. **Surface:** metalled. ◖ 01/01-31/12
Distance: 🚂3km ⊗500m.

| 🛁 S | **Landstuhl** | 16D3 |

Bahnstraße. **GPS:** n49,41595 e7,57092.
2 ⬛free 🚰 Ch 🔌 free. **Surface:** asphalted. ◖ 01/01-31/12
Distance: 🚶on the spot ⛽350m 🛒Aldi 100m.

| 🛁 S | **Lauterecken** ⛲ | 16D2 |

Wohnmobilstellplatz Villa Toskana, Friedhofweg 3a. **GPS:** n49,65056 e7,58806. ⬆➡.

30 ⬛€8 🚰€ 1/80liter Ch 🔌(18x)€ 1/8h. **Surface:** grassy/gravel. ◖ 01/01-31/12
Distance: 🚂300m ⊗on the spot ⛽100m.
Remarks: Bread-service.

| 🍴 S | **Leiwen** ⛲ | 16C2 |

Moselblick, Flurgartenstrasse 2/ Weinallee. **GPS:** n49,82580 e6,88148. ⬆.

15 ⬛€7,50 🚰 Ch 🔌 WC ⬛ 1 🗑. **Surface:** grassy.
Distance: 🏊on the spot ⊗on the spot ⛽300m 🚶500m.

| 🛁 | **Linz am Rhein** 🌿⛲ | 9B6 |

B42. **GPS:** n50,56291 e7,27982. ⬆.

6 ⬛free. **Surface:** asphalted. ◖ 01/01-31/12
Distance: 🏊on the spot ⊗50m.

| 🛁 S | **Löf** | 9B6 |

SOG Dahmann, In der Mark 2. **GPS:** n50,23194 e7,43750. ⬆.

9 ⬛free 🚰 Ch 🔌(4x) WC. **Surface:** metalled. ◖ 01/01-31/12

| 🌿 S | **Longuich/Mosel** ⬛ | 16C2 |

Feiten, Rioler weg 2. **GPS:** n49,80288 e6,77894. ⬆.

30 ⬛€5 🚰€ 0,50/60liter Ch 🔌€ 2 WC ⬛ 1. **Surface:** grassy. ◖ 01/01-31/12
Distance: 🚂300m 🏊on the spot 🚶on the spot ⊗on the spot ⛽1km.

| 🍴 S | **Longuich/Mosel** ⬛ | 16C2 |

WeinKulturgut Longen Schlöder, Kirchenweg 9. **GPS:** n49,81023 e6,76496. ⬆.

8 ⬛€5 🚰€ 1 🔌(3x)€ 1,50 WC ⬛ 2. **Surface:** metalled. ◖ 01/01-31/12 ⬛ Tue.
Distance: ⊗on the spot ⛽500m.

| 🛁 S | **Losheim am See** | 16C2 |

Reisemobilplatz am Stausee, Zum Stausee. **GPS:** n49,51999 e6,74123. ➡.

20 🅂€5 ⊟ 🄲Ch ✎ WC ⊟included. **Surface:** asphalted/grassy. ⬛
01/01-31/12
Distance: 🚶1km ⊗100m 🚲1km.
Remarks: Parking at lake, in front of Tourist-Information, incl. use sanitary and service on campsite 1km.

8 🅂€6/pp, dog €1,50 ⊟ € 0,50/100liter 🄲Ch ✎€ 2,50 WC ⊟. **Surface:** metalled. ⬛ 15/03-31/10
Distance: 🚶800m ⊗800m 🚲800m ▢on camp site.

🅂 **Lösnich** 16D1
Stellplatz am Moselufer, Gestade. **GPS:** n49,97560 e7,04276.⬆

🍴🅂 **Manderscheid** 16C1
Hotel Heidsmühle, Mosenbergstrasse 22. **GPS:** n50,08504 e6,80021.

96 🅂€6 ⊟ 🄲Chincluded ✎ €1,50. **Surface:** grassy. ⬛ 01/03-01/11
Distance: 🚲3km.
Remarks: Along ther Moselle river, baker every morning.

20 🅂free ⊟ ✎€ 2,50. **Surface:** unpaved. ⬛ 01/01-31/12

🅂 **Mayen** 9B6
Wohnmobilstellplatz am Viehmarkt, Polcherstrasse. **GPS:** n50,32194 e7,22806.⬆

🅂 **Lutzerath** 16C1
Trierer Strasse. **GPS:** n50,13015 e7,01002.

10 🅂€5/day ⊟€ 0,50 🄲Ch ✎(6x)€ 0,50/kWh. **Surface:** asphalted. ⬛ 01/01-31/12
Remarks: Check in at Hotel Restaurant Maas, Trierer Str. 30.

6 🅂free ⊟€ 1/80liter 🄲Ch WC. **Surface:** grassy. ⬛ 01/01-31/12
Distance: 🚶100m ⊗100m 🚲100m.

🅂 **Maikammer** 17A3
Sporthalle Kalmit, Johannes Dammstrasse. **GPS:** n49,30307 e8,13219.⬆➡

🅂 **Mayschoss** 9A6
Ahruferplatz, Am Bahnhof. **GPS:** n50,51736 e7,01948.⬆

🅂€ 4/day. **Surface:** asphalted. ⬛ 01/01-31/12
Distance: 🚶100m ⊗nearby 🚲nearby.

75 🅂€5,50 ⊟€ 0,50/100liter 🄲Ch WC. **Surface:** metalled. ⬛ 01/01-31/12
Distance: 🚶on the spot ⊗100m 🚲on the spot 🚗50m.
Remarks: Parking at station, along the Ahr.

🅂 **Manderscheid** 16C1
Campingplatz Vulkaneifel, Herbstwiese. **GPS:** n50,09650 e6,80159.➡

🅂 **Mehring** 16C2
Weingut Zellerhof, Zellerhof 1. **GPS:** n49,79395 e6,81987.

41 ⌁ 6 🚰 € 0,50/70liter 🔌Ch ⚡€ 0,50/kWh WC 🚽€ 1,50. **Surface:** grassy/metalled. ⏻ 01/01-31/12
Distance: 🚶100m 🏊on the spot ⊗on the spot 🍴100m.

12 ⌁€ 6,50 🚰€ 1 ⚡€ 1 Ch ⚡ 🗑. **Surface:** grassy/gravel. ⏻ 01/01-31/12
Distance: 🚶2km ⊗on the spot 🍴2km.
Remarks: Check in at swimming pool.

Wohnmobilstellplatz del Mosel, Moselweinstrasse 1. **GPS:** n49,79423 e6,81976.

Cloef-Atrium, An der Cloef, Mettlach-Orscholz. **GPS:** n49,50394 e6,53225.

60 ⌁€ 5, 2 pers.incl 🚰€ 0,50/100liter 🔌Ch ⚡€ 2 WC 🚽€ 1. **Surface:** grassy. ⏻ 01/01-31/12
Distance: 🚶100m ⊗on the spot 🍴200m.

⌁€ 5 🚰 WC. **Surface:** gravel.
Remarks: Max. 24h.

Schwimmbad Meisenheim, In der Heimbach. **GPS:** n49,71472 e7,65750. ⬆.

Mettlacher Abtei-Bräu, Bahnhofstrasse 32. **GPS:** n49,49484 e6,59804.

12 ⌁€ 5 🚰€ 1/4minutes 🔌Ch ⚡(12x)€ 1/kWh. **Surface:** gravel. ⏻ 01/01-31/12
Distance: 🚶1,6km ⊗on the spot 🍴500m.

⌁€ 5 🚰 🔌Chfree. **Surface:** gravel. ⏻ 01/01-31/12
Distance: 🚶500m ⊗on the spot.

Tourist information Mettlach:
👁M Erlebniszentrum Villeroy&Boch. ⏻ Mo-Fr: 9.30-19h, Sa 9.30-18h.
🛍 Villeroy&Boch Outletcenter, Freiherr-vom-Stein-Strasse 4-6. ⏻ Mo-Fr: 9.30-19h, Sa 9.30-18h.

Vulkanmuseum Lava-Dome, Brauerstraße 7–9. **GPS:** n50,37955 e7,28631.
20 ⌁free 🚰€ 1 🔌Ch ⚡(8x)€ 0,50/kWh. **Surface:** gravel. ⏻ 01/01-31/12
Distance: ⊗Vulkanbrauhaus&Felsenkeller.

Reisemobilpark Minheim. **GPS:** n49,86500 e6,94111.

Yachthafen Merzig, Saarwiesenring 10. **GPS:** n49,44205 e6,63566. ➡.

15 ⌁€ 7 🚰 🔌Ch ⚡€ 0,50/kWh WC 🚽. **Surface:** metalled. ⏻ 01/04-31/10
Distance: 🚶1km ⊗on the spot 🍴800m.

88 ⌁€ 6,50 🚰€ 1/100liter 🔌Ch ⚡€ 1,50. **Surface:** grassy/gravel. ⏻ 01/01-31/12
Remarks: Along the Moselle river, next to football ground.

Das Bad, Saarwiesenring 3. **GPS:** n49,44470 e6,62769. ➡.

Reisemobilhafen Morbach, Zum Camping 15, Hoxel. **GPS:** n49,77855 e7,10695. ⬆➡.

DE

40 🛏€ 5/night 🚰€ 1/80liter 🅲Ch🧹(40x)€ 2/night. **Surface:** grassy. 🅾 16/03-15/11

Distance: ⊗300m 🛒300m.

Weingut Mauch-Michels, Mühlenweg 4. **GPS:** n49,91058 e7,00640.

3 🛏€ 7,50 🚰🧹WC🎽. **Surface:** metalled. 🅾 01/01-31/12

Distance: 🚶2km ⊗on the spot 🛒500m.

Wohnmobilstellplatz Zum Frauenberg. GPS: n50,09455 e7,13730.

50 🛏€6 🚰🅲Ch🧹(42x)€ 2/24h, 4Amp. **Surface:** grassy. 🅾 Easter-15/10

Remarks: Along the Moselle river, nearby sports fields.

Wohnmobilstellplatz Efferz, Im Feldchen. **GPS:** n50,38271 e7,70331.

20 🛏€8 🚰€ 1 🅲Ch🧹(12x)€ 1/2kWh WC🎽📶. **Surface:** metalled. 🅾 01/01-31/12

Distance: 🚶250m ⊗250m 🛒250m 🚌100m > Koblenz.

Remarks: Bread-service.

Yachthafen Neumagen, Moselstrasse 21. **GPS:** n49,85357 e6,89373.⬆

30 🛏<9m € 6, >9m € 8 + € 2,50/pp 🚰🅲Ch🧹€ 0,60/kWh WC🎽included 📶 € 3/24h. **Surface:** gravel. 🅾 01/01-31/12

Distance: 🚶100m ⚓on the spot 🚲on the spot ⊗on the spot 🛒1,3km.

Remarks: Check in at harbourmaster.

Gaststatte Beim Ketsch, Brückenstrasse 14/ In der Zeil. **GPS:** n49,86449 e6,90321.⬆➡

100 🛏€ 5 🧹€ 1,50/3kWh WC🎽€ 2,50. 🅾 01/01-31/12

Distance: 🚶200m ⊗on the spot 🛒500m.

Remarks: Bread-service.

Volkssonnengarten, Zweibrücker Straße 148. **GPS:** n49,32766 e7,19375.⬆

20 🛏€ 8 🚰🅲Ch🧹WC🎽📶included.

Surface: grassy. 🅾 01/03-31/10

Distance: 🚶3km 🏊1,7km ⊗1,4km.

Dammstrasse-Ost, Hambach. **GPS:** n49,33083 e8,13139.⬆

20 🛏free 🚰€ 1 🎽€ 1 Ch. **Surface:** grassy. 🅾 01/01-31/12

Distance: 🚶nearby ⊗nearby 🛒nearby.

Parkplatz am Rebenmeer, Am Falltor, Duttweiler. **GPS:** n49,30148 e8,21192.⬆

10 🛏free. **Surface:** metalled. 🅾 01/01-31/12

Reisemobilstellpatz Stadtzentrum, Martin-Luther-Strasse. **GPS:** n49,35485 e8,15255.

30 🛏€ 2,50/24h. **Surface:** asphalted. 🅾 01/01-31/12

Distance: 🚶300m ⊗250m 🛒Aldimarkt 50m.

Weingut Schäfer, Schiessmauer 56, Mussbach. **GPS:** n49,36335 e8,17111.

DE

5 ⱬ€6 ⵜ🍴Ch ✍ 🍴€ 4. ⬛ 01/01-31/12
Remarks: Reservation recommended: 0 63 27 21 55.

| | Neustadt/Weinstrasse | 17A3 |

Weingut Andres, Langensteinstrasse 22, Lachen-Speyersdorf. **GPS:** n49,33631 e8,20579.
3 ⱬfree.

| S | Neustadt/Weinstrasse | 17A3 |

Esso-Tankstelle, Martin-Luther-Strasse. **GPS:** n49,35948 e8,15160.
ⵜ🍴Chfree. ⬛ 01/01-31/12

| S | Neuwied | 9B6 |

Yachthafen Neuwied, Rheinstrasse 180. **GPS:** n50,43415 e7,47685.⬆

30 ⱬ€7, 2 pers.incl. ⵜ🍴Ch ✍€ 0,50/kWh WC🍴. **Surface:** metalled.
⬛ 01/01-31/12
Distance: 🚶2km ⊗on the spot 🛒2km.

| | Nohfelden | 16D2 |

P3 Surferbasis, Gonnesweiler. **GPS:** n49,57010 e7,08410.⬆

50 ⱬ€8. **Surface:** grassy. ⬛ 01/01-31/12
Distance: ⊗500m 🛒3km.

| S | Nohfelden | 16D2 |

Campingplatz Bostalsee, L325, Bosen. **GPS:** n49,56039 e7,06113.⬆➡

10 ⱬ€8/24h ⵜ€ 0,50/50liter 🍴Ch ✍€ 1/2kWh. **Surface:** metalled. ⬛
01/01-31/12
Distance: 🚶500m 🏊200m ⊗on the spot 🛒800m.

| | Nonnweiler | 16C1 |

Stellplatz Am Hallenbad, Triererstrasse 2. **GPS:** n49,97225 e6,97186.⬆

---

5 ⱬfree. **Surface:** grassy/metalled. ⬛ 01/01-31/12
Distance: 🚶on the spot ⊗on the spot 🛒800m.
Remarks: Parking swimming pool, max. 48h.

| S | Ober-Hilbersheim | 17A1 |

Napoleonshöhe, Sprendlingers Straße. **GPS:** n49,89785 e8,02421.⬆

40 ⱬfree ⵜ🍴Ch. **Surface:** grassy. ⬛ 01/01-31/12
Distance: 🛒300m.

| S | Ober-Olm | 17A1 |

Wohnmobilplatz Mainz, Draiser Straße. **GPS:** n49,94298 e8,19237.
25 ⱬ€10 ⵜ🍴Ch ✍included. **Surface:** grasstiles. ⬛ 01/01-31/12
Distance: 🚲3,8km 🛒500m.

| S | Oberbrombach | 16D2 |

Wohnmobilstellplatz Höhenblick, Sonnenberger Strasse. **GPS:** n49,69481 e7,25960.
30 ⱬ€7 ⵜ🍴Ch ✍(20x)€ 2/24h. **Surface:** grassy/gravel. ⬛ 01/01-31/12
Distance: 🚶400m ⊗600m.

| S | Oberwesel/Rhein | 17A1 |

Camping Schönburgblick, Am Hafendamm / B9. **GPS:** n50,10294 e7,73663.⬆

20 ⱬ€8,50/24h ⵜ🍴 ✍€ 0,50/kWh WC🍴€ 2 🔲🛜€ 2. **Surface:**
grassy. ⬛ 15/03-31/10
Distance: 🚶800m 🏊on the spot 🚤on the spot ⊗on the spot 🛒200m
🚗400m.

| S | Oppenheim 🍴 | 17B1 |

Womoland Oppenheim, An der Festwiese. **GPS:** n49,85673 e8,36502.⬆➡

20 🍴€7 🚰€ 1/50liter 🗑€ 1 Ch 💧€ 3/24h. **Surface:** grassy. ⬛ 01/01-31/12 ⬛ week before/after Whitsuntide.
Distance: 🚶500m ⊗500m 🛒500m.

🏕 S Osthofen 17B2
Festplatz Wonnegauhalle, Wonnegaustrasse. **GPS:** n49,69913 e8,32691. ⬆➡.

50 🍴free 🚰 🗑 Chfree. **Surface:** gravel. ⬛ 01/01-31/12
Distance: 🚶500m 🛒500m.

🏕 S Osthofen 17B2
Sommerried Stadion, L439. **GPS:** n49,69222 e8,32805. ⬆.

10 🍴free. **Surface:** grassy/sand. ⬛ 01/01-31/12
Distance: 🛒800m.
Remarks: Max. 48h.

🏕 S Osthofen 17B2
Weingut Borntaler Hof, Alter Westhofer Weg. **GPS:** n49,69985 e8,29860. ⬆➡.

4 🍴€5 🚰 🗑 💧 WCincluded. **Surface:** metalled. ⬛ 01/01-31/12

🏕 S Ottweiler 🌿🏛🌳 16D3
Stellplatz Wingertsweiher, Am Wingertsweiher. **GPS:** n49,41250 e7,18083. ⬆➡.

12 🍴€5/24h 🚰€ 1/150liter 🗑€ 1 Ch 💧 (6x)€ 3/8h. **Surface:** grassy/metalled. ⬛ 01/01-31/12
Distance: 🚶1,5km ⊿on the spot 🚣on the spot ⊗on the spot 🛒1,5km 🚌1km.
Remarks: Max. 7 days.

Tourist information Ottweiler:
ℹ Tourist-Information Ottweiler, Schloßhof 5, www.ottweiler.de.

🏕 S Palzem 16B2
Weingut E. Pauly, Obermoselstrasse 5. **GPS:** n49,56402 e6,37581. ⬆➡.

5 🍴€ 7,50, free for clients 🚰 🗑 💧 WC.
Surface: metalled. ⬛ 01/01-31/12
Distance: ⊗50m 🛒4km.
Remarks: Not suitable for big motorhomes.

🏕 S Perl 16C2
Auf dem Sabel. **GPS:** n49,47906 e6,38508. ⬆.

6 🍴€ 8, payment with SMS 🚰 🗑 Ch 💧€ 2/8h. **Surface:** metalled. ⬛ 01/01-31/12
Distance: 🚶500m ⊿3,5km ⊗500m 🛒500m.

🏕 S Piesport 16C1
Piesporter Goldtröpfchen, Moselstrasse. **GPS:** n49,87199 e6,92703.

30 🍴€6 🚰€ 1/80liter 🗑Ch 💧€ 1,50.
Surface: gravel. ⬛ 01/01-31/12
Distance: 🚶100m ⊿on the spot ⊗on the spot 🛒500m.
Remarks: Bread-service mo-sa.

🏕 S Piesport 16C1
Weingut Spang, Reisemobilplatz Rebengarten, In den Dur 11. **GPS:** n49,88282 e6,92669. ⬆➡.

4 🍴€ 6/pppd, guests free 🚰 💧€ 0,50/kWh WC 🗑. **Surface:** gravel. ⬛ 01/01-31/12
Distance: 🚶on the spot ⊿100m ⊗100m 🛒500m 🚌500m.
Remarks: Bread-service.

DE

DE

⬛S Piesport 16C1
Wohnmobilstellplatz Loreleyblick, Loreleyblick 20. **GPS:** n49,87380 e6,92535.

5 ⬛€6 ⛽🔌Ch ☄(5x) ⬛€ 1. **Surface:** gravel. ⬛ 01/01-31/12
Distance: 🚶on the spot ⊗1km ⬛300m.

70 ⬛€6 ⛽🔌Chfree ☄(36x)€ 1,50.
Surface: grassy. ⬛ 01/03-31/10
Distance: 🚶500m ⊗450m.
Remarks: Along the Moselle river.

⬛S Polch 9B6
Niesmann&Bisschof, Clou-strasse 1. **GPS:** n50,30680 e7,30684.⬆

25 ⬛free ⛽🔌Ch ☄€ 0,50/kWh. ⬛ 01/01-31/12
Distance: ⊗on the spot ⬛on the spot.

⬛S Reipoltskirchen 17A2
Wasserburg, Kegelbahnstrasse. **GPS:** n49,63448 e7,66373.⬆

7 ⬛free ⛽€ 1/4minutes 🔌Ch ☄€ 1/12h. **Surface:** metalled. ⬛ 01/01-31/12
Distance: 🚶150m ⊗on the spot ⬛bakery 100m.

⬛S Pronsfeld 16B1
Am Alten Bahnhof, Bahnhofstrasse. **GPS:** n50,16336 e6,33733.⬆➡

⬛S Reipoltskirchen 17A2
Stellplatz Ausbacherhof, K42, Ausbacherhof. **GPS:** n49,61210 e7,65630.⬆

50 ⬛€5 ⛽€ 0,50/60liter 🔌Ch ☄€ 0,50/kWh. **Surface:** gravel. ⬛ 01/01-31/12
Distance: 🚶600m ⊗600m ⬛700m 🚆500m.

4 ⬛free. **Surface:** gravel. ⬛ 01/01-31/12

⬛S Remagen 9B6
Wohnmobilhafen Goldene Meile, Simrockweg 9–13. **GPS:** n50,57583 e7,25111.
15 ⬛€12 ⛽€ 1/90liter 🔌Ch ☄€ 1/6h. **Surface:** grassy. ⬛ 01/01-31/12

⬛S Pünderich 16D1
Wohnmobilstellplatz Pünderich. GPS: n50,04355 e7,12548.⬆

⬛S Rheinbreitbach 9B6
Wohnmobilstellplatz Siebengebirgsblick, Rolandsecker Weg 8. **GPS:** n50,62193 e7,22812.⬆
12 ⬛€8 ⛽€ 1 🔌Ch ☄€ 1/2kWh. **Surface:** grassy/gravel. ⬛ 01/01-31/12
Distance: ⊗500m.

⬛ Rhodt unter Rietburg 17A3
Rhodt, Edesheimerstrasse, L506. **GPS:** n49,26926 e8,10974.⬆

40 ⬛€6 ⛽🔌Ch ☄(12x)€ 1,50/24h.
Surface: grassy. ⬛ 01/04-31/10
Distance: 🚶on the spot ⬛on the spot ⊗300m ⬛500m.

⬛S Reil/Mosel 16D1
Am Moselufer, Moselstrasse. **GPS:** n50,02566 e7,11493.⬆

6 ⬛€ 4. **Surface:** asphalted. ⬛ 01/01-31/12

Distance: ⚓nearby ⊗nearby 🍴nearby.

🏕S **Rhodt unter Rietburg** 17A3

Fader Kastanienhof, L506. **GPS:** n49,26921 e8,10997. ⬆

12 ⛽€ 10 🚿🗑Ch ✦. **Surface:** gravel. ⭕ 01/01-31/12
Distance: ⚓on the spot ⊗on the spot 🍴on the spot.
Remarks: Sep-Oct on reservation.

🏕S **Rockenhausen** 17A2

Reisemobilhafen Rockenhausen, Obermühle. **GPS:** n49,62136 e7,82146. ⬆
5 ⛽free 🚿€ 1/80liter 🗑Ch ✦€ 1/6h.
Surface: gravel. ⭕ 01/01-31/12
Distance: ⚓800m 🍴on the spot.
Remarks: At swimming pool.

🏕S **Saarbrücken** 🏖🏸🍴 16C3

Reisemobilhafen Calypso, Deutschmühlental 7. **GPS:** n49,23027 e6,96222. ⬆

30 ⛽€ 6 + reduction swimming pool 🚿🗑Ch ✦€ 1/24h. **Surface:**
metalled. ⭕ 01/01-31/12
Distance: ⚓on the spot ⊗on the spot 🍴500m.
Remarks: To pay at swimming pool.

Tourist information Saarbrücken:
ℹ Tourist Information, Reichsstrasse 1 - Saar Galerie, www.die-region-saarbruecken.de.

🏕S **Saarburg** 16C2

Reisemobilpark Saarburg, Am Saarufer. **GPS:** n49,60098 e6,55549. ⬆

72 ⛽€ 8 🚿€ 1 🗑Ch ✦€ 0,50/kWh WC.
Distance: ⚓10 min walking 🍴100m.
Remarks: Bread-service.

🏕S **Saarlouis** 16C3

In den Fliesen, Sankt Nazairer Allee. **GPS:** n49,32225 e6,74334.
30 ⛽free 🚿🗑Ch. **Surface:** metalled. ⭕ 01/01-31/12
Remarks: At sports centre.

🏕S **Sankt Aldegund** 16D1

Am Moselstausee. **GPS:** n50,07899 e7,13119.

40 ⛽€ 6 🚿🗑Ch included ✦€ 1,50. **Surface:** grassy/metalled. ⭕
01/04-01/12
Distance: ⚓250m.

🏕S **Sankt Ingbert** 🍴 16D3

Reisemobilplatz 'Das Blau', Spieser Landstraße. **GPS:** n49,28652 e7,13194. ⬆
➡

8 ⛽free 🚿€ 1/80liter 🗑Ch. **Surface:** grassy. ⭕ 01/01-31/12
Distance: ⚓1,5km ⊗100m 🍴1,7km.
Remarks: Next to parking swimming pool.

🏕S **Sankt Julian** 16D2

An der Ölmühle, An der Lenschbach. **GPS:** n49,60758 e7,51480.
10 ⛽free 🚿€ 1 🗑Ch ✦€ 1/kWh. ⭕ 01/04-31/10
Distance: ⚓on the spot 🍴300m.

🏕 **Sankt Martin** 17A3

Edenkoperstrasse. **GPS:** n49,29702 e8,10838. ⬆

19 ⛽€ 6/day. **Surface:** asphalted. ⭕ 01/01-31/12
Remarks: Max. 1 night.

🏕 **Sankt Martin** 17A3

Winzer Holger Schneider, Riedweg. **GPS:** n49,29814 e8,10824. ⬆

⛽free for clients. **Surface:** gravel.

S **Sankt Martin** 17A3

Riedweg. **GPS:** n49,29814 e8,10824. ⬆
🚿€ 1 🗑Ch.

🏕S **Sankt Wendel** 16D2

Am Wendelinuspark, Tholeyer Straße. **GPS:** n49,46907 e7,14267. ⬆

DE

22 ⛺ € 5 � 🔌 Ch ✎ free. **Surface:** metalled. ⬛ 01/01-31/12
Distance: ⚓1km ⊗on the spot 🚰100m 🚌20m.

⚜S Schleich 16C2
Zum Moselufer, Kapellenstrasse 13. **GPS:** n49,81335 e6,84228. ⬆➡

6 ⛺ € 5 ⟦ Ch ✎ € 2 WC. **Surface:** grassy. ⬛ 01/01-31/12
Distance: ⚓on the spot ⊗on the spot 🚌200m.

📷S Schwabenheim/Selz 17A1
Reisemobilstellplatz Schwabenheim, Ingelheimer Straße. **GPS:** n49,93284 e8,09430.

10 ⛺ free ✎. **Surface:** gravel. ⬛ 01/01-31/12
Distance: ⚓200m 🛒200m.
Remarks: Max. 72h.

📷S Schweich/Mosel bei Trier 16C2
Wohnmobilpark zum Fahrturm, Am Yachthafen. **GPS:** n49,81517 e6,75076.

40 ⛺ ⟦ Ch ✎ € 0,50/kWh,.
Surface: grassy.
Distance: ⚓on the spot 🚶on the spot ⊗on the spot 🛒on the spot 🚌50m.

📷S Simmern/Hunsrück 16D1
Wohnmobilstellplatz Simmern, Gemündener Straß. **GPS:** n49,98011 e7,52283. ⬆➡

3 ⛺ free ⟦. **Surface:** metalled.
Distance: ⚓on the spot ⊗250m 🛒200m.

📷S Sinzig 9B6
Wohnmobilhafen Stellplatz 1 Sportpark, Bäderstrasse. **GPS:** n50,55142 e7,21746. ⬆

10 ⛺ € 4/24h ⟦ € 1 ⟦ Ch. **Surface:** gravel. ⬛ 01/01-31/12

📷 Sinzig 9B6
Sinziger Schloß, Jahnstrasse. **GPS:** n50,54684 e7,24844. ⬆

20 ⛺ free. **Surface:** metalled.
Distance: ⚓100m.

⚜S Sinzig 9B6
Wohnmobilhafen Stellplatz 2 Am Kurgarten, Bäderstrasse. **GPS:** n50,54912 e7,21749. ⬆

50 ⛺ € 4/24h, electricity incl ⟦ € 1 ⟦ Ch ✎. **Surface:** metalled. ⬛ 01/01-31/12
Distance: ⊗50m.

📷S Speyer 17B3
Techniek Museum Speyer, Geibstrasse. **GPS:** n49,31222 e8,45009. ⬆

⛺ € 19 ⟦ Ch ✎ WC ⌐ included. **Surface:** grassy. ⬛ 01/01-31/12
Remarks: Bread service, discount museum/theater.

Tourist information Speyer:
Ⓜ Technik Museum Speyer/Imax Filmtheater, Geibstrasse. ⬛ Mo-Fr 9-18h, Sa-Su 9-17h.

📷S Sprendlingen 17A1
Wiesbach, Bachgasse/Bleichstrasse. **GPS:** n49,85424 e7,98538. ⬆

DE

30 🗆free 🏕€ 2/10minutes 🗆Ch 🧹€ 2/day. **Surface:** asphalted. ⬛ 01/01-31/12
Distance: 🚶700m 🚲3,4km ⊗500m.
Remarks: Parking at swimming pool, entrance swimming pool € 2/day.

| 🏞S | Sprendlingen | 17A1 |

Eura Mobil Stellplatz, Graf-von-Sponheimstrasse. **GPS:** n49,86297 e7,97612.⬆.

10 🗆free 🏕€ 1 🗆Ch 🧹(10x)free.
Surface: metalled. ⬛ 01/01-31/12
Distance: 🚶600m 🚲4,4km 🚋300m.
Remarks: Workdays from 9h guided tours (free).

| 🏞S | Stromberg | 17A1 |

Reisemobilplatz Michels Land, Königsberger Straße. **GPS:** n49,94709 e7,78818.
6 🗆€5 🏕🗆Ch 🧹€ 0,50/kWh. **Surface:** unpaved. ⬛ 01/01-31/12
Distance: 🚶500m 🚋50m Lidl.

| 🏞S | Thalfang 🏔❄ | 16C2 |

Festplatz Thalfang, Talstrasse 2. **GPS:** n49,75028 e6,99944.⬆.

40 🗆€5 🏕🗆Ch 🧹(6x)free. **Surface:** gravel. ⬛ 01/01-31/12
Distance: 🚶200m ⊗on the spot 🚋200m.
Remarks: Check in at swimming pool, max. 4 nights.

| 🏞 | Thallichtenberg 🌿 | 16D2 |

Burg Lichtenberg, K23. **GPS:** n49,55716 e7,35975.⬆➡.

4 🗆free. **Surface:** asphalted. ⬛ 01/01-31/12
Distance: ⊗300m 🚋1km.
Remarks: Max. 3 days.

| 🏞 | Tholey | 16D2 |

Parkplatz Am Schaumburg, Am Schaumberg. **GPS:** n49,48965 e7,03804.⬆➡.

±20 🗆free. **Surface:** metalled. ⬛ 01/01-31/12
Distance: ⊗100m.

| 🏞S | Traben-Trarbach 🌿🏔〰 | 16D1 |

Rißbacher Straße. **GPS:** n49,96583 e7,10583.⬆.
45 🗆€10 🏕🗆Ch 🧹WC 🗆📶. **Location:** Comfortable. **Surface:** grassy.
⬛ 01/10-31/12
Distance: 🚶2km.
Remarks: Along the Moselle river.

| 🏞 | Trier | 16C2 |

Reisemobilpark Treviris, In den Moselauen. **GPS:** n49,74092 e6,62502.

120 🗆€ 0,10/h 10-18h, € 6/18-10h 🏕€ 1/100liter 🗆Ch 🧹(30x)€ 0,50/kWh WC 🧹€ 1.
Surface: grasstiles. ⬛ 01/01-31/12
Distance: 🚌on the spot.
Remarks: Along the river Moselle.

Tourist information Trier:
ℹ Tourist Information, An der Porta Nigra, www.trier.de.Old Roman city with the best kept and also largest Roman gate in Europe: Porta Nigra.
ℹ Triercard.Free city bus and discount at museums, boat trips, swimming pool etc. 🎫 € 9 family card € 15 3 days.

| 🏞S | Trittenheim | 16C2 |

Moselpromenade, Moselstrasse. **GPS:** n49,82436 e6,90295.⬆➡.

50 🗆€5 🏕€ 0,50/100liter 🗆Ch 🧹(30x)€ 2,50/24h. **Surface:** metalled. ⬛ 01/01-31/12
Distance: 🚶500m 🏊on the spot 🎣on the spot ⊗300m 🚋400m.
Remarks: Bread-service.

| 🏞S | Unkel | 9B6 |

P3, Parkplatz Hallenbad, Kamenerstrasse. **GPS:** n50,59776 e7,21962.⬆.

6 🛏free 🚰€ 1/80liter ⬛Ch WC. **Surface:** asphalted. 🔲 01/01-31/12
Distance: 🚶100m 🚏100m 🛒150m.

⬛S Urmitz/Rhein 9B6
Wohnmobilhafen am Rhein, Kaltenengerser Straße 3. **GPS:** n50,41716 e7,52506.
15 🛏€5 🚰⬛Ch 🔌. **Surface:** metalled. 🔲 01/01-31/12
Distance: 🚶on the spot ⊗350m 🚏300m.
Remarks: Along the Rhine river.

⬛S Ürzig 16C1
Panorama-Mobilstellplatz Ürzig, Moselufer B53. **GPS:** n49,97870 e7,00768.

25 🛏€8 🚰⬛Ch 🔌€ 1,50/day. **Surface:** grassy. 🔲 01/04-31/10
Distance: 🛒bakery 150m.
Remarks: Along the Moselle river.

⬛S Vallendar 9B6
Rheinufer. **GPS:** n50,39749 e7,61277.
3 🛏free 🚰⬛Ch. **Surface:** metalled. 🔲 01/01-31/12
Distance: 🚶centre 500m ⊗200m 🛒Aldi 200m.
Remarks: Along railwayline.

⬛ Valwig 16D1
Moselweinstrasse. **GPS:** n50,14271 e7,21292.⬆

40 🛏€5. **Surface:** grassy.
Distance: 🚶100m ⊘on the spot ⊗100m.

⬛S Veldenz 16D1
Wohnmobilpark Veldenz, Hauptstrasse, K88. **GPS:** n49,89222 e7,01944.

40 🛏€6 🚰⬛Ch 🔌(24x)included 🗑€ 2. **Surface:** grassy. 🔲 01/01-

---

31/12
Distance: 🚶300m ⊗300m 🛒300m 🚏200m.

⬛S Völklingen 16C3
Weltkulturerbe Völklinger Hütte, Rathausstraße. **GPS:** n49,24730 e6,84492.
5 🛏free 🚰⬛Ch 🔌.
Surface: asphalted. 🔲 01/01-31/12
Distance: ⛵1,1km ⊗400m 🛒850m.

⬛S Wadern 16C2
An der Stadthalle. **GPS:** n49,54377 e6,89465.⬆

10 🛏free 🚰🔌€ 1,50/day. **Surface:** metalled. 🔲 01/01-31/12
Distance: 🚶on the spot ⊼3km ⊗on the spot 🛒100m.
Remarks: Parking in centre.

⬛ Wadern 16C2
Noswendeler See, Noswendel. **GPS:** n49,53906 e6,88992.⬆

5 🛏free. 🔲 01/01-31/12
Distance: 🚶on the spot ⊼on the spot ⊗on the spot 🛒3km.

⬛ Wadern 16C2
Zum Wiesental, Nunkirchen. **GPS:** n49,48905 e6,83679.⬆➡

5 🛏free. 🔲 01/01-31/12
Distance: 🚶on the spot ⊗on the spot 🛒on the spot.

🍽 Wadern 16C2
Hotel Pension Steil, Schlossstrasse, Lockweiler. **GPS:** n49,52765 e6,90158.

4 🛏guests free. **Surface:** metalled. 🔲 01/01-31/12
Distance: 🚶1km ⊗on the spot 🛒500m.

🍴 **Wadern** 16C2

Hotel Restaurant Reidelbacher Hof, Reidelbach 6, Reidelbach. GPS: n49,57694 e6,86056.
5 € 5, guests free. 01/01-31/12
Distance: 3km ⊗on the spot 3km.

Tourist information Wadern:
ℹ️ Tourist Information, Marktplatz 13, www.wadern.de.Nature reserve Saar Hunsrück, many signposted cycle and hiking routes.
♖ Schloß Dagstuhl.
Weiherhof, Nunkirchen.Golf court, 9 holes. Sunday 10-12 Schnuppergolf, free try-out.

Waldalgesheim 17A1

An der Keltenhalle, Niedergasse. GPS: n49,95371 e7,83614.

25 € 4/night 1 Ch € 2/6h. **Surface:** metalled. 01/01-31/12
Distance: 500m.

Waldfischbach-Burgalben 17A3

In den Bruchwiesen, Carentaner Platz. GPS: n49,28155 e7,64772.
6 free Ch. **Surface:** asphalted. 01/01-31/12
Distance: 600m ⊗100m.

Waldfischbach-Burgalben 17A3

Camping Clausensee. GPS: n49,27562 e7,72125.
10 € 15,50-19,50 Ch. **Surface:** grasstiles. 01/01-31/12
Distance: 8km ⊗on the spot on the spot.

Waxweiler 16B1

Wohnmobilplatz Waxweiler, Bahnhofstrasse. GPS: n50,09401 e6,35669.

20 € 5 1 Ch € 2. **Surface:** metalled. 01/01-31/12
Distance: on the spot ⊗100m 500m.

Weiskirchen 16C2

Am Kurpark, Burgstrasse. GPS: n49,55868 e6,81810.

6 € 1,40/pp 0,50 € 0,50 Ch € 0,50. **Surface:** metalled.
01/01-31/12
Distance: on the spot ⊗500m 300m.
Remarks: Parking at the health resort, max. 2-3 days.

Westhofen 17A2

Parkplatz Nickelgarten, Am Nickelgarten. GPS: n49,70559 e8,24672.

15 free (12x)€ 1/8h. **Surface:** metalled. 01/01-31/12
Distance: 100m 4km 100m.
Remarks: Max. 3 days.

Westhofen 17A2

Weingut Dreihornmühle, An der Brennerei. GPS: n49,70375 e8,25288.

3 € 5, guests free € 1/day. **Surface:** grassy. 01/01-31/12
Distance: 600m ⊗600m 150m.

Westhofen 17A2

Tankstelle Raiffeisen. GPS: n49,70039 e8,24699.
Ch. 01/01-31/12
Remarks: Coins at petrol station.

Wintrich 16C1

Mosel Stellplatz Wintrich, Moselstrasse. GPS: n49,88417 e6,94833.

90 € 7 1/100liter Ch (90x)included WC € 1 free.
Surface: grassy/metalled. 01/01-31/12
Distance: 100m on the spot on the spot ⊗100m bakery 300m.

Wintrich 16C1

Weingut Clemens, Kurfürstenstrasse 11. GPS: n49,89000 e6,95416.

10 € 5 2 Ch € 2. **Surface:** metalled. 01/01-31/12
Distance: on the spot ⊗on the spot 1km.

Wittlich 16C1

Zweibächen, Hasenmühlenweg. GPS: n49,99470 e6,87595.

DE

30 �€ 5/24h ⌐€ 1/80liter 🔲Ch. **Surface:** grassy. ⬛ 01/01-31/12
Distance: 1km 🚲1km 🚂1km.
Remarks: Max. 3 days.

| 🔲S | Worms | 17B2 |

Wohnmobilhafen, Kastanienallee. **GPS:** n49,63458 e8,37513. ⬆➡.

30 �€ 4/24h ⌐ 🔲Ch 🧹.
Surface: gravel.
⬛ 01/01-31/12
Distance: 15 min walking 🏊Rhine promenade 🚲300m 🚂500m 🚌on the spot.
Remarks: Along river, service at Gaststätte Hagenbräu 300m from the parking.

Tourist information Worms:
ℹ Tourist Info, Neumarkt 14, www.worms.de.City with several curiosities, wine-city, Liebfraumilch.
Ⓜ Raschi-Haus, Hintere Judengasse 6.Jewish history, cemetery and synagogue.
⬛ Tue-Su 10-12.30h, 13.30-17/16.30h.
🚲 Gasthaus Brauerei Hagenbräu, Am Rhein 3.Restaurant with its own brewery.

| 🔲S | Zell/Mosel | 16D1 |

Wohnmobilstellplatz Römerquelle, Am Freizeitzentrum, Kaimt. **GPS:** n50,01632 e7,17662. ⬆➡.

70 �€ 6 ⌐€ 0,50/90liter 🔲Ch. **Surface:** grassy/metalled. ⬛ 01/01-31/12
Distance: 1km 🏊on the spot 🚌on the spot 🚲500m 🚂1km.
Remarks: Along the Moselle river, bread-service.

| 🔲S | Zell/Mosel | 16D1 |

Am Fussgängerbrücke. GPS: n50,02729 e7,17811. ⬆.

23 �€ 6 ⌐€ 0,50/90liter 🔲Ch. **Surface:** asphalted. ⬛ Easter-31/10
Distance: 300m 🏊on the spot 🚌on the spot 🚲200m 🚂300m.

| 🔲S | Zweibrücken | 16D3 |

Eitel's Wohnmobil-Stellplatz, Californiastraße. **GPS:** n49,26477 e7,36112.
25 �€ 7 ⌐€ 0,50 🔲Ch 🧹 included. **Surface:** asphalted. ⬛ 01/01-31/12
Distance: 🚌100m.

Hesse

| 🔲 | Aarbergen | 9C6 |

Hauptstraße 58, Michelbach. **GPS:** n50,23093 e8,05926. ⬆.
10 �37free. **Surface:** metalled.

| 🔲S | Alsfeld 🌼 | 10A5 |

Erlenstadion, Fulder Weg. **GPS:** n50,74882 e9,27882. ⬆➡.

10 �37free ⌐€ 0,50 🔲€ 0,50 Ch. **Surface:** grasstiles.
Distance: 200m 🚲1,8km.

| 🍴 | Alsfeld 🌼 | 10A5 |

Hotel zum Schaferhof, A20 dir Eudorf. **GPS:** n50,76742 e9,29048.

20 �37free. **Surface:** metalled. ⬛ 01/01-31/12
Distance: 🚌on the spot 🚲on the spot.

| 🔲S | Alsfeld 🌼 | 10A5 |

Fina-tankstelle, Pfefferhöhe. **GPS:** n50,73366 e9,24128.

5 �37free ⌐€ 0,50 🔲€ 0,50 WC 🔲€ 2,50. **Surface:** metalled. ⬛ 01/01-31/12
Distance: 🚲on the spot.

Bad Arolsen 🏕️ S 9D3
Reisemobilhafen Twistesee, Bericher Seeweg 1, Wetterburg. **GPS**: n51,38396 e9,06546.
100 🛏️ € 6-8,50, tourist tax incl 🚰 1/100liter 🔌Ch 🧹 € 2/day. **Surface:** grassy/gravel. 🅿️ 01/01-31/12
Distance: 🚣on the spot ⊗on the spot.
Remarks: At lake, bread-service.

Bad Emstal 🏕️ S ♨️ 10A4
Am Mineral-Thermalbad, Karlsbader Straße 4, Sand. **GPS**: n51,24858 e9,24952.
7 🛏️ € 7, tourist tax incl 🚰 1/100liter 🔌Ch 🧹 € 1/8h. **Surface:** metalled.
🅿️ 01/01-31/12
Distance: 🚲1km ⊗on the spot.

Bad Endbach 🏕️ S 9D5
Kultur-, Sport- und Freizeitzentrum, Zur Kurmittelhaus. **GPS**: n50,75669 e8,47875.⬆️.

18 🛏️ € 5 🚰 🔌Ch 🧹 WC 🚽. 🅿️ 01/01-31/12
Distance: 🚲1km ⊗on the spot 🚆100m.
Remarks: Excl. tourist tax, service: Kläranlage, 2km, Mo/Thu 7-16h, Fri 7-12.30h, Sa/Su 8-10h.

Bad Hersfeld 🏕️ S 10A5
Acqua-fit, Kolpingstrasse 6. **GPS**: n50,86771 e9,72951.
20 🛏️ € 3 🚰 🔌Ch 🧹. **Surface:** metalled. 🅿️ 01/01-31/12
Distance: 🚴2km.
Remarks: Swimming pool.

Bad Hersfeld 🏕️ S 10A5
Geistalbad, Am Schwimmbad. **GPS**: n50,87485 e9,70025.⬆️➡️.

20 🛏️ € 5 🚰 € 1/80liter 🔌Ch 🧹 (6x)€ 0,50/kWh. **Surface:** asphalted/metalled. 🅿️ 01/01-31/12
Distance: 🚲50m 🚴3,9km.
Remarks: Parking swimming pool.

Bad Hersfeld 🏕️ 10A5
Auf der Unteraue. **GPS**: n50,86231 e9,70340.⬆️.

3 🛏️free. **Surface:** metalled. 🅿️ 01/01-31/12
Remarks: At tennis-court.

Bad Hersfeld 🍴 10A5
Waldhotel Glimmesmühle, Hombergerstrasse. **GPS**: n50,88420 e9,66984.⬆️.

10 🛏️free with a meal.
Surface: metalled. 🅿️ 01/01-31/12
Distance: ⊗on the spot.

Tourist information Bad Hersfeld:
ℹ️ Tourist Information, Am Markt 1, www.bad-hersfeld.de/touristik.Medieval healt resort and festival city on the Fulda river.
☀️ Lullusfest.Traditional folk festival for the honour of the founder of the city.
🅿️ week 16/10.

Bad Karlshafen Ⓒ S 10A3
Am Rechten Weserufer, Am rechten Weserufer 2. **GPS**: n51,64508 e9,44953.
15 🛏️ € 9 🚰 🔌Ch 🧹 € 1. **Surface:** asphalted. 🅿️ 01/01-31/12
Remarks: Max. 4 days.

Bad Nauheim 🏕️ 9D6
Usa-Wellenbad, Friedberger Strasse 16-20. **GPS**: n50,35352 e8,74305.⬆️.

40 🛏️ € 5. 🅿️ 01/01-31/12
Distance: 🚲1km ⊗on the spot 🚆300m 🚌on the spot.
Remarks: Check in at Wellenbad, 8-20h.

Bad Orb 🏕️ S ♨️ 10A6
Am Busbahnhof, Austraße. **GPS**: n50,23014 e9,34659.⬆️.
4 🛏️ € 6 🚰 🔌Ch 🧹. **Surface:** metalled. 🅿️ 01/01-31/12
Distance: ⊗450m 🚆300m.

Bad Salzschlirf 🏕️ S 10A5
Riedstrasse. **GPS**: n50,62090 e9,50304.⬆️.

3 🛏️free 🚰 € 1 🔌Ch.
Surface: asphalted. 🅿️ 01/01-31/12
Distance: 🚲100m.

Tourist information Bad Salzschlirf:
ℹ️ Kur und Tourismus GmbH Bad Salzschlirf, Bahnhofstr. 22, www.bad-salzschlirf.de.Health resort.

Bad Schwalbach 🏕️ S 17A1
Am Kurpark, Reitallee 21. **GPS**: n50,13988 e8,06362.⬆️.
4 🛏️free 🚰 € 0,50/50liter 🔌Ch 🧹 € 0,50/kWh. **Surface:** metalled. 🅿️ 01/01-31/12
Distance: 🚲500m ⊗400m.

Bad Soden-Salmünster   10A6

Wohnmobilplatz am Kurpark, Parkstraße, Bad Soden. **GPS**: n50,28544 e9,35917.

30 €5 € 1/70liter Ch € 1/2kWh. **Surface:** metalled. 01/01-31/12

Distance: on the spot on the spot on the spot.
Remarks: To pay at pay-desk of the Therme.

Bad Sooden-Allendorf   10B4

Reisemobilhafen Franzrasen, Am Alten Festplatz, Allendorf. **GPS**: n51,27149 e9,97209.

100 € 4, incl tourist tax 1 pers € 0,50/5minutes € 0,50 Ch € 0,50/kWh, 16Amp. **Surface:** grassy/metalled. 01/01-31/12
Distance: 200m.

Tourist information Bad Sooden-Allendorf:
Tourist Information, Landgraf-Philipp-Platz 1-2, www.bad-sooden-allendorf.de. Health resort with many half-timbered houses.

Bad Wildungen   9D4

Wohnmobilstellplatz Bad Wildungen, Bahnhofstrasse. **GPS**: n51,12008 e9,13631.

16 free, voluntary contribution € 1/pppd € 1/45liter Ch € (14x)€ 1/kWh. **Surface:** metalled. 01/01-31/12
Distance: 1,5km.
Remarks: Max. 7 days.

Bad Zwesten   10A4

Hotel Altenburg, Hardtstrasse 1a. **GPS**: n51,05706 e9,17748.

---

3 € 10 WC included. **Surface:** metalled. 01/01-31/12
Distance: 400m on the spot 300m.

Battenberg ❄   9D4

Ederberglandhalle, Am Wingertsberg. **GPS**: n51,01233 e8,63411.
3 free. 01/01-31/12
Distance: on the spot 100m on the spot on the spot.
Remarks: Service: Esso-Station, Battenfelderstr. 6.

Battenberg ❄   9D4

Festhalle Battenberg, Festplatzweg. **GPS**: n51,00972 e8,63861.

3 free Ch.
01/01-31/12
Remarks: At community centre, service: Esso-station, Battenfelderstr. 6.

Tourist information Battenberg:
Tourist-Information Ederbergland Touristik e. V, Untermarkt 12, www.ederbergland-touristik.de. Small town high above the Eder valley.
Besucherbergwerk Burgbergstollen. 150 years old mine shaft, can be reached from Marktplatz. 01/05-30/09 1st Su of the month 14-17h.
Stadtmuseum. Mining and hunting. Wed, Su 14-17h.
In winter cross-country trails on the Röhrberg.

Baunatal   10A4

Parkstadion. GPS: n51,25865 e9,39956.
12 € 5/24h € 1/100liter Ch € 0,50/kWh. 01/01-31/12
Distance: 500m 4km.
Remarks: Max. 3 days.

Bebra   10B4

Natur- und Freizeitpark Fuldaue Breitenbachen Seen, Hersfelder Straße. **GPS**: n50,95899 e9,78764.

25 free € 1/100liter Ch € (18x)€ 0,50/kWh. **Surface:** grassy. 01/01-31/12
Distance: 1km on the spot on the spot.

Bebra   10B4

Annastrasse 17. **GPS**: n50,97464 e9,79836.

4 free. **Surface:** asphalted. 01/01-31/12
Distance: 400m.
Remarks: Parking swimming pool.

Bebra — 10B4

Mehrzweckparkplatz, Bei Laupfütze/Rathausstrasse. **GPS**: n50,97000 e9,79000.

5 free. **Surface:** metalled. 01/01-31/12
Distance: on the spot.

Beerfelden — 17C2

Parkplatz NordicCenter, Seeweg. **GPS**: n49,56034 e8,97557.
4 free € 0,50/50liter Ch € 0,50/kWh. **Surface:** asphalted.
01/01-31/12
Distance: 1km.

Biedenkopf — 9D5

Freizeitzentrum Sackpfeife, An der Berggaststätte. **GPS**: n50,93160 e8,51839.

6 € 5 (6x)€ 1. **Surface:** concrete. 01/01-31/12
Distance: on the spot on the spot.
Remarks: Max. 3 days.

Biedenkopf — 9D5

Lahnauenbad, Am Freibad 7. **GPS**: n50,91293 e8,52310.
Ch.

Biedenkopf — 9D5

Parkplatz Stadtwerke, Mühlweg. **GPS**: n50,90904 e8,52653.

4 € 5/24h € 1/12h. **Surface:** metalled. 01/01-31/12
Distance: 200m.

Biedenkopf — 9D5

Perfstausee, Hauptstrasse. **GPS**: n50,91117 e8,46015.

5 free. **Surface:** gravel. 01/01-31/12
Distance: 5km on the spot on the spot 5km 12km 12km.
Remarks: Parking at artificial lake, max. 3 days.

Biedenkopf — 9D5

Parkhotel Bürgerhaus, Auf dem Radeköppel 2. **GPS**: n50,91183 e8,53515.

5 free with a meal. 01/01-31/12
Distance: on the spot on the spot 500m 12km 12km.

Biedenkopf — 9D5

Restaurant Der Katzenbacher, Ortstrasse 12, Katzenbach. **GPS**: n50,89949 e8,57239.

8 € 5. 01/01-31/12
Distance: 10km 15km on the spot 10km 15km on the spot.
Remarks: Not suitable for big motorhomes.

Tourist information Biedenkopf:
Tourist Information, Hainstr. 63, www.hessennet.de/biedenkopf.Old part of town with half-timbered houses.
Hinterlandmuseum Schloß Biedenkopf.Regional and cultural history.
01/04-15/11 10-18h Mo.
Freizeitzentrum Sackpfeife.

Braunfels — 9C6

Wohnmobilstation Schloss Braunfels, Jahnplatz. **GPS**: n50,51478 e8,38609.
4 € 5 Ch included. **Surface:** metalled. 01/01-31/12
Distance: on the spot 350m.

Breuberg — 17C1

Bahnhofstraße 4, Neustadt. **GPS**: n49,81576 e9,04063.
4 free € 1/60liter € 1 Ch € 0,50/kWh. **Surface:** asphalted.
01/01-31/12
Distance: on the spot 300m 550m.

Burghaun — 10A5

Oberste Straße. **GPS**: n50,69179 e9,73203.
4 free € 1/100liter Ch € 0,50/kWh. **Surface:** asphalted.
01/01-31/12
Distance: 500m on the spot on the spot.

Calden — 10A3

Waldschwimmbad Calden. **GPS**: n51,40958 e9,40218.

3 free. **Surface:** grassy. 01/01-31/12

DE

Distance: 🚶1km ⊗1,5km 🛒2km.

© **Diemelsee** **9D4**

Terrassenparkplatz Hohes Rad, Hohes Rad 1. **GPS**: n51,33533 e8,75319.⬆.

20 📷€ 5. **Surface**: metalled. ⬜ 01/01-31/12

S **Dillenburg** **9C5**

Aquarena-Bad, Stadionstrasse. **GPS**: n50,73994 e8,27815.

8 📷free ⚡€ 1/90liter ⛲Ch ⚡(6x)€ 1/kWh. **Surface**: asphalted. ⬜ 01/01-31/12

Distance: 🚶300m.

🍽 **Dillenburg** **9C5**

Hotel Kanzelstein, Fasanenweg 2. **GPS**: n50,74538 e8,31473.
10 📷free with a meal. **Surface**: asphalted.
Distance: 🚶3km ⊗on the spot 🛒3km.

S **Edermünde** **10A4**

Aueweg, Grifte. **GPS**: n51,21252 e9,44905.⬆.
12 📷€ 5/15h electricity incl ⚡⛲Ch ⚡included. 🚐 **Location:**
Comfortable. **Surface:**
Distance: ⊗300m 🛒100m 🚲Premium-Radweg R1.

S **Edertal** **9D4**

Kraftwerkstrasse. **GPS**: n51,17022 e9,05096.⬆➡.

5 📷free ⚡ 1/5minutes ⛲€ 1 Ch ⚡(6x)€ 0,50/kWh. **Surface:**
metalled. ⬜ 01/01-31/12
Distance: 🚶750m ⊗100m 🛒100m 🚍100m.

S **Eschwege** ❄ **10B4**

Reisemobilhafen Werratalsee, Am werratalsee 2. **GPS**: n51,19196 e10,06728.
⬆.

32 📷€ 7 ⚡⛲Ch ⚡€ 2/5kWh WC€ 3/pppd 📷€ 2,50. **Surface:**
metalled. ⬜ 01/01-31/12
Distance: 🚶2km.
Remarks: Motorhome parking nearby Knaus Campingpark, pay at bistro.

Tourist information Eschwege:
🛈 Tourist Information, Hospitalplatz 16, www.werratal-tourismus.de.Small
half-timbered city in the Werra valley, many fishing opportunities.
👁 Besuchbergwerk Grube Gustav, Höllethal, Meissner, Abterode.Slate mine. ⬜
15/03-31/10 Tue -Su 13-16h.
Ⓜ😊 Wild- und Erholungspark, Waldwichtelhaus, Meissner, Germerode.Game
preserve and gnome museum. ⬜ 01/04-31/10 Tue-Su 10-18h, 01/11-31/03
Sa-Su 10-17h 📷 15/12-15/01.
Ⓜ Eschweger Zinnfigurenkabinett, In der Kemenate, Hospitalstrasse 7.Tinware.
⬜ Wed, Sa, Su 14-17h.
Ⓜ Grensmuzeum Schifflergrund, Asbach-Sickenberg.The history of the Eastern
border. ⬜ 01/03-31/10 10-17h, 01/11-28/02 10-16h, Sa-Su 13-16h.
🎿 Skigebiet Hohen Meissner.

S **Flörsbachtal-Lohrhaupten** **17C1**

Am Schwimbad, Mühlweg. **GPS**: n50,12453 e9,47830.⬆➡.

20 📷€ 6 ⚡€ 1 ⛲Ch ⚡€ 1. **Surface**: grassy. ⬜ 01/01-31/12
Distance: 🚶1km ⊗100m 🛒1km.
Remarks: Service closed during wintertime, check in at Gartenstrasse 10a.

S **Frankenberg/Eder** **9D4**

Ederberglandhalle, Teichweg 3. **GPS**: n51,05613 e8,80195.⬆.
10 📷free ⚡€ 1 ⛲Ch ⚡€ 0,50/kWh. **Surface**: grassy/gravel. ⬜ 01/01-
31/12
Distance: 🚶500m ⊗200m 🛒1,5km.

🍽 **Friedberg** **13B1**

Jagdhaus, Florstädterstrasse 67, Ossenheim. **GPS**: n50,32546 e8,80536.

S **Eltville** **17A1**

Parkplatz Weinhohle, Weinhohle. **GPS**: n50,02832 e8,12406.
+20 📷free ⚡⛲Ch ⚡. **Surface**: metalled.
Distance: 🚶400m ⊗400m 🛒50m.

S **Erbach** **17C2**

Alexanderbad, In der Stadtwiese. **GPS**: n49,66349 e8,98863.⬆.

5 🛏free.
Distance: ⚓1km ⊗on the spot.

4 🛏free. ☐ 01/01-31/12
Distance: ⚓100m.
Remarks: Parking at swimming pool.

🅿S Frielendorf 10A4
Wohnmobilpark Silbersee, Zum Silbersee. **GPS:** n50,98389 e9,34667. ⬆➡.

⑪🅿S Gilserberg 9D5
Landgasthof Steller, Marburgerstrasse 3. **GPS:** n50,95047 e9,06220. ⬆.

50 🛏€8 ⚡🍽 Ch ⚡€ 2/day. **Location:** Rural, comfortable, quit. **Surface:** grassy/metalled. ☐ 01/04-01/11
Distance: ⚓250m ⛵250m.

2 🛏€ 5, clients € 2,50 ⚡€ 2,50 🍽⚡€ 2,50 WC. **Surface:** asphalted. ☐ 01/01-31/12

🅿 Fritzlar 10A4
Grauen Turm. GPS: n51,13221 e9,26974. ⬆➡.

⑪🅿S Gladenbach 9D5
Restaurant Rosengarten, Hoherainstrasse 45. **GPS:** n50,77462 e8,57952. ⬆➡.

10 🛏€ 5.
Surface: metalled. ☐ 01/01-31/12
Distance: ⚓100m ⊗100m.

Tourist information Fritzlar:
ℹ Tourist Information, Zwischen den Krämen 5, www.fritzlar.de. Small medieval town.
✎ Stadtführingen. Guided tour around the historic city center. ☐ 01/04-31/10 Tue-Sa 10.30h, Su 11h. 🎫 € 2,50.

3 🛏€ 5,50 ⚡🍽⚡. **Surface:** grassy. ☐ 01/01-31/12
Distance: ⊗on the spot.
Remarks: Pay and key at restaurant.

🅿S Grebenhain 10A6
Reisemobilstellplatz am Kurpark, Hindenburgstraße, Hochwaldhausen. **GPS:** n50,51910 e9,31756. ⬆.
🛏€ 7,50 ⚡🍽 Ch ⚡. **Surface:** gravel. ☐ 01/01-31/12

🅿S Fulda 10A5
Weimarerstrasse. **GPS:** n50,55685 e9,66663. ⬆.

🅿S Grünberg 9D5
Gallusplatz, Gerichtsstraße. **GPS:** n50,59477 e8,95439. ⬆.
10 🛏free ⚡€ 0,50 🍽 Ch ⚡€ 0,50/kWh. **Surface:** gravel. ☐ 01/01-31/12
Distance: ⚓Old city centre 300m ⊗100m 🛒Aldi 400m.

🅿 Helsa 10A4
Sportplatzweg. **GPS:** n51,25444 e9,68638. ⬆➡.

30 🛏€ 0,10/h ⚡€ 1 🍽 Ch ⚡€ 1/2kWh WC🍽. **Surface:** asphalted. ☐ 01/01-31/12
Distance: ⚓400m 🛒200m.

🅿 Gelnhausen 10A6
Am Hallenbad. **GPS:** n50,20125 e9,17795.

4 🛏free. **Surface:** metalled. ☐ 01/01-31/12
Distance: ⚓800m ⊗800m 🛒700m 🚰400m.

Herbstein 🏕 S 10A5

An der VulkanTherme Herbstein, Zum Thermalbad 1. **GPS**: n50,56883 e9,34647. ⬆

11 ⚡€ 5 + €0,80/pp tourist tax ⚓🔌 Ch 🔌.
Surface: metalled. ⬤ 01/01-31/12
Distance: ⛽1,1km ✕800m.
Remarks: Coins available at pay-desk of theTherme.

Hessisch Lichtenau S 10A4

Sportcenter Fürstenhagen, Breslauer strasse 18. **GPS**: n51,20416 e9,72722. ⬆ ➡

10 ⚡€ 5/24h ⚓€ 1/80liter ⚡Ch 🔌€ 0,50/kWh 🚿. **Surface:** metalled. ⬤ 01/01-31/12
Distance: ⛽3km ✕1km 🚂2km.

Hessisch Lichtenau 10A4

Alter Bahnhof, Bahnhofstrasse 5. **GPS**: n51,20055 e9,77833.

8 ⚡€ 10. **Surface:** asphalted. ⬤ 01/01-31/12
Distance: ⛽5km 🚂1km.

Hessisch Lichtenau 10A4

Wohnmobilstellplatz am Hallenbad, Freiherr vom Stein strasse 12. **GPS**: n51,20445 e9,72655. ⬆

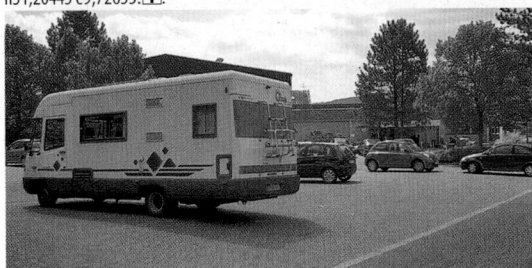

6 ⚡free. **Surface:** metalled. ⬤ 01/01-31/12
Distance: ⛽600m.
Remarks: Parking swimming pool.

Hessisch Lichtenau 🍴 S 10A4

Berggasthof Hohe Meissner, Hoher Meissner 1. **GPS**: n51,20376 e9,84852.
10 ⚡free ⚓. ⬤ 01/01-31/12
Distance: ⛽10km ✕on the spot 🏂on the spot 🚠on the spot.

Tourist information Hessisch Lichtenau:
ℹ Kultur- und Verkehrsamt, Rathaus, Zimmer 21, Landgrafenstrsse 52, www.hessisch-lichtenau.de.Characteristic 13th century small town, cycle and hiking routes available.

Hirzenhain 10A6

Festplatz Hirzenhain, Robert-Eichenauerweg. **GPS**: n50,39259 e9,13593. ➡

6 ⚡free. **Surface:** metalled. ⬤ 01/01-31/12
Distance: ⛽100m.

Hirzenhain S 10A6

Müller-Mobil, Junkerwiese 2. **GPS**: n50,40004 e9,14744.

5 ⚡free ⚓€ 1/130liter ⚡🔌. **Surface:** metalled. ⬤ 01/01-31/12
Distance: ⛽1,5km.

Hofgeismar S 10A3

Am Sälber Tor. **GPS**: n51,49521 e9,37547. ⬆

100 ⚡free ⚓€ 1/80liter ⚡Ch 🔌€ 1/2kWh WC. **Surface:** gravel.
Distance: ⛽on the spot 🚿300m.

Tourist information Hofgeismar:
ℹ Tourist-Info Märchenwald Reinhardswald, Markt 5, www.reinhardswald.de.

Homberg/Efze S 10A4

Wassmuthshäuserstrasse, Dresdener Alee. **GPS**: n51,02757 e9,41470. ⬆ ➡

6 ⚡free ⚓⚡Ch 🔌free. **Surface:** metalled. ⬤ 01/01-31/12
Distance: ⛽on the spot ✕1km 🚿500m.

Tourist information Homberg/Efze:
ℹ Tourist Information, Obertorstrasse 4, www.homberg-efze.de.Medival city with some half-timbered houses.

Hünfeld 10B5

Hessisches Kegelspiel, Zu den Unaben. **GPS**: n50,67626 e9,77622. ⬆ ➡

DE

18 🛏€5 ⛽€ 1/120liter 🚽Ch ⚡€ 1/2kWh. 🅿 01/01-31/12
Distance: 🛒500m ⊗250m 🚉500m.

25 🛏€ 10, dogs € 2/day ⛽€ 1 🚽Ch ⚡€ 2,50/day. **Surface:** metalled.
Distance: 🛒5km 🏊4,9km ≈20m 🚲on the spot ⊗20m.

Testplatz Haselgrund, Zum Haselsee. **GPS:** n50,67798 e9,77679.

Bleiche/Festplatz auf der grosse Bleiche, Bleichstrasse. **GPS:** n50,63849 e9,40444.

50 🛏free ⛽Ch ⚡WC. **Surface:** metalled.
Distance: 🛒600m ⊗on the spot 🚉600m.

20 🛏free. 🅿 01/01-31/12
Distance: 🛒100m 🚉on the spot.

Wohnmobilplatz Kassel, Am Sportzentrum/Giessenallee, Kassel-süd. **GPS:** n51,29250 e9,48750.➡

Freizeitzentrum, Am Sportfeld. **GPS:** n50,62758 e9,39288.⬆

12 🛏€ 7/day ⛽€ 1/100liter 🚽€ 1 Ch ⚡€ 0,50/kWh. 🅿 01/01-31/12
Distance: 🏊1,4km ⊗500m 🚌50m.
Remarks: With parking ticket free public transport (2 pers).

8 🛏free. **Surface:** metalled. 🅿 01/01-31/12
Distance: 🛒800m ⊗on the spot.

David-Eifertstrasse. **GPS:** n50,64288 e9,39393.
⛽€ 1 🚽Ch. 🅿 01/01-31/12
Distance: 🛒300m.
Remarks: Industrial area Hopfengarten.

Tourist information Kassel:
ℹ Kassel Tourist, Obere Königsstrasse 15, www.kassel.de.Capital of the German Märchenstrasse, fairy-tale trail.
👁🍵 Treppenstrasse, shopping promenade, modern architecture.

Festplatz, Am Steckkopf. **GPS:** n51,28525 e9,61956.⬆➡

Parkplatz Kappstrasse, Kappstrasse. **GPS:** n49,68018 e8,78294.⬆➡

4 🛏free ⛽€ 2 🚽Ch. **Surface:** metalled. 🅿 01/01-31/12
Distance: ⊗300m 🚉500m.

18 🛏free ⛽€ 1/80liter 🚽Ch ⚡(4x)€ 0,50/6h WC. 🅿 01/01-31/12
Distance: 🛒on the spot ⊗on the spot.

Campingplatz Seepark, Brunnenstrasse 20. **GPS:** n50,81400 e9,52000.⬆➡

Tourist information Lindenfels:
ℹ Health resort with historical centre.

Karolingerplatz Lorsch, Klosterstraße. **GPS:** n49,65359 e8,57220.

15 ⌚free ⟝🍳. **Surface:** gravel. 🚫 01/01-31/12

⌚Ⓢ Marburg 🌿🍴 9D5
Jahnstraße. **GPS:** n50,80354 e8,77544.⬆️➡️.

8 ⌚€7 ⟝€ 1/100liter ✂️(4x)€ 1/4h.
Surface: gravel. 🚫 01/01-31/12
Distance: 🚶300m 🚉500m.

⌚Ⓢ Michelstadt 🌿 17C2
Am Festplatz, Wiesenweg. **GPS:** n49,68038 e9,00143.⬆️.

10 ⌚free ⟝€ 1/70liter 🔵Ch ✂️€ 1/2kWh. **Surface:** gravel.
Distance: 🚶200m ⊗200m 🚉50m.

⌚Ⓢ Neukirchen 25D2
Birkenallee, Knüllgebirge. **GPS:** n50,86567 e9,34478.
5 ⌚free ⟝against payment. 🚫 01/01-31/12
Distance: 🚶500m.

Tourist information Neukirchen:
ℹ️ Small health resort with half-timbered houses and city walls.

⌚Ⓢ Oberaula 10A5
Am Golfplatz 1. **GPS:** n50,83590 e9,46211.⬆️➡️.

2 ⌚free. **Surface:** grassy. 🚫 01/01-31/12
Remarks: Parking golf court, max. 4 days.

⌚Ⓢ Oberaula 10A5
Sportplatz, Schwimbadstrasse. **GPS:** n50,85421 e9,45908.⬆️.

5 ⌚free. **Surface:** asphalted. 🚫 01/01-31/12

⌚Ⓢ Oberaula 10A5
Teichstrasse. **GPS:** n50,85900 e9,47300.➡️.

10 ⌚free. **Surface:** metalled.
Remarks: Parking tennis-courts, max. 4 days.

⌚Ⓢ Ottrau 10A5
Am Schwimmbad 10. **GPS:** n50,80400 e9,38500.⬆️.

5 ⌚free ⟝🍳 ✂️ WC ⌐. **Surface:** asphalted. 🚫 01/01-31/12
Distance: 🚶on the spot.

⌚Ⓢ Poppenhausen 👥 10B6
Sport- und Freizeitgelände Lüttergrund, Sebastian-Kneippweg, Wasserkuppe.
GPS: n50,49012 e9,87689.⬆️➡️.

10 ⌚€4 ⟝€ 1 🔵Ch ✂️€ 1/6h. **Surface:** metalled. 🚫 01/01-31/12
Distance: 🚶300m ⊗300m 🚉300m.

⌚Ⓢ Rasdorf 10B5
Sport- und Freizeitgelände, Setzelbacher Straße. **GPS:** n50,71422 e9,90306.
4 ⌚€4 ⟝€ 1/120liter 🔵Ch ✂️€ 1/10h. **Surface:** metalled. 🚫 01/01-
31/12
Distance: 🚶850m 🚉500m.
Remarks: Max. 3 days.

⌚Ⓢ Reichelsheim/Odenwald 17B2
Reichenbergschule, Beerfurhterstrasse. **GPS:** n49,71507 e8,84234.⬆️➡️.

20 ⌚free ⟝€ 1 🔵Ch ✂️(8x)€ 0,50/kWh. **Surface:** asphalted. 🚫 01/01-
31/12
Distance: 🚶500m ⊗100m.

Reinhardshagen 10A3

Freibad, Klinkersweg. **GPS**: n51,48694 e9,59194. ↑→.

5 free. **Surface**: asphalted.
Distance: 2km 2km 2km.
Remarks: Parking swimming pool, OT Veckerhagen.

Ringgau 10B4

Am Festplatz, In der Röste, Gandenborn. **GPS**: n51,08139 e10,04239.
20 free Ch . **Surface**: gravel. 01/01-31/12
Distance: 200m.

Rotenburg a/d Fulda 10A4

Wohnmobilpark Am Wittlich, Braacher Straße 14. **GPS**: n51,00040 e9,71932.
40 €4 € 1 Ch € 0,50/kWh.
Surface: metalled. 01/01-31/12
Distance: Old city centre 650m.

Rotenburg a/d Fulda 10A4

Am Kuckucksmarktgelände, Braach. **GPS**: n51,00583 e9,69361.→.

15 free. 01/01-31/12
Distance: 200m on the spot 200m.

Rotenburg a/d Fulda 10A4

Im Heienbach. **GPS**: n51,00223 e9,74141. ↑→.

10 free. 01/01-31/12
Remarks: Parking swimming pool.

Rotenburg a/d Fulda 10A4

Biergarten Hof Hafermas, Rotenburgerstrasse 13, Braach. **GPS**: n51,00325 e9,69019.

3 free € 1 Ch. **Surface**: gravel. 01/01-31/12
Distance: on the spot on the spot.

Tourist information Rotenburg a/d Fulda:
Verkehrs- und Kulturamt, Weingasse 3.Motorhome friendly town, worth seeing, with historic old part and half-timbered houses, hiking and mountain bike trails.
Kuckucksmarkt, Braach.Farmers market. 01/05-30/09 last weekend of the month10-18h.

Schlitz 10A5

Damenweg. **GPS**: n50,66909 e9,56908.
3 free . **Surface**: gravel. 01/01-31/12
Remarks: At swimming pool.

Schwalmstadt 10A5

Altstad Schwalmstadt-Treysa. **GPS**: n50,91447 e9,19327.

10 free Ch. 01/01-31/12
Distance: on the spot.
Remarks: Nearby, indicated on site.

Schwalmstadt 10A5

Ziegenhain, Fünftenweg. **GPS**: n50,91753 e9,24633.

10 free Ch. 01/01-31/12
Distance: on the spot.
Remarks: Parking swimming pool, service indicated.

Tourist information Schwalmstadt:
Schwalm-Touristik e.V, Paradeplatz 7, www.schwalmstadt.de.
Museum der Schwalm, Ziegenhain.Collection of costumes. Tue-Fri en Su 10/11-12h, 15-17h, Sa 14-17h.
In-line skating.Signposted routes.

Schwalmtal 10A5

Reisemobilplatz, Friedenstrasse, Schwalmtal-Storndorf. **GPS**: n50,65579 e9,26935. ↑→.

8 free € 0,50/80liter Ch (6x)€ 0,50/kWh. **Surface**: asphalted.
01/01-31/12
Distance: 300m.
Remarks: Nearby sports park.

Sontra 10B4

Langhelle/Jahnstrasse. **GPS**: n51,07227 e9,94673.

5 ⌃free ⌁🏠Ch🚰€ 2/24h WC. **Surface:** asphalted/metalled. ◨
01/01-31/12
Distance: 🚶600m 🚌on the spot.
Remarks: Parking behind swimming pool.

| ⌃ | Steinau a/d Strasse | 10A6 |

Am Steines. **GPS:** n50,31605 e9,46029.

3 ⌃free. **Surface:** asphalted. ◨ 01/01-31/12
Distance: 🚶1km 🚋150m.
Remarks: Parking next to bus stop, at sports centre.

| ⌃S | Tann/Rhön | 10B5 |

Festplatz Tann, Am Unsbach. **GPS:** n50,64264 e10,01948.
10 ⌃€5 ⌁€ 1/120liter 🏠Ch🚰€ 1/2kWh. **Surface:** gravel. ◨ 01/01-
31/12
Remarks: Max. 3 days.

| ⌃S | Ulrichstein | 10A5 |

Reisemobilstellplatz Panoramablick, Erlenweg. **GPS:** n50,57588 e9,20619.
⬆➡.

14 ⌃€5 ⌁€ 1/80liter 🏠Ch🚰(6x)€ 0,50/kWh. **Surface:** asphalted. ◨
01/01-31/12
Distance: 🚶1km ⊗1km 🚋1km.
Remarks: Beautiful view.

| ⌃ | Villmar | 9C6 |

P3, König-Konrad-Straße. **GPS:** n50,39102 e8,18625. ⬆➡.

10 ⌃free. **Surface:** metalled.
Distance: ⊗on the spot.

Remarks: Parking at the river.

| 🅲 | Vöhl | 9D4 |

Camping-und Ferienpark Teichmann, Herzhausen. **GPS:** n51,17472 e8,89103.
3 ⌃€10. **Surface:** metalled. ◨ 01/01-31/12
Distance: ⊗on the spot.
Remarks: Max. 1 night, >22h.

| ⌃S | Wahlsburg | 10A3 |

Landhotel "Zum Anker", Weserstrasse 14. **GPS:** n51,62447 e9,55212.⬆.

50 ⌃€6 ⌁€ 0,50 🏠Ch🚰(20x)€ 0,50/kWh WC 📶. **Surface:** grassy.
◨ 01/01-31/12
Distance: 🚶1km ⊗on the spot 🚋1km.
Remarks: Bread-service.

| 🍴S | Waldeck | 9D4 |

Seeblick Wohnmobil, Güldener Ort 12. **GPS:** n51,20309 e9,05004.
⌃€ 10, 2 pers.incl ⌁🏠Ch🚰WC 🚽.
Surface: grasstiles. ◨ 01/01-31/12
Distance: ⚓50m ⊗on the spot.
Remarks: At Edersee.

| ⌃S | Wanfried | 10B2 |

In der Weeraaue. **GPS:** n51,86667 e10,16736.⬆➡.

12 ⌃€3 ⌁€ 2 🏠Ch🚰(12x)€ 2/24h. **Surface:** grassy/metalled. ◨
01/01-31/12
Distance: 🚶50m 🚋50m.

| ⌃S | Weilburg | 9C6 |

An der Hainallee. GPS: n50,48385 e8,25848. ⬆➡.

20 ⌃€7,50 ⌁🏠Ch🚰included. **Surface:** metalled. ◨ 01/01-31/12
Distance: 🚶on the spot ⊗on the spot.
Remarks: In front of Feuerwehrstützpunkt, caution key € 15.

| ⌃S | Weilmünster | 9C6 |

Am Froschgraben, L3054. **GPS:** n50,43345 e8,37343. ⬆➡.

DE

20 🛏free ⟷ 🔌Ch free ⚡€ 2/16h. ◻ 01/01-31/12
Distance: 🚰on the spot ⊗100m 🚮100m.

54 🛏€ 12,50, 2 pers.incl ⟷ 1/100liter 🔌Ch ⚡€ 1/8h WC ⟷€
1/10minutes. **Surface:** metalled. ◻ 01/01-31/12

🏕S | **Weilrod** | 9C6

Taunus Mobilcamp, Hochtaunussstrasse. **GPS:** n50,31138 e8,42581.⬆.

Remarks: Discount at subtropical swimming pool and indoor skating rink.

🏕S | **Witzenhausen** | 10B4

Reisemobilplatz Diebesturm, Oberburgstrasse. **GPS:** n51,34110 e9,85435.⬆.
➡.

30 🛏€ 5 + € 1/pp, dog € 1 ⟷ 1/20liter 🔌Ch ⚡€ 0,50/kWh WC⟷.
Surface: metalled. ◻ 01/01-31/12
Distance: ⊗300m 🚮6km.

🏕S | **Wetzlar** 🌼 | 9D6

Lahninsel. **GPS:** n50,55506 e8,49794.⬆.
5 🛏€ 0,25/h, overnight stay free 🔌WC.
Surface: asphalted. ◻ 01/01-31/12
Distance: 🚰300m 🚤1,5km ⊗250m.

4 🛏€ 2,50 ⟷€ 0,50 🔌Ch ⚡(4x)€ 0,50. **Surface:** metalled. ◻ 01/01-
31/12
Distance: 🚰500m ⊗on the spot 🚮500m.

🏕S | **Witzenhausen** | 10B4

Reisemobilplatz Josef-Pott-Platz, Laubenweg. **GPS:** n51,34477 e9,85503.
10 🛏€ 2,50 ⟷€ 1/100liter 🔌Ch ⚡€ 0,50/kWh. **Surface:** metalled. ◻
01/01-31/12
Distance: ⊗800m 🚮Aldi 100m.

🏕S | **Wiesbaden** ♈ | 17A1

Reisemobilhafen Wiesbaden, Wörther-See-Strasse/Saarstrasse. **GPS:** n50,05583
e8,20972.⬆.

🏨S | **Witzenhausen** | 10B4

Haus des Gastes, Ringkopfstrasse, Dohrenbach. **GPS:** n51,31061 e9,83372.

32 🛏€ 12 ⟷€ 1/80liter 🔌Ch ⚡(32x)€ 0,50/kWh. ◻ 01/01-31/12
Distance: ⊗800m 🚮800m.

🏕 | **Wiesbaden/Frauenstein** | 17A1

Alfred-Delp-Strasse/Frauenstein. **GPS:** n50,06755 e8,16526.

8 🛏€ 3 ⟷ 🔌Ch ⚡free.
Surface: metalled. ◻ 01/01-31/12
Distance: 🚰on the spot ⊗on the spot 🚮300m.

Tourist information Witzenhausen:
⚜ Kesperkirmes.Village fair. ◻ beginning Jul.

🏕S | **Wolfhagen** | 10A4

Freizeitanlange Bruchwiesen, Siemensstrasse. **GPS:** n51,32944 e9,17083.⬆.
➡.

10 🛏free. ◻ 01/01-31/12
Distance: 🚰4km.
Remarks: Parking in front of sports park.

🏕S | **Willingen** | 9D4

Wohnmobilpark Willingen, Am Hagen. **GPS:** n51,29050 e8,61278.⬆.

27 🛏free 🚰€ 1/80liter 🗑Ch🧹(12x)€ 1/8h. **Surface:** gravel. 🅾 01/01-31/12
Distance: 🚶on the spot ⊗500m 🛒200m.

| 😊 S | Ziegenhagen | 10A3 |

Erlebnispark Ziegenhagen, Ziegenberg 3. **GPS:** n51,37191 e9,76472.➡️

30 🛏€5 🚰€ 1 🗑Ch. 🅾 01/03-31/10
Distance: 🚶6km.

Thuringia

| 📷 S | Asbach/Sickenberg | 10B4 |

Grenzmuseum Schifflersgrund, Sickenberger Straße 1. **GPS:** n51,28667 e10,01052.
6 🛏free 🚰🗑Ch🧹. **Surface:** gravel.

| 📷 S | Bad Berka ♨ | 10D4 |

P2, Bleichstrasse. **GPS:** n50,89969 e11,28528.⬆️➡️

3 🛏free 🚰€ 1/3minutes 🗑€ 1 Ch🧹(3x)€ 1/3h. **Surface:** asphalted.
🅾 01/01-31/12
Distance: 🚶200m 🏊on the spot ⊗200m 🛒200m.
Remarks: 10/7/10 during inspection service out of order.

| 📷 S | Bad Colberg/Heldburg | 10C6 |

Rainbrünnlein. **GPS:** n50,27967 e10,73063.⬆️

10 🛏free 🚰🗑Chfree. **Surface:** metalled.
Distance: 🚶100m ⊗200m 🛒200m.
Remarks: At sports park.

| 🏕 S | Bad Frankenhausen/Kyffhäuser ♨ | 10C3 |

Bornstraße, B85. **GPS:** n51,35550 e11,10333.⬆️➡️

6 🛏€ 12 🚰🗑🧹 included. **Location:** Rural. **Surface:** metalled. 🅾 01/01-31/12
Distance: 🚶500m ⊗200m 🛒300m.
Remarks: Check in at pay-desk of the Therme.

| 🏕 S | Bad Klosterlausnitz | 11A4 |

Kristall Sauna-Wellnesspark/Soletherme, Köstritzerstrasse 16. **GPS:** n50,91190 e11,87242.⬆️➡️

15 🛏€ 10 + € 1,30/pp Kurtaxe 🚰€ 1/80liter 🗑Ch🧹€ 1/2kWh WC🚽.
Surface: gravel. 🅾 01/01-31/12
Distance: 🚶800m 🚴2,8km ⊗on the spot.

| 🏕 S | Bad Langensalza ♨ | 10C4 |

Friederiken Therme, Böhmenstrasse. **GPS:** n51,11535 e10,64440.⬆️➡️

8 🛏€ 2, tourist tax € 1,20/pp 🚰€ 1 🗑Ch🧹(8x)€ 1/10h. **Surface:** metalled. 🅾 01/01-31/12
Distance: 🚶1km ⊗1km 🛒200m.
Remarks: Parking spa resort.

| 🏕 | Bad Liebenstein | 10B5 |

Stadthalle, Ruhlaerstrasse 2. **GPS:** n50,81698 e10,34963.
5 🛏overnight stay free. **Surface:** metalled.
Distance: 🚶100m ⊗100m 🛒200m.

| 🍴 S | Bad Liebenstein | 10B5 |

Villa Georg, Friedensallee 12. **GPS:** n50,81876 e10,35517.⬆️
🛏€ 11 🚰🗑Ch🧹 WCincluded. **Surface:** gravel. 🅾 01/01-31/12
Distance: 🚶500m ⊗on the spot 🛒800m.

| 🏕 S | Bad Lobenstein | 10D6 |

Ardesia Therme, Parkstrasse 8. **GPS:** n50,44981 e11,64294.⬆️➡️

11 🛏€ 2,50, free with use of therme 🚰 2 🍴Ch 🔌 € 0,50/kWh WC 🗑.
Surface: metalled. 🅾 01/01-31/12
Distance: 🚶200m 🛒on the spot 🚲200m 🚌on the spot.

Bad Salzungen 🌱🛒♨ 10B5
Werrastrasse. **GPS:** n50,81191 e10,23019.

15 🛏free. **Surface:** gravel. 🅾 01/01-31/12
Distance: 🚶500m 🛒250m 🚲500m.
Remarks: At health resort next to the first German Keltenbad, max. 3 days, service Hersfelderstrasse 4.

Bad Salzungen 🌱🛒♨ 10B5
Am Haad. **GPS:** n50,81867 e10,23376. ⬆➡.

40 🛏€ 3/day 🔌 € 2/day. **Surface:** grassy. 🅾 01/01-31/12
Distance: 🚶2km 🛒2km 🚲2km.
Remarks: Max. 3 days.

Bad Salzungen 🌱🛒♨ 10B5
Am Flössrasen, Flössrasen 1. **GPS:** n50,81541 e10,23748. ⬆.

10 🛏free 🔌 (8x)€ 1/kWh. **Surface:** asphalted/grassy. 🅾 01/01-31/12
Distance: 🚶500m 🛒400m 🚲400m.
Remarks: Max. 3 days.

Bad Salzungen 🌱🛒♨ 10B5
Werrastrasse. **GPS:** n50,81521 e10,22558. ⬆.
🚰🗑Ch.

Tourist information Bad Salzungen:
ℹ Tourist Information, Am Flössrasen 1. Health resort, several guided city walks available.

Breitungen 10B5
Hotel Jagdhaus Seeblick, Seeblick. **GPS:** n50,74250 e10,32306. ⬆➡.
30 🛏€ 5 🚰 🔌 WC. **Surface:** grassy. 🅾 01/01-31/12
Distance: 🚶2km 🏊1km 🛒on the spot 🚲2km.

Dankmarshausen 10B5
Am Werraufer, Bootsanleger. **GPS:** n50,92695 e10,02092.
3 🛏free.

Dankmarshausen 10B5
Gaststätte Rhädenblick, Blumenweg 2. **GPS:** n50,92760 e10,01093. ⬆.

10 🛏customers free 🚰🗑.
Distance: 🚶500m 🛒on the spot 🚲300m.

Dankmarshausen 10B5
Hotel Waldschlösschen, Waldstrasse 31. **GPS:** n50,92573 e10,00726. ⬆.
5 🛏free with a meal 🚰 🔌. **Surface:** grasstiles.
Distance: 🚶500m 🛒on the spot 🚲300m.

Eisenach 🌱🚡 10B4
Burg Wartburg. **GPS:** n50,96775 e10,30989.

10 🛏€ 5. **Surface:** metalled. 🅾 01/01-31/12
Remarks: Nearby castle Wartburg.

Eisenach 🌱🚡 10B4
Karl Marxstrasse. **GPS:** n50,97861 e10,32083. ⬆.

3 🛏9-17h max. € 6, free overnight stay.
Surface: gravel. 🅾 01/01-31/12
Distance: 🚶500m 🛒100m 🚲100m.

Eisenach 🌱🚡 10B4
Wohnmobile A. Waldhelm, Ringstrasse 27. **GPS:** n51,00194 e10,32667. ⬆.

6 🛏€6 ⚡€ 2,50 🚽Ch ⚡€ 2,50/day. **Surface:** grasstiles. 🅿 01/01-31/12
Distance: 🚶1km ⊗1km 🛒1km 🚌Shuttle bus.

4 🛏free. **Surface:** asphalted. 🅿 01/01-31/12
Distance: 🚶200m ⊗200m 🛒300m 🚌on the spot.
Remarks: Max. 48h, parking, southern Altstadt.

🚽	Eisfeld	10C6

Weihbach. **GPS:** n50,42370 e10,90480. ⬆.
3 🛏free. **Surface:** asphalted. 🅿 01/01-31/12
Distance: ⊗on the spot 🛒on the spot.

🏨🍴S	Eisfeld	10C6

Waldhotel Hubertus, Coburgerstrasse 501. **GPS:** n50,41649 e10,91312. ⬆➡.
20 🛏free, use of a meal desired ⚡€ 2 ⚡€ 2. **Surface:** asphalted/grassy.
🅿 01/01-31/12
Distance: 🚶3km ⊗on the spot 🛒2km 🚌on the spot.

🚽S	Erfurt 🌿⚓🍴	10D4

Domplatz, An den Graden. **GPS:** n50,97591 e11,02455.

🚗	Erfurt 🌿⚓🍴	10D4

Juri-Gagarin-Ring. **GPS:** n50,98111 e11,03472. ⬆.

2 🛏free. **Surface:** asphalted. 🅿 01/01-31/12
Distance: 🚶Old city centre 1km ⊗500m 🛒500m.
Remarks: Max. 48h, parking, eastern Altstadt.

🚗	Erfurt 🌿⚓🍴	10D4

P&R Parkplatz Messe, Gothaerstrasse. **GPS:** n50,95818 e10,98296. ⬆.

4 🛏€8 ⚡ ⚡(3x)€ 2. **Surface:** gravel. 🅿 01/01-31/12
Distance: 🚶on the spot ⊗on the spot 🛒on the spot 🚌on the spot.

🚽S	Erfurt 🌿⚓🍴	10D4

Am Saunabad Trautmann, Paulinzellerweg 46, Melchendorf. **GPS:** n50,95404 e11,06654.
15 🛏€ 4,50,with electricity € 6 ⚡🚽Ch ⚡WC 🗑€ 1,50 ▣ washing machine/dryer € 3,50. **Surface:** gravel. 🅿 01/01-31/12
Distance: 🛒300m.
Remarks: Discount on access sauna/wellness.

🚽S	Erfurt 🌿⚓🍴	10D4

P&R, Am Urbicher Kreuz. **GPS:** n50,94992 e11,09456. ➡.

4 🛏free. **Surface:** asphalted. 🅿 01/01-31/12
Distance: 🚶centre 4km 🚌Bus <23.00h.
Remarks: Parking exhibition ground.

🚗	Erfurt 🌿⚓🍴	10D4

P&R Parkplatz Thüringerhalle, Werner-Seelenbinderstrasse. **GPS:** n50,95771 e11,03605. ⬆.

15 🛏free ⚡🚽Ch. **Surface:** asphalted. 🅿 01/01-31/12
Distance: 🚶7km 🛒Total-shop 🚌Tram till 24am.
Remarks: Service at petrol station Total. A4 > Erfurt Ost > L1052.

🚗	Erfurt 🌿⚓🍴	10D4

Eichenstrasse. **GPS:** n50,97327 e11,02737. ➡.

10 🛏free. **Surface:** gravel. 🅿 01/01-31/12
Distance: 🚶2,6km 🚌Tram till 23am.
Remarks: Nearby B4, south edge of the city.

Tourist information Erfurt:
ℹ️ Erfurt-Card.Card gives for free entrance on among other things public transport and city museums, and discount on a lot of curiosities, guided tours, swimming pools, theater, souvenirs. 🎫 € 14,90.
ℹ️ Tourist Information, Benediktsplatz 1, www.erfurt-tourist-info.de.Medieval centre with a lot of curiosities.

DE

✐ Stadtführung, Tourist Information, Benediktsplatz 1.Guided tour around the historic city center. ⚑ 01/04-31/12 Mo-Fri 13h, Sa-Su 11h, 13h, 01/01-31/03 Sa-Su 11h, 13h. 🎫 € 5,50.

Friedrichroda ♒ — 10C5

Wohnmobilstellplatz Ortlepp, Bahnhofstrasse 32a. **GPS:** n50,85981 e10,57631. ⬆➡.

40 🏕 € 5,50, € 1,20/pp tourist tax 🚐 ⛽ Ch ⚡ (6x)€ 0,50/kWh WC. **Surface:** grassy. ⬛ 01/01-31/12
Distance: 🛒300m ⊗200m 🍺 on the spot.

Geschwenda — 10C5

Kickelhanchen. **GPS:** n50,73051 e10,81395. ⬆.
3 🏕 free. **Surface:** asphalted. ⬛ 01/01-31/12
Distance: 🛒1km ⊗on the spot 🍺700m.
Remarks: Parking at sports park.

Geschwenda — 10C5

Waldbad. **GPS:** n50,72395 e10,81752. ⬆.
5 🏕 free. **Surface:** metalled. ⬛ 01/01-31/12
Distance: 🛒1,5km.

Geschwenda — 10C5

Gasthof Diemelsee, Neue Sorge 38. **GPS:** n50,73138 e10,82000. ⬆.
5 🏕 free with a meal. **Surface:** gravel. ⬛ 01/01-31/12
Distance: ⊗on the spot 🍺600m.

Geschwenda — 10C5

Lippert Reisemobile, Dieselstrasse. **GPS:** n50,72169 e10,82832. ⬆.
3 🏕 free 🚐 ⛽ Ch 🚰 free. **Surface:** asphalted.
Remarks: Motorhome dealer.

Ichtershausen — 10C5

Autohof, Thöreyerstrasse. **GPS:** n50,88824 e10,93478. ⬆.

20 🏕 € 6,50/24h, first hour free 🚐 € 0,50 ⛽ Ch€ 0,50 WC. **Surface:** asphalted. ⬛ 01/01-31/12
Distance: 🛒4km ⊗on the spot 🍺Esso-shop.
Remarks: A4 Ausfahrt 44.

Ichtershausen — 10C5

Freizeitfahrzeuge Mobilease, Feldstrasse 1. **GPS:** n50,86907 e10,96563. ⬆.

5 🏕 € 5 🚐 ⛽ Ch ⚡ (4x)€ 2,50 WC during opening hours. **Surface:** gravel. ⬛ 01/01-31/12

Distance: 🛒3km ⊗500m 🥖bakery 500m.

Ilfeld — 10C3

Gasthof Brauner Hirsch, Dorfstrasse 42, Sophienhof. **GPS:** n51,63467 e10,79223. ⬆.

15 🏕 € 5 🚐 ⛽ Ch ⚡ (3x)€ 0,25/kWh WC 🚰 2 ⚓. **Surface:** metalled. ⬛ 01/01-31/12
Distance: ⊗on the spot 🚗3km 🦌on the spot 🍺on the spot.

Ilmenau — 10C5

Festhalle, Naumannstrasse. **GPS:** n50,68139 e10,90472. ⬆.

10 🏕 free 🚐 € 1/80liter ⛽ Ch. **Surface:** asphalted. ⬛ 01/01-31/12
Distance: 🛒500m ⊗500m 🍺500m.
Remarks: Max. 24h.

Lauscha ❄ — 10D5

Parkplatz Am Pappenheimer Berg, Im Steinachgrund. **GPS:** n50,48721 e11,17246.

🏕free. **Surface:** metalled. ⬛ 01/01-31/12
Distance: 🛒600m ⊗500m 🍺1km.
Remarks: Parking at ski-lift.

Lauscha ❄ — 10D5

Parkplatz Obermühle. **GPS:** n50,48026 e11,16795. ⬆.

10 🏕free. **Surface:** asphalted. ⬛ 01/01-31/12
Distance: 🛒300m ⊗100m 🍺1km.

Linda — 11A5

Knappmühle, Ortsstraße. **GPS:** n50,68473 e11,78324. ⬆.

10 🛏6 ⛽🔌 Ch 🚿 (6x)€ 1/kWh.
Surface: grassy/gravel. 🅿 01/03-31/10
Distance: 🚶300m 🚲5km 🚂3km 🛒5km.

10 🛏voluntary contribution ⛽€ 0,50 🔌Ch 🚿 (7x)€ 0,50/kWh. **Surface:** grasstiles.
Distance: 🚶300m 🚲300m.

🏕🅂	**Meiningen**	10C5

Grossmutterwiesen, Werrastrasse. **GPS:** n50,56172 e10,41266. ⬆➡

🏕🅂	**Nordhausen**	10C3

Am Badehaus, Grimmelallee 40. **GPS:** n51,50450 e10,78508. ⬆➡

5 🛏free. **Surface:** concrete. 🅿 01/01-31/12
Distance: 🚶on the spot 🚲200m 🛒100m.
Remarks: Service possible at Kläranlage.

2 🛏€5 ⛽€ 2 🚿€ 1 Ch€ 1 🔌€ 1 🛒€ 3. **Location:** Very simple.
Surface: metalled.
Distance: 🚶800m 🚲500m 🛒300m.

🏕🅂	**Meiningen**	10C5

Volkshausplatz, Landsbergerstrasse. **GPS:** n50,57427 e10,41369. ⬆➡

🏕🅂	**Nordhausen**	10C3

Am Kuhberg, Parkallee. **GPS:** n51,51502 e10,78492. ⬆

5 🛏free. **Surface:** metalled. 🅿 01/01-31/12
Distance: 🚶200m 🏊on the spot 🚲200m 🛒200m.
Remarks: Service possible at Kläranlage.

10 🛏free. **Surface:** asphalted. 🅿 01/01-31/12
Distance: 🚶2km 🚲on the spot 🛒500m.

🏕🅂	**Oberhof** 👭 ❄	10C5

🍴🅂	**Neustadt/Orla** 👭	11A5

Gaststätte & Pension Heinrichs-Ruhe, Heinrichsruhe 1, Rodaer Strasse. **GPS:** n50,75545 e11,75595. ⬆

Wohnmobilstellplatz Winkler, Zeallerstrasse. **GPS:** n50,70278 e10,72694. 150 🛏€ 9/24h ⛽🔌 Ch 🚿€ 2.
Surface: asphalted.
🅿 01/01-31/12
Distance: 🚶on the spot 🚲200m 🛒500m 🛝on the spot.

Tourist information Oberhof:
ℹ Oberhof-Information, Crawinkler strasse 2, www.oberhof.de.Small winter sports resort, 150 days of snow per year. Snow-telephone 036842 201 95.
👁 Rennsteiggarten Oberhof.Botanical garden. 🅿 01/05-30/09 9-18, 01/10-31/10 9-17h.
Ⓜ Thüringer Wintersportausstellung, Crawinkler strasse 1 / Oberer Hof.Winter sport museum. 🅿 10-13h, 14-17h.
◉ Rennsteig Thermen.Swimming pool complex. 🅿 daily 10-22h.

10 🛏free 🔌 (6x)€ 0,50/kWh. **Surface:** grassy/gravel. 🅿 01/01-31/12 ◉
Restaurant: Mo.
Distance: 🚶2,6km 🚴12,2km 🚲on the spot 🛒2,6km.

🍴🅂	**Reichenbach**	11A4

Heidlbergers Gastlichkeit und Freizeitsport, Rodaer Landstrasse. **GPS:** n50,86118 e11,87607. ⬆

🏕🅂	**Nimritz**	10D5

Wohnmobilstellplatz Nimritz, Ortsstrasse 29. **GPS:** n50,70079 e11,64858. ⬆ ➡.

DE

50 🛏€7, guests free ⚡1 🔲Ch 💧(15x)€ 2/day WC🗑€ 2/pp. **Surface:** concrete. 🅾 01/01-31/12
Distance: ⛽2km ⊗on the spot 🛒bakery 500m.

| 🚻S | Rudolstadt | 10D5 |

Freizeit- und Erlebnisbad Saalemaxx, Hugo-Trinckler-Straße 6. **GPS:** n50,70635 e11,31659.
9 🛏€7/24h ⚡€ 1/80liter 🔲€ 1 Ch 💧€ 0,50/kWh. **Surface:** gravel. 🅾 01/01-31/12
Distance: ⛽2km ➖100m.
Remarks: Discount at swimming pool.

| 🚻S | Ruhla | 10B4 |

Am Sportplatz, Burgstrasse. **GPS:** n50,91806 e10,39528.⬆.
🛏€ 6/24h. **Surface:** metalled.
Distance: ⛽300m ⊗300m 🛒400m.

| 🚻S | Saalfeld | 10D5 |

Reschwitzerstrasse, B281. **GPS:** n50,63720 e11,36751.⬆➡.

10 🛏free. **Surface:** gravel. 🅾 01/01-31/12
Distance: ⛽2,8km.
Remarks: Parking at swimming pool.

| 🅿S | Saalfeld | 10D5 |

Saalfelder Feengrotten, Feengrottenweg 2. **GPS:** n50,63468 e11,33982.⬆➡.

30 🛏free ⚡€ 3/5minutes 🔲€ 3 Ch 💧(6x)€ 0,50/kWh WC🗑. **Surface:** grassy. 🅾 01/01-31/12
Distance: ⛽2,3km ⊗on the spot 🛒bakery 500m ➖500m.

| 🍴S | Schleiz | 11A5 |

Spitzbergs Zollhaus, Burgkerstrasse 25. **GPS:** n50,55507 e11,73438.⬆➡.

5 🛏€ 5, free with a meal ⚡🔲Ch 💧(7x)€ 2/24h. **Surface:** gravel/metalled. 🅾 01/01-31/12 ⏺ Mo.
Distance: ⛽7km 🏊5,4km ⊗on the spot 🛒7km.

| 🚻S | Schleiz | 11A5 |

HEM-Großtankstelle, Saalburgerstrasse. **GPS:** n50,55717 e11,78706.⬆.

8 🛏€2 ⚡€ 1 🔲€ 1 Ch WC.
Surface: asphalted. 🅾 01/01-31/12
Distance: ⛽5km ⊗on the spot 🛒shop.
Remarks: Max. 24h, industrial area.

| 🏔 | Sitzendorf | 10D5 |

Sitzendorfer Porzellanmanufaktur, Hauptstrasse 26. **GPS:** n50,63174 e11,16788.⬆.
5 🛏free. **Surface:** asphalted. 🅾 01/01-31/12
Distance: ⛽on the spot ⊗200m 🛒200m.

| 🚻S | Sondershausen | 10C3 |

P7 zur Windleite, Hospitalstrasse. **GPS:** n51,37824 e10,86234.⬆➡.

5 🛏free ⚡€ 1 🔲Ch 💧(4x)€ 1/2h.
Surface: metalled. 🅾 01/01-31/12
Distance: ⛽2,5km ⊗500m 🛒100m.

| 🎡 | Sondershausen | 10C3 |

Freizeitpark Possen, Possen 1. **GPS:** n51,33800 e10,86265.

10 🛏€ 2/stay. **Surface:** metalled. 🅾 01/01-31/12
Distance: ⛽5km ⊗on the spot.

| 🚻S | Stadtlengsfeld | 10B5 |

Am Schwimmbad, Eisenacher Straße. **GPS:** n50,79065 e10,11373.

6 🛏 free ⚡ ✂. **Surface:** asphalted. 🅾 01/01-31/12
Distance: 🚶1,5km.

| 🏕 S | Tambach-Dietharz | 10C5 |

Festplatz, Burgstallstraße. **GPS:** n50,78902 e10,60897.
4 🛏 free ⚡ 🍴 Ch ✂. **Surface:** gravel. 🅾 01/01-31/12
Distance: 🚶on the spot ⊗on the spot.

| 🏕 S | Tambach-Dietharz | 10C5 |

Erlebnispark Lohmühle, Lohmühle 4. **GPS:** n50,81056 e10,62778.⬆.
40 🛏 € 6 + € 4/pp, dog € 2 ⚡ € 2,50 🍴 Ch ✂ WC.
Surface: grassy.
Distance: ⊗on the spot 🚆3km.
Remarks: Museum, Barefoot park.

| 🏕 S | Themar | 10C6 |

Am Hexenturm, Mauerstrasse. **GPS:** n50,50512 e10,61194.

5 🛏 free ⚡€ 1/50liter 🍴 Ch ✂€ 1/kWh. **Surface:** grasstiles. 🅾 01/01-31/12
Distance: 🚶100m ⊗300m 🚆400m.
Remarks: Along the river Werra.

| 🏕 S | Tiefenort | 10B5 |

Krayenberg, Heerstatte. **GPS:** n50,83444 e10,16306.⬆➡.

5 🛏 free ✂€ 2/day. **Surface:** metalled. 🅾 01/03-31/10
Distance: 🚶on the spot ⊗on the spot 🚆100m.

| 🏕 S | Treffurt | 10B4 |

Unter den Linden. **GPS:** n51,13398 e10,23659.⬆➡.

20 🛏 free ⚡€ 0,50 🍴 Ch ✂(4x)€ 0,50/kWh. **Surface:** grasstiles/grassy.
🅾 01/01-31/12 🔲 15/07-31/07.
Distance: 🚶300m ⚓on the spot ⊗50m 🚆500m.
Remarks: Along the river, water closed during wintertime.

Tourist information Treffurt:
ℹ Small town with half-timbered houses and medival castle Normannstein.

Hermann Brill-Platz. **GPS:** n50,98501 e11,31701.⬆➡.

| 🏕 | Weimar | 10D4 |

20 🛏 € 4 (8-18h), overnight stay free. **Surface:** metalled. 🅾 01/01-31/12
Distance: 🚶Weimar centre 1,2km ⊗on the spot 🚆500m.

| 🍴 S | Weimar | 10D4 |

Saunabad Weimar, In der Buttergrube 11, Legefeld. **GPS:** n50,93573 e11,28678.
⬆.

10 🛏 € 5 ⚡ ✂(10x)included. **Surface:** metalled. 🅾 01/01-31/12
Distance: 🚶Weimar centre 6km.
Remarks: Use of sauna obligatory.

| 🍴 S | Zella-Mehlis | 10C5 |

Toschis Station, An der Quelle 5. **GPS:** n50,64375 e10,68436.⬆.

20 🛏 € 5 ⚡ 🍴 Ch ✂(20x) 📶. **Surface:** grassy/gravel. 🅾 01/01-31/12
Distance: ⊗on the spot 🚆300m.
Remarks: Check in at reception.

| 🏕 S | Zeulenroda | 11A5 |

Badewelt Waikiki, Am Birkenwege 1. **GPS:** n50,66543 e11,99355.
6 🛏 free ⚡ 🍴 Ch ✂ water and electricity € 10/day. **Surface:** metalled.
🅾 01/01-31/12

Baden Württemberg

| 🏕 S | Aalen | 18A4 |

Hirschbach, Hirschbachstrasse 68. **GPS:** n48,84524 e10,10712.⬆➡.

10 🛏 free ⚡€ 1/80liter 🍴 Ch. **Surface:** asphalted. 🅾 01/01-31/12
Distance: 🚶800m ⊗100m 🚌200m.
Remarks: At swimming pool, max. 3 days.

DE

Aalen 18A4

Limes-Thermen, P1, Osterbucher Steige. **GPS**: n48,82047 e10,07918. ⬆.

12 🛏 free. **Surface**: metalled. 🔲 01/01-31/12
Distance: ✕100m.

Achern 17A5

Wohnmobilstellplatz Achern, Kapellenstrasse/Badstrasse. **GPS**: n48,62436 e8,07359. ⬆.

12 🛏 € 4 🔌€ 1/100liter 🍴 Ch 🔧(12x)€ 1/16h. 🏠 **Location**: Urban, quit.
Surface: gravel/metalled. 🔲 01/01-31/12
Distance: 500m 4,8km 650m on the spot on the spot.

Albstadt 17C5

Badkap. GPS: n48,21402 e8,97844. ⬆.

25 🛏 free 🔌 🍴Chfree 🔧€ 2,50/day.
Surface: metalled.
🔲 01/01-31/12
Distance: 1km ✕200m 500m.
Remarks: Parking swimming and sauna centre, max. 3 days.

Tourist information Albstadt:
ℹ Tourist Information, Marktstrasse 35, www.albstadt.de.Mountain village with half-timbered houses, known for its textile industry.

Allensbach 24C1

Campingplatz Himmelreich, Strandweg 34. **GPS**: n47,71038 e9,08044. ⬆➡.

6 🛏 € 12,50, tourist tax € 1,50 🔌 🍴 Ch 🔧(6x)€ 0,50/kWh WC 🗑€ 0,90
🗑€ 2 🧺. **Surface**: grasstiles/metalled. 🔲 15/03-15/10
Distance: 800m on the spot ✕on the spot 800m 300m.

Allensbach 24C1

Gaststätte Zum Riesenberg, Professor-Schmider-strasse 10. **GPS**: n47,71544 e9,07629.
🔌.

Allensbach 24C1

Landgasthaus Mindelsee, Gemeinmärk 7. **GPS**: n47,74279 e9,04411. ⬆.

15 🛏 € 8. **Surface**: metalled. 🔲 01/01-31/12 🔴 Tue.
Distance: 5km ✕on the spot.
Remarks: Max. 1 night.

Amtzell 24D1

Wohnmobilanlage Büchelweisen, Haus 3. **GPS**: n47,70871 e9,76684. ⬆➡.

17 🛏 € 9 🔌 🍴 Ch 🔧(24x) 🗑€ 1,50/pp. **Surface**: grasstiles. 🔲 01/01-31/12
Distance: 1,5km 1km 1km on the spot 1,5km.
Remarks: Bread-service.

Aspach 17C3

Wanderparkplatz Fautenhau, Im Fautenhau, Hohrot. **GPS**: n48,97823 e9,39483. ⬆.

5 🛏 free. **Surface**: metalled. 🔲 01/01-31/12
Remarks: Max. 1 night.

Aspach 17C3

Wanderparkplatz Heiligental, Heiligentalstrasse, Rietenau. **GPS**: n48,99158 e9,40519. ⬆.
5 🛏 free. **Surface**: asphalted/grassy. 🔲 01/01-31/12
Remarks: Max. 1 night.

Aspach 17C3

Wanderparkplatz Kelter, Kelterstrasse, Allmersbach. **GPS**: n48,99543 e9,39006. ⬆.

DE

5 🛏free. **Surface:** asphalted. 🅿 01/01-31/12
Remarks: Max. 1 night.

| 🛈 | Aspach | 17C3 |

Wanderparkplatz Lapidarium, Ortsstrasse, Kleinaspach. **GPS:** n48,99738 e9,35711.⬆.
5 🛏free. 🅿 01/01-31/12
Distance: 🛒on the spot ⊗1km 🍴1,5km.
Remarks: Max. 1 night.

| 🛈 | Aulendorf | 17D6 |

Schwaben-Therme, Ebisweilerstrasse 5. **GPS:** n47,95797 e9,63728.➡.

20 🛏free. **Surface:** metalled. 🅿 01/01-31/12
Distance: 🛒500m ⊗on the spot 🍴500m.
Remarks: Parking swimming pool, max. 2 nights.

| 🛏 S | Backnang | 17D4 |

Gartenstrasse. **GPS:** n48,95041 e9,45281.⬆.

4 🛏free ⛽€ 1/90liter 🗑Ch. **Surface:** gravel. 🅿 01/01-31/12

| 🛏 S | Bad Bellingen 🛈 | 24A1 |

Balinea Thermen, Badstrasse 14. **GPS:** n47,72963 e7,55233.⬆.

31 🛏€ 10 + € 1,45-2,25 tourist tax ⛽€ 1/80liter 🗑Ch 🔌(24x)€ 1/kWh
WC 🚽€ 1,50. 🚲 **Location:** Urban, noisy. **Surface:** asphalted/metalled. 🅿
01/01-31/12
Distance: 🛒500m 🚴5,5km ⊗on the spot 🍴on the spot.

| 🛏 S | Bad Buchau | 17D6 |

Seegasse. **GPS:** n48,06801 e9,60977.

17 🛏€ 7,50 ⛽€ 1/80liter 🗑Ch 🔌(17x)€ 0,50/kWh. **Surface:** metalled.
🅿 01/01-31/12
Distance: 🛒500m.
Remarks: Adelindis Therme 300m.

| 🛏 S | Bad Buchau | 17D6 |

Am Freibad, Friedhofstrasse. **GPS:** n48,06292 e9,61714.⬆.

10 🛏€ 6 + € 1,50/pp tourist tax 🔌included. **Surface:** asphalted. 🅿 01/01-31/12
Distance: 🛒700m.

| 🛏 S | Bad Buchau | 17D6 |

Adelindis Therme, Am Kurpark. **GPS:** n48,06865 e9,60653.⬆.

21 🛏€ 9,50 ⛽€ 1/80liter 🗑Ch 🔌(21x)€ 0,50/kWh. **Surface:** metalled.
🅿 01/01-31/12
Distance: 🛒500m.

| 🛈 S | Bad Buchau | 17D6 |

Federseemuseum. **GPS:** n48,07051 e9,60949.

12 🛏€ 9,50 🔌included WC 🚽. **Surface:** asphalted. 🅿 01/01-31/12
Distance: 🛒800m.
Remarks: Adelindis Therme 500m.

| 🛏 S | Bad Ditzenbach 🛈 | 17D4 |

Vinzenz Therme, Badstraße 20. **GPS:** n48,59003 e9,70553.
10 🛏€ 5 ⛽🗑Ch 🔌. **Surface:** asphalted. 🅿 01/01-31/12

| 🛏 S | Bad Dürrheim | 17B6 |

Reisemobilhafen Bad Dürrheim, Huberstraße 34/2. **GPS:** n48,01204 e8,53506.
⬆➡.

DE

300 ⌘€8 ⌁€ 1/100liter ⌘Ch ✎WC€ 2 ⌐. **Surface:** gravel. ❑ 01/01-31/12
Distance: ⊗on the spot.
Remarks: Special health arrangement possible, bread service. Follow Solemar Parkplatz.

16 ⌘€8 + €2/pp tourist tax ⌁⌘Ch ✎(16x)WC ⌐included ▣€ 3 ⌁
⌁.⚑ **Location:** Rural, very simple, noisy. **Surface:** metalled/sand. ❑ 01/01-31/12
Distance: ⚒on the spot ⚓17km ⊗500m ⚏100m ⇌on the spot ⚴on the spot ⚱on the spot.

Ⓤ Ⓢ	Bad Herrenalb ⚑⚏⚓	17B4

Therme Siebentäler, Schweizer Wiese. **GPS:** n48,80334 e8,44067. ⬆.

⚏ Ⓢ	Bad Mergentheim	17D2

Festplatz beim Freibad, Erlenbachweg. **GPS:** n49,49194 e9,79167. ⬆.

10 ⌘€4,10 + €2,50/pp ⌁€ 1 ⌘€ 1 Ch€ 1 ✎(4x)€ 1.
Location: Rural.
Surface: asphalted.
❑ 01/01-31/12
Distance: ⚒500m ⊗100m ⚏200m ⇌200m ⚴on the spot ⚱on the spot.
Remarks: Max. 2 nights, discount on access terme.

Tourist information Bad Herrenalb:
ℹ Tourismusbüro, Bahnhofsplatz 1, www.bad-herrenalb.de.Health resort.
⚐ Quellenerlebnispfad, Kurpark Herrenalb.Hiking trails past 60 fountains.

50 ⌘€5 ⌁€ 1/10minutes ⌘Ch ✎(16x)€ 1/20h. **Surface:** metalled. ❑ 01/01-31/12
Distance: ⚒1,5km ⊗200m ⚏2km ⇌100m.
Remarks: Check in at restaurant tennispark.

⚏ Ⓢ	Bad Rappenau ⚓	17C3

Weinbrennerstrasse. **GPS:** n49,23517 e9,11396. ⬆➡.

Ⓒ Ⓢ	Bad Krozingen ⚑⚓	17A6

Vita Classica Therme - Bad Krozingen

mail@bad-krozingen.info - www.bad-krozingen.info

Thermalbad
Saunaparadies
Wellness

Vita Classica Therme, Thürachstraße. **GPS:** n47,91763 e7,68821. ⬆➡.
75 ⌘€ 10, from 7th night € 8,50 ⌁⌘Ch included ✎h € 2,50/4 Amp, € 3,50/16Amp WC⌐€ 3 ▣⌁.⚑ **Location:** Rural, comfortable. **Surface:** asphalted/metalled. ❑ 01/01-31/12
Distance: ⚒500m ⚓2km ⊗50m ▣1km ⚱1km ⇌500m.
Remarks: Bread-service, trailer € 5.

Ⓒ Ⓢ	Bad Liebenzell ⚑⚓	17B4

Campingpark Bad Liebenzell, Pforzheimer strasse 34. **GPS:** n48,77850 e8,73120. ⬆.

30 ⌘€ 3/pp, child € 2 ⌁€ 1/80liter ⌘Ch ✎(16x)€ 1/4h. **Location:** Comfortable. **Surface:** metalled. ❑ 01/01-31/12
Distance: ⚒1km ⊗50m ⚏1km.
Remarks: Therme 400m.

⛰ Ⓢ	Bad Rappenau ⚓	17C3

Autohof Bad Rappenau, A6, Wilhelm-Hauff-Straße 43, Fürfeld. **GPS:** n49,21043 e9,06927. ⬆.
15 ⌘€ 10, free for clients ⌁⌘Ch▣. **Location:** Highway, very simple.
Surface: metalled. ❑ 01/01-31/12
Distance: ⚓300m ⊗on the spot ⚏on the spot.
Remarks: Breakfast-servic.

⚏ Ⓢ	Bad Säckingen ⚓	24A1

Reisemobilplatz Am Rheinufer, Ausstrasse. **GPS:** n47,54903 e7,94765. ⬆➡.

30 🔲€ 10/24h 🚰 € 0,50/100liter 🔲€ 0,20 Ch 🔌 WC.
Surface: gravel.
🔲 01/01-31/12 🔲 beginning Mar, end Oct.
Distance: 🚶300m 🚲6km 🚉50m 🚌on the spot.
Remarks: Several offers, i.e. free public transport.

Tourist information Bad Säckingen:
ℹ️ Kurverwaltung GmbH, Waldshuter Stasse 20, www.bad-saeckingen.
de.'Trumpet city' with colourfull centre, health resort.
Ⓜ️ TrompeterSchloß.Trumpeting museum. 🔲 Tue, Thu, Su 14-17h.
🔪 Nachtwächterführungen.Evening tour guided by night watch in historical clothing and lantern. Information and booking: Kurverwaltung. 🔲 € 2.

🔲S	Bad Saulgau	17D6

GolfPark Bad Saulgau, Koppelweg 103. **GPS:** n47,97928 e9,48623.⬆️
30 🔲€ 10, shady pitch € 26, golfers free 🚰 Ch 🔌 📶. **Surface:** metalled.
🔲 01/03-31/10
Distance: 🚶4km ⊗on the spot 🚉4km.

🔲S	Bad Saulgau	17D6

Wohnmobilstellplatz Sonnenhof-Therme, Am Schönen Moos. **GPS:** n48,01703 e9,48838.⬆️

69 🔲€ 8, 1/11-30/4 € 9 🚰 € 0,50/80liter 🔲Ch € 0,50 🔌 (69x)included, 16Amp 🔲. **Surface:** metalled. 🔲 01/01-31/12
Distance: 🚶on the spot ⊗on the spot 🚉on the spot.
Remarks: Discount on access terme.

🔲S	Bad Schönborn ♨	17B3

Reisemobilhafen WellMobilPark, Kraichgaustraße 16. **GPS:** n49,21839 e8,67144.⬆️➡️

90 🔲€ 8, >10m € 12 🚰 € 1/80liter 🔲Ch 🔌 (112x)€ 0,50/kWh 🔲€ 1,50
🔲 📶. **Location:** Rural, luxurious. **Surface:** metalled. 🔲 01/01-31/12
Distance: 🚶500m ⊗on the spot 🚉1km 🚌200m.
Remarks: Bread-service, swimming pool.

🔲S	Bad Schussenried	17D6

Am Zellersee, Zellerseeweg. **GPS:** n48,00160 e9,64724.⬆️

10 🔲€ 7 + € 1,20/pp tourist tax 🚰 🔲Ch 🔌. **Surface:** metalled. 🔲
01/01-31/12
Distance: 🔲on the spot.

🔲S	Bad Schussenried	17D6

Bierkrugmuseum, Wilhelm Schussenstrasse 12. **GPS:** n48,00325 e9,65902.⬆️

30 🔲free 🚰 🔲Ch 🔌 € 5, reduction for guests WC.
Surface: metalled.
🔲 01/01-31/12
Distance: 🚶on the spot ⊗150m.
Remarks: Brewery and brewery museum.

Tourist information Bad Schussenried:
ℹ️ Tourist Info, Klosterhof 5, www.bad-schussenried.de.Holiday resort and health resort.
Ⓜ️ Bierkrugmuseum.Collection of beer jugs. 🔲 Tue-Su 10-17h.
Ⓜ️ Kloster Schussenried.History of the monastry. 🔲 Easter-Oct 13.30-17.30h.

🔲S	Bad Teinach 🏰♨	17B4

Zavelsteiner strasse. **GPS:** n48,68890 e8,69440.

20 🔲free. **Location:** Rural. **Surface:** asphalted. 🔲 01/01-31/12
Distance: 🚶50m ⊗100m 🚉100m 🚌on the spot 🚲on the spot 🧍on the spot.
Remarks: Parking swimming pool, max. 24h.

🔲S	Bad Urach 🏕🏰♨❄♨	17C5

Wohnmobilstellplatz Bad Urach, Bäderstrasse. **GPS:** n48,50060 e9,37713.⬆️

26 🔲€ 8 🚰 € 0,50 🔲€ 0,50 Ch 🔌 included. **Surface:** asphalted. 🔲
01/01-31/12

DE

Distance: 🚶on the spot 🚲5km ⊗200m 🛒800m 🚮200m ⚒10km 🚊10km.

| 🚐 | **Bad Waldsee** ⚓ | 17D6 |

Friedhofstrasse. **GPS:** n47,91806 e9,75727.
4 🚐. **Surface:** metalled. 🅾 01/01-31/12
Remarks: Parking at cemetery.

| 🚐 | **Bad Waldsee** ⚓ | 17D6 |

Strandbad. **GPS:** n47,92464 e9,75502.
🚐. 🅾 01/01-31/12

| 🚿S | **Bad Waldsee** ⚓ | 17D6 |

Bauernhof Lott, Mattenhaus 4. **GPS:** n47,95113 e9,75838.

10 🚐€ 9, 2 pers.incl 🚰 🚽Ch 🔌(10x)€ 0,40/kWh WC 🚿▣€ 4. 🅾
01/03-30/11
Distance: 🚶3,5km 🏊3km 🚲3km ⊗200m 🛒3km.
Remarks: Bread-service. B30, dir Ulm, ± 3 left, after Gasthof.

| 🚿S | **Bad Waldsee** ⚓ | 17D6 |

Waldsee-Therme, Unterurbacher weg. **GPS:** n47,91441 e9,76047. ⬆➡

45 🚐€ 4 🚰 1 🚽 1 Ch 🔌€ 0,50/kWh. **Surface:** metalled. 🅾 01/01-
31/12
Distance: 🚶1km 🏊1km 🚲1km ⊗500m 🛒1km 🚮500m.
Remarks: Bread-service.

| 🚿S | **Bad Wildbad** 🏰⚓ | 17B4 |

Kernerstrasse. **GPS:** n48,74132 e8,54740. ⬆.

16 🚐€ 5, tourist tax € 2,90/pp 🚰€ 1/60liter 🚽Ch 🔌(16x)€ 2/8h. 🚆
Location: Rural, very simple, noisy.
Surface: asphalted. 🅾 01/01-31/12
Distance: 🚶500m ⊗500m 🛒300m 🚮on the spot 🚲on the spot 🚶on the spot.
Remarks: Max. 3 days.

| 🚐 | **Bad Wimpfen** ⚓ | 17C3 |

Am alter Bahnhof, Carl Ulrichstrasse 1. **GPS:** n49,22942 e9,16745. ⬆.

10 🚐€ 2, overnight stay free. **Location:** Urban. **Surface:** gravel. 🅾 01/01-
31/12
Distance: ⊗400m 🚲400m 🚮50m 🚲on the spot.

| 🚿S | **Bad Wimpfen** ⚓ | 17C3 |

An der Alten Saline 2. **GPS:** n49,23604 e9,15630. ⬆.

8 🚐€ 8, tourist tax excl 🚰€ 1/70liter 🚽Ch 🔌(8x)€ 1/12h WC. **Location:**
Rural, comfortable, quit. **Surface:** asphalted. 🅾 01/01-31/12
Distance: 🚶800m.
Remarks: Parking at health resort.

| 🚿S | **Bad Wurzach** ⚓ | 17D6 |

Wohnmobilstellplatz Vitalium, Riedhalde. **GPS:** n47,91437 e9,90363. ⬆➡

17 🚐€ 5,50, € 1,50/pp tourist tax 🚰€ 0,50 🚽€ 0,50 Ch 🔌WC 🚿.
Surface: asphalted. 🅾 01/01-31/12
Distance: 🚶500m ⊗300m 🛒500m.

| 🚿S | **Baden-Baden** ⚓ | 17B4 |

Wohnmobilparkplatz, Hubertusstraße 2, Badenscheunern. **GPS:** n48,78193
e8,20388. ⬆➡

28 🚐€ 8 🚰€ 1/100liter 🚽Ch 🔌(28x)€ 0,50/kWh. 🚆 **Location:** Urban,
comfortable, noisy. **Surface:** metalled. 🅾 01/01-31/12
Distance: 🚶Baden-Baden 4km 🚃1km ⊗100m 🛒150m 🚮on the spot
🚲on the spot 🚶on the spot.
Remarks: Max. 4 days, terrain with video surveillance.

| 🚿S | **Baiersbronn** ⚓ | 17B5 |

Schelklewiesen, Neumühleweg/Lochweg. **GPS:** n48,51016 e8,37272. ⬆➡

DE

15 € 6 € 1/80liter Ch (12x)€ 0,50/kWh. **Location:** Rural, quit. **Surface:** metalled. 01/01-31/12
Distance: 300m on the spot 100m 200m on the spot on the spot.

Balingen 17C5

Wohnmobilstellplatz an der Eyach, Heinzlerstrasse. **GPS**: n48,27028 e8,85222.

10 free € 1 Ch (8x)€ 0,50/kWh. **Surface:** asphalted. 01/01-31/12
Distance: on the spot 500m 300m 300m.
Remarks: Max. 4 days.

Benningen am Neckar 17C4

Parkplatz Gemeindehalle, Max - Eyth Strasse. **GPS**: n48,94574 e9,23363.

4 free. **Surface:** metalled. 01/01-31/12
Distance: on the spot 50m 1km.

Bernau im Schwarzwald 24A1

Sportzentrum Spitzenberg, Sportplatzstraße. **GPS**: n47,80614 e8,02803.

10 summer free € 3,50 + € 3,50/pp Ch WC included cold shower. **Surface:** grassy/gravel. 01/01-31/12
Distance: 500m 1km 500m.
Remarks: Tourist tax € 1,80 p p.

Besigheim 17C3

Wohnmobilstellplatz bei der Minigolfanlage, Auf dem Kies 32. **GPS**: n48,99771 e9,14863.

6 € 5 € 1/80liter Ch (6x)€ 0,50/kWh. **Location:** Rural, comfortable, quit. **Surface:** metalled. 01/01-31/12
Distance: 500m 500m 200m 500m 200m on the spot on the spot.
Remarks: After 2 nights € 20/night.

Tourist information Besigheim:
Stadtverwaltung, Marktplatz 12, www.besigheim.de.

Beuron 17C6

Kloster Beuron, Abteistraße. **GPS**: n48,05306 e8,96704.

± 4 free. **Surface:** gravel. 01/01-31/12
Remarks: Parking monastery.

Beuron 17C6

Besi-Kanu-Sport, Bahnhofstrasse 29. **GPS**: n48,08597 e9,09559.

10 € 5 Ch WC included. **Surface:** gravel.
Distance: 1km 200m 5km.
Remarks: Canoe rental.

Biberach/Riss 17D6

Rissstrasse. **GPS**: n48,10401 e9,79582.

10 free Ch free. **Surface:** asphalted. 01/01-31/12 service: 01/11-28/02.
Distance: 700m.
Remarks: Max. 3 days.

Bietigheim-Bissingen 17C4

Wohnmobilstellplatz an der Enz, Mühlwiesenstrasse. **GPS**: n48,96110 e9,13329.

DE

9 ⌧€5 🛢€ 0,50/80liter 🗑Ch ✂ (8x)€ 0,50/kWh. **Location:** Urban.
Surface: metalled. ⬛ 01/01-31/12
Distance: 🚶200m ⛱1km 🚲1km ⊗100m 🚆100m 🚌100m.
Remarks: Max. 4 days, check in at Lama Bar.
Tourist information Bietigheim-Bissingen:
ℹ️ Tourist-Information, Marktplatz 10, www.bietigheim-bissingen.de.

🛏S | **Blaubeuren** | 17D5
Parkplatz P6, Dodelweg. **GPS:** n48,41351 e9,79102. ➡️

20 ⌧€5 🛢€ 1/5minutes 🗑Ch€ 1.
Surface: metalled. ⬛ 01/01-31/12
Distance: 🚶1km ⊗1km 🚆1km 🚌800m.
Remarks: Parking swimming pool, max. 2 days.

🛏S | **Blumberg** | 17B6
P1, Festplatz, Oberes Ried. **GPS:** n47,83943 e8,54226. ⬆️➡️

48 ⌧€7,50 🛢🗑Ch ✂ (36x)€ 1. **Surface:** gravel/metalled. ⬛ 01/01-31/12
Distance: 🚶800m 🚆80m.

🛏S | **Blumberg** | 17B6
P2, Parkplatz Bahnhof Zollhaus, Achdorf. **GPS:** n47,83767 e8,55777. ⬆️

10 ⌧€7,50 🛢. **Surface:** gravel. ⬛ 01/01-31/12
Distance: 🚶1,5km.

🛏S | **Blumberg** | 17B6
P3, Achdorfer Tal. GPS: n47,83528 e8,49833. ⬆️

10 ⌧€7,50 🛢€ 1 🗑Ch ✂€ 1, winter € 1,50. **Surface:** gravel. ⬛
01/01-31/12
Distance: 🚶4km.
Remarks: Caution key € 10 (connection electricity).

🛏S | **Böblingen** | 17C4
Parkplatz an der Sporthalle, Rudolf-Diesel-strasse/Stetner strasse. **GPS:** n48,67693 e9,01651. ⬆️

3 ⌧free 🛢🗑Chfree. **Surface:** metalled. ⬛ 01/05-30/10
Distance: 🚶1km 🚲7km ⊗500m 🚆250m 🚌100m.
Remarks: Max. 3 nights.

🛏S | **Bonndorf** | 17B6
Wohnmobilstellplatz Holzschlag, Schulstrasse/Bonndorfer Strasse, Bonndorf-Holzschlag. **GPS:** n47,84970 e8,26784. 🚶.
⌧€5 🛢🗑Ch.

🛏S | **Bönnigheim** | 17C3
Mineralfreibad Bönnigheim, Bachstrasse 40. **GPS:** n49,03910 e9,08439. ⬆️

4 ⌧free 🛢🗑. **Location:** Rural. **Surface:** grasstiles/metalled. ⬛ 01/01-31/12
Distance: 🚶500m ⊗500m 🚆1km.
Remarks: Caution key water € 10.

🍴S | **Bopfingen** | 18A4
Gasthof zum Bären, Nördlinger strasse 3. **GPS:** n48,85715 e10,35508. ⬆️

⌧€6 🛢€ 1 🗑€ 1 Ch ✂€ 1. **Surface:** asphalted. ⬛ 01/01-31/12
Distance: 🚶on the spot 🚲16km ⊗on the spot 🚆100m.

Boxberg 17D2

Gasthof Forellenhof Hagenmühle, Uiffinger strasse 74. **GPS:** n49,48710 e9,61299. ⬆➡.

20 ☕5 ⬅ (8x)€ 2,50. **Surface:** grassy/gravel. ☐ 01/01-31/12
Distance: 🚶2km ⊗on the spot 🚲1km 🚉200m.

Brackenheim 17C3

Weingut und Besenwirtschaft 'Zum Alten Pflug', Seebergweg. **GPS:** n49,10261 e9,04994. ⬆.

3 ☕€ 6, free for clients ⬅ 🗑 Ch ✎ (3x)€ 2 WC 🕳€ 2. **Surface:** metalled. ☐ 01/01-31/12
Distance: 🚶3km 🚲3km.
Remarks: Sunday on demand.

Brackenheim 17C3

Weingut Winkler, Stockheimer strasse 13. **GPS:** n49,08001 e9,06270. ⬆.

5 ☕€ 5 ⬅ 🗑 ✎ included. **Location:** Rural. **Surface:** grassy/metalled. ☐ 01/01-31/12
Distance: 🚶on the spot ⛰10km ⛵10km ⊗300m 🚲1km 🚉300m.

Breisach/Rhein 16D4

Wohnmobil-Parkplatz, Josef-Buebstrasse. **GPS:** n49,02944 e7,57576. ⬆➡.

80 ☕free 8-20h, € 6/night, 2 nights € 10, 3 nights € 13, winter free ⬅€ 1/100liter 🗑€ 1 Ch€ 1. 🏠 **Location:** Urban. **Surface:** asphalted. ☐ 01/01-31/12 ◐ Other parking in case of festivities.
Distance: 🚶300m ⛰on the spot 🚌on the spot ⊗300m 🚲1,5km.
Remarks: Ground of wine festival, bread-service.

Breisach/Rhein 16D4

Restaurant Am Rhein, Hafenstrasse 11. **GPS:** n49,04292 e7,57378. ⬆.

5 ☕free. **Location:** Very simple.
Surface: metalled. ☐ 01/01-31/12
Distance: 🚶2km ⊗on the spot 🚲500m.
Remarks: Guests only.

Tourist information Breisach/Rhein:
ℹ Tourist Information, Marktplatz 16, www.breisach.de.City wall and towers.
⏰ Tue-Su.
Ⓜ Museum für Stadtgeschichte, Rheintor.Town history. 🎫 free.
☀ Weinfest Kaiserstuhl Tuniberg.Wine festivals. ☐ end Aug.

Bretten 17B3

Reisemobil-Stellplatz Bretten, Willi-Hesselbacher-Weg. **GPS:** n49,02980 e8,71914.
4 ☕free ⬅€ 1/100liter ✎€ 1/10h. **Surface:** metalled.
Distance: 🚶city centre 1,5km.
Remarks: Max. 2 days.

Bruchsal 17B3

Giesgrabenweg. **GPS:** n49,13227 e8,58981. ⬆.

2 ☕free. **Location:** Urban, central.
Surface: metalled. ☐ 01/01-31/12
Distance: 🚶1km ⛵4km ⊗100m 🚲1km 🚌on the spot.
Remarks: At sports centre, max. 48h.

Bruchsal 17B3

Autohaus Konrad, Murgstrasse 9-13, Gewerbegebiet Stegwiesen. **GPS:** n49,13700 e8,59437. ⬆.

3 ☕free ⬅€ 1/80liter 🗑Ch ✎ (4x) WC 🕳. **Location:** Urban. **Surface:** metalled. ☐ 01/01-31/12
Distance: 🚶2km ⛵3km ⊗2km 🚲200m 🚌300m.
Remarks: Max. 3 nights, service use during shop opening hours. Follow signs TÜV.

Buchen (Odenwald) 17C2

Wohnmobilhafen Morretal, Mühltalstraße. **GPS:** n49,52888 e9,31020.
12 ☕€ 5/24h, 3 days € 20 ⬅€ 1/100liter 🗑Ch ✎€ 1/kWh WC 🕳 📶€ 1/h. **Surface:** metalled. ☐ 01/01-31/12
Remarks: Use sanitary only during opening hours swimming pool.

DE

Buchenbach 17A6
Wanglerhof, Vogtweg 1. **GPS:** n47,96820 e7,99269. ⬆.

10 🍴€ 10 + € 1,20/pp tourist tax 🚰🔌Chincluded ⚡€ 2/day. 🚿
Location: Rural. **Surface:** grassy. 🅾 01/01-31/12
Distance: 🚶1km ⊗100m 🚲1km.

Bühl 17A4
Wohnmobilstellplatz am Schwarzwaldbad, Ludwig-Jahn-strasse 8. **GPS:** n48,68862 e8,12995. ⬆➡.

50 🍴€ 5 🚰€ 2/100liter 🔌€ 2 Ch ♻.🏠 **Location:** Urban, noisy. **Surface:** metalled. 🅾 01/01-31/12
Distance: 🚶1km 🚴6km 🚲500m 🚲1km 🚶on the spot 🚶on the spot.
Remarks: Bread-service.

Calw 17B4
Wohnmobilstellplatz Am Alten Bahnhof, Bahnhofstrasse. **GPS:** n48,70592 e8,73808. ⬆➡.

6 🍴free 🚰€ 1/80liter 🔌€ 1 Ch€ 1 ⚡(4x)€ 0,50/kWh. **Location:** Rural, noisy. **Surface:** asphalted. 🅾 01/01-31/12
Distance: 🚶1km 🚲100m 🚲200m 🚶on the spot 🚶on the spot.

Cleebronn/Tripsdrill 17C3

Erlebnispark Tripsdrill - Cleebronn

info@tripsdrill.de - www.tripsdrill.de
Located near amusement park
Located in a quit location
BBQ area

Erlebnispark Tripsdrill. GPS: n49,03102 e9,05096. ⬆➡.
100 🍴free.
Location: Rural, isolated, quit.
Surface: grassy.
🅾 23/03/2013-03/11/2013
Distance: 🚶1km ⊗on the spot 🚲3km 🚲400m.
Remarks: Max. 3 days.
Tourist information Cleebronn/Tripsdrill:
🌐 Erlebnispark Tripsdrill.Amusement park. 🅾 9-18h.

Crailsheim 17D3
Autohof Euro Rastpark, Marco-Polo-Straße 1, Satteldorf. **GPS:** n49,18146 e10,06889.
10 🍴€ 5, free with a meal 🚰🔌. **Surface:** metalled. 🅾 01/01-31/12
Distance: 🚲600m ⊗on the spot.

Dettenheim 17B3
Kartbahn Liedolsheim, Kartbahnring 1. **GPS:** n49,14326 e8,43118.

20 🍴free 🚰🔌Ch ⚡(8x)€ 3 WC 🔌€ 2,50. **Location:** Rural, isolated.
Surface: grassy/metalled. 🅾 01/01-31/12
Distance: 🚶2km 🚴2km 🚲2km ⊗on the spot 🚲5km.
Remarks: Parking at Karting.

Dettingen 17D4
Wanner + Freizeit GmbH, Lindengarten. **GPS:** n48,63005 e9,45320.

8 🍴free 🚰🔌Ch ⚡WCfree. 🅾 01/01-31/12
Remarks: Service: Mo/Fri 9-18h, za 9-13h.

Donaueschingen 17B6
Fürstenbergstrasse. GPS: n47,95250 e8,50667. ⬆➡.

10 ⛺free. **Surface:** metalled. 🅾 01/01-31/12
Distance: 🚶300m.
Remarks: Max. 2 days.

| ⓢ | Donaueschingen | 17B6 |

Prinz Fritz Allee. **GPS:** n47,94746 e8,51183.

10 ⛺free. **Surface:** grassy. 🅾 01/01-31/12
Remarks: Max. 2 days, service, 300m, at Danube cycle route.

| ⓢ | Donaueschingen | 17B6 |

Haberfeld. **GPS:** n47,94931 e8,52209.
🚰🧹Chagainst payment.
🅾 01/01-31/12
Remarks: Follow signs Kläranlage.

Tourist information Donaueschingen:
ℹ️ Tourismus- und Sportamt, Karlstrasse 58, www.donaueschingen.de.Horse
city, named after the source of the River danube.
Ⓜ Museum Karlsbau, Karlsplatz 7.Art collection Furstenberg. 🅾 Tue-Sa 10-
13h, 14-17h, Su 10-17h. 🎫 € 5.
⬦ Der Donau Radweg.Signposted cycle route along the Donau.

| ⓢ | Durbach | 17A5 |

Grol/Festplatz, Almstrasse. **GPS:** n48,49407 e8,01105.⬆️➡️.

15 ⛺€ 6 ⬦ (8x)€ 1/8h. 🚌
Surface: gravel. 🅾 01/01-31/12 ⬤ festivities.
Distance: 🚶500m ⬦10km 🚏50m.

| ⓢ | Durbach | 17A5 |

Halle am Durbach, Wiesenstraße, Ebersweier. **GPS:** n48,50122 e7,98940.⬆️➡️.

6 ⛺€ 6 🚰€ 1/80liter 🧹Ch ⬦(6x)4h. 🚌 **Location:** Rural. **Surface:**
grasstiles. 🅾 01/01-31/12
Distance: 🚶500m ⬦ 10km 🚏750m 🚉200m.

| ⓢ | Eberbach 🌳⛱️🏖️ | 17C2 |

Wohnmobilstellplatz In der Au, In der Au. **GPS:** n49,46162 e8,97812.⬆️.

7 ⛺free 🚰 ⬦(6x)€ 1 🚾. **Location:** Isolated. **Surface:** gravel. 🅾 01/01-
31/12 ⬤ 16/08-31/08.
Distance: 🚶1km 🏊on the spot.
Remarks: Max. 2 nights.

| ⓢ | Eberbach 🌳⛱️🏖️ | 17C2 |

Wohnmobilstellplatz Neckarlauer, B37, Uferstrasse. **GPS:** n49,46012 e8,98652.
⬆️.

10 ⛺free. **Location:** Central. **Surface:** metalled. 🅾 01/01-31/12 ⬤ high
water.
Distance: 🚶300m ⊗300m 🚉500m.

| ⓢ | Eberbach 🌳⛱️🏖️ | 17C2 |

Kläranlage, B37 dir Heidelberg. **GPS:** n49,45743 e8,95648.⬆️.
🚰🧹Ch. 🅾 01/01-31/12: Mo-Thu 7-12h, 13-16h, Fr 7-12.30h

| ⓢ | Ebringen | 17A6 |

An der Schönberghalle, Schulstraße 8. **GPS:** n47,95639 e7,77667.⬆️➡️.

3 ⛺free. **Surface:** grasstiles. 🅾 01/01-31/12
Distance: ⬦7,6km 🏊on the spot.
Remarks: Max. 6.5m, max. 2 days.

| ⓢ | Ehingen 🌳⛱️⛲🎡 | 17D5 |

Wohnmobilstellplatz, Am Stadion. **GPS:** n48,28053 e9,73571.⬆️.

DE

10 ⌂free ⌁€ 1/100liter ☐Ch ⌇(4x)€ 1/4h. **Surface:** metalled. ☐
01/01-31/12
Distance: ⌁1km ⌁1km ⊗on the spot ⌁500m ⌁10m.

Eichstetten 17A6
Weingut Köbelin, Altweg 131. **GPS:** n48,09472 e7,72083.

5 ⌂€ 13 ⌁☐Ch ⌇included. **Location:** Rural, comfortable, isolated,
quit. **Surface:** gravel/sand.

Eigeltingen 17C6
Landgasthof Mönchhof, Mönchhof. **GPS:** n47,88094 e8,95278.

4 ⌂guests free ⌁☐Ch ⌇. **Surface:** metalled. ☐ 01/01-31/12
Distance: ⌁6km ⊗on the spot ⌁4km.

Eisenbach 17B6
Reisemobilpark Höchstberg. GPS: n47,94938 e8,25441.☝

20 ⌂€ 8 + Kurtaxe € 1,60/pp ⌁€ 1/100liter ☐Ch ⌇included. **Surface:**
grassy/gravel. ☐ 01/01-31/12
Remarks: At sports park, altitude 1033m.

Ellwangen 18A3
Wohnmobilstellplatz Schießwasen, P1, Am Schießwasen. **GPS:** n48,96235
e10,12657.☝➡

8 ⌂€ 8/night ⌁€ 0,50/80liter ☐Ch ⌇(8x)€ 0,50/kWh. **Surface:**
asphalted. ☐ 01/01-31/12
Distance: ⌁500m.

Ellwangen 18A3
Maxi-Autohof Ellwangen, Max-Eyth-Strasse 1. **GPS:** n48,95628 e10,18319.
50 ⌂€ 5/night ⌁☐Ch WC ⌇against payment. **Surface:** asphalted.

☐ 01/01-31/12
Distance: ⌁3km ⊗on the spot ⌁1km.

Emmendingen 17A6
Wohnmobilstellplatz am Sportfeld, Am Sportfeld. **GPS:** n48,11869 e7,84154.
☝

20 ⌂free ⌁€ 1/80liter ☐Ch. **Location:** Urban. **Surface:** asphalted. ☐
01/01-31/12
Distance: ⌁1km ⊗400m ⌁600m.
Remarks: Max. 3 days, in front of swimmingpool.

Endingen am Kaiserstuhl 17A6
P2 Stadthalle, Freiburger Weg. **GPS:** n48,13830 e7,70321.☝➡

20 ⌂free.
Location: Urban, very simple, central. **Surface:** asphalted/metalled.
Distance: ⌁200m ⊗200m.

Eppingen 17C3
Wohnmobilhalt am Parkweg, Am Altstadring. **GPS:** n49,13793 e8,91402.☝

4 ⌂free ⌁€ 1/80liter ☐€ 1 Ch€ 1 ⌇(4x)€ 1. **Location:** Rural,
comfortable. **Surface:** metalled. ☐ 01/01-31/12
Distance: ⌁500m ⊗on the spot ⌁500m ⌁on the spot ⌁on the spot.

Eschenau 17C3
Weingut Wendel, Wieslendorferstrasse 39, Obersulm. **GPS:** n49,14111 e9,40910.
⌂.

Esslingen am Neckar 17C4
Äußerer Burgplatz, Mülbergerstraße. **GPS:** n48,74150 e9,31900.☝

2 ⌂free. **Surface:** metalled. ☐ 01/01-31/12

Distance: 1km 1km 1km 300m.

Tourist information Esslingen am Neckar:

Esslinger Stadtmarketing, Marktplatz 2, www.esslingen-tourist.de.

| | S | **Ettenheim** | 17A5 |

Ernst Caravan und Freizeit Center, Rudolf Hell Straße 32-44. **GPS**: n48,27431 e7,78161.

30 free € 1 € 1 Ch € 1 (12x)€ 0,50/kWh. **Location:** Highway.
Surface: metalled. 01/01-31/12
Distance: 500m.
Remarks: Motorhome dealer, accessory shop, repairs.

| | S | **Ettlingen** | 17B4 |

Wohnmobilstellplatz Am Freibad, Schöllbronner strasse. **GPS**: n48,93561 e8,41747.

14 free € 1 Ch (8x)€ 1/kWh. **Location:** Urban, very simple.
Surface: asphalted. 01/01-31/12
Distance: 100m 3,3km 100m 700m on the spot on the spot on the spot.
Remarks: Parking swimming pool, max. 48h.

| | S | **Filderstadt** | 17C4 |

Parkplatz P2, Tübinger Strasse 40. **GPS**: n48,67347 e9,21456.

8 € 5/24h € 1/80liter Ch (8x)€ 0,50/kWh, 16Amp. 01/01-31/12
Distance: 500m 500m 500m 500m.
Remarks: Follow Filharmonie.

| | S | **Freiburg** | 17A6 |

Reisemobilplatz Freiburg, Bissierstrasse / Am Eschholzpark. **GPS**: n47,99915 e7,82643.

80 € 8, motorhome >7m + € 0,50/50cm € 1/100liter Ch (20x)€ 0,50/kWh free.
Location: Urban, comfortable.
Surface: asphalted/gravel. 01/01-31/12
Distance: Old city centre 1,5km 4,3km 450m.
Remarks: Max. 3 days, green zone: environmental badge obligatory.

| | S | **Freiburg** | 17A6 |

WV-Südcaravan, Hanferstrasse 30, Hochdorf. **GPS**: n48,04146 e7,81473.

6 free € 1/80liter Ch.
Location: Urban, very simple.
Surface: asphalted/metalled.
01/01-31/12
Distance: Old city centre 10km 3km 300m 3km.
Remarks: During opening hours.

Tourist information Freiburg:

Freiburg Wirtschaft und Touristik GmbH & Co. KG, Rotteckring 14, www.freiburg.de.University town, city centre with many curiosities.

Augustinermuseum, Salzstrasse 32.Medieval ecclesiastical treasures.

Münster Unserer Lieben Frau, Münsterplatz.Built as a cemetery. Tue-Su.

Bergwelt Schauinsland.

| | S | **Freudenberg** | 17C2 |

Hauptstrasse. **GPS**: n49,74001 e9,31938.

7 € 5/night € 1/15minutes Ch (6x)€ 1/8h, 16Amp. **Surface:** metalled. 01/01-31/12
Distance: 50m 20m 20m 300m 500m.

| | S | **Friedrichshafen** | 24D1 |

Neue Messe Friedrichshafen, Allmannsweilerstrasse. **GPS**: n47,67727 e9,51279.

€ 15 Ch (32x) WC . **Surface:** asphalted/metalled. during fair
Distance: 3km on the spot.

| | S | **Friedrichshafen** | 24D1 |

Stellplatz Friedrichshafen, Lindauerstrasse 2. **GPS**: n47,65025 e9,49597.

20 € 10 € 1/80liter Ch WC . **Surface:** asphalted/metalled. 01/01-31/12
Distance: 200m 200m on the spot.
Remarks: Max. 3 nights. Follow signs campsite.

S Gaildorf 17D3

Bleichgärten. **GPS**: n49,00224 e9,76587.

7 free Ch (4x)free, 16Amp.
Surface: metalled. 01/01-31/12
Distance: 500m 400m 500m 500m.

Gammertingen 17C5

Reutlingerstrasse. **GPS**: n48,25611 e9,21056.

10 free. **Surface:** grassy/gravel. 01/01-31/12
Distance: 1km 1km 1km.

S Geisingen 17B6

Reisemobilstellplatz Geisingen, Am Espen 8. **GPS**: n47,92016 e8,65153.
37 € 7 € 1/80liter Ch € 1/4kWh. **Surface:** unpaved. 01/01-31/12
Distance: 500m.

S Gernsbach 17B4

Parkplatz Murginsel, Schlossstrasse/Klingelstrasse. **GPS**: n48,75934 e8,33900.

8 € 5 € 1/100liter Ch (8x)€ 1/12h WC. **Location:** Rural.
Surface: asphalted. 01/01-31/12
Distance: 500m on the spot 500m 1km on the spot on the spot on the spot.

Remarks: Max. 7 days.

Gernsbach 17B4

Am Schwimmbad 1, Oberstrot. **GPS**: n48,74239 e8,34186.

5 free.
Location: Rural, very simple. **Surface:** grassy. 01/01-31/12
Distance: 200m 200m on the spot on the spot.
Remarks: At swimming pool.

S Giengen 18A4

Reisemobilstation Charlottenhöhle, Lonetalstrasse 60, Hürben. **GPS**: n48,58430 e10,20908.

15 € 5/night Ch (6x)€ 2/12h, 16Amp WC included € 2.
Surface: gravel. 01/01-31/12
Remarks: At prehistoric cave.

Giengen 18A4

Reisemobilstation Schwage, Gluckstraße 10. **GPS**: n48,62414 e10,23566.

10 free.
Surface: asphalted. 01/01-31/12
Distance: 600m.

Tourist information Giengen:
Charlottenhöhle.Caves. 8.30-11.30h, 13.30-16.30h, Su 8.30-16.30h.
M Margarete Steiff Museum.Cuddling animals. Mo-Fri 13-16h, Sa 8.30-12h.
T free.

S Göppingen 17D4

Hohen Staufenhalle, P1, Lorcherstrasse. **GPS**: n48,71176 e9,64816.

10 free Ch . 01/01-31/12

Distance: 1km ⊗1km 1km.
Remarks: Max. 2 nights.

| 🏕 | **Grossbottwar** 🌿 | 17C3 |

Parkplatz an der Wunnensteinhalle, In den Frauengärten/ August-Lämmle-weg. **GPS:** n49,00363 e9,28739. ⬆️➡️.

3 🏕 free. **Surface:** metalled. 🅾 01/01-31/12
Distance: 400m ⊗400m 200m.
Remarks: Max. 3 nights.

| 🏕 S | **Gschwend** | 17D4 |

Joosenhofer Sägmühle. **GPS:** n48,92312 e9,77393. ⬆️➡️.
2 🏕 free ⚡€ 1/80liter 🚿Ch. **Surface:** asphalted. 🅾 01/01-31/12

| 🏕 | **Gschwend** | 17D4 |

Naturbadesee, Frickenhofer Strasse. **GPS:** n48,93603 e9,75143. ⬆️.

20 🏕 free. **Location:** Urban. **Surface:** metalled. 🅾 01/01-31/12
Distance: 50m ⊗150m 500m 🚌100m.

| 🏕 | **Haslach/Kinzigtal** 🚣 | 17A5 |

Parkplatz Eichenbach-sporthalle, Strickerweg. **GPS:** n48,27854 e8,07968. ⬆️.

3 🏕 free. **Surface:** gravel. 🅾 01/01-31/12
Distance: 1,5km.

| 🏕 S | **Güglingen** | 17C3 |

Oberes Tal. **GPS:** n49,06492 e8,99489. ⬆️➡️.

10 🏕 free. **Location:** Very simple. **Surface:** metalled. 🅾 01/01-31/12
Distance: 500m 300m.

| 🏕 | **Haslach/Kinzigtal** 🚣 | 17A5 |

Waldseeparkplatz, Waldseeweg. **GPS:** n48,27161 e8,09148. ⬆️.

6 🏕 free ⚡€ 1 🚿Ch.
Location: Rural. **Surface:** metalled. 🅾 01/01-31/12
Distance: 700m ⊗500m Aldi-Lidl 500m 🚲 on the spot 🚶 on the spot.
Remarks: At swimming pool, max. 5 nights.

| 🏕 S | **Haigerloch** | 17C5 |

Wohnmobilstellplatz Haigerloch, Weildorfer Kreuz 1. **GPS:** n48,36875 e8,79384.
10 🏕 free ⚡🚿Ch 🔌. **Surface:** asphalted. 🅾 01/01-31/12
Distance: 300m.
Remarks: Max. 4 days.

| 🏕 | **Haslach/Kinzigtal** 🚣 | 17A5 |

Klosterplatz, Ringstraße. **GPS:** n48,27572 e8,08509. ⬆️.

10 🏕 free. **Location:** Rural, very simple. **Surface:** asphalted. 🅾 01/01-31/12
Distance: 1km ⊗200m 1km.

| 🏕 S | **Hausach** | 17A5 |

Waldstadion, Waldstraße. **GPS:** n48,28058 e8,17829. ⬆️➡️.

4 🏕 free ⚡WC. **Location:** Rural, very simple. **Surface:** gravel/sand. 🅾 01/01-31/12
Distance: 500m ⊗100m.

| 🏕 | **Hausach** | 17A5 |

Badepark, Schanze 3. **GPS:** n48,28620 e8,16589. ⬆️➡️.

DE

6 🎫free. **Location:** Very simple. **Surface:** metalled. ⬛ 01/01-31/12
Distance: ⊗on the spot 🛢500m.
Remarks: Nearby swimming pool.

🛢S | **Hechingen** | 17C5
Weiher, Niederhechingerstrasse. **GPS:** n48,35797 e8,96093.

12 🎫€6 🚰€ 1 Ch.🔌€ 0,50/kWh.
Surface: metalled. ⬛ 01/01-31/12
Remarks: Parking at sports park, adjacent walking and bicycle area.

🛢S | **Heidenheim** | 18A4
In den Seewiesen. **GPS:** n48,69455 e10,16410. ⬆➡.

22 🎫€ 2/day 🚰€ 1/70liter 🔋€ 1 Ch.🔌(22x)€ 1/6h, 16Amp. **Surface:** asphalted/gravel. ⬛ 01/01-31/12
Distance: 🛢1km.

🛢S | **Heilbronn** 🌿🚲🧁🍴 | 17C3
Wertwiesenpark, Neckarhalde. **GPS:** n49,13047 e9,20469. ⬆➡.

20 🎫free 🚰€ 1/100liter 🔋Ch.🔌(12x)€ 0,50/kWh. **Location:** Comfortable. **Surface:** metalled. ⬛ 01/01-31/12
Distance: 🚶2km ⛵7km ⊗100m 🚌500m.

🛢S | **Heiligenberg** 🌿 | 17C6
Sennerei Schläge, Betenbrunner strasse. **GPS:** n47,81892 e9,31445. ⬆➡.

10 🎫€ 5/16-09h 🚰€ 0,50, 🔋€ 0,50, Ch.🚐 **Surface:** grassy/metalled. ⬛ 01/01-31/12
Distance: 🚶300m 🏊300m 🛒300m ⊗200m 🛢bakery 200m.
Remarks: Max. 2 nights.

🛢 | **Herbrechtingen** 🌿 | 18A4
P7 Eselstalparkplatz, Baumschulenweg. **GPS:** n48,58412 e10,21203. ⬆.

15 🎫free. **Surface:** asphalted. ⬛ 01/01-31/12
Remarks: Max. 3 days.

🛢S | **Hessigheim** | 17C3
Fasanenhof, Römerweg 1. **GPS:** n49,00939 e9,18877. ⬆.
15 🎫€ 5 🚰.
Location: Rural, very simple. **Surface:** . ⬛ 01/01-31/12
Distance: 🚲3,5km ⊗on the spot 🛢shop with farm products 🍴on the spot 🚶on the spot.
Remarks: Farm/restaurant/Biergarten/shop.

🛢S | **Hessigheim** | 17C3
Felsengarten Kellerei Besigheim e.G., Am Felsengarten 1. **GPS:** n48,99612 e9,18068. ⬆.

5 🎫guests free 🚰🔌. **Surface:** asphalted. ⬛ 01/01-31/12
Distance: 🚶1km ⊗on the spot 🛢1km.
Remarks: Max. 2 nights.

🛢S | **Höchenschwand** | 24B1
Natursportzentrum. **GPS:** n47,73652 e8,15990. ⬆➡.
10 🎫€ 7 🔋Ch.🔌€ 1/6h. **Surface:** metalled. ⬛ 01/01-31/12
Distance: 🚶400m ⊗100m 🚌600m 🌳on the spot.

🛢 | **Holzmaden** | 17D4
Urwelt-Museum Hauff, Aichelbergerstrasse 75/90. **GPS:** n48,63482 e9,52771.
6 🎫free. **Surface:** metalled. ⬛ 01/01-31/12
Distance: 🚶3km ⛵2,2km.
Remarks: Max. 1 night.

🍴🛢 | **Hornberg** 🍴🚲❄ | 17B6
Hotel Schöne Aussicht, Schöne Aussicht 1, Niederwasser. **GPS:** n48,19443 e8,18494.
4 🎫€ 8 🚰🔌included.
Distance: ⊗on the spot.

DE

Hüfingen 17B6
Bräunlinger Straße. **GPS**: n47,92361 e8,48707.

22 ⭤€5 ⭢€ 1 ⬛Ch ⚡ 1. **Surface:** grasstiles. ⬛ 01/01-31/12
Distance: ⭢300m ⬁300m.

Hülben 17D5
Phönix-Wohnmobihafen, Kaltentalstrasse. **GPS**: n48,52620 e9,41227.➡.

10 ⭤free ⭢€ 0,50/80liter ⬛Ch ⚡(6x)€ 0,50/kWh. **Surface:** gravel. ⬛
01/01-31/12
Distance: ⭢400m ⬁400m ⬅500m.
Remarks: Max. 5 days.

Ihringen 17A6
Kaiserstuhl Camping, Nachtwaid 5. **GPS**: n48,03083 e7,65778.⬆➡.

6 ⭤€ 14,60 + tourist tax ⭢⬛Ch ⚡€ 1,80/3kWh WC ⬛ⵌincluded.⬛
Location: Rural, comfortable.
Surface: asphalted/metalled. ⬛ 31/03-30/10
Distance: ⭢600m ⬁200m.

Ippesheim 18A2
Kempe's Autohof Gollhofen, Industriestraße 1. **GPS**: n49,58546 e10,17579.
25 ⭤€5 ⭢WC ⬛. **Surface:** asphalted. ⬛ 01/01-31/12
Distance: ⬁on the spot.

Isny 25A1
Parkplatz An der Untere Mühle, Seidenstrasse 43. **GPS**: n47,69457 e10,03780.
⬆➡.

10 ⭤€ 7,50, tourist tax € 1/pp ⭢€ 1/80liter ⬛Ch ⚡(8x)€ 0,50/kWh.
Surface: asphalted/gravel. ⬛ 01/01-31/12

Distance: ⭢300m ⬁100m ⬛300m ⬅200m.
Remarks: Max. 2 nights.

Isny 25A1
Caravans Dethleffs, Rangenbergweg. **GPS**: n47,69938 e10,05490.⬆.

8 ⭤€ 5 + € 1/pp tourist tax ⭢⬛Ch ⚡ included. **Surface:** metalled. ⬛
01/01-31/12
Distance: ⭢1km ⬈1km ⬅1km ⬁1,4km ⬛500m.
Remarks: Max. 3 nights.

Ittlingen 17C3
Freizeitheim Friedenshort, Sagmulhlstrasse 12. **GPS**: n49,19617 e8,93307.⬈.

20 ⭤free ⭢⬛Ch ⚡WC. **Location:** Rural. **Surface:** asphalted. ⬛
01/01-31/12
Distance: ⭢1km ⬁10m ⬅300m ⛹on the spot ⬈on the spot.
Remarks: Parking at sports park.

Kaisersbach 17D4
Schwaben-Park, Hofwiesen 11, Gmeinweiler. **GPS**: n48,90304 e9,65484.➡.

⭤free. ⬛ 01/04-31/10
Tourist information Kaisersbach:
⬤ Schwaben-Park. Amusement park. ⬛ Easter-Oct 9-18h.

Kappelrodeck 17A5
Wohnmobileck am Heidenhof, Grüner Winkel. **GPS**: n48,58370 e8,12650.⬆
➡.

18 ⭤€ 5/day, 3 days € 10, 7 days € 20 ⭢€ 1/100liter ⬛Ch ⚡(8x)€
1/2kWh.⬛
Location: Rural, quit. **Surface:** gravel/metalled. ⬛ 01/01-31/12

DE

Distance: 🚲800m ⊗150m 🏊500m 🚐on the spot 🚶on the spot.
Remarks: Max. 6 nights.

🚐S **Kehl** 🚽 17A5

Reisemobilstellplatz Hurst, An den Sportanlagen 1, Kehl-Auenheim. **GPS:** n48,60653 e7,83146.⬆️.

18 🗑️€6 🚰€ 1 🔌Ch 🔧(12x)€ 2/2kWh WC 🗑️ 1.🚿 **Location:** Rural, quit. **Surface:** asphalted/grassy. 🅾 01/01-31/12
Distance: 🚲500m ⊗on the spot 🏊500m 🚶on the spot 🚶on the spot.
Remarks: Check in at cafe zum Ganz.

🚐S **Kehl** 🚽 17A5

Am Wasserturm, Schwimbadstrasse. **GPS:** n48,56381 e7,81498.⬆️.

40 🗑️€6 🚰€ 1/100liter 🔌Ch 🔧(16x)€ 0,50/kWh. 🏠 **Location:** Urban, comfortable, quit. **Surface:** grassy/metalled. 🅾 01/01-31/12
Distance: ⊗100m 🏊500m 🚐on the spot 🚴on the spot 🚶on the spot.
Remarks: Max. 3 days.

🚐S **Kehl** 🚽 17A5

Bürstner-Service-Centrum, Elsässer strasse 80, Kehl-Neumühl. **GPS:** n48,57010 e7,84042.⬆️.

6 🗑️free 🚰€ 1/100liter 🔌Ch 🔧(6x)€ 1/kWh WC 🗑️. **Location:** Rural. **Surface:** asphalted. 🅾 01/01-31/12
Distance: 🚲1km ⊗100m 🏊600m 🚴on the spot 🚶on the spot.

🚐S **Kenzingen** 17A6

Ritter's Weingut, Rossleiteweg 1. **GPS:** n48,18739 e7,78343.⬆️➡️.

15 🗑️€ 10/incl. 2 pers + € 2/pp 🚰🔌 🔧 2,50/day WC 🗑️included. 🚿
Location: Comfortable. **Surface:** grassy/gravel. 🅾 01/01-31/12

Distance: 📐7,5km ⊗on the spot.

🚐 **Kirchberg/Jagst** 17D3

Wanderparkplatz Kirchberg-Tal, Hohen Loher Strasse. **GPS:** n49,20367 e9,98344.⬆️.

10 🗑️free. **Surface:** gravel. 🅾 01/01-31/12

🚐S **Kisslegg** 17D6

Strandbad Obersee, Strandbadweg. **GPS:** n47,79602 e9,87950.

10 🗑️free 🚰€ 1/50liter 🔌Ch 🔧(5x)€ 1/3h WC 🗑️. **Surface:** grassy/gravel. 🅾 01/01-31/12
Distance: 🚲800m 🏊100m 🏊100m ⊗100m 🏊1km 🚐400m.
Remarks: Max. 2 nights.

🚐 **Kisslegg** 17D6

Familiefreizeitgelände St Anna, Le Pouliguenstrasse. **GPS:** n47,79119 e9,87229 ⬆️➡️

3 🗑️free. **Surface:** grassy/metalled. 🅾 01/01-31/12
Distance: 🚲800m ⊗500m 🏊500m.

🍴 **Kisslegg** 17D6

Seminarhotel Sonnenstrahl, Sebastian Kneipp strasse 1. **GPS:** n47,78421 e9,87973.
3 🗑️free. **Surface:** asphalted/metalled. 🅾 01/01-31/12
Distance: 🚲800m ⊗on the spot 🏊800m.
Remarks: Max. 2 nights.

🚐S **Königschaffhausen** 17A6

Wohnmobilgarten im Kirschenhof Schmidt, Königsweg 5. **GPS:** n48,14277 e7,66273.⬆️➡️.

DE

16 🛏 € 11 + tourist tax € 1/pp 🚰 🗨 Ch 🚿 WC included 🗑 € 1 🔊 in Caffl.
Location: Rural, comfortable. **Surface:** gravel/metalled. 🅾 01/01-31/12
Distance: 🚶500m ⊗on the spot.
Remarks: Wifi in café.

⛺ S	**Königsfeld**	17B6

Reisemobilpark Bregnitzhof, Buchenberger Strasse 34. **GPS:** n48,14028
e8,40583. ⬆️➡️.

21 🛏 € 8/night 🚰 € 0,50 🗨 Ch 🚿 € 1/8h. **Surface:** gravel. 🅾 01/01-
31/12
Distance: 🚶1km ⊗10 min walking.
Remarks: Saunalandschaft Bregnitzhof, 18-holes golf course.

⛺ S	**Konstanz**	24C1

Parkplatz Döbele, Döbeleplatz. **GPS:** n47,65794 e9,16933. ⬆️➡️.

12 🛏 € 1/h, € 15/24h 🚰 🗨 Ch 🚿 WC included. **Surface:** asphalted/
metalled. 🅾 01/01-31/12
Distance: 🚶1km ⛵800m 🚲800m 🛒200m 🚊800m 🚌500m.
Remarks: Max. 1 night.

⛺ S	**Konstanz**	24C1

Bauernhof Gebhardshof, Zum Hofgut 4, Wallhausen. **GPS:** n47,74321 e9,13702.
⬆️➡️.

3 🛏 € 15 + tourist tax € 2/pp 🚰 🗨 Ch 🚿 WC 🗑 € 0,50. **Surface:** grassy/
metalled. 🅾 01/01-31/12
Distance: 🚶1km ⛵250m 🚲250m 🛒500m 🚊500m 🚌Free bus.
Remarks: Call before arrival: 0049/01742048535.

⛺ S	**Korb**	17C4

Reisemobilstellplatz Unterm Korber Kopf, Brucknerstrasse 14. **GPS:** n48,84597
e9,35544. ⬆️.

6 🛏 € 3 🚰 € 0,50/80liter 🗨 Ch 🚿 (6x)€ 0,50/kWh. **Surface:** metalled. 🅾
01/01-31/12
Distance: 🚶400m ⊗Gaststätte 🚊300m 🚌500m.

⛺ S	**Kressbronn**	24D1

Wohnmobilstellplatz Dorfkrug Tunau, Tunauerweg 4. **GPS:** n47,58999
e9,57512. ⬆️➡️.

40 🛏 € 18 🚰 🗨 Ch 🚿 (40x) WC 🗑 € 1,50/pp 🔊. **Surface:** asphalted/
grassy. 🅾 01/04-31/10
Distance: 🚶1km ⛵1km 🚲1km ⊗on the spot 🚊1km.

⛲ S	**Kressbronn**	24D1

Gohren am See. **GPS:** n47,58818 e9,56256.
11 🛏 € 12 🚰 🗨 Ch 🚿 € 3/12h. 🅾 01/04-15/10

⛺ S	**Külsheim**	17D2

Am Schloss Külsheim, Kirchbergweg. **GPS:** n49,67123 e9,52255. ⬆️.

8 🛏 free 🚰 € 0,50/80liter 🗨 Ch 🚿 (6x)€ 0,50/kWh. **Surface:** metalled. 🅾
01/01-31/12 ⬛ 10/09-25/09.
Distance: 🚶300m.

⛺ S	**Ladenburg** 🍰	17B2

Wohnmobilstellplatz Ladenburg, Heidelberger Straße. **GPS:** n49,46596
e8,61460. ⬆️.

34 🛏 € 10 🚰 € 1/80liter 🗨 Ch 🚿 € 1/2kWh 🔊. 🖥 **Location:** Urban,
comfortable, central, quit. **Surface:** grassy. 🅾 01/01-31/12
Distance: 🚶Altstadt 500m, Heidelberg 10km 🚴3km ⊗200m 🚊200m.

DE

🏕 Langenbrettach 17C3

Freibad Langenbeutingen, Schwabbacker Strasse 24, Langenbeutingen. **GPS:** n49,21196 e9,40759.⬆️.

3 🏕free. **Surface:** asphalted.
Remarks: Parking swimming pool.

🏕 Langenburg 17D3

Am Freibad, In der Strut 5. **GPS:** n49,24973 e9,86681.⬆️.
3 🏕free. **Surface:** gravel. 🅾 01/01-31/12
Distance: 🚶1km.
Remarks: Not accessible coming from the west.

🏕S Lauchringen 24B1

An der Wutach, Badstrasse. **GPS:** n47,62556 e8,31361.➡️.

20 🏕free, 01/04-01/11 € 5 🚰🔲Ch 🔌 included. **Surface:** gravel. 🅾 01/01-31/12 🔘 service: 01/11-01/04.
Distance: 🚶on the spot.

🏕 Lauda-Königshofen ⛱ 17D2

Badstrasse, Lauda. **GPS:** n49,55886 e9,70099.⬆️.

4 🏕free. **Surface:** asphalted. 🅾 01/01-31/12
Distance: 🚶1km.
Remarks: Parking at swimming pool.

🍴S Lauda-Königshofen ⛱ 17D2

Gasthaus Zur Lamm, St. Josefstrasse 30-32, Marbach. **GPS:** n49,56568 e9,72834.⬆️.

10 🏕€ 5/24h 🚰🔲Ch 🔌 (10x)included. **Surface:** asphalted. 🅾 01/01-31/12

Distance: ⊗on the spot.

🏕S Laufenburg 24A1

Laufenburg Baden P6, Andelsbachstraße. **GPS:** n47,56585 e8,06677.
6 🏕free 🚰€ 2 🔲€ 2 Ch 🔌€ 0,50/kWh. **Surface:** metalled. 🅾 01/01-31/12
Remarks: Along the Rhine river.

🏕S Laupheim 17D5

Schloß Grosslaupheim, Klaus-Graf-Stauffenberg-Strasse. **GPS:** n48,23128 e9,88872.⬆️.

7 🏕€ 8 🚰🔲Ch 🔌. **Surface:** metalled. 🅾 01/01-31/12
Distance: 🚶on the spot.

🏕 Leonberg 17C4

Parkplatz Steinstrasse, Steinstrasse. **GPS:** n48,79705 e9,01751.⬆️.

5 🏕€ 1/night. **Surface:** metalled. 🅾 01/01-31/12 🅿 Sa 5-13h.
Distance: 🚶400m ⊗150m 🛒300m 🚌on the spot.

🏕S Leutkirch im Allgäu 18A6

Wohnmobilstellplatz Leutkirch, Kemptener Straße. **GPS:** n47,82228 e10,03939. ⬆️.
14 🏕€ 6 🚰€ 1/100liter 🔲Ch 🔌€ 0,50/kWh. **Surface:** asphalted. 🅾 01/01-31/12
Distance: 🚶1km ⊗300m.

🏕S Löffingen 17B6

Waldbad Löffingen, Am Waldbad. **GPS:** n47,90017 e8,33287.⬆️.

7 🏕€ 8 + € 2/pp, winter free 🚰🔲 🔌 included. **Surface:** metalled. 🅾 01/01-31/12 🔘 service 01/10-01/05.
Tourist information Löffingen:
😊 Schwarzwaldpark.Game preserve and summer toboggan slide (€ 1.02 a time). 🅾 Easter-Oct 9-18h.

🏕S Malsch 17B4

Gast Caravanning, Daimlerstr. 20b. **GPS:** n48,89079 e8,30747.⬆️.

6 ⌁free ⌁€ 1/80liter ⚑Ch. **Location:** Very simple. **Surface:** asphalted/metalled. ◘ 01/01-31/12
Distance: ⚓7,6km.
Remarks: Motorhome dealer, accessory shop.

| ⌁S | **Mannheim/Friedrichsfeld** | 17B2 |

Güma Reisemobile, Steinzeugstrasse 21. **GPS:** n49,44570 e8,56780.⬆.

3 ⌁free ⌁⚑Ch⌁ WC free.
Location: Noisy.
Surface: metalled. ◘ 01/01-31/12
Distance: ⚓10km ⚓1km ⚓1km ⚓300m.
Remarks: Max. 3 nights, sanitary use during shop opening hours.

| ⌁S | **Marbach am Neckar** | 17C4 |

Parkplatz Bolzplatz, Poppenweiler/Weimarstrasse. **GPS:** n48,93389 e9,26278.⬆.

5 ⌁€5 ⌁⚑Ch. **Surface:** metalled. ◘ 01/01-31/12
Distance: ⚓1km ⚓6,2km ⊗100m ⚓600m ⚓500m.
Remarks: Max. 2 nights, service: Gruppenklärwerk Häldenmühle, L1100.

| ⌁ | **Markelsheim** | 17D2 |

Engelsbergstrasse. **GPS:** n49,47537 e9,83474.⬆➜.

2 ⌁free. **Surface:** asphalted. ◘ 01/01-31/12 ◉ week of Whitsuntide.
Distance: ⚓300m ⚓300m.
Remarks: Max. 2 nights.

| ⌁S | **Meckenbeuren** | 24D1 |

Wohnmobilplatz Besenwirtschaft Georgshof, Pfingstweiderstrasse 10-12/1, Reute. **GPS:** n47,68022 e9,55308.⬆➜.

10 ⌁€8 ⌁⚑Ch⌁(9x)€ 0,35/kWh ⌁€ 1. **Surface:** grassy/gravel. ◘ 01/01-31/12
Distance: ⚓on the spot ⊗200m ⚓100m.

| ⌁S | **Meersburg/Bodensee** 🌿⚓ | 24C1 |

Ergeten, Allmendweg. **GPS:** n47,70160 e9,26898.⬆.

35+60 ⌁€ 10/24h ⌁€ 1/100liter ⚑€ 1 Ch⌁€ 0,50/kWh WC.⌁⚑
Surface: metalled. ◘ 01/01-31/12
Distance: ⚓1km ⊗100m ⚓50m ⚓shuttle to centre.
Remarks: At edge of city, + 2x parking Allmendweg P1 n47.70211, o 9.26983, P2 n47,70159, o 9,27172.

Tourist information Meersburg/Bodensee:
🛈 Gästeinformation, Kirchstrasse 4, www.meersburg.de. Tourist town with historical centre and promenade along Lake Constance.

| ⌁S | **Meißenheim** | 17A5 |

Wohnmobilpark Ortenau, Winkelstrasse 36. **GPS:** n48,41616 e7,77736.⬆➜.

24+24 ⌁€ 5/day ⌁€ 1/120liter ⚑⌁(24x)€ 1/kWh. ⚓ **Location:** Rural, comfortable. **Surface:** gravel/metalled. ◘ 01/01-31/12
Distance: ⚓500m ⚓800m.

| ⌁S | **Memmingen** ⬡ | 18A6 |

Wohnmobilstellplatz Memmingen, Colmarer Straße/Hemmerlestraße. **GPS:** n47,99531 e10,18245.⬆➜.

20 ⌁€ 1/2h, € 5/24h ⌁€ 1/100liter ⚑Ch⌁(18x)€ 0,50/kWh.⌁⚑
Location: Urban. **Surface:** metalled. ◘ 01/01-31/12
Distance: ⚓900m ⚓2,2km ⊗700m ⚓Lidl 600m.
Remarks: Max. 3 days.

S Mengen 17C6

Südsee III, Uferweg 25. **GPS**: n48,03117 e9,28265.

20 €7 € 1/80liter Ch (16x)€ 0,50/kWh. **Surface:** gravel. 01/01-31/12

Distance: 500m on the spot 500m.

S Messkirch 17C6

Messplatz P2, Am Stachus. **GPS**: n47,99381 e9,11514.

5 free € 1/80liter Ch WC. **Surface:** metalled. 01/01-31/12, service 01/04-30/09

Distance: 500m 400m 200m 500m.

S Metzingen 17C5

Reisemobilplatz Outletcity Metzingen, Stetterstrasse 4. **GPS**: n48,53241 e9,27574.

20 €10 Ch included (6x)€ 2, 16Amp. **Surface:** gravel. 01/01-31/12

Distance: 800m 800m 800m 800m shuttle every 15 min.

S Mosbach 17C3

Wasemweg. **GPS**: n49,36139 e9,14833.

10 free € 1/150liter Ch (10x)€ 1/12h. **Location:** Rural, comfortable, quit. **Surface:** concrete. 01/01-31/12

Distance: 800m.

S Mössingen 17C5

Wohnmobilstellplatz Firstwald, Firstwaldstraße, Kernstadt. **GPS**: n48,41348 e9,06915.

10 free € 1 € 1 Ch (10x)€ 0,50/kWh, 16Amp. **Surface:** grasstiles. 01/01-31/12

Distance: 1,5km 500m 1km 100m.

Muggensturm 17B4

Muggensturm, Vogesenstraße. **GPS**: n48,87946 e8,28721.

3 free. **Location:** Urban, very simple. **Surface:** gravel. 01/01-31/12

Distance: 1,5km 4,4km beach 100m.

S Mühlberg 18A6

Ferienhof Musch, Unterer weg 7. **GPS**: n47,98534 e9,98697.

4 € 10, 2 pers.incl Ch (3x) WC € 3. **Surface:** grassy/ metalled. 01/01-31/12

Distance: 10km 100m 100m 10km 10km.

Müllheim 24A1

Am Engelberg, Hügelheim. **GPS**: n47,83282 e7,62320.

2 free. **Location:** Rural, very simple, isolated, quit. **Surface:** . 01/01-31/12

Distance: 500m 1,5km.

Müllheim 24A1

Am Nüsslegarten, Am Nüsslegarten, Britzingen. **GPS**: n47,82891 e7,67336.

DE

2 free.
Location: Rural, very simple, quit. **Surface:** . 01/01-31/12

| Müllheim | 24A1 |

Freibad Müllheim, Ziegleweg 7. **GPS:** n47,80237 e7,63403.

3 free.
Location: Urban, very simple. **Surface:** asphalted. 01/01-31/12
Remarks: Next to swimming pool.

| Müllheim | 24A1 |

Parkplatz Nußbaumallee, Nußbaumallee. **GPS:** n47,80942 e7,62985.
3 free.
Location: Urban, very simple. **Surface:** asphalted. 01/01-31/12
Remarks: Max. 2 days.

| S | Müllheim | 24A1 |

Markgräfler Kräuterhof, Im Käppeleacker 3, Hügelheim. **GPS:** n47,83237 e7,62045.

4 free. free. **Location:** Urban, very simple. **Surface:** grasstiles.
01/01-31/12
Distance: 500m 1km.
Remarks: Herbery, herb-Stube.

| S | Münsingen | 17D5 |

Wiesentalstadion, Grafenecker Straße. **GPS:** n48,40939 e9,48580.
18 € 5/24h, 3 days € 12 € 1/100liter Ch € 1/6h. **Surface:** gravel.
01/01-31/12
Distance: 1km within walking distance on the spot.

| S | Murrhardt | 17D3 |

Parkplatz Festhalle, Kaiser-Ludwig-Straße 25. **GPS:** n48,97960 e9,57461.

3 free € 1/90liter Ch. **Surface:** asphalted. 01/01-31/12
Distance: 400m 100m.

| Nagold | 17B5 |

Wohnmobilhafen, Am Glockenrain. **GPS:** n48,56389 e8,72306.

12 free € 1/80liter € 1 Ch € 1 (12x)€ 1/kWh. **Location:** Rural, quit. **Surface:** gravel/metalled. 01/01-31/12
Distance: 1km 25m 900m 400m on the spot on the spot.

| Nagold | 17B5 |

Am Bahnhof, Bahnhofstraße. **GPS:** n48,55791 e8,72748.

4 free. **Location:** Rural, very simple, noisy. **Surface:** asphalted. 01/01-31/12
Distance: 700m 100m on the spot on the spot on the spot.
Remarks: Max. 4 nights.

| S | Nattheim | 18A4 |

Ramensteinbad, Dieselstrasse 22. **GPS:** n48,70261 e10,23745.

3 free € Ch free.
Surface: gravel. 01/01-31/12 25/04-07/05.
Distance: 500m 300m 200m.
Remarks: Parking swimming pool, max. 3 days, caution key € 10 (water).

| S | Neckarsulm | 17C3 |

Aquatoll, Reisachmühlweg. **GPS:** n49,18802 e9,24302.

DE

50 ⊖free ⏚€ 2/60liter ⬛Ch. **Location:** Rural. **Surface:** asphalted/gravel. ◘ 01/01-31/12
Distance: ⚓4km.
Remarks: Parking swimming pool, max. 24h.

8 ⊖voluntary contribution ⏚€ 1 ⬛€ 1 Ch ⚹ (9x). **Surface:** metalled. ◘ 01/01-31/12
Distance: ⚓300m ⊗500m ⚲1km 🚌300m 🚲2km 🚶2km.
Remarks: Max. 3 nights.

🛉🚿 **Neckarwestheim** 17C3	🚿🚿 **Neunkirchen** 🏞 17C3

Wohnmobilstellplätze Im Bühl, Liebensteiner Strasse. **GPS:** n49,04186 e9,18797.⬆️.

Festplatz, Zwingenbergerstrasse. **GPS:** n49,38818 e9,01531.⬆️.

2 ⊖free ⏚€ 2 ⬛Ch ⚹ (4x)€ 2/8h.
Surface: metalled. ◘ 01/01-31/12
Distance: ⚓500m ⊗200m ⚲500m.
Remarks: From 4th night € 25/night.

8 ⊖free ⏚€ 1/90liter ⬛Ch. **Location:** Quit. **Surface:** asphalted. ◘ 01/01-31/12
Distance: ⚓300m.
Remarks: Service next to: Autohaus Weishaupt, Industriestrasse 3 (200m).

🛉🛉 **Nellingen** 17D5	🚿🚿 **Nordheim** 17C3

Landgasthof Krone, Aicherstrasse 7-9. **GPS:** n48,54179 e9,79136.

Lauffener Straße. **GPS:** n49,10461 e9,13552.⬆️.

DE

⊖guests free. **Surface:** metalled.
Distance: ⚓on the spot ⊗on the spot ⚲200m.

2 ⊖€ 5/3 days ⏚⬛Ch ⚹included. **Surface:** asphalted. ◘ 01/01-31/12 🚲on the spot 🚶on the spot.
Remarks: Max. 3 days, in front of swimmingpool.

🚿🚿 **Neresheim** 🚂🛉 18A4	🛏🚿 **Nordheim** 17C3

Stellplatz Alter Bahnhof, Dischinger Straße 11. **GPS:** n48,75102 e10,33957.⬆️.

Müllers Weingut und Weinstube, Im Auerberg 3. **GPS:** n49,10236 e9,13810.

5 ⊖free ⏚€ 1 ⬛Ch ⚹ (4x)€ 1/4h. **Location:** Noisy. **Surface:** metalled. ◘ 01/01-31/12
Distance: ⚓on the spot ⚓12km ⊗on the spot.
Remarks: Service during opening hours.

2 ⊖€ 5,with electricity and water € 8 ⏚⬛Ch ⚹. **Location:** Rural.
Surface: .
Distance: ⚓800m ⊗on the spot 🚌on the spot 🚲on the spot 🚶on the spot.

🚿🚿 **Neuhausen ob Eck** 🛉 17C6	

Beim Friedhof. **GPS:** n47,97473 e8,92397.⬆️.

Schwarzwald-Panorama Wohnmobilstellplatz, Im Dorf 29. **GPS:** n48,39873 e8,07927.⬆️➡️.

8 🛏free ⚡€ 1/10liter 🔵Ch ✎ (8x)6h. **Location:** Rural, central. **Surface:** metalled. 🔲 01/01-31/12
Distance: 🚶100m 🛒100m.

📷S **Nürtingen** 17C4

Reisemobilstellplatz, B313, Plätschwiesen, Oberensingen. **GPS**: n48,63645 e9,33051. ⬆.

12 🛏€ 5/24h ⚡€ 1 🔵Ch ✎ (8x)€ 1. **Surface:** metalled.
Distance: 🚶1km 🛒500m.
Remarks: Max. 7 days.

📷S **Oberkirch** 17A5

Am Renchtalstadion, Renchallee. **GPS**: n48,52972 e8,07250. ⬆➡.

21 🛏€ 5, € 7/2 days + €2 tourist tax ⚡€ 1/80liter 🔵€ 1 Ch ✎ (30x)€ 0,50/kWh. 🔲 **Location:** Rural, quit. **Surface:** grassy/gravel. 🔲 01/01-31/12 ⬤ week before and week after 1st weekend Sep.
Distance: 🚶100m ⊗100m 🛒100m 🚲on the spot 🚶on the spot.

📷S **Oberkirch** 17A5

Waldparkplatz Schauenburg, Burgstraße 29. **GPS**: n48,53812 e8,09452. ⬆.

4 🛏€ 8 ✎ (4x)€ 2 🔵. 🔲 **Location:** Very simple, isolated, quit. **Surface:** grassy/sand. 🔲 01/01-31/12
Distance: ⊗500m.
Remarks: € 8 voucher, max 4 days.

Tourist information Oberkirch:
ℹ www.oberkirch.de. Wine city with historical centre. Many hiking routes.

📷S **Oberndorf/Neckar** 17B5

Neckarhalle, Austrasse 12. **GPS**: n48,28222 e8,58472. ⬆➡.

8 🛏free ⚡€ 1/70liter 🔵Ch ✎ (4x)€ 1/kWh. **Location:** Rural, noisy. **Surface:** asphalted. 🔲 01/01-31/12
Distance: 🚶2km ⊗300m 🛒200m 🚰50m 🚲on the spot 🚶on the spot.

📷 **Oberstenfeld** 17C3

Mineralfreibad, Beilsteiner Strasse 100. **GPS**: n49,03160 e9,31890. ➡.

4 🛏free. **Surface:** asphalted. 🔲 01/01-31/12

📷S **Oberteuringen** 24D1

Ferienhof Kramer, St. Georg strasse 8. **GPS**: n47,73948 e9,47278. ⬆➡.

8 🛏€ 7 + € 5,50/pp ⚡Ch ✎ (8x)€ 2 WC 🔵✎ 4. **Surface:** gravel/metalled. 🔲 01/03-31/10
Distance: 🚶2km 🏊on the spot ⊗300m 🛒300m.

📷S **Offenburg** 17A5

Strandbad Gifizsee, Platanenallee 15. **GPS**: n48,45785 e7,93663.
11 🛏€ 12 + € 3 /pp (peak season) ⚡€ 1/80liter 🔵Ch ✎ (11x)€ 0,50/kWh WC 🔲 🔊. 🔲 **Surface:** grasstiles. 🔲 01/04-31/10
Distance: 🚶2,5km 🚲3,8km 🏊100m 🚲on the spot 🛒150m.
Remarks: Bread-service, dog € 1,50/night.

📷 **Offenburg** 17A5

Bürgerpark, Stegermattstraße 26a. **GPS**: n48,46565 e7,94566. ⬆.

2 🛏free. **Location:** Urban, very simple, quit. **Surface:** asphalted/metalled. 🔲 01/01-31/12
Distance: 🚶500m ⊗300m.
Remarks: In front of swimmingpool.

Offenburg 17A5

Camping Kuhn, Im Drachenacker 4. **GPS**: n48,48039 e7,92776.

10 free € 0,50/50liter Ch (8x)free. **Location:** Urban. **Surface:** metalled. 01/01-31/12
Distance: 2km 3,7km 500m.
Remarks: Service during opening hours.

Öhningen/Schienen 24C1

Landgasthof Schienerberg, Schienerbergstrasse 56. **GPS**: n47,69595 e8,90698.

6 free. **Surface:** gravel/metalled. 01/01-31/12 Tue.
Distance: 800m on the spot 800m.

Öhringen 17D3

P Frei- und Hallenbad, Pfaffenmühlweg. **GPS**: n49,19771 e9,51137.

20 free. **Surface:** metalled. 01/01-31/12
Distance: 1km 100m.
Remarks: Parking swimming pool, max. 3 days.

Öhringen 17D3

Firma Weissert, Kuhallmand 26. **GPS**: n49,19673 e9,49860.

5 € 5/24h € 1/80liter Ch included. **Surface:** metalled. 01/01-31/12
Distance: 500m.

Tourist information Öhringen:

Tourist Information, Markplatz 15, www.oehringen.de.Many signposted hiking routes.

RADius.Cycle route, 18km.

Öllingen 18A5

Parking Rathaus, Hauptstrasse. **GPS**: n48,52449 e10,14433.

5 free € 4 Ch . **Surface:** grasstiles. 01/01-31/12

Oppenau 17A5

Hauptstrasse. **GPS**: n48,47639 e8,16972.

6 free € 1/100liter Ch (6x)€ 1/8h. **Location:** Rural, quit. **Surface:** gravel. 01/01-31/12
Distance: 300m 150m bakery 300m on the spot on the spot.

Oppenweiler 17D3

Caravanstation, Murrwiesenstraße 15. **GPS**: n48,97999 e9,45898.

3 free € 1/80liter Ch. **Surface:** asphalted. 01/01-31/12
Distance: 600m.
Remarks: Max. 2-3 days.

Ottenhöfen im Schwarzwald 17A5

Bauernhof Murhof, Murhof 1. **GPS**: n48,56005 e8,15350.

15 € 10, 2 pers.incl € 1/100liter Ch (15x)€ 0,50/kWh WC €0,50. **Location:** Rural, quit.
Surface: grassy/metalled. 01/04-31/10
Distance: 1km 500m 500m on the spot.
Remarks: Swimming pool 200m.

Pforzheim 17B4

Reisemobilplatz Oststadt am Enzauenpark, Wildersinnstraße. **GPS**: n48,89784 e8,72232.

15 🛏free ⛽€ 1/80liter ⚡(4x)€ 1/kWh.
Location: Urban, noisy.
Surface: metalled. 🅾 01/01-31/12
Distance: 🚶1,5km ⊗200m 🚰100m 🚮on the spot 🚿on the spot 🚾on the spot.
Remarks: Max. 7 days, service 200m. In front of Ensauenpark, behind P&R.

| | | Pforzheim | 17B4 |

Parkplatz 2 Wildpark, Tiefenbronnerstraße. **GPS:** n48,87651 e8,71749.
🛏€ 2-4/24h. **Location:** Urban. **Surface:** .
Remarks: Max. 1 night.

| S | | Pforzheim | 17B4 |

Hohwiesenweg. **GPS:** n48,89750 e8,72674.⬆
4 ⛽€ 1/80liter 🛏€ 1 Ch€ 1 ⚡(2x)€ 1/kWh. **Location:** Very simple, noisy. **Surface:** metalled.
Distance: 🚶1,5km ⊗50m 🚰100m 🚮on the spot 🚾on the spot 🚿on the spot.

| S | | Pfullendorf | 17C6 |

Seepark Linzgau, P-Ost, Bannholzerweg 18. **GPS:** n47,93097 e9,23728.
15 🛏€ 4/24h ⛽. **Surface:** unpaved. 🅾 01/01-31/12

| S | | Pfullingen | 17C5 |

Wohnmobilplatz Schönbergbad, Klosterstraße. **GPS:** n48,45537 e9,22812.
7 🛏free ⛽€ 1 🛏Ch€ ⚡€ 1/2kWh. **Surface:** grassy. 🅾 01/01-31/12
Distance: 🚶1,5km ⊗nearby.
Remarks: Max. 4 days.

| S | | Radolfzell | 24C1 |

Stellplatz Hartplatz, Strandbadstrasse. **GPS:** n47,73784 e8,98007.⬆

10 🛏€ 8/24h ⛽€ 1/50liter 🛏Ch⚡(6x)€ 0,50/kWh. **Surface:** asphalted.
🅾 01/01-31/12
Distance: 🚶500m 🚰700m 🚮700m ⊗500m 🚰700m 🚾100m.
Remarks: Max. 2 nights.

| S | | Radolfzell | 24C1 |

Stellplatz in den Herzen, Zeppelinstrasse. **GPS:** n47,73888 e8,95331.

15 🛏€ 8/24h ⛽€ 1/80liter 🛏Ch⚡(12x)€ 0,50/kWh. **Surface:** metalled.
🅾 01/01-31/12
Distance: 🚶1km ⊗500m 🚰1km.
Remarks: Max. 2 nights.

| C S | | Radolfzell | 24C1 |

Campingplatz Böhringer See, Hindenburgstrasse. **GPS:** n47,76176 e8,93488.
⬆

10 🛏€ 10 ⛽🛏Ch⚡(5x) WC 🚾€ 1.
Surface: metalled. 🅾 01/01-31/12
Distance: 🚶1km ⊗on the spot 🚰1km.

| S | | Rastatt | 17A4 |

Leopoldring. **GPS:** n48,85409 e8,19970.⬆➡

5 🛏€ 5 ⛽€ 1/10minutes 🛏Ch⚡(8x)€ 1/6h. 🚿 **Surface:** metalled. 🅾
01/01-31/12
Distance: 🚶500m 🏊3,8km.
Remarks: Pay-desk of the swimming pool, Discount at swimming pool/sauna.

| S | | Ravensburg | 17D6 |

Mühlbruckstrasse. **GPS:** n47,78196 e9,60001.⬆➡

12 🛏€ 5 ⛽€ 1/80liter 🛏Ch⚡(6x)€ 0,50. **Surface:** metalled. 🅾
01/01-31/12
Distance: 🚶2km ⊗500m 🚰200m 🚾250m.
Remarks: Max. 3 nights.

| S | | Ravensburg | 17D6 |

Carthago Reisemobilbau, Okatreut, Schmalegg. **GPS:** n47,79729 e9,54906.
6 🛏free ⛽🛏Chfree. **Surface:** gravel. 🅾 01/01-31/12

Tourist information Ravensburg:
ℹ Bodensee-Erlebniskarte.Card gives free access to all boats, telpher carriers, beaches etc. Around the Lake Constance in Germany, Switzerland and Austria.
🎫 € 54/3 days.
ℹ Tourist Information, Kirchstrasse 16.City of the Tore und Turme, gates and towers.

| S | | Rechberghausen | 17D4 |

Sportpark Lindach, Am Desenbach. **GPS:** n48,72405 e9,63594.➡

6 ⑤free ⚡€ 0,50/80liter 🔧Ch.💧(6x)€ 0,50/kWh. **Surface:** grassy. ⬛ 01/04-01/10
Distance: 🚶1km ⛽500m 🚲1km 🏪1km 🚌500m.

🛶S | **Reichenau** ⛵🏊 | 24C1

Zum Sandseele. **GPS:** n47,69887 e9,04711.⬆.

12 ⑤€8 ⚡€ 1/80liter 🔧Ch.💧(8x)€ 1/2kWh. **Surface:** asphalted/metalled. ⬛ 01/01-31/12
Distance: 🚶1,5km ⛽on the spot 🚲on the spot 🏪100m 🚆2km.
Remarks: Max. 1 night. Follow signs campsite.

🏞S | **Reutlingen** | 17C5

Am Südbahnhof/Marktstrasse. **GPS:** n48,48280 e9,22982.

3 ⑤free ⚡🔧Ch. **Surface:** gravel. ⬛ 01/01-31/12
Distance: 🚶3km 🚲on the spot 🚌on the spot.
Remarks: In front of motorhome dealer Berger.

🛶S | **Rheinau** 🌿 | 17A5

Weberhaus World of Living, Am Erlenpark 1, Linx.
GPS: n48,61944 e7,88709.⬆.

10 ⑤free ⚡🔧Ch.💧(4x)€ 1. **Location:** Rural, quit. **Surface:** metalled. ⬛ 01/01-31/12
Distance: 🚲100m 🚶on the spot 🏪on the spot.
Remarks: Parc for building and living.

🏞S | **Rheinmünster** ⛵🏊 | 17A4

Freizeit Center Oberrhein, Am Campingpark 1. **GPS:** n48,77312 e8,04044.⬆.

20 ⑤€8 ⚡€ 1/80liter 🔧Ch.💧(20x)€ 0,50/kWh. 🏪**Location:** Rural, comfortable, quit. **Surface:** grassy. ⬛ 01/01-31/12
Distance: 🏊on the spot 🚲200m 🚶on the spot 🚶on the spot.

🏞S | **Riedlingen** | 17D6

Stadthalle, Hindenburgstraße. **GPS:** n48,15189 e9,47766.
3 ⑤free ⚡€ 1 🔧Ch.💧€ 1. **Surface:** asphalted. ⬛ 01/01-31/12
Distance: 🚶300m.

🏞S | **Rottenburg/Neckar** 🌿⛵🍴🌊 | 17C5

Wohnmobilhafen am Neckarufer, Ulmenweg 4. **GPS:** n48,47213 e8,95010.
⬆➡.

12 ⑤free ⚡€ 1/80liter 🔧Ch.💧€ 0,50/kWh. **Surface:** asphalted. ⬛ 01/01-31/12
Distance: 🚶800m ⛽800m 🚲800m 🏪800m.
Remarks: Max. 4 days.

🏞S | **Rottenburg/Neckar** 🌿⛵🍴🌊 | 17C5

Weggentalstrasse. **GPS:** n48,48072 e8,92769.

5 ⑤free. **Surface:** gravel. ⬛ 01/01-31/12
Distance: 🚶500m 🏪500m 🚌100m.
Remarks: Along the Neckar river.

🏞S | **Rottweil** | 17B6

Parkplatz, Stadionstrasse. **GPS:** n48,15556 e8,62861.

20 ⑤free ⚡€ 1 🔧Ch.💧(16x)€ 1/8h. **Surface:** gravel. ⬛ 01/01-31/12
Distance: 🚶1km 🚲1km 🏪1km 🚌500m.
Remarks: Parking stadium.

DE

Rust 27B2

Europapark Rust, Europa-Parkstrasse. **GPS:** n48,27189 e7,71745.⬆➡.

200 🏕8-20h € 2/h (max. € 6), 20-8h € 2/h (max. € 22) ⛽€ 1 🗑
Ch ⚡ WC ▯included.▯🏠
Surface: asphalted.
🔵 03/04-07/11, 27/11-09/01 9-18
Distance: ⊗on the spot.

Tourist information Rust:
😊 Europa-park, Europa-Park-Straße 2.Large amusement and theme park with
Europe as theme. 🔵 03/04-07/11, 27/11-09/01 9-18h.

Sankt Blasien 24A1

Rehbachweg, Sankt Blasien. **GPS:** n47,81306 e8,06933.
20 🏕€ 6, tourist tax ⛽🗑 ⚡€ 3. **Surface:** unpaved. 🔵 01/01-31/12
Distance: 🚂St Blasien 8km.
Remarks: Parking ski-lifts.

Sankt Blasien 24A1

Am Dom, Fürstabt-Gerbert-Straße. **GPS:** n47,76039 e8,12923.⬆.
5 🏕free. **Surface:** metalled. 🔵 01/01-31/12
Distance: 🚂on the spot ⊗200m.

Sankt Blasien 24A1

Sportzentrum, Sebastian-Kneipp-Straße. **GPS:** n47,77176 e8,11311.
20 🏕free. **Surface:** asphalted/grassy. 🔵 01/01-31/12

Sasbachwalden 17A5

Wohnmobilstellplatz "Alde Gott" - Sasbachwalden

info@sasbachwalden.de - www.sasbachwalden.de

Beautiful view
Restaurant with regional specialties
Pleasant tourist resort

Wohnmobilstellplatz "Alde Gott", Talstraße 2. **GPS:** n48,61945 e8,12094.⬆
➡.
30 🏕€ 7 ⛽€ 1/100liter 🗑Ch ⚡ (20x)€ 2/24h. ▯🏠 **Location:** Rural,
comfortable, quit. **Surface:** gravel/metalled. 🔵 01/01-31/12
Distance: 🚂centre ±300m 🚲9km 🚶9km ⊗100m 🍴250m 🛒250m
🚶100m 🚴on the spot 🎿on the spot.
Remarks: Waterfall 1km, swimming pool 800m.

Saulgau 17D6

Sonnenhof Therme, Am Schönen Moos. **GPS:** n48,01372 e9,48166.
69 🏕1/5-31/10 € 7,1/11-30/4 € 8, tourist tax € 1, dog € 1 ⛽€ 0,50 🗑
Ch ⚡ WC▯€ 1,50 🗑📷 🔵 01/01-31/12
Distance: 🚂1km 🚲2km ⊗on the spot 🍴2km.
Remarks: Parking next to the spa resort.

Tourist information Saulgau:
ℹ Tourist Information, Lindenstrasse 7, www.t-b-g.de.Tourist town and health
resort.
😊 Sonnenhof Therme, Am Schönen Moos.Recognized health resort. 🔵 8-21h.

Schiltach 17B5

P1, Lehewiese. **GPS:** n48,29111 e8,34250.⬆➡.
10 🏕free ⛽ ⚡ (3x). **Location:** Quit.
Surface: gravel. 🔵 01/01-31/12
Distance: 🚂200m ⊗50m 🍴50m 🚶on the spot 🚴on the spot 🎿on the
spot.
Remarks: Busy parking during the day.

Schluchsee 24B1

P Aqua Fun, Faulenfürster Straße. **GPS:** n47,81569 e8,18113.
20 🏕free. **Surface:** metalled. 🔵 01/01-31/12
Distance: 🏊200m.
Remarks: Max. 1 night.

Schönach 17B6

Parkplatz Obertal, Obertalstrasse. **GPS:** n48,14977 e8,18018.

30 🏕€ 5 ⛽€ 1 🗑Ch ⚡. **Surface:** metalled.
Distance: 🎿nearby 🚴on the spot.
Remarks: Parking after swimming pool, coins available at tourist office,
mountainbike-, hiking- and winter cross-country trails.

Schonach im Schwarzwald 17B6

Parkplatz Obertal, Schwimmbadweg. **GPS:** n48,14573 e8,18872.⬆.

10 🏕€ 7 ⛽€ 1 🗑€ 0,50 Ch ⚡ (8x)€ 1/8h. **Surface:** grasstiles. 🔵
01/01-31/12
Distance: 🚂1km 🍴650m 🎿on the spot 🚴on the spot.
Remarks: Free entrance swimming pool, ski-lift and public transport, max. 3
nights.

Schorndorf 17D4

Gmünder Straße 84/1. **GPS:** n48,80539 e9,54187.
7 🏕€ 5 + € 4/pp ⛽🗑Ch ⚡ WC▯.
Surface: metalled. 🔵 01/01-31/12
Distance: 🚂10min.

Schramberg 17B5

Bahnhofstraße, B462. **GPS:** n48,23017 e8,38323.⬆.
2 🏕free ⛽€ 1/80liter 🗑€ 1 Ch€ 1. **Location:** Rural, very simple, noisy.
Surface: metalled. 🔵 01/01-31/12
Distance: 🚂on the spot ⊗100m 🍴50m 🚶10m 🚴on the spot 🎿on the
spot.

DE

Schwäbisch Gmünd — 17D4
Schiesstalplatz, Schiesstalstraße. **GPS:** n48,80543 e9,81308.⬆️

8 🚐free ⛽️€ 1/50liter 🗑️Ch ⚡️(8x)€ 0,50/kWh. **Surface:** gravel. ⬛ 01/01-31/12
Distance: 🚶1km ⊗50m 🚌500m.
Remarks: Motorhome < 7m.

Schwäbisch Hall — 17D3
P5 Weilerwiese, Johanniterstrasse. **GPS:** n49,11666 e9,73269.⬆️

4 🚐8-18 max. € 5, 18-8 max. € 2 ⛽️🗑️Ch ⚡️(4x)€ 1/3h. **Surface:** asphalted. ⬛ 01/01-31/12
Distance: 🚶200m.
Remarks: Follow P5.

Schwaigern — 17C3
Wohnmobilstellplatz Schaigern, Gemminger Straße 91. **GPS:** n49,14576 e9,04529.⬆️

2 🚐free ⛽️€ 1 🗑️Ch ⚡️free. **Surface:** asphalted. ⬛ 01/01-31/12
Distance: 🚶1km ⊗300m 🚲on the spot 🏊on the spot.

Schwetzingen — 17B3
Ketscher Landstrasse. **GPS:** n49,37803 e8,55820.⬆️

12 🚐free ⛽️€ 3/80liter 🗑️Ch. **Surface:** grasstiles/metalled. ⬛ 01/01-31/12
Distance: 🚶500m ⊗on the spot 🍴on the spot 🚲on the spot 🏊on the spot.
Remarks: Max. 3 night, noisy place.

Seelbach — 17A5
Reisemobil-Wellness-Stellplatz Schwarzwälder Hof, Am Tretenbach. **GPS:** n48,30042 e7,94497.⬆️

16 🚐€ 18 ⛽️€ 1/90liter 🗑️Ch ⚡️(16x)1kWh WC 🛜 📶 **Location:** Rural, comfortable. **Surface:** metalled. ⬛ 01/01-31/12
Distance: 🚶600m ⊗100m.
Remarks: Including access to swimming pool, use sanitary facilities, entrance 1p wellness/sauna.

Seewald — 17B5
P4, L362. **GPS:** n48,55111 e8,48444.⬆️➡️

17 🚐free ⛽️🗑️Ch WC free. **Location:** Rural, quit. **Surface:** asphalted. ⬛ 01/01-31/12 ⬤ service 01/11-31/03.
Distance: 🚶15min 🚌25m ⊗5 min 🛒Lidl 700m.

Sigmaringen — 17C6
Wohnmobilplatz Sigmaringen, Georg Zimmerer Straße 4. **GPS:** n48,08545 e9,21029.
20 🚐€ 5 ⛽️🗑️Ch ⚡️. **Surface:** metalled. ⬛ 01/01-31/12

Sindelfingen — 17C4
RALL-Caravanning GmbH, Mahdentalstrasse 84. **GPS:** n48,70583 e9,02808.⬆️

3 🚐free ⛽️€ 1/5minutes 🗑️€ 1 Ch€ 1 ⚡️(2x)free. **Surface:** asphalted/metalled. ⬛ 01/01-31/12
Distance: 🚶1km.
Remarks: Max. 1 night.

Singen — 24C1
Schaffhauserstrasse. **GPS:** n47,75992 e8,82766.⬆️➡️

20 ⛺free ⛽ 🔧 Ch 💧(16x)€ 1/12h. **Surface:** grassy/gravel. ⬤ 01/01-31/12, service 15/03-15/11
Distance: 🚶1km ⊗on the spot 🚗200m.
Remarks: Max. 72h.

| S | **Sinsheim** | 17C3 |

Schwimmbadweg 11b. **GPS:** n49,24778 e8,88667. ⬆️➡️.

5 ⛺free ⛽ 🔧 Ch WC 🔧. **Location:** Rural, comfortable, quit. **Surface:** asphalted. ⬤ 01/01-31/12
Distance: 🚶1,5km ⊗1,5km.
Remarks: Sanitairy at swimming pool.

| S | **Steinheim** | 17C4 |

Jürgen Sigrist Wohwagenabstellplätze, Boschstrasse 11. **GPS:** n48,96698 e9,26796. ⬆️.
2 ⛺ ⛽€ 1/80liter 🔧Ch.
Surface: asphalted. ⬤ Mo-Fri 8-17.30, Sa 8-12
Remarks: Service only during opening hours.

| S | **Stetten** 🌿 | 24C1 |

Alte Brennerei, Riedetsweilerstrasse 5. **GPS:** n47,69326 e9,29788. ⬆️.

15 ⛺€7 ⛽ 1 🔧 1 Ch 💧(6x)€ 0,50/kWh. **Surface:** grassy/gravel. ⬤ 01/01-31/12
Distance: 🚶300m ⛵2km 🚲2km ⊗300m 🛒300m 🚗300m.

| S | **Stockach/Bodensee** | 17C6 |

Reisemobilhafen 'Papiermühle', Johann-Glatt-strasse 3. **GPS:** n47,84169 e8,99945. ⬆️.

85 ⛺€10 ⛽ 0,50/50liter 🔧Ch 💧(118x) WC 🔧. **Surface:** gravel/metalled. ⬤ 01/01-31/12
Distance: 🚶1,5km ⊗on the spot 🚗700m.

| S | **Sulz am Neckar** 🚉 ⚓ | 17B5 |

Stellplatz Wöhrd, Ludwigstraße. **GPS:** n48,36427 e8,63681. ⬆️➡️.

6 ⛺free ⛽€ 1/80liter 🔧€ 1 Ch 💧(4x)€ 0,50,/kWh. **Location:** Rural, quit. **Surface:** metalled. ⬤ 01/01-31/12
Distance: 🚶300m ⊗100m 🛒100m 🚗on the spot 🚲on the spot 🚶on the spot.

| C S | **Sulzburg** 🚉 | 17A6 |

Camping Sulzbachtal, Sonnmatt 4. **GPS:** n47,84773 e7,69868. ⬆️➡️.

10 ⛺€15 + tourist tax + Ecotaxe ⛽ 🔧 Ch 💧(10x)€ 0,70/kWh WC 🔧 🖥️ 📶included. 🧺 🧼 **Location:** Comfortable. **Surface:** grassy/gravel. ⬤ 01/01-31/12
Distance: 🚶500m ⊗on the spot.

| S | **Tauberbisschofsheim** | 17D2 |

P Freibad, Vittryallee. **GPS:** n49,62155 e9,66632. ⬆️.

3 ⛺free ⛽ 🔧 Ch WC free 🔧€ 0,50, during opening hours. **Surface:** asphalted. ⬤ 01/01-31/12
Distance: 🚶500m ⊗300m 🛒300/600m 🚗500m.
Remarks: Service: Kläranlage.

| S | **Tettnang** | 24D1 |

Loretostrasse. **GPS:** n47,66425 e9,59175. ⬆️➡️.

14 ⛺€5 ⛽€ 1 🔧€ 1 Ch€ 1 💧(8x)€ 1/8h. 🚐 **Surface:** grassy/metalled. ⬤ 01/01-31/12
Distance: 🚶800m ⊗200m 🛒200m 🚗200m.

| C S | **Tettnang** | 24D1 |

Gutshof Camping Badhütten, Badhütten, Laimnau. **GPS:** n47,63370 e9,64668. ⬆️.

DE

70 ⌁€20 ⌁€ 1 Ch ⚡€ 1/3kWh WC ⌁€ 1. **Surface:** grassy. 🅾️ 01/01-31/12

4 ⌁free. **Surface:** metalled. 🅾️ 01/01-31/12
Distance: ⚓3km ⊗on the spot ⚑on the spot.
Remarks: Max. 2 nights.
Tourist information Trochtelfingen:
ℹ️ Historical little town with half-timbered houses.

© S | **Titisee** | 17A6
Camping Bankenhof, Bruderhalde 31a. **GPS:** n47,88643 e8,13046. ⬆️.
8 ⌁€ 12, 2 pers.incl ⌁ Ch ⚡ WC ⌁ 📶included. **Surface:** gravel/sand.
🅾️ 01/01-31/12
Distance: ⚓Titisee 600m.

🅿️S | **Trossingen** | 17B6
Reisemobilplatz am Naturbad Troase, Steppach 5. **GPS:** n48,07703 e8,62192.
⬆️➡️

🅿️S | **Todtmoos** ♈ | 24A1
Jägermatt, Vordertodtmoos. **GPS:** n47,73390 e8,00285. ⬆️➡️.

30 ⌁€5 ⌁ Ch ⚡included.
Surface: gravel/metalled. 🅾️ 01/01-31/12
Distance: ⚓1km ⚑50m.

8 ⌁€4 ⌁€ 1/100liter Ch ⚡€ 1/12h.
Surface: gravel. 🅾️ 01/01-31/12

🅿️S | **Triberg im Schwarzwald** | 17B6
Sommerauer Strasse, Nußberg. **GPS:** n48,13161 e8,25294. ⬆️➡️.

🅿️S | **Tuttlingen** 🛁 | 17C6
Stellplatz Donaupark, Stuttgarter strasse. **GPS:** n47,98490 e8,81316. ⬆️.

20 ⌁free. **Surface:** gravel. 🅾️ 01/01-31/12
Distance: ⚓300m.

10 ⌁free ⌁€ 1/5minutes ⌁€ 1 Ch 📶. **Surface:** metalled. 🅾️ 01/01-31/12
Distance: ⚓500m ⊗500m ⚑500m 🚌500m.
Remarks: Max. 3 nights.

🅿️S | **Trochtelfingen** 🌿🛁🍰 | 17C5
Eberhard-von Werderberg-Halle, Siemensstrasse. **GPS:** n48,30811 e9,23546.
➡️.

🅿️S | **Überlingen** ♈ | 24C1
Reisemobilhafen Überlingen, Kurt-Hahn-strasse. **GPS:** n47,77617 e9,15046.

20 ⌁€ 3 ⌁€ 1/80liter Ch ⚡(4x)free, 16Amp. **Surface:** gravel. 🅾️ 01/01-31/12
Distance: ⚓Old city centre ⚑500m 🚌500m.

20 ⌁€ 6-10 ⌁€ 0,50/70liter ⌁€ 0,50 Ch ⚡(30x)€ 0,50/2kWh WC.
Surface: asphalted/gravel. 🅾️ 01/01-31/12
Distance: ⚓1km ⚓1km ⚓1km ⊗200m ⚑1,5km 🚌200m.
Remarks: Price incl. bus transport (max. 5 pers) to the city centre.

🅿️ | **Trochtelfingen** 🌿🛁🍰 | 17C5
Kräuter- und Erlebnisgarten Alb-Gold Nudelfabrik, Grindel 1. **GPS:** n48,32838 e9,24001.

🅿️S | **Uhldingen-Mühlhofen** | 24C1
Ehbachstrasse. **GPS:** n47,72535 e9,23649. ⬆️.

DE

19 🚐 € 10 🚰 € 1 🚽 € 1 Ch WC. **Surface:** grasstiles/metalled. 🅾 01/01-31/12
Distance: 🚶1km ⛰2km 🏊2km 🛒kiosk on the spot.
Remarks: Parking at edge of the village, max. 24h.

Tourist information Uhldingen-Mühlhofen:
ℹ️ Tourist Information, Schulstrasse 12, www.seeferien.com. Tourist town on the Lake Constance.
Ⓜ️ Pfalbaumuseum. Reconstruction village from 4000-850 before Christ. 🅾 01/04-31/10 daily 8-18/17h, 01/11-31/03 Sa-Su 9-16h.

🚐S	Ulm	17D5

P+R Friedrichsau, Wielandstrasse. **GPS:** n48,40774 e10,00929.

50 🚐free 🚰 € 1 🚽 Ch. **Surface:** metalled. 🅾 01/01-31/12
Distance: 🚻175m 🍴on the spot.
Remarks: Max. 3 days, green zone: environmental badge obligatory.

Tourist information Ulm:
ℹ️ Ulm Touristik, Neue strasse 45, www.tourismus.ulm.de.

🚐S	Ummendorf	17D6

Bräuhaus Ummendorf, Bachstrasse 10. **GPS:** n48,06340 e9,83252. ⬆️➡️

5 🚐free 🚰 🚿 (5x)€ 3 WC 🚽 € 3 🚰.
Surface: metalled. 🅾 01/01-31/12
Distance: 🚶300m 🚻on the spot 🍺800m 🍴100m.
Remarks: 3 days free stay.

🚐S	Unterkirnach 🌿⛰🏛	17B6

Reisemobilhafen Am Rathaus, Rathausplatz. **GPS:** n48,07719 e8,36707. ⬆️

16 🚐 € 9 🚰 🚽 Ch 🚿 included. **Surface:** metalled. 🅾 01/01-31/12
Distance: 🚶on the spot ⛰400m 🏊500m 🚻200m 🍺300m 🍴200m 🏥150m 🛒400m.
Remarks: Behind townhall, alternative arrangement if full.

🍴S	Unterkirnach 🌿⛰🏛	17B6

Ackerloch-Metzgerei-Grillschopf, Unteres Ackerloch 2. **GPS:** n48,08473 e8,36573.
20 🚐 € 4 + €1,80/pp tourist tax 🚰 🚽 Ch 🚿 WC. **Surface:** unpaved.
Distance: 🚻on the spot.

Tourist information Unterkirnach:
ℹ️ Tourismusbüro Unterkirnach, Hauptstraße 5, www.unterkirnach.de.

🚐S	Untermünkheim	17D3

Wohnmobilpark Ostertag, Kupfer Straße 20, Übrigshausen. **GPS:** n49,17603 e9,71321.
10 🚐 🚰 🚽 Ch 🚿. **Surface:** metalled. 🅾 01/03-30/11

🚐S	Villingen/Schwenningen 🌿⛰🏛🏔❄️	17B6

Messegelände VS-Schwenningen, Waldeckweg. **GPS:** n48,05028 e8,54056. ⬆️
4 🚐free 🚰 € 1 🚽 Ch. **Surface:** asphalted. 🅾 01/01-31/12
Distance: 🚶1km 🍺500m.

🍴S	Villingen/Schwenningen 🌿⛰🏛🏔❄️	17B6

Wohnmobilstellplatz Alte Ölmühle, Stumpenstraße 27, Obereschach. **GPS:** n48,10381 e8,47890.
12 🚐 € 7,50 🚰 🚽 Ch 🚿 WC 🚽 🚰. 🅾 01/01-31/12
Distance: 🚻on the spot.

🚐	Vogtsburg im Kaiserstuhl	17A6

Hauptstraße/L115, Oberrotweil. **GPS:** n48,09000 e7,64361.

8 🚐free. **Location:** Rural, very simple, isolated, quit. **Surface:** . 🅾 01/01-31/12
Distance: 🚶800m.

🚐S	Waiblingen 🌿⛰🏛🏔	17C4

Parkplatz Hallenbad, An der Talaue. **GPS:** n48,83029 e9,32540.

20 🚐 € 6/24h, 19-9h € 2 🚰 € 1/80liter 🚽 Ch 🚿 (6x)€ 1, 16Amp WC.
Surface: gravel. 🅾 01/01-31/12
Distance: 🚶500m ⛰500m 🚻50m 🍺300m 🍴600m.
Remarks: Parking swimming pool, during congresses special tariff.

🚐S	Waldkirch 🍴🏔	17A6

Reisemobilstellplatz Am Stadpark, Am Stadtrain. **GPS:** n48,09023 e7,95833. ⬆️

10 🍴free 🚰€ 1/80liter 🚽€ 1 Ch€ 1. **Location:** Urban, central. **Surface:** asphalted. ⬛ 01/01-31/12
Distance: 🚶500m.
Remarks: Max. 2 days.

📷S **Waldshut-Tiengen** 24B1
Wohmobil-Park Waldshut-Tiengen, Jahnweg 22, Waldshut. **GPS:** n47,61121 e8,22513.⬆.
44 🍴€10 🚰€ 1/100liter 🚽Ch 🔌(54x)€ 1/kWh ⬛ 0,50. **Surface:** metalled. ⬛ 01/01-31/12
Distance: ⊗on the spot.
Remarks: Along the Rhine river, bread-service.

📷S **Walldürn** 17C2
Auerbergzentrum, Theodor-Heuss-Ring. **GPS:** n49,58506 e9,35421.⬆.

50 🍴free 🚰€ 1/80liter 🚽Ch 🔌(4x)€ 0,50/kWh, 6Amp. **Surface:** metalled. ⬛ 01/01-31/12
Distance: 🚶800m ⊗on the spot 🍴300m 🚌on the spot.

📷S **Walldürn** 17C2
Goldschmitt Technik-Center, Industrieparkstrasse. **GPS:** n49,58977 e9,39339.

30 🍴free 🚰€ 1/80liter 🚽Ch 🔌(12x)€ 0,50/kWh. **Surface:** asphalted. ⬛ 01/01-31/12
Distance: 🚶800m.

📷S **Wangen im Allgäu** 24D1
P17, Am Klösterle. **GPS:** n47,68160 e9,83401.⬆➡.

40 🍴€8 🚰€ 0,50/120liter 🚽Ch 🔌(28x) WC. **Surface:** metalled. ⬛ 01/01-31/12

Distance: 🚶on the spot 🚲500m 🚌500m ⊗on the spot 🍴on the spot 🚌on the spot.
Remarks: Tourist tax € 1.

Tourist information Wangen im Allgäu:
ℹ Tourist Information, Parkplatz 1, Rathaus.Traditional small Bavarian town. Every Thursday city walk through historical city centre, 15.30-17. 🕐 free. 🚶 ⬛ Wed.

📷S **Wehr** 24A1
Ludingarten. **GPS:** n47,62515 e7,90582.
7 🍴free 🚰€ 1/100liter 🚽Ch 🔌€ 1/8h WC. **Surface:** metalled. ⬛ 01/01-31/12
Remarks: At park.

📷S **Weikersheim** 17D2
P HL-Wöhr, Heiliges Wöhr. **GPS:** n49,48197 e9,89708.⬆.

4 🍴free. **Surface:** metalled. ⬛ 01/01-31/12
Distance: 🚶200m 🍴300m.

📷S **Weikersheim** 17D2
Parkplatz Tauberwiesen, Romantische Strasse. **GPS:** n49,48389 e9,89599.

10 🍴free. **Surface:** grasstiles. ⬛ 01/01-31/12
Distance: 🚶300m 🍴400m.

©S **Weikersheim** 17D2
Campingplatz Schwabenmühle, Weikersheimer Strasse 21, Laudenbach. **GPS:** n49,45795 e9,92691.⬆.

10 🍴€7 🚰🚽Ch 🔌 against payment . **Surface:** gravel. ⬛ 01/01-31/12
Distance: 🚶300m 🚌200m.

📷S **Weil der Stadt** 17C4
Festplatz, Jahnstrasse. **GPS:** n48,75268 e8,87453.⬆➡.

4 🛏free ⚡€ 1/80liter 🔲€ 1 Ch€ 1 ⚡(4x)€ 1/kWh. **Location:** Urban, noisy. **Surface:** asphalted. ⬛ 01/01-31/12
Distance: 🚶300m ⊗300m 🚉250m ⚓on the spot ⚘on the spot.
Remarks: Max. 3 days.

🔲S	Weingarten	17D6

Festplatz, Abt Hyller Strasse 55. **GPS:** n47,81009 e9,63041.⬆️.
8 🛏€ 5 ⚡€ 2 🔲 Ch ⚡€ 2. **Surface:** metalled. ⬛ 01/01-31/12
Distance: 🚶1km.

🔲S	Weinsberg	17C3

Eugen-Diez-Straße 2. **GPS:** n49,14846 e9,28464.⬆️➡️.
6 🛏free ⚡€ 1 🔲 Ch ⚡(6x)€ 0,50/kWh. **Location:** Rural, quit. **Surface:** grasstiles. ⬛ 01/01-31/12
Distance: 🚶500m ⚘2km ⚓on the spot ⚘on the spot.

🔲S	Welzheim	17D4

Aichstruter Stausee, Seiboldsweiler, Aichstrut. **GPS:** n48,90020 e9,63719.⬆️.

12 🛏€ 5 ⚡€ 1/80liter 🔲 Ch WC. **Surface:** gravel. ⬛ 01/01-31/12
Distance: 🚶5km ⊗on the spot.
Remarks: At artificial lake.

🔲S	Wertheim	17D1

Wohnmobilstellplatz An der Taubermündung, Linke Tauberstrasse. **GPS:** n49,76040 e9,51425.⬆️➡️.

54 🛏€ 5/24h ⚡€ 1/90liter 🔲Ch. **Surface:** gravel. ⬛ 01/01-31/12 ⬤ 2nd sa of the month + high water.
Distance: 🚶500m.
Remarks: Along the Tauber river, max. 3 days.

🔲S	Wertheim	17D1

Expocamp, Wertheim Caravaning & Freizeit, Hymerring 1. **GPS:** n49,77368 e9,58034.⬆️.

90 🛏free ⚡€ 1/90liter 🔲Ch ⚡€ 1/3h WC during opening hours.
Surface: asphalted. ⬛ 01/01-31/12
Distance: ⊗400m 🚉3,7km.
Remarks: Bread-service mo-sa.

Tourist information Wertheim:

ℹ️ Tourist Information, Wenzelplatz 2, www.tourist-wertheim.de.Small tourist town with historical centre.
Ⓜ️ Glasmuseum, Mühlenstrasse 24. ⬛ 01/04-31/10 Tue-Fri 10-12h, 14-17h, Sa-Su 14-17h.
🛒 Wertheim Village, Almosenberg.Outlet-shopping.

🔲S	Wolfach	17B5

Trendcamping Schwarzwald, Schiltacher Straße 80, Halbmeil. **GPS:** n48,29053 e8,27763.⬆️.

6 🛏€ 15 + tourist tax ⚡🔲 Ch WC ⬛included 🔲 📶€ 2 ⚡🧺. **Location:** Quit. **Surface:** grassy/sand. ⬛ 10/04-15/10
Distance: ⊗on the spot.

🔲S	Wolfach	17B5

Ferienhof Bartleshof, Ippichen 6, Ippichen. **GPS:** n48,30183 e8,26264.⬆️➡️.

5 🛏€ 15 ⚡🔲 Ch ⚡(2x). 🧺 **Location:** Rural. **Surface:** grassy/gravel. ⬛ 01/01-31/12
Distance: ⊗on the spot.
Remarks: € 10, reduction at restaurant.

🔲	Wolfegg/Allgäu	17D6

Gemeindehalle, Rötenbacher strasse 13. **GPS:** n47,81636 e9,79780.⬆️.

4 🛏free. **Surface:** metalled. ⬛ 01/01-31/12

DE

Distance: 🚶200m ⛰2km 🚲2km ⊗500m 🛒500m 🚌500m.
Remarks: Max. 3 nights.

| 🏕 | Wolfegg/Allgäu | 17D6 |

Hofgarten, Alttaner strasse. **GPS:** n47,82105 e9,79487. ⬆.

2 🏕free. **Surface:** gravel/metalled. ⚪ 01/01-31/12
Distance: 🚶on the spot.
Remarks: Max. 2 nights.

| 🍴🚿S | Wolfegg/Allgäu | 17D6 |

Gasthaus Adler, Eintürnerstrasse 38, Molpertshaus. **GPS:** n47,87029 e9,80622. ⬆.

4 🏕€4 🚰🔌€ 0,50 Ch 🔌€ 0,50/kWh. **Surface:** gravel/metalled. ⚪ 01/01-31/12
Distance: 🚶on the spot ⊗on the spot.

| 🚻 | Wolfegg/Allgäu | 17D6 |

Gasthof zum Bräuhaus, Rossberg 1. **GPS:** n47,86776 e9,78182. ⬆.

3 🏕free. **Surface:** metalled. ⚪ 01/01-31/12
Distance: ⊗on the spot.

| 🍴 | Wolfegg/Allgäu | 17D6 |

Hotel-Gasthof zur Post, Rötenbacher strasse 5. **GPS:** n47,81978 e9,79339.

4 🏕. ⚪ 01/01-31/12
Distance: 🚶on the spot ⊗on the spot.

| 🛁 | Wolfegg/Allgäu | 17D6 |

Kurpark Wolfegg-Altann. **GPS:** n47,83861 e9,78750.
2 🏕free.
Remarks: Max. 2 nights.

Tourist information Wolfegg/Allgäu:
ℹ️ Tourist Information, Rötenbacher strasse 13
.Health resort.
Ⓜ️ Automobilmuseum.200 oldtimers. ⚪ 01/04-31/10 9.30-18h, 01/11-31/03
Su 10-17h.
Ⓜ️ Bauernhaus-museum.Open air museum. ⚪ 01/04-31/10 Tue-Su 10-18/17h
⚫ Mo Apr Oct.

| 🍴🚿S | Wutöschingen | 24B1 |

Wohnmobilplatz Degernau, Ofteringer Strasse 1, Degernau. **GPS:** n47,66639
e8,37917. ⬆➡.

12 🏕€6/day, 2 pers.incl 🚰€ 1 🔌Ch🔌 (12x)€ 0,50/kWh WC 🚿€ 1 ⊡€
3. **Surface:** grassy/gravel. ⚪ 01/03-31/10
Distance: 🛒10 min walking 🚌on the spot.
Remarks: Sauna, solarium.

| 🏕S | Zell am Harmersbach ⛰ | 17A5 |

Stellplatz am Schwimmbad, Nordracher Strasse. **GPS:** n48,35146 e8,05942. ⬆
➡.

14 🏕€3/20-12h 🚰€ 1/10minutes 🔌Ch🔌 (8x)€ 1/10h. 📷 **Location:**
Rural, quit. **Surface:** gravel. ⚪ 01/01-31/12
Distance: 🚶2km 🛒2km.

Tourist information Zell am Harmersbach:
ℹ️ Tourist Info, Alte Kanzlei, www.zell.de.Old centre worth seeing.
Ⓜ️ Storchenturmmuseum.Town history. ⚪ 01/04-31/10 14-17h. 🎫 € 1,50.

Bavaria

| 🏕S | Absberg | 18B3 |

Badehalbinsel Brombachsee, Gunzenhausen-Pleinfeld Ausfart Absberg. **GPS:**
n49,13770 e10,87389.

150 🏕€8/24h 🚰€ 0,20/60liter 🔌Ch🔌 (80x)€ 0,50/kWh WC 🚿€ 0,50.
📷 **Location:** Rural, comfortable, quit.
Surface: grassy. ⚪ 01/04-01/10
Distance: 🚶1km ⛰on the spot ⊗on the spot 🛒1km 🚴on the spot 🚶on
the spot.

Tourist information Absberg:
ℹ️ Health resort on the Kleiner Brombachsee and Igelsbachsee.

DE

▤ Adelsdorf 18B2
Neuhauser Hauptstrasse. **GPS:** n49,68500 e10,87556.

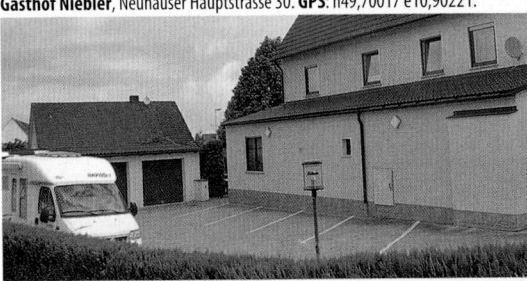

▤free. **Surface:** metalled.
Remarks: Next to sports fields.

▯▯S Adelsdorf 18B2
Gasthof Niebler, Neuhauser Hauptstrasse 30. **GPS:** n49,70017 e10,90221.

4 ▤guests free 🚰 🧹. **Surface:** metalled.
Distance: 🛒on the spot ⊗on the spot.

▤ Ahorn 10C6
Freizeitzentrum Wittman, Badstrasse 20, Eicha. **GPS:** n50,22537 e10,90252.

4 ▤free. **Surface:** metalled. ⬛ 01/01-31/12
Distance: 🛒on the spot 🚰5km.

▤S Aichach 18B5
Reisemobilplatz, Franz-Beck-Strasse. **GPS:** n48,45889 e11,12611.⬆.

4 ▤€5 🚰 ⬛Chfree. ♨ **Location:** Urban, very simple, quit. **Surface:** grassy/gravel. ⬛ 01/01-31/12
Distance: 🛒500m ⊗500m 🚰100m.

▤S Albertshofen 18A1
An der Fähre Mainstockheim-Albertshofen, Mainstraße. **GPS:** n49,77254 e10,15749.⬆.

10 ▤€5 🚰 ⬛Ch 🧹 included. **Surface:** gravel. ⬛ 01/01-31/12
Distance: 🛒on the spot 🏊on the spot ⊗50m.
Remarks: Along Main river, closed when high water.

▯▯S Altenstadt 18A5
Gasthof Sonne, Bahnhofstrasse 8-10. **GPS:** n48,16040 e10,11045.

3 ▤free with a meal 🚰.

▯▯S Altmannstein 18C3
Gasthof Forster, Schulstrasse 9. **GPS:** n48,90125 e11,69559.

20 ▤guests free 🚰 🧹 (4x)€ 2/night.
Surface: asphalted. ⬛ 01/01-31/12
Distance: 🛒on the spot ⊗on the spot 🚰3km.
Remarks: Check in before 19h (Mo-Tue 16h), bread service.

▤S Altötting 19A5
Griesstraße. **GPS:** n48,22946 e12,67493.⬆.

8 ▤free 🚰€ 1/80liter ⬛Ch 🧹 (8x)€ 1/4h WC. **Location:** Urban, very simple, noisy. **Surface:** grasstiles. ⬛ 01/01-31/12
Distance: 🛒5 min ⊗on the spot 🚰on the spot.
Remarks: Max. 3 days.

▤S Altötting 19A5
P2 Dultplatz, Traunsteinerstrasse. **GPS:** n48,22287 e12,67921.⬆.

7 🛏free ⚡€ 1/10liter 🔌 💧(8x)€ 1/4h. **Location:** Urban, central. **Surface:** gravel. 🅿 01/01-31/12
Distance: 🚶700m.
Remarks: Max. 3 days.

Tourist information Altötting:
ℹ Verkehrsbüro Altötting im Rathaus, Kapellplatz 2a, www.altoetting-touristinfo.de.

🛏S Altusried 18A6
Am Freibad, Im Tal 4. **GPS:** n47,79915 e10,21934. ⬆➡

10 🛏€5 ⚡€ 1 🔌Ch 💧€ 0,50/1kWh. 🏠**Location:** Rural, quit. **Surface:** grassy/gravel. 🅿 01/01-31/12
Distance: 🚶500m 🚊700m.
Remarks: Parking at swimming pool.

🛏S Alzenau 17C1
Wenzel's Weinscheune, Schlossbergstrasse 5. **GPS:** n50,07023 e9,07752.

10 🛏guests free ⚡ 💧.
Distance: 🚶on the spot ⊗on the spot 🚊1km.

🛏S Amberg 18C2
Gasfabrikstraße. **GPS:** n49,44139 e11,86222. ⬆➡

10 🛏free ⚡€ 1/80liter 🔌Ch 💧(12x)€ 1/12h. **Surface:** asphalted. 🅿 01/01-31/12
Distance: 🚶500m ⊗1km 🚊1km.

Tourist information Amberg:
ℹ Tourist Information, Zeughausstrasse 1a, www.amberg.de. 🅣 € 2.

🛏S Ansbach 18A3
Freizeitbad Aquella, Am Stadion 2. **GPS:** n49,30459 e10,55852. ⬆➡

12 🛏free ⚡€ 0,50/50liter 🔌Ch 💧(12x)€ 0,50/kWh. **Location:** Central. **Surface:** metalled. 🅿 01/01-31/12
Distance: 🚶1km 🚲7,7km ⊗on the spot 🚊1km 🚌on the spot.
Remarks: At swimming pool.

🛏 Ansbach 18A3
Autohof Ansbach, Vetterstrasse 1. **GPS:** n49,26295 e10,58381.
50 🛏€ 6, reduction for guests. **Surface:** asphalted. 🅿 01/01-31/12
Distance: 🚶2km 🚲700m ⊗on the spot 🚊on the spot.

🍴S Arnbruck 19A3
Landhotel Rappenhof, Rappendorf 5. **GPS:** n49,13517 e12,95069.

5 🛏€ 10 ⚡🔌Ch 💧WC ⌐included. **Surface:** grassy. 🅿 01/01-31/12
Distance: 🚶2km ⊗on the spot 🚊2km 🏊10km 🚠8km.
Remarks: Use of sauna against payment.

🛏 Arnstein 17D1
Badesee, Am Alten Schwimmbad. **GPS:** n49,97667 e9,95917. ⬆

3 🛏free. **Surface:** grassy. 🅿 01/01-31/12
Distance: 🚶100m ⊗snack 100m.
Remarks: At the old swimming pool.

🛏 Arnstein 17D1
Cancale Platz. **GPS:** n49,97625 e9,96564.

5 🛏free. **Surface:** metalled. 🅿 01/01-31/12
Distance: 🚶100m ⊗100m 🚊100m.

Arnstein   17D1

Caravaning Arnstein, Michael Wenzstrasse 9. **GPS:** n49,97361 e9,98444.

2 free   Ch free. **Surface:** metalled. 01/01-31/12

Arzberg   11A6

Am Rathausplatz. **GPS:** n50,05528 e12,18870.
2 free. **Surface:** metalled. 01/01-31/12
Distance: 250m 300m 250m.

Aschaffenburg   17C1

Grossostheimerstrasse. **GPS:** n49,97139 e9,13722.

25 € 3/24h Ch (18x)€ 0,50/kWh.
Surface: grassy/gravel.
01/01-31/12
Distance: historical centre 500m 8km.
Remarks: Parking along the Main, Altstadt, being indicated with with small signs, max. 3 days.

Tourist information Aschaffenburg:
Tourist Information, Schlossplatz 1, www.info-aschaffenburg.de.Historical centre.
Schloß Johannisburg.
Automuseum Rosso Bianco, Obernauer strasse 125.Collection of sports cars containing many makes including Porsche, Alfa Romeo, Ferrari, Lamborghini.
Su 10-18h 24/12-01/01. € 9, family card (5pers) € 23.
Stadtfest.City celebration. end Aug.
Voksfest, Volksfestplatz am Mainufer.Large folk festival. 2 week Jun.

Asschheim   18C5

Gasthof Zur Post, Ismaningerstrasse 11. **GPS:** n48,17433 e11,71490.

10 € 10. **Surface:** asphalted. 01/01-31/12
Distance: on the spot on the spot 300m.

Aufseß   18B1

Brauerei-Gasthof Reichold, Hochstahl 24. **GPS:** n49,88389 e11,26855.

38 € 5 1/90liter Ch (38x)€ 1 WC . **Surface:** grassy/metalled. 01/01-31/12
Distance: on the spot.
Remarks: Bread-service, breakfast buffet € 6/pp.

Augsburg   18B5

Schillstraße 109, Lechhausen. **GPS:** n48,38914 e10,90435.

4 € 5 Ch 1/2kWh WC . Location: Urban. **Surface:** gravel. 01/01-31/12
Distance: 3,2km Sportgastätte 200m on the spot on the spot.
Remarks: At sports centre.

Augsburg   18B5

Wohnmobilstellplatz Wertach, Bürgemeister Ackermann strasse 1. **GPS:** n48,36944 e10,87750.

12 € 8 1/90liter Ch 1/6h. Location: Urban, very simple.
Surface: gravel. 01/01-31/12
Distance: on the spot 4,5km on the spot on the spot 500m 500m.

Bad Abbach   18D3

Kaiser-Therme, Kurallee 4. **GPS:** n48,92712 e12,04044.

28 € 8 + € 1,80/pp 1/4minutes Ch (16x) WC . **Surface:** grasstiles/grassy. 01/01-31/12
Distance: 2km.
Remarks: Check in at pay-desk of the Therme.

DE

⛫Ⓢ Bad Aibling ⚓ ♉ 18D6

Stellplatz an der Therme P13, Lindenstrasse/Heubergstrasse. **GPS**: n47,85639 e12,00583. ⬆➡

25 ⌧€7 ⛽€ 🔌Ch ⚡€ 0,50/kWh. **Location:** Comfortable. **Surface:** grasstiles/metalled. ⬛ 01/01-31/12
Distance: 🚶500m ⛰400m ⊗500m 🛒600m 🚌100m.

⛫Ⓢ Bad Bayersoien 25B1

Wohnmobilstellplatz Bad Bayersoien, Am Bahnhof 6. **GPS**: n47,68798 e10,99820. ➡

12 ⌧€ 9/24h ⛽€ 1/90liter 🔌Ch ⚡€ 1/2kWh. **Location:** Rural, quit.
Surface: gravel. ⬛ 01/01-31/12
Distance: 🚶400m ⛰300m 🚲300m ⊗400m 🛒400m.

©Ⓢ Bad Birnbach ♉ 19B4

Camping Arterhof, Hauptstraße 3, Lengham. **GPS**: n48,43512 e13,10939. ⬆

10 ⌧€ 10 ⛽ 🔌Ch WC ⤵ 📶included. **Location:** Rural, quit. **Surface:** gravel.
⬛ 01/01-31/12
Distance: ⊗on the spot.

⛫Ⓢ Bad Bocklet ♉ 10B6

Aschacherstrasse. **GPS**: n50,26490 e10,07486. ⬆➡

13 ⌧€ 6 ⛽€ 1/80liter 🔌Ch ⚡(13x)€ 0,50/kWh. **Surface:** metalled. ⬛
01/01-31/12
Distance: 🚶500m 🚌Free bus to Bad Kissingen.

⛫Ⓢ Bad Brückenau 10B6

Schlosspark König Ludwig I, Schlüchterner Straße. **GPS**: n50,30556 e9,74861.
⬆➡

10 ⌧€8 ⛽€ 1/100liter 🔌Ch ⚡€ 0,50/kWh. **Surface:** asphalted. ⬛
01/01-31/12
Distance: 🚶4km 🚌50m.

⛫Ⓢ Bad Brückenau 10B6

Sinnflut, Industriestrasse P5. **GPS**: n50,31212 e9,79607. ⬆➡

8 ⌧€3 ⛽🔌Ch ⚡(8x). **Surface:** gravel. ⬛ 01/01-31/12
Distance: 🚶250m ⊗250m 🛒250m.
Remarks: Parking swimming pool.

⛫Ⓢ Bad Brückenau 10B6

Stellplatz Bahnhofstrasse, Buchwaldstrasse. **GPS**: n50,30667 e9,78556. ⬆

8 ⌧free ⚡€ 0,50. **Surface:** metalled. ⬛ 01/01-31/12
Distance: 🚶50m ⊗on the spot 🛒on the spot 🚌on the spot.

⛺Ⓢ Bad Brückenau 10B6

Pension Breitenbach, D286, Römershag. **GPS**: n50,31944 e9,82000.

3 ⌧free, use of a meal desired ⚡WC. **Surface:** asphalted/metalled. ⬛
01/01-31/12
Distance: 🚶2km ⊗on the spot.

⛺ Bad Feilnbach 18D6

Gasthof Tiroler Hof, Aiblinger strasse 95. **GPS**: n47,76476 e12,03857. ⬆⬆.

3 🛏guests free.
Location: Isolated. **Surface:** gravel. ☐ 01/01-31/12
Distance: 🚶on the spot ⊗on the spot ☎1km.

30 🛏€ 8-10 + tourist tax € 2,10/pp, 7><16 € 1,60, <7 € 0,90 ⟿ 1/100liter
🍴Ch 🔌€ 0,50/kWh WC⌷€ 1 🔊. 🚿 **Location:** Rural, luxurious, quit.
Surface: grassy/gravel. ☐ 01/01-31/12
Distance: ⊗on the spot ☎1km 🧍on the spot.

© Ⓢ | **Bad Füssing** 🏊 | 19B5
Campingplatz Holmerhof, Am Tennispark 10. **GPS:** n48,35798 e13,30658.⬆.

© Ⓢ | **Bad Hindelang** 🏔❄ | 25A1
Wohnmobilplatz Bergheimat, Passstraße 60, Oberjoch. **GPS:** n47,51791
e10,42142.⬆ .

9 🛏€ 9,10 ⟿ 1/30liter 🍴Ch 🔌(9x)€ 2/kWh WC⌷€ 2. **Location:**
Rural, very simple. **Surface:** metalled. ☐ 01/01-31/12
Distance: 🚶1km ⊗on the spot ☎1km.
Remarks: Max. 3 days, swimming pool available, use sanitary € 5/motorhome.

10 🛏€ 15, dog € 3,50 ⟿ 🍴Ch 🔌WC⌷€ 1 🔊.🚿 **Location:** Rural, very
simple, noisy. **Surface:** grassy/gravel. ☐ 01/01-31/12
Distance: ⊘on the spot 🛁on the spot.

🛏Ⓢ | **Bad Gögging** 🏊 | 18C4
Limes-Therme, Am Brunnenforum 1. **GPS:** n48,81857 e11,78868.⬆.

🛏Ⓢ | **Bad Kissingen** 🌿🏊🏊 | 10B6
KissSalis Therme, Heiligenfelder Allee 16. **GPS:** n50,18861 e10,06139. ⬆➡.

+20 🛏€ 8, tourist tax excl ⟿€ 1 🍴Ch. **Surface:** asphalted. ☐ 01/01-31/12
Distance: 🚶150m ⊗150m ☎150m.
Remarks: Check in at pay-desk of the Therme.

18 🛏€ 4 + € 3,30/pp ⟿€ 1/90liter 🍴Ch 🔌€ 1/8h. **Surface:** asphalted.
☐ 01/01-31/12
Distance: 🚶500m 🛁on the spot.

🛏Ⓢ | **Bad Griesbach** 🏊 | 19B4
Mobilhafen Dreiquellenbad, Singham 40. **GPS:** n48,42023 e13,19261.⬆.

© Ⓢ | **Bad Kohlgrub** | 25B1
Kur-Camping Waldruh, Sonnen 93. **GPS:** n47,65789 e11,04393.⬆.

29 🛏€ 16, incl tourist tax ⟿€ 1/80liter 🍴Ch 🔌(29x)€ 0,60/kWh
⌷included 🔊€ 5. **Location:** Rural, quit. **Surface:** metalled. ☐ 01/01-31/12
Distance: 🚶2km ⊗on the spot.
Remarks: Thermal-Vital-Oase incl., max. 3 days.

16 🛏€ 10,40 + € 2,50/pp ⟿ 🍴Ch 🔌€ 0,40/kWh WC⌷€ 2,50 🔊📷
Surface: gravel. ☐ 01/01-31/12
Distance: 🚶1,5km 🛁1,5km.

🛏Ⓢ | **Bad Hindelang** 🏔❄ | 25A1
Wiesengrund Wohnmobilpark, Parkplatz Wiesengrund 1. **GPS:** n47,49931
e10,37218. ⬆➡.

🛏Ⓢ | **Bad Kohlgrub** | 25B1
Sanatorium Kurhaus Dr. Lauter, Kurhausstrasse 81. **GPS:** n47,66412 e11,04315.
⬆ .

DE

4 ⌾ € 12 ⚒ ⚓.
Location: Rural, quit. **Surface:** gravel. ⬛ 01/01-31/12
Distance: ⚒1,5km ⊗on the spot ⚓1,5km ⚒1km ⚓1km.

⬆Ⓢ Bad Königshofen — 10C6
Frankentherme, Am Kurzentrum 1. **GPS:** n50,30003 e10,47503. ⬆➡.

77 ⌾ € 8,50 ⚒ € 1 ⬛Ch.⚒ € 0,50/kWh WC⬛. **Surface:** grasstiles/met-
alled. ⬛ 01/01-31/12
Remarks: Special health arrangements possible, washing-machine/dryer
available, if full 2 alternatives will be given.

Tourist information Bad Königshofen:
ℹ Kurverwaltung Königshofen, Am Kurzentrum 1, www.bad-koenigshofen.
de.Traditional small town with half-timbered houses, cycle and hiking routes in
the surroundings.

⬆Ⓢ Bad Kötzting ⛰🏠❄ — 19A3
Kaitersbacher Hof, Kaitersbach 40. **GPS:** n49,15520 e12,89467.

10 ⌾ € 5, free with a meal ⚒ ⬛ ⚒ € 2,50. **Surface:** grassy/gravel. ⬛
01/12-31/10
Distance: ⚒4km ⊗on the spot ⚓Aldi 2km ⚒10km ⚓8km.

⬆Ⓢ Bad Neustadt — 10B6
Parkplatz An der Saale. **GPS:** n50,31637 e10,22205. ⬆➡.

60 ⌾ € 8 ⚒ € 1/50liter ⬛Ch.⚒.
Surface: grasstiles. ⬛ 01/01-31/12
Distance: ⚒500m.

⬆Ⓢ Bad Reichenhall ♨ — 19A6
Wohnmobilpark Rupertus Therme, Hammerschmiedweg. **GPS:** n47,73466
e12,87536. ⬆➡.

25 ⌾ € 13, 2 pers.incl ⚒ € 1/80liter ⬛Ch.⚒ included. **Location:**
Comfortable. **Surface:** gravel. ⬛ 01/01-31/12
Distance: ⚒500m ⚓on the spot.

⬆Ⓢ Bad Rodach — 10C6
Wohnmobilplatz Thermenaue, Thermalbadstrasse. **GPS:** n50,33452 e10,77499.

30 ⌾ € 2,50 ⚒ € 2 ⬛Ch.⚒ € 2 WC⬛. **Surface:** metalled.
Distance: ⚒on the spot ⊗on the spot ⚓500m.

⬆Ⓢ Bad Steben ♨ — 10D6
An der Therme, P3, Steinbacher Straße. **GPS:** n50,36250 e11,63239. ⬆.

12 ⌾ € 5 + €0,50/pp tourist tax ⚒ € 0,50/80liter ⬛Ch.⚒ € 0,50/kWh.
Surface: metalled. ⬛ 01/01-31/12
Distance: ⚒500m ⊗200m ⚓500m.

⬆Ⓢ Bad Tölz ❀❄☼ — 18C6
Bürgermeister Stohlreiterpromenade. **GPS:** n47,76252 e11,55142. ⬆➡.

30 ⌾ € 8/24h ⚒ € 1/50liter ⬛Ch. **Location:** Rural. **Surface:** asphalted. ⬛
01/01-31/12
Distance: ⚒1km ⊗500m ⚓500m ⚓500m.
Remarks: Max. 48h, Kurkarte incl.

Tourist information Bad Tölz:
ℹ Tourist Information, Max-Höfler-Platz 1.Health resort in the mountains of
Upper Bavaria.
☻ Alpamare.Large swimming pool complex with wave machine, alpa, slides,

sauna etc. ▢ Su-Thu 8-21h, Fri-Sa 8-22h, 24/12-01/01 8-16h.
☻ Blombergbahn.Summer toboggan slide, 1226m. ▢ 01/04-30/09 9-18h.
Ⓣ € 4.
⛷ 40 km skiruns, 22 ski-lifts, ski schools.

🏕S	Bad Wiessee	18C6

Parkplatz am Strandbad Grieblinger, Am Strandbad. **GPS:** n47,72068 e11,72569.⬆➡.

6 🅟 € 5/12h, € 10/24h 🚰 1/50liter 🔌Ch 🔌 € 1/6h. 🚐 **Location:** Rural, quit. **Surface:** gravel. ▢ 01/01-31/12
Distance: 🚶1km ⛱on the spot ⊗500m 🚰300m.
Remarks: Max. 3 days.

🏕S	Bad Windsheim ♨	18A2

Phoenix Reisemobilhafen, Bad Windsheimer Strasse 7. **GPS:** n49,51361 e10,41722.⬆➡.

100 🅟 € 10 🚰 1/100liter 🔌Ch 🔌(80x)€ 0,50/kWh. WC 🔌 € 1 ▣ washing machine/dryer € 2,50 📶. **Surface:** gravel. ▢ 01/01-31/12
Distance: 🚶1km ⊗100m 🚰500m.
Remarks: Bread-service.

📷	Bad Windsheim ♨	18A2

Fränkisches Freilandmuseum, Eisweiherweg. **GPS:** n49,49705 e10,41667.⬆➡.

20 🅟 € 5 + € 1/pp. **Surface:** grassy. ▢ 01/01-31/12
Distance: 🚶1km ⊗500m 🚰500m.

🏕S	Bad Wörishofen ♨	18B6

Therme Bad Wörishofen, Thermenallee 1. **GPS:** n48,02120 e10,59100.⬆.

25 🅟 € 9 🚰 1/100liter 🔌Ch 🔌included WC. 🚿 **Location:** Urban.
Surface: asphalted. ▢ 01/01-31/12
Distance: 🚶1,5km ✈4,3km ⊗on the spot 🚰500m 🚰on the spot.
Remarks: Check in at pay-desk of the Therme, <8m, max. 3 nights, bread-service.

🏕S	Balderschwang 🏔❄	25A1

Wohnmobilplatz Schwabenhof, Schwabenhof 23. **GPS:** n47,45745 e10,12963. ⬆.

50 🅟 € 11-16 🚰 🔌Ch 🔌 € 3,50/day WC 🔌 € 0,50. 🚿 **Location:** Rural, comfortable, luxurious. **Surface:** grassy/gravel. ▢ 01/01-31/12
Distance: 🚶3km ⊗on the spot 🚰3km 🚰100m ⛷100m 🚡100m.
Remarks: Bread-service.

🏕S	Bamberg	18B1

Wohnmobilplatz, Am Heinrichsdamm. **GPS:** n49,88583 e10,90221.⬆.

25 🅟 € 12 🚰 1/100liter 🔌Ch 🔌 € 0,50/kWh. 🚐 **Surface:** gravel. ▢ 01/01-31/12
Distance: 🚶10 min walking.
Remarks: Max. 24h.

🍴S	Bärnau 🏔🍴❄	18D1

Gasthof und Wald-Pension Blei, Altglashütte 4. **GPS:** n49,77222 e12,38880.

30 🅟 free 🚰 🔌Ch WC customers free. **Surface:** asphalted/grassy. ▢ 01/01-31/12
Distance: 🚶6km ⊗on the spot 🚰6km ⛷100m.

📷	Baunach	18B1

Sportplatz-Festplatz, Bahnhofstrasse 14-4. **GPS:** n49,98750 e10,85444.

5 free. **Surface:** grassy/metalled. ◻ 01/01-31/12
Remarks: Parking at the edge of nature reserve Haßberge, in the old part of the city, max. 2 nights.

Bayerbach 19B4

Wohnmobilhafen Vital, Huckenham 11. **GPS:** n48,41537 e13,13010.

10 € 12,50 2 pers.incl, dog € 2,50 Ch (8x)€ 0,50/kWh WC included € 1. **Location:** Rural, quit. **Surface:** metalled. ◻ 01/01-31/12
Distance: 500m on the spot.
Remarks: Max. 3 nights, use sanitary facilities at campsite.

Bayreuth 18C1

Lohengrin Therme Bayreuth, Kurpromenade 5. **GPS:** n49,94319 e11,62861.

24 € 6 WC. **Surface:** metalled. ◻ 01/01-31/12
Distance: 1,5km 3,5km 500m 1km.
Remarks: Swimming pool available.

Bayrischzell 18D6

Wohnmobilstellplatz Bayrischzell, Seebergstraße. **GPS:** n47,67189 e12,01023.

20 € 10 € 0,50/80liter Ch (12x)€ 0,50/kWh. **Location:** Comfortable, central. **Surface:** gravel. ◻ 01/01-31/12
Distance: 400m 400m 400m 400m bus 5min on the spot.

Beilngries 18C3

An der Altmühl, An der Altmühl. **GPS:** n49,02655 e11,47121.

20 € 10 Ch WC included. **Location:** Urban, comfortable, central, quit. **Surface:** grassy.

Remarks: Check in at reception.

Beilngries 18C3

Landgasthof Euringer, Dorfstrasse 23. **GPS:** n49,01054 e11,50261. .

6 guests free Ch . **Location:** Urban, very simple, central. **Surface:** metalled. ◻ 01/01-31/12
Distance: 4km on the spot 4km.

Benediktbeuern 18C6

Wohnmobilstellplatz Benediktbeuren, Schwimmbadstraße 37. **GPS:** n47,69920 e11,41556. .

8 € 7 Ch included € 1/6h. **Location:** Rural, comfortable, quit. **Surface:** asphalted. ◻ 15/03-01/11
Distance: 1km.
Remarks: Max. 3 nights, Alpenwarmbad 01/05-01/09 (swimming pool).

Beratzhausen 18C3

Landgasthof Friesenmühle, Friesenmühle 1. **GPS:** n49,08534 e11,81176. .

10 free, use of a meal desired (2x) WC. **Surface:** grassy/gravel. ◻ 01/01-31/12
Distance: 1km on the spot 1km.
Remarks: Apply< 22h.

Berching 18C3

Stellplatz Schiffsanleger, Uferpromenade. **GPS:** n49,10972 e11,43910. .
12 € 5 € 1 Ch € 1/8h. **Surface:** grasstiles/metalled. ◻ 01/01-31/12
Distance: 200m 50m on the spot 300m 100m.

Berchtesgaden 19B6

Reisemobilplatz Rasp, Renothenweg 15, Oberau. **GPS:** n47,65172 e13,07038. .

20 🛏 € 8 + € 2,10/pp tourist tax 🚰 € 2 🔵 Ch 🚿 € 2 WC. **Location:** Central, quit. **Surface:** gravel. 🅿 Easter-30/11
Distance: 🚶500m 🚏500m.

| 🅿 | Bergen/Chiemgau ❄ | 19A6 |

Parkplatz Hochfelln-Seilbahn, Maria-Eck-Straße 8. **GPS:** n47,79710 e12,59079. ⬆.

10 🛏 € 5. 🚐
Location: Very simple. **Surface:** metalled. 🅿 01/01-31/12
Distance: 🚶1,2km ⊗on the spot 🚲on the spot.
Remarks: Parking ski-lift, max. 1 night.

| 🍴S | Bernried | 19A3 |

Altes Gasthaus Artmeier, Innenstetten 45. **GPS:** n48,89675 e12,90262.⬆.

10 🛏 € 5 🚰 € 1/100liter 🔵 🚿 (4x)€ 1/day. **Location:** Rural, very simple, quit. **Surface:** gravel/sand.
Distance: 🚶3km ⊗on the spot 🛒on the spot.

| 🅿S | Betzenstein ❄ | 18C2 |

Ferienhotel Eibtaler Hof, Spies 8. **GPS:** n49,63551 e11,40437.

20 🛏 guests free 🚰 🚿 € 5 WC].
Distance: 🚶on the spot ⊗on the spot 🛒5km 🚲1km.

| 🍴S | Biesenhofen | 18B6 |

Gasthof Stegmühle, Stegmühle 2. **GPS:** n47,82437 e10,64428.⬆.

4 🛏 € 5, free with a meal 🚰🔵 Ch 🚿 WC]. 🚿 **Surface:** gravel/metalled. 🅿 01/01-31/12
Distance: 🚶1km ⊷1km ⊗on the spot 🚲1km.

| 🅿S | Bischofsgrün ❄ | 18C1 |

Rangenweg. **GPS:** n50,05407 e11,79292.⬆➡.

8 🛏 tourist tax € 1 to be paid at tourist office 🚰 € 1 🔵 Ch 🚿 (6x)€ 1.
Surface: metalled. 🅿 01/01-31/12
Distance: 🚶250m 🚲500m 🛒nearby.

| 🅿S | Bischofsheim an der Rhön | 10B6 |

Viehweg 1, Haselbach. **GPS:** n50,39506 e9,99593.⬆➡.

12 🛏 € 5 🚰 € 1/80liter 🔵 Ch. **Surface:** asphalted. 🅿 01/01-31/12
Distance: 🚶on the spot ⊗on the spot 🚲on the spot.
Remarks: Parking swimming pool in Haselbach.

| 🍴 | Bischofswiesen | 19A6 |

Götschen Alm, Kollertradte 21, Loipl. **GPS:** n47,64817 e12,93631.

20 🛏 guests free. **Surface:** gravel. 🅿 01/04-30/11
Distance: 🚶2km ⊗on the spot 🛒2km 🚲on the spot 🚲on the spot.

| 🅿S | Blaichach | 25A1 |

Alpen-Rundblick Mobil Camping, Am Eichbichl 1. **GPS:** n47,54615 e10,25917. ⬆➡.

DE

60 ⅏ € 9,50/11,50 + € 1,20/pp ⚡ € 1/80liter Ch ⚡ (54x)€ 0,50/kWh
WC 🚻 € 1,50 ⚡ € 2,50. 🚿 **Location:** Luxurious. **Surface:** grassy/gravel. ◻
01/01-31/12
Distance: 🚶300m 🏊 3,3km ⛷ on the spot 🚌 on the spot ⊗500m 🍺500m
🚲 5km 🏪 1km.

5 ⅏ € 10 ⚡ € 2 Ch ⚡ (5x)€ 2/8h. **Surface:** grassy/metalled. ◻
01/01-31/12
Distance: 🚶300m 🏪 Edeka 100m.
Remarks: Check in at pay-desk of swiming pool.

🚻 S **Bodenmais** 🌿 ⛵ 🏕 🌳 ❄ 19A3
Concorde-Reisemobil-Stellplatz, Kötztinger Straße. **GPS:** n49,07147 e13,09273.
⬆.

🚻 S **Burgbernheim** 18A2
Wohnmobilstellplatz im Gründlein, Freibadstrasse. **GPS:** n49,44627 e10,31869.
⬆ ➡.

12 ⅏ € 7 + tourist tax ⚡ € 0,50/100liter Ch ⚡ € 0,50/kWh.
Surface: asphalted.
◻ 01/01-31/12
Distance: 🚶800m ⊗200m 🍺200m.
Remarks: Use swimming pool, sauna, fitness-studio incl.

12 ⅏ free ⚡ € 1/100liter Ch ⚡ € 0,50/kWh. **Surface:** grasstiles. ◻
01/01-31/12
Distance: 🚶500m ⊗500m 🍺500m 🚌500m.

🍴 S **Burghaslach** 18A1
Hotel-Restaurant Steigerwaldhaus, Oberrimbach 2. **GPS:** n49,72764
e10,53542. ⬆.

10 ⅏ € 6, guests free. **Surface:** grassy. ◻ 01/01-31/12
Distance: 🚶500m ⊗on the spot 🍺5km.

🚻 S **Bodenmais** 🌿 ⛵ 🏕 🌳 ❄ 19A3
Kerzenwelt, Bahnhofstrasse. **GPS:** n49,06972 e13,09972. ⬆.

🚻 S **Burghausen** 🌿 19A5
Waldpark Lindach, Berghamer Strasse 1. **GPS:** n48,15443 e12,80859. ⬆ ➡.

5 ⅏ € 8/20h. **Surface:** metalled. ◻ 01/01-01/11
Distance: 🚶nearby ⊗nearby 🍺nearby 🚲500m 🏪nearby.

🍴 S **Bodenwöhr** 18D2
Gasthof zum Troidlwirt, Bodenwöhrer strasse 6. **GPS:** n49,28305 e12,26272. ⬆.

16 ⅏ € 5/24h ⚡ € 1/80liter Ch ⚡ (16x)€ 0,50/kWh WC 🚻. ◻
Location: Rural, comfortable, quit. **Surface:** gravel. ◻ 01/01-31/12 ◻
sanitary 01/11-31/03.
Distance: 🚶1,5km ⊗500m 🍺1,5km.
Remarks: Check in at Bürgerhaus Marktlerstr. 15a, caution key sanitary building
€ 20.

🚻 S **Burgkirchen** 19A5
Peterhof, Peterhof 24. **GPS:** n48,15096 e12,75025. ⬆.

40 ⅏ € 5/24h, guests free ⚡ Ch ⚡ (12x)€ 1 WC 🚻 € 1. **Surface:** grassy/
gravel. ◻ 01/01-31/12
Distance: 🚶on the spot ⊗on the spot 🍺bakery 300m.

🚻 S **Bogen** 19A3
Volksfestplatz, Kotaustraße 12. **GPS:** n48,90744 e12,68877. ⬆.

3 🛏€ 12,50, 2 pers.incl 🚰🍴 ♨ WCincluded 🖥📶. **Location:** Rural, quit.
Surface: grassy. 🅾 01/01-31/12
Distance: 🚶2km ⊗2km 🚲2km.

Burgkunstadt 🎋 10D6

Burgkunstadt

rathaus@burgkunstadt.de - www.burgkunstadt.de
Paved and flat motorhome pitches
Swimming pool
Ideal base for walking and cycling

Alter Postweg. **GPS:** n50,13965 e11,25017.⬆
4 🛏free 🚰€ 1 Ch.
Location: Rural. **Surface:** gravel. 🅾 01/01-31/12
Distance: 🚶100m 🚲15km 🚃100m ⊗300m 🛒300m 🚲 on the spot 🚶 on the spot.
Remarks: Max. 48h.

Cadolzburg 🌾 18B2

Parkplatz Am Höhbuck, Am Höhbuck. **GPS:** n49,46123 e10,85188.
8 🛏free 🚰♨Ch 🚲. **Surface:** metalled. 🅾 01/01-31/12
Distance: 🚶on the spot.

🍴 Chammünster 🎋 19A2

Berggasthaus Oedenturm, Am Oedenturm 11. **GPS:** n49,21056 e12,70444.⬆

2 🛏free, use of a meal desired.
Surface: grassy/gravel. 🅾 01/01-31/12
Distance: 🚶5km ⊗on the spot.

Coburg 10C6

Ketschenanger, Schutzenstrasse. **GPS:** n50,25306 e10,96417.⬆

9 🛏free. **Surface:** asphalted.
Distance: 🚶on the spot ⊗on the spot.
Remarks: Parking next to gymnasium, max. 48h.

🅂 Coburg 10C6

Aral-station, Bambergerstrasse. **GPS:** n50,24833 e10,96639.

3 🛏free 🚰€ 1 ♨Ch.
Surface: metalled.
🅾 01/01-31/12
Distance: 🚶on the spot.

Tourist information Coburg:
ℹ Tourist Information, Herrngasse 4, www.coburg-tourist.de.Old residence city of the Sachsen-Coburg family. The Sachsen-Coburg family is related to several Eurpean Royal Houses.
🅼🏰 Die Veste Coburg.Medieval fortress.
🅼 Coburger Puppenmuseum, Rückertstrasse 2/3, neben Schloss Ehrenburg.Doll museum. 🅾 9-17h.
🏰 Schloß Ehrenburg. 🅾 guided tour Tue-Su.

Deggendorf 19A3

Konstantin-Bader-Strasse, Konstantin-Bader-Straße. **GPS:** n48,82656 e12,96367.⬆
3 🛏free. **Location:** Very simple. **Surface:** asphalted. 🅾 01/01-31/12
Distance: 🚶centre 500m ⊗250m.

🅂 Deiningen 18A4

Cowabanga, Am Sportpark. **GPS:** n48,86292 e10,58042.➡

10 🛏free 🚰 🚲€ 2,50 WC⏚. **Location:** Urban, very simple. **Surface:** asphalted. 🅾 01/01-31/12
Distance: 🚶2km ⊗on the spot.
Remarks: Parking sports centre.

🍴🅂 Denkendorf 18C3

Gasthof Lindenwirt, Hauptstrasse 43. **GPS:** n48,92806 e11,45568.⬆

10 🛏€4 🚰 🚲 included. 🛁 **Location:** Urban. **Surface:** gravel/sand. 🅾 01/01-31/12
Distance: 🚶on the spot 🚲700m ⊗on the spot 🛒200m 🚲 on the spot 🚶 on the spot.

🅂 Dettelbach 18A1

Zur Mainfähre, Mainsondheimerstrasse. **GPS:** n49,80076 e10,16751.⬆➡

DE

35 ⛺ € 5 ⚡ 1 Ch ⚡ (24x)€ 0,50/kWh. **Surface:** grassy. ☀ 01/01-
31/12 high water season.
Distance: 100m ⊗100m 100m.

| | | **Dießen** | | 18B6 |

Seestraße. **GPS:** n47,95220 e11,10598.⬆.
12 ⛺ € 8 ⚡ 1 Ch ⚡ (12x)€ 4/8h. **Surface:** gravel. ☀ 01/01-
31/12
Distance: ⟂200m 200m ⊗150m 150m.
Remarks: Max. 3 days.

| | | **Dingolfing** | | 19A4 |

Wohnmobilstellplatz Dingolfing, Wollanger/Prasserweg. **GPS:** n48,62827
e12,50206.⬆ ➡.

12 ⛺ free ⚡€ 1/80liter Ch ⚡ (12x)€ 1/12h. **Location:** Rural,
comfortable, quit. **Surface:** gravel. ☀ 01/01-31/12
Distance: 400m 4,6km ⊗250m.
Remarks: Nearby swimming pool.

| | | **Dittelbrunn** | | 18A1 |

Gasthaus Goldene Flasche, Strohgasse 1, Haubach. **GPS:** n50,09787 e10,20763.
⬆.

3 ⛺ € 1. **Surface:** metalled. ☀ 01/01-31/12
Distance: on the spot ⊗on the spot 200m.

| | | **Donauwörth** | | 18B4 |

Wohnmobilstellplatz am Festplatz, Neue Obermayerstrasse. **GPS:** n48,71490
e10,77874.⬆ ➡.

20 ⛺ free ⚡€ 1/80liter Ch ⚡€ 1/8h. **Location:** Urban, very simple.

Surface: asphalted. ☀ 01/01-31/12
Distance: on the spot ⊗on the spot 500m.
Remarks: Max. 1 night.

| | | **Ebelsbach** | | 18A1 |

Hotel-Gasthof Klosterbräu, Georg-Schäfer-Strasse 11. **GPS:** n49,98356
e10,67406.

7 ⛺ € 7,50 ⚡ Ch ⚡ WC included. ☀ 01/01-31/12
Distance: 150m.
Remarks: Apply < 21h.

| | | **Ebermannstadt** | | 18B1 |

P2, Oberes Tor. **GPS:** n49,78222 e11,18946.⬆ ➡.

10 ⛺ free. **Surface:** metalled. ☀ 01/01-31/12
Distance: 750m 100m.

| | | **Ebermannstadt** | | 18B1 |

P8, Bahnhofstrasse. **GPS:** n49,77750 e11,18722.⬆ ➡.

2 ⛺ free. **Surface:** metalled. ☀ 01/01-31/12

| | | **Ebern** | | 18A1 |

Wohnmobilhafen am Festplatz, Walk-Strasser-Anlage. **GPS:** n50,09312
e10,79496.

30 ⛺ € 5 ⚡ Ch ⚡ € 2 WC ⟂included. **Surface:** metalled. ☀ 01/01-
31/12
Distance: on the spot ⟂1km 2km ⊗100m 200m 100m.

| | | **Ebern** | | 18A1 |

Dietz, Bahnhofstrasse. **GPS:** n50,10167 e10,78917.

DE

4 ᗕfree 🚰🔌Ch🐾 WC 🚽. **Surface:** asphalted/grassy. 🅾 01/01-31/12

Tourist information Ebern:

ℹ️ Fremdenverkehrsamt, Rittergasse 3, www.tourismus-ebern.de.

Ⓜ️ Heimatmuseum am Grauturm, Marktplatz.History of the city. 🅾 holidays Tue-Fri 14.30-17.30h, remaining Su 13.30-17.30h.

| ᗕⓈ | Ebrach | 18A1 |

Naturbad, Schwimmbadweg. **GPS:** n49,84639 e10,48306.⬆️➡️

5 ᗕfree 🚰€ 1 🔌ChWC. **Surface:** metalled. 🅾 01/01-31/12

Distance: 🚲2km ⊗2km 🛒2km 🚆500m.

Remarks: Parking swimming pool.

| ᗕ | Eggenfelden | 19A4 |

P2, Birkenallee. **GPS:** n48,40185 e12,77579.⬆️

5 ᗕfree. **Location:** Very simple, quit. **Surface:** grassy/metalled. 🅾 01/01-31/12

Distance: 🚲1km.

Remarks: Max. 3 days.

| ᗕⓈ | Eggenfelden | 19A4 |

Tankstelle Breitner Shell, Tiefstadt 10. **GPS:** n48,39591 e12,76621.

ᗕ€3 🚰🔌. **Location:** Very simple. **Surface:** asphalted.

Remarks: Max. 1 night.

| ⒸⓈ | Eging am See | 19B4 |

Bavaria Kur-Sport Camping Park, Grafenauer Str. 31. **GPS:** n48,72120 e13,26519.⬆️➡️.

---

10 ᗕ€ 15 🚰🔌Ch🐾(10x)included. **Location:** Rural, quit. **Surface:** asphalted. 🅾 01/01-31/12

Remarks: Max. 2 days, check in at reception, use sanitary facilities at campsite.

| ᗕⓈ | Eibelstadt 🚤 | 17D2 |

Wassersportclub Eibelstadt - Eibelstadt

info@wsc-eibelstadt.de - www.wsc-eibelstadt.de

Located near marina
Located directly at the river
Restaurant on the spot

Wassersportclub Eibelstadt, Mainparkring. **GPS:** n49,73146 e9,98701.⬆️. 35 ᗕ€ 10 🚰€ 1/5minutes 🔌Ch🐾, 6Amp WC included 🚽€ 1/time 🔌€ 5. **Surface:** grassy/gravel. 🅾 01/01-31/12

Distance: 🚲2km ⛵50m ⊗50m 🚆1km.

Remarks: Along the river Meno.

| ᗕⓈ | Eichstätt | 18B4 |

Schottenwiese/Volkfestplatz. GPS: n48,88400 e11,19816.➡️

50 ᗕ€7 🚰🔌Ch🐾(30x)€ 0,50/kWh WC 🚽€ 0,50. 🚌 **Location:** Urban, central, quit. **Surface:** metalled. 🅾 01/01-31/12 🅾 Eichstätter Volksfest.

Distance: 🚲500m 🛒500m 🍴 on the spot 🧍 on the spot.

Remarks: From Ingolstadt dir Volkfestplatz, follow Wohnmobil Stellplatz and P+R.

Tourist information Eichstätt:

ℹ️ Tourist Information, Domplatz 8, www.altmuehlnet.de.Baroque city in nature parc Altmühl, cycle and hiking routes.

👁️ Fossiliensuchen, Steinbruch.Searching for fossils. 🅾 01/04-31/10 8-20h.

🎪 Flohmarkt, Volkfestplatz.Flea market. 🅾 08/05, 19/06, 17/07, 18/09, 02/10.

☀️ Altstadtfest, Innenstad.City celebration. 🅾 01/07-03/07.

☀️ Eichstätter Volksfest, Volkfestplatz.Folk festival. 🅾 02/09-11/09.

🌿 Informationszentrum Naturpark Altmühltal, Notre Dame 1, voormalig klooster.Information centre nature reserve. 🅾 01/04-31/10 Mo-Sa 9-17h, Su 10-17h, 01/11-31/03 Mo-Thu 8-12h, 14-17h, Fri 8-12h. 🅣 free.

DE

⬡S Einsiedl 🏰🌳❄ 25C1

Wohnmobilstellplatz, B11. **GPS:** n47,57000 e11,30389. ⬆➡

80 ◌€5 ⛽€ 1/70liter ✎€ 1/6h. **Location:** Rural, comfortable, quit.
Surface: asphalted/gravel. ◌ 01/01-31/12
Distance: 🚰500m 🏊on the spot 🛒on the spot ⊗500m 🚂3,5km ✈1,5km
🚲1,5km.
Remarks: Max. 3 nights.

⬡S Eisenheim 18A1

Weingut Herbert Schuler, An der Mainaue, Obereisenheim. **GPS:** n49,88883 e10,17942.

60 ◌€5 ⛽€ 1/80liter 🔧Ch ✎€ 0,50. **Surface:** grassy/metalled. ◌
01/01-31/12
Distance: 🚰on the spot 🏊on the spot ⊗on the spot.
Remarks: Along the river Meno.

⬡ Eltmann am Main 🚢 18A1

Parkplatz, Mainlände. **GPS:** n49,97306 e10,66250. ⬆➡

20 ◌free. **Surface:** gravel. ◌ 01/01-31/12
Distance: 🚰500m 🛒on the spot ⊗100m 🚂300m.

⬡S Enderndorf 🌿🏖🏰🌳 18B3

Wohnmobilstellplatz Panorama, Kreisstraße, Spalt-Enderndorf. **GPS:** n49,15028 e10,91083. ⬆

60 ◌€7,50 ⛽€ 0,20/10liter 🔧Ch ✎(60x)€ 0,60/kWh 🧺. **Surface:**
metalled. ◌ 01/04-31/10
Distance: 🚰400m 🏊400m 🛒400m ⊗400m 🚂3km 🚍150m.

⬡S Enderndorf 🌿🏖🏰🌳 18B3

Reisemobil-Stellplatz Enderndorf-West, Zum Hafen. **GPS:** n49,14777 e10,91126. ⬆

25 ◌€8/24h ⛽€ 0,20/100liter 🔧Ch ✎€ 0,50/kWh. 🚐 **Location:** Rural,
isolated, quit. **Surface:** grasstiles. ◌ 01/01-31/12
Distance: 🚰200m 🏊150m ⊗200m 🚂200m 🚲on the spot 🚶on the spot.

⬡S Erbendorf 18C1

Am Stadtpark, Bahnhofstraße 21. **GPS:** n49,84144 e12,04769. ⬆➡

20 ◌free ⛽€ 1 🔧Ch. **Surface:** gravel. ◌ 01/01-31/12
Distance: 🚰100m ⊗200m 🚂200m.

⬡S Erding 🍸 18D5

Wohnmobilpark Erding, Thermenallee. **GPS:** n48,29332 e11,88707. ⬆

55 ◌€10/day ⛽€ 1/80liter 🔧Ch ✎(55x)€ 1/2kWh. **Surface:** grasstiles/
metalled. ◌ 01/01-31/12
Distance: 🚰2km ⊗2km 🚂2km 🚍50m.

⬡ Erding 🍸 18D5

Therme Erding, Thermenallee 1. **GPS:** n48,29332 e11,88707. ⬆➡

25 ◌free. **Surface:** metalled. ◌ 01/01-31/12
Distance: 🚰2km ⊗2km 🚂2km 🚍50m.
Remarks: Max. 7 nights, swimming pool.

⬡S Escherndorf 18A1

Campingplatz Escherndorf, An der Güß 9a. **GPS:** n49,85996 e10,17632. ⬆

22 ⌂ € 8 ⚡ ⊏ Ch ✎. **Surface:** grassy. ◑ 01/04-31/10
Distance: 🚶300m 🚊300m.

| 🚐 S | Ettenbeuren | 18A5 |

Wohnmobilpark Kammelaue, Zum Sportplatz 12. **GPS:** n48,37679 e10,36195.

40 ⌂ € 13, 2 pers.incl ⚡ ⊏ Ch ✎ WC ⊐. **Surface:** grasstiles/metalled. ◑
01/04-31/10
Distance: 🚶500m ⊗4km 🚊500m.

| 🚐 S | Feucht | 18B2 |

Am Freibad Feuchtasia, Chormantelweg. **GPS:** n49,37848 e11,22495.

12 ⌂ € 8 + € 1,95/pp tourist tax ⚡€ 1 ⊏€ 1 Ch ✎ (12x)€ 1/12h. 🛁
Location: Rural. **Surface:** asphalted.
Distance: 🚶1,2km 🚊on the spot 🚴on the spot 🚶on the spot.
Remarks: Pay at Sportpark, Mühlenstraße 55.

| 🚐 S | Forchheim | 18B1 |

Auf der Sportinsel. **GPS:** n49,72120 e11,04939. ⬆➡.

10 ⌂ € 3 ⚡€ 3 ⊏ Ch WC ⊐. **Surface:** metalled. ◑ 01/01-31/12
Distance: 🚶5 min walking ⊗on the spot 🚊on the spot.

| 🚐 S | Frasdorf | 18D6 |

Bauernhof Lederstube, Lederstube 3. **GPS:** n47,79521 e12,28774. ⬆⬆.

9 ⌂ € 7 ⚡€ 1/80liter ⊏ Ch ✎ (8x)€ 1/2kWh ⊐. **Surface:** grasstiles. ◑
01/01-31/12
Distance: 🚶1km 🚊900m.

| ⊙ | Fichtelberg | 18C1 |

Automobilmuseum, Eckert Naglerweg 9. **GPS:** n49,99760 e11,85820. ⬆.

6 ⌂ € 7 ⚡€ 1,50 ⊏ Ch ✎ € 3. **Location:** Rural, very simple, isolated, quit.
Surface: grassy/gravel. ◑ 01/03-30/09
Distance: 🚶500m ⛰800m 🚊800m 🚶800m.

| 🚐 | Freilassing | 19B6 |

Stellplatz Freilassing, Salzburgerstrasse. **GPS:** n47,84031 e12,98599. ⬆.

5 ⌂ free. **Surface:** asphalted. ◑ 01/01-31/12
Distance: 🚶6km 🚏100m.

Tourist information Freilassing:
🎪 Flea market.

| 🚐 S | Freyung 🍴🌳🎭🏖❄ | 19B3 |

Freizeitpark Solla, Solla. **GPS:** n48,80104 e13,54125. ⬆➡.

5 ⌂ free. **Surface:** asphalted/metalled. ◑ 01/01-31/12
Distance: ⊗100m.
Remarks: Parking museum.

| 🚐 S | Fischen 🏔🎭 | 25A1 |

Wohnmobil-Stellplatz Fischen, Mühlenstraße. **GPS:** n47,44950 e10,26946. ⬆.

DE

12 🛏 € 5 📶 € 1/80liter 🗑 Ch 🔌 (12x)€ 0,50/kWh. **Location:** Rural, quit.
Surface: grasstiles. 🅾 01/01-31/12
Distance: 🛁2km ⊗500m 🚲on the spot ⛵on the spot.

| 🏕 | Freyung 🍴🏰⛲❄ | 19B3 |

Parking Freibad, Zuppinger Straße. **GPS:** n48,80515 e13,54102. ⬆.

10 🛏free.
Location: Urban, very simple, quit.
Surface: metalled. 🅾 01/01-31/12
Distance: 🛁1km ⊗1km 🍷1km.

Tourist information Freyung:
ℹ www.freyungurlaub.de.Glass city, air health and winter sports resort.
Ⓜ Bergglashütte.Glass-blowing and exhibition of engraving. 🅾 Mo-Fri 9-18h,
01/05-30/09 Mo-Fri 9-18h, Su 10-12h, 14-16h.
Ⓜ Schloß Wolfstein.Hunting and fishery museum. 🅾 Tue-Su 10-17h ⬛
01/11-15/12.
⛷ Cross-country skiing in Freyung-Kreuzberg, 36 km trails.

| 🏕 | Friedberg | 18B5 |

Seestraße. **GPS:** n48,36540 e10,96529. ⬆→.

4 🛏free. **Location:** Rural, very simple, quit. **Surface:** asphalted. 🅾 01/01-
31/12
Distance: 🛁1,8km ⚓5km 🏖on the spot ⊗400m 🚲on the spot 🚶on the
spot.

| 🏕 S | Friedenfels 🏔🏰❄ | 18D1 |

Freibad, Badstrasse. **GPS:** n49,88639 e12,10417. ⬆.

15 🛏 € 3,50 📶 ⬛. **Surface:** metalled. 🅾 01/01-31/12

Distance: 🛁1,5km.
Remarks: Max. 3 days, service during opening hours.

| 🏕 | Friedenfels 🏔🏔🏰❄ | 18D1 |

Steinwaldhalle Zentral, Am Hammerweiher. **GPS:** n49,88102 e12,10297. ⬆.

15 🛏 € 3,50. **Surface:** metalled. 🅾 01/01-31/12
Distance: 🛁on the spot 🍷25m.
Remarks: Max. 3 days, pay at tourist office, Café Am Steinwald, Gemmingenstr.
19.

| 🏕 | Friedenfels 🏔🏔❄ | 18D1 |

Stellplatz 'Ruhig', Weisteinerweg, Frauenreuth. **GPS:** n49,89278 e12,08556. ⬆.

5 🛏 € 3,50. **Surface:** metalled. 🅾 01/01-31/12
Distance: 🛁1,5km.
Remarks: Max. 3 days.

Tourist information Friedenfels:
ℹ Touristic region, signposted routes for Nordic Walking.

| 🏕 S | Füssen 🌿🍴🏰🏔❄♒ | 25B1 |

Camper's Stop, Abt Hafnerstrasse 9. **GPS:** n47,58186 e10,70080. ⬆→.

120 🛏 € 12,50, trailer € 5 📶 € 0,50/150liter 🗑Ch 🔌€ 1/1kWh WC 💧€
0,50 🚿€ 2. **Location:** Urban, comfortable, noisy. **Surface:** gravel/metalled.
🅾 01/01-31/12
Distance: 🛁1,5km 🏊600m ⛵600m ⊗terrace 🍷50m 🚗250m 🚲4km
⛷400m.

| 🏕 S | Füssen 🌿🍴🏰🏔❄♒ | 25B1 |

Wohnmobilstellplatz Füssen, Abt Hafnerstrasse 1. **GPS:** n47,58224 e10,70355.
⬆.

DE

30 ⌃€ 13,50 ⌲⌁ Ch ✎ (6x)€ 2,50 WC ⌑€ 0,50 ⌁€ 2.⌁
Location: Noisy.
Surface: metalled. ◼ 01/01-31/12
Distance: ⌂1,8km ⌂1km ⊗200m ⌁300m ⌁500m ⌁on the spot 🚶on the spot ⌁on the spot ⌁on the spot.
Tourist information:
ℹ Füssen Tourismus, Kaiser-Maximilian-Platz 1, www.stadt-fuessen.de.Located on the Forggen Lake in a spur of the Alpes.

⌁ S   **Garmisch-Partenkirchen** ⌁⌁⌁ ❄   25B1
Alpencamp am Wank, Wankbahnstraße 2. **GPS:** n47,50573 e11,10802.⌁.

110 ⌃€ 9, tourist tax > 16 € 2/pp, € 1 Umwelttaxe ⌲50liter ⌁ Ch ✎ (110x)€ 1/1kWh WC ⌑€ 1 ⌁ ⌁.⌁ **Location:** Rural, comfortable. **Surface:** asphalted. ◼ 01/01-31/12
Distance: ⌂1km ⌂2km ⊗50m ⌁700m ⌁50m ⌁2,5km ⌁1,5km.
Tourist information Garmisch-Partenkirchen:
ℹ www.garmisch-partenkirchen.de.Famous winter sports resort on the Zugspitze.
Ⓜ Werdenfelsermuseum.Local museum. ◼ Tue-Fri 10-13h, 15-18h, Sa-Su 10-13h.
⌁⌁ Ski school and ski rental, cross country trails, skating rink, swimming pools.

⌁ S   **Gerolzhofen**   18A1
P3 Zur Volkach, Schallfelderstrasse. **GPS:** n49,89808 e10,35169.⌁➜.

2 ⌃€ 5 ⌲€ 1 ⌁ Ch ✎ (4x)€ 0,50/kWh. **Surface:** metalled. ◼ 01/01-31/12
Distance: ⌂on the spot.
Remarks: Max. 3 days.

⌁   **Gerolzhofen**   18A1
P1 Geomaris. **GPS:** n49,89980 e10,36035.⌁.

6 ⌃free. **Surface:** asphalted. ◼ 01/01-31/12
Distance: ⌂750m.
Remarks: Parking swimming pool.

⌁ S   **Geslau**   18A2
Bauernhof Mohrenhof, Lauterbach 3. **GPS:** n49,34630 e10,32500.⌁➜.

20 ⌃€ 10-12 ⌲⌁ Ch ✎ € 0,50/kWh WC ⌑€ 0,50 ⌁€ 3 ⌁€ 2,50/2h.
Surface: grassy. ◻ Easter-31/10
Distance: ⌂500m ⌂on the spot.
Remarks: Bread-service.

⌁ S   **Goldkronach** ⌁⌁ ❄   18C1
Schulstrasse. **GPS:** n50,01265 e11,68276.⌁➜.

4 ⌃free ⌲€ 1/10minutes ⌁ Ch ✎ (4x)€ 1/10h. **Surface:** gravel. ◼ 01/01-31/12
Distance: ⌂500m ⌁2km.

⌁ S   **Grafenau**   19B3
Grafenauer Kurpark, Freyunger Straße. **GPS:** n48,85605 e13,40456.⌁➜.

10 ⌃€ 5 Kurtaxe incl ⌲€ 1/80liter ⌁ Ch ✎ included ⌁free.
Location: Urban, quit.
Surface: gravel. ◼ 01/01-31/12
Distance: ⌂500m ⊗600m ⌁550m ReWe 🚶on the spot.
Remarks: Wifi in Touristinformation + 1/2h free internet in Stadtbücherei.

⌁ S   **Gräfendorf**   17D1
Roßmühle, Weickersgrüben. **GPS:** n50,10660 e9,78309.

4 ⌃free ⌲€ 2/100liter ⌁ Ch. **Surface:** metalled. ◼ 01/04-31/10
Distance: ⌂on the spot ⌁on the spot ⊗on the spot.
Remarks: Max. 24h, check in at shop.

⌁   **Greding**   18C3
Am Hallenbad. **GPS:** n49,04409 e11,35551.⌁.

DE

20 🛏free.
Location: Urban. **Surface:** metalled. 🅿 01/01-31/12
Distance: 🚶Old city centre 300m 🚲500m ⊗250m 🚆250m 🚄on the spot 🏃on the spot.
Remarks: Parking at city wall in front of swimming pool.
Tourist information Greding:
ℹ City wall and towers.
🕷 Christmas fair. 🅿 Dec 13-19h.

🍴S | **Großheubach** | 17C2
Weingut Gasthaus "Zur Bretzel", Kirchstraße 1. **GPS:** n49,72620 e9,22083.
25 🛏€ 15 🚽🛁Ch included 🔌€ 1. **Surface:** grassy/gravel.
Remarks: € 10, reduction.

🍴S | **Großweil** 🏔 👫 | 25C1
Aplengasthof Kreut-Alm, Kreut 1. **GPS:** n47,66184 e11,28286.⬆

15 🛏customers free 🚰 🔌. **Location:** Rural, very simple, isolated, quit.
Surface: asphalted. 🅿 01/03-31/10
Distance: 🚲3,2km ⊗on the spot.

😊 | **Großweil** 🏔 👫 | 25C1
Freilichtmuseum Glentleiten, An der Glentleiten 4. **GPS:** n47,66495 e11,28506.
⬆➡

10 🛏free. **Surface:** gravel.
Distance: 🚶2km 🚲3,5km ⊗Gaststätte - Biergarten 🚆1km.
Remarks: Open air museum, only overnight stays.

♿S | **Günzburg** | 18A5
Gutshof Donauried, Heidenheimerstrasse 115. **GPS:** n48,48721 e10,25632.
20 🛏€ 8 + € 1,50/pp 🚽€ 0,50 🛁Ch 🔌€ 0,50/kWh WC 🔌€ 0,50. 🚽 🅿
01/01-31/12
Distance: 🚌on the spot.

♿S | **Günzburg** | 18A5
Waldbad, Heidenheimerstrasse. **GPS:** n48,46287 e10,26944.

10 🛏€ 5/24h 🚽€ 1/100liter 🛁🔌€ 0,50/kWh. 🅿 01/01-31/12
Remarks: Parking swimming pool.

🛁S | **Gunzenhausen** | 18B3
Surfzentrum Schlungenhof. **GPS:** n49,12790 e10,74559.⬆

80 🛏€ 10/24h 🚽€ 1 🛁Ch 🔌included WC 🔌€ 1 📶.🚌 **Location:**
Rural, comfortable, quit. **Surface:** grassy/gravel. 🅿 01/04-30/10
Distance: 🏊100m ⊗on the spot 🚆1,8km.

| **Gunzenhausen** | 18B3
Altmühlsee, Seezentrum Mühr. **GPS:** n49,13145 e10,73534.

40 🛏€ 3 day/€ 6 night. 🚌 **Location:** Rural, comfortable, isolated, quit.
Surface: grassy. 🅿 01/01-31/12
Distance: 🏊on the spot ⊗200m 🚄on the spot 🏃on the spot.
Remarks: Max. 3 days.

🛁S | **Hammelburg** | 17D1
Am Bleichrasen, P2, Am Weiher. **GPS:** n50,11390 e9,88820.⬆

25 🛏€ 6/24h 🚽🛁Ch 🔌€ 0,50/kWh WC. **Surface:** asphalted. 🅿
01/01-31/12
Distance: 🚶200m ⊗200m 🚆300m.

🛁S | **Hammelburg** | 17D1
Schloß Saaleck, Am Schlossberg. **GPS:** n50,11194 e9,87778.

10 ⬛€4 🚰 ⬛ ⚡€ 0,50/kWh WC. **Surface:** asphalted/metalled. 🅾️ 01/01-31/12
Distance: 🚰on the spot.

6 ⬛€6 🚰 1 ⬛Ch ⚡€ 1/6h. **Surface:** gravel. 🅾️ 01/01-31/12
Distance: 🚰on the spot ⊗200m 🚾200m.
Remarks: Check in at pay-desk of the Therme.

🍴	Hammelburg	17D1

Restaurant Nöth, Morlesauer Strasse 3. **GPS:** n50,11707 e9,80313.
5 ⬛. **Surface:** grassy.
Distance: ⚓on the spot.

⬛S	Herzogenaurach	18B2

Freizeitbad Atlantis, Würzburger Straße 35. **GPS:** n49,57251 e10,86641.
12 ⬛€6/24h 🚰⬛Ch ⚡ (12x). **Surface:** gravel. 🅾️ 01/01-31/12
Distance: ⊗on the spot.
Remarks: € 2 reduction swimming pool.

⬛S	Hassfurt ⬛ ⬛	18A1

Festplatz am Gries, Ringstrasse. **GPS:** n50,03068 e10,50094. ⬆️➡️

⬛	Hilpoltstein	18B3

Seezentrum Heuberg am Rothsee, Heuberg. **GPS:** n49,20954 e11,18595.

22 ⬛€5/night 🚰€ 1 ⬛Ch ⚡ 1 WC. **Surface:** asphalted. 🅾️ 01/01-31/12
Distance: 🚰200m ⚓10m ⊗200m 🚾200m.
Remarks: Parking along the Main, follow signs.

50 ⬛€ 7,50 🚰⬛Ch. **Surface:** metalled. 🅾️ 01/01-31/12 🅾️ Service: winter.
Distance: ⚓200m 🚰200m.

⬛	Herrieden	18A3

Volksfestplatz an der Altmühl, Staatsstrasse 2248. **GPS:** n49,23191 e10,49588. ⬆️.

⬛	Hilpoltstein	18B3

Am Main-Donau Kanal. GPS: n49,20455 e11,18813.

30 ⬛€ 6. ⬛ **Surface:** grassy. 🅾️ 15/04-30/10
Distance: 🚰1,9km ⚓Canal ⊗1,9km 🚾1km ⬛on the spot 🏊on the spot.
Tourist information Hilpoltstein:
ℹ️ Amt für Kultur und Tourismus, Maria-Dorothea-strasse 8, www.hilpoltstein.de.City on the Rothsee.
🎉 Burgfeste.Festival with events. 🅾️ beginning Aug.

10 ⬛free. **Surface:** asphalted. 🅾️ 01/01-31/12
Distance: 🚰100m ⊗200m 🚾200m.
Remarks: Parking at the old mill bridge.

⬛S	Herrieden	18A3

ARAL-station, Am Eichelberg 2. **GPS:** n49,25820 e10,50239. ⬆️.

⬛	Hof/Saale	11A6

Park Theresienstein, Ritter von Münch Strasse. **GPS:** n50,32956 e11,92041. ⬆️.

10 ⬛free 🚰€ 1,50 ⬛Ch WC. **Surface:** asphalted. 🅾️ 01/01-31/12
Distance: 🚰3km ⊗on the spot 🚾on the spot.

⬛S	Hersbruck	18C2

Fackelmanntherme Hersbruck, Badestaße. **GPS:** n49,51142 e11,44267. ⬆️.

20 ⬛free. **Surface:** metalled. 🅾️ 01/01-31/12
Distance: 🚰2,5km 🚾1km.

DE

Remarks: Max. 24h.

🖼 **Hof/Saale** 11A6

Utreusee, Wilhelm Löhe strasse. **GPS:** n50,28583 e11,91361.⬆.

20 🍴free. **Surface:** asphalted/metalled. ⬛ 01/01-31/12
Distance: ⚓100m ⊗50m ⛵500m.
Remarks: Max. 24h.

🖼S **Hof/Saale** 11A6

Clean Park Buchta, Hofeckerstrasse/Ernst Reuterstrasse. **GPS:** n50,32641 e11,89248.⬆.

4 🍴€5 🚰€1 ⚡Ch.⚡.
Surface: metalled.
⬛ 01/01-31/12
Distance: 🚲2km ⊗800m.
Remarks: Max. 72h.

Tourist information Hof/Saale:

ℹ️ Tourist-Information, am Rathaus, www.hof.de.Modern industrial town.
👁 Bürgerpark Theresienstein.Landscape park according English example. ⬛
9-18h, winter 9-16h.
😊 Untreusee.Lake with water sports.

🖼S **Hofheim in Unterfranken** 10C6

Wohnmobilplatz Hofheim, Johannisstraße 28. **GPS:** n50,14185 e10,51957.⬆.
➡.

30 🍴€5 🚰€ 1/100liter ⚡Ch.⚡€ 0,50/kWh WC ⃞⃞. **Surface:**
grasstiles. ⬛ 01/01-31/12
Distance: 🚲750m ⛵750m.

🖼S **Hohenberg an der Eger** 11A6

Wiesenfestplatz, Selberstrasse. **GPS:** n50,09762 e12,22085.

10 🍴free 🚰 ⚡WC. **Surface:** metalled. ⬛ 01/01-31/12
Distance: 🚲200m ⊗50m.
Remarks: Beautiful view.

🍴🍴S **Huisheim** 18B4

Waldparkplatz im Schwalbtal, Waldschenke 1, Gosheim. **GPS:** n48,84932
e10,71530.⬆➡.

10 🍴€ 5, guests free 🚰. **Location:** Rural, very simple, quit. **Surface:**
asphalted. ⬛ 01/01-31/12
Distance: ⊗on the spot.

🍴S **Immenstadt** 25A1

P 3 Viehmarktplatz, Badeweg. **GPS:** n47,56192 e10,20857.⬆➡.
6 🍴free 🚰Ch WC. **Location:** Urban, comfortable. **Surface:** asphalted. ⬛
01/01-31/12
Distance: ⛵700m.

🍴S **Ingolstadt** 18C4

Parkplatz Hallenbad, Jahnstrasse. **GPS:** n48,76025 e11,42038.⬆➡.

8 🍴€ 5 (9-17h), overnight stay free 🚰€ 1/80liter ⚡Ch.⚡included ⃞.🛈
Location: Urban, comfortable. **Surface:** metalled. ⬛ 01/01-31/12
Distance: 🚲on the spot 🏊1,6km ⊗on the spot ⛵on the spot 🚲on the spot
🚶on the spot.
Remarks: Parking sports park, max. 3 days.

©S **Inzell** ♨ 19A6

Camping Lindlbauer, Kreuzfeldstraße 44. **GPS:** n47,76717 e12,75417.

12 🍴€ 16 🚰 ⚡Ch.⚡WC ⃞📶included. **Location:** Rural. **Surface:**
metalled. ⬛ 01/01-31/12

Distance: 🛇 1km.
Remarks: Max. 1 night, health resort 500m.

⬛S **Iphofen** **18A2**
Einesheimer Tor. GPS: n49,70260 e10,26459. ⬆.

8 ⬛free ⛽€ 1 🛇Ch WC. **Surface:** asphalted. ◘ 01/01-31/12
Distance: 🚶200m.
Remarks: Parking at city wall.

⬛S **Kastl/Oberpfalz** 🌿🕊 **18C2**
Wanderparkplatz Am Alten Bahnhof, Amberger Straße. **GPS:** n49,36657 e11,68388. ⬆.

5 ⬛free ⛽🛇Ch WC free. **Surface:** gravel. ◘ 01/01-31/12
Distance: 🚶200m ⊗200m 🛇100m 🚎50m.

⬛S **Kaufbeuren** **18B6**
Wohnmobilplatz Kaufbeuren, Buronstraße. **GPS:** n47,89885 e10,61650. ⬆.
8 ⬛free ⛽🛇Ch free ⚡(6x)€ 0,50/2kWh. **Location:** Urban. **Surface:** gravel.
Distance: 🚶historical centre 3km.
Remarks: Max. 3 days.

⬛S **Kelheim** 🚤 **18C3**
Volksfestplatz, Am Pflegerspitz. **GPS:** n48,91331 e11,87657. ⬆➡.

50 ⬛€ 6, 01/11-31/03 free ⛽🛇Ch ⚡(18x)€ 1/2kWh WC. **Surface:** metalled. ◘ 01/01-31/12 ◉ service 01/11-31/03.
Distance: 🚶500m ⊗500m.
Remarks: Hindmost part, max. 3 nights.

Tourist information Kelheim:
ℹ Tourist Information, Ludwigsplatz 14, www.kelheim.de. Historical little town on the Danube river.
Ⓜ Archäologisch Museum im Herzogkasten, Lederergasse 11. Archeological museum and history of the city. ◘ 01/04-31/10 Tue-Su 10-16h.

⬛S **Kemnath** **18C1**
Wohnmobilstellplatz Kemnath, Am Eisweier 8. **GPS:** n49,87219 e11,88774.

5 ⬛free ⛽€ 1 🛇Ch ⚡(6x)€ 1/6h WC. **Surface:** concrete. ◘ 01/01-31/12
Distance: 🚶650m ⊗650m 🛇650m.

⬛S **Kempten** **25A1**
Illerstadion, Illerdamm/Jahnstrasse. **GPS:** n47,72915 e10,31940. ⬆➡.

6 ⬛€ 5 ⛽€ 1 🛇. ◫ **Location:** Urban, noisy. **Surface:** metalled. ◘ 01/01-31/12
Distance: 🚶500m 🚗2,7km.

⬛S **Kiefersfelden** 🏔🚤❄ **25D1**
Hödenauer See, Wasserstrasse. **GPS:** n47,62881 e12,18949. ⬆➡.

10 ⬛€ 5 WC ◫€ 0,50. **Location:** Very simple. **Surface:** gravel/sand. ◘ 01/01-31/12
Distance: 🚶2km 🚲3km ⛱on the spot ⊗50m 🚎300m.
Remarks: Max. 3 days.

⬛ **Kiefersfelden** 🏔🚤❄ **25D1**
Rathausplatz. GPS: n47,61303 e12,18981. ⬆.

20 ⬛€ 10. **Location:** Very simple. **Surface:** asphalted. ◘ 01/01-31/12
Distance: 🚶on the spot 🚲2km ⊗100m.
Remarks: Max. 3 days.

Tourist information Kiefersfelden:
ℹ Kur- und Verkehrsamt, Dorfstrasse 23, www.kiefersfelden.de. Mountain village in Oberbayern.
Ⓜ Blaahaus museum. Museum about daily living in ancient times. ◘ 01/05-31/10 Thu, Su 14-17h, 01/11-30/04 1st Su of the month 14-17h.

Kirchenlamitz | S | 11A6

REWE-Markt, Weißenstädter Straße. **GPS**: n50,14905 e11,94055. ⬆️➡️.

12 ⬛free 🚰🔌Ch 🔌 free, voluntary contribution. **Location:** Comfortable. **Surface:** asphalted. ⬛ 01/01-31/12
Distance: 🚶500m 🚰10m.

Kirchham | S | 19B5

Erlebnispark Haslinger Hof, Ed 1. **GPS**: n48,34947 e13,29115. ⬆️.

25-30 ⬛Overnight stay € 17 (incl. € 9 voucher) 🚰🔌Ch. **Location:** Rural, very simple, quit. **Surface:** gravel. ⬛ 01/01-31/12
Distance: ⊗on the spot.

Kitzingen | S | 18A2

Wohnmobilpark Am Main, Bleichwasen, Etwashausen. **GPS**: n49,74274 e10,16491. ⬆️.

30 ⬛€ 5/24h 🚰€ 1/80liter 🔌Ch 🔌€ 0,50/kWh WC. **Surface:** asphalted. ⬛ 01/01-31/12
Distance: 🚶300m 🏊on the spot.
Remarks: Between Alter Mainbrücke and Nordbrücke.

Tourist information Kitzingen:
ℹ️ Tourist Information, Schrannenstraße 1.

Klingenberg | | 16D2

Sonja's Wohnmobilhafen, Zur Einladung. **GPS**: n49,78370 e7,17805.

55 ⬛€ 6,50 🚰€ 1 🔌Ch 🔌 (30x)€ 2. **Surface:** grassy. ⬛ 01/01-31/12
Distance: 🚶500m.

Königsberg | S | 18A1

Am Sportgelände, Buchweg. **GPS**: n50,08472 e10,57028. ⬆️➡️.

6 ⬛free 🚰Ch. **Surface:** metalled. ⬛ 01/01-31/12
Distance: 🚶300m ⊗300m 🚰300m.
Remarks: Parking sports park.

Kronach | S | 10D6

Hammermühle, Am Sand. **GPS**: n50,23195 e11,32735. ⬆️➡️.

10 ⬛€ 2/24h 🚰🔌Ch 🔌 (4x)€ 0,50/kWh. **Surface:** asphalted. ⬛ 01/01-31/12
Distance: 🚶10min 🚶on the spot ⊗200m 🚰on the spot.

Kronach | S | 10D6

Lucky Stable Ranch, Mostrach 1. **GPS**: n50,21840 e11,34012. ⬆️.

5 ⬛€ 5, 2 pers.incl 🚰🔌 🔌 WCincluded 🛗€ 1,50 🚰€ 1,50 🔔. **Surface:** grassy/metalled. ⬛ 01/01-31/12
Distance: 🚶2km 🚶on the spot 🚰on the spot.
Remarks: At manege.

Krün 🌿🌲🏔️🎪📷❄️ | S | 25C1

Tennsee Reisemobilhafen, Am Tennsee 1. **GPS**: n47,49083 e11,25444. ⬆️➡️.

37 ⬛€ 12,50-18,50 + tourist tax € 1,50/pp, Umwelttaxe € 0,60/pp 🚰🔌Ch 🔌€ 0,70/kWh WC 🛗€ 3 🔔€ 3/h ☕ 🍴. **Location:** Rural, comfortable, luxurious, quit. **Surface:** grassy/gravel. ⬛ 01/01-31/12 ⬤ 07/11-15/12.
Distance: 🚶2,5km 🏊800m 🚶3km ⊗on the spot 🚰on the spot 🚲100m 🚴on the spot 🚶on the spot 📷5km 🌳300m.

Kulmbach 🌿 | S | 10D6

Wohnmobilstellplatz Kulmbach, Am Schwedensteg. **GPS**: n50,11063 e11,45698. ⬆️➡️.

DE

25 🏕€ 3 🚰€ 1/100liter 🗑Ch 🚿(25x)€ 1/2kWh. **Surface:** gravel. ⬛
01/01-31/12 ⬤ water disconnected in winter.
Distance: 🛒on the spot.

Wohnmobilstellplatz Kümmersbruck, Am Butzenweg. **GPS:** n49,41978
e11,89651.⬆.

8 🏕free. **Surface:** metalled. ⬛ 01/01-31/12
Distance: 🛒1km ⊗1km.
Remarks: At sports centre.

Wohnmobilstellplatz Weber, Euschertsfurth 34. **GPS:** n48,83222 e13,14444.➡.

8 🏕€ 8 🚰🗑Chincluded 🚿(10x)€ 0,30/kWh 🚿 1,50. 🐾 **Location:**
Rural, comfortable, quit. **Surface:** grassy/metalled. ⬛ 01/04-30/11
Distance: 🛒1,5km ⊗100m.
Remarks: Incl. swimming pool.

Lalling-Freizeitgelände, Waldstrasse. **GPS:** n48,84139 e13,13778.⬆.

2 🏕free 🚰€ 1/80liter 🗑Ch 🚿€ 3/day. **Location:** Rural, very simple, quit.
Surface: metalled/sand. ⬛ 01/01-31/12
Distance: 🛒2km.
Remarks: At tennis-courts.

Familie Stelzer, Euschertsfurth 141. **GPS:** n48,83222 e13,13917.➡.

4 🏕€ 4 🚰 Service € 1 🚿. **Location:** Rural, very simple, quit. **Surface:**
asphalted/grassy.

Distance: 🛒1km ⊗1km.

Lallinger Hof, Hauptstrasse 23. **GPS:** n48,84560 e13,13851.⬆.

4-5 🏕guests free 🚿against payment. **Location:** Rural, very simple, quit.
Surface: . ⬛ 01/04-31/10
Distance: 🛒250m ⊗250m.
Remarks: Check in at restaurant.

Sieglinde, Obstgarten 13, Hunding. **GPS:** n48,84502 e13,14939.⬆.

3 🏕€ 5 🚰🗑Chincluded 🚿(2x)€ 2/day WC🚿. **Location:** Rural, very
simple, quit. **Surface:** grassy. ⬛ 01/04-31/12
Distance: ⊗700m.

Gasthof zur Post, Pfarrweg. **GPS:** n48,84405 e13,14064.⬆.

15 🏕free. **Location:** Rural, very simple, quit. **Surface:** metalled.
Distance: 🛒200m ⊗200m.

Erikas Wohlfühlplatz, Kleinfeld 6, Hunding. **GPS:** n48,84333 e13,17944.⬆.

10 🏕€ 5 + € 0,50/pppn 🚰🚿(10x)€ 1/day WC🚿€ 3. **Location:** Rural, very
simple, quit. **Surface:** grassy/sand. ⬛ 01/04-31/10
Distance: 🏊on the spot 🛒on the spot ⊗3km 🍺200m 🍽on the spot 🛶
on the spot.
Remarks: Check in at Kleinfeld 6.

Feng Shui Kurpark, Euschertsfurther Straße. **GPS:** n48,84137 e13,13952.⬆.

DE

€1.
Surface: gravel. 01/01-31/12
Remarks: Not indicated.

Tourist information Lalling:

Verhehrsamt Lallinger Winkel, Hauptstrasse 28, www.lalling.de.Holiday and fruit region Lallinger Winkel.

Töpferwerkstatt Pflugk, Pfarrweg 2, Lallinger Winkel.Pottery. Mo-Sa.

Fahrzeug- und kunstmuseum, Lalinger Winkel.Approx. 100 cars and 100 motorbikes. 01/03-31/10, 15/12-15/01 Fri-Su 13-17h.

S **Landau/Isar** 19A4

Am Festplatz, Harburger Straße 20/B20. **GPS**: n48,67712 e12,68323.

± 20 free € 1/100liter Ch (6x)€ 0,50/kWh. **Surface:** grassy/gravel. 01/01-31/12
Distance: 1,5km 2,3km McDonalds 200m bakery 200m.

S **Landsberg am Lech** 18B6

Waitzinger Wiese, Gottesackerangerweg. **GPS**: n48,05534 e10,87371.

8 € 1/24h € 1/100liter Ch (8x)€ 0,50/6h WC € 0,50.
Location: Urban, very simple. **Surface:** metalled. 01/01-31/12
Distance: 400m 300m.

S **Lechbruck am See** 25B1

Wohnmobilpark via Claudia, Via Claudia 6. **GPS**: n47,71556 e10,82139.

52 € 12,50-13,30 2 pers.incl, dog € 3-3,50 Ch WC € 1,50 € 2,50 . **Location:** Rural, comfortable, luxurious. **Surface:** gravel. 01/01-31/12
Distance: 5km on the spot on the spot on the spot on the spot on the spot 10km on the spot.

S **Lenggries** 25C1

Dürrachstrasse, Fall. **GPS**: n47,57039 e11,53380.

25 € 0,50/h, € 4/24h € 2 WC. **Location:** Isolated, quit. **Surface:** metalled. 01/01-31/12
Distance: 250m 250m 150m 8km on the spot on the spot.
Remarks: Max. 7 days.

S **Lindau** 24D1

Blauwiese, P1. **GPS**: n47,55869 e9,70130.

34 € 0,70/h € 0,50 € 0,50 Ch WC. **Surface:** metalled. 01/01-31/12
Distance: on the spot 1km 1km 500m 500m on the spot.

S **Lindau** 24D1

Campingplatz Lindau am See, Frauenhoferstrasse, Lindau-Zech. **GPS**: n47,53764 e9,73148.

15 € 10/24h Ch included. 15/03-31/10

Tourist information Lindau:

Tourist Information, Ludwigstrasse 68, www.lindau-tourismus.de.

Lindau Insel.Promenade along the lake with Mangturm, 700 years old lighthouse.

St Maria Kirche.Former monastery-church.

Haus zum Cavazzen, Marktplatz.Mechanical musical instruments, from musical boxes to jukeboxes. Tue-Su 10-12h, 14-17h.

Lindauer Hafen Konzerte, Promenade. summer Tue-Su.

S **Lohr/Main** 17D1

Lohrer Mainlände, Osttangente. **GPS**: n49,99429 e9,58053.
20 € 5 € 1/100liter Ch € 1/4h. **Surface:** metalled. 01/04-31/10
Distance: 300m.
Remarks: Along Main river, max. 3 days.

Mainbernheim 18A2

Goldgrubenweg. **GPS**: n49,71484 e10,22028.

DE

10 🛏free. **Surface:** metalled. 🚻 01/01-31/12
Distance: 🚰on the spot.

🚐S **Mainstockheim** ⚓ **18A1**
Wohnmobilhafen Mainstockheim, Albertshöfer strasse an de Fähre. **GPS:** n49,77173 e10,15595.⬆➡.

30 🛏€5 🚰🔌Ch✎. **Surface:** gravel. 🚻 01/01-31/12
Distance: 🚰on the spot 🏊on the spot ⊗100m 🛒100m.

🚐S **Manching** **18C4**
Am Braunweiher. GPS: n48,71078 e11,49602.⬆.

50 🛏free 🚰€ 1/80liter 🔌Ch. **Surface:** grasstiles/metalled. 🚻 01/01-31/12
Distance: 🚰1,5km ⚓1,3km 🛒Edeka 1km.

🚐S **Markt Wald** 📶⚓ **18A5**
Wohnmobilpark Markt Wald, Bürgle 1a. **GPS:** n48,14602 e10,57517.⬆➡.

20 🛏€7 🚰€ 1/100liter 🔌Ch✎€ 0,50/kWh WC 🔌€ 2.🐾
Location: Rural, comfortable, quit.
Surface: grassy/gravel. 🚻 01/01-31/12
Distance: 🚰1km 🏊on the spot 🚣on the spot ⊗on the spot 🛒1km 🚌on the spot 🐾on the spot 🎣on the spot.
Remarks: At small lake, use sanitary facilities at campsite, bread-service.

🚐 **Marktbreit** **18A2**
Am Kranen, Staatstraße. **GPS:** n49,66878 e10,14241.⬆.

3 🛏free. **Surface:** metalled. 🚻 01/01-31/12
Distance: 🚰on the spot ⊗on the spot.
Remarks: Max. 1 day.

🚐S **Marktleuthen** **11A6**
Am Angerparkplatz. GPS: n50,12965 e11,99479.⬆.

10 🛏free 🚰🔌Chfree ✎(10x)included 🔌€ 0,50. **Surface:** metalled. 🚻 01/01-31/12
Distance: 🚰250m ⊗150m 🛒200m.
Remarks: Bread-service.

🚐S **Marktredwitz** **18D1**
Wohnmobilstellplatz am Auenpark, Dörflaser Platz, Fabrikstraße. **GPS:** n49,99710 e12,08640.⬆➡.

20 🛏free 🚰€ 0,50 🔌€ 0,50 Ch✎(6x)€ 0,50/kWh. **Surface:** asphalted/gravel. 🚻 01/01-31/12
Distance: 🚰300m ⊗50m 🛒150m.
Remarks: At park.

🚐 **Marktredwitz** **18D1**
Angerplatz, Egerland-Kulturhaus, Fikentscherstrasse. **GPS:** n50,00379 e12,09506.⬆➡.

6 🛏free. **Surface:** asphalted. 🚻 01/01-31/12
Distance: 🚰1km ⊗500m.

🚐S **Massing** **19A5**
Am Freilichtmuseum, Spirknerstraße. **GPS:** n48,39528 e12,60056.
10 🛏free 🚰✎On demand. **Surface:** asphalted.
Distance: ⊗Museumstüberl.

Remarks: Parking open air museum, busy parking during the day.

| ⌂S | **Mehlmeisel** | 18C1 |

Parkplatz „Am Park". **GPS:** n49,97615 e11,85471. 🏕 .

⌂free. **Surface:** metalled. ⬤ 01/01-31/12
Distance: ⊗250m 🍴100m.
Remarks: Max. 3 nights.

| ⌂S | **Mellrichstadt** | 10B6 |

Malbachweg. **GPS:** n50,43139 e10,30972. ⬆ .

7 ⌂free 🚰€ 1/80liter 🔌Ch ⚡€ 0,50/kWh. **Surface:** asphalted. ⬤
01/01-31/12
Distance: 🚶500m ⊗750m 🍴750m.

| ⌂S | **Miltenberg** | 17C2 |

Jahnstrasse/Luitpoldstrasse. **GPS:** n49,70464 e9,25860. ⬆➡ .

20 ⌂free 🚰🔌Ch WC.
Distance: 🚶200m ⊗200m.

| ⌂S | **Miltenberg** | 17C2 |

Oberhof. **GPS:** n49,70523 e9,25901.
⌂🚰€ 1 🔌Ch.

| ⌂S | **Mistelgau** | 18B1 |

Therme Obernsees, An der Therme 1, Obernsees. **GPS:** n49,91630 e11,37831. ⬆ .

20 ⌂€ 8 🚰€ 1/50liter 🔌Ch ⚡€ 1/12h. **Surface:** grasstiles/metalled. ⬤
01/01-31/12
Distance: 🚶1km ⊗Therme-Bistro.
Remarks: Discount on access terme.

| ⌂S | **Mittenwald** 🏔 | 25C1 |

Wohnmobil-Stellplatz Karwendel, Albert-Schott-Straße. **GPS:** n47,43792
e11,26411. ⬆➡ .

30 ⌂€ 7/24h + € 4/pp tourist tax 🚰€ 1/80liter 🔌Ch ⚡(30x)€ 0,80/kWh.
Location: Noisy. **Surface:** asphalted/gravel. ⬤ 01/01-31/12
Distance: 🚶250m 🚌on the spot.
Remarks: Along railwayline.

| ⌂S | **Mitterteich** | 18D1 |

Am Freibad, Am Bad 1. **GPS:** n49,95060 e12,22468.

2 ⌂free. **Surface:** gravel. ⬤ 01/01-31/12
Distance: 🚶1km 🚲1,2km.

| ©S | **Mitterteich** | 18D1 |

Freizeithugl Großbüchlberg, Großbüchlberg 32. **GPS:** n49,97286 e12,22496.
15 ⌂€ 12, 2 pers.incl 🚰🔌Ch ⚡WC 🚽📷 against payment. ⬤
01/01-31/12
Distance: ⊗200m.
Remarks: Bread-service.

| ⌂S | **Monheim** 🌿🍴🛒 | 18B4 |

An der Stadthalle, Schulstraße. **GPS:** n48,84503 e10,85329. ⬆➡ .

7 ⌂free 🚰€ 1 🔌Ch ⚡€ 1/10h. **Location:** Very simple, central. **Surface:**
grasstiles. ⬤ 01/01-31/12
Distance: 🚶400m ⊗500m 🍴500m.

| ⌂S | **Moosbach** 🌳🍴 | 18D2 |

Am Badeweiher Tröbes, Friedhofgasse. **GPS:** n49,59076 e12,41193. ⬆➡ .

6 ⌂€ 5 🚰🔌Ch ⚡. **Surface:** gravel. ⬤ 01/01-31/12

Distance: 🚶250m ⊗250m ♿250m.
Remarks: Check in at Gästeinformation.

| 📷S | München | 18C5 |

Allianz-Arena Wohnmobilstellplätze, Werner-Heisenberg-Allee 25, Munich (München). **GPS:** n48,22089 e11,62505.⬆️

110 📷€ 15 🚰€ 0,20/20liter 🔌 (10x)€ 1/kWh. **Surface:** asphalted.
Distance: ⊗on the spot 🚐on the spot.

| 📷S | München | 18C5 |

Messe Riem, De-Gasperi-Bogen, MÜnchen-Riem, Munich (München). **GPS:** n48,13342 e11,70746.
1000 📷€ 35/incl. 2 pers, € 15/pers 🚰 🔧Ch 🧹WC 🪣included. **Surface:** metalled. 🅾️ Oktoberfest
Distance: 🚇metro 300m.

| 📷S | München | 18C5 |

Wohnmobilstellplatz Oktoberfest, Siegenburger Straße 58, Laim, Munich (München). **GPS:** n48,12788 e11,52190.
250 📷€ 18 + € 3/pp 🚰 🔧Ch 🧹WC 🪣included.
Surface: metalled.
🅾️ Oktoberfest
Distance: ⊗100m 🚐500m.

Tourist information Munich (München):
ℹ️ Fremdenverkehrsamt München, Sendlinger Str. 1; Hauptbahnhof, Bahnhofstrasse 2, www.muenchen.de.The capital of Bavaria. There are many beer gardens, old city with centre worth visiting.
ℹ️ München Welcome Card.Card gives for free entrance on among other things public transport and 50% discounts on curiosities. 🎫 € 11/day 2 pers.
👁️ Agustinerbräu, Neuhauserstrasse 16.Brewery from 1644.
🏛️ Schloß Nymphenburg.Former summer residence of the Witelbacher monarchs. 🕐 Tue-Su 9-12.30h, 13.30-17h.
♟️ Neumarkt.Ruins of citadel dominating the city.
🎇 Oktoberfest.Beer festival, special motorhome parking

| 📷S | Münnerstadt | 10B6 |

Lache, P1, Seminarstrasse. **GPS:** n50,24957 e10,19086.

5 📷free 🚰€ 1/90liter 🔧Ch 🧹€ 0,50 WC 🪣. **Surface:** metalled. 🅾️ 01/01-31/12
Distance: 🚶350m.

| 📷S | Murnau am Staffelsee | 25C1 |

Am Bahnhof Murnau, Am Bahnhof. **GPS:** n47,68005 e11,19447.⬆️➡️

6 📷€ 1/day 🚰€ 1/100liter 🔧Ch 🧹€ 1/2kWh. **Location:** Rural, comfortable, central, quit.
Surface: grasstiles/metalled. 🅾️ 01/01-31/12
Distance: 🚶500m 🚲10km ⊗400m ♿300m 🚐on the spot.
Remarks: Max. 72h.

| 📷S | Naila | 11A6 |

Bahnhofstrasse. GPS: n50,33071 e11,71127.⬆️

2 📷free 🚰 1 📷 1 Ch€ 1. **Surface:** metalled. 🅾️ 01/01-31/12
Distance: 🚶100m ♿300m.
Remarks: Parking left side of the station.

| 📷S | Nesselwang | 🏔️🌲👫❄️ | 25A1 |

An der Riese, Altspitzbahn. **GPS:** n47,61995 e10,49830.⬆️➡️

70 📷€ 8 🚰 1 🔧Ch 🧹(62x)€ 1/1kWh 📶. 📱 **Location:** Rural, comfortable. **Surface:** gravel/metalled. 🅾️ 01/01-31/12
Distance: 🚶500m 🚲3,8km ⛰️1km 🚂3km ⊗200m ♿500m 🚐500m 🚶‍♂️on the spot 🚴200m 🎿200m.
Remarks: Baker every morning, code internet at tourist office. Follow parking P1.

Tourist information Nesselwang:
ℹ️ Tourist Information, Lindenstrasse 16, www.nesselwang.de.

| 📷S | Neualbenreuth ♨️ | 18D1 |

Reisemobilhafen Sibyllenbad, Parkplatz P2, Kurallee. **GPS:** n49,98099 e12,42406.⬆️

21 📷€ 8 + € 1/pp tourist tax 🚰 🔧Ch 🧹(20x)€ 0,50/kWh WC 🪣. **Surface:** metalled. 🅾️ 01/01-31/12

DE

Distance: 1,5km.
Remarks: Bread-service.

| ⛟S | **Neuburg/Donau** 🌿 | 18B4 |

Parkplatz P1, Schlösslwiese, Zur Ringmeierbucht. **GPS:** n48,74022 e11,18434.

30 free € 1 Ch. **Location:** Urban, very simple, central, quit. **Surface:** gravel/sand. 01/01-31/12
Distance: 100m 400m on the spot on the spot.
Remarks: On the Danube river.

| ⛟S | **Neuhaus/Inn** | 19B4 |

Rast & More - Neuhaus am Inn

info@rastandmore-neuhaus.de - www.rastandmore-neuhaus.de

Reservations possible
Sanitary facilities
Convenient for longer stays

Rast & More, Straßfeld 7. **GPS:** n48,46228 e13,40720.
20 € 12 Ch (17x)€ 2/day WC . **Location:** Rural, comfortable, quit. **Surface:** gravel. 01/02-30/11
Distance: 700m 5,2km 8km 500m 700m 700m.

| | **Neumarkt/Oberpfalz** | 18C2 |

Woffenbacherstrasse. **GPS:** n49,28211 e11,44722.

30 free. **Surface:** grassy. 01/01-31/12
Remarks: At sports centre.

| ⛟S | **Neumarkt/Oberpfalz** | 18C2 |

Fritz Berger, Fritz-Berger-Str. 1. **GPS:** n49,30500 e11,48444.

free Ch free. **Surface:** grassy. 01/01-31/12
Distance: 2km 2km.

| | **Neusäß** | 18B5 |

Titania-Therme, Birkenallee 1. **GPS:** n48,40089 e10,82508.

5 free. **Location:** Urban, very simple, central, quit. **Surface:** metalled. 01/01-31/12
Distance: 1,2km 3km 1,2km on the spot on the spot.

| ⛟S | **Neustadt/Aisch** | 18A2 |

Am Festplatz, Bei den Sommerkeller/Riedfelder Ortstrasse. **GPS:** n49,58187 e10,60271.

8 free € 1 Ch € 1. **Surface:** gravel. 01/01-31/12
Distance: 500m 500m 500m 500m on the spot.

| ⛟S | **Neustadt/Aisch** | 18A2 |

Am Waldwad, Eilersweg. **GPS:** n49,57462 e10,62993.

6 free. **Surface:** grasstiles. 01/01-31/12
Distance: 3,5km 4km 4km 1km.

| ⛟S | **Niederwerrn** | 17D1 |

Jahnstrasse. **GPS:** n50,06073 e10,17526.

30 ⌖free ⟋€ 3 ⚑ Ch WC ⌷. **Surface:** asphalted. ◔ 01/01-31/12
Distance: ⌂on the spot ⊗on the spot.
Remarks: Max. 3 nights, near sports fields.

| ⛺ S | **Nordheim am Main** 🚲 | 18A1 |

Zehnthofstrasse. **GPS:** n49,85952 e10,17909.⬆.

30 ⌖voluntary contribution ⟋ ⚑Chfree. **Surface:** metalled. ◔ 01/01-31/12
Distance: ⌂200m.
Remarks: Along the river Meno.

| ⛺ S | **Nördlingen** | 18A4 |

Kaiserwiese. **GPS:** n48,85488 e10,48445.⬆.

30 ⌖free ⟋€ 2 ⚑€ 2 Ch ⚡€ 2/kWh WC. **Location:** Urban, quit.
Surface: asphalted. ◔ 01/01-31/12
Distance: ⌂on the spot ⊗McDonalds.
Remarks: Max. 48h.

| ⛺ | **Nürnberg** | 18B2 |

Volkspark Dutzendteich, Munchener Strasse. **GPS:** n49,42403 e11,10586.⬆➡.

10 ⌖free. **Surface:** asphalted. ◔ 01/01-31/12
Distance: ⌂4km ⚖.700m.
Remarks: Max. 3 nights.

| ⛺ | **Nürnberg** | 18B2 |

Volkspark Marienburg, Kilianstrasse. **GPS:** n49,47495 e11,09606.⬆➡.

8 ⌖free. **Surface:** grasstiles/metalled. ◔ 01/01-31/12
Distance: ⌂centre 4km ⊗800m ⚖.800m ⇌on the spot.
Remarks: Max. 3 nights.

| ⛺ | **Nürnberg** | 18B2 |

Wöhrder See, Rechenberganlage, Dr Gustav Heinemannstrasse. **GPS:** n49,46041 e11,11548.⬆.

2 ⌖free.
Surface: metalled. ◔ 01/01-31/12
Distance: ⌂3km ⚖.500m.
Remarks: Max. 3 nights.

Tourist information Nürnberg:
🛈 City walk through old city centre, daily from Tourist Information, Hauptmarkt. ◔ 14.30h.
🛈 Königstrasse 93; Hauptmarkt, www.tourismus.nuernberg.de.Large living city with a long history and many curiosities.
🛈 Nürnberg Card.Card gives for free entrance on among other things public transport and museums, discounts on purchases, boat trips, city walks etc.
Ⓜ Albrecht Dürerhaus.The life and work of Albrecht Bürer. ◔ Su 10-17h, 01/07-30/09 Su, Mo 10-17h.
Ⓜ Spielzeugmuseum, Karlstrasse 13-15.Toy museum. ◔ Tue-Su 10-17h, Wed 10-21h.
Ⓜ Technisch Uhrenmuseum, Allerbergerstrasse 95.Watch collection of Karl Gebhardt. ◔ 8-20h. Ⓣ free.
✖ Die Burg.Palace. ◔ 01/04-30/09 9-12h, 12.45-17h, 01/10-31/03 9.30-12h, 12.45-16h. Ⓣ € 3.
🐾 Tiergarten.Zoo. ◔ 01/04-30/09 8-19.30h, 01/10-31/03 9-17h.

| ⛺ S | **Oberammergau** 🏔 💧 ❄ | 25B1 |

Campingpark Oberammergau, Ettalerstrasse 56B. **GPS:** n47,59028 e11,06861.⬆➡.

30 ⌖€ 8 ⟋ ⚑ Ch ⚡ WC ⌷🗑against payment. 🛒 **Surface:** gravel. ◔ 01/01-31/12
Distance: ⌂1,2km ⌂400m ⊗100m ⚖.1,2km 🎿1km.
Remarks: Max. 24h.

| ⛺ S | **Oberaudorf** 🏔 💧 ⛷ | 18D6 |

Pechler Hof, Tatzlwurmstrasse 5. **GPS:** n47,66132 e12,16890.⬆➡.

5 🛏 €9 🚰 🔌 ✎ included. **Location:** Central, quit. **Surface:** grassy. ⬛ 01/01-31/12

Distance: 🚶1km ⊗500m 🛒200m 🏊100m.

80 🛏 €10 + € 2,60/pp Kurtaxe, dog € 3 🚰 🔌 Ch ✎ € 0,70/kWh WC 🚽 🔌 📶 🚿 🧺 **Surface:** grassy. ⬛ 01/01-31/12

Distance: 🚶150m (skibus) 🚴 on the spot 🧗 on the spot.

Remarks: Bread-service.

🏨 S | Oberaudorf 🏔 🎋 | 18D6
Hotel Feuriger Tatzlwurm, Tatzlwurm, B307. **GPS:** n47,67223 e12,08448.

10 🛏 guests free 🚰. **Location:** Rural, very simple. **Surface:** gravel/metalled. ⬛ 01/01-31/12

Distance: 🏊 on the spot ⊗ on the spot.

🏨 S | Oberelsbach | 10B6
Wohnmobilstellplatz Oberelsbach, Gangolfstrasse. **GPS:** n50,44234 e10,11412. ⬆️

6 🛏 €5 🔌 € 1/80liter 🔌 Ch ✎ (6x)€ 0,50/kWh. ⬛ 01/01-31/12

Distance: 🚶500m ⊗on the spot.

Remarks: Max. 3 days.

🏨 S | Obermaiselstein 🏔 ❄ | 25A1
Wohnmobilplatz Allgäu, Am Goldbach 3, Niederdorf. **GPS:** n47,44422 e10,24288. ⬆️ ➡️

30 🛏 €10 + € 1,30/pp Kurtaxe 🚰 🔌 Ch ✎ (25x)€ 2/day WC 🚽 € 1 🔌. 🚿 **Location:** Rural, comfortable, luxurious. **Surface:** asphalted/gravel. ⬛ 01/01-31/12

Distance: ⊗on the spot.

🏨 S | Oberstdorf 🏔 🎋 🏔 ❄ 🎋 | 25A1
Rubi-Camp, Rubinger Straße 34. **GPS:** n47,42340 e10,27772. ⬆️

🏨 S | Oberstdorf 🏔 🎋 🏔 ❄ 🎋 | 25A1
Wohnmobilstellplatz Oberstdorf, Enzenspergerweg 10. **GPS:** n47,40856 e10,28625. ⬆️

150 🛏 € 12, tourist tax € 2,60/pp 🚰 🔌 Ch ✎ € 2,50/24h WC 🚽 🚿

Location: Rural, luxurious.

Surface: grassy/metalled. ⬛ 01/01-31/12

Distance: 🚶on the spot ⊗250m 🛒100m 🏊on the spot 🚵500m 🚲800m.

Tourist information Oberstdorf:

ℹ️ Tourist Information, Marktplatz 7, www.oberstdorf.de.Mountain village with many sporting possibilities in summer and winter.

🏨 S | Oberthulba | 10B6
Reisemobilstellplatz Thulbatal. **GPS:** n50,17419 e9,92499. ⬆️

25 🛏 € 6,50, 2 pers.incl 🚰 🔌 Ch ✎ € 2 WC 🚽 € 0,80 🔌 € 2,30. **Surface:** grasstiles. ⬛ 15/03-15/11

Distance: 🚶1km 🏊on the spot ⊗150m.

🏨 S | Oberviechtach | 18D2
Am Freibad, Im Wiesengrund. **GPS:** n49,45296 e12,42458. ⬆️ ➡️

+5 🛏 free 🚰 🔌 Ch ✎ (3x)free. **Surface:** asphalted. ⬛ 01/01-31/12

Distance: 🚶1km ⊗600m.

🏨 S | Oettingen | 18A3
Schießwasen. **GPS:** n48,95690 e10,60894. ⬆️

4 🛏 free ⛽ € 1/10minutes 🚰 Ch 💧 (4x)€ 1/8h. **Location:** Quit. **Surface:** metalled. 🅿 01/01-31/12 🔴 last weekend Jul, 1st weekend Aug.
Distance: 🚶10 min walking 🛒500m.

| 🅂 | Ostheim 〰🚉⛵ | 10B6 |

Streuwiesenparkplatz, Nordheimer Straße/Alexander Straße. **GPS:** n50,45820 e10,22656.⬆.

6 🛏 € 3 ⛽ € 1/80liter 🚰 Ch 💧 € 0,50.
Surface: metalled. 🅿 01/01-31/12
Distance: 🚶300m ⊗300m 🛒300m.

| 🅂 | Ottobeuren ⚜ | 18A6 |

Parking Sportwelt, Galgenberg 4. **GPS:** n47,94907 e10,29649.⬆.

10 🛏 free ⛽ € 0,50/100liter 🚰 Ch 💧 (6x)€ 0,50/kWh.
Location: Urban, comfortable.
Surface: metalled. 🅿 01/01-31/12
Distance: 🚶1km 🛵 on the spot.
Remarks: Coins available at Sportwelt (9-23h).

| 🅂 | Parkstein 🏰⛲ | 18D1 |

Basaltkegel von Parkstein, Basaltstrasse 16. **GPS:** n49,73179 e12,07127.

20 🛏 free. **Surface:** metalled. 🅿 01/01-31/12
Distance: 🚶200m ⊗50m.
Remarks: Nearbij Gasthof Bergstüberl, beautiful view.

| 🅂 | Passau | 19B4 |

Güterbahnhof, Regensburger strasse. **GPS:** n48,57406 e13,44495.⬆.

15 🛏 € 3/h, max. € 13/day ⛽ 🚰 Ch. 🚌 **Location:** Urban, very simple, noisy.
Surface: metalled. 🅿 01/01-31/12
Distance: 🚶500m ⊗500m 🛒500m 🚉100m.
Remarks: Price incl. bus transport to the city centre.

| 🅂 | Passau | 19B4 |

Winterhafen, Regensburgerstrasse/Racklau. **GPS:** n48,57412 e13,42690.⬆➡.

60 🛏 free. **Surface:** gravel. 🅿 01/01-31/12 🔴 high water.
Distance: 🚶2km 🏊On the Danube river 🎣on the spot ⊗500m 🛒500m 🚉300m.

| 🍴🅂 | Pechbrunn | 18D1 |

Ferien- und Reiterhof Timber Canyon, Silberrangen 1. **GPS:** n49,98393 e12,14844. ⬆.
8 🛏 € 8/pp ⛽ 🚰 Ch 💧 WC 🚿included. 🅿 01/01-31/12
Distance: 🚶2,5km.

| 🅂 | Petting | 19A6 |

Stellplatz Schneiderhof, Seestrasse 11a. **GPS:** n47,91375 e12,81120.

4 🛏 € 14 incl. 2 pers., tourist tax incl ⛽ 🚰 Ch 💧 € 0,50/kWh WC 🚿included.
Surface: grassy.
Distance: 🚶300m 🏊1km ⊗300m 🛒300m 🚉500m.

| 🅂 | Petting | 19A6 |

Wolferstätte, Stubern 1. **GPS:** n47,88988 e12,78455.

3 🛏 € 12, 2 pers.incl ⛽ € 2/100liter 🚰 Ch 💧 WC 🚿. **Surface:** grassy. 🅿 01/05-30/10
Distance: 🚶4km 🏊5km 🛒2km.
Remarks: Farm.

DE

Pfronten ❄ 25B1

Wohnmobilstellplatz Wohlfahrt, Am Wiesele 7, Weißbach. **GPS:** n47,59829 e10,55240. ⬆️➡️.

45 🛏️€ 10, 2 pers.incl ⚓€ 0,50 🔌Ch ⚡(48x) WC included 🚿€ 0,50 ⚡€ 3. 🚰 **Surface:** gravel. ⏰ 01/01-31/12
Distance: 🚌Skibus 🚲5km ⛷on the spot.

Plattling 19A4

Freizeit- und Sportzentrum Plattling, Georg-Ecklstrasse. **GPS:** n48,77226 e12,87331. ⬆️➡️.

20 🛏️free ⚓€ 1/80liter 🔌Ch ⚡(4x)€ 0,50/kWh. **Location:** Rural.
Surface: metalled. ⏰ 01/01-31/12
Distance: 🏊500m ⛴500m.

Plech 18C2

Freizeitpark Fränkisches Wunderland, Zum Herrlesgrund 13. **GPS:** n49,65929 e11,46552. ⬆️.

10 🛏️free. **Surface:** gravel.
Distance: 🏊1km ⛴1km.
Tourist information Plech:
🎡 Freizeitpark Fränkisches Wunderland, Zum Herrlesgrund 13.Amusement park. ⏰ 01/05-30/09. 🎫 € 12,50.

Pleystein 18D1

Reisemobilplatz Pleystein, Vohenstraußer Straße/Galgenbergweg. **GPS:** n49,64429 e12,40548. ⬆️.

10 🛏️free ⚓🔌 WC free. **Surface:** gravel. ⏰ 01/01-31/12
Distance: 🏊350m.

Poppenricht 18C2

Wohnmobilstellplatz an der Vils, Vilsstrasse. **GPS:** n49,48184 e11,83119. ⬆️.

20 🛏️free. **Surface:** gravel. ⏰ 01/01-31/12
Distance: 🏊1km ⛽on the spot ⊗2km ⛴1km.
Remarks: At sports centre, along the historic "Goldenen Straße" from Nürnberg to Prague.

Pottenstein 18C1

Wohnmobilpark Pottenstein, Am langen Berg. **GPS:** n49,76294 e11,40826. ➡️.

25 🛏️€ 7 ⚓€ 1/100liter 🔌⚡(6x)€ 1/kWh.
Surface: gravel.
⏰ 01/01-31/12 ⚪ Service: winter.
Distance: 🏊1km ⛴Aldi 200m.
Tourist information Pottenstein:
🏛 Verkehrsbüro Pottenstein, Forchheimer strasse 1, www.pottenstein.de.City centre with half-timbered houses.
👁 Teufelshöhle.Caves, constant temperature 9ºC and atmospheric humidity 98%. ⏰ 01/04-31/10 9-17h.
🏰 Burg Pottenstein.1000 Jaar oude burcht. ⏰ Tue-Su 10-17h.
😊 Sommerrodelbahn.Toboggan slide 1km, on the B470. ⏰ 10-17h.

Prichsenstadt 18A1

Wohnmobilstellplatz Schützengesellschaft 1752, Wiesentheider Straße 3. **GPS:** n49,81649 e10,34981. ⬆️.

5 🛏️€ 5 ⚓€ 1 ⚡€ 2,50. **Surface:** gravel. ⏰ 01/01-31/12
Distance: 🏊300m ⊗on the spot.

Prien am Chiemsee 18D6

Wohnmobilstellplatz Strandbad Schraml, Harrasser Strasse 39. **GPS:** n47,85400 e12,36679. ⬆️➡️.

250 🛏 € 8-12 ⚡ € 0,20/10liter 🍳 Ch ⚡ € 0,75/kWh WC 🚿. **Location:** Rural, quit. **Surface:** grassy/metalled. 📷 01/01-31/12
Distance: 🚶1km 🚉200m 🚏on the spot 🚲 on the spot.
Remarks: Shuttle bus to ski-piste, use sanitary € 4,50-6/pppn.

Reit im Winkl 🏔️ ❄️   19A6
Wohnmobilpark Seegatterl, Seegatterl 7. **GPS:** n47,65898 e12,54213. ⬆️➡️.

100 🛏 € 8-10, tourist tax excl ⚡ € 0,20/10liter 🍳Ch ⚡ € 0,75/kWh WC 🚿.
Location: Rural, quit.
Surface: grassy/gravel. 📷 17/12-10/04, 01/06-15/10
Distance: 🚶4km 🚉1,5km 🚏150m 🚲 on the spot.

Reit im Winkl 🏔️ ❄️   19A6
Gasthof Stoaner, Birnbacher Straße 34. **GPS:** n47,67900 e12,44930.
15 🛏 € 10, 2 pers.incl., winter € 12 ⚡🍳Ch ⚡ WC 🚿included. **Surface:** unpaved.
Remarks: At golf court.

Riedenburg 🏔️ 🌳   18C3
Volksfestplatz, Austraße. **GPS:** n48,96446 e11,68181. ⬆️.

40 🛏 € 6 ⚡ 🍳Ch ⚡ € 1/8h. **Surface:** gravel/metalled. 📷 01/01-31/12
📷 last week of Aug.
Distance: 🚶450m 🚏300m 🚉20m.
Remarks: At the Main-Danube Canal.

Röslau   11A6
Festplatz Geiersgarten, Eisnerstrasse. **GPS:** n50,08666 e11,97559. ⬆️.

3 🛏free. **Surface:** grassy/gravel. 📷 01/01-31/12
Distance: 🚶1km 🚏1km 🚉1km.
Remarks: Max. 1 night.

Rothenburg ob der Tauber   18A2
Parkplatz P2, Nördlinger Strasse. **GPS:** n49,36661 e10,18580.

---

30 🛏 € 9/night, € 2,50/day ⚡🍳Ch 3 ⚡ WC. **Location:** Rural, isolated.
Surface: grassy/sand. 📷 01/04-15/10
Distance: 🚶1,5km 🚴6km 🚏on the spot 🚉500m 🚏on the spot.
Remarks: Steep ramp.

Tourist information Prien am Chiemsee:
ℹ️ Tourist Information, www.tourismus.prien.de.De Chiemsee is one of the biggest lakes of the Bavaria region, tourist area.

Rain/Lech   18B4
Wohnmobilstellplatz Rain, Fasanenweg. **GPS:** n48,69195 e10,90699.
8 🛏free ⚡ € 1 🍳Ch ⚡ € 1/6h. **Surface:** gravel.
Distance: 🚶1,6km.

Ramsthal   17D1
Festplatz am Feuerwehrhaus, Hauptstrasse, K6-4. **GPS:** n50,13750 e10,06111. ⬆️

6 🛏free ⚡ € 1/100liter 🍳Ch ⚡ WC 🚿 € 1.
Surface: metalled.
📷 01/01-31/12
Distance: 🚶on the spot 🚏Gasthof Wahler, Gaststätte zum Beck 🚏on the spot.

Reichelshofen   18A2
Landwehr-Bräu. GPS: n49,43906 e10,21188.

5 🛏free. **Surface:** asphalted.
Remarks: Brewery.

Reit im Winkl 🏔️ ❄️   19A6
Wohnmobilpark Reit im Winkl, Am Waldbahnhof 7, Groissenbach. **GPS:** n47,67013 e12,48358. ⬆️➡️.

25 🛏€10 🚰€ 1 🚿Ch 🔌€ 0,50/kWh WC. **Surface:** metalled. 🔲 01/01-31/12

Distance: 🚶within walking distance.

🚐S Rothenburg ob der Tauber 18A2

Parkplatz P3, Weinsdorfer strasse. **GPS:** n49,38222 e10,18889.⬆️.

30 🛏€10 🚰€ 1/100liter 🚿Ch WC.
Surface: metalled.
🔲 01/01-31/12

Distance: 🚶on the spot.

Tourist information Rothenburg ob der Tauber:

ℹ️ Rothenburg Tourismus Service, Marktplatz, www.rothenburg.de.Small medieval town surround by ramparts.
Ⓜ️ Mittelalterliches Kriminalmuseum, Burggasse 3.History of 1000 years of jurisdiction. 🔲 01/04-31/10 9.30-18h, 01/11-28/02 14-16h, 01/12-31/12, 01/03-31/03 10-16h.
✳️ Schäfertanz.Traditional celebration. 🔲 27/03, 15/05, 04/09.

🚐S Rothenkirchen 10D6

Waldschwimmbad. GPS: n50,37389 e11,31583.

40 🛏€5 🚰€ 0,50 🚿Ch€ 1 🔌(16x)WC🍴included. **Surface:** metalled.
🔲 01/04-31/10

Distance: 🚶1,5km.
Remarks: Parking swimming pool.

🚐S Röthlein 18A1

Freizeit Reisch, Mühläckerstrasse 11. **GPS:** n49,98722 e10,22556.
1 🛏🚰€ 0,50/50liter 🚿Ch 🔌€ 0,50. **Surface:** asphalted. 🔲 01/01-31/12

🚐S Röthlein 18A1

Sportanlage TSV/Bundeskegelbahn, Friedhofstrasse. **GPS:** n49,98694 e10,21583.⬆️.

10 🛏free. **Surface:** grassy.
Distance: 🚶on the spot.

🚐S Röttingen 17D2

Wohnmobilplatz an der Tauber, Neubronner Straße. **GPS:** n49,50724 e9,96995.
20 🛏€5 🚰€ 1 🚿Ch 🔌€ 2/24h WC🍴€ 1,20. **Surface:** gravel. 🔲 01/04-31/10 🔲 last 2 weeks of august.

Distance: 🚶300m ⊗500m.
Remarks: Along the Tauber river.

🏭S Roßhaupten 🌾🏕️🍴🌳⛷️❄️ 25B1

Wohnmobilstellplatz Miller, Augsburger Strasse 23. **GPS:** n47,65889 e10,71944. ⬆️.

25 🛏€ 9, 4 pers.incl 🚰🚿Ch 🔌(3x)€ 2 WC🍴€ 1. **Surface:** metalled. 🔲 01/01-31/12

Distance: 🚶50m ⛰️1,2km 🚶1,2km ⊗200m 🛒150m 🚃150m 🚲1km ⛴️500m.
Remarks: Next to Camping- und Freizeitmarkt, reparation work.

©S Ruhpolding 19A6

Campingplatz Ortnerhof, Ortsstraße 5. **GPS:** n47,74260 e12,66303.⬆️➡️.

16 🛏€ 9 🚰🚿Ch 🔌€ 1,50 + € 0,60/kWh WC🍴€ 3 🚿€ 3/24h.
Location: Rural. **Surface:** gravel. 🔲 01/01-31/12
Distance: 🚶3km ⊗on the spot 🚶2km ⛴️on the spot.
Remarks: At golf court, max. 1 night.

🚐S Scheidegg 🌿 24D1

Wohnmobilpark am Kurhaus, Am Hammerweiher 1. **GPS:** n47,57351 e9,84545. ⬆️.

20 🛏€ 6, € 1,70/pp tourist tax 🚰🚿Chincluded 🔌€ 3 🍴€ 1,50 🚿.
Surface: gravel/metalled. 🔲 01/01-31/12
Distance: 🛒Minishop.
Remarks: Bread-service.

🚐S Scheinfeld 18A2

Freibad Scheinfeld, Badstrasse 5. **GPS:** n49,67434 e10,46173.

2 € 6 Ch. **Surface:** gravel. 01/01-31/12
Remarks: At swimming pool.

S Schliersee 18D6

Am Spitzingsee, Spitzingstraße. **GPS**: n47,66648 e11,88851.

+10 summer € 12, winter € 9 (no service) Ch.
Location: Rural, very simple, isolated, quit. **Surface:** gravel. 01/01-31/12
Service: winter.
Distance: 5,4km on the spot 500m on the spot on the spot on the spot.
Remarks: At lake, altitude 1085m.

S Schlüsselfeld 18A1

Bambergerstrasse. **GPS**: n49,75878 e10,62104. .
5 free € 1/80liter. **Surface:** gravel. 01/01-31/12
Distance: on the spot.

S Schlüsselfeld 18A1

Concorde, Concorde-Straße 2–4. **GPS**: n49,76745 e10,56478.

20 free € 1/100liter Ch € 0,50/kWh. **Surface:** metalled. 01/01-31/12
Distance: 1km 1km 1km.
Remarks: At motohome manufacturer.

S Schnelldorf 18A3

BP-Truckstop Feuchtwangen, Rudolph Dieselstrasse 1. **GPS**: n49,17149 e10,24124.

20 € 6 € 1/80liter Ch (3x) WC € 2. **Surface:** metalled. 01/01-31/12

Distance: 300m on the spot on the spot.
Remarks: Reduction at restaurant € 5.

S Schöllkrippen 17C1

Naturerlebnisbad, Häfner-Ohnhaus-Straße. **GPS**: n50,08444 e9,25306.
35 € 5/24h € 1 Ch € 0,50/kWh. **Surface:** grassy. 01/01-31/12
Distance: 500m.

S Schongau 18B6

Festplatz, Lechuferstrasse. **GPS**: n47,80906 e10,89815.

70 € 5 € 1/5liter Ch WC.
Location: Urban. **Surface:** asphalted. service: 20/03-05/11 25/07-08/08.
Distance: 400m 100m 400m on the spot.
Remarks: Caution sanitary € 30, guests free.

Tourist information Schongau:
Tourist Information, Münzstrasse 1 - 3, www.schongau.de.City wall, towers and gates.

S Schonungen 18A1

Behr Reisemobile, An der Kemenate 6, Abersfeld, B303. **GPS**: n50,07352 e10,39366. .

5 free Ch free. **Surface:** metalled. 01/01-31/12
Distance: 8km.
Remarks: Motorhome dealer, accessory shop.

Schrobenhausen 18C4

Am Klostergarten. GPS: n48,55835 e11,26234.

4 free. **Surface:** metalled. 01/01-31/12
Distance: 500m 500m 500m.

S Schrobenhausen 18C4

Kläranlage, Köningslachenerweg 12. **GPS**: n48,57420 e11,26930.
Ch.
Remarks: Mo-Thu 7-12h, 13-16h, Fr 7-12h.

S Schwandorf 18D2

Festplatz, Angerring, Krondorf. **GPS**: n49,33230 e12,10247.

DE

30 ⛺free ⛽🔌♻Chfree. **Surface:** asphalted/grassy. 🅿 01/01-31/12 ◗
week before/after Whitsuntide.
Distance: 🚶500m ⊗200m 🛒500m.
Remarks: Along the Naab river.

| 🏕🆂 | Schwangau ❄❅🏔🌿☀🌷 | 25B1 |

Wohnmobilpark Schwangau, Münchenerstrasse 151. **GPS:** n47,59167
e10,77250.⬆.

24 ⛺€ 12,50-17,50, dog € 2 ⛽🔌♻Ch🧹 (24x)€ 2,50 WC🍽◗.🚿📷
Location: Urban, comfortable. **Surface:** grassy/gravel. 🅿 01/01-31/12
Distance: 🚶2km 🏊on the spot 🍞on the spot ⊗on the spot 🛒on the spot
🚍on the spot 🚲1km 🚤on the spot.

| 🆂 | Segnitz | 18A2 |

Mainstraße. **GPS:** n49,67012 e10,14242.⬆.

4 ⛺free. **Surface:** metalled.
Distance: 🏊on the spot 🍞on the spot.
Remarks: Max. 1 day.

| 🍴🆂 | Segnitz | 18A2 |

Gasthaus zum Goldenen Anker, Mainstraße 8. **GPS:** n49,67063 e10,14344.⬆.

17 ⛺€ 7,50 ⛽🔌♻Ch🧹. **Surface:** grassy/gravel. 🅿 01/01-31/12 ◗
Restaurant: Thu.
Distance: 🏊on the spot ⊗on the spot.
Remarks: Along the river Meno.

| 📷 | Selb | 11A4 |

Wundsiedler Weiher. **GPS:** n51,15581 e12,13455.➡.

20 ⛺free. **Surface:** gravel. 🅿 01/01-31/12
Distance: 🚶2km ⊗200m.
Remarks: Hiking trails.

| 🏕🆂 | Selbitz | 11A6 |

Autohof Bayers, Stegenwaldhauser Strasse. **GPS:** n50,32469 e11,78524.

⛺free ⛽€ 1/80liter ♻Ch. **Surface:** asphalted. 🅿 01/01-31/12
Distance: ⊗10m.
Remarks: Parking vans.

| 🍴🆂 | Siegsdorf | 19A6 |

Gasthof Hörterer der Hammerwirt, Schmiedstrasse, B306, Hammer. **GPS:**
n47,80096 e12,70392.⬆➡.

10 ⛺guests free ⛽WC 📶. **Location:** Rural. **Surface:** metalled. 🅿 01/01-
31/12 ◗ Wed.
Distance: ⊗on the spot 🛒100m 🚍100m 🚲2,5km 🚤300m.
Remarks: Max. 3 nights.

| ♨ | Sonthofen ♨ | 25A1 |

Erlebnisbad Wonnemar, Stadionweg 5. **GPS:** n47,50344 e10,27883.⬆➡.

12 ⛺free.
Location: Urban, very simple. **Surface:** gravel. 🅿 01/01-31/12
Distance: 🚲2,3km ⊗on the spot 🚍on the spot 🚶on the spot.
Remarks: Max. 1 night.

| 🆂 | Steinach/Straubing | 19A3 |

Firma Hubert Brandl Caravantastic, Gewerbering 11. **GPS:** n48,95639
e12,62250.⬆.

3 🛌 free ⚡€ 1 🔌 💧. **Surface:** grassy. 📷 01/01-31/12
Distance: 🚿1,5km ⊗2km 🚰1km.
Remarks: Connection electricity < 18h.

| ⊙ S | Steinberg am See 🏖️🏔️👥 | 18D2 |

Movin'G'round, Am Steinberger See. **GPS:** n49,28247 e12,17357. ⬆️

10 🛌 free, use of a meal desired ⚡🔌Ch 💧. **Surface:** grassy. 📷
Whitsuntide-30/09
Distance: 🚿500m ⊘on the spot ⊗on the spot.

| S | Steinhausen | 17D6 |

Parkplatz, Am Reiterhof 1. **GPS:** n48,02746 e9,69476.

5 🛌.
Distance: ⊗180m.

| S | Suben | 19B4 |

Raststätte Hotel Servus Europa Suben, Etzelshofen 125. **GPS:** n48,40078
e13,42593.
+10 🛌€ 10 ⚡🔌Ch 💧included. **Surface:** asphalted. 📷 01/01-31/12
Distance: ⚓50m ⊗50m.

| S | Sulzbach-Rosenberg 🌿 | 18C2 |

Großparkplatz, Bayreuther Straße. **GPS:** n49,50583 e11,74500. ⬆️➡️

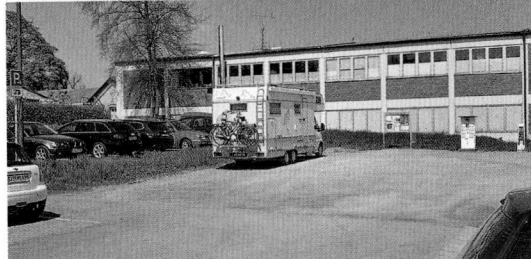

4 🛌 free ⚡€ 1/80liter 🔌Ch 💧 (4x)€ 0,50/kWh. **Surface:** metalled. 📷
01/01-31/12
Distance: 🚿300m ⊗500m 🚰500m.

| S | Sulzemoos | 18C5 |

Der Freistaat Caravaning, Ohmstrasse. **GPS:** n48,28267 e11,26084. ⬆️

40 🛌 free ⚡€ 1/80liter 🔌Ch 💧 (20x)€ 1/kWh WC. **Surface:** gravel. 📷
01/01-31/12
Distance: 🚿800m ⚓800m ⊗McDonalds 800m 🚰800m 🚌600m.

| S | Tauberrettersheim | 17D2 |

GPS: n49,49609 e9,93495.

6 🛌 free. **Surface:** grassy. 📷 01/01-31/12
Distance: 🚿on the spot ⊘on the spot.
Remarks: Parking at the Tauber.

| S | Thierstein 🌿🏔️❄️ | 11A6 |

Kaiserstein, Hirtweg. **GPS:** n50,10610 e12,10490. ⬆️➡️

10 🛌€ 4 ⚡🔌Ch 💧included 📶voluntary contribution. 🚪 **Surface:**
metalled. 📷 01/01-31/12 📷 01/10-31/03 water disconnected.
Distance: 🚿500m ⊗500m 🚰500m.
Remarks: Max. 2 nights, beautiful view.

Tourist information Thierstein:
ℹ️ www.thierstein.de.Town in the Fichtel mountains, with ruins of a former
fortress.

| ℹ️ S | Thüngersheim | 17D1 |

Parkplatz Main-Aue, Am Schwimbad. **GPS:** n49,88084 e9,83717.
10 🛌 free ⚡🔌 💧. **Surface:** grassy. 📷 01/04-31/10
Distance: 🚿500m.
Remarks: Along the river Meno.

| 🍴 S | Traunstein | 19A6 |

Gasthaus Jobst, Balthasar Permoserstrasse 64, Rettenbach. **GPS:** n47,91188
e12,64899. ⬆️.

DE

10 ⬚€3, guests free ⬚€ 2 ⬚Ch ⬚€ 2,50. **Surface:** metalled. ◻ 01/01-31/12 ◻ Wed.

Traunstein 19A6

Firma Grüaugl, Schmidhamerstrasse 31. **GPS:** n47,88227 e12,59941.

12 ⬚€5 ⬚€ 2 ⬚€ 2 Ch ⬚€ 0,50/kWh. **Location:** Isolated. **Surface:** metalled. ◻ 01/01-31/12
Distance: ⊗on the spot.
Remarks: Camping equipment store.

Treuchtlingen 18B3

Reisemobilstellplatz am Kurpark, Kästleinmühlenstrasse 20. **GPS:** n48,96028 e10,91778. ↑➔.

44 ⬚€9 ⬚Ch ⬚€ 1/8h WC ⬚included. **Location:** Urban, comfortable, quit. **Surface:** grasstiles. ◻ 01/01-31/12
Distance: 800m on the spot.

Übersee/Chiemsee 19A6

Bauernhof Steiner, Almfischer 11, Stegen. **GPS:** n47,80963 e12,49136. ↑➔.

25 ⬚€ 11, 2 pers.incl ⬚Ch ⬚€ 0,40/kWh WC ⬚€ 1,50. **Surface:** gravel. ◻ 01/01-31/12
Distance: Übersee 2km 4,6km Chiemsee 6km 1km.

Übersee/Chiemsee 19A6

Wohmobilstellplatz Dusenhof, Stegen 4. **GPS:** n47,81237 e12,48843. ↑➔.

28 ⬚€ 11, 2 pers.incl ⬚Ch ⬚€ 0,50/kWh ⬚€ 1. **Surface:** grassy/gravel. ◻ 01/01-31/12
Distance: Übersee 1km 4km Chiemsee 5km.
Remarks: Bread-service.

Viechtach 19A3

P1, Stadtmitte, Bierfeldstraße. **GPS:** n49,07876 e12,88235. ↑.

6 ⬚free. **Surface:** metalled. ◻ 01/01-31/12
Distance: 400m ⊗150m 50m.
Remarks: In front of supermarket Edeka, max. 3 nights.

Viechtach 19A3

P2, Stadthalle, Friedhofstrasse. **GPS:** n49,07722 e12,88528. ↑.

3 ⬚free. **Surface:** metalled. ◻ 01/01-31/12
Remarks: Max. 3 nights.

Viechtach 19A3

P5, TÜV, Karl-Gareis-Straße. **GPS:** n49,08222 e12,88306. ↑.

⬚free. **Surface:** asphalted. ◻ 01/01-31/12
Distance: 500m 500m.
Remarks: Small pitches, max. 3 nights.

Viechtach 19A3

Fam. Reisinger, Eging 1. **GPS:** n49,05417 e12,91333. ↑.

3 ⬚free ⬚. **Surface:** grassy. ◻ 01/01-31/12
Distance: Viechtach 4,5km.

Viechtach 19A3

Johann Ebner, Lohmühlweg 2, Pirka. **GPS:** n49,10694 e12,87583. ↑➔.

3 ⌁ € 8,50, electricity incl ⌁ ✦. **Surface:** grassy. ⬛ 01/04-01/10
Distance: 🚶8km.

| 🍴S | Viechtach 🏕️🏔️❄️ | 19A3 |

Landhotel Miethaner, Höllenstein 13. **GPS:** n49,12917 e12,87667.⬆️.

4 ⌁free ✦ € 1/12h. **Surface:** asphalted. ⬛ 01/01-31/12
Distance: 🚶7km 🛒1km ⊗on the spot 🚂on the spot ⛷️10km ⛵2km.

| 🍴 | Viechtach 🏕️🏔️❄️ | 19A3 |

Berghütte 'Zum Pröller', Hinterviechtach 3, Kollnburg. **GPS:** n49,02939 e12,83892.⬆️.

3 ⌁free. **Surface:** gravel. ⬛ 01/01-31/12
Distance: 🚶Viechtach 7km ⛷️20m.
Remarks: Parking at skipistes.

| S | Viechtach 🏕️🏔️❄️ | 19A3 |

Am Regenufer 1. **GPS:** n49,08303 e12,88824.⬆️.
⌁€ 1 ⌁€ 1 Ch.
⬛ 01/01-31/12

Tourist information Viechtach:

ℹ️ Tourist Information, Spitalgasse 5, www.viechtach.de.Many hiking routes.
👁️ Agayrischen Gewölbe, Spitalgasse 5.Oldest building of the city. Discover the mysterious treasures of the past, the mysteries of the Farao and the Tarot game.
⬛ 01/04-31/10 Tue-Su 10-16h.
Ⓜ️ Kristallmuseum, Linprunstrasse 4.600 crystals, glass and gems. ⬛ 9-18h, Sa-Su 10-16h.
🌲 Stadtplatz.Week market. ⬛ Wed 7-17h.

| ⌁S | Vilshofen 🏕️⛵ | 19B4 |

Yachthafen Vilshofen, Am Bootshafen. **GPS:** n48,63870 e13,18785.⬆️➡️.

10 ⌁€ 12 ⌁🦆Ch ✦(10x)€ 3/day WC ⌁€ 1. **Location:** Comfortable, quit. **Surface:** gravel. ⬛ 01/04-30/11
Distance: 🚶500m ⛵On the Danube river.

| ⌁ | Vilshofen 🏕️⛵ | 19B4 |

Schiffanleger, Donaukade. **GPS:** n48,63833 e13,18000.⬆️➡️.

12 ⌁free. **Location:** Noisy. **Surface:** asphalted. ⬛ 01/01-31/12
Distance: 🚶500m ⛵On the Danube river 🛒on the spot ⊗500m 🍴500m.
Remarks: Max. 1 night.

| ⌁S | Vohenstrauss | 18D2 |

Stadthalle, Neuwirtshauser 11. **GPS:** n49,61872 e12,34523.

20 ⌁free ⌁🦆WC. **Surface:** gravel. ⬛ 01/01-31/12
Distance: 🚶100m 🚲800m ⊗50m 🍴100m.

| ⌁ | Volkach 🌿🏕️⛵ | 18A1 |

Mainschleife, Am Main. **GPS:** n49,86389 e10,22139.⬆️➡️.

40 ⌁€ 5,50. **Surface:** gravel. ⬛ 01/01-31/12
Distance: 🚶500m ⛵on the spot 🛒on the spot ⊗500m 🍴500m.

| ⌾S | Wackersberg 🌿🏕️🏞️❄️ | 18C6 |

Camping Demmelhof, Stallau 148. **GPS:** n47,75056 e11,49992.⬆️.

12 ⫷€ 15, 2 pers.incl 🚿 Ch. ⚡€ 0,60/kWh WC ⫸€ 0,50 ▣€ 3.
Surface: grassy. ⬛ 01/01-31/12
Distance: 🚶5km ⊗500m 🚲600m.
Walder Badeweiher, Am Sportplatz. **GPS:** n47,72294 e10,56348. ⬆➡.
Wald 25B1

10 ⫷€5 🚿 Ch. **Location:** Rural, quit. **Surface:** gravel. ⬛ 01/01-31/12
Distance: 🚶500m ⊘on the spot ⊗250m on the spot ⚲on the spot.
Karoli-Badepark, VDK Heimstrasse 1. **GPS:** n48,72222 e13,60278.⬆.
Waldkirchen 19B4

16 ⫷free 🚿€ 1/50liter Ch. (10x)€ 0,50/kWh WC. **Location:** Rural, quit. **Surface:** gravel. ⬛ 01/01-31/12
Distance: 🚶1km ⊗25m 2km 🚲on the spot ⚲on the spot.
Remarks: Parking skating rink-swimming pool, use sanitary only during opening hours swimming pool, against payment.
Waldsassen 18D1
P2 Schwanenwiese, Schwanengasse. **GPS:** n50,00526 e12,30739.⬆.

2x2 ⫷free ⚡€ 2/10h. **Surface:** metalled. ⬛ 01/01-31/12
Distance: 🚶500m ⊗500m ⚲500m.
Remarks: Max. 3 days.
Waldsassen 18D1
Joseph-Wiesnetstrasse. **GPS:** n50,00250 e12,30361.⬆.

2 ⫷free. **Surface:** metalled. ⬛ 01/01-31/12
Distance: 🚶100m ⊗100m ⚲100m.
Remarks: Max. 3 days.
Wassertrüdingen 18A3
Parkplatz Entengraben. GPS: n49,03926 e10,59494.⬆➡.

12 ⫷voluntary contribution 🚿€ 1/80liter Ch. (6x)€ 1/8h. **Location:** Urban, quit. **Surface:** metalled. ⬛ 01/01-31/12
Distance: 🚶on the spot ⊘on the spot 🚲on the spot ⚲1km.
Weidenberg 18C1
Am Sportpark, In der Au. **GPS:** n49,93781 e11,73068.⬆.

10 ⫷free. **Surface:** gravel. ⬛ 01/01-31/12
Distance: 🚶750m ⊗Chinese restaurant 100m ⚲1,5km.
Weilheim in Oberbayern 18B6
Reisemobilplatz, Lohgasse. **GPS:** n47,84012 e11,13583.⬆.

8 ⫷€ 4/24h 🚿€ 0,50/50liter Ch. ⚡€ 0,50/kWh WC. **Location:** Urban, central. **Surface:** asphalted. ⬛ 01/01-31/12
Distance: 🚶Old city centre 500m 🚲100m ⚲200m.
Remarks: Along the Ammer river.
Weismain 10D6
Kraus-Gelände, Burgkunstadterstrasse. **GPS:** n50,08639 e11,23872.⬆.

6 ⛲free ⟊€ 0,50 ♨Ch ✎ (6x)€ 0,50. **Surface:** asphalted. ◗ 01/01-31/12
Distance: 🚶on the spot.
Remarks: Parking in centre.

Kirchweihplatz, Limesbad, Badstrasse 5. **GPS:** n49,02476 e10,97180.⬆.

⛲free ⟊€ 1/80liter ♨Ch. **Location:** Urban. **Surface:** metalled. ◗ 01/04-31/10
Distance: 🚶Old city centre 300m ⊗La Fattoria, Frauentorstrasse 11; Mai Tai, Bismarckanlage 16; Wittelsbacher Hof, Fr.Ebertstrasse 21 🚃on the spot.

Camping Grüntensee, Grüntenseestraße 41. **GPS:** n47,61003 e10,44704.⬆➡.

12 ⛲€ 15 + tourist tax € 1/pp ⟊ ♨Ch ✎ (12x)€ 0,50/kWh.🚽🚿 **Location:** Rural, luxurious, quit. **Surface:** gravel. ◗ 01/01-31/12
Distance: 🚶2,5km 🚲600m ⛱on the spot 🚂on the spot ⊗on the spot 🚊1,5km 🚃1,5km 🐎on the spot 🎿on the spot 🐟on the spot 🐕on the spot.

Wohnmobilpark Wertingen, Am Bahnhof 4. **GPS:** n48,55948 e10,69065.

12 ⛲€7 ⟊€ 1 ♨Ch ✎€ 2/day.🚽 **Location:** Urban, comfortable, central, quit. **Surface:** grassy/gravel. ◗ 01/01-31/12
Distance: 🚶800m 🚂300m.

Wohnmobilstellplatz Streitberg, Bahnhofstrasse, B470. **GPS:** n49,80782 e11,21636.

7 ⛲€ 2 ⟊♨Chfree. **Surface:** gravel. ◗ 01/01-31/12
Distance: 🚶500m 🚲500m ⊗500m 🚂500m 🚃300m.

Schwimm- & Erlebnisbad Wolnzach, Hanslmühlweg 6. **GPS:** n48,59718 e11,62792.⬆.

4 ⛲free ⟊€ 1/80liter ♨Ch ✎ (4x)€ 0,50/kWh. **Surface:** metalled. ◗ 01/01-31/12
Distance: 🚶600m 🚲500m 🚂600m.

Gasthof Alpenblick, Traunsteiner Straße 21, Weibhausen. **GPS:** n47,89880 e12,69123.

5 ⛲free, use of a meal desired.
Location: Very simple. **Surface:** gravel.
Distance: ⊗on the spot.

Ludwigstraße/Rot-Kreuz-Strasse. **GPS:** n50,03638 e11,99351.⬆.

6 ⛲€ 5/24h ⟊♨Ch ✎ included. **Surface:** gravel. ◗ 01/01-31/12 ◖ water: Nov-March.
Distance: 🚶600m 🚂1km.
Remarks: Pay at tourist office.

Altstadtparkplatz, Mittelweg. **GPS:** n50,00667 e10,59583.⬆.

DE

5 🛒free. **Surface:** metalled. 🅾 01/01-31/12

| | Zeil am Main | 18A1 |

Parkplatz Tuchanger, Oskar Winkler strasse. **GPS:** n50,01083 e10,59056.↑→

20 🛒free. **Surface:** metalled. 🅾 01/01-31/12
Distance: 🚶1km ⊗1km 🚉1km.
Remarks: Parking gymnasium.

Tourist information Zeil am Main:
ℹ Tourist Information, www.zeil-am-main.de.Beer and wine region.
⊗ Brauereigasthof Göller"Zum alten Freyung".Brewery restaurant with regional specialities and Göller-beer. 🅾 Mo-Su 9.30-01h.
☀ Altstadt Weinfest.Wine festivals. 🅾 06/08-08/08.
🌿 Wein-Wander-Weg.Hiking trail through wine region.

| S | Zellingen | 17D1 |

Am Freibad, Badstraße. **GPS:** n49,89621 e9,82665.
5 🛒free 🚰🗑Ch 🧺€ 3. **Surface:** metalled. 🅾 01/01-31/12

| 00 | Zirndorf | 18B2 |

Playmobil Funpark, Brandstätterstrasse. **GPS:** n49,43087 e10,93935.
40 🛒€ 2. **Surface:** metalled.
Distance: ⊗on the spot.

SWITZERLAND

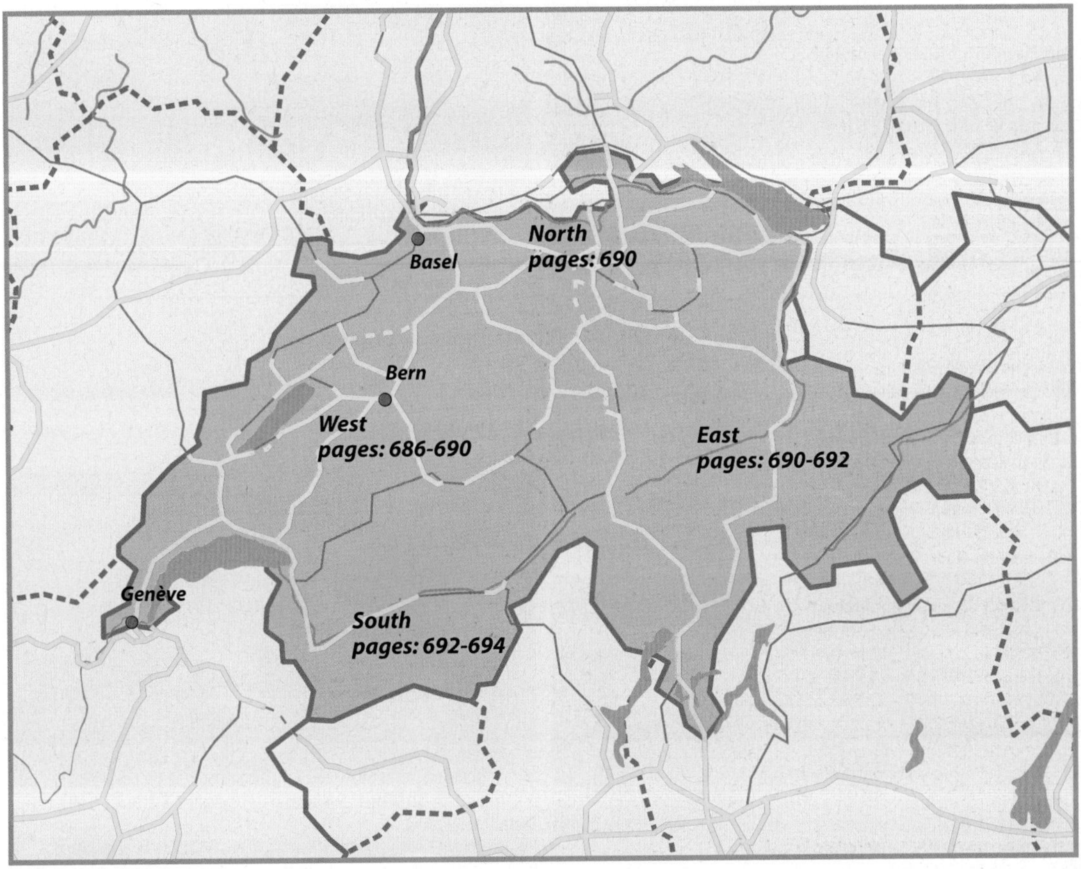

North
pages: 690

Basel

Bern

West
pages: 686-690

East
pages: 690-692

Genève

South
pages: 692-694

Capital: Bern
Government: Direct democracy, Federal republic
Official Language: German, French, Italian, Romansh
Population: 7,700,000 (2010)
Area: 41,284 km².

General information
Dialling code: 0041.
Currency: Swiss franc (CHF), 1 CHF = € 0,83 (October 2012)

Regulations for overnight stays
Overnight parking is allowed, max 15 hours.

Opening hours
Shops: Monday-Friday 8am-12noon and 1.30pm-6.30pm, closed on Monday morning, Saturday 8am-12noon and 1.30pm-16/17pm
Banks: Monday-Friday 8.30am-4.30pm, often in small towns 8.30am-12noon and 1.30pm-4.30pm.

Switzerland

Switzerland West

| △ | Aeschi | 24A3 |

Panorama, Scheidgasse 272. **GPS**: n46,65399 e7,70070.
🚿. ⬛ 15/05-15/10

| △ | Avenches | 23D3 |

Port-Plage. **GPS**: n46,90351 e7,04918.
🚿. ⬛ 01/04-01/10

| △ | Boltigen | 23D4 |

Jaunpass. **GPS**: n46,59208 e7,33758.
🚿. ⬛ 01/01-31/12

| △ | Böningen | 24A3 |

Seeblick, Campingstrasse 14. **GPS**: n46,68987 e7,89398.
🚿. ⬛ Easter-01/10

| △ | Brienz 🏔🚠❄ | 24A3 |

Aaregg. **GPS**: n46,74634 e8,04844.
🚿. ⬛ 01/04-01/11

Tourist information Brienz:
ℹ Alpen Region Brienz-Meiringen-Hasliberg, Bahnhofstrasse 22, Meiringen, www.alpenregion.ch.Village of wood-cutters.
⬛ during school hours ⬛ 01/07-31/08.
🚂 Brienz Rothorn Bahn.Steam rack-railway. ⬛ 01/06-31/10 8.45h.
🚂 CHF 46.
Ⓜ Freilichtmuseum Ballenberg.Open air museum. ⬛ 15/04-31/10 10-17h.

| 🍴S | Bullet | 23C3 |

Restaurant Les Cluds. **GPS**: n46,84248 e6,55991.

4 🚿free 🚰CHF 10 🗑Ch 🧹. **Surface**: asphalted.
Distance: ⊗on the spot.

| △ | Burgdorf | 24A2 |

Waldegg, Waldeggweg. **GPS**: n47,05407 e7,62895.
🚿. ⬛ 01/04-31/10

| △ | Château-d'Oex | 23D4 |

Le Berceau. **GPS**: n46,46673 e7,12529.
🚿. ⬛ 01/01-31/12

| 🚿S | Cheyres 🚤 | 23C3 |

Route de Crevel. **GPS**: n46,81651 e6,78501.

🚿free 🚰🗑Chfree. **Surface**: asphalted. ⬛ 01/01-31/12
Remarks: Parking at station.
Tourist information Cheyres:
🍇 Fête de vendanges.Wine festivals. ⬛ beginning Oct.

| 🚿S | Concise 🚤 | 23C3 |

Rue de Gare. **GPS**: n46,85057 e6,72218.⬆➡.

4 🚿free 🚰CHF 3 🗑Ch. **Surface**: gravel.
Remarks: At station and harbour.

| 🚿S | Couvet | 23C3 |

Sportzentrum Val de Travers. **GPS**: n46,92819 e6,64038.
🚿free 🚰CHF 2 🗑Ch.
Distance: 🚶nearby.

Tourist information Couvet:
🎉 12e Fête de l'Absinthe, Boveresse.

| 🚿S | Cudrefin | 23D3 |

Route de Neuchâtel. **GPS**: n46,96000 e7,02750.⬆.
🚰🗑Chfree.
Remarks: In front of camping Le Chablais.

| 🚿S | Delémont | 23D2 |

Route de Porrentruy. **GPS**: n47,36120 e7,33855.⬆➡.

5 🚿free 🚰🗑Ch🚌free. **Surface**: grassy/metalled. ⬛ 01/01-31/12
Distance: 🚌200m.

| 🚿S | Dürrenroth 🏔👥 | 24A2 |

Reisemobilstellplatz Blueberry Hill, Brunnen. **GPS**: n47,06563 e7,76553.⬆.

4 🚿CHF 8 🧹CHF 2. **Location**: Rural, comfortable, quit. **Surface**: gravel. ⬛ 01/01-31/12
Distance: 🚌Dürrenroth 3,5km.
Remarks: Panoramic view.

| 🚿S | Echallens | 23C4 |

Chemin du Pont. **GPS**: n46,63945 e6,64096.⬆➡.

5 🛌free ⚡🔌Ch free. **Surface:** asphalted. ⬜ 01/01-31/12

| △ | Estavayer-le-Lac | 23C3 |

Nouvelle-Plage. GPS: n46,85602 e6,84801.
🛌. ⬜ 01/04-01/10

| △ | Frutigen | 24A4 |

Grassi. GPS: n46,58178 e7,64213.
🛌. ⬜ 01/01-31/12

| △ | Gampelen | 23D3 |

Fanel, Seestraße. **GPS:** n47,00702 e7,05973.
🛌. ⬜ Easter-01/10

| △ S | Grandson | 23C3 |

Le Pécos, Rue du Pécos. **GPS:** n46,80371 e6,63575.
4 🛌⚡🔌Ch. ⬜ 01/04-01/10
Remarks: Next to campsite.

| △ | Grindelwald 🏔️⚡❄️ | 24A4 |

Eigernordwand. GPS: n46,62135 e8,01683.
🛌. ⬜ 01/01-31/12

Tourist information Grindelwald:
ℹ️ Grindelwald Tourismus, www.grindelwald.com. Area of glaciers and permanent snow.
👁️ Jungfraubahn. Train journey to the highest train station of Europe.

| △ S | Gryon | 23D4 |

Place de la Barboleuse. **GPS:** n46,28222 e7,07028.

4 🛌⚡CHF 5 🔌Ch. **Surface:** asphalted.
Distance: 🚶200m.
Remarks: To be paid at office de tourisme.

| △ | Gstaad | 23D4 |

Bellerive. GPS: n46,48106 e7,27328.
🛌. ⬜ 01/01-31/12

| ⏸️ S | Gündlischwand 🏔️👤 | 24A4 |

Säumertaverne, Am Chienbach 96. **GPS:** n46,63692 e7,92636.
🛌guests free ⚡. **Location:** Rural, central. **Surface:** asphalted.
Distance: ⚡7km 🏊on the spot 🍽️on the spot ⊗on the spot 🍺on the spot 🚲6km 🚶on the spot.

| △ | Gwatt-Thun | 24A3 |

Betllereiche. GPS: n46,72749 e7,62760.
🛌. ⬜ 01/04-01/10

| △ | Hinterkappelen | 23D3 |

Kappelenbrucke, Wohlenstrasse 62. **GPS:** n46,96433 e7,38361.
🛌. ⬜ 01/01-31/12

| ⏸️ S | Huttwil 🏔️👤 | 24A2 |

Firma Flyer E-Bike, Luzernstrasse. **GPS:** n47,11527 e7,86795.⬆️

20 🛌free ⚡🔌Ch ⚡ free. **Location:** Rural. **Surface:** gravel.
Distance: 🚶500m.
Remarks: E-bike factory.

| △ | Interlaken 🌿⛵🏔️🍦❄️ | 24A3 |

Hobby, Lehnweg 16. **GPS:** n46,68079 e7,82793.
🛌. ⬜ 01/04-01/10

| △ | Interlaken 🌿⛵🏔️🍦❄️ | 24A3 |

Jungfr' ablick, Gsteigstraße 80. **GPS:** n46,67581 e7,86597.
🛌. ⬜ 01/05-01/10

| △ | Interlaken 🌿⛵🏔️🍦❄️ | 24A3 |

Lazy-Rancho, Lehnweg 6. **GPS:** n46,68079 e7,82793.
🛌. ⬜ 01/04-01/10

Tourist information Interlaken:
ℹ️ Interlaken Tourismus, Höheweg 37, www.interlaken-tourism.ch. Jungfrau region, mountains and water.
👁️ Heimwehfluhbahn. Telpher carrier from 1906. ⬜ 01/04-31/10.
👁️ Mistery Park. Attractions and themepark. ⬜ 10-18h ⬜ 25/12-01/01.

| 🛌 S | La Brévine | 23C3 |

Les Varodes. **GPS:** n46,97195 e6,58860.

10 🛌free ⚡🔌Ch free. **Surface:** asphalted. ⬜ 01/01-31/12
Distance: 🚶3km 🏊on the spot.
Remarks: Parking at Lac des Tailleres.

| 🛌 S | La Chaux-de-Fonds ❄️ | 23C2 |

Bois du Couvent. **GPS:** n47,09334 e6,83593. ⬆️➡️
2 🛌free ⚡🔌Ch free. **Surface:** asphalted. ⬜ 01/05-30-09
Remarks: In front of campsite du Bois du Couvent.

Tourist information La Chaux-de-Fonds:
ℹ️ Tourisme neuchâtelois - Montagnes, Espacité 1, Place Le Corbusier. Capital of the clock industry.
Ⓜ️ Musée International d'Horlogerie, Rue des Musée 29. Watch museum. ⬜ 10-17h ⬜ Mo, 25/12-01/01.
Ⓜ️ Musée paysan et artisanal, Rue des Crêtets 148. The farmers' life and old crafts industry. ⬜ 01/04-31/10 14-17h, 01/11-28/02 Wed, Sa, Su 14-17h

| 🏠 S | Langenthal | 24A2 |

Lexa-Wohnmobile, Bern-Zürichstrasse 49b. **GPS:** n47,22461 e7,77944. 🚶

5 🛌free ⚡🔌Ch ⚡ free. **Surface:** asphalted. ⬜ 01/01-31/12
Distance: 🚶2km.

| 🛌 S | Lausanne 🌿⛵🏔️🍦 | 23C4 |

GPS: n46,51734 e6,59777.

10 ⌇CHF 20 ⌐CHF 3 ⬛Ch. **Surface:** grassy/metalled.
Remarks: Next to campsite the Vidy, free bus to centre.

Tourist information Lausanne:
ℹ️ Lausanne Tourisme, Avenue de Rhodanie 2, www.lausanne-tourisme. ch.Parking at the port, rack-railway to city centre.
Ⓜ️ Musée Olympique, Quai d'Ouchy 1.All about the Olympic games. ⬛ 9-18h
⬤ Mo, 01/10-30/04.

| △ | Lauterbrunnen ❄ | 24A4 |

Jungfrau. GPS: n46,58834 e7,90882.
⌇. ⬛ 01/01-31/12

| △ | Lauterbrunnen ❄ | 24A4 |

Schützenbach. GPS: n46,59047 e7,91194.
⌇. ⬛ 01/01-31/12

Tourist information Lauterbrunnen:
ℹ️ Lauterbrunnen Tourismus, Bahnhofplatz, www.wengen-muerren.ch/.Large winter sports area.
👁 Jungfraubahn, Grindelwald.Train journey to the highest train station of Europe.
👁 Klöppelstube, Altes Schulhaus.Making of bobbin lace. ⬛ Tue 14-17h. 🅣 free.
👁 Trümmelbachfälle, Lauterbrunnen dir Stechelberg.Underground waterfalls.
⬛ 01/04-30/11 9-17h.

| | Le Landeron | 23D3 |

Camp des Pêches. GPS: n47,05257 e7,06993.
⌇. ⬛ 01/04-15/10

Tourist information Le Landeron:
⊗ Restaurant Le Carnotzet, Rue de la Gare 22.Restaurant with regional specialities. ⬛ Tue-Sa 11-14h, 17-23h ⬤ Mo, Su.

| S | Les Brenets ◀ | 23C2 |

Champ de la Fontaine. GPS: n47,06588 e6,69898.

⌐CHF 5 ⬛Ch⚡. ⬛ 01/01-31/12
Remarks: Nearby campsite Lac de Brenets.

| S | Les-Ponts-de-Martel | 23C3 |

Rue du Bugnon. **GPS:** n46,99644 e6,73065. ⬆➡

2 ⌇free ⌐⬛Chfree. **Surface:** asphalted.
Remarks: At community centre.

| ⬛S | Malvilliers | 23C3 |

Hotel-Restaurant La Croisée, Route de Neuchâtel. **GPS:** n47,03200 e6,86779. ⬆
5 ⌇CHF5 ⌐⬛Ch⚡ included. **Surface:** asphalted. ⬛ 01/01-31/12

| △S | Morges | 23C4 |

Le Petit Bois. GPS: n46,50446 e6,48894.
⌇⌐⬛Chagainst payment. ⬛ 01/04-01/10
Remarks: Service at entrance campsite.

| ⬛S | Moutier | 23D2 |

Chemin de la Piscine. **GPS:** n47,27365 e7,37923. ⬆➡

5 ⌇free ⌐⬛Chfree.
Remarks: At swimming pool.

| ⬛S | Neuchâtel 🌿⛱🏠🏔🌊 | 23D3 |

Route des Falaises. **GPS:** n47,00145 e6,95735. ⬆

8 ⌇free ⌐⬛Ch⚡ free. **Surface:** grasstiles.
Distance: ⬛city centre 2km ⬛300m ⬛100m.
Remarks: Max. 24h.

Tourist information Neuchâtel:
ℹ️ Tourisme neuchâtelois, Hôtel des Postes.Medieval city on lake of same name.
Ⓜ️ Château de Boudry, Boudry.Wine museum. ⬛ Wed-Su 14-17h. 🅣 CHF 10.
✖ Château.Guided tour in French, German and English language. ⬛ 01/04-30/09 each hour. 🅣 free.
🌿 Le Creux-du-Van, Val-de-Travers.Nature reserve. ⬛ 01/01-31/12.

| ⬛S | Nyon 🌿⛱🏠🌊 | 23B4 |

Piscine de Colovray, Route de la Piscine. **GPS:** n46,36989 e6,22842.

10 ⌇free ⌐⬛Ch WC free. **Surface:** asphalted.
Distance: ⬛1km ⊗1km ⬛1km.

Tourist information Nyon:
ℹ️ Nyon Région Tourisme, www.nyon.ch.Old Roman city on the lake.
Ⓜ️ Musée du Léman, Quai Louis-Bonnard 8.Nature and culture of the lake. ⬛ 01/04-31/10 10-12h, 14-18h, 01/11-31/03 14-18h ⬤ Mo.
🌿 Fête de la Musique.Annual music festival. ⬛ 3rd weekend Jun. 🅣 free.

| ⬛S | Oron-la-Ville | 23C4 |

Chemin de Botollie. **GPS:** n46,57222 e6,81889. ⬆

CH

5 🛏free ⛽🍽Chfree. **Surface:** asphalted.

2 🛏free ⛽🍽Chfree. **Surface:** metalled.
Distance: ⚓on the spot ⊗on the spot 🛒on the spot.
Remarks: Near office de tourisme.

Tourist information Romont:

ℹ️ Office du Tourisme de Romont, Rue du Château 112, www.romont.ch.
Ⓜ️ Musée Suisse du Vitrail, Château.Glass painting art. 🕐 01/04-31/10 Tue-Su 10-13h, 14-18h, 01/11-31/03 Thu-Su 10-13h, 14-17h.
☀️ Pleureuses de Romont.Procession. 🕐 Good Friday.

| 🏕🅂 | Payerne | 23D3 |

Place de la Concorde. **GPS:** n46,81976 e6,93757.

| 🏕🅂 | Saignelégier | 23D2 |

Chemin de la Tuilerie. **GPS:** n47,25239 e7,00428.⬆️

🛏free ⛽🍽Ch🔌against payment. **Surface:** metalled. 🕐 01/01-31/12
Distance: ⚓700m.

| 🅰️ | Satigny | 23B5 |

Bois de Bay, Route du Bois-de-Bay 19. **GPS:** n46,19856 e6,04724.
🛏. 🕐 01/01-31/12

2 🛏free ⛽🍽Chfree. **Surface:** asphalted. 🕐 01/01-31/12
Distance: ⊗on the spot 🛒on the spot.

| 🏕🅂 | St.Aubin | 23C3 |

Port de St-Aubin-Sauges. GPS: n46,89181 e6,77427.⬆️➡️

| 🏕🅂 | Portalban 🌊⛵🌾 | 23D3 |

Route du Port. **GPS:** n46,92131 e6,95614.⬆️

17 🛏CHF 20, 2 pers.incl ⛽🍽Ch🚿WC🪣included. **Surface:** grasstiles. 🕐 01/01-31/12
Distance: ⚓on the spot ⊗on the spot 🛒on the spot.
Remarks: In port, nearby campsite.

10 🛏CHF 20 ⛽🍽Ch🚿WC🪣included. 🕐 01/01-31/12
Remarks: Parking port, nearby the capitainerie.

| 🅰️ | Prêles | 23D2 |

Prêles, Route de la Neuveville 61. **GPS:** n47,08404 e7,11262.
🛏. 🕐 01/04-15/10

| 🏕🅂 | St.Blaise | 23D3 |

Chemin des Pêcheurs. **GPS:** n47,01139 e6,98778.⬆️➡️

| 🏕🅂 | Reconvilier | 23D2 |

La Vie des Crêts. GPS: n47,22975 e7,22494.⬆️

10 🛏free ⛽CHF 5/100liter 🍽Ch🔌CHF 5/1h. **Surface:** metalled. 🕐 01/01-31/12
Distance: ⚓on the spot.
Remarks: Near Salle des Fêtes.

12 🛏CHF 8/24h ⛽🍽Ch🚿WC🪣included. **Surface:** asphalted.
Distance: ⚓Neuchâtel 5km.

| 🅰️ | Rolle | 23C4 |

Aux Vernes, Chemin des Vernes. **GPS:** n46,46152 e6,34457.
🛏. 🕐 01/04-01/10

| 🏕🅂 | Romont 🌊⛵🏔🐏 | 23D3 |

Rue de Château. **GPS:** n46,69535 e6,91877.⬆️➡️

CH

⬛S Ste.Croix ❄ 23C3
Grand-Rue, Auberson. **GPS:** n46,82019 e6,47230.

4 🚐free 🔌🛢Ch 🚿free. **Surface:** asphalted.
Distance: 🚶2km ⊗on the spot.
Tourist information Ste.Croix:
ℹ️ Office du tourisme Sainte-Croix, Rue Neuve 6.

△ Vesenaz 23B5
Pointe a la Bise. GPS: n46,24517 e6,19331.
🚐. ◻ 01/01-31/12

△ Zweisimmen 23D4
Vermeille, Eygässli 2. **GPS:** n46,56265 e7,37766.
🚐. ◻ 01/01-31/12

Switzerland North

⬛S Bellerive 23D3
Hep, Route de Vallamand. **GPS:** n46,91813 e7,02063.⬆

🚐€7 🔌🛢Ch 🚿CHF 3 WC. **Surface:** grassy.

△ Brunnen 24B3
Hopfraeben. GPS: n46,99700 e8,59300.
🚐. ◻ 01/05-01/10

△ Engelberg 24B3
Eienwäldli, Wasserfallstraße 108. **GPS:** n46,81009 e8,42243.
🚐.

⬛S Frick 24A1
Hotel Engel, Hauptstraße 101. **GPS:** n47,50576 e8,02430.

20 🚐free WC. **Surface:** gravel. ◻ 01/01-31/12
Distance: 🚶300m ⚓1,6km ⊗on the spot 🍴50m 🚌50m.
Remarks: Behind the hotel.
Tourist information Frick:
ℹ️ Tourismus Rheinfelden, Rheinfelden, www.rheinfelden.ch.
Ⓜ Sauriermuseum, Im Schulhaus, Schulstrasse 22. ◻ 1st, 3rd Su of the month.
🎫 CHF 3.

△ Horw 24B3
Steinibachried. GPS: n47,01100 e8,31100.
🚐. ◻ 01/04-01/10

△ Luzern 🌿🍽🏔🥖 24B2
Lido, Lido Straße 19. **GPS:** n47,05097 e8,33694.
🚐. ◻ 15/03-15/11

Tourist information Luzern:
ℹ️ Tourist Information, Zentralstrasse 5.Historical town centre with among other things die Kapelbrücke.
Ⓜ Gletchergarten, Denkmalstrasse 4.Nature monument. ◻ 01/04-31/10 9-18h, 01/11-31/03 10-17h.
Ⓜ Richard Wagner Museum, In Tribschen. ◻ Tue-Su 10-12h, 14-17h 🔲 01/12-31/03.
⚓ Stadtbummel.Guided tour around the historic city center, 2 hours. ◻ 01/05-31/10 daily 9.45h, 01/11-30/04 Wed, Sa 9.45h. 🎫 CHF 18.

△ Reinach 24A1
Waldhort, Heideweg 16. **GPS:** n47,49923 e7,60296.
🚐. ◻ 15/03-15/10

△ Sempach 24B2
Seeland. GPS: n47,12500 e8,18800.
🚐. ◻ 01/04-01/10

⬛S Weggis 🌿🏔🏔🥖❄ 24B2
Bauernhof Gerberweid, Eichistrasse. **GPS:** n47,03616 e8,41213.

15 🚐€ 18 🔌🛢Ch 🚿 included. **Surface:** grassy. ◻ 01/04-15/10
Distance: 🚶2km ⊗1km 🍴1km 🚌500m.

⬛S Willisau 24A2
Bisangmatt. GPS: n47,11937 e7,99829.⬆

4 🚐free 🔌 🚿(4x)free. **Surface:** metalled. ◻ 01/01-31/12
Distance: 🚶500m ⊗500m 🍴500m.
Remarks: At fire-station.

△ Zug 24B2
Zugersee, Chamer Fussweg 36. **GPS:** n47,17758 e8,49358.
🚐. ◻ 01/04-01/10
Remarks: Max. ^3.17m.

Switzerland East

△ Andeer 24D3
Sut Baselgia. GPS: n46,60651 e9,42630.

⬛S Appenzell 🌿🏔🏔❄ 24D2
Restaurant Eggli, Egglistrasse. **GPS:** n47,32104 e9,46565.
10 🔌🛢Ch guests free. **Surface:** asphalted. ◻ 01/01-31/12
Remarks: The most beautiful panorama of Appenzell.

⬛S Bivio 🏔❄ 24D4
Wohnmobilplatz der Skilifte. GPS: n46,46304 e9,65597.

CH

20 ⌫CHF 15/day ⌫⌐🔌Ch🔌 CHF 3,50. **Surface:** grasstiles. ◘ 01/01-31/12

Distance: 🎿nearby.

Remarks: Parking ski-lifts.

Tourist information Bivio:

ℹ️ Kur- und Verkehrsverein Bivio, www.bivio.ch/.Holliday village, 1769m, 260 inhabitants, winter sports destination with guaranteed snow.

Breil/Brigels 24C3

Bergbahnen BWA. **GPS:** n46,77104 e9,06770.⬆️

20 ⌫CHF 5+ 2,90/pp ⌐CHF 2 🔌Ch🔌. **Surface:** metalled. ◘ 01/05-31/10

Distance: 🏊600m 🛶on the spot 🍴Imbiss on the spot, restaurants 600m 🍺600m 🎿nearby.

Tourist information Breil/Brigels:

ℹ️ Informationsbüro & Center Turistic Brigels-Dorf, Raiffeisenbank, www.brigels.ch.Summer: cycle and hiking routes, winter: cross-country skiing trails and 75km skiruns. ◘ Mo-Fri 9-12, 14-18, summer Mo-Fri 9-12, 14-18, Sa 14-16h.

Churwalden 24D3

Pradafenz, Girabodawag 34. **GPS:** n46,77636 e9,54178.

⌫. ◘ 01/01-31/12

Davos 24D3

Rinerlodge Talstation, Rinerhornbahn, Davos Glaris. **GPS:** n46,74150 e9,77814.

10 ⌫CHF 29 ⌐🔌Ch🔌 CHF 2. **Surface:** gravel.

Distance: 🏊1km 🛶on the spot 🍴on the spot 🎿on the spot 🚲on the spot. **Remarks:** Max. 24h.

Tourist information Davos:

ℹ️ Davos Tourismus, Promenade 67, Davos Platz, www.davos.ch.Spectacular summer and winter sports resort.

👁 Davos Alpengarten.Botanical garden. ◘ 01/05-30/09 9-17h.

🍴 Berghaus Stafelalp, Frauenkirch.250 Year old inn where they still cook on a wood oven and shimmer paraffin lamps are lit.

Ennetbühl 24C2

Stellplatz Gill, Schwägalpstrasse 1336. **GPS:** n47,24111 e9,21861.

15 ⌫CHF10 ⌐🔌Ch🔌 (9x)CHF 0,40/kWh WC⌐CHF 1 🔲. **Surface:** metalled.

Distance: 🏊400m 🛶on the spot 🍴400m 🍺400m.

Eschenz 24C1

Hüttenberg. **GPS:** n47,64480 e8,86003.

7⌫€ 13 ⌐🔌Ch🔌 WC🔌included. ◘ 01/01-31/12

Remarks: In front of campsite.

Kreuzlingen 24C1

Fischerhaus, Promenadestraße 52. **GPS:** n47,64745 e9,19898.

⌫. ◘ 01/04-01/11

Müstair 25B3

Clenga. **GPS:** n46,62900 e10,45400.

⌫. ◘ 01/05-20/10

Neuhausen 24B1

Parkplatz Fischacker, Nohlstrasse. **GPS:** n47,67373 e8,60866.

50 ⌫€ 7 ⌐🔌Ch WC 🔌. **Surface:** grassy/metalled.

Distance: 🏊200m 🛶on the spot 🍴200m 🍺1km.

Tourist information Neuhausen:

👁 Der Rheinfall.Water falls.

Pontresina 25A4

Plauns. **GPS:** n46,46200 e9,93400.

⌫. ◘ 01/06-15/10, 15/12-15/04

Samnaun 25A2

Wohnmobilplatz. **GPS:** n46,94906 e10,36705.

18 ⌫CHF 25-35/day, CHF 5,80/pp ⌐🔌Ch🔌 WC🔌. ◘ 01/01-31/12

Distance: 🎿on the spot.

Remarks: Possibility for reservation: www.samnaun.ch/de/forms/motorhome_form.cfm. Between Samnaun-Dorf and Samnaun Ravaisch.

Sankt Moritz 24D4

Olympiaschanze. **GPS:** n46,47800 e9,82600.

⌫. ◘ 15/05-01/10

Tourist information Sankt Moritz:

ℹ️ Kur-& Verkehrsverein St. Moritz, Via Maistra 12, www.stmoritz.ch.Famous exclusive holiday resort.

🚩 Clean Energy Tour.Hiking trail, nature, energy, climate and weather adventure. Sign up at Kur- und Verkehrsverein St. Moritz. ◘ 15/06-01/10 Wed 13.45h duration 2,5 hours.

Savognin 24D3

Veia Sandeilas. **GPS:** n46,59660 e9,59226.

20 ⌫CHF 12 +CHF 6/pp ⌐🔌Ch.

Remarks: Near the chair-lift, summer: parking at campsite Julia.

Splügen 24D4

Auf dem Sand. **GPS:** n46,54922 e9,31399.

⌫. ◘ 01/01-31/12

Steckborn 24C1

Parkplatz P4, Schützengraben. **GPS:** n47,66684 e8,98474.⬆️

Switzerland South

🔺 Agno	24C5

Eurocampo, Via di Molinnazzo. **GPS:** n45,99547 e8,90063.
🍽. 🅾 01/04-01/10

🔺 Avegno	24C5

Piccolo Paradiso. GPS: n46,20100 e8,74300.
🍽. 🅾 01/03-01/11

⛟S Bellinzona 🌿❄️	24C5

Centro Sportivo, Viale Giuseppe Motta. **GPS:** n46,20116 e9,01729.⬆️

7 🍽CHF 10 🚰🔌Ch against payment. **Surface:** asphalted. 🅾 01/01-31/12
Distance: 🚶1,5km 🚃4km.
Remarks: Max. 48h.

Tourist information Bellinzona:
ℹ️ Bellinzona Tourismus, Viale Stazione 18, www.bellizonaturismo.ch.Turrita, city of the towers, walls and castles.
🏰 Castelgrande. 🅾 01/01-31/12 10-18h.
🏰 Castello di Montebello. 🅾 01/03-30/11 10-18h.
🏰 Castello di Sasso Corbaro. 🅾 01/03-30/11 10-18h.
😊 Palestra di Roccia San Paolo, Palazo Civico.Climbing garden for beginners and experienced, 30.000²m, 23 climbing trails.

8 🍽CHF 12/24h 🚰🔌Ch 🔧 (8x)included. **Surface:** metalled.
Distance: 🚶400m 🚃400m ✖️400m 🛒300m.

⛟S Vaduz/Lichtenstein 🌿🎣🏔️❄️	24D2

Rheinparkstadion, Rheindamm. **GPS:** n47,14022 e9,50945.⬆️

🍽free 🚰🔌Ch WC free. **Surface:** asphalted. 🅾 01/01-31/12
Distance: 🚃1,8km.
Remarks: Parking near stadium, max. 24h.

Tourist information Vaduz/Lichtenstein:
ℹ️ Liechtenstein Tourismus, Städtle 37, www.vaduz.li.Monarchy on the Austrian-Swiss border.
Ⓜ️ Briefmarkenmuseum, Städtle 37.Postage stamp museum. 🅾 10-12h, 13-17h. 🎫 free.
Ⓜ️ Kunstmuseum Lichtenstein, Städtle 32. 🅾 Tue-Su 10-17h.
Ⓜ️ Skimuseum, Fabrikstrasse 5.100 years ski history. 🅾 Mo-Fri 14-18h.
😊 Erlebniswelt Neuguthof, Neugutweg 30.Maize labyrinth with wild-west city.
🅾 15/06-30/09 Wed 13-18h, Sa-Su 10-20h, holidays Mo-Fri 10-20h, Sa-Su 10-22h.

⛟S Vals	24C3

Bergbahnen Vals. GPS: n46,60891 e9,17438.

10 🍽CHF 10 + 2,20/pp 🚰free. **Surface:** metalled. 🅾 summer
Distance: 🚶300m 🚃on the spot ✖️300m 🛒300m 🎿on the spot.
Remarks: Parking funicular railway.

🔺 Zürich 🌿🎣🏔️🚣	24B2

Seeburcht, Seestrasse 559. **GPS:** n47,33641 e8,53960.
🍽. 🅾 01/05-01/10

Tourist information Zürich:
ℹ️ Zürich Tourismus, Im Hauptbahnhof, www.zuerich.com.Historical city with large pedestrian area.
👁️ Scot & Scotch, Wohllebgasse 7, Schipfe.Wiskey-shop in the old city, 750 diferent kinds, also tastery. 🅾 Tue-Fri 12-18.30h, Sa 12-17h.
🎆 Sechseläuten.Traditional spring celebration. 🅾 3rd Mo Ap.
😊 Zoo Zürich, Zürichbergstrasse 221.Zoo. 🅾 01/03-31/10 9-18h, 01/11-28/02 9-17h.

🔺 Bouveret	23C4

Rive Bleue. GPS: n46,38645 e6,86041.
🍽. 🅾 01/04-30/09
Remarks: Autoroute Leman, exit Villeneuve-Evian.

🔺 Brig	24A4

Brigerbad. GPS: n46,29995 e7,93617.
🍽.

⛟S Champéry	23C5

Route de la Fin. GPS: n46,17478 e6,87022.

6 🍽CHF 15 + CHF 2,20/pp 🚰🔌Ch🔧included. **Surface:** asphalted. 🅾 01/01-31/12
Remarks: Parking supermarket, nearby the téléphérique.

🔺 Evolène	24A5

Evolène. GPS: n46,11075 e7,49654.
🍽. 🅾 01/01-31/12

🔺 Gordevio	24C4

Bella Riva. GPS: n46,22293 e8,74313.
🍽. 🅾 01/04-01/10

⛟S Grimentz 🌿🎣🏔️🐄❄️	24A5

Aire camping-car l'Ilôt Bosquet. GPS: n46,17432 e7,57271.⬆️

CH

20 🛏free 🚰🔌Ch 🚽CHF 3. **Surface:** gravel. ⬛ 01/01-31/12
Distance: 🛒on the spot ⊗on the spot ⚓on the spot �on the spot 🏊nearby 🚶nearby.
Remarks: Coins available at Office du Tourisme, tourist tax CHF 2/pp.

Tourist information Grimentz:
ℹ️ Grimentz/St.Jean Tourisme, www.grimentz.ch.Many signposted cycle and hiking routes.
👁 La Maison bourgeoisiale.Life of the citizens of Grimentz. ⬛ guided tour Mo. 🎫 free.

🛏S	Grimselpas 🏔🌲	24B4

Hotel Grimselblick, Totensee. **GPS:** n46,56115 e8,33673.
20 🛏free 🚰. **Surface:** asphalted.
Distance: 🏊on the spot.
Remarks: Service at hotel.

⛺	La Fouly	23D5

Les Glaciers. GPS: n45,93351 e7,09361.
🛏. ⬛ 15/05-30/09

⛺	Les Haudères	24A5

Molignon. GPS: n46,09061 e7,50776.
🛏. ⬛ 01/01-31/12

🛏S	Leukerbad 🏔🌲❄	24A4

Winterstellplatz, Parkplatz Fischweiher. **GPS:** n46,37907 e7,63004.
🛏CHF 8/day. ⬛ 01/11-15/04

⛺	Locarno 🌊🚤	24C5

Parco della Pace, Via Gioacchino Respini. **GPS:** n46,16011 e8,80255.⬆➡

50 🛏€ 10/24h. **Surface:** gravel.
Distance: 🛒900m ⛵100m ⊗100m.
Remarks: Max. 24h.

Tourist information Locarno:
ℹ️ Ente Turistico Lago Maggiore, Via B. Luini 3, www.maggiore.ch.City with the mildest climate of Switzerland.
👁 Rasa.Touristic car-free miniature village, can be reached by first taking the Centrovall-track, till Verdasio, then the small telpher carrier to Rasa.
🚢 Tenero-Locarno-Tenero.Free boat service. ⬛ 31/05-30/09.

🛏S	Martigny 🌊🚤🏔❄	23D5

Place de la Fondation Gianadda. **GPS:** n46,09585 e7,07143.⬆

5 🛏free 🚰🔌Ch 🚽free. **Surface:** asphalted.

⛺	Martigny 🌊🏔❄	23D5

Les Neuvilles, Rue du Levant 68. **GPS:** n46,09787 e7,07930.
🛏. ⬛ 01/02-31/12

Tourist information Martigny:
ℹ️ Office de Tourisme de Martigny, Place Centrale 9, www.martignytourism.ch.Gallo-Roman city with many archeological curiosities.
Ⓜ Fondation Pierre Gianadda, Rue du Forum.Art and culture museum with archeological museum. ⬛ 01/06-30/11 9-19h, 01/12-31/05 10-18h.
💧 Gorges du Durnand.Hiking trail through the gorge of the river Durnand.

⛺	Meride	24C5

Parco al Sole. GPS: n45,88806 e8,94944.
🛏. ⬛ 01/05-01/10

⛺	Molinazzo di Montegio	24C5

Tresiana. GPS: n45,98990 e8,81576.
🛏. ⬛ Easter-01/11

⛺	Muzzano-Lugano	24C5

Piodella di Agnuzzo. GPS: n45,99463 e8,90857.
🛏. ⬛ 01/01-31/12

⛺	Raron	24A4

Santa Monica, Kantonstrasse 56. **GPS:** n46,30007 e7,82374.
🛏. ⬛ 01/01-31/12

⛺	Reckingen	24B4

Ellbogen. GPS: n46,45790 e8,25355.
🛏. ⬛ 01/05-01/11

🛏S	Saas Fee	24A5

Parkplatz P4. GPS: n46,11090 e7,93208.⬆
100 🛏CHF 22/24h 🚰🔌Ch 🔌included. ⬛ 01/01-31/12 ⬛ service in winter.

🍴S	Saillon	23D5

Relais de Sarvaz. GPS: n46,15951 e7,16542.⬆

5 🛏free 🚰CHF 5 🔌Ch.

Tourist information Saillon:
ℹ️ Office du tourisme, Bains de Saillon.Small medieval town.
Ⓜ La fausse monnaie au grand jour.Museum of counterfeit money. ⬛ Wed-Su 14-17h.
♨ Bains de Saillon.Thermal centre. ⬛ 8-21h.
🚶 Sentier des Vitraux.Hiking trail, 45 minutes, through wine region.

⛺	Sierre 🌊🚤🏔❄	24A4

Bois de Finges. GPS: n46,29362 e7,55777.
🛏. ⬛ 01/05-01/10

🍴S	Sierre 🌊🚤🏔❄	24A4

Auberge de la Promenade, Sous-Géronde 41. **GPS:** n46,28476 e7,53683.
10 🛏 🚰🔌Chagainst payment.

Tourist information Sierre:

🚹 Office du Tourisme de Sierre, Salgesch et environs, Place de la Gare 10, www.
sierre-anniviers.ch.Cité du Soleil, city of the sun, wine region.

Ⓜ Musée Valaisan de la Vigne et du Vin, Château de Villa, Rue Sainte-Catherine
4.2 museums connected by wineroute. ◑ 01/04-30/11, Tue-Su 14-17h. Ⓣ
CHF 5, family CHF 12.

🎋 Marche des Cépages.March of the vine, information: sierre@sierre-anniviers.ch.

☺ Happyland New, Route Foulon, Granges.Amusement park. ◑ 01/03-31/10
11-18h.

🅂	Simplon	24A4

Col du Simplon. GPS: n46,24944 e8,03056.⬆.
🛏free 🚰🍴Chfree.

ⓐ	Sion 〽🏖🏕❄☀	23D5

Botza, Route du Camping 1, Vétroz. **GPS**: n46,20585 e7,27855.
🛏. ◑ 01/01-31/12

Tourist information Sion:

⊗ Restaurant Cave de Tous Vents, Rue des Châteaux 16.Restaurant in the arched
cellars of the city. ◑ 17-24h.

🅂	St.Léonard	23D5

Place du Lac Souterrain. **GPS**: n46,25564 e7,42600.➡.

5 🛏CHF 10/night 🚰🍴Ch ⚡ WC included. **Surface:** asphalted/grassy.
Distance: ⚐5,5km.
Remarks: To pay at Bar Domino.

ⓐ	Tenero 🏖🏕🏄	24C5

Campofelice, Via Alle Brere 7. **GPS**: n46,17353 e8,85401.
🛏. ◑ 01/04-27/10

ⓐ	Tenero 🏖🏕🏄	24C5

Lido Mappo, Via Mappo. **GPS**: n46,17850 e8,84519.
🛏. ◑ 15/03-01/11

ⓐ	Tenero 🏖🏕🏄	24C5

Tamaro, Via Mappo 32. **GPS**: n46,17525 e8,84779.
🛏. ◑ 15/03-01/11

Tourist information Tenero:

🚹 Ente turistico di Tenero, Via ai Giardini, www.tenero-tourism.ch.Holiday
village on Lake Maggiore.

⊗ Grotto Scalinata, Via Contra.Restaurant with regional products.

⚐ Verzascadal.Walking route of arts, information at VVV.

🅂	Trient 🏕	23D5

GPS: n46,04645 e6,99499.
🛏CHF 4 🚰.

🅂	Vétroz	23D5

Restaurant L'As de Pique. GPS: n46,20556 e7,27833.
🚰🍴Ch ⚡ CHF 15, guests free.

Tourist information Vétroz:

🚹 Office du Tourisme, Rue Lombarde 24, Le Bourg, Conthey.

⊗ Relais du Valais Ancienne Abbay, Rte de l'Abbaye 35.Restaurant in former
abbey.

CH

AUSTRIA

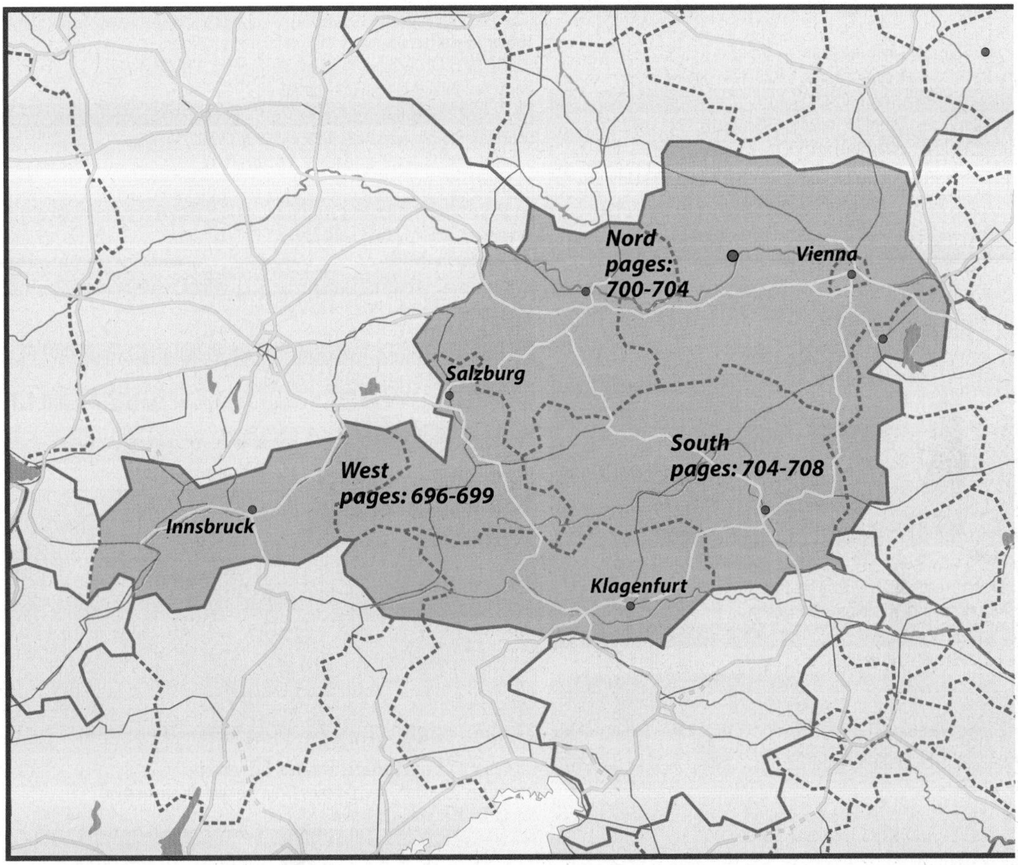

Nord
pages:
700-704

Vienna

Salzburg

West
pages: 696-699

South
pages: 704-708

Innsbruck

Klagenfurt

Capital: Vienna
Government: federal, parliamentarian, democratic
republic
Official Language: German
Population: 8,300,000 (2010)
Area: 83,857 km^2

General information
Dialling code: 0043.
Currency: Euro.

Regulations for overnight stays
In general overnight parking is allowed, except: Tyrol,
Vienna, nature reserves and in areas where locally
prohibited. No "camping" activities allowed and
disposal wastewater must be at official places.

Opening hours
Shops: Monday-Friday 8am-12noon and 4pm-6pm,
Saturday 8am-1pm
Bank: Monday-Friday 8am-1.30pm and 1.30pm-3pm,
Thursday until 5.30pm.

Austria

Austria West

Achenkirch 🏔️🎋🌲❄️ 25C1

Camping Achensee, Achenkirch 17. **GPS**: n47,49947 e11,70655.
8 🗓️ from € 13 2 pers incl 🚰🍽️Ch 🚿 WC ⬜ included. **Surface**: gravel. ⬛
01/01-31/12
Distance: 🏊 on the spot 🚠 on the spot.
Remarks: Extra pers € 7, electricity winter € 0,70/kWh, dog € 4,50.

Altenmarkt im Pongau 26B1

Bauernhof Kellerbauer, Kellerdörfl Palfen 7. **GPS**: n47,37015 e13,42923.
10 🗓️ € 12 🚰🍽️Ch 🚿. ⬛ 01/01-31/12

Aschau im Zillertal 25D1

Aufenfeld, Distelberg 1. **GPS**: n47,26318 e11,90063.
🗓️ 19-€ 32,70 🚰🍽️Ch 🚿 WC ⬜.

Biberwier 🏔️🎋❄️ 25B1

Marienbergstrasse 15. **GPS**: n47,37528 e10,88944.

15 🗓️ € 10 🚰🍽️Ch 🚿 € 1 ⬜ € 2. **Surface**: grassy. ⬛ 01/01-31/12
Distance: 🏊 on the spot 🚲 2km 🎿 on the spot 🚠 on the spot.
Remarks: Nearby campsite Alpencamp Marienberg.

Bichlbach 25B1

Almkopfbahn. **GPS**: n47,42367 e10,78116.

15 🗓️. ⬛ 01/01-31/12
Distance: 🏊 5km 🎿 on the spot 🚠 on the spot 🚲 on the spot.
Remarks: Parking next to valley station.

Tourist information Bichlbach:
ℹ️ Tourismusbüro, Kirchhof 22.

Bregenz 🌊🏔️🎋🌲 24D1

Parkplatz Talstation Pfänderbahn. **GPS**: n47,50538 e9,75308. ⬆️➡️
🗓️ € 9/day, overnight stay free.

Tourist information Bregenz:
ℹ️ Bregenz Tourismus & Stadtmarketing, Bahnhofstraße 14, www.tiscover.at/bregenz.Historical city on the Lake Constance.
👁️ Altes Rathaus, Oberstadt.Half-timbered house 1661.
👁️ Pfänderbahn.Panorama gondola to station Pfänder 1064. ⬛ 9-19h ⬜ 08/11-19/11.
Ⓜ️ Vorarlberger Landesmuseum, Kornmarktplatz 1.Culture and art history. ⬛ Tue-Su 9-12h, 14-17h. 🎫 € 1,45.
✝️ Kloster Mehrerau, Mehrerauersraßbe 66.Abbey, 1097, with neo-Roman church.

Breitenwang 25B1

Seespitze. **GPS**: n47,47417 e10,78472.
🗓️. ⬛ 01/05-15/10

Breitenwang 25B1

Sennalpe. **GPS**: n47,48639 e10,83972.
🗓️. ⬛ 15/12-15/10

Bruck an der Großglocknerstraße 26A1

Woferlgut. **GPS**: n47,28361 e12,81667.

🗓️. ⬛ 01/01-31/12

Tourist information Bruck an der Großglocknerstraße:
😊 Wild- und Freizeitpark Ferleiten, Großglocknerstrasse.Zoo and amusement park. ⬛ 01/05-30/11 8h-sunset.

Ehrwald 25B1

Tiroler Zugspitze, Obermoos. **GPS**: n47,42731 e10,94096.
10 🗓️€ 15/17.00-10.00h 🚿 against payment. ⬛ 01/01-31/12
Remarks: Parking in front of campsite.

Faschina 25A2

Sportcafé Domig, Haus nr 92. **GPS**: n47,27263 e9,90717.
5 🗓️€ 11 🚰🍽️Ch 🚿 included. ⬛ 01/01-31/12
Remarks: At B193.

Feichten/Kaunertal 25B2

Kaunertal. **GPS**: n47,05333 e10,75056.
🗓️. ⬛ 01/05-30/09

Fieberbrunn 26A1

Tirol-camp. **GPS**: n47,46833 e12,55389.
🗓️. ⬛ 01/01-31/12

Fügen 25D1

Zillertal Hell. **GPS**: n47,35934 e11,85198.
10 🗓️ against payment 🚰🍽️Ch 🏊 against payment. **Surface**: metalled. ⬛ 01/01-31/12

Galtür 🏔️❄️ 25A2

Silvretta-Bundesstraße, B188, Wirl. **GPS**: n46,96570 e10,16390.

🗓️€ 15 🚰🍽️Ch. **Surface**: metalled. ⬛ winter
Distance: ✕100m 🚠 on the spot 🎿 on the spot 🚲 on the spot.
Remarks: Free skibus to Ischgl.

Gerlos 🏔️❄️☀️ 25D2

Bauernhof Schönachhof, Schönachtal 242. **GPS**: n47,22639 e12,05476.

10 🗓️€ 12 🚰🍽️Ch 🚿 WC ⬜. ⬛ 01/01-31/12

Tourist information Gerlos:
ℹ️ Tourismusverband Gerlos, Haus Nr. 141.Mountain village.
😊 Activ Wellness.Free wellness program. ⬛ 01/07-30/09.

Gries am Brenner 25C2

Alpengasthof, Nößlach 483. **GPS**: n47,04229 e11,47455.
50 🗓️ 🚰 WC free.
Remarks: Brenner highway exit Nößlach.

Haiming 25B2

Center-Oberland, Bundeßtraße 9a. **GPS**: n47,24147 e10,87755.
🗓️🚰🍽️Ch 🚿. ⬛ 01/01-31/12

Hall in Tirol 🌊🎋🏔️❄️☀️ 25C2

Wohnmobilpark, Scheidensteinstraße 24. **GPS**: n47,28444 e11,49665. ⬆️

10 🍴€ 15 ⚡🔌Ch⚡ included. 🅾 01/05-30/09
Distance: 🚰400m ⊗200m Gaststätte 🍺300m.

Tourist information Hall in Tirol:
ℹ Tourismusverband, Wallpachgasse 5, www.tiscover.at/hall.Historical little town.

| 🍴S | **Hochfilzen** | 26A1 |

Schulgasse. **GPS:** n47,47000 e12,62250. ⬆➡.

5 🍴free ⚡🔌Chfree. **Surface:** gravel.
Distance: 🏔on the spot.
Remarks: Behind fire-station, max. 3 nights.

| 🍴S | **Hütten** 🏔❄ | 26A1 |

Parkplatz Asitzbahn, Sportarena Leogang, B164. **GPS:** n47,43963 e12,72040.
50 🍴€ 5 + tourist tax ⚡🔌Ch⚡ (9x) WC🔌€ 2.
Distance: 🚰3,5km.

| 🍴S | **Hüttschlag** | 26B2 |

Bauernhof Stockham-Camping. **GPS:** n47,14775 e13,28947.
5 🍴€ 10 ⚡🔌Ch⚡. 🅾 01/01-31/12
Distance: 🚰6km ⊗150m 🍺6km.

| 🍴S | **Ischgl** 🏔❄ | 25A2 |

Mathoner Straße 5, Ischgl-Mathon. **GPS:** n46,98967 e10,24751.
15 🍴€ 15 ⚡🔌Ch⚡🔌. **Surface:** metalled. 🅾 01/01-31/12
Distance: 🚰1km.
Remarks: Free skibus to Ischgl and Galtür.

| 🔺 | **Itter** | 25D1 |

Schloßberg. **GPS:** n47,46641 e12,13975.
🍴. 🅾 01/01-31/12

| 🍴 | **Jenbach** | 25D1 |

Gasthof Rieder, Fischl 3. **GPS:** n47,40131 e11,77500.

5 🍴against payment.
Remarks: Only for guest of the restaurant.

| 🔺 | **Kitzbühel** | 26A1 |

Schwarzsee. **GPS:** n47,45924 e12,36209.
🍴. 🅾 01/01-31/12

| 🔺 | **Kössen** | 19A6 |

Wilder Kaiser. **GPS:** n47,65369 e12,41560.
🍴. 🅾 01/01-31/12

| 🔺 | **Kramsach** | 25D1 |

Seeblick Toni. **GPS:** n47,46175 e11,90664.
🍴. 🅾 01/01-31/12

| 🔺 | **Krimml** | 25D2 |

P2. **GPS:** n47,21805 e12,17519.

🍴free.

| 🍴S | **Krimml** | 25D2 |

Hotel Krimmlerfälle, Wasserfallstraße 42. **GPS:** n47,21617 e12,17185.

10 🍴€ 11 ⚡🔌Ch⚡. 🅾 15/05-25/10

| 🔺 | **Kufstein** | 25D1 |

Kufstein. **GPS:** n47,57576 e12,15910.
🍴. 🅾 01/05-01/11

| 🔺 | **Landeck** 🏔❄ | 25B2 |

Riffler. **GPS:** n47,14250 e10,56139.
🍴. 🅾 01/06-30/04

Tourist information Landeck:
ℹ See.Farmer village and winter sports resort.
ℹ Tourismusverband TirolWest.Holiday resort in the mountains. Many ski areas in surroundings.
❌ Schloss Landeck, Schlossweg.Renovated castle. 🅾 01/05-30/09 Tue-Su 10-17h, 1/10-26/10 Tue-Su 14-17h.

| 🔺 | **Längenfeld** | 25B2 |

Ötztal. **GPS:** n47,07228 e10,96434.
🍴. 🅾 01/01-31/12

| 🔺 | **Leutasch** | 25C1 |

Holiday-Camping. **GPS:** n47,39861 e11,17936.
🍴. 🅾 10/12-31/10

| 🔺 | **Lienz** 🏔❄ | 26A2 |

Seewiese, Tristachersee. **GPS:** n46,80655 e12,80313.

🍴. 🅾 15/05-30/09

Tourist information Lienz:
ℹ Tourismusverband Lienzer Dolomiten, Europaplatz 1, www.tiscover.com/Lienz.Capital East Tyrol.
❌ Schloß Bruck, Schloßberg 1.Regional museum. 🅾 01/06-15/09 10-18h, 16/09-31/10 Tue-Su 10-17h. 🎫 € 6, family card € 12.

AT

🛏S	**Maria Alm**	26A1

Stegerbauer, Schattberg 11. **GPS**: n47,39767 e12,90355.
6 🏕 € 8, tourist tax excl ⚡🔌Ch ♿€ 2,50. 🅿 01/01-31/12
Distance: 🚰1km ⊗500m 🛒1km 🚌1km 🚲1km.

🛏	**Matrei**	26A2

Matreier Tauernhaus. GPS: n47,11833 e12,49778.
100 🏕 € 4. 🅿 01/05-30/11

🛏S	**Maurach am Achensee**	25D1

Rofan Seilbahn P2, Bundesstrasse. **GPS**: n47,42445 e11,75224.

5 🏕 ⚡🔌Ch. 🅿 01/04-30/11
Distance: 🚰400m.

🔺	**Maurach am Achensee**	25D1

Wimmer, Buchau 8. **GPS**: n47,43319 e11,73456.
🏕 🅿 01/01-31/12

🔺S	**Nassereith**	25B2

Roßbach, Roßbach 325. **GPS**: n47,31153 e10,85270.

🏕 € 16 ⚡🔌Ch ♿included. **Surface:** grassy. 🅿 01/01-31/12
Distance: 🛒500m.

🔺	**Natters**	25C2

Natterer See. GPS: n47,23749 e11,34195.
🏕 🅿 15/04-15/10

🔺	**Nenzing**	24D2

Alpencamping Nenzing. GPS: n47,18258 e9,68216.
🏕 🅿 01/01-31/12

Tourist information Nenzing:
ℹ Tourismusbüro Nenzing, Landstraße 1.

🍴S	**Neukirchen**	14B6

Panoramastellplatz, Scheffau 96. **GPS**: n47,23862 e12,24083.

9 🏕 € 6,50, guests free ⚡🔌Ch ♿. **Surface:** gravel. 🅿 01/01-31/12
Distance: 🚰4km ⊗on the spot 🚲on the spot 🛒on the spot.
Remarks: Bread-service.

🔺S	**Neustift** 🛶🏔❄	25C2

Edelweiss, Volderau. **GPS**: n47,06801 e11,25295.
🏕 € 16, 2 pers.incl ⚡🔌Ch ♿included. 🅿 01/01-31/12

🔺	**Neustift** 🛶🏔❄	25C2

Stubai. GPS: n47,11021 e11,30895.
🏕 🅿 01/01-31/12

Tourist information Neustift:
ℹ Fulpmes.Health resort and winter sports centre.
ℹ Tourismusverband Neustift, www.tourismus-tirol.com/neustift.
⚑ Stubaier Gletsjerpfad.Trail (45min) from Station Eisgrat.

🔺	**Nüziders** 🏔❄	24D2

Sonnenberg. GPS: n47,16939 e9,80722.
🏕 🅿 01/05-01/10

Tourist information Nüziders:
ℹ Ms Brigitte Burtscher, Sonnenbergstr. 21 a.Tourist information.
ℹ Tourismus & Freizeit Bludenz, Werdenbergerstr. 42, Bludenz.Alps city.

🍴S	**Oberndorf in Tirol**	26A1

Gasthof zum Schnitzel Profi, Paß Thurnstraße 10. **GPS**: n47,47709 e12,38391.
6 🏕guests free ⚡♿.
Remarks: Max. 1 night.

🍴S	**Obersteig**	25B2

Gasthof zum Lenz, Gschwent 282. **GPS**: n47,30930 e10,94482.

18 🏕 € 15 ⚡🔌Ch ♿included. 🅿 01/01-31/12
Distance: 🚲on the spot.

🛏S	**Pfunds** ⚑	25B2

Wohnmobilplatz Via Claudiasee, Rauth 714. **GPS**: n46,95429 e10,51171.⬆
🏕 € 7 + tourist tax € 1,50/pp ⚡🔌Ch ♿WC 🏕
Surface: grassy/metalled.
Distance: 🚰2km ⊗200m.
Remarks: Bread-service.

🔺	**Radstadt**	26B1

Tauerncamping Lerchenhof. GPS: n47,38728 e13,46107.
🏕 🅿 01/01-31/12

🔺	**Ried im Oberinntal** 🌄🏔❄	25B2

Dreiländereck. GPS: n47,05594 e10,65638.

🏕 🅿 01/01-31/12
Tourist information Ried im Oberinntal:
ℹ Serfaus.High car-free mountain village, large ski area.

🛏S	**Schwaz**	25C1

Swarovskistraße. **GPS**: n47,34655 e11,70436.⬆

AT

10 free € 2 Ch € 2.
01/01-31/12
Distance: 500m.

Tourist information Schwaz:
Tourismusverband Silberregion Karwendel, Franz-Josef-Straße 2, www.silberregion-karwendel.at.
Schwazer Silberbergwerk. 01/05-31/10.

Seefeld in Tirol	25C1

Alpin Seefeld. GPS: n47,33731 e11,17861.
01/01-31/12

Sölden	25B2

Sölden. GPS: n46,95782 e11,01200.
15/06-01/05

Söll	25D1

Franzlhof. GPS: n47,50772 e12,18975.
01/01-31/12

St.Johann im Pongau	26B1

Kastenhof. GPS: n47,34185 e13,19751.
01/01-31/12

St.Johann im Tirol	26A1

Michelnhof. GPS: n47,51056 e12,40893.
01/01-31/12

St.Martin bei Lofer	26A1

Park Grubhof. GPS: n47,57510 e12,70834.
01/05-01/10

Stams	25B2

Eichenwald-Stams. GPS: n47,27506 e10,98645.
01/01-31/12

Steinach am Brenner	25C2

Gasthaus Wolf, Brennerstraße 36. **GPS:** n47,06704 e11,48574.
5 guests free .
Remarks: At the old Brennerstraße.

Stumm	25D1

Gasthof Rißbacher Hof, Ahrnbachstraße 37. **GPS:** n47,27951 e11,89347.

3 € 8.

Tweng	26C1

Landhotel Postgut, Tweng 2. **GPS:** n47,19058 e13,60210.

5 € 8. **Surface:** metalled. 01/01-31/12
Distance: on the spot on the spot.

Waidring	26A1

Steinplatte. GPS: n47,58344 e12,58286.
01/01-31/12

Walchsee	18D6

Seespitz. GPS: n47,64863 e12,31436.
01/01-31/12

Wenns/Piller	25B2

Gasthof Sonne, Piller 41. **GPS:** n47,13581 e10,69390.

3 € 5 .
Remarks: Altitude 1350m.

Werfen	26B1

Vierthaler. GPS: n47,44567 e13,21223.
15/04-30/09

Tourist information Werfen:
Village with citadel Hohenwerfen. Easter-Oct 9-17h.
Eisriesenwelt.Largest ice caves in the world. Route to the caves is rather steep, caves can also be reached by telpher carrier. 01/05-31/10 9-15.30h.

Wiesing	25D1

Inntal. GPS: n47,40585 e11,80536.

01/01-31/12

Zell am See	26A1

Seecamp. GPS: n47,33973 e12,80907.
01/01-31/12

Tourist information Zell am See:
Zell am See Information, Brucker Bundesstrasse 1a, www.zellamsee.com. Tourist town, summer and winter.
Gletscherskigebiet Kitzsteinhorn, Kaprun.Large winter sports area. Summer skiing on glacier.

Zell am Ziller	25D2

Hofer. GPS: n47,22818 e11,88585.
01/01-31/12

Tourist information Zell am Ziller:
www.zell.at.Former mining village, place of finding gold.

AT

👁 Zillertalbahn.Steam train Zell-Jenbach.
❄ Gauderfest.Traditional folk festival. ◘ 1st weekend May.

Austria North

⌂S Aggsbach Markt — 27A1
Badestrand. GPS: n48,29814 e15,40497.

16 ⌂€ 3,20, € 1,90/pp 🚰⌐Ch ⚡€ 1.
Distance: 🚶500m ⊗50m Donaustüberl 🚻500m.
Remarks: Parking at the Danube river.

⌂S Alland — 27B1
ÖMV-tankstelle Groschner&KarrerOHG, Gewerbestraße 550. **GPS:** n48,06734 e16,06364.

20 ⌂free 🚰⌐Chagainst payment. **Surface:** asphalted. ◘ 01/01-31/12
Remarks: Parking motorway.

Tourist information Alland:
ℹ Ehemalig Jagdschloss, Mayerling. ◘ summer 9-12.30h, 13.30-18h, winter 9-12.30h, 13.30-17h ◐ 05/04-06/04.
👁 Tropfsteinhöhle.Caves. ◘ 01/04-30/09 Sa, Su 9-17h, 01/07-31/08 Mo-Fri 15-16.30h Sa-Su 9-17h ◐ 01/11-31/03. 🎫 € 1,90/3.

⑪S Altenmarkt an der Triesting — 27B1
Gasthof Zum Kleinen Semmering, Hafnerberg 15. **GPS:** n48,01762 e16,01383.

10 ⌂free 🚰WC. **Surface:** metalled.
Distance: 🚶2,3km 🚻2,3km.

S Altlengbach — 27B1
Latra Wohnwagen, Reitermühlstraße 16. **GPS:** n48,15481 e15,91520.
🚰Ch.
Remarks: A1 exit Altlengbach, 40 km west of Vienna.

⌂S Arbesbach — 27A1
Am Ganser. GPS: n48,49123 e14,95683.
15 ⌂free 🚰⌐. ◘ 01/01-31/12
Distance: 🚶500m ⊗500m 🚻500m 🚌500m.
Remarks: Check in at town hall.

⌂S Armschlag — 27A1
Mohndorf. GPS: n48,45222 e15,21944.
5 ⌂€ 3 🚰⌐Ch⚡. **Surface:** asphalted. ◘ 01/01-31/12
Distance: 🚻2km.

⌂S Aschbach Markt — 27A1
Fam. Edtbauer, Auckental 1 u. 2. **GPS:** n48,10682 e14,69988.
8 ⌂🚰⌐⚡€ 2. ◘ 15/04-30/10
Distance: 🚶7km ⚡3km 🚻7km.

⌂S Bad Großpertholz — 27A1
Busparkplatz Naturpark Nordwald, Scheiben. **GPS:** n48,61765 e14,81548.
⌂.

⌂S Bernhardsthal — 27B1
Schulstrasse. **GPS:** n48,69402 e16,87481. ⬆➡.

5 ⌂free. **Surface:** grassy. ◘ 01/01-31/12
Distance: 🚶500m ⌂on the spot ⚡on the spot ⊗weekends only.

⌂S Deutsch Jahrndorf — 27C1
Söldnergasse 19. **GPS:** n48,00777 e17,11073. ⬆➡.

17 ⌂voluntary contribution 🚰⌐Ch. **Surface:** grassy. ◘ 01/01-31/12
Distance: 🚶500m ⊗500m 🚻on the spot.
Remarks: Max. 3 nights.

⌂S Ebensee — 19C6
Busparkplatz am Traunsee, Trauneck. **GPS:** n47,81283 e13,77730.
⌂.

⌂S Eferding — 19C4
Parkplatz direkt an der Donau, Brandstatt, Pupping. **GPS:** n48,33503 e14,02698.
⌂.

⌂S Eggenburg 🏛📶 — 27B1

Stellplatz an der Stadtmauer, Erzherzog-Karl-Ring 19. **GPS:** n48,64513 e15,81745.
8 ⌂€ 4 🚰⌐€ 1/10minutes ⌐Ch⚡(8x)€ 1/8h. **Surface:** metalled. ◘ 01/04-31/10

AT

Distance: 🚶on the spot 🏊35km ⚓creek ⊗300m 🛒200m 🚌500m 🧍on the spot.

| 🍴S | **Erlauf** | 27A1 |

Gasthof Plaika Wirt, Plaika 1. **GPS:** n48,16866 e15,16436.
10 🛌guests free 🚰.
Remarks: A1, between exit Ibbs and Pöchlarn.

| 🛌 | **Gallneukirchen** | 19D4 |

Freizeitcentrum, Veitsdorfer Weg 10. **GPS:** n48,36045 e14,40797.
5 🛌free. ⚫ 01/01-31/12
Distance: 🚶1km 🛒1km.

| 🛌 | **Gaming** | 27A2 |

Kartause. GPS: n47,92463 e15,08223.

| 🛌 | **Gars am Kamp** | 27B1 |

Gföhler Strasse/Strandgasse, Thunau am Kamp. **GPS:** n48,59300 e15,65723.⬆.

5 🛌free. **Surface:** gravel. ⚫ 01/01-31/12
Distance: 🚶200m ⊗on the spot 🛒200m.
Remarks: Nearby swimming pool.

| 🛌 | **Geboltskirchen** | 19C5 |

Parkplatz Badesee Geboltskirchen, Leithen. **GPS:** n48,16472 e13,66235.
🛌.

| 🛌S | **Gmünden** | 19C5 |

Gasthof Egger, Ohlsdorferstr. 1. **GPS:** n47,92807 e13,79623.
5 🛌€5 🚰Ch. ⚫ 01/01-31/12
Distance: 🚶2km ⚓3km 🛒1km.

| 🍴S | **Gosau** | 19B6 |

Hotel Gosauschmied, Gosau 57. **GPS:** n47,55072 e13,51607.
10 🛌€10 🚰Ch🔌On demand. **Surface:** asphalted. ⚫ 01/01-31/12
Distance: 🚶3km ⊗on the spot 🛒3km 🚌on the spot 🎿500m ⛷on the spot.

| S | **Gumpoldskirchen** | 27B1 |

Neustiftgasse. GPS: n48,04423 e16,27552.
🚰🛒Ch.

| 🛌 | **Hainburg/Donau** | 27B1 |

Parkplatz an der Donau, Parkweg. **GPS:** n48,15110 e16,94440.

🛌. **Surface:** asphalted. ⚫ 01/01-31/12
Distance: 🚶500m ⊗on the spot.

| 🍴S | **Haslach** | 19C4 |

Gasthof Furtmühle, Schwackerreith 20, St.Oswald. **GPS:** n48,60497 e14,01967.
15 🛌🔌against payment. ⚫ 01/01-31/12
Remarks: 5km north of Haslach.

| 🍴S | **Hohenau/March** | 27B1 |

Freizeitzentrum, Kindergartenstrasse. **GPS:** n48,61095 e16,91010.

🛌free. **Surface:** asphalted. ⚫ 01/01-31/12
Remarks: Swimming pool 200m.

| 🍴S | **Hollenstein/Ybbs** | 27A2 |

Gasthof Staudach, Walcherbauer 5. **GPS:** n47,80703 e14,76687.
4 🛌€14, 4 pers.incl 🚰🛒Ch🔌.
Distance: 🚶200m ⊗10m 🛒200m.

| 🍴 | **Kefermarkt** | 27A1 |

Schloßbrauerei Weinberg, Weinberg 2. **GPS:** n48,44856 e14,53957.
5 🛌guests free.

| 🛌S | **Klosterneuburg** | 27B1 |

Euromobil Campers, Bahnhofplatz 16, Kritzendorf. **GPS:** n48,33582 e16,29863.

4 🛌€4 🚰🛒Ch. ⚫ 01/01-31/12
Distance: 🏊12,5km ⊗nearby 🛒nearby.
Remarks: Lock-up parking, guarded. Motorhome parking at S-Bahnstation.

| 🏕 | **Klosterneuburg** | 27B1 |

Donaupark. GPS: n48,31055 e16,32710.
🛌. ⚫ 01/03-01/12

Tourist information Klosterneuburg:
ℹ Tourismusverein Klosterneuburg, Niedermarkt 4, www.klosterneuburg.net.
✝ Stift Klosterneuburg, Stiftsplatz 1.Monastery.

| S | **Königswiesen** | 27A1 |

Freibad, Badgasse 4. **GPS:** n48,40450 e14,84080.
3 🛌€1 + €1/pp + tourist tax 🚰🛒Ch WC. ⚫ 01/01-31/12
Distance: 🚶500m ⊗10m Freibadbuffet 🛒300m.
Remarks: Parking swimming pool, service at water purification plant.

| 🛌 | **Kremsmünster** | 19C5 |

Parkplatz Benediktiner Stift, Fuxjägerstraße. **GPS:** n48,05407 e14,12607.

| 🛌S | **Laimbach am Ostrong** | 27A1 |

Bauernhof Stoiber, Wagmühle 34. **GPS:** n48,31711 e15,11636.⬆.
5 🛌€12 🚰🛒Ch🔌.
Distance: 🚶300m ⊗300m 🛒300m.

| 🛌 | **Langschlag-Mitterschlag** | 27A1 |

Freizeitanlage Frauenwieserteich, Böhmerwald-Bundesstraße. **GPS:** n48,58038 e14,83507.
10 🛌free. ⚫ 01/01-31/12
Distance: 🚶5km 🛒5km.

| 🛌 | **Marchtrenk** | 19C5 |

Imbiß Koutek, Eichenstraße 2. **GPS:** n48,19055 e14,11893.
10 🛌. ⚫ 01/01-31/12
Distance: 🚶1km 🏊2,3km ⊗on the spot 🛒50m.

| 🍴S | **Maria Laach** | 27A1 |

Haberghütte Zum Gießhübler, Gießhübl 1. **GPS:** n48,32072 e15,35938.

AT

20 🛏 € 8 ⚡ 🔌 Ch ✦ (20x). **Surface:** grassy/metalled.
Distance: 🚶3,5km ⊗on the spot 🚊2,5km.
Remarks: Via Maria Laach.

Mondsee 🏕️ 19B6
Geflügelhof Schweighofer, Schwand 10. **GPS:** n47,88186 e13,31105.
5 🛏 € 10 ⚡🔌Ch✦. ⬜ 01/01-31/12
Remarks: A1, exit Mondsee, after <Gasthof Kasten>to the left, second farm.

Tourist information Mondsee:
ℹ️ Tourismusverband Mondseeland, Dr. Franz Müller Straße 3, www.mondsee.
at.Holiday region.
Ⓜ Heimat- und Pfahlbaumuseum, Marschall-Wrede-Platz 1.Historical museum.
⬜ 01/05-31/10 10-17h.
Ⓜ Rauchhaus, Hilfbergstraße 5.Farm museum. ⬜ 10-18h, Sa-Su 10-17h.

Naarn 27A1
Bauernhof Mostschenke, Dirnwagram 1. **GPS:** n48,21750 e14,61972.
5 🛏 € 5, free with a meal ⚡🔌Ch✦WC.
Remarks: Max. 4 days, arrival till 19.30. Naarn dir Mitterkirchen, at garage to the right, then first farm at the right.

Nußdorf am Attersee 19B6
Seecamping Gruber. **GPS:** n47,87965 e13,52444.
🛏. ⬜ 15/04-15/10

Orth/Donau 27B1
P2, Am Rosenhügel. **GPS:** n48,14523 e16,70383.

🛏free. **Surface:** metalled. ⬜ 01/01-31/12
Distance: 🚶on the spot.

Ottenschlag 27A1
Florianigasse. **GPS:** n48,42361 e15,22750.⬆️.

8-10 🛏 € 5 ⚡ € 1/10minutes 🔌 Ch ✦ € 1/8h. **Surface:** metalled.
Distance: 🚶500m ⊗Gaststätte 🚊500m.

Pillichsdorf 27B1
Am Tennisclub, Bahnstraße 8A. **GPS:** n48,36167 e16,53750.➡️.

8 🛏free, use facilities clubhouse € 10 ⚡🔌Ch ✦WC🔌. ⬜ 01/01-31/12
Distance: 🚶500m, Wien 15km ⊗300m 🚊500m 🚐on the spot.
Remarks: Use facilities clubhouse possible.

Pulkau 27B1
Rat-Cumfe Straße. **GPS:** n48,70430 e15,86637.⬆️➡️.

8 🛏 € 5 ⚡ € 1/10minutes 🔌Ch ✦ € 1/6h. **Surface:** gravel. ⬜ 01/01-31/12
Distance: 🚶500m ⊗300m 🚊on the spot 🚐on the spot.

Purgstall an der Erlauf 27A1
Purgstall. **GPS:** n48,05625 e15,12973.
🛏. ⬜ 01/01-31/12

Ranshofen 19A5
Vereinslokal, Scheuhub 2. **GPS:** n48,23228 e12,99893.
10 🛏free ⚡🔌✦. ⬜ 01/01-31/12
Distance: 🚶2km 🚊2km 🚐2km.

Reichenau/Rax 27B2
Kaiserbrunn, Bundesstraße Höllental 27. **GPS:** n47,73480 e15,79188.

🛏free. **Surface:** metalled.

Reichenau/Rax 27B2
Gasthof Flackl Wirt, Hinterleiten 12. **GPS:** n47,69056 e15,82778.

5 🛏 € 11,50 breakfast incl ⚡✦ included WC at restaurant.
Distance: 🚶1,5km ⊗on the spot.
Remarks: From B27 follow Gasthof.

AT

Retz — 27B1
Stellplatz Retz, Jahnstraße. **GPS:** n48,75382 e15,95105.

5 ⬛free. **Surface:** asphalted.
Distance: 500m 500m.
Tourist information Retz:
ℹ️ Tourismusbüro, Hauptplatz 30, www.weinerlebnis-retz.at.

Rossatzbach — 27A1
Aggsteiner-Bundesstraße. **GPS:** n48,38750 e15,51722.

12 ⬛€ 10 ⬛ Ch (12x) WC included. 🔘 01/01-31/12
Distance: 300m on the spot 1,5km.
Remarks: Vinotheek 300m.

Rust — 15D5
Reisebus-Parkplatz, Amhafen. **GPS:** n47,80405 e16,67873.

⬛ Ch.

Scharnstein — 19C5
Camping Schatzlmühle, Viechtwang 1A. **GPS:** n47,91578 e13,97353.
5 ⬛€ 8, tourist tax excl. 🔘 01/01-31/12
Distance: 2km on the spot 600m on the spot on the spot.

Schönberg — 27B1
Freizeitzentrum, Badgasse. **GPS:** n48,52063 e15,69377.

5 ⬛€ 5, first night free ⬛ (1x) WC included € 1. **Surface:** asphalted.
🔘 01/01-31/12, service Easter-01/11
Distance: 200m on the spot on the spot 200m.
Remarks: Shower during opening hours. Along river.

Schremms — 27A1
Parkplatz Stadthalle. GPS: n48,79142 e15,07113.
⬛. 🔘 01/01-31/12
Distance: 500m.
Remarks: Max. 1 night.

St.Martin am Ybbsfelde — 27A1
Gemeindeparkplatz. GPS: n48,16465 e15,01995.
⬛. 🔘 01/01-31/12

St.Pankraz — 19C6
Parkplatz Klauser Stausee, Klaus an der Pyhmbahn. **GPS:** n47,82733 e14,15703.

St.Wolfgang — 19B6
Appesbach. GPS: n47,73231 e13,46374.
⬛. 🔘 01/04-01/11

Steyregg — 19D4
Campingshop Weber, Pulgarn 14. **GPS:** n48,28083 e14,39972.
25 ⬛€ 5 + € 2/pp ⬛ Ch € 2,50 WC. 🔘 01/01-31/12
Distance: 1,5km 1,5km 1,5km 1,5km.

Stockerau — 27B1
Hallenbad Wellness Oase, Pestalozzigasse. **GPS:** n48,39385 e16,21912.

7 ⬛free ⬛ € 2 ⬛ Ch WC sanitary in swimming pool. **Surface:** gravel.
🔘 01/01-31/12
Distance: 1,5km.

Traisen — 27B1
Traisen. GPS: n48,04216 e15,60294.
⬛. 🔘 15/02-15/11

Tulln an der Donau — 27B1
Donaupark Tulln. GPS: n48,33324 e16,07151.
⬛. 🔘 01/05-01/10

Unterach am Attersee — 19B6
Inselcamping. GPS: n47,80096 e13,48251.
⬛. 🔘 15/05-15/09
Tourist information Unterach am Attersee:
ℹ️ Ferienregion Attersee Infobüro Unterach, Hauptstraße 9, www.
oberoesterreich.at/unterach.Holiday resort at Lake Atter.
🌾 Naturlehrpfad Edelkastanienwald.Hiking trail through nature reserve.

Waldhausen im Strudengau — 27A1
Badesee, Schloßberg. **GPS:** n48,28420 e14,95883.
6 ⬛free ⬛ € 1/10minutes Ch. 🔘 01/01-31/12
Distance: 2km on the spot on the spot 2km 2km.

Weistrach — 27A1
Parkplatz Sportplatz. GPS: n48,05475 e14,58167.
10 ⬛free. 🔘 01/01-31/12
Distance: 200m 200m.

Wien — 27B1
Kurpark Oberlaa, Filmteichstrasse 5, Vienna (Wien). **GPS:** n48,15211 e16,39767.

Wien — 27B1
Neue Donau, Am Kleehäufel, Vienna (Wien). **GPS:** n48,20836 e16,44602.
⬛. 🔘 Easter-30/09
Remarks: East of Vienna.

Wien — 27B1
Wien Süd, Breitenfursterstraße, Vienna (Wien). **GPS:** n48,14969 e16,30030.
⬛. 🔘 01/05-30/09

Wien — 27B1
Weingut Heuriger Schilling, Langenzersdorferstraße 54, Wien-Strebersdorf,
Vienna (Wien). **GPS:** n48,29856 e16,38421.

AT

2 ⌇ € 5, guests free ⌐ ⌐Ch ⌐ WC. **Surface:** gravel. ▢ Feb, Apr, Jun. Aug, Oct ▢ other months.
Distance: Wien 15km on the spot.
Remarks: Max. 3 days. A22, exit Strebersdorf.

| S | Wien | | 27B1 |

Waldrebengasse 3. **GPS:** n48,22552 e16,46271.
⌐ ⌐Ch. ▢ Mo-Fri 7-16.30

Tourist information Vienna (Wien):
ℹ Overnight parking prohibited.
ℹ Tourist-Info, Albertinaplatz 1, info.wien.at/.Imperial city, many curiosities, capital of the classic music.
ℹ Wien-Karte.Card gives entrance to public transport and discounts on museums, curiosities. Available at Tourist-Info and hotels. Ⓣ € 16,90.
👁 Spanische Hofreitschule, Michaelerplatz 1.Spanish Riding School, morning-training can be visited without reservation. ▢ 9.40-12.30h.
Ⓜ Kunsthistorisches Museum, Maria Theresien-Platz.Important painting collection. ▢ Tue-Su 10-18h, Thu 10-21h. Ⓣ € 10, family card € 20.
😊 Wurstelprater.Amusement park. ▢ 15/03-15/10 10-24h.

| S | Wiener Neustadt | | 27B2 |

Parkplatz Stadion, Stadionstrasse. **GPS:** n47,82156 e16,25629.

20 ⌇. ▢ 01/01-31/12
Distance: 500m on the spot.

| S | Wilfersdorf | | 27B1 |

Schloss Wilfersdorf, Parkplatz am Schloss. **GPS:** n48,58600 e16,64514.⬆.

3 ⌇ € 4 ⌐ ⌐WC. ▢ 01/01-31/12
Distance: 100m 300m on the spot.
Remarks: Check in at Schloss, 10-16h tue/su.

| S | Zwettl | | 27A1 |

Wirtshaus zur Minidampfbahn, 47, Teichhäuser bei Zwettl. **GPS:** n48,66278 e15,15444.⬆➡.

6-10 ⌇free ⌐free Ch€ 2,50 ⌐ € 2. **Surface:** grassy/metalled. ▢ 01/01-31/12
Distance: 2km 200m on the spot 2,5km.

Austria South

| S | Andau | | 27C2 |

Puszasee. GPS: n47,77536 e17,03265.
⌇ € 11 ⌐ ⌐Ch ⌐ € 1,85. ▢ 15/04-15/10

| S | Annenheim | | 26C3 |

Ossiachersee. GPS: n46,65631 e13,89168.
⌇ € 20,8- € 26,4 ⌐ ⌐Ch ⌐ WC ⌐ included. ▢ 01/05-15/09

Tourist information Annenheim:
⚔ Treffen.Former residence of the counts of Treffen.

| S | Bad Gams | | 27B3 |

Freizeitzentrums GamsBad, Bad Gams 2. **GPS:** n46,86730 e15,22743.⬆.

6 ⌇ € 5 ⌐ ⌐Ch. **Surface:** grasstiles/metalled. ▢ 01/01-31/12
Distance: 200m on the spot 200m 100m 200m.
Remarks: Check in at Gamsbad.

| | Bad Sankt Leonhard | | 27A3 |

Bachwegbrücke. GPS: n46,96037 e14,79358.

8 ⌇free. ▢ 01/01-31/12
Remarks: Parking behind Spar-supermarket.

| | Bleiburg | | 27A3 |

Grabenstraße. **GPS:** n46,59130 e14,79550.

4 ⌇free. **Surface:** grasstiles. ▢ 01/01-31/12

AT

Distance: 🚶on the spot ⊗100m 🛒on the spot 🚲200m.

| 🏕 | **Deutschlandsberg** 🌿♨🍴⛰ | 27B3 |

Koralmhalle, Höhe Frauentalerstraße 51. **GPS:** n46,81783 e15,22248.⬆

2 🛏free. **Surface:** asphalted. ◐ 01/01-31/12
Distance: 🚶200m ⊗on the spot 🛒100m 🚲on the spot.

| 🏕 | **Döbriach** 🏖⛰🌊 | 26C2 |

Brunner am See. GPS: n46,76778 e13,64806.
🛏. ◐ 01/01-31/12

| 🏕 | **Döbriach** ⛰🌊 | 26C2 |

Mössler. GPS: n46,77444 e13,65556.
🛏. ◐ 01/04-01/11

Tourist information Döbriach:
ℹ Tourismusbüro Millstatt, Marktplatz 8, Millstatt.Tourist town and health resort to the Millstättersee.

| 🏕 | **Drobollach** | 26C3 |

Marhof. GPS: n46,59031 e13,91340.
🛏. ◐ 01/05-01/10

Tourist information Drobollach:
👁 Terra Medica, Bad Bleiberg.Cave with beneficial effect. 🆃 € 16 1h therapy.
👁 Terra Mystica, Bad Bleiberg.Miners cave. ◐ 01/05-31/10 10-15h, 01/07-31/08 9.30-16.30h.

| 🏕 | **Eberndorf** | 27A3 |

Gösseldorfersee. GPS: n46,57532 e14,62319.
🛏. ◐ 01/05-01/10

| 🏕 | **Eberndorf** | 27A3 |

Rutar Lido. GPS: n46,58455 e14,62615.
🛏. ◐ 01/01-31/12

| 🏕 | **Faak/See** | 26C3 |

Gruber. GPS: n46,57254 e13,93242.
🛏. ◐ 01/05-01/10

| 🏕 | **Faak/See** | 26C3 |

Poglitsch. GPS: n46,56972 e13,90694.
🛏. ◐ Easter-15/10

| 🏕S | **Ferlach** | 26D2 |

Messeparkplatz Schloß Ferlach. GPS: n46,52633 e14,29750.⬆

30 🛏€ 4 🚰€ 1/10minutes 🔌Ch 💧€ 1. **Surface:** metalled. ◐ 01/01-31/12
Distance: 🚶500m 🏊on the spot ⊗300m 🛒300m 🚲300m.
Remarks: Max. 3 days.

| 🍴S | **Gamlitz** | 27B3 |

Schloßweingut Melcher, Eckberger Weinstraße. **GPS:** n46,72054 e15,55409.

10 🛏🚰💧WC free with a meal. ◐ 8-23h
Distance: 🚶on the spot ⊗on the spot 🛒150m.
Remarks: After restaurant, go up to the right.

| 🏕 | **Gleinstätten** | 27B3 |

Gleinstätten. GPS: n46,75167 e15,36111.
🛏. ◐ 01/04-01/10

| ⒸS | **Hermagor** 🏖⛰🌊❄ | 26C3 |

Schluga. GPS: n46,63147 e13,39532.
6 🛏€ 12, dog € 3,90. **Surface:** grassy. ◐ 01/01-31/12
Distance: 🚌winter free huttle to piste.

| 🏕 | **Hermagor** 🏖⛰🌊❄ | 26C3 |

Max Presseggersee. GPS: n46,63022 e13,45423.
🛏. ◐ 01/05-01/10

Tourist information Hermagor:
🌿 Presseggersee.Nature reserve, no motorboats allowed.

| 🍇S | **Horitschon** | 27B2 |

Weingut Duschanek, Hauptstraße 104. **GPS:** n47,59162 e16,53493.⬆

6 🛏€ 3, guests free 🚰🔌Ch 💧€ 2 WC. **Surface:** metalled. ◐ 01/01-31/12
Distance: 🚶600m ⊗on the spot 🛒600m 🚲on the spot.

| 🛏S | **Jagerberg** | 27B3 |

GPS: n46,85692 e15,74292.⬆➡

5 🛏free 🚰€ 0,50/60liter 🔌Ch. **Surface:** gravel. ◐ 01/01-31/12
Distance: 🚶200m ⊗200m 🛒200m 🚲200m.
Remarks: Follow 'Sportanlage'.

| 🏕 | **Jennersdorf** | 27B2 |

Jennersdorf. GPS: n46,94558 e16,13372.
🛏. ◐ 01/04-01/11

| 🛏S | **Judenburg** 💦 | 26D1 |

Erlebnisbad, Fichtenhainstraße. **GPS:** n47,16407 e14,65308.⬆➡

5 🛏 € 5 🚰 🔌 Ch WC free. **Surface:** gravel. ⬛ 01/01-31/12
Distance: 🚶500m ✕200m 🛒200m.

🍴 S	Kötschach–Mauthen	26B3

Gasthof Gailberghöhe, Gailberg 3. **GPS:** n46,71525 e12,96753.
70 🛏 € 14,50, 2 pers.incl. 🚰 🔌 Ch 🔧 WC included. **Surface:** asphalted/gravel. ⬛ 01/05-15/11, 15/12-15/03
Distance: 🚶7km ✕on the spot 🛒7km 🏊2km 🎣7km.

🔺	Ledenitzen	26C3

Ferien am Walde. **GPS:** n46,57046 e13,95161.
🛏 ⬛ 01/05-01/10

🛏 S	Liezen	27A2

Sportzentrum, Friedau. **GPS:** n47,56500 e14,23333. ⬆️➡️.

3 🛏 free 🚰 ⃣ € 1. **Surface:** gravel. ⬛ 01/01-31/12
Distance: 🚶1km ✕300m 🛒1km 🚰on the spot.

🔺	Malta 🌿🏔	26C2

Maltatal. **GPS:** n46,94958 e13,50975.
🛏 ⬛ 01/04-01/11

Tourist information Malta:
ℹ️ Gmünd.Small fortified medieval town.
Ⓜ️ Porsche Museum, Gmünd.Former place of residence of Ferdinand Porsche, 1944-1950. ⬛ 15/05-15/10 9-18h, 16/10-14/5 10-16h.

🛏	Mörbisch/Neusiedlersee	27B2

Seefestspiele, P3, Seestrasse. **GPS:** n47,75470 e16,69592.

30 🛏 € 3,50. **Surface:** grassy. ⬛ 01/01-31/12
Distance: 🚶2km 🏊on the spot.
Remarks: Parking at marina.

🍴 S	Mörtschach	26B2

Gasthof Suntiger, Mörtschach 35. **GPS:** n46,92287 e12,91348.

4 🛏 guests free 🚰 🔧. **Surface:** grassy.

🔺	Mühlen	26D2

Am Badesee. **GPS:** n47,03719 e14,48780.
🛏 ⬛ 01/05-30/09

🍴 S	Murfeld	27B3

Gasthof Dorfheuriger Rom Thomas, Dorfstrasse 1, Unterschwarza. **GPS:** n46,71612 e15,67612. ⬆️➡️.

50 🛏 € 5 🚰 🔌 Ch WC 📶. **Surface:** grassy. ⬛ 01/01-31/12
Distance: 🚶200m ✕on the spot.
Remarks: Bread-service.

🛏 S	Oberrakitsch	27B3

Ölmühle Sixt, Oberrakitsch 115. **GPS:** n46,73863 e15,74605.

10 🛏 € 12 🚰 🔌 Ch 🔧 WC. **Surface:** gravel. ⬛ 01/01-31/12
Distance: 🚶1km 🛒on the spot ✕1km 🏊3km 🚰4km.

🔺	Obervellach	26B2

Sport Erlebnis. **GPS:** n46,92658 e13,20195.

🔺 S	Oberwölz 🌿	26D1

Schloß Rothenfels. **GPS:** n47,20697 e14,28051.
🛏 € 18,50, 2 pers.incl 🚰 🔌 Ch 🔧 WC included. ⬛ 01/04-01/11

Tourist information Oberwölz:
ℹ️ Urlaubsregion Murau, Am Bahnhof, St. Lorenzen/Murau.Oldest small town of Styria.
Ⓜ️ Blasmusikmuseum.Music museum. ⬛ 10-15h. 🎫 € 3.

🔺	Ossiach 🚣🏔	26D3

Kalkgruber. **GPS:** n46,68730 e14,01941.
🛏 ⬛ 01/05-01/10

🔺	Ossiach 🚣🏔	26D3

Kölbl. **GPS:** n46,66200 e13,97267.
🛏 ⬛ 01/04-01/11

🔺	Ossiach 🚣🏔	26D3

Lampele. **GPS:** n46,68267 e13,99865.
🛏 ⬛ 01/05-01/10

🔺	Ossiach 🚣🏔	26D3

Ossiach. **GPS:** n46,66367 e13,97452.
🛏 ⬛ 01/05-01/10

Ossiach 🏕️🏔️🌊 26D3
Parth. GPS: n46,66517 e13,97697.
🚐. 🅾 01/01-31/12
Tourist information Ossiach:
ℹ️ www.ossiach.at/.Tourist town.

Pölfing-Brunn 🏔️🎏 27B3
Kipferlbad, Badstraße 13. **GPS:** n46,72422 e15,29268.

10 🚐free. **Surface:** grassy. 🅾 01/01-31/12
Distance: 🚶1km 🏊on the spot ⊗on the spot 🚰1km 🚮1km.

Schiefling am See 26D3
Weißes Rössl. GPS: n46,61810 e14,10428.
🚐. 🅾 01/05-01/10

Schladming 🎿⛷️❄️ 26C1
Talstation Planai-West. GPS: n47,39005 e13,67638.
30 🚐€ 17 excl. tourist tax 🚱🚰Ch🔌. 🅾 winter
Distance: 🎿25m 🎿on the spot.
Remarks: Valley station ski-lift.

Schwanberg 🏔️🎏 27B3
Freibad, Badgasse. **GPS:** n46,76361 e15,20639.

4 🚐free 15/09-15/05, € 6 16/05-14/09 🚱🔌On demand WC. **Surface:** gravel. 🅾 01/01-31/12
Distance: 🚶500m 🏊on the spot ⊗on the spot 🚰500m 🚮500m.

Soboth 27A3
Parkplatz Soboth-Stausee. GPS: n46,68142 e15,03805.

🚐free. **Surface:** asphalted.
Distance: 🚶5km.
Remarks: Parking at artificial lake.

St Stefan im Rosental 27B2
Schichenauerstraße 6. **GPS:** n46,90634 e15,71431. ⬆️➡️.
6 🚐free 🚱€ 1/100liter 🚰Ch🔌(6x)€ 0,60/kWh. **Surface:** gravel. 🅾 01/01-31/12
Distance: 🚶200m ⊗200m 🚰200m.

St.Andrä 27B2
Zicksee. GPS: n47,79205 e16,91428.
🚐. 🅾 01/04-01/10

St.Primus 26D3
Turnersee. GPS: n46,58588 e14,56568.
🚐. 🅾 01/05-01/10

Stainz 27B3
Parkplatz 3, Ettendorfer Straße. **GPS:** n46,89377 e15,26823.

3 🚐free. **Surface:** metalled.
Distance: 🚶100m ⊗100m 🚰100m.
Tourist information Stainz:
ℹ️ Region Süd-Weststeiermark, Hauptplatz 34, www.stainz.at.Das Land des Schilcher, country of the Austrian rosé wine.
👁️ Der Stainzer Flascherlzug.Narrow-gauge steam train. 🅾 01/05-31/10 Sa-Su 15h.
👁️ Ren(nt)t a Traktor, Anton Nettwall, Sommereben 95, St. Stefan ob Stainz.With a tractor through Schilcherland. 🎫 € 50 1/2 day.

Unterlamm 27B2
Stefan's Heuriger Sieglhof, Magland 44. **GPS:** n46,98152 e16,09172. ⬆️.

15 🚐€ 1/pp 🚱🚰Ch. 🅾 01/01-31/12
Distance: 🚶4km ⊗on the spot 🚰on the spot 🚮on the spot.

Veitsch 27B2
Marktgemeindeamt. GPS: n47,57896 e15,48961. ⬆️.

3 🚐free. **Surface:** asphalted. 🅾 01/01-31/12
Distance: 🚶300m ⊗100m 🚰100m 🚮100m.

Villach 🏕️🏔️🌊 26C3
Berghof. GPS: n46,65290 e13,93307.
🚐. 🅾 01/04-15/10
Tourist information Villach:
ℹ️ Villach Tourismus, Rathausplatz 1, www.villach.at.Tourist town. 🅾 Mo-Fri 10-17h.
👁️ Therme Warmbad, Kadischenallee 25-27.Thermal bath and health centre.

Vordernberg 27A2
Hauptplatz 2. **GPS:** n47,48617 e14,99202. ⬆️.

AT

6 🥄 🚰 € 1/10minutes 🗑 Ch 🧹 € 1/8h. **Surface:** gravel. ▢ 01/01-31/12
Distance: 🚶500m ⊗500m 🍽500m 🚌on the spot.

AT

ITALY

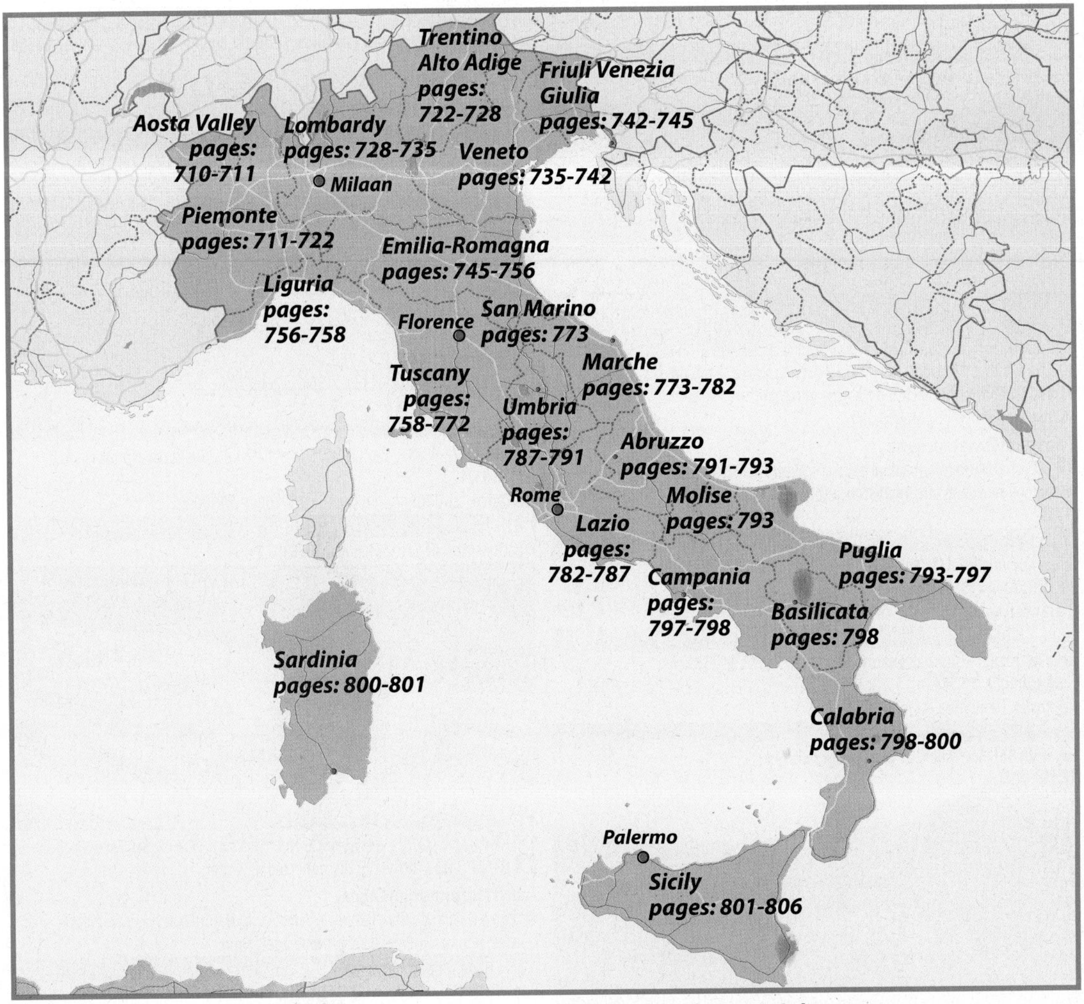

Aosta Valley
pages:
710-711

Lombardy
pages: 728-735

Trentino
Alto Adige
pages:
722-728

Friuli Venezia
Giulia
pages: 742-745

Veneto
pages: 735-742

● Milaan

Piemonte
pages: 711-722

Emilia-Romagna
pages: 745-756

Liguria
pages:
756-758

Florence ●

San Marino
pages: 773

Marche
pages: 773-782

Tuscany
pages:
758-772

Umbria
pages:
787-791

Abruzzo
pages: 791-793

Rome ●

Molise
pages: 793

Lazio
pages:
782-787

Campania
pages:
797-798

Puglia
pages: 793-797

Basilicata
pages: 798

Sardinia
pages: 800-801

Calabria
pages: 798-800

Palermo
●

Sicily
pages: 801-806

IT

Capital: Rome
Government: parliamentarian republic
Official Language: Italian
Population: 59,000,000 (2010)
Area: 301,318 km^2

General information
Dialling code: 0039.
Currency: Euro
Credit cards are accepted almost everywhere.

Regulations for overnight stays
Wild camping is allowed with permission of
municipality, police or property owner when no
problems occur.

Opening hours
Shops: Monday-Saturday 9.am-1pm and 4pm-8pm.
Banks: Monday-Friday 8.30am-1pm and 3pm-4pm.

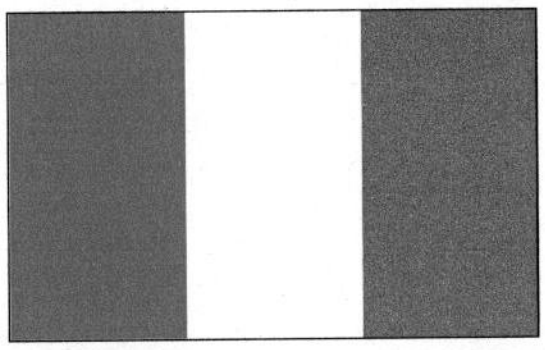

Aosta Valley

S Antey-Saint-André 24A6

Località Filey, SR46. **GPS**: n45,81246 e7,58898.
15 free Ch. **Surface:** metalled. 01/01-31/12
Distance: 850m.

S Aosta 23D6

Via Cadutti del Lavoro. **GPS**: n45,73600 e7,33035.

30 € 6/12h € 1/100liter € 2 Ch. **Surface:** asphalted. 01/01-31/12 Thu-morning closed because of market.
Distance: on the spot 4,5km.

Tourist information Aosta:
U.I.A.T. (Ufficio Informazioni e di Accoglienza Turistica), Piazza Chanoux, 8, www.regione.vda.it/turismo.Historical city. 9.30-12h, 14-17.30h, summer 9-19h.

S Aymavilles 23D6

Strada Comunale del Moulins. **GPS**: n45,70125 e7,23960.
20 € 8/24h . **Surface:** metalled. 01/05-31/10
Distance: on the spot 2km.

S Bionaz 23D5

Area Attrezzata Bosco di Lexert. **GPS**: n45,87458 e7,42381.
€ 10/night Ch.
Remarks: Picnic area at small lake.

S Brusson 24A6

Foyer du Ski, Rue Vollon. **GPS**: n45,76617 e7,71117.

50 € 10/24h Ch included. **Surface:** grassy/metalled. 01/01-31/12
Distance: on the spot.
Remarks: At lake. On the road dir Campoluc.

S Cervinia/Breuil 24A5

GPS: n45,92614 e7,62026.

50 € 7/24h Ch. **Surface:** asphalted. 01/01-31/12
Distance: 1km Lago Blu 400m on the spot.
Remarks: Shuttle to centre. 1km before entering the village, nearby cross roads with Cieloalto.

S Champorcher 24A6

Area pic-nic, Loc. Chardonney. **GPS**: n45,62153 e7,60654.
free free. **Surface:** grassy/metalled.
Remarks: Nearby parking funicular railway.

S Chatillon 24A6

Area Camper attrezzata Chatillon, Località Chopine. **GPS**: n45,74889 e7,62388.
€ 6/12h Ch . **Surface:** metalled. 01/01-31/12
Distance: centro storico 500m.

S Cogne 23D6

Fraz. Lillaz. **GPS**: n45,59602 e7,38815.

38 € 8, 1/7-31/8 + 24/12-6/1 € 10 Ch. **Surface:** asphalted. 01/01-31/12
Distance: 100m on the spot 100m 100m.

S Cogne 23D6

Fraz. Revettaz. **GPS**: n45,60840 e7,35830.

120 € 8, 1/7-31/8 + 24/12-6/1 € 10 Ch € 2. **Surface:** asphalted. 01/01-31/12 water disconnected in winter.

Tourist information Cogne:
Parco Nacionale Gran Paradiso, Vall d'Aosta.Nature reserve, information centres: Dégioz, Rhêmes-Notre-Dame and Cogne.

S Courmayeur 23D6

Funivia Val Veny. **GPS**: n45,81428 e6,95612.
free . **Surface:** metalled. 01/01-31/12
Distance: 3km on the spot.

S Gressoney 24A5

P Weissmatten, Via Bildschocke, Saint Jean. **GPS**: n45,76028 e7,83556.

15/12-31/03 - 01/07-31/08 € 10/24h . **Surface:** asphalted. 01/01-31/12
Remarks: Parking funicular railway.

S Gressoney 24A5

Tschaval, La Trinité. **GPS**: n45,85657 e7,81362.

IT

36 ⬛€ 12/24h, May-Oct € 10 ⬛⬛Ch ⬛€ 3 WC ⬛. **Surface:** metalled. ⬛ 01/01-31/12, 24/24h

Distance: ⬛2 restaurants ⬛300m ⬛on the spot ⬛on the spot ⬛200m.

Hône ⬛   24A6

Via Raffort. **GPS:** n45,61169 e7,73262.⬛.

10 ⬛€ 8 ⬛⬛Ch ⬛ included. **Surface:** metalled. ⬛ 01/01-31/12

Distance: ⬛350m ⬛7km.

Remarks: Max. 48h.

⬛S La Thuile ⬛⬛❄   23D6

Area Azzura. **GPS:** n45,70823 e6,95335.

75 ⬛€ 12/24h ⬛⬛Ch ⬛(45x)€ 3 ⬛. **Surface:** metalled. ⬛ 01/01-31/12

Distance: ⬛500m ⬛500m ⬛100m.

Pont-Saint-Martin   24A6

Piazzale Palazzetto dello Sport. GPS: n45,60025 e7,79338.

⬛free. **Surface:** asphalted.

Distance: ⬛1km.

⬛S Rhemes Notre Dame   23D6

Loc. Chanavey. **GPS:** n45,57960 e7,12392.

⬛€ 5 ⬛⬛⬛ included. **Surface:** metalled.

Distance: ⬛on the spot.

⬛S Rhemes Notre Dame   23D6

Frazione Bruil. **GPS:** n45,57148 e7,11848.

20 ⬛free. **Surface:** asphalted.

⬛S Saint-Denis ⬛   24A6

Strada Regionale del Col Saint Pantaléon, Loc. Plaù. **GPS:** n45,77129 e7,56092.

10 ⬛free ⬛⬛Ch ⬛free. **Surface:** grasstiles/grassy.

Distance: ⬛16km.

⬛S Saint-Oyen ⬛❄   23D6

Rue de Flassin. **GPS:** n45,82133 e7,20822.⬛.

⬛€ 12/24h ⬛⬛Ch ⬛ WC included ⬛€ 1. ⬛ 01/01-31/12

Distance: ⬛22km ⬛on the spot ⬛on the spot.

⬛S Torgnon   24A6

Plan Prorion. **GPS:** n45,80397 e7,55490.⬛⬛.

25 ⬛€ 8/24h ⬛⬛Ch ⬛. **Surface:** asphalted. ⬛ 01/01-31/12

Distance: ⬛50m.

⬛S Valgrisenche ⬛   23D6

Frazione Bonne. **GPS:** n45,61931 e7,05930.

20 ⬛€ 10/24h ⬛⬛Ch ⬛€ 3. **Surface:** grassy/sand.

Remarks: At weir.

⬛S Valsavarenche ⬛   23D6

GPS: n45,59229 e7,20839.⬛.

⬛€ 5/12h ⬛⬛Ch. **Surface:** grasstiles. ⬛ 01/01-31/12

Distance: ⬛100m.

Remarks: Check in at town hall Tabaccheria or Bar Lo Fourquin, with registration number motorhome.

⬛S Verrès ⬛   24A6

Via Stazione. **GPS:** n45,66214 e7,69356.⬛.

6 ⬛€ 5 ⬛⬛free. **Surface:** asphalted.

Distance: ⬛1,5km.

Piedmont

⬛S Acqui Terme ♨   31B2

SS456, Viale Einaudi. **GPS:** n44,66533 e8,47228.⬛.

4 ⬛€ 5 ⬛⬛ ⬛(4x). **Surface:** metalled. ⬛ 01/01-31/12

⬛S Alba   19B6

Alba Village, Corso Piave 219, loc. San Cassiano. **GPS:** n44,68537 e8,01019.

20 ⬛€ 8 ⬛€ 0,50/30liter ⬛Ch ⬛free ⬛. **Surface:** grassy. ⬛ 01/01-31/12

Distance: ⬛2km ⬛on the spot ⬛100m ⬛on the spot.

Remarks: Nearby Hotel&Camping Alba Village, max. 48h, guarded parking, check in at reception.

IT

S̶ Avigliana 🌿 🏔️ 30D1
Piazzale Grande Torino, Via Pontetto. **GPS:** n45,07342 e7,39075.

⌇free ⟋—⟍Chfree. **Surface:** asphalted.
Distance: ⎯1km ⚓4,6km.
Remarks: Nearby sports complex.

Tourist information Avigliana:
🛈 Ufficio Informazioni e di Accoglienza Turistica, Piazza del Popolo, 2. Historical city.
⛺ 🅿️ Thu.

S̶ Bairo 31A1
SP 41, Via Cornaletto. **GPS:** n45,38681 e7,75796.

⌇free ⟋—⟍Chfree. **Surface:** gravel. 🅿️ 01/01-31/12
Remarks: Max. 3 days.

S̶ Barge 30D2
Via Fiorita. **GPS:** n44,72684 e7,32028. ⬆️→

5 ⌇free ⟋—⟍Chfree. **Surface:** asphalted.
Distance: ⎯800m ⎯on the spot.

S̶ Baveno 24B5
Area Comunale, Piazza Umberto Giordano. **GPS:** n45,91139 e8,50056. ⬆️

40 ⌇€ 12/24h ⟋—⟍Ch 🚰WC included. 🚿
Surface: metalled.
🅿️ 01/01-31/12
Distance: ⎯500m ⚓2,8km 🏊Lago Maggiore 300m 🛒300m.
Remarks: Max. 72h, no camping activities.

S̶ Biella 24B6
Area Comunale, Piazzale Sandro Pertini. **GPS:** n45,55559 e8,06760. ⬆️

30 ⌇free ⟋—⟍free.
Location: Urban. **Surface:** asphalted. 🅿️ 01/01-31/12
Distance: ⎯on the spot ⊗100m ⎯station 100m.
Remarks: Square next to station F.S San Paolo.

Tourist information Biella:
🛈 A.T.L. (Agenzia Turistica Locale), Piazza V. Veneto, 3.

S̶ Bielmonte 🏔️ 👣 24B6
Piazzale 2, SS232. **GPS:** n45,66250 e8,08472.
8 ⌇€ 3,50 ⟋—⟍Ch included. 🔌€ 3,50.
Remarks: Follow Panoramica Zegna, funicular railway 500m.

S̶ Borgo San Dalmazzo 31A3
P Area Camper, Strada Communale Del Cimitero. **GPS:** n44,32889 e7,49167. ⬆️
→

⌇free ⟋—⟍Chfree. **Surface:** asphalted.
Distance: ⎯100m.
Remarks: At sports park.

S̶ Borgosesia 24B6
Piazza Valentino milanaccio, Via Varallo. **GPS:** n45,72005 e8,27408. ⬆️

8 ⌇free ⟋—⟍Chfree. **Location:** Urban. **Surface:** asphalted. 🅿️ 01/01-31/12 🌙 Jun.
Distance: ⎯300m.
Remarks: Sa market.

S̶ Bra 31A2
Piazza XX settembre. **GPS:** n44,69550 e7,85883.
⌇ ⟋ 🅿️ Tue-Sa 8-12, 14-19
Remarks: Near covered market.

S Bra 31A2
Via Senator Satori. **GPS:** n44,71333 e7,70333.
⟋—⟍ 🅿️ Tue-Sa 8-12, 14-19
Remarks: Parking car washing centre, in opposite of Coop.

S̶ Candelo 24B6
Area Comunale, Via C. Pavese/Via F. Bianco. **GPS:** n45,54244 e8,11524. ⬆️

10 ⃞free ⌐⊐⊣ Chfree. **Location:** Urban, quit. **Surface:** gravel. ⃝ 01/01-31/12
Distance: 400m 400m 100m.
Remarks: Nearby sports center.

| ⃞S | Canelli | 31B2 |

Piazza Unione Europea. **GPS:** n44,72039 e8,29369.↑.
⃞free ⌐⊐⊣ Chfree. **Surface:** asphalted.

| ⃞S | Cannobio | 24C5 |

Area Comunale, Via Al Fiume / Via San Rocco. **GPS:** n46,06179 e8,69242.↑→.

20 ⃞€ 15/24h ⌐⊐ Ch WC free. ⃞ **Location:** Rural. **Surface:** grasstiles. ⃝
01/01-31/12
Distance: 500m on the spot 500m 300m.
Remarks: Along river, max. 3 days.

Tourist information Cannobio:
ℹ U.I.A.T. (Ufficio Informazioni e di Accoglienza Turistica), Viale V. Veneto,
4.Historical little town with palace and Renaissance church.
⌂ ⃞ Su.

| ⃞S | Carcoforo ❀🏔🎄🍂❄ | 24B5 |

Le Giare, SP11, Loc. Tetto Minocco. **GPS:** n45,90769 e8,05130.↑.

100 ⃞€ 10/day, € 15/weekend, € 40/week ⌐⊐⊣ Chfree (16x)€ 1,50
WC ⃞€ 1. **Surface:** grassy. ⃝ 01/03-30/09
Distance: on the spot 50m 300m.
Remarks: Along the Egua river.

| ⃞S | Casale Monferrato | 31B1 |

Palazzetto dello Sport Paolo Ferraris, Via Visconti. **GPS:** n45,12556 e8,46194.
⃞.
Distance: 1,5km 3,6km.
Remarks: At sports centre.

| ⃞S | Casale Monferrato | 31B1 |

Parcheggio Castello. **GPS:** n45,13722 e8,44806.

⃞free. **Surface:** asphalted.
Distance: 200m 4km.

| ⃞S | Castelletto Stura | 31A2 |

Via Cuneo. **GPS:** n44,44194 e7,63444.

⃞free ⌐⊐⊣free. **Surface:** gravel.
Remarks: Nearby sports park.

| ⃞S | Castiglione Tinella | 31B2 |

Camperstop Ai Ciuvin, Agriturismo, Strada Manzotti 3. **GPS:** n44,73357 e8,18140.↑→.

12 ⃞€ 10, free for clients ⌐⊐⊣ Ch WC ⃞. ⃝ 01/01-31/12
Distance: on the spot 20km.
Remarks: Max. 48h.

| ⃞S | Cavour | 30D2 |

Via Giacomo Puccini. **GPS:** n44,78861 e7,37667.↑→.

18 ⃞free ⌐⊐⊣ Chfree. **Surface:** metalled.
Distance: 400m 100m.
Remarks: Nearby SP152.

| ⃞S | Ceresole Reale | 30D1 |

Borgata Chiapili Inferiore, SP50. **GPS:** n45,45142 e7,18587.↑.
⃞€ 8 ⌐⊐ 4 Ch € 3. **Surface:** unpaved.
Distance: 4km Ristorante Lo Sciatore 2km.
Remarks: Along the Orco river, National Park 'Gran Paradiso'.

| ⃞S | Ceresole Reale | 30D1 |

Borgota Villa, SP50. **GPS:** n45,44053 e7,21066.

40 🛏free ⛽ WC free. **Surface:** grassy/gravel.
Distance: 🏪Ceresole Reale 2km 🏊on the spot ⊗200m.
Remarks: Altitude 1350m, National Park 'Gran Paradiso'.

📷S | **Cesana Torinese** ⛰❄ | 30D2
Area Sosta Camper Casa Cesana, Viale Sen. Bouvier. **GPS:** n44,94782 e6,79516. ⬆.

12 🛏 💶€ 10/24h ⛽ 🔌 Ch included 🚿(12x)€ 3/day, 6Amp. **Surface:** asphalted. ⬜ 01/01-31/12
Distance: 🏪300m ⊗50m.

📷S | **Cherasco** | 31A2
Viale della Sibila. **GPS:** n44,64946 e7,85529. ⬆➡.

8 🛏free ⛽ 🔌(4x)free, 16Amp. **Surface:** asphalted.
Distance: 🏪400m 🚲3,7km.
Remarks: Max. 48h.

📷S | **Chieri** | 31A1
Piazza Quarini, via Bernardo Vittone. **GPS:** n45,00488 e7,82724.

12 🛏free ⛽ Ch free. **Surface:** asphalted.
Distance: 🏪on the spot.
Remarks: Behind Barracks.

📷S | **Chivasso** | 31A1
Piazza Libertini. **GPS:** n45,18514 e7,89296. ⬆.

🛏free ⛽€ 2 🔌. **Surface:** asphalted.
Distance: 🏪300m.
Remarks: Parking swimming pool.

📷S | **Chivasso** | 31A1
Via Ceresa. **GPS:** n45,19470 e7,88955.

🛏free ⛽€ 2 🔌. **Surface:** asphalted.
Distance: 🏪300m.
Tourist information Chivasso:
ℹ Ufficio Informazioni, Palazzo del Lavoro Lungo Piazza D'Armi. Tourist information.

📷S | **Collegno** | 31A1
Collegno Area Sosta Camper, Corso Pastrengo. **GPS:** n45,08070 e7,58313. ⬆.

30 🛏free ⛽€ 0,50 🔌Ch 💶€ 0,50. **Surface:** asphalted.
Distance: 🚲4km 🚍on the spot.
Remarks: Terrain with video surveillance, coins available at Autolavaggio Il Draghetto.

📷S | **Cravagliana** | 24B5
Pian delle Fate, Loc. Brugarolo, SP di Valle Mastallone. **GPS:** n45,85223 e8,22473. ⬆.

30 🛏 💶€ 14/24h ⛽ 🔌Ch 🚿(4x) WC ⅃included. **Surface:** grassy. ⬜ 15/03-15/10
Distance: 🏪on the spot ⊗on the spot.

📷S | **Cuceglio** | 31A1
Area Camper Erbaluce, Via Porta Pia 69/71. **GPS:** n45,34724 e7,81168.
🛏free ⛽. **Surface:** metalled.

714

IT

Cuneo 31A3
Via Discesa Bellavista. **GPS:** n44,39495 e7,54878.⬆️➡️.

🏕free 🚰🗑️Chfree. **Surface:** asphalted.
Distance: 🚶250m.
Remarks: Dir Torino/Saluzzo, before the old bridge over the Stura river.

Tourist information Cuneo:
ℹ️ U.I.A.T. (Ufficio Informazioni e di Accoglienza Turistica), Piazza Bovens, www.cuneoholiday.com.Historical city.
🎭 Piazza Galimberti. ⭕ Tue.

Demonte 30D3
Via G. Nicolai. **GPS:** n44,31551 e7,29495.
🏕. **Surface:** asphalted.
Remarks: Market square.

Donato 24A6
Area Camper Fabrizio de André, Via S. Pertini, SP405. **GPS:** n45,52774 e7,90944.
⬆️.

6 🏕€ 3/night 🚰🗑️ WC free. **Location:** Rural. **Surface:** grasstiles. ⭕ 01/01-31/12
Distance: 🚶300m ⊗300m.
Remarks: Pay at Tabaccheria in the village.

Entracque 31A3
Parcheggio Camper Real Park, Ponterosso. **GPS:** n44,26111 e7,37750.⬆️.

66 🏕€ 6 🚰 ⚡ included. **Surface:** grassy.
Distance: 🚶3km ⊗on the spot 🚌on the spot 🍴6km.
Remarks: Max. 2 days, recreation park.

Entracque 31A3
Centro Sci Nordico Gelas. GPS: n44,22852 e7,38927.
20 🏕€ 10/24h, € 15/48h 🚰🗑️. **Surface:** grassy/sand.
Distance: ⊗on the spot 🍴20m.

Entracque 31A3
Via del Mulino. **GPS:** n44,23389 e7,39723.
65 🏕€ 10/24h, € 15/48h 🚰🗑️⚡ included.
Distance: 🚶300m.

Fenestrelle 30D1
Le Casermette. GPS: n45,03671 e7,05090.
25 🏕€ 10 🚰🗑️Ch ⚡ € 3. **Surface:** unpaved.

Fenestrelle 30D1
GPS: n45,03889 e7,04583.

9 🏕free. **Surface:** grassy.
Remarks: Next to cemetery.

Frabosa Soprana 31A3
Grotta di Bossea. GPS: n44,24077 e7,83939.
🏕free 🚰🗑️Chfree. ⭕ 01/01-31/12
Remarks: Parking at the caves.

Genola 31A2
Grosso Vacanze, Via Divisione Alpina Cuneense 2, SS20. **GPS:** n44,59751 e7,65982.
🏕free 🚰🗑️Ch⚡. **Surface:** metalled. ⭕ 01/01-31/12
Remarks: Motorhome dealer, accessory shop.

Giaveno 30D1
GPS: n45,04137 e7,36135.

🏕free 🚰🗑️free. **Surface:** metalled.
Distance: ⊗100m.
Remarks: SP187 Roundabout dir Torino.

Grinzane Cavour 31A2
Piazza Ugo Genta, Via Bricco. **GPS:** n44,65515 e7,98936.
🏕free 🚰🗑️Ch. **Surface:** asphalted. ⭕ 01/01-31/12

Ivrea 24A6
La Dora d'Ivrea, Via Dora Baltea. **GPS:** n45,46334 e7,87621.

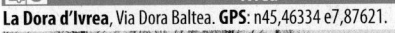

8 🏕€ 5 🚰 € 3 🗑️Ch. **Surface:** asphalted. ⭕ 01/01-31/12
Distance: 🚶500m ⛵ 4,5km 🛒Ipermercato 800m 🚌350m.
Remarks: Along the river side.

Tourist information Ivrea:
ℹ️ I.A.T. (Ufficio Informazioni e di Accoglienza Turistica), Corso Vercelli, 1.

Locana 31A1
Via Nusiglie. **GPS:** n45,41361 e7,46278.
€ 5/24h 🚰 ⚡ € 3/24h WC.

Macugnaga 24A5
Pecetto, Di Iacchine Pierluigi Loc. Pecetto. **GPS:** n45,97015 e7,95352.⬆️.

IT

28 ⌧€ 10, 2 nights € 15 🚰 🔌 Ch WC free. 🚿 **Location:** Rural, quit. **Surface:** concrete. 🅾 01/05-30/11
Distance: 🚲1km ⊗100m 🛒500m 🚌100m 🚶on the spot.
Remarks: At ski-lift.

15 ⌧€ 4/24h 🚰 🔌 Ch 🔧 included. 🚿 **Location:** Urban, quit. **Surface:** grasstiles. 🅾 01/01-31/12
Distance: 🚲900m.
Remarks: At sports centre.

🛉 S	Madonna del Sasso	24B6

Area Comunale, Via Santuario, Fraz. Boleto. **GPS:** n45,78974 e8,37222.⬆️

🛉 S	Montalto Dora	24A6

La vecchia stazione. **GPS:** n45,49067 e7,85903.⬆️
⌧€ 7/24h 🚰 🔌 Ch 🔧. **Surface:** asphalted. 🅾 01/01-31/12
Distance: 🚲10km ⊗100m 🛒200m.

🛉 S	Montiglio Monferrato	31A1

Via Padre Carpignano. **GPS:** n45,06261 e8,10045.
25 ⌧free 🚰 🔧.

🐾 S	Niella Tanaro	31A2

Agriturismo i Fornelli, Via Fornello 1. **GPS:** n44,41418 e7,90988.
3 ⌧against payment 🚰 🔧. **Surface:** grassy/gravel.

🛉 S	Nizza Monferrato	31B2

Piazzale Sandro Pertini. **GPS:** n44,77140 e8,35346.⬆️➡️

8 ⌧free 🚰 🔌 Ch free. **Surface:** grasstiles. 🅾 01/01-31/12
Distance: 🚲200m 🏊Lago d'Orta 700m ⊗100m 🚌50m.
Remarks: Narrow entrance, view at Lago d'Orta.

🛉	Maglione	31A1

SP78, Via Cigliano. **GPS:** n45,34338 e8,01456.

14 ⌧€ 5 🚰 🔌Ch 🔧included.
Surface: grassy.
Remarks: Gate closed, first call Motorhome Club Nicese between 9-20h.

🛉 S	Novi Ligure	31B2

Viale Pinan Cichero, zona stadio comunale. **GPS:** n44,77006 e8,78200.⬆️

20 ⌧free. **Surface:** grassy.
Distance: 🚲on the spot ⊗50m.
Remarks: Art city. Nearby SS44, dir Borgo d'Ale.

🛉 S	Marsaglia	31A2

Via della Stazione, SP115. **GPS:** n44,45228 e7,97929.
18 ⌧€ 13 🚰 🔌Ch 🔧 WC 🚽. **Surface:** asphalted/grassy. 🅾 01/01-31/12
Distance: 🚲on the spot.

🛉 S	Mirabello Monferrato	31B1

SS31. **GPS:** n45,03016 e8,52946.⬆️
8 ⌧free 🚰 🔌Ch. **Surface:** asphalted. 🅾 01/01-31/12
Distance: 🚲900m 🛒50m.

🐾 S	Mombaruzzo	31B2

Club Agrisportivo Mombaruzzo, Via Piero Boidi 32. **GPS:** n44,77554 e8,44821.
⌧€ 8 🚰 🔌Ch 🔧 € 2. 🅾 01/01-31/12

🛉 S	Mondovi	31A3

Piazza Republica. **GPS:** n44,38964 e7,81930.⬆️➡️
⌧free 🚰 🔌Ch WC free. **Surface:** asphalted.
Distance: 🚲400m.
Remarks: Nearby the old station.

🛉 S	Mongrando	24A6

Area Comunale, Via dei Giovanni. **GPS:** n45,52543 e8,00595.⬆️

⌧free 🚰 🔌free. **Surface:** asphalted.
Remarks: Parking gymnasium.

🛉 S	Occimiano	31B1

Via Circonvallazione. **GPS:** n45,05834 e8,50940.
5 ⌧free 🚰 🔌Ch 🔧. **Surface:** asphalted. 🅾 01/01-31/12
Distance: 🚲250m.

🛉 S	Oggebbio	24C5

Fiesta, Via Martiri Oggebbiesi 6. **GPS:** n45,99680 e8,65304.⬆️➡️

IT

20 🍴€ 18/24h 🚰🔌Ch 🚿 WC included 🍴€ 1 📶€ 5, /24h.🚽
Location: Luxurious.
Surface: gravel. 🅿 01/06-31/12
Distance: ⚓on the spot ⊗700m.
Remarks: Attention: narrow road, view on Lago Maggiore.

🏕🅂	**Omegna**	24B5

Lido di Omegna, Via Caduti di Bologna. **GPS:** n45,86340 e8,39840.⬆.

25 🍴€ 8-15 🚰🔌Ch 🚿 € 3. **Surface:** metalled. 🅿 01/01-31/12
Distance: ⚓1,8km ⛱beach.
Remarks: Caution key electricity € 30.

🏕🅂	**Ormea**	31A3

Via Orti della Rana. **GPS:** n44,14532 e7,90751.
10 🍴€ 10 🚰🔌Ch. **Surface:** grassy. 🅿 01/01-31/12
Distance: ⚓500m.

🏕🅂	**Oropa** 🌿⛲🎋	24A6

Area di Santuari, Via Santuario di Oropa. **GPS:** n45,62864 e7,97530.⬆➡.

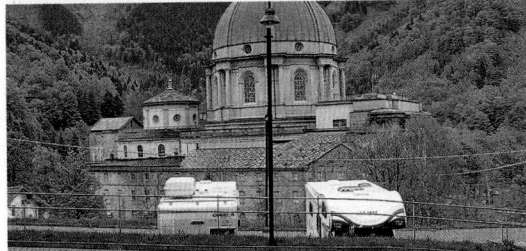

31 🍴€ 10, 01/05-30/09 € 15, 01/07-31/08 € 21 🚰🔌Ch 🚿 WC 🍴.
Location: Rural. **Surface:** metalled. 🅿 01/01-31/12 ❄ snow.
Distance: ⊗500m.

🏕🅂	**Orta San Giulio**	24B6

Via Panoramica. **GPS:** n45,79729 e8,41527.⬆.

20 🍴€ 10/24h 🚰🔌Ch. 🚽 **Surface:** asphalted. 🅿 01/01-31/12
Distance: ⚓500m ⛱Lago d'Orta 500m ⊗100m.

🏕	**Orta San Giulio**	24B6

Parco del Sacro Monte, Via Sacro Monte. **GPS:** n45,79732 e8,41204.⬆.

8 🍴free. **Surface:** gravel. 🅿 01/01-31/12
Distance: ⚓900m ⊗400m.
Remarks: Max. 48h.

🏕🅂	**Ovada**	31B2

Via Gramsci. **GPS:** n44,64084 e8,64920.⬆➡.

🍴free 🚰🔌WC free. **Surface:** metalled.
Distance: ⚓300m 🏊3km.

🏕	**Paesana**	30D2

Via Roma. **GPS:** n44,68139 e7,27639.

🍴free. **Surface:** grassy.
Distance: ⚓on the spot.
Remarks: To provincial route along the left bank of the Po river.

🏕🅂	**Piatto**	24B6

Area Comunale, Fraz. Malina. **GPS:** n45,58908 e8,13630.⬆.

10 🍴free 🚰🔌Ch.
Location: Urban. **Surface:** asphalted. 🅿 01/01-31/12
Remarks: At sports park.

🏕🅂	**Pietraporzio**	30D3

Via Nazionale, SS21. **GPS:** n44,34868 e7,01831.
10 🍴€ 5/24h 🚰🔌Ch 🚿. **Surface:** asphalted. 🅿 01/01-31/12

🏕🅂	**Pinerolo**	30D2

Parco Olimpico, Piazza Carlo Alberto Dalla Chiesa. **GPS:** n44,88917 e7,35111.⬆.

IT

10 ⌷free ⌷🔲Ch 🖉 (10x)against payment. **Surface:** metalled.
Distance: ⊗300m 🚊300m 🚌200m.
Remarks: Nearby sports park.

⌷S **Pollone** 🔺👥 24A6
Burcina di Pollone, Via Felice Piacenza. **GPS:** n45,58548 e8,00521.⬆️➡️.

20 ⌷€ 10/24h ⌷🔲Ch 🖉 WCincluded ⌷€ 2.🏠 **Location:** Rural,
comfortable. **Surface:** grasstiles. 🅾️ 01/01-31/12
Distance: 🚶600m ⊗on the spot.
Remarks: At parco Naturale Burcina.

◉S **Pombia** 24C6
Safari Park, SS 32 km 23,4. **GPS:** n45,64167 e8,61740.
⌷free ⌷ WC. **Surface:** asphalted.

⌷S **Ponderano** 24B6
Area Comunale, Strada Vicinale al Cimitero. **GPS:** n45,53683 e8,04949.⬆️.

10 ⌷free ⌷🔲free.
Location: Urban. **Surface:** gravel. 🅾️ 01/01-31/12
Distance: 🚶400m.
Remarks: Nearby sports park.

⌷S **Pont Canavese** 31A1
Via Roma. **GPS:** n45,42153 e7,60020.
12 ⌷€7 ⌷€ 2 ⌷Ch 🖉€ 2. **Surface:** grassy. 🅾️ 01/01-31/12
Distance: ⊿on the spot.
Remarks: Max. 48h.

⌷S **Pontechianale** 30D2
Area Camper, Fraz Maddalena. **GPS:** n44,62158 e7,02776.
⌷€ 8/24h ⌷🔲. **Surface:** grassy.

⌷S **Pragelato** 30D1
Fraz. Pattemouche, Valtroncea. **GPS:** n44,98736 e6,92090.

⌷€ 8/24h ⌷🔲Ch 🖉. **Surface:** unpaved. 🅾️ 01/01-31/12
Distance: 🎿on the spot.
Remarks: Former camsite, service only during winter period.

⌷S **Prali** ❄️ 30D2
Fraz.Ghigo. **GPS:** n44,89150 e7,04982.⬆️.

⌷free ⌷🔲free. **Surface:** grassy.
Distance: 🚶300m 🏊on the spot.
Remarks: Nearby SP169, along the river.

⌷S **Prato Nevoso** 🏔️❄️ 31A3
Area Stalle Lunghe, Via Galassia. **GPS:** n44,25668 e7,77946.
⌷€ 15-20 ⌷🔲Ch 🖉. **Surface:** asphalted. 🅾️ 01/01-31/12
Distance: 🚶on the spot 🚲A6 33km ⊗on the spot 🚊50m 🎿on the spot.

⌷S **Rimasco** 24B5
Il Laghetto, Strada del Lago. **GPS:** n45,86109 e8,06450.⬆️.

20 ⌷€ 10/24h ⌷🔲Ch 🖉€ 2/day WC ⌷included. **Surface:** grassy. 🅾️
01/05-30/09 🍽️ Restaurant: Tue.
Distance: ⊿on the spot ⊗on the spot.

⌷S **Riva Valdobbia** 🛶 24A6
Area Lo Chalet, Fraz Gabbio. **GPS:** n45,83467 e7,95469.⬆️.

48 ⌷€ 13/24h ⌷🔲Ch 🖉€ 3 WC included ⌷. **Surface:** grassy/metalled.
🅾️ 01/04-31/10
Distance: ⊿on the spot ⊗on the spot.
Remarks: Along river.

⌷S **Rivoli** 31A1
Campo sportivo, Via Isonzo. **GPS:** n45,08147 e7,51037.⬆️.

IT

⑃free ⛽🚰free. **Surface:** asphalted.
Distance: 🏊 1,5km.
Remarks: Parking sports park.

| 🅿 | **Rivoli** | 31A1 |

Piazzale Mafalda di Savoia. **GPS:** n45,06994 e7,51097.
⑃free. **Surface:** asphalted.
Distance: 🚶500m 🚲2,5km.
Remarks: Parking castle.

| 🅿 S | **Romano Canavese** | 31A1 |

Piazza Bachelet, via Montalenghe, SP82. **GPS:** n45,38782 e7,86396.⬆

8 ⑃free ⛽🚰 (2x). **Surface:** grassy/metalled. ☐ 01/01-31/12
Distance: 🏊2,2km.

| 🅿 S | **Rosta** | 31A1 |

Via Buttigliera Alta 2, Via Piave. **GPS:** n45,07106 e7,46333.
⑃free ⛽€ 2 🚰Ch€ 2. **Surface:** asphalted. ☐ 01/01-31/12
Distance: 🍺on the spot 🚂train > Turin 19min.

| 🏭 | **Saluzzo** | 31A2 |

Distributore AGIP, Via Torino. **GPS:** n44,65609 e7,49798.
⑃free ⛽🚰free.
Remarks: At petrol station.

| 🅿 S | **San Damiano d'Asti** | 31A2 |

Via Monsignor Franco. **GPS:** n44,82659 e8,05921.
⑃free ⛽🚰Ch. ☐ 01/01-31/12
Distance: 🚶1km.
Remarks: At cemetery.

| 🅿 S | **San Damiano d'Asti** | 31A2 |

Azienda Agricola Cascina Piana, Fraz S.Grato. **GPS:** n44,85136 e8,07417.
150 ⑃€ 8-10 ⛽🚰Ch✎WC🚽. **Surface:** grassy. ☐ 01/09-30/06
Remarks: Farm products.

| 🅿 S | **Sanfront** | 30D2 |

Via Montebracco, SP26. **GPS:** n44,64944 e7,32056.⬆➡

⑃free ⛽🚰Chfree. **Surface:** gravel.
Remarks: At sports park, max. 24h.

| 🅿 S | **Santa Maria Maggiore** ⛷ | 24B5 |

Area Verde Attrezzata, Via Alfredo Belcastro/via Pineta. **GPS:** n46,13219 e8,45500.⬆➡

32 ⑃€ 15/24h ⛽🚰Ch✎.🚐
Location: Rural.
Surface: gravel. ☐ 01/01-31/12
Distance: ✕200m 🚴 on the spot.
Remarks: Max. 48h. Follow 'Centro del Fondo'.

| 🅿 S | **Santa Maria Maggiore** ⛷ | 24B5 |

Agriturismo Al Piano delle Lutte, Via Domodossola 57. **GPS:** n46,13569 e8,44753.

3 ⑃€ 10/24h ⛽🚰Ch✎ consumption WC🚽.🚿 **Location:** Rural.
Surface: grassy/gravel. ☐ 01/01-31/12
Distance: ⊙on the spot.

| 🍴 S | **Sant'Antonino di Susa** | 30D1 |

Area Sosta Il Sentiero Dei Franchi, Borgo Cresto 16/1. **GPS:** n45,09973 e7,27754.
20 ⑃€ 10/24h ⛽🚰Ch✎. **Surface:** gravel. ☐ 01/01-31/12
Distance: ✕on the spot.

| 🍴 S | **Sant'Antonino di Susa** | 30D1 |

Area Sosta Il Sentiero Dei Franchi, Borgo Cresto 16/1. **GPS:** n45,09973 e7,27754.
20 ⑃€ 10 ⛽🚰Ch✎€ 2. **Surface:** grassy/gravel. ☐ 01/01-31/12
Distance: ✕on the spot.

| 🅿 S | **Sestriere** ⛰❄ | 30D1 |

Lago Losetta, Strada Azzurri d'Italia. **GPS:** n44,96465 e6,88141.
120 ⑃€ 10/24h ⛽🚰Ch✎. **Surface:** gravel. ☐ 01/01-31/12
Distance: 🚶800m 🚌Shuttle bus to ski-piste.

| 🅿 S | **Susa** | 30D1 |

Piazza Repubblica. **GPS:** n45,13861 e7,05389.

12 ⑃free ⛽🚰Ch✎free. **Surface:** asphalted. ☐ 01/01-31/12
Distance: 🚶300m.

| 🅿 S | **Tagliolo Monferrato** | 31B2 |

Via Mazzini 16. **GPS:** n44,63760 e8,67029.
⑃€ 5/24h ⛽🚰Ch. **Surface:** gravel. ☐ 01/01-31/12
Distance: 🚶150m.

| 🅿 S | **Torino** 🎭🍴 | 31A1 |

Piazza d'Armi, Corso Monte Lungo, Turin (Torino). **GPS:** n45,04848 e7,65651.
25 ⑃free ⛽🚰Chfree. **Surface:** grassy/metalled.

IT

Distance: 🚶city centre 3km 🚐on the spot.
Remarks: In opposite of police station.

| 🅂 | Torino 〰️ | 31A1 |

Corso Casale 327. **GPS:** n45,08084 e7,72993.

🚰free 🚐🗑️free. **Surface:** asphalted.
Distance: 🚶800m 🚐nearby.

| 🅂 | Torino 〰️ | 31A1 |

Parco Ruffini, Corso Lione/Corso Carlo Piaggia, Turin (Torino). **GPS:** n45,05686 e7,63166.

🚰free 🚐🗑️free. **Surface:** asphalted.

| 🅂 | Torino 〰️ | 31A1 |

Strada Castello di Mirafiori/via Artom, zona sud. **GPS:** n45,00900 e7,64873.⬆️.
🚰free 🚐Chfree. **Surface:** asphalted.

Tourist information Turin (Torino):

ℹ️ U.I.A.T. (Ufficio Informazioni e di Accoglienza Turistica), Piazza Castello, 161. Important industrial city with a lot of monuments and museums. Olympic Winter Games 2006.
Ⓜ️ Mole Antonelliana.National filmmuseum.
Ⓜ️ Museo Nazionale dell'Automobile, Corso Unità d'Italia 40.Museum of motor-cars. 🕐 Tue-Sa, 10-18.30h, Su 10-20.30h 🔴 Mo.
Ⓜ️ Palazzo Madame.Historical art.
✖️ Palazzo Reale.Royal palace.
✝️ Cathedral, 1498.
✝️ Basilica di Superga.Baroque basilica.

| 🅂 | Usseaux 〰️ | 30D1 |

Fraz. Fraisse-Pourrieres, SR23. **GPS:** n45,04170 e6,98518.
🚰€15 🚐Ch 🔧 WC. **Surface:** grassy.

| 🅂 | Usseaux 〰️ | 30D1 |

Lago del Laux, Via Lago 7. **GPS:** n45,04166 e7,02222.
100 🚰€10 🚐Chincluded 🔧€2. **Surface:** grassy. 🕐 01/06-31/10
Distance: 🚶500m 🚲200m 🚢5km.

| 🅂 | Valdieri | 30D3 |

Centro Alpino S.Anna, Loc. S. Anna. **GPS:** n44,24513 e7,32548.⬆️➡️.

40 🚰€12 🚐Ch 🔧 included. **Surface:** grassy/gravel.
Distance: 🚶100m 🏊on the spot ⊗100m.
Remarks: Narrow entrance (bridge).

| 🅂 | Valdieri | 30D3 |

Parco Alpi Marittime, Terme di Valdieri. **GPS:** n44,20546 e7,26840.
🚰€6 🚐Ch 🔧. **Surface:** metalled. 🕐 01/01-31/12

| 🅂 | Valenza | 31B1 |

SS494. **GPS:** n45,00400 e8,63895.⬆️.

🚰free 🚐🗑️free. **Surface:** asphalted.
Distance: 🚶1km.
Remarks: Parking sports park.

| 🅂 | Valle Mosso | 24B6 |

Piazza Alpini d'Italia. **GPS:** n45,63316 e8,14629.⬆️.

3 🚰free 🚐🗑️Chfree. **Location:** Urban. **Surface:** asphalted. 🕐 01/01-31/12
Distance: 🚶on the spot 🛒Conad 20m 🚐50m.

| 🅂 | Varallo | 24B6 |

Area Comunale, Via Sant'Antonio. **GPS:** n45,81797 e8,24857.⬆️.

8 🚰€10/24h 🚐Ch 🔌 included. **Location:** Urban, quit. **Surface:** gravel/sand. 🕐 01/01-31/12
Distance: 🚶500m ⊗500m.
Remarks: To be paid at town hall.

| 🅂 | Venaria Reale | 31A1 |

Relax and Go, Via Scodeggio 15. **GPS:** n45,14108 e7,62404.
15 🚰€15 🚐Ch 🔧. **Surface:** grassy.
Distance: ⊗650m 🚐bus GTT, tram 11>Turin.

| 🅂 | Venasca | 31A2 |

SP8, Via Provinciale. **GPS:** n44,56620 e7,39328.⬆️.

20 ⬛free ⬛free. **Surface:** sand.
Distance: 600m.

⬛S Verbania 24B5
Area Comunale, Viale Sant´Anna. **GPS:** n45,92896 e8,56468.⬆.

6 ⬛free ⬛free. **Location:** Urban, very simple. **Surface:** asphalted. ⬛
01/01-31/12
Distance: on the spot 100m 200m.

⬛S Verbania 24B5
Area Zone Arena, Via San Bernardino. **GPS:** n45,93143 e8,57106.⬆.
13 ⬛€ 10/24h included. **Surface:** asphalted. ⬛ 01/01-31/12
Distance: 600m 50m 100m 250m.

⬛S Vercelli 31B1
Via Trento, c/o piazzale Pala-hockey. **GPS:** n45,33417 e8,41861.⬆.

⬛free ⬛free. **Surface:** asphalted.
Distance: 1,5km.

Tourist information Vercelli:
ℹ U.I.A.T. (Ufficio Informazioni e di Accoglienza Turistica), www.turismovalsesiavercelli.it.
✝ Basilica di Sant'Andrea.Basilica, part of abbey.

⬛S Vialfrè 31A1
Via Luigi Emanuel, SP55. **GPS:** n45,38298 e7,81754.⬆.

⬛free ⬛free. **Surface:** metalled.
Distance: 6km 300m 300m.

⬛S Vidracco 31A1
Damanhur Crea, Via Baldissero 21. **GPS:** n45,42884 e7,75327.⬆.

⬛€ 8/24h Ch (24x) WC ⬛included. **Surface:** asphalted.
Distance: cafetaria on the spot.
Tourist information Vidracco:
👁 Damanhur Crea, Via Baldissero 21.Extraordinary Italian artistic and spritual community.

⬛S Villar Focchiardo 30D1
Area Camper Villar Focchiardo, Via Fratta, SS24. **GPS:** n45,11336 e7,22408.⬆.
➡

52 ⬛€ 5, weekend € 8 ⬛Chfree. **Surface:** grassy. ⬛ 01/01-31/12 ⬛
camper service: 01/11-31/03.
Distance: 4,5km.
Tourist information Villar Focchiardo:
ℹ Susa.Small medieval mountain village.

⬛S Villar Pellice 30D2
Parco Flissia, Via Cave del Fin. **GPS:** n44,80472 e7,15083.

⬛€ 6 ⬛free. **Surface:** grassy.
Distance: on the spot on the spot fishing permit obligatory agriturismo.
Remarks: Nearby SP161.

⬛S Vinadio 30D3
Area di Sosta Communale, Bagni di Vinadio, Fraz. Strapesi. **GPS:** n44,28747 e7,07534.⬆.

30 ⬛€ 11/24h ⬛Ch ⬛free. **Surface:** gravel.
Distance: 300m on the spot on the spot.

Remarks: Parking at the spa resort of Strapeis, altitude 1350m.

⛶ S — Vinadio ♈ — 30D3

Piazza d'Armi, SS21. **GPS:** n44,30667 e7,17083. ⬆️

🚿1/6-31/8 € 5 🚰 💺 Ch free. **Surface:** asphalted.
Distance: 🚶400m.

⛶ S — Volpedo — 31C2

Lungo Curone Matteotti. **GPS:** n44,88512 e8,98707. ⬆️➡️

6 🚿free 🚰 💺 Ch free. **Surface:** grassy/gravel.
Distance: 🚶600m.
Remarks: At sports park.

⛶ S — Zubiena — 24A6

Prà Gros Agriturismo, SS338, Casale Montino. **GPS:** n45,49812 e7,98934. ⬆️

6 🚿 🚰 💺. **Location:** Rural. **Surface:** gravel/metalled.
Distance: ⊗on the spot.

Trentino South Tyrol

⛶ S — Andalo — 25C4

Via Rindole, 6, Loc. Rindole. **GPS:** n46,16113 e11,00647.

80 🚿 € 15 🚰 💺 Ch 🔧 € 5. **Surface:** asphalted. ☐ summer
Distance: 🚶200m ⊗on the spot.
Remarks: Beautiful view, service only € 5.

⛶ S — Arco — 25B5

Piazzale Carmellini, Viale Paolina Caproni. **GPS:** n45,92232 e10,89032. ⬆️

13 🚿€ 1/4h, max. € 10/24h. **Surface:** asphalted. ☐ 01/01-31/12
Distance: 🚶200m ⊗200m.

S — Arco — 25B5

Viale Rovereto. **GPS:** n45,91820 e10,89225. ⬆️
🚰 💺 Ch free.

⛶ S — Barbiano 🏰 — 25C3

Kollmann Stop, Frazione Colma, SS12. **GPS:** n46,58728 e11,52401. ⬆️

15 🚿€ 10, in envelope in mail box 🚰 💺 Ch 🔧 included. **Location:** Very simple, noisy. **Surface:** gravel. ☐ 01/01-31/12
Distance: 🚶300m ⛵9km ⊗300m 🚉300m 🚏on the spot 🚲 on the spot.
Remarks: Max. 48h, along the through road.

⛶ S — Bolzano/Bozen 🌼🍴🏔 — 25C4

Parking Fiera Messe, Via Bruno Buozzi. **GPS:** n46,47417 e11,32617. ⬆️

30 🚿free 🚰 💺 Ch free. **Location:** Urban, very simple, noisy. **Surface:** asphalted. ☐ 01/01-31/12
Distance: 🚶centre 4km ⛵1,1km ⊗on the spot 🚉4km 🚏on the spot.
Remarks: Along railwayline.

⛶ S — Bolzano/Bozen 🌼🍴🏔 — 25C4

Via Maso della Pieve. **GPS:** n46,47327 e11,33693. ⬆️

8 🚿€ 0,70/h mo-fr 8-19h, sa 8-13, overnight stay free 🚰 💺 Ch. 🚆 **Location:** Urban, noisy. **Surface:** asphalted. ☐ 01/01-31/12
Distance: 🚶city centre 3km 🚉100m 🚏on the spot.

🚿 S — Borgo Valsugana 🌼🍴🏔🌳 — 25C5

Via Tommaso Temanza. **GPS:** n46,05444 e11,46361.

IT

18 🛏 € 10/24h ⚡ 🚿 Ch 🚰 included. **Surface:** metalled.
Distance: 🚶100m 🏊20m 🎣20m ⊗100m 🛒100m.
Remarks: Max. 48h, service only € 5.

30 🛏 € 10, Jul € 13, Aug € 15 ⚡ 🚿 🚰 € 6. **Surface:** asphalted. ⬛ 01/04-30/09
Distance: 🚶2km ⊗200m 🛒2km.

Braies 🏔🏞   25D3
P2, Lago di Braies, Fraz. San Vito. **GPS:** n46,70265 e12,08520. ➡️.

Caldonazzo   25C5
Via al Lago. **GPS:** n46,00501 e11,26307. ⬆️.

25 🛏 € 5-15 🛏 € 0,50. 🚲 **Location:** Rural, quit. **Surface:** gravel. ⬛ 30/05-31/10
Distance: 🚶Braies 5km 🏊Lago di Braies 250m ⊗250m 🛒5km 🚵on the spot 🥾on the spot.

20 🛏 € 6/21-9h (1/6-30/9). **Surface:** grassy/sand. ⬛ 01/01-31/12
Distance: 🏊500m ⊗300m.

Cavalese   25C4
P Fondovalle, SP232. **GPS:** n46,28438 e11,47256. ⬆️.

Brentonico 🏔🎣🏔   25C5
Via al Dosset. **GPS:** n45,81540 e10,95581. ⬆️➡️.

11 🛏 € 7 ⚡ 🔌 2 🚿 Ch 🚰 € 3. **Surface:** asphalted. ⬛ 01/01-31/12
Distance: 🚶400m 🏊10km ⊗250m 🛒300m.

Brunico/Bruneck 🏔🎣🪣🏔❄   25D3
P2, Piazza Mercato di Stegona. **GPS:** n46,79558 e11,93006. ⬆️.

50 🛏 € 10 ⚡ 🚿. **Surface:** grasstiles/metalled. ⬛ 01/01-31/12

Chiusa 🏔🏔❄   25C3
Gamp, Via Gries 10. **GPS:** n46,64128 e11,57244. ➡️.

>25 🛏 free.
Location: Urban, noisy. **Surface:** gravel. ⬛ 01/01-31/12
Distance: 🚶800m ⊗500m 🛒500m 🚌on the spot 🚵on the spot 🥾on the spot.

20 🛏 € 14/24h 2 pers. + 2 children incl, dog € 2 ⚡ 🚿 Ch 🚰 included.
Location: Rural. **Surface:** grassy. ⬛ 01/01-31/12
Distance: 🚶300m 🚴800m ⊗on the spot 🛒mini market 🚌100m 🚵on the spot 🥾on the spot.

Tourist information Brunico/Bruneck:
ℹ️ Associazione Turistica, Via Europa,24.Fortified city, 14th century.
Ⓜ️ Regional museum.
✳️ Annual fair. ⬛ last week Oct.

Corvara in Badia   25D3
P Corvara, Strada Planac SS244. **GPS:** n46,54105 e11,88388. ⬆️.

Caldes   25B4
Rafting Val di Sole, Loc. Contrè. **GPS:** n46,36139 e10,94528.

IT

10 🛏 free.
Location: Rural, isolated. **Surface:** gravel. ⬛ 01/01-31/12
Distance: 🚶3,5km 🚲3,5km.

🛏S Dimaro 25B4

Camper Solander, Loc. Rovina. **GPS:** n46,32488 e10,86215.⬆️.

10 🛏 € 20/24h, € 10/night 🚰🍽Ch 🧹 WC⬛ included. **Surface:** gravel. ⬛ 01/01-31/12
Distance: ⊗on the spot.
Remarks: Near campsite Dolomiti.

🛏S Dimaro 25B4

Hotel Belvedere, SS239. **GPS:** n46,29734 e10,86765.
🛏€ 15/24h 🚰🍽Ch 🧹 included. **Surface:** asphalted. ⬛ 01/01-31/12

🛏S Folgaria 🌿⛰🏕🍴❄ 25C5

Parcheggio, Via Andrea Maffei, SS350, Fraz. Costa. **GPS:** n45,91688 e11,18656.⬆️.

20 🛏 free. **Surface:** gravel. ⬛ 01/01-31/12
Distance: 🚶on the spot ⊗100m 🚲100m 🐎on the spot 🚲on the spot.

🛏S Gargazzone 🌿⛰🏕🍴 25C3

Weisshof-Törgelle-Keller, Landstrasse 65 SS38. **GPS:** n46,58500 e11,20528.⬆️.

10 🛏€ 10 🚰🍽Ch 🧹 € 2/24h WC⬛ € 1.
Location: Rural, quit.
Surface: grassy/gravel. ⬛ 01/01-31/12
Distance: 🚶2km 🚲1,5km ⊗500m 🚲2km 🚌on the spot 🐎on the spot 🚲on the spot.
Remarks: Reservation for Christmas holidays, tel.: +39 (0)473 292448.

Tourist information Gargazzone:

ℹ️ Consorzio Turistico, Via Maria Trost, 5, Merano, www.meranerland.com.Place with medicinal sources.
🏛 Castel Tirolo, 4km N. de Merano.Regional museum. ⬛ 01/03-31/12.
🎭 Merano. ⬛ Tue, Fri.
🎉 Festa della Città, Merano. ⬛ 1st weekend Aug.

🛏S Glorenza 25B3

Glurns Camping im Park, > SS41. **GPS:** n46,67067 e10,54520.⬆️➡️.

40 🛏€ 10/12 🚰🍽Ch 🧹 € 2 WC⬛. **Surface:** grassy.
Distance: 🚶500m 🚲on the spot.
Remarks: Along the Adige river.

🛏S La Villa in Badia 🏔❄ 25D3

Odlina, Strada Ninz, 49. **GPS:** n46,58889 e11,90028.➡️.

45 🛏 summer € 20, winter € 30 🚰🍽Ch 🧹 WC⬛ included 📶 € 5 📶 € 3.
🏠 **Location:** Rural, luxurious, quit. **Surface:** metalled. ⬛ 01/01-31/12
Distance: 🚶400m ⊗150m 🚲150m 🚌on the spot 🐎on the spot 🧍on the spot 🚲300m.
Remarks: Use of sauna against payment, reservation for Christmas holidays: info@odina.it.

🛏S Lavarone 🏔⛰🍴❄ 25C5

Turismo Lavarone Spa - Lavarone

info@lavaroneski.it - www.lavaroneski.it
Located in the mountains
Alpine skiing
Pleasant tourist resort

Prà Grando, Via Padova. **GPS:** n45,93602 e11,27099.
40 🛏€ 14 May/June/July, € 15 Aug, € 18 Dec-April 🚰🍽Ch 🧹 included.
Surface: grassy/gravel. ⬛ 01/05-30/09, 01/12-31/03
Distance: 🚶300m 🚲32km 🚲Lago di Lavarone 1km 🚌1km ⊗300m 🚲300m 🚲300m 🐎1km 🚲1km.

🛏S Lavarone 🏔⛰🍴❄ 25C5

SS 349, Loc Moar. **GPS:** n45,94575 e11,26397.⬆️.

10 ⛺ € 0,40/h 🚰 € 0,50 🗑 Ch. 🏠 **Surface:** metalled.
Distance: 🚶800m ⛵Lago di Lavarone 1,9km ⊗500m.

🛉 S | **Levico Terme** 🌿⛲🏕🎾❄🚡 | 25C5
Lago di Levico, Loc Pleina. **GPS:** n46,00655 e11,28793. ⬆➡.

50 ⛺ € 12, € 18 (24/12-9/1, 23/4-24/6, 4/9-1/10), € 26 (25/6-3/9) 🚰🗑
Ch 🧹 included. **Surface:** metalled. ⏻ 01/01-31/12
Distance: 🚶800m ⛵200m ⊗200m 🚉100m.

⛺ S | **Molveno** | 25B4
Via Lungolago,Loc. Ischia. **GPS:** n46,14165 e10,95727. ⬆.

35 ⛺ € 15 🚰 Ch WC. **Surface:** grassy. ⏻ 01/01-31/12
Distance: 🚶1,3km ⛵200m, Lido di Levico 1,1km ⊗50m 🚉50m 🚌on the spot.

🍴 S | **Levico Terme** 🌿⛲🏕🎾❄🚡 | 25C5
Bici Grill, Via Antonio Tararotti. **GPS:** n46,00099 e11,24571.

20 ⛺ € 9, € 14 (24/12-9/1, 23/4-24/6, 4/9-1/10), € 22 (25/6-3/9) 🚰🗑 Ch 🧹
included. **Surface:** metalled. ⏻ 01/01-31/12
Distance: 🚶1km ⛵400m ⊗200m 🚉100m.

⛺ S | **Pergine Valsugana** 🌿 | 25C5
Soleando Camperparking, Via al lago 23/A. **GPS:** n46,05184 e11,22494.

6 ⛺guests free 🚰🗑Ch.

🍴 S | **Moena** 🏔❄ | 25D4
Bar Il Giardino, SS 48 Forno di Moena. **GPS:** n46,35238 e11,63149.➡.

10 ⛺ €12/day 🚰🗑Ch.
Surface: gravel.
Distance: 🚶600m ⛵lake 1km ⊗300m 🚉300m 🚌100m.
Remarks: Dir'Lago di Caldenazzo'.

Tourist information Pergine Valsugana:
ℹ️ www.apt.trento.it.City at the foot of the Dolomites with historical centre.
Ⓜ️ Palazzo Pretorio, Trento.Ecclesiastical museum. ❄.

⛺ S | **Predazzo** 🏔❄ | 25D4
Latemar 2200, SS48, dir Moena. **GPS:** n46,32582 e11,59970.⬆.

50 ⛺ € 10-12 🚰🗑 Ch included 🧹 € 4/24h. **Location:** Rural, comfortable,
central. **Surface:** grassy/metalled. ⏻ 01/01-31/12
Distance: 🚶3,5km ⊗500m 🚉2km 🚌300m 🚡on the spot 🥾on the spot
🚴on the spot.
Remarks: Max. 48h, skibus comes at parking.

⛺ S | **Molveno** | 25B4
Area attrezzata per camper Lago di Molveno, Via Lungolago, 25, Loc. Ischia.
GPS: n46,14018 e10,96011. ⬆➡.

50 ⛺free, peak season € 7-10/24h 🚰🗑Ch included. 🏠 **Location:** Rural,
noisy. **Surface:** asphalted/gravel. ⏻ 01/01-31/12
Distance: 🚶2,5km 🚉2,5km 🚌on the spot 🚴on the spot 🥾on the spot
⛷on the spot 🚴on the spot.
Remarks: Parking ski-lifts.

⌂S Rabbi 25B4
Area camper Plan, Loc. Plan, Bagni di Rabbi. **GPS**: n46,40619 e10,82629. ⬆➡

105 € 14-21, 2 pers.incl. Ch WCincluded against payment ▣.
Surface: metalled. 🕙 01/06-30/09
Distance: 600m.
Remarks: Former campsite, max 48h.

Racines 25C3
Sportzone Ratschings, Belprato, Stanghe. **GPS**: n46,88254 e11,38383.

20 free.
Location: Rural, very simple.
Surface: gravel. 🕙 01/01-31/12
Distance: 400m 5km ⊗400m ⊠400m 400m Gilfenklammroute.

⌂S Riva del Garda 25B5
Via Monte Brione. **GPS**: n45,87986 e10,85872.

41 € 8/day Ch included. **Surface**: grasstiles.
Distance: 1,5km 200m.
Remarks: Max. 48h.

Tourist information Riva del Garda:
ℹ A.P.T. (Azienda di Promozione Turistica), Giardini di Porta Orientale 8, www.gardatrentino.de. Tourist town at Lake Garda.
Ⓜ Museo Civico, Piazza Battisti.

⌂S Rovereto 25C5
Stadio Quercia, Via Palestrina. **GPS**: n45,90232 e11,03704. ⬆➡

8 free Ch free. **Surface**: asphalted. 🕙 01/01-31/12
Distance: 1,5km 2km.

Tourist information Rovereto:
ℹ A.P.T. (Azienda di Promozione Turistica), Via Dante, 63, www.apt.rovereto.tn.it.
Ⓜ Castello di Rovereto. War museum. 🕙 Tue-Su ◉ 01/01-28/02.
✖ Castel Beseno. 🕙 Tue-Su.

⌂S San Candido 26A3
Area di Sosta Camper, Via Prato alla Drava, 1/A. **GPS**: n46,73924 e12,36559. ➡

90 € 15 Ch WCincluded € 2.
Location: Rural, comfortable, quit.
Surface: gravel. 🕙 01/01 - 31/12
Distance: 6km ⊗on the spot 500m on the spot on the spot on the spot 2km 500m.
Remarks: Bicycle rental. Nearby the frontier station.

⌂S San Guiseppe al Lago 25C4
Posteggio Camper Lago di Caldero, San Guiseppe 18. **GPS**: n46,39038 e11,25663. ➡

35 € 15/night Ch WC. Location: Rural, comfortable, quit.
Surface: gravel. 🕙 13/03-15/11
Distance: 5km Caldero Private beach ⊗50m Nearby campsite.
Remarks: Max. 4 days.

⌂S San Martino di Castrozza 25D4
Area camper Tognola, Loc. Tognola. **GPS**: n46,25373 e11,80158. ⬆

80 € 12 included Ch € 1/80minutes. Location: Rural, comfortable, quit. **Surface**: gravel. 🕙 01/01-31/12
Distance: 1,5km ⊗500m on the spot on the spot on the spot.
Remarks: Next to ski-lift, free shuttle bus.

S San Vigilio di Marebbe 25D3
Restaurant Pizzeria Rittenkeller, Ras-Costa 2. **GPS**: n46,70630 e11,92920. ➡

IT

120 🗻01/04-30/11 € 20, 01/12-31/03 € 25 ⛽🔌Ch ✂ included.
Location: Rural, quit.
Surface: gravel. ◘ 01/01-31/12
Distance: 🚲600m 🚶500m ⊗on the spot 🛒600m 🚐600m 🚶on the spot
🏊600m.
Remarks: Next to ski-lift, reservation for Christmas holidays: info@ritterkeller.it.

Santa Cristina Valgardena 🏔 25D3
P1 Monte Pana, Strada Pana. **GPS:** n46,55174 e11,71624. ⬆ .

50 🗻free, peak season € 4/day. 🏠 **Location:** Isolated, quit. **Surface:** gravel.
◘ 01/01-31/12
Distance: 🚲2,5km 🛒2,5km.
Remarks: Max. 7 days, narrow entrance road, altitude 1650m.

Selva di Val Gardena 🏔❄ 25D3
Piz Sella, Strada Plan de Gralba. **GPS:** n46,53204 e11,77230. ⬆ .

15 🗻free, Winter € 6/day, € 6 night. **Location:** Rural. **Surface:** gravel. ◘
01/01-31/12
Distance: 🚲4km ⊗150m 🚶on the spot 🚶on the spot.
Remarks: Inclining pitches.

Sesto/Sexten 🏔❄🎿 26A3
Caravanpark Sexten, SS52 St Josefstrasse 54. **GPS:** n46,66741 e12,39996. ➡ .

36 🗻€ 23-29 ⛽🔌Ch ✂ WCincluded 🗑🔌€ 4 📶€ 2. **Location:** Rural,
luxurious, quit. **Surface:** grasstiles. ◘ 01/01-31/12
Distance: 🚲3km ⊗on the spot 🛒on the spot 🚐on the spot 🚲on the spot
🚶on the spot 🚶900m 🏊on the spot.
Remarks: Sauna and spa.

Silandro 🏔 25B3
Via Ospedale, Silandro/. **GPS:** n46,62721 e10,78185.

🗻free. **Surface:** grasstiles.
Distance: 🚲500m ⊗500m.

Siusi 🌿🏕🌳❄ 25C3
Seiseralm, Via Rosegarten. **GPS:** n46,54048 e11,56600. ⬆ .

>25 🗻free WC. **Location:** Rural, quit. **Surface:** gravel.
Distance: 🚲500m ⊗on the spot 🛒500m 🚐on the spot 🚶on the spot 🚶on
the spot.
Remarks: Parking at Seiseralm-lift.

Smarano 🏔🏕🌳 25C4
Area Sosta Ostaria del Filò, Viale Merlonga 48/a. **GPS:** n46,34962 e11,10956. ⬆ .

43 🗻€ 10-13-15 ⛽🔌Ch ✂ WC 🗑🔌. **Surface:** grassy. ◘ 01/01-31/12
Distance: 🚲1km ⊗on the spot.
Remarks: Check in at restaurant.

Tirolo 25C3
Via principale. **GPS:** n46,68636 e11,15904. ⬆ .

15 🗻€ 10,50/night ⛽ WC. 🚿 **Location:** Rural, quit. **Surface:** asphalted. ◘
01/01-31/12
Distance: 🚲200m ⊗50m 🛒200m 🚐50m 🚲on the spot 🚶on the spot.

Tonadico 🏔❄ 25D4
Lanterna Verde, Via Zocchet 10. **GPS:** n46,18216 e11,84318. ➡ .

IT

45 🔲 €15 🔧 Ch 🔩 included WC. **Location:** Rural, comfortable, quit. **Surface:** grasstiles. ⭕ 01/01-31/12
Distance: 🚶1km ⊗100m 🛒1km 🚌on the spot 🚴on the spot 🚶on the spot 🚂15km 🚏15km.
Remarks: Max. 48h, check in at restaurant.

🔲S	Trento	25C5

P Zuffo, Loc. Vela. **GPS:** n46,07650 e11,11050. ⬆➡.

20 🔲 €5 🔧 €1 🔩 Ch. **Surface:** asphalted. ⭕ 01/01-31/12
Distance: 🚶1,8km 🏊150m 🚌200m.
Remarks: A22, slip-road Trento Centro.

🔲S	Trento	25C5

Parking Trentino, Via Santi Cosma e Damiano 64. **GPS:** n46,07674 e11,10411. ⬆.

20 🔲 €15 🔧 Ch 🔩 included. **Surface:** grassy. ⭕ 01/01-31/12
Distance: 🚶1,8km 🏊300m ⊗300m.
Remarks: Call for entrance code: 3389004343 Mr. Pisetta.

🔲	Trento	25C5

P3 Giardino Botanico Fondo Viote, SP85. **GPS:** n46,02445 e11,03973.

100 🔲 free. **Location:** Rural, isolated, quit. **Surface:** asphalted. ⭕ 01/01-31/12
Distance: 🚶18km Trento ⊗150m.
Remarks: Max. 48h.

Tourist information Trento:
ℹ️ I.A.T. (Ufficio Informazioni e di Accoglienza Turistica), Via Romagnosi, 3.

🔲S	Tres	25C4

A Monte del Paese, SP della Predaia. **GPS:** n46,32040 e11,10202. ⬆.

15 🔲 €10/24h 🔧 Ch 🔩 WC included. **Surface:** gravel. ⭕ 01/01-31/12
Distance: 🚶800m.

Lombardy

🔲S	Alzano Lombardo	24D6

Via Europa. **GPS:** n45,73690 e9,72007. ⬆➡.

3 🔲 🔧. **Surface:** asphalted.
Remarks: At sports park.

🔲S	Biassono	24D6

Via al Parco/Via della Sciavatera. **GPS:** n45,63102 e9,28865. ⬆➡.

🔲 free 🔧 Ch free. **Surface:** asphalted. ⭕ 01/01-31/12
Distance: 🚶500m 🛒Centro Commerciale Vilasanta 4km 🚂train > Milan 500m.

🔲S	Borgofranco sul Po	32A1

Via Filipo Turati. **GPS:** n45,04775 e11,20524. ⬆➡.

🔲 free 🔧 Ch free.
Surface: grassy. ⭕ 01/01-31/12 water: frost.
Distance: 🚶600m ⊗200m.

🔲S	Bormio	25A4

Bormio 2000, Via Battaglion Morbegno. **GPS:** n46,46260 e10,37190. ⬆.

⌗€ 8/24h 🚰🔌Ch included. **Surface:** sand. 🅾 01/01-31/12
Distance: 🚶500m ⊗500m 🍴on the spot.
Remarks: Parking funicular railway, service only € 5.

Tourist information Bormio:
ℹ Ufficio Informazioni e di Accoglienza Turistica, Via Roma, 131/b.Alps city, large winter sport area, also summer skiing.
⚑ Parco Nazionale dello Stelvio.Region with 50 glacier lakes and high mountain peaks. Access around Bormio.

⌗S	Campione	25B5

Area Camper Campione del Garda, Via Verdi. **GPS:** n45,75651 e10,74985.⬆.

30 ⌗€ 10/24h 🚰. **Surface:** unpaved. 🅾 01/04-31/10
Distance: 🚶500m 🏊on the spot ⊗200m.

⌗S	Capo di Ponte	25A5

Concarena, Via Santo Stefano. **GPS:** n46,02447 e10,34325.⬆➡.

12 ⌗€ 8/24h, 1/10-28/2 free 🚰🔌Ch 🧹 WC ⬛included. **Surface:** asphalted. 🅾 01/01-31/12
Distance: 🚶300m ⊗300m 🛒300m.

⌗S	Certosa di Pavia ⚓	31C1

Parking Certosa, Via di Vittorio, SP27. **GPS:** n45,25702 e9,14152.⬆.

⌗€ 4/night, € 4/day 🚰🔌Ch free. **Surface:** gravel. 🅾 01/01-31/12 🔵
water disconnected in winter.
Distance: ⊗200m.
Remarks: Monastery Certosa di Pavia 450m.

⌗S	Certosa di Pavia ⚓	31C1

Località Certosa Monumento. **GPS:** n45,25574 e9,14632.⬆.

⌗€ 4/night, € 4/day 🚰🔌Ch WC free.
Surface: sand. 🅾 01/01-31/12
Distance: ⊗500m.
Remarks: Monastery Certosa di Pavia 80m.

⌗S	Chiavenna	24D4

Piazzale Leonardo da Vinci, Via A. Moro, SS36. **GPS:** n46,31424 e9,39631.⬆➡.

⌗free 🚰🔌Ch free. **Surface:** asphalted.
Distance: 🚶800m 🛒200m.

Tourist information Chiavenna:
ℹ U.I.A.T.(Ufficio Informazioni e Accoglienza Turistica), Via Vittorio Emanuele II, 2.

⌗S	Chiesa in Valmalenco	25A4

Loc. Vassalini. **GPS:** n46,27020 e9,85670.⬆.

⌗free 🚰€ 3 🛒. **Surface:** gravel.
Distance: 🚶1km 🍴200m.

⌗S	Clusone	25A5

Busgarina, Via Vago 6, loc Fiorine. **GPS:** n45,87312 e9,91642.⬆.

80 ⌗€ 13 🚰🔌Ch 🧹 (33x)€ 2 ⬛€ 1/7minutes. 🅾 01/01-31/12
Distance: ⊷on the spot.

⌗S	Clusone	25A5

Viale Vittorio Veneto. **GPS:** n45,88926 e9,95812.⬆.

IT

5 🛏free 🚰🔧Chfree. **Surface:** asphalted.
Distance: ⬇Nearby centre 🛒on the spot.
Remarks: Max. 48h.

| 🏕S | **Colico** | 24D5 |

L'Ontano, Via Montecchio Nord. **GPS:** n46,14213 e9,37452.⬆➡.

25 🛏€ 15/24h 🚰🔧Ch 🚿 WC 🍴€ 1/3minutes. **Surface:** metalled. ⬤ 01/02-31/12
Distance: ⬇500m 🏊on the spot 🍴on the spot.
Remarks: View on Lake Como.

| 🏕S | **Cremona** | 31D1 |

Piazzale della Croce Rossa, Via Mantova. **GPS:** n45,13744 e10,03464.⬆.

🛏free 🚰🔧Chfree. **Surface:** asphalted. ⬤ 01/01-31/12
Distance: ⬇on the spot 🚲3km 🍴on the spot 🚌200m 🚍on the spot.
Remarks: Nearby stadium.

| 🍴🍴S | **Desenzano del Garda** 🚤🛶 | 25B6 |

Pit-Stop La Spiaggia, Via Valtenesi, 19. **GPS:** n45,48783 e10,52468.

70 🛏€ 10/24h 🚰🔧Chincluded. **Surface:** gravel. ⬤ 01/01-31/12
Distance: 🏊200m 🍴Pizzeria Stella Del Garda 🚍10m.

| 🍴🍴S | **Esine** | 25A5 |

Parco e Ristorante Le Fontanelle, Via Toroselle 12, SS42. **GPS:** n45,90302 e10,21820.

15 🛏 🚰🔧Ch. **Surface:** grassy. ⬤ 01/01-31/12
Distance: ⬇4km 🍴on the spot.

| 🏕S | **Gandino** | 25A5 |

Via Giovanni Pascoli. **GPS:** n45,81286 e9,90538.⬆➡.

2 🛏free 🚰🔧Chfree. **Surface:** metalled. ⬤ 01/01-31/12
Distance: ⬇centro storico 250m.
Remarks: Max. 48h.

| 🏕S | **Gavirate** | 24C5 |

Via Cavour. **GPS:** n45,83913 e8,72105.⬆.

30 🛏€ 8/day 🚰🔧Ch 🚿€ 1/12h. **Surface:** grassy/metalled. ⬤ 01/01-31/12
Distance: ⬇200m 🏊10m.

| 🏕S | **Germignaga** 🚤🛶 | 24C5 |

Via A. Bodmer. **GPS:** n45,99630 e8,72421.⬆.

6 🛏€ 15/24h 🚰€ 2 🔧Ch🔌€ 2. **Surface:** asphalted. ⬤ 01/01-31/12
Distance: ⬇500m 🏊on the spot 🍴500m.

| 🏕S | **Iseo** | 25A6 |

Via Gorzoni. **GPS:** n45,65360 e10,04379.

IT

⚓free. **Surface:** unpaved. ◻ 01/01-31/12
Distance: ⚓1km ⚓250m ⚓600m.

Tourist information Iseo:
🛈 I.A.T. (Ufficio Informazioni e di Accoglienza Turistica), Lungolago Marconi,
2.Old fishermen's village.
🏕 Week market. ◻ Fri.

| ⚓S | **Lecco** | 24D5 |

Via Arturo Toscanini, Loc. Bione di Lecco. **GPS:** n45,83136 e9,40779.⬆

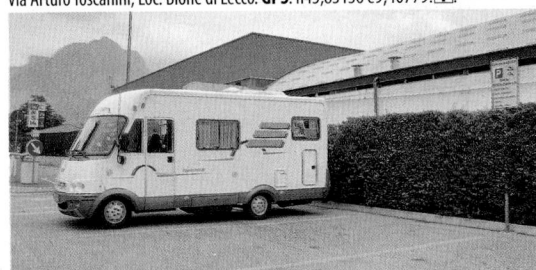

12 ⚓free ⚓🔌Ch free. **Surface:** asphalted.
Distance: ⚓2,8km.
Remarks: At lake Garlate, cycle routes.

| ⚓S | **Livigno** | 25A4 |

Stella Alpina, Via Palipert 570. **GPS:** n46,50515 e10,11958.⬆

28 ⚓€15 ⚓🔌Ch ⚓€ 3 WC 🚽. **Surface:** gravel. ◻ 01/01-31/12
Distance: ⚓400m 🚌Free bus.

| ⚓S | **Livigno** | 25A4 |

Trepalle, SS301. **GPS:** n46,52655 e10,17578.⬆

50 ⚓€10 ⚓🔌Ch free. **Surface:** asphalted.
Distance: ⚓Livigno 6,6km ⚓200m 🚌bus to Livigno every 40 minutes 🚲on
the spot.

Tourist information Livigno:
🛈 U.A.I.T.(Ufficio Informazioni e Accoglienza Turistica), Via Saroch.
👁 Latteria di Livigno, Via Pemonte 911.Discover the secrets of dairy products
from Livigno. On Wednesday the possibility of preparing meals, costs € 7, from

14h. ◻ summer Mo-Fr 8-20h.

| ⚓S | **Lodrino** | 25A6 |

Via Kennedy, Localité Dade. **GPS:** n45,71450 e10,28107.⬆

3 ⚓free ⚓🔌Ch ⚓free. **Surface:** asphalted. ◻ 01/01-31/12
Distance: ⚓500m.

| 🍴S | **Luino** | 24C5 |

Via Gorizia. **GPS:** n45,97406 e8,75019.⬆➡

16 ⚓€9 ⚓€ 3. **Surface:** asphalted/grassy. ◻ 01/01-31/12
Distance: ⚓3km ⚓on the spot.
Remarks: Next to sports fields.

| ⚓S | **Magnacavallo** | 32A1 |

Via Salvador Allende. **GPS:** n45,00587 e11,17906.⬆➡

⚓free ⚓🔌Ch free. **Surface:** asphalted. ◻ 01/01-31/12
Distance: ⚓200m.
Remarks: At sports park.

| ⚓S | **Mandello del Lario** | 24D5 |

Area Cima, Via Giulio Cesare. **GPS:** n45,91830 e9,31589.➡

12 ⚓free ⚓🔌Ch. **Surface:** asphalted. ◻ 01/01-31/12
Distance: ⚓800m ⚓Lago di Lecco 400m.

| ⚓S | **Mantova** ⚓🚢 | 32A1 |

Parco Paganini, Via Fiera 11, Grazie di Curtatone, Curtatone. **GPS:** n45,15333
e10,69111.⬆

IT

✝ Duomo.History of Gothic architecture. ☐ Tue-Su.
⚱ Via Fauché. ☐ Tue, Sa.
⚱ Mercatone del Naviglio Grande, Naviglio Grande.Antiques market, 400 stalls.
☐ last Su of the month.
� Galleria.

🅂 Moglia 32A1
Via Tazio Nuvolari. **GPS**: n44,93639 e10,91582.⬆.

14 🅂free ⌁🅂 Chfree. **Surface:** asphalted. ☐ 01/01-31/12
Distance: 🚶300m ✈A22 7km ⊗300m.
Remarks: At swimming pool.

🅂 Monte Marenzo 24D6
Via Papa Gionvanni. **GPS**: n45,77639 e9,45222.⬆.

6 🅂free ⌁🅂free. **Surface:** gravel. ☐ 01/01-31/12
Distance: 🚶300m.

🅂 Monzambano 25B6
Area attrezzata camper Comunale di Monzambano, Via Degli Alpini n. 9. **GPS**: n45,38916 e10,69277.⬆➡.

140 🅂€ 10/24h ⌁🅂 ✍(24x) 🔌 included. **Surface:** gravel. ☐ 01/01-31/12
Distance: ⊗100m 🚊300m, bakery 100m.
Remarks: Max. 48h.

Tourist information Monzambano:
ℹ I.A.T. (Ufficio Informazioni e di Accoglienza Turistica), Piazza Tito Zaniboni, 2.

🅂 Niardo 25A5
Area di sosta Mr. Sanders, Località Crist. **GPS**: n45,97690 e10,31959.⬆.

108 🅂€ 10 ⌁🅂€ 3 Ch€ 3 ✍ WC included. **Surface:** asphalted/grassy.
☐ 01/03-13/11
Distance: 🚶300m, Mantova 6km ⊗300m🚊4km, bakery 300m.

🅂 Mantova 32A1
Anconetta. **GPS**: n45,15322 e10,79864.

🅂free. **Surface:** asphalted. ☐ 01/01-31/12
Distance: 🏊on the spot.
Remarks: Marina.

Tourist information Mantova:
ℹ I.A.T. (Ufficio Informazioni e di Accoglienza Turistica), Piazza Mantegna, 6, www.mantova.it.

🅂 Merate 24D6
Via Papa Giovanni Paolo I, loc. Sartirana. **GPS**: n45,71326 e9,41865.⬆.

7 🅂€ 5,50 ⌁🅂 Ch✍. **Surface:** grasstiles.

🅂 Milano 24D6
Ripamonti SNC, Via Ripamonti 481, Milan (Milano). **GPS**: n45,40914 e9,20937.

30 🅂€ 20/24h ⌁🅂 Ch✍€ 5 WC included. **Surface:** asphalted.
Distance: ☐on the spot 🚋Milan 40min.
Remarks: Monitored parking.

Tourist information Milan (Milano):
ℹ U.I.A.T. (Ufficio Informazioni e di Accoglienza Turistica), Via Marcon, 1, www.milanoinfotourist.it.Large city and economic heart of the country.
🅼✖ Castello Sforzesco.
🅼 Palazzo Reale.Contemporary art.

IT

20 ⬚€ 10 🚰 🍴Ch 🔌€ 2 WC 🚽. **Surface:** metalled. ⬛ 01/01-31/12
Distance: 🚶Niardo 1,3km 🚲on the spot 🛒on the spot.
Remarks: Bread-service.

⬚S **Nova Milanese** 24D6
Via G. Brodolini. **GPS:** n45,58298 e9,19668. ⬆️➡️

4 ⬚free 🚰 ⬚free. **Surface:** asphalted. ⬛ 01/01-31/12
Distance: 🚶500m 🚲 1,6km 🛒200m.

⬚ **Novate Mezzola** 〰️ 24D4
Via al Lido. **GPS:** n46,21083 e9,45000. ⬆️➡️

25 ⬚free. **Surface:** grassy/gravel.
Distance: 🚶800m 🏊40m ⚓800m.
Remarks: At lake Novate, signposted cycle route.

⬚S **Olginate** 24D6
Via Cesare Cantù. **GPS:** n45,79523 e9,41610. ⬆️

40 ⬚€ 8/12h 🚰 🍴Ch 🔌. **Surface:** metalled. ⬛ 01/01-31/12 ◖
Thu>16h-Fri<16h (market).
Distance: 🚶200m 🏊on the spot.
Remarks: At Olginate lake.

⬚S **Pizzighettone** 🏛️ 31D1
Via De Gasperi. **GPS:** n45,18538 e9,79402. ⬆️➡️

4 ⬚free 🚰 🍴Chfree. **Surface:** gravel. ⬛ 01/01-31/12
Distance: 🚶400m ⚓Lidl 100m.

⬚S **Rovetta** 25A5
Campo sportivo, Via Papa Giovanni XIII. **GPS:** n45,88892 e9,98224. ⬆️

⬚free 🚰 🍴Ch. **Surface:** asphalted.
Remarks: Parking at gymnasium.

🍴S **Ruino** 🌿🌲👥 31C1
Agriturismo Adriana Tarantani, Loc. Tre Venti. **GPS:** n44,92833 e9,26311.

6 ⬚free with a meal 🚰 🍴Ch 🔌.
Surface: grassy/gravel. ⬛ 01/01-31/12
Distance: 🚶1km 🛒on the spot.

⬚S **Sabbioneta** 🏛️ 32A1
Via Piccola Atene. **GPS:** n44,99459 e10,48849. ⬆️

15 ⬚free 🚰 ⬚free. **Surface:** metalled. ⬛ 01/01-31/12
Distance: 🚶200m 🛒400m.

⬚S **Santa Caterina Valfurva** 25B4
Baita de Naségn, Via Forni, loc. Nassegno. **GPS:** n46,40917 e10,50833. ⬆️➡️

⬚€ 12 🚰 🍴Ch 🔌€ 3. **Surface:** grassy.
Distance: 🚶on the spot 🚲on the spot.
Tourist information Santa Caterina Valfurva:
ℹ️ I.A.T. (Ufficio Informazioni e di Accoglienza Turistica), Piazza Magliavaca.

⬚S **Saronno** 🏛️ 24C6
Via E.H.Grieg. **GPS:** n45,61265 e9,04274. ⬆️

IT

🔲free 🚰€ 1/100liter 🚽Ch. **Surface:** asphalted. ⬛ 01/01-31/12
Distance: 🚶1,5km 🏊3,5km 🛒500m 🚌200m.

| 📷S | Saronno | 24C6 |

Via Dalmazia 11. **GPS**: n45,62446 e9,02469.⬆.

150 🔲€ 18/day 🚰🚽Ch 🚿€ 3 WC 🚽📶included. **Surface:** gravel. ⬛
15/03–31/10
Distance: 🚶1,5km 🏊Lake Garda 🛒100m 🍴1km 🚌100m.

| 📷S | Sirmione 🌿 | 25B6 |

Piazzale Montebaldo. **GPS**: n45,48694 e10,61028.⬆→.

2 🔲free. **Surface:** concrete. ⬛ 01/01-31/12
Remarks: Max. 24h.

| 📷S | Sartirana Lomellina 🍴 | 31B1 |

Via Cavour. **GPS**: n45,11337 e8,66936.⬆.

21 🔲from € 2,50 1/2h till-€ 21/24h 🚽Ch. **Surface:** asphalted. ⬛ 01/01-31/12
Distance: 🚶200m 🏊on the spot 🛒50m 🍴200m.
Remarks: Parking on entering the village, in opposite of castle.
Tourist information Sirmione:
ℹ️ I.A.T. (Ufficio Informazioni e di Accoglienza Turistica), Viale Marconi, 2.City around medieval castle.

| 📷S | Sondrio | 25A5 |

Area Sportiva, Via Vanoni. **GPS**: n46,16064 e9,86957.⬆.

3 🔲free 🚰🚽Chfree. **Surface:** asphalted. ⬛ 01/01-31/12 ⬛ Sa-morning market.
Distance: 🚶100m 🛒200m 🍴100m 🚌on the spot.

| 📷S | Seriate | 24D6 |

Corso Europa. **GPS**: n45,67920 e9,72897.⬆.

6 🔲free 🚰🚽Chfree. **Surface:** asphalted.
Distance: 🚶600m.
Remarks: Parking sports park.

| 📷S | Sorico | 24D5 |

La Punta, Boschetto III Traversa. **GPS**: n46,16386 e9,38158.⬆.

🔲free 🚰🚽Chfree. **Surface:** asphalted.
Distance: 🚶700m 🛒50m.
Remarks: In front of supermarket UNES.

| 📷S | Sirmione 🌿 | 25B6 |

Camper Park Sirmione, Via Cantarane. **GPS**: n45,46083 e10,63333.⬆.

53 🔲€ 18/day 🚰🚽🚿€ 2/kWh WC 🚽€ 1. **Surface:** metalled. ⬛ 01/01-31/12
Distance: 🚶400m 🏊on the spot 🛒on the spot.
Remarks: View on Lake Como.

| 📷S | Stezzano | 24D6 |

Via Pietro Mascagni. **GPS**: n45,65594 e9,65301.⬆.

🛏free 🚰🧺Chfree. **Surface:** asphalted.

120 🛏€ 30/24h, € 48/48h 🚰🧺Ch 🔧 WC 🍴🔋included. **Surface:** grassy. 🚻 01/01-31/12

🛏S **Sulzano** 25A6

Distance: 🛬on the spot 🏖on the spot ⊗on the spot 🍴on the spot.

Parking Gerolo, Via Tassano 14. **GPS:** n45,63546 e10,07665.⬆➡.

Remarks: Along Lake Garda, max. 48h.

Ⓒ S **Toscolano Maderno** 🛶🏄 25B6

Area Sosta Maderno, Via Promontorio. **GPS:** n45,63487 e10,61103.⬆➡.

25 🛏€ 13/24h, € 15/24h (1/3-30/9), € 10/night 🚰🧺Ch WC 🍴. **Surface:** grassy. 🚻 01/01-31/12

Distance: 🛬300m 🏖400m 🍴300m.

🛏S **Ternate** 24C6

Via Roma. **GPS:** n45,78006 e8,69780.⬆.

25 🛏€ 25 🚰🧺Ch 🔧 WC 🍴included 🚲.

Surface: grassy. 🚻 01/01-31/12

Distance: 🏖500m.

🛏S **Treviglio** 24D6

Via al Malgari. **GPS:** n45,53142 e9,59710.⬆.

8 🛏free 🚰🧺Ch 🔧(2x)free. **Surface:** unpaved. 🚻 01/01-31/12

Distance: 🏖on the spot ⊗100m 🚴on the spot 🏃on the spot.

Remarks: At Comabbio lake.

🛏S **Tirano** 🛫 25A4

4 🛏free 🚰🧺Chfree. **Surface:** metalled. 🚻 01/01-31/12

Distance: 🛬700m 🍴400m.

Remarks: At sports park.

Area Camper Tirano, Via Polveriera/Via Sala Piero. **GPS:** n46,21361 e10,15722. ⬆➡.

🛏S **Varzi** 31C2

Strada Circonvallazione. **GPS:** n44,82172 e9,19727.⬆➡.

20 🛏€ 10/24h 🚰🧺Ch 🔧included. **Location:** Comfortable. **Surface:** metalled.

Distance: 🛬1km 🚉station 800m.

Tourist information Tirano:

ℹ Bernina Express. The highest-altitude trans-Alpine line in Europe, with one of the steepest gradients in the world between Tirano (It) and Chur (Ch). UNESCO's List of World Heritage. 🚂 ± € 100/pp return ticket (Tirano-Chur), ± € 45/pp return ticket (Tirano-Pontresina).

🛏S **Torbole** 🌿🛫🏔🛶🌳 25B5

Tr@ns.it, Via Al Cor. **GPS:** n45,87264 e10,87260.⬆➡.

30 🛏free, summer € 10 🚰🧺Chfree. **Surface:** asphalted/metalled. 🚻 01/01-31/12

Distance: 🛬200m 🏖on the spot.

Remarks: Along the Staffora river.

Veneto

🛏S **Arquà Polesine** 32B1

Ostello Canalbianco, SS 16, n15. **GPS:** n44,99665 e11,76243.

12 🛏€ 10 🚰🔧.

Distance: ⊗on the spot.

Asiago 25C5
P Verdi Mosele, SS349, Via Giuseppe Verdi. **GPS:** n45,87129 e11,50026. ⬆.

20 ⬚€ 1/h, € 4/day. **Surface:** asphalted. ⬤ 01/01-31/12
Distance: 300m 500m.

Asolo 25D5
Area Camper Communale, Via Forestuzzo. **GPS:** n45,79637 e11,91283. ⬆➡.

12 ⬚€7 ⌁ Ch (14x)included.
Surface: grassy/sand. ⬤ 01/01-31/12
Distance: 400m ⊗400m 400m.
Remarks: Entrance 8-19.30h, barbecue place, picnic area.

Auronzo di Cadore 26A3
Taiarezze, SR48, Via Reaneloc. **GPS:** n46,56217 e12,41640. ⬆.

30 ⬚€ 8, 20/07-31/08 and 24/12-06/01 € 12 ⌁ Chincluded. **Location:**
Rural, quit. **Surface:** asphalted. ⬤ 01/01-31/12
Distance: 1,5km on the spot ⊗on the spot on the spot on the spot
on the spot on the spot 1,6km 1,6km.
Remarks: Max. 48h, payment only with coins.

Barbarano Vicentino 25D6
Viale Vittorio Veneto 66. **GPS:** n45,40725 e11,54654. ⬆.

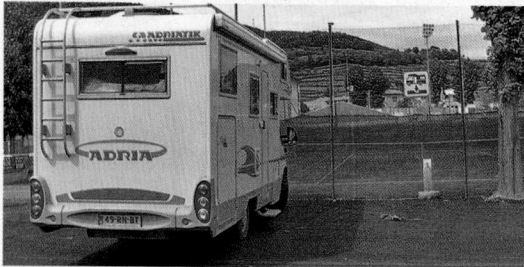

3 ⬚free ⌁ free. **Surface:** asphalted. ⬤ 01/01-31/12
Distance: 200m ⊗200m 200m.
Remarks: In village.

Bardolino 25B6
P Prandini, Piazzale Prandini. **GPS:** n45,55083 e10,72341.

10 ⬚€ 15/24h ⌁.
Remarks: Along the through road.
Tourist information Bardolino:
ℹ I.A.T. (Ufficio Informazioni e di Accoglienza Turistica), Piazzale Aldo Moro.

Bassano del Grappa 25D5
Parcheggio Gerosa, Via Kolbe. **GPS:** n45,75831 e11,73091. ⬆➡.

20 ⬚€ 10 ⌁Ch included. **Surface:** asphalted. ⬤ 01/01-31/12
Distance: 300m ⊗300m 300m on the spot.
Remarks: Max. 48h.

Bassano del Grappa 25D5
Prato Santo Caterina, Via Chini 6. **GPS:** n45,76009 e11,73413.
⬚free.
Distance: on the spot.

Tourist information Bassano del Grappa:
ℹ I.A.T. (Ufficio Informazioni e di Accoglienza Turistica), Largo Corona D'Italia,
35.

Belluno 26A4
Rio Cavalli, Via Sagrogna 74. **GPS:** n46,15646 e12,26136. ⬆.

20 ⬚€ 10, electricity included € 15 ⌁ 5 .
Location: Comfortable, central, quit.
Surface: grassy/sand. ⬤ 01/01-31/12
Distance: 3km 6km on the spot ⊗on the spot 3km on the spot.

Belluno 26A4
Viale dei Dendrofori, loc. Lambioi. **GPS:** n46,13712 e12,21371. ⬆➡.

12 ⌇8-18 € 0,80/h, overnight stay free ⌐⌐ 🔲 Ch free. **Location:** Central, noisy.
Surface: grasstiles/metalled. 🔲 01/01-31/12
Distance: 🚶100m ⊗100m 🚊100m.
Remarks: Nearby swimming pool and skating rink.

🔲S Bibione 26B5
Strada Brussa. **GPS:** n45,62458 e12,95866. ⬆️.

100 ⌇€ 7/day, overnight stay free ⌐⌐ WC 🔲. **Location:** Rural, isolated, quit.
Surface: grassy. 🔲 25/04-30/09
Distance: ⌇sandy beach 250m.
Remarks: Dogs permitted on the beach, guarded during the day.

🔲S Borghetto di Valeggio sul Mincio 🌿 25B6
Camper parking Visconteo, Strada provinciale 55. **GPS:** n45,35537 e10,72017.
⬆️.
60 ⌇€ 10/24h ⌐⌐ 3 🔲 Ch ✦€ 1/12h. **Location:** Rural, comfortable.
Surface: gravel.
Distance: 🚶on the spot ⌇Lake Garda 13km ⊗250m 🚶on the spot 🏃on
the spot.
Remarks: Borghetto 200m.

🔲S Caorle 🚢🌊 26B5
Area di sosta Ai Parchi, Via Traghete. **GPS:** n45,60490 e12,88500. ⬆️.

65 ⌇€ 11-16/24h ⌐⌐ 🔲 Ch ✦ (60x)€ 4/kWh WC 🔲€ 1/3minutes 📶.
Location: Comfortable, isolated, noisy.
Surface: gravel.
🔲 01/01-31/12
Distance: 🚶historical centre 1,1km ⌇500m ⊗300m 🚊300m 🎯350m
🚌150m.
Remarks: Max. 72h, guarded parking, Luna Park 150m, Parco Acquatico 150m.

🔲 Cavallino-Treporti 🚢🌊 26A6
Spiaggia di Cà Ballarin, Via Gabrielle Berton. **GPS:** n45,45998 e12,51659. ⬆️.

4 ⌇free.
Location: Central, quit. **Surface:** sand. 🔲 01/05-31/10
Distance: 🚶1km ⌇on the spot ▸on the spot ⊗on the spot 🚊1km
🚌300m.
Remarks: Beach parking.

Tourist information Cavallino-Treporti:
ℹ️ I.A.T. (Ufficio Informazioni e di Accoglienza Turistica), Via Ramo II Delle Saline,

23.
🛒 Week market. 🔲 Tue-Thu morning.

🔲S Chioggia 32C1
Centro Sport 2000, Isola dell'Unione. **GPS:** n45,22194 e12,29583. ⬆️.

⌇8-23h € 1/h, 23-8h € 8 ⌐⌐ 🔲 ✦. **Surface:** asphalted.
Distance: 🚶300m.

🔲S Conegliano 🟢 26A5
Area de Sosta Campeggio Club Conegliano, Via Don Bosco, SS13. **GPS:**
n45,87799 e12,30111. ⬆️➡️.

30 ⌇€ 12/24h ⌐⌐ 🔲 Ch ✦ (16x)included WC 🔲. **Location:** Central, quit.
Surface: grassy. 🔲 01/01-31/12
Distance: 🚶2km ⊗nearby 🚊on the spot.

🔲S Cortina d'Ampezzo 🏔️🎪❄️ 25D3
Fiames, SS51. **GPS:** n46,57504 e12,11650. ⬆️.

>100 ⌇free, peak season € 12-15 ⌐⌐ 🔲 Ch. 🚉 **Location:** Rural, comfortable,
quit. **Surface:** grassy/metalled. 🔲 01/01-31/12
Distance: 🚶5km ⊗on the spot 🚊5km 🚌200m 🚶on the spot 🏃on the spot
🎿5km ⛷️5km.
Remarks: Max. 48h.

Tourist information Cortina d'Ampezzo:
ℹ️ Ufficio Informazioni, Piazzetta S.Francesco, 8.Famous winter sports resort.

🔲S Domegge di Cadore Belluno 🏔️❄️⛷️ 26A3
Camping Cologna, Vallesella di Cadore. **GPS:** n46,44605 e12,40658. ⬆️.

30 ⌇€ 10 ⌐⌐ 🔲 Ch.
Location: Rural, quit. **Surface:** grassy. 🔲 01/05-20/10

IT

Distance: 🚶1km ⚓At the lake ▸on the spot ⊗on the spot 🚰1km 🚐1km 🍴on the spot 🅰 on the spot.
Remarks: Max. 24h, narrow entrance road.

| 📷S | **Feltre** | 25D5 |

Piazale Pra del Vescovo, Viale A. Gaggia. **GPS:** n46,02013 e11,90792.⬆.

15 🅿free 🚰🔧Chfree. **Surface:** metalled. ⬛ 01/01-31/12
Distance: 🚶500m ⊗500m 🚰500m 🚐500m.
Remarks: Max. 48h.

| 📷S | **Ferrara di Monte Baldo** | 25B6 |

Via Chiesa. **GPS:** n45,67794 e10,85491.⬆.

16 🅿free 🚰🔧Ch🔧 (16x). **Location:** Rural, isolated, quit. **Surface:** gravel.
⬛ 01/01-31/12
Distance: 🚶300m ⊗300m 🚰300m 🍴on the spot 🅰 on the spot.

| 📷S | **Garda** | 25B6 |

P Centro, SS249. **GPS:** n45,57501 e10,71019.

20 🅿€ 13/24h 🚰 WC. **Surface:** metalled. ⬛ 01/01-31/12
Distance: 🚶200m ⊗on the spot 🚰on the spot.

| 📷S | **Garda** | 25B6 |

Via Preite. **GPS:** n45,57620 e10,71404.⬆▸.
30 🅿free, easter-31/10 € 12 🚰🔧Ch. **Surface:** metalled. ⬛ service:
Easter-31/10
Distance: 🚶300m ⚓Lake Garda 300m.

Tourist information Garda:
ℹ I.A.T. (Ufficio Informazioni e di Accoglienza Turistica), Piazza Donatori di
Sangue, 1.

| 📷 | **Lazise** | 25B6 |

Parking Lazise Dardo, Via San Martino, SP31. **GPS:** n45,50623 e10,73584.

15 🅿€ 17/24h. **Surface:** asphalted. ⬛ 01/01-31/12
Distance: 🚶200m 🚲5,8km ⊗200m 🚰200m 🚐200m.

| 📷S | **Lido di Jesolo** | 26B6 |

Area camping Albatros, Via Correr 102/A. **GPS:** n45,52477 e12,68995.⬆.

131 🅿€ 9-17 🚰🔧Ch 🔧 WC ⊐included. **Location:** Comfortable, isolated,
quit. **Surface:** grassy. ⬛ 01/03-31/10
Distance: 🚶500m 🚲700m ⊗100m 🚰100m 🖥100m 🚐100m.

| 📷S | **Lido di Jesolo** | 26B6 |

Boscopineta, Via Vettor Pisani. **GPS:** n45,52278 e12,69178.⬆.

250 🅿€ 10-20 🚰🔧Ch 🔧 WC ⊐. **Location:** Comfortable, central. **Surface:**
grassy. ⬛ 01/01-31/12
Distance: ⚓400m.

| 📷S | **Lido di Jesolo** | 26B6 |

Camping Park dei Dogi, Viale Oriente. **GPS:** n45,52146 e12,68828.⬆.

200 🅿€ 14-26, 4 pers.incl. 🚰🔧Ch 🔧 WCincluded ⊐€ 0,50 🖥📶.
Location: Comfortable, central, quit.
Surface: grassy. ⬛ 01/01-31/12
Distance: 🚶200m ⚓sandy beach 200m ⊗40m 🚰40m 🚐20m.

| 📷S | **Lido di Jesolo** | 26B6 |

Jesolo Camper Don Bosco, Via Oriente/via G.Don Bosco. **GPS:** n45,52188
e12,68943.⬆▸.

250 🦽€ 10-20 🚰🔌 Ch 🧹 € 3/1kWh WC 🚿 1 🚽 € 5.
Surface: grassy/gravel. ⏺ 01/01-31/12
Distance: 🚶within walking distance 🏊100m ⊗on the spot 🛒100m 🚌on the spot. **Remarks:** Bus to Venice stops in front of motorhome parking.

🦽S   Lido di Jesolo   26B6
Parcheggio Mare d'Oriente, Viale Oriente, Lido di Jesolo est. **GPS:** n45,52083 e12,68556.⬆️.

🦽€ 10/24h, € 13/Sunday, Aug 🚰🔌 Ch 🧹included 🚽. **Location:** Very simple, central, quit. **Surface:** grassy. ⏺ summer
Distance: 🚶100m 🏊100m ⊗on the spot 🛒on the spot 🚌on the spot.
Remarks: Servicepoint at Don Bosco, incl.

🦽S   Livinallongo del Col di Lana 🏔️🌳❄️ 25D3
Sportbar del Ghiaccio, Via Piagn,6 Arabba. **GPS:** n46,49678 e11,87692.⬆️.

50 🦽€ 10/24h, Jul-Aug-Dec € 14 🚰🔌 Ch 🧹(17x)🔌 3/24h WC 🚿 € 3.
Location: Rural, comfortable, quit.
Surface: grassy/gravel. ⏺ 01/01-31/12
Distance: 🚶on the spot ⊗on the spot 🛒200m 🚌200m 🚴on the spot 🧍on the spot 🚲200m.
Remarks: At the skating rink, check in at bar.

ⒸS   Malcesine   25B5
Camping Lombardi, Via Navene, loc. Campagnola. **GPS:** n45,78429 e10,82187.⬆️.

20 🦽€ 15/24h 🚰 1 🔌Ch 🧹 WC 🚿 € 1. **Surface:** unpaved. ⏺ 01/04-31/10
Distance: 🚶3km 🏊Lake Garda 500m.

Remarks: Max. 48h.

P   Marghera   26A6
Parcheggio Terminal Service, Via dei Petroli 1/3 angolo via della Libertà. **GPS:** n45,46806 e12,26589.

🦽€ 10/24h.
Location: Very simple, central, quit. **Surface:** . ⏺ 01/01-31/12
Distance: 🚌> Venice.
Remarks: Monitored parking.

🦽S   Mirano   26A6
Camper Club Mirano, Via viasana, 4. **GPS:** n45,49322 e12,08968.⬆️.

🦽€ 12/24h 🚰🔌 Ch 🧹.
Location: Comfortable. **Surface:** grasstiles.
Distance: 🚶historical centre 1,5km 🚲8km 🚌300m Padua-Venice.
Remarks: For entrance email: camperclubmirano@libero.it of phone 3479831010.

🦽S   Misurina 🏔️⛰️🌊❄️ 26A3
Piazzale Loita, Via Monte Piana. **GPS:** n46,58839 e12,25737.➡️.

50 🦽€ 8, 20/07-31/08 - 24/12-06/01 € 12 🚰🔌 Chincluded. 🚐
Location: Rural, very simple, central, noisy.
Surface: gravel. ⏺ 01/01-31/12
Distance: 🚶300m 🏊500m ⊗50m 🛒300m 🚌on the spot 🚴on the spot 🧍on the spot 🚲3km.

🦽   Misurina 🏔️⛰️🌊❄️ 26A3
P camper Rifugio Auronzo, Rifugio Auronzo. **GPS:** n46,61267 e12,29342.➡️.

40 🦽€ 33 toll road incl., extra night € 15. 🚐 **Location:** Rural, isolated.

IT

Surface: gravel. 🔲 01/05-30/10
Distance: 🚶Misurina 12km ⊗on the spot 🚰12km ➡on the spot ⚞Tre Cime di Lavadero 🎿15km.
Remarks: Beautiful view.

| ♿S | Montagnana | 32B1 |

Via Circonvallazione. **GPS:** n45,23528 e11,46639.⬆➡.

20 🚐free 🗑Ch WC free. **Surface:** asphalted. 🔲 01/01-31/12
Distance: 🚶200m ⊗200m 🚰200m.
Remarks: At sports centre.

| ♿S | Padova 🌿 | 25D6 |

P1, Piazza della Pace Ytzhak Rabbin, Via cinquantottesimo Fanteria, Padua (Padova).
GPS: n45,39686 e11,87673.⬆.

🚐8-20h € 10, 20-8h € 10, 18-10h € 20 🚰🗑Ch. **Surface:** asphalted. 🔲 01/01-31/12
Distance: 🚶on the spot 🚲6km ⊗on the spot 🚰on the spot ➡on the spot.

Tourist information Padua (Padova):
ℹ U.I.A.T. (Ufficio Informazioni e di Accoglienza Turistica, Galleria Pedrocchi, www.turismopadova.it.Old university city.
👁 Caffe Pedrocchi, Via Oberdan.Café, meeting point for students.
👁 Capella degli Scrovegni.Chapel.

| ♿S | Peschiera del Garda | 25B6 |

P4, Via Milano 67. **GPS:** n45,44179 e10,67768.⬆.

33 🚐€ 15/24h 🚰🗑Ch free. **Surface:** asphalted. 🔲 01/01-31/12
Distance: 🚲5km 🚤Lake Garda 300m ⊗100m ➡nearby.
Remarks: Parking nearby campsite Bella Italia.

Tourist information Peschiera del Garda:
ℹ Tourist town at Lake Garda.
⚞ 🔲 Mo-morning.

| ♿S | Porto Tolle | 32C1 |

Via del Mare, loc. Barricata. **GPS:** n44,84470 e12,46580.
🚐free. **Surface:** grassy/sand.
Remarks: Beach parking.

| ♿S | Punta Sabbioni 🏖🌊 | 26A6 |

Agricampeggio Al Bateo, Lungomare Dante Alighieri 19A. **GPS:** n45,44278 e12,42260.⬆.

26 🚐€ 20-25, 2 pers.incl 🚰🗑Ch 🧹WC 🚿.

Location: Rural.
Surface: grassy. 🔲 01/02-30/10
Distance: 🚶500m 🚤2,5km ⊗50m 🚰500m 🎯3km ➡ferry Venice 500m.
Remarks: Sale of vegetables, summer: shuttle to the beach.

| ♿S | Punta Sabbioni 🏖🌊 | 26A6 |

Parking Dante Alighieri, Dante Alighieri 26. **GPS:** n45,44132 e12,42131.⬆.

36 🚐€ 17-20 + € 3/pp 🚰🗑Ch 🧹€ 3 WC 🚿🎯€ 3.
Location: Central, quit.
Surface: grassy. 🔲 01/01-31/12
Distance: 🚶on the spot 🚤1,5km 🚰700m ⊗on the spot ➡free shuttle to beach.
Remarks: Monitored parking, arrival <22h, ferry boat to Venice 500m.

| 🏴S | Punta Sabbioni 🏖🌊 | 26A6 |

Agricamping da Scarpa, Via Pealto 17. **GPS:** n45,44279 e12,44055.

15 🚐€ 14-16 + € 5/pp 🚰🗑Ch 🧹WC included 🚿. **Surface:** grassy. 🔲 01/01-31/12
Distance: 🚤500m ⊗on the spot 🚰500m ➡ferry Venice 1,5km.

| ♿S | Recoaro Terme ⚞🏔🍽❄ | 25C6 |

Area Communale, Via Della Restistenza. **GPS:** n45,70469 e11,22874.⬆⬆➡.

16 🚐€ 5/24h 🚰€ 0,10/10liter 🗑Ch 🧹(16x)€ 0,50/2h, 6Amp. 🔲 01/01-31/12
Distance: 🚶on the spot ⊗on the spot 🚰on the spot ➡on the spot 🎿on the spot.

| ♿S | Santo Stefano di Cadore 🏔🏕 | 26A3 |

Albergo Gasperina, Loc. Cima Canale, Val Visdende. **GPS:** n46,60835 e12,63053.⬆➡.

49 ⬛€ 11/24h, Aug € 12 ⛽🪑Ch ⚡(49x)€ 3/day WC included ⬛€ 2.
Surface: gravel.
⭕ 25/04-01/10
Distance: 🚂12km ➡️300m ⊗on the spot 🛒6km 🚲on the spot 🧍on the spot.
Remarks: Check in at restaurant, bread-service.

8 ⬛free ⛽🪑Ch ⚡(8x)free, 16Amp. ⭕ 01/01-31/12
Distance: 🚂200m ➡️3km ⊗on the spot ⊗200m 🛒200m 🚗300m.

| ⬛S | Torre di Mosto | 26B5 |

Agriturismo La Via Antiga, Via S. Martino 13. **GPS:** n45,64389 e12,67056.⬆️

| ⬛S | Sappada 🏔️❄️ | 26A3 |

Area Camper, Borgata Palù. **GPS:** n46,56254 e12,67991.⬆️➡️

60 ⬛€ 10/24h ⛽🪑Ch ⚡(24x)included. ⬛**Location:** Rural, quit.
Surface: gravel. ⭕ 01/01-31/12
Distance: 🚂1,1km ⊗500m 🛒1km 🚲on the spot 🧍on the spot 🚴100m.
Remarks: Keycard at townhall, caution key € 5.

| ⬛S | Schio 🎣🏔️❄️ | 25C5 |

Parking Palasport, Viale dell'Industria. **GPS:** n45,71389 e11,37599.⬆️

8 ⬛€ 15/day ⛽🪑Ch ⚡(5x)included. **Location:** Isolated, quit. **Surface:** grassy/gravel. ⭕ 01/03-30/09
Distance: 🚂7km.

| ⬛S | Treviso 🍃 | 26A5 |

Parking ex Foro Boario, Via Castello d'Amore. **GPS:** n45,67014 e12,25733.⬆️

4 ⬛free ⛽🪑Ch free. **Surface:** asphalted. ⭕ 01/01-31/12
Distance: 🚂1km ⊗1km 🛒1km 🚴on the spot 🚲on the spot.

| ⬛S | Sernaglia della Battaglia | 26A5 |

Area attrezzata Le Grave, Via Passo Barca, Falzè di Piave. **GPS:** n45,85676 e12,16566.⬆️➡️

13 ⬛free ⛽🪑Ch free. **Surface:** metalled. ⭕ 01/01-31/12
Distance: 🚂500m 🚢11,5km ⊗500m 🛒500m 🚗200m.
Remarks: Max. 48h.

| ⬛S | Treviso 🍃 | 26A5 |

Via Giovanni Boccaccio. **GPS:** n45,66769 e12,26361.⬆️➡️

26 ⬛€ 5/12h, € 8/24h ⛽🪑Ch included ⚡€ 2/24h. **Surface:** grassy. ⭕ 01/01-31/12
Distance: 🚂150m 🏊on the spot ⊗100m 🛒150m 🚗300m.

| ⬛S | Soave 🍃🍇 | 25C6 |

Via Invalidi del Lavoro. **GPS:** n45,42340 e11,24541.⬆️➡️

40 ⬛free ⛽🪑Ch free. **Location:** Central, noisy. **Surface:** asphalted. ⭕ 01/01-31/12
Distance: 🚂1km ⊗500m 🛒500m 🚗300m.
Remarks: Along railwayline.

Tourist information Treviso:
ℹ️ U.I.A.T. (Ufficio Informazioni e di Accoglienza Turistica), Piazza Monte di Pieta, 8.Fortified small town with canals.
🏛️ Sile.Fish-market on island.

| ⬛S | Venezia 🍃🏛️🍦🌊 | 26A6 |

Parcheggio Al Tronchetto, Venice (Venezia) . **GPS:** n45,44146 e12,30514.⬆️

IT

€ 21/0-12h, 12-24h € 16 Ch ☕. **Location:** Urban, central, quit. **Surface:** asphalted. 01/01-31/12 **Distance:** 2km on the spot ferry Venice.

🅂 Venezia 26A6

Parco di San Giuliano, Via San Giuliano, Venice (Venezia). **GPS:** n45,46742 e12,27916.

100 € 10/24h € 3 Ch WC. **Location:** Central, quit. **Surface:** grassy. 01/01-31/12 **Distance:** ferry Venice 100m.

Tourist information Venice (Venezia):
ℹ A.P.T. (Azienda di Promozione Turistica), www.turismovenezia.it.Historical city consits of 117 islands, 150 canals and 400 bridges.
Ⓜ Murano.Famous for its glass industry, museum.

🅂 Verona 25C6

Area sosta camper Porta Palio, Via dalla Bona. **GPS:** n45,43354 e10,97879.

37 € 5/4h, € 10/24h Ch included. **Surface:** asphalted. 01/01-31/12

Distance: 500m Pizza (ordering service) bus 62 > centre.

🅂 Verona 25C6

Agricamping Corte Finiletto, Strada Bresciana, 41. **GPS:** n45,44651 e10,91917.

€ 18, 2 pers.incl Ch € 2 WC. **Surface:** grassy/gravel.

Tourist information Verona:
ℹ U.I.A.T. (Ufficio Informazioni e di Accoglienza Turistica), Piazza XXV Aprile-c/o stazione "Porta Nuova".Historical city with palaces and squares.
Ⓔ Arena.Large anfiteatro, in July/August opera performances.
Ⓔ Via Capella.Known for the love drama of Romeo and Juliet.
Ⓣ Piazza dellen Erbe. daily.

🅂 Vicenza 25D6

Park Interscambio CentroBus, Via Bassano, Zona sud-est. **GPS:** n45,54321 e11,55886.

40 € 8,40/24h WC included. **Surface:** asphalted. 01/01-31/12 during event. **Distance:** 2km on the spot Free bus to centre, every 15 min. **Remarks:** At stadium.

🅂 Vicenza 25D6

Park Interscambio CentroBus, Viale Cricoli, Zona nord. **GPS:** n45,56418 e11,54903.

18 € 8,40/24h Ch WC included. **Surface:** asphalted. 01/01-31/12 **Distance:** 1,6km on the spot on the spot Free bus to centre. **Remarks:** Ring-road dir Bassano.

Tourist information Vicenza:
ℹ U.I.A.T. (Ufficio Informazioni e di Accoglienza Turistica), Piazza Matteotti, 12, www.vicenzae.org.City with many palaces, former residence of 16th century architect.
Ⓔ La Rotonda.Famous villa designed by Palladio. summer: Wed.
Ⓔ Quartiere delle Barche.District with palaces in Venetian style.

Friuli Venezia Giulia

🅂 Andreis 26A4

SP20. **GPS:** n46,19880 e12,61157.

€ 5/day . **Surface:** grassy/gravel. **Distance:** little stream.

🅂 Barcis 26A4

Loc. Portuz, SS251. **GPS:** n46,19055 e12,56507.

IT

20 🛀 € 12/24h 🚰🔌 Ch ⚓. **Location:** Comfortable, isolated, quit. **Surface:** grasstiles/metalled. ⬛ 01/01-31/12
Distance: 🚶400m ⛱on the spot ⊗500m 🛒500m.
Remarks: At the lake of Barcis.

| 🚐 S | **Corno di Rosazzo** | 26C4 |

Via dei Pini. **GPS:** n45,98955 e13,43917. ⬆➡.

8 🛀 free 🚰🔌.
Location: Rural, quit. **Surface:** asphalted. ⬛ 01/01-31/12
Distance: 🚶300m.

| 🚐 S | **Dolegna del Collio** | 26C4 |

Frazione Vencò. **GPS:** n46,00370 e13,47700. ⬆.

🛀 free 🚰🔌 Ch 🚆. **Surface:** asphalted.
Distance: 🚶Dolegna del Collio 4km.
Remarks: Picnic area, 50m from border with Slovenia.

| 🚐 S | **Forni di Sopra** 🏔️ 🌼 ❄ | 26A3 |

Santa Viela, SS52. **GPS:** n46,42500 e12,57036. ⬆.

20 🛀 € 7-9 🚰🔌 Ch free. 🐕 **Location:** Rural, noisy. **Surface:** asphalted. ⬛ 01/01-31/12
Distance: 🚶800m ⊗on the spot 🛒800m 🚌400m 🚲on the spot 🚶on the spot 🎣on the spot 🚣on the spot.
Remarks: No camping activity. Parking outside the village, dir Lorenzago di Cadore.

| 🚐 S | **Gemona del Friuli** | 26B4 |

Piazzale Mons. Battista Monai. **GPS:** n46,27585 e13,13728. ⬆.
🛀 free 🚰🔌 Ch free. **Location:** Very simple, central, noisy. **Surface:** asphalted.
Distance: 🚶on the spot 🚲3,3km.

| 🚐 S | **Gorizia** ⛲ | 26C4 |

Viale Antonio Oriani. **GPS:** n45,94554 e13,61603. ⬆.

30 🛀 free 🚰🔌 Ch free.
Location: Quit. **Surface:** asphalted. ⬛ 01/01-31/12
Distance: 🚶centre 500m.

| 🚐 S | **Gradisca d'Isonzo** | 26C5 |

Viale Trieste. **GPS:** n45,88577 e13,49582. ⬆.

3 🛀 free 🚰🔌 Ch free. **Location:** Central. **Surface:** asphalted.
Distance: 🚶on the spot 🚲2,3km ⊗on the spot 🛒on the spot.
Remarks: Max. 48h.

| 🚐 S | **Grado** | 26C5 |

Viala Italia. **GPS:** n45,68218 e13,41230. ⬆➡.

40 🛀 € 12 🚰🔌 Ch 🔌 included. 🚿 **Surface:** asphalted. ⬛ 01/01-31/12
Distance: 🚶1km 🚲4km ⛱600m.

| 🚐 S | **Montereale Valcellina** | 26A4 |

Via dell'Omo. **GPS:** n46,15168 e12,66122. ⬆➡.

15 🛀 free 🚰🔌 Ch.
Location: Urban. **Surface:** asphalted. ⬛ 01/01-31/12
Distance: 🚶500m 🛒300m.

| 🚐 S | **Pordenone** | 26A5 |

Agip, SS13, Pordenone. **GPS:** n45,97236 e12,64332. ⬆.

IT

8 🅿€3/24h 🚰🔌Ch. **Location:** Urban, very simple, isolated, quit. **Surface:** asphalted. 🅾 01/01-31/12
Distance: 🚆1km 🚤3km ⊗200m 🛒200m.
Remarks: To be paid at petrol station.

Tourist information Pordenone:
ℹ️ Infopoint Turismo, Via Damiani 2c.

San Daniele del Friuli 🏕️   26B4
Via Udine, SP16. **GPS:** n46,15610 e13,01368.⬆️.

20 🅿free 🚰🔌Chfree. **Location:** Comfortable, central, quit. **Surface:** grasstiles. 🅾 01/01-31/12
Distance: 🚆300m ⊗on the spot 🛒300m 🚌200m.
Remarks: Parking sports park.

San Vito al Tagliamento   26B5
Area di sosta San Vito al Tagliamento, Via Pulet. **GPS:** n45,91224 e12,86590.
⬆️➡️.

12 🅿€5/12h, €8/24h, €15/48h 🚰€1 🔌Ch🛀. **Location:** Rural, isolated, quit. **Surface:** asphalted. 🅾 01/01-31/12
Distance: 🚆500m 🚤15km ⊗500m 🛒500m 🚌500m.
Remarks: Open the gate manually.

Sauris 🏔️   26A3
Prosciuttificio Wolf Sauris, Sauris di Sotto 88. **GPS:** n46,46756 e12,70833.⬆️.
10 🅿free 🚰🛀free WC 🚽.
Location: Rural, quit. **Surface:** asphalted.
Distance: 🚆on the spot ⊗150m 🚶on the spot.

Tarcento   26B4
Plein-air Torre, Via Sotto Colle Verzan. **GPS:** n46,21496 e13,22503.⬆️.

10 🅿free 🚰🔌Ch🛀free. **Location:** Quit. **Surface:** grasstiles.
Distance: 🚆200m ⊗200m 🛒200m.
Remarks: Nearby sports center, no camping activity, max. 72h.

Tarvisio 🏔️❄️   26C3
Parcheggio P3, Via Armando Diaz. **GPS:** n46,50426 e13,57157.⬆️➡️.

25 🅿€0,60/h 🚰🔌Ch.🚐
Location: Urban, central. **Surface:** metalled.
Distance: 🚆on the spot ⊗100m 🛒100m.

Trieste 🌊🏕️🍴   26C5
Via Von Bruck, Torre del Lloyd. **GPS:** n45,63710 e13,76990.⬆️➡️.

50 🅿€4 🚰🔌Chfree. **Location:** Highway, very simple, noisy. **Surface:** asphalted. 🅾 01/01-31/12
Distance: 🚆3km 🚌shuttle to centre.
Remarks: Pitches under motorway, max. 72h.

Trieste 🌊🏕️🍴   26C5
Piazzale 11 settembre 2001, Viale Miramare. **GPS:** n45,68250 e13,75138.

20 🅿free. **Location:** Urban, quit. **Surface:** metalled.
Distance: 🚆on the spot.
Remarks: In front of porticciolo di Barcola, quiet at night.

Trieste 🌊🏕️🍴   26C5
Via Ottaviano Augusto. **GPS:** n45,64599 e13,75654.

IT

🛏free. **Location:** Urban. **Surface:** asphalted. ⬛ 01/01-31/12
Distance: 🚶centre 500m ⊗100m 🚌on the spot.
Remarks: In opposite of Piazza Unitá d'Italia.
Tourist information Trieste:
ℹ A.I.A.T (Agenzia di Informazione e di Accoglienza Turistica), Via San Nicolo, 20, www.triestetourism.it.Large port city with many place of interest.
👁 Grotta del Giganta.Caves. ⬛ Tue-Su, 01/07-31/08 Mo-Su.

🛏S	Zoppola	26B5

Via Manteghe. **GPS:** n45,96502 e12,78019.⬆➡.

2 🛏free 🚐🍽Chfree. **Location:** Rural, isolated, quit. **Surface:** metalled. ⬛
01/01-31/12
Distance: 🚶centre ±800m.
Remarks: At gymnasium.

Emilia-Romagna

🛏S	Anita	32C2

Agriturismo Prato Pozzo, Via Rotta Marinella 34/a. **GPS:** n44,54892 e12,13322. ⬆➡.

60 🛏€ 5/pp, guests free 🚐🍽Ch🔌(12x)€ 2,50 WC 🍽included ▣against payment. **Surface:** grassy/metalled. ⬛ 01/01-31/12
Distance: 🚶1km 🚊500m 🚐500m ⊗on the spot 🚉1km 🚌1km.

🛏S	Argenta	32B2

Via Galassi. **GPS:** n44,61345 e11,83983.⬆➡.

10 🛏free 🚐🍽free. **Surface:** metalled. ⬛ 01/01-31/12
Distance: 🚶200m ⊗200m 🚉200m 🚌200m.

Remarks: At tennis-courts.
Tourist information Argenta:
ℹ U.I.A.T.(Ufficio Informazzioni e di Accoglienza Turistica), Piazza Marconi, 1.

🛏S	Bagnacavallo	32C2

Parcheggio bocciodromo, Via Stradello. **GPS:** n44,42191 e11,97390.⬆.

🛏free 🚐🍽free. **Surface:** asphalted. ⬛ 01/01-31/12
Distance: 🚶700m 🚲2,5km ⊗700m 🚉200m.

🛏	Bagno di Romagna 🏔🌳	32C3

Via Lungo Savio 1. **GPS:** n43,84108 e11,96532.

10 🛏free. **Surface:** metalled. ⬛ 01/01-31/12
Distance: 🚶500m 🚲1km ⊗500m 🚉500m.
Remarks: Parking swimming pool.
Tourist information Bagno di Romagna:
ℹ U.I.A.T.(Ufficio Informazzioni e di Accoglienza Turistica), Via Fiorentina, 38.
🌾 Week market. ⬛ Fri 7.30-12.30h.

🛏S	Bellaria-Igea Marina	32C3

Parking delle Robinie, Via Pinzon 258, Igea Marina, Zona sud. **GPS:** n44,12783 e12,48873.

106 🛏€ 10, 01/06-30/09 € 12-€ 14 🚐🍽Ch🔌€ 2 🍽€ 1. **Surface:** grassy/gravel. ⬛ 01/03-31/10, 8-23h
Distance: 🚊10m ⊗200m 🚉100m 🚌50m.

🛏S	Bellaria-Igea Marina	32C3

Mare d'Inverno, Via Murri, 13. **GPS:** n44,11639 e12,49972.⬆.

55 🛏€ 9,50, peak season € 11 🚐🍽Ch🔌€ 2 🍽€ 1. **Surface:** grassy. ⬛

IT

Easter-30/09
Distance: 🛒800m ⛱100m ⊗800m 🍴1,5km, bakery 800m 🚌100m.

📷🅂 **Bellaria-Igea Marina** `32C3`
Area di sosta Rio Pircio, Via Beniviene 4, Igea Marina. **GPS:** n44,12688 e12,48849.

68 📷€ 12-16/24h 🔧 🗑Ch 🚿 € 2 WC 🗂 hot shower € 1. **Surface:** grassy.
🅾 01/01-31/12
Distance: ⛱100m ⊗200m 🍴250m.

📷🅂 **Bellaria-Igea Marina** `32C3`
L'Adriatico Parking, Via Benivieni, 12. **GPS:** n44,12644 e12,48740.

60 📷€ 12-16/24h 🔧 🗑Ch 🚿 € 2 🗂 hot shower € 0,80.
Surface: grassy.
Distance: ⛱250m.

Tourist information Bellaria-Igea Marina:
ℹ U.I.A.T.(Ufficio Informazzioni e di Accoglienza Turistica), Via Leonardo da Vinci, 2.

📷🅂 **Berceto** `31D2`
Via P. Salas. **GPS:** n44,51123 e9,98589. ⬆➡.

20 📷€ 7 🔧 🗑Ch 🚿 WCincluded.
Surface: asphalted. 🅾 01/01-31/12
Distance: 🛒200m 🚲4km ⊗200m 🍴200m 🎣 on the spot 🧍on the spot.
Remarks: Key at kiosk in front of restaurant Rina, caution key € 20.

📷🅂 **Bertinoro** 🏔🎎🌴 `32C3`
Via Superga, SP 83, fraz Fratta Terme. **GPS:** n44,13788 e12,10355. ⬆➡.

📷free 🔧 🗑Chfree. **Surface:** asphalted. 🅾 01/01-31/12

Distance: 🛒1km ⊗1km 🍴1km 🚌300m.
Remarks: Near spa resort and sports centre.

📷🅂 **Bertinoro** 🏔🎎🌴 `32C3`
Azienda agricola Achille Budellacci, Via Palmeggiana 516, loc. Capocolle. **GPS:** n44,15214 e12,16325. ⬆➡.
2 📷€ 5, free for clients 🔧 € 1/100liter 🗑Ch 🚿 WC 🗂included. 🅾 01/01-31/12
Distance: 🛒5km ⊗5km 🍴5km.

📷🅂 **Bomporto** `32A2`
Piazza dello Sport, Via Verdi. **GPS:** n44,72886 e11,03585.

10 📷free 🔧 🗑free.
Location: Urban, very simple. **Surface:** metalled.
Distance: 🛒500m 🍴500m.
Remarks: Parking at sports park.

📷 **Borello** `32C3`
Via Fiera. **GPS:** n44,05315 e12,17847.

5 📷free. **Surface:** asphalted. 🅾 01/01-31/12
Distance: 🛒100m 🚲1,2km ⊗500m 🍴100m 🚌100m.
Remarks: Near post office.

📷🅂 **Brisighella** 🏔🎎 `32B2`
Piazzale Donatori di Sangue. **GPS:** n44,22168 e11,77883. ⬆➡.

18 📷free 🔧 🗑Chfree. **Surface:** asphalted. 🅾 01/01-31/12
Distance: 🛒1km ⊗1km 🍴1km 🚌500m.

📷🅂 **Brisighella** 🏔🎎 `32B2`
Agriturismo Torre del Marino, Via Torre del Marino 45. **GPS:** n44,25447 e11,75867. ⬆➡.

4 ⌂free ⌖Ch ⚡(3x) WC. **Surface:** asphalted. ◻ 01/01-31/12
Distance: ⓘ8km ⊗on the spot.
Remarks: Restaurant is closed on Monday.

⌂S	Carpi	32A1

Piazzale delle Piscine. **GPS:** n44,78444 e10,86817. ⬆.

⌂free ⌖⚊Chfree. **Surface:** metalled.
Distance: ⓘ300m ⊗50m 🚂on the spot.
Remarks: Parking swimming pool.

⌂S	Casal Borsetti	32C2

Area Sosta Camper Mare e Parco, Via Ortolani. **GPS:** n44,55000 e12,27997. ⬆.

238 ⌂€ 7, 01/06-01/10 € 10 ⌖⚊Chincluded ⚡€ 2,50/24h WC ◻.
Surface: grassy/metalled. ◻ 01/01-31/12
Distance: ⚓150m ⓘ150m.

⌂S	Casola Valsenio 🌳👄	32B2

Viale Domenico Neri. **GPS:** n44,22483 e11,62392. ⬆.
4 ⌂free ⌖free. **Surface:** asphalted. ◻ 01/01-31/12
Distance: ⓘ100m ⊗500m 🚂100m.

⌂S	Casola Valsenio 🌳👄	32B2

Via don Milani/Via Antonio Gramsci. **GPS:** n44,22597 e11,62953. ⬆➡.

3 ⌂free. **Surface:** asphalted. ◻ 01/01-31/12
Distance: ⓘ300m ⊗500m 🚂500m.
Remarks: At old city centre.

Tourist information Casola Valsenio:
🛈 I.A.T.(Ufficio Informazzioni Turistica), Via Roma, 48/a.

⌂S	Castel Bolognese	32B2

Via Donati, SS 9. **GPS:** n44,31611 e11,79280. ⬆➡.

50 ⌂free ⌖⚊Chfree.
Distance: ⓘ300m.
Remarks: At sports park.

⌂S	Castel San Pietro Terme ♒	32B2

Via Oriani. **GPS:** n44,39725 e11,59197. ⬆➡.

100 ⌂free ⌖€ 1 ⚊Ch WC€ 0,20. **Surface:** asphalted. ◻ 01/01-31/12
Distance: ⓘ300m ⚡4,2km ⊷200m ⊗250m 🚂250m 🚂250m.
Remarks: Nearby hospital.

⌂S	Castellarano 🌿	32A2

Parco Don Reverberi, Via Don Reverberi. **GPS:** n44,50777 e10,73419. ⬆➡.

5 ⌂free ⌖⚊Chfree. **Location:** Rural, very simple. **Surface:** asphalted. ◻
01/01-31/12
Distance: ⓘ500m ⚓500m ⊷500m ⊗500m 🚂500m.

⌂S	Castelnovo ne' Monti 🏔	32A2

Impianti Sportivi, Zona PEP, Via Fratelli Cervi, SS63. **GPS:** n44,43277 e10,41133.
⬆.

4 ⌂free ⌖⚊Chfree. **Location:** Very simple, quit. **Surface:** asphalted. ◻
01/01-31/12
Distance: ⓘ500m 🚶on the spot.
Remarks: On entering the village from Reggio Emilia.

⌂S	Cervia	32C2

Via Aldo Ascione, Cervia-nord. **GPS:** n44,28151 e12,32459.

IT

50 🏕free ⚒🔧♻Chfree. **Surface:** asphalted. ⬛ 01/01-31/12

🚿S | **Cervia** | 32C2

Viale Tritone, Fraz. Pinarella. **GPS:** n44,23984 e12,35883.

40 🏕free ⚒🔧♻Chfree. **Surface:** asphalted. ⬛ 01/01-31/12
Distance: 🏖900m ⊗on the spot.

🏕S | **Cervia** | 32C2

Terme di Cervia, Viale C. Forlanini, Cervia-nord. **GPS:** n44,27335 e12,32964.⬆️.

50 🏕€ 8/24h 🔧€ 2. **Surface:** grassy/gravel. ⬛ 01/02-30/11
Distance: 🏖3km ⊗50m.
Remarks: Parking spa resort.

Tourist information Cervia:
ℹ️ U.I.A.T.(Ufficio Informazzioni e di Accoglienza Turistica), Vale Matteotti, 39-41, www.turismo.comunecervia.it.
🏕 Week market. ⬛ Thu.

🏕S | **Cesena** | 32C3

Agriturismo Macin, Via San Mauro 5280. **GPS:** n44,13592 e12,16953.⬆️.

2 🏕€ 5, free for clients ⚒🔧Ch 🔧 WC ♻included. **Surface:** grassy/metalled. ⬛ 01/01-31/12
Distance: 🏖5km ⚓8,4km ⊗5km 🏖5km.

🏕S | **Cesenatico** | 32C2

Piazzale della Rocca. **GPS:** n44,19855 e12,39086.⬆️.

---

35 🏕free ⚒🔧♻Chfree. **Surface:** metalled. ⬛ 01/01-31/12
Distance: 🏖500m ⚓2km 🏖200m 🏖500m 🚌200m.
Remarks: 2nd parking.

©S | **Cesenatico** | 32C2

Via Mazzini, zona Ponente. **GPS:** n44,21408 e12,38008.

16 🏕€ 7/24h ⚒🔧♻Ch 🔧 included.
Surface: grassy/gravel. ⬛ 01/01-31/12
Distance: 🏖centre 3,5km ⚓800m.
Remarks: At entrance campsite Cesenatico, max. 48h.

🏕S | **Civitella di Romagna** | 32C3

Agriturismo Acero Rosseo, Via Seggio. **GPS:** n44,00200 e11,97539.⬆️➡️.

20 🏕guests free ⚒free ♻. **Surface:** grassy. ⬛ 01/01-31/12
Distance: 🏖5km ⊗on the spot 🏖5km.

🏕S | **Collecchio** | 31D2

Via Spezia. **GPS:** n44,75178 e10,22265.⬆️➡️.

8 🏕free ⚒🔧♻Ch. **Location:** Very simple. **Surface:** asphalted. ⬛ 01/01-31/12
Distance: 🏖500m.

🏕S | **Comacchio** 🌟 | 32C1

Area di sosta Cavallari, Via Villaggio San Carlo 9. **GPS:** n44,70297 e12,16862.⬆️.
100 🏕€ 15 ⚒🔧♻Ch 🔧 WC 🔧. **Surface:** grassy. ⬛ 01/01-31/12
Distance: 🏖1km.

🏕 | **Comacchio** 🌟 | 32C1

Via Fattibello. **GPS:** n44,69095 e12,18447.⬆️.
🏕free. **Surface:** grassy. ⬛ 01/01-31/12

IT

Distance: 🚶300m.

Conselice 32B2

Agriturismo Massari, Via Coronella 110, Chiesanuova di Conselice. **GPS:** n44,53167 e11,81856. ⬆️➡️.

10 🅿️ € 9/pp, guests free 🚰🔌Ch 💧WC 🔲 📶included ♻️. **Surface:** metalled. 🅿️ 01/01-31/12

Distance: 🚶1,5km 🚆200m ⊗on the spot 🚉1,5km.

Cusercoli 32C3

Agriturismo Ca'Bionda, Via San Giovanni 41. **GPS:** n44,04153 e11,97544. ⬆️➡️.

20 🅿️free 🚰🔌Ch 💧free WC. **Surface:** metalled.

Distance: 🚶3,5km ⊗on the spot 🚉3,5km.

Remarks: Last 3km narrow road, swimming pool.

Faenza 32C2

Via Proventa. **GPS:** n44,31272 e11,89289. ⬆️.

2 🅿️free 🚰🔌Ch free. **Surface:** asphalted. 🅿️ 01/01-31/12

Distance: 🚶4km ⚓2km.

Remarks: Industrial area, A14 exit Faenza, SP8 dir centre.

Faenza 32C2

Agriturismo Trerè, Via Casale 19. **GPS:** n44,29968 e11,80368. ⬆️➡️.

5 🅿️ € 8 + € 5/pp, guests free 🚰🔌Ch 💧€ 2 WC. **Surface:** metalled. 🅿️ 01/01-31/12

Distance: 🚶7km 🚆on the spot 🚉200m ⊗on the spot.

Remarks: Dog € 1, swimming pool € 5. Follow Agriturismo Trerè.

Faenza 32C2

Agriturismo Il Laghetto del Sole, Via Pittora 37. **GPS:** n44,25128 e11,88717. ⬆️➡️.

20 🅿️ € 5 🚰🔌Ch 💧(4x) WC ♻️. **Surface:** metalled. 🅿️ 01/02-31/10

Distance: 🚶4,5km 🚉200m 🚆200m ⊗on the spot 🚉4km.

Faenza 32C2

Centro vendita Faenza Caravan, Via Emilia Ponent 76/c. **GPS:** n44,30353 e11,84294.

🅿️free 🚰🔌Ch free. **Surface:** metalled. 🅿️ 01/01-31/12

Distance: 🚶3km ⊗350m.

Remarks: Service during opening hours.

Tourist information Faenza:

ℹ️ I.A.T.(Ufficio Informazioni e di Accoglienza Turistica), VOLTONE DELLA MOLINELLA, 2.

Ferrara 🌿🏛️🍴 32B1

Via Darsena 40/Corso Isonzo. **GPS:** n44,83468 e11,60795. ⬆️➡️.

30 🅿️ € 6/24h 🚰€ 1/100liter 🔌€ 2 Ch € 1. **Surface:** metalled. 🅿️ 01/01-31/12

Distance: 🚶800m ⚓6,5km 🚉250m 🚉500m 🚆50m.

Tourist information Ferrara:

ℹ️ U.I.A.T. (Ufficio Informazioni e di Accoglienza Turistica), Castello Estense. Historical city.

Ⓜ️ Museo della Cattedrale. 🎁 gift.

⚔️ Castello Estence.

⚔️ Palazzo Scifanoia.

🏛️ 🅿️ Mo, Fri.

Fontanellato 🌿 31D1

Via Caduti di Cefalonia. **GPS:** n44,88195 e10,17762. ⬆️.

IT

30 🚐free 🚰🚽free. **Location:** Very simple, quit. **Surface:** asphalted. 📅 01/01-31/12
Distance: 🏘centre 500m 🛣5,4km 🛒500m.
Remarks: At cemetery.

[🚐][S] Fontanellato 31D1

Via Nazionale Emilia. **GPS**: n44,87797 e10,16987.[↑][→].

20 🚐free 🚰🚽Ch ⚡(16x) WC free.
Surface: asphalted. 📅 01/01-31/12
Distance: 🏘300m 🛣6km 🍴200m 🛒500m.

[🚐] Forlimpopoli 32C2

Via De Gasperi. **GPS**: n44,19044 e12,12608.

🚐free. **Surface:** asphalted. 📅 01/01-31/12
Distance: 🏘100m 🍴100m 🛒100m 🥖100m.
Remarks: Nearby railway station.

[S] Forlimpopoli 32C2

Palazzetto dello Sport, Via del Tulipano. **GPS**: n44,18432 e12,11843.
🚰🚽Chfree.
Remarks: In front of gymnasium.

[🚐][S] Gropparello 31D2

Via D. Aligieri. **GPS**: n44,83521 e9,73051.[↑][→].

🚐€ 10 🚰🚽free. 🚿 **Location:** Rural, quit. **Surface:** asphalted. 📅 01/01-31/12
Distance: 🏘100m 🍴500m.
Remarks: Castello di Gropparello 300m.

[🚐][S] Guastalla 32A1

Piazzale Ugo Foscolo. **GPS**: n44,92364 e10,65148.[↑].

🚐free 🚰🚽free ⚡(6x)€ 3. **Surface:** asphalted. 📅 01/01-31/12
Distance: 🏘historical centre 300m 🏖1,5km 🍴600m 🥖100m.
Remarks: Cycle route along the Po river.

[🚐][S] Imola 32B2

Via 1° Maggio, Via Salvador Allende. **GPS**: n44,37083 e11,72093.

🚐free 🚰free. **Surface:** asphalted. 📅 01/01-31/12
Distance: 🏘1,5km 🛣2,7km 🍴trattoria Ca' del Pozzo 🛒500m 🚌100m.
Remarks: Industrial area.

[🚐][S] Imola 32B2

Via Pirandello. **GPS**: n44,34628 e11,70922.

30 🚐free 🚰🚽free. **Surface:** grassy/sand. 📅 01/01-31/12
Distance: 🏘700m 🚆50m 🍴80m 🛒50m supermercato Famila.
Remarks: In front of the Ferrari Circuit. Follow signs autodromo.

Tourist information Imola:
[i] I.A.T.(Ufficio Informazioni e di Accoglienza Turistica), Via Emilia, 135.
⛱ Piazza Gramsci. 📅 Mo-Thu, Sa 8-12.30h.

[🍴][S] Lagosanto 32C1

Ristorante Il Varano, Via Valle Oppio 6, Marozzo di Lagosanto. **GPS**: n44,78167 e12,12533.[↑].

50 🚐€ 12, guests free 🚰🚽Ch ⚡ WC 🚿 🧺. **Surface:** gravel. 📅 01/01-31/12
Distance: 🏘3km 🏖12km 🍴on the spot 🛒500m.

Langhirano 31D2
Salumificio La Perla, Quinzano. **GPS**: n44,58748 e10,23783.

50 free ⚡. **Location:** Rural, very simple, quit. **Surface:** gravel. ⬛ 01/01-31/12
Distance: 3km on the spot 3km on the spot.
Remarks: Producer Parma ham.

Langhirano 31D2
La Fazenda, Cascinapiano di Langhirano. **GPS**: n44,63322 e10,27410.
50 € 10, guests € 5 WC included. **Location:** Quit. **Surface:** grassy/gravel. ⬛ 01/01-31/12
Distance: 1km on the spot on the spot 500m.

Maranello 32A2
Area Camper Maranello, Via Fondo Val Tiepido 77, Torre Maina. **GPS**: n44,50008 e10,87384.
10 € 5 Ch WC. **Location:** Rural, comfortable, quit.
Surface: unpaved. ⬛ 01/01-31/12
Distance: on the spot shuttle Bologna-Modena on the spot.
Remarks: Entrance code available at bar.

Marzaglia 32A2
Area di sosta Marzaglia, Strada Pomposiana 305. **GPS**: n44,63514 e10,80733.

30 € 5/pppd Ch € 1,50/day WC. **Location:** Rural, comfortable, quit. **Surface:** gravel. ⬛ 01/01-31/12
Distance: Modena 10km 7km.

Mesola 32C1
Oasi Park II, via Cristina 84, Bosco Mesola. **GPS**: n44,86822 e12,24898.

€ 8-15 Ch € 2 WC. **Surface:** grassy. ⬛ 01/01-31/12
Distance: 100m.
Remarks: Borrow cycles for free.

Mesola 32C1
Via 2 Giugno. **GPS**: n44,92331 e12,23469.

6 free Ch free. **Surface:** asphalted. ⬛ 01/01-31/12
Distance: 400m 400m 150m.
Remarks: Parking sports park.

Mesola 32C1
Agriturismo Ca'Laura, SP 27, Bosco Mesola. **GPS**: n44,87122 e12,24444.

6 € 15 Ch WC. **Surface:** metalled. ⬛ 01/01-31/12
Distance: 10km on the spot 1km 1km.
Remarks: Swimming pool, training golf course.

Mirandola 32A1
Via Luigi Galvani. **GPS**: n44,89812 e11,06199.
10 free Ch free.
Location: Very simple, quit. **Surface:** gravel.
Distance: 500m 1km 1km 500m.
Remarks: At cemetery.

Misano Adriatico 32D3
Via Taveleto 53. **GPS**: n43,96694 e12,67306.

€ 16 Ch WC included.
Distance: 500m 5km 500m 500m.

Modena 32A2
Camper Club Mutina, Strada Collegarola 76/A, zona Vaciglio. **GPS**: n44,61361 e10,94444.

32 € 15/24h Ch WC included. **Location:** Rural, comfortable, luxurious, quit. **Surface:** asphalted. ⬛ 01/01-31/12
Distance: 600m 3km 600m on the spot.

IT

Modena 32A2

Ristorante Pizzeria Taverna Napoleone, Via San Lorenzo 44. **GPS:** n44,57567 e10,96415.

10 free free.
Location: Rural. **Surface:** metalled. 01/01-31/12
Distance: 5km 2,8km pizzeria 5km.
Remarks: 10% discount at restaurant. A1 exit Modena-sud.

Tourist information Modena:
U.I..A.T. (Ufficio Informazioni e di Accoglienza Turistica), Piazza Grande, 17, www.comune.modena.it/infoturismo/guidaturismo.City with factories of Ferrari and Masserati.
Galleria Ferrari, Via Dino Ferrari 43, Maranello.Museum of motor-cars.

Monticelli d'Ongina 31D1

Piazza Resistenza. **GPS:** n45,09050 e9,93537.

10 free Chfree. **Location:** Very simple, quit. **Surface:** asphalted.
01/01-31/12
Distance: centre ±300m 6,2km 300m 300m.

Parma 31D2

Area Camper Parma, Largo XXIV Agosto 1942, n° 21/a. **GPS:** n44,80931 e10,28495.

30 € 1/8-22h, € 8/night Ch consumption WC € 1.
Surface: grasstiles.
01/01-31/12
Distance: centre 3,5km 7km Lidl 100m.
Remarks: Monitored parking, motorhome washing place 50m.

Tourist information Parma:
U.I.A.T. (Ufficio Informazioni e di Accoglienza Turistica), Via Melloni,1, turismo. comune.parma.it/turismo.
Palazzo Pilotta. morning.
Via Verdi.Week market. Wed-Sa 7-14h.

Pavullo nel Frignano 32A2

Via Degli Abeti. **GPS:** n44,34294 e10,83309.

12 free Chfree.
Location: Comfortable, quit. **Surface:** gravel/sand.
Distance: 700m 600m 600m 600m.
Remarks: Picnic area.

Porto Corsini 32C2

Pro Loco, Via G. Guizzetti. **GPS:** n44,49620 e12,27950.

155 01/04-30/09 € 8 Ch WC.
Distance: 500m 200m 300m 300m 300m.

Portomaggiore 32B2

Via Giuseppe Mazzini. **GPS:** n44,69584 e11,81389.

10 free free. **Surface:** asphalted. 01/01-31/12
Distance: 500m 500m 500m.
Remarks: Nearby cemetery.

Tourist information Portomaggiore:
Valli di Comacchio.Nature reserve, in winter whereabouts birds.

Premilcuore 32B3

Parcheggio Fluviale, Loc. Fontanalba. **GPS:** n43,97618 e11,77615.

free, 15/05-15/09 € 5. **Surface:** metalled. 01/01-31/12
Distance: 500m 20m 500m 50m.
Remarks: Along river.

Ravenna 32C2

Parking Bus-Camper, Via E.Ferrari. Loc.Classe. **GPS:** n44,37849 e12,23461.

IT

30 🛏free 🚰🗑free. **Surface:** metalled. 🅾 01/01-31/12
Distance: Ravenna centre 6km.
Remarks: Nearby basilica.

| 🅂 | Ravenna | 32C2 |

Piazza della Resistenza. **GPS:** n44,41433 e12,18852.⬆.

10 🛏 🚰🗑Chfree. 🅾 01/01-31/12
Distance: historical centre 500m 🏊5km ⊗150m 🚉500m 🚌50m.

| 🅂 | Ravenna | 32C2 |

Via Chiavica Romea/via Pomposa. **GPS:** n44,42570 e12,21081.

10 🛏free 🚰🗑Ch. **Surface:** metalled. 🅾 01/01-31/12
Distance: 500m 🏊5km ⊗350m 🚉500m.

| 🅂 | Ravenna | 32C2 |

Via Teodorico. **GPS:** n44,42317 e12,20981.

10 🛏free 🚰🗑Ch. **Surface:** metalled. 🅾 01/01-31/12
Distance: 500m ⊗on the spot.
Remarks: In front of the Mausoleum.

| | Ravenna | 32C2 |

Via Brancaleone/circonvallazione S. Gaetanino. **GPS:** n44,42339 e12,20478.

25 🛏free. **Surface:** metalled. 🅾 01/01-31/12
Distance: 200m 🏊5km 📡100m ⊗200m 🚉200m 🚌10m.
Remarks: Next to Rocca Brancaleone.

| 🅂 | Ravenna | 32C2 |

Parco Divertimenti Mirabilandia, SS16, via Romea Sud 463. **GPS:** n44,33290 e12,26966.⬆.

400 🛏€ 9 🚰🗑free.
Surface: gravel.
Distance: Ravenna centre 10km ⊗McDonalds.
Remarks: Arrival < 18h, max. 48h.

Tourist information Ravenna:
ℹ️ U.I.A.T. (Ufficio Informazioni e di Accoglienza Turistica), Via Salara, 8/12, www.turismo.ravenna.it.City of the mosaics, historical city with many curiosities.
🏵 Piazza Garibaldi.Antiques market. 🅾 3rd weekend of the month.
😊 Parco Divertimenti Mirabilandia, SS16, via Romea Sud 463.Amusement park.
🅾 01/04-15/09.

| 🅂 | Reggio nell'Emilia | 32A2 |

Parking Ex Foro Boario, Via XX Settembre. **GPS:** n44,70941 e10,62463.⬆➡.

200 🛏free 🚰🗑Chfree. **Location:** Urban, very simple. **Surface:** grasstiles.
🅾 01/01-31/12
Distance: 1km 🚴3,7km ⊗100m 🚉500m 🚌Free bus to centre.

| 🅂 | Riccione | 32D3 |

Piazza 1° Maggio. **GPS:** n44,00392 e12,65115.⬆➡.

10 🛏free 🚰€ 4 🗑Ch. **Surface:** asphalted. 🅾 01/01-31/12 ⬛ Service: winter.

Distance: 🏖100m ⛰500m ⊗500m 🛒100m 🚉50m.

S | Rimini 🌿⛱🌊 32C3

Park Settebello, Via Roma 86. **GPS:** n44,06068 e12,57572.⬆➡.

150 🅿€10/24h ⚡€ 4 🔌€ 2. **Surface:** metalled. ⭕ 01/01-31/12
Distance: 🏖200m ⛰400m.
Remarks: Next to cinema Settebello.

S | Rimini 🌿⛱🌊 32C3

Sostaverde La Valletta, Via Della Lama, SS 16. **GPS:** n44,09889 e12,49867.⬆➡.

150 🅿€10/24h ⚡🧹€ 3 WC included. **Surface:** grassy/gravel. ⭕ 01/04-30/09
Distance: 🏖Rimini 11km 🏄3,8km ⛰2km ⊗800m 🚉800m.
Remarks: Beachshuttle.

S | Rimini 🌿⛱🌊 32C3

P30 Chiabrera, Via Chiabrera. **GPS:** n44,04803 e12,59548.
🅿01/05-30/09 € 7,75. **Surface:** metalled.

Tourist information Rimini:
ℹ U.I.A.T. (Ufficio Informazioni e di Accoglienza Turistica), Piazzale Frederico Fellini, 3, www.riminiturismo.it/.Popular bathing resort.
⊗ Casa Zanni, Via Casale, 205, Villa Verucchio.Restaurant with authentic Italian cuisine.

S | Ro 32B1

Mulino sul Po. GPS: n44,95498 e11,75668.⬆.

4 🅿free ⚡🧹free. **Surface:** metalled.
Distance: 🏖1km 🚲on the spot 🚶on the spot.
Remarks: Along the Po river.

S | Rubiera 32A2

Via della Chiusa. **GPS:** n44,64229 e10,77765.⬆➡.

🅿free ⚡🔌Ch. **Location:** Very simple, quit. **Surface:** asphalted. ⭕ 01/01-31/12
Remarks: At sports park.

S | Sala Baganza 31D2

Via Vittorio Emanuele, 42. **GPS:** n44,70856 e10,23070.⬆.

2 🅿free ⚡🔌Ch🧹(4x)free. **Location:** Rural, quit. **Surface:** asphalted. ⭕ 01/01-31/12
Distance: 🏖500m 🏄15km 🚉500m.

S | Salsomaggiore Terme ♨ 31D2

Via Antonio Gramsci. **GPS:** n44,82005 e9,98981.⬆.

20 🅿free ⚡free. **Location:** Urban, very simple, quit. **Surface:** gravel. ⭕ 01/01-31/12
Distance: 🏖800m.
Remarks: Parking next to station.

S | Saludecio ⛰ 32D3

Agriturismo Fattoria Eby, Via Tassinara 81, loc. Pulzona. **GPS:** n43,89771 e12,72701.⬆➡.

10 🅿€ 16, guests free ⚡🔌Ch🧹WC included. ⭕ 01/01-31/12, restaurant Fr/Sa/Su
Distance: 🏖4km ⊗on the spot.
Remarks: SP 38 dir Tavullia.

S | San Piero in Bagno 32C3

Via G.Mazzini. **GPS:** n43,86353 e11,97692.⬆.

5 ⌇free. **Surface:** asphalted. ◐ 01/01-31/12
Distance: 🚶500m 🚲1km ⊗500m 🛒500m 🚌200m.

| 🛁 S | Santa Sofia 🏔🎭 | 32C3 |

Piazzale K. Marx. **GPS:** n43,94165 e11,90930.⬆.

⌇free 🚰🗑Ch. **Surface:** asphalted. ◐ 01/01-31/12
Distance: 🚶200m.

Tourist information Santa Sofia:
⤵ Foreste Casentinesi.National nature reserve.

| Serramazzoni 🏔🚡🏔🎭❄ | 32A2 |

Piazza Olimpico. **GPS:** n44,42223 e10,79402.⬆➡.

20 ⌇free 🚰🗑Ch free. **Location:** Urban. **Surface:** asphalted. ◐ 01/01-31/12
Distance: 🚶300m ⊗100m 🛒300m 🚲300m 🚶300m 🚴800m.

| 🍴 S | Serramazzoni 🏔🚡🏔🎭❄ | 32A2 |

Via Giardini Nord, Montagnana di Serramazzoni. **GPS:** n44,47250 e10,82005.⬆.

15 ⌇free 🚰🗑.
Location: Rural, quit. **Surface:** gravel. ◐ 01/01-31/12
Distance: 🚶8km Maranello 🛒8km.
Remarks: Maranello: Ferrari factory and museum.

Tourist information Serramazzoni:
ℹ Ufficio Turistico, Piazzo Tasso,7.

| 🛁 S | Soragna 🏔 | 31D1 |

Via Matteotti / via Gramsci. **GPS:** n44,92988 e10,12566.⬆.

10 ⌇free 🚰🗑Ch free. **Location:** Urban, very simple, quit. **Surface:** asphalted. ◐ 01/01-31/12
Distance: 🚶120m ⊗200m 🛒200m.

| 🛁 | Suviana | 32A3 |

Via Lungo Lago. **GPS:** n44,12039 e11,04592.

60 ⌇Free, hollidays € 9. 🚣 **Location:** Rural, very simple, quit. **Surface:** asphalted.
Distance: 🏊on the spot 🛒on the spot ⊗on the spot.
Remarks: At lake Suviana.

| 🛁 S | Terenzo 🏔🏔🎭 | 31D2 |

Loc. Bardone. **GPS:** n44,62528 e10,10083.⬆.

10 ⌇€ 13 🚰🗑Ch 💧WC included. 🚣 **Location:** Rural, comfortable, quit. **Surface:** metalled. ◐ 01/01-31/12
Distance: 🚶200m 🚲12km 🛒12km 🚶on the spot.

| 🛁 S | Tredozio 🏔🎭 | 32B3 |

Via Salvo D'Acquisto. **GPS:** n44,07431 e11,73228.⬆➡.

10 ⌇€ 5 🚰🗑Ch. **Surface:** metalled. ◐ 01/01-31/12
Distance: 🚶1,5km ⊗200m camping 🛒1,5km.
Remarks: Next to campsite Le Volte, max. 48h, reductions at restaurant/swimming-pool.

| 🛁 S | Tresigallo | 32B1 |

Fraz. Finale di Rero. **GPS:** n44,81643 e11,90050.
⌇free 🚰🗑.
Remarks: Nearby sports park.

Vergato 32A2

SS 64, Bologna-Pistoia. **GPS**: n44,28952 e11,11270.⬆️.

25 free ⌁ Ch free. **Location**: Rural, very simple. **Surface**: asphalted. ⬛
01/01-31/12
Distance: 400m 400m 500m 500m.
Remarks: On entering de village from Bologna.

Liguria

Borghetto Santo Spirito 31B3

Via Tevere. **GPS**: n44,11548 e8,23758.⬆️➡️.

150 € 10 ⌁ Ch (50x)€ 3/day, 16Amp. **Surface**: gravel.
Distance: 1,1km 2,5km 400m.
Remarks: Along the river Varatella.

Castelnuovo Magra 31D3

Agriturismo Cascina dei Peri, Via Montefrancio 71. **GPS**: n44,10355 e10,00734.
⬆️➡️.

6 € 8/pp, children free ⌁ Ch WC included ⬛ € 5. **Surface**:
grassy/gravel. ⬛ 01/01-31/12
Distance: 2,4km.
Remarks: Dinner € 20/pp wine incl. (to order <16h), selling of wine and olive oil, swimming pool from june.

Cengio 31B3

Area Attrezzata Cengio Isole, Via Isole. **GPS**: n44,39083 e8,20194.⬆️➡️.

free ⌁ Ch free. **Surface**: asphalted.
Distance: 600m on the spot on the spot.

Remarks: Nearby sports park.

Cervo 31B3

Via Steria. **GPS**: n43,92833 e8,10527.⬆️➡️.

130 € 8-12/day ⌁ Ch € 3/24h.
Surface: gravel. ⬛ 01/01-31/12
Distance: 2,5km.

Diano Marina 31A3

Oasi Park, Via Sori 5. **GPS**: n43,90667 e8,07083.⬆️.

300 € 5-15/day ⌁ Ch € 2 WC. **Surface**: grassy/gravel. ⬛
01/01-31/12
Distance: 600m 6,8km 700m 600m 600m 600m.
Remarks: Beachshuttle.

Diano Marina 31A3

Il bowling di Diano, Via Diano S. Pietro, 71 - Diano Castello. **GPS**: n43,91683 e8,07576.

€ 5-10-15/day ⌁ Ch. **Surface**: unpaved.
Distance: 500m 5,5km 500m on the spot 50m.
Remarks: Swimming pool, bar, bowling.

Diano Marina 31A3

Al Roseto, Via Case Parse, San siro, Diano Castello. **GPS**: n43,91983 e8,07733.⬆️.

€ 12, free for clients ⌁ Ch WC € 2. ⬛ 01/01-31/12
Distance: 5,5km.
Remarks: At Floriculturist, shuttle to beach.

Tourist information Diano Marina:
ℹ️ I.A.T. (Ufficio Informazioni e di Accoglienza Turistica), Corso Garibaldi, 60.

IT

🚐 [S] Finale Ligure 31B3

Loc. Caprazoppa. **GPS**: n44,16549 e8,33750.
100 🚐 € 8/12h, € 15/24h 🚰 🗑 Chagainst payment.
Distance: 🏙 4km 🏖 on the spot.

🚐 [S] La Spezia 🐚 ⛱ 🌊 31D3

Viale San Bartolomeo. **GPS**: n44,10417 e9,85917.

100 🚐 voluntary contribution 🚰 🗑 free. **Surface:** grassy. 🕐 8-20h ⛔ 12.30-13.30h.
Distance: 🚶 4km.
Remarks: Monitored parking.

Tourist information La Spezia:
ℹ Lerici.Former fishing village, nowadays holiday resort.
ℹ Cinque Terre.Protected coast area.
🏰 Castello di Lerici, Lerici. 🕐 01/04-31/10.
🛍 Lerici. 🕐 Sa-morning.

🚐 [S] Levanto 31D3

SP556, Loc. Moltedi. **GPS**: n44,17476 e9,61836. ⬆ ➡.

16 🚐 € 10/12h, € 15/24h, € 20/36h 🚰 🗑 Chfree. 🕐 01/01-31/12
Distance: 🚶 500m 🏖 1km 🚆 train 100m.
Remarks: Behind railway station, good location for visiting the Cinque Terre by train.

🚐 [S] Loano 🐚 31B3

Camper Park, Via Silvio Amico, via delle Fornaci.. **GPS**: n44,13111 e8,24111. ⬆ ➡.

44 🚐 € 10/24h 🚰 🗑 Ch 🔌 6Amp WCincluded. **Surface:** gravel.
Distance: 🚶 1,4km 🏙 7km 🏖 1,5km 🛒 200m.
Remarks: Max. 48h.

Tourist information Loano:
ℹ U.I.A.T. (Ufficio Informazioni e di Accoglienza Turistica), Toirano, www.italianriviera.com.Small medieval town.
👁 Grotta di Santa Lucia, Toirano.Stalactites and stalagmites.
⛰ Grotta della Basura, Toirano.Man and beast from the stone age.

🚐 [S] Pietra Ligure 31B3

Area Camper, Via Crispi 43. **GPS**: n44,15484 e8,28397. ⬆ ➡.

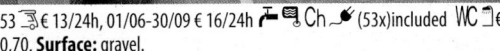

53 🚐 € 13/24h, 01/06-30/09 € 16/24h 🚰 🗑 Ch 🔌 (53x)included WC 🚿 € 0,70. **Surface:** gravel.
Distance: 🏖 200m.

🚐 [S] San Bartolomeo al Mare 31B3

Via Manzoni. **GPS**: n43,92432 e8,10489.
10 🚐 € 8/24h 🚰 🗑 free. **Surface:** gravel.
Distance: 🏙 2,5km.
Remarks: Along the river Stera, max. 48h.

🚐 [S] San Remo 🐚 ⛱ 🌊 31A4

Loc. Pia di Poma S.S. Aurelia. **GPS**: n43,80278 e7,74806.

🚐 16/09-14/06 € 7, 15/06-15/09 € 10 🚰 🗑 Chfree.
Distance: 🏙 5km.
Remarks: Max. 36h.

Tourist information San Remo:
ℹ Bussana Vecchia.International artists village.
ℹ A.P.T. (Azienda di Promozione Turistica), Largo Nuvoloni, 1, www.apt.rivieradeifiori.it.Famous holiday resort.
🛍 Corso Garibaldi.Flowers market. 🕐 morning.

🚐 San Rocco 🐚 31C3

Viale Franco Molfino/Camogli. **GPS**: n44,33472 e9,16084.

9 🚐 € 9/8-20h. **Surface:** asphalted.
Distance: 🚆 on the spot.
Remarks: Marked hiking trails in Parco di Portofino (45min-2h).

🚐 [S] Santo Stefano al Mare 🌊 31A4

Camper Village, Strada Porsani. **GPS**: n43,84378 e7,90824. ⬆.

IT

60 ⛽€ 12-20/24h 🚿🚰 Ch ♨💧 3 WC 🗑. **Surface:** gravel.
Distance: 🏖10km 🏊800m 🚋on the spot.
Remarks: Free shuttle.

🚐S **Torriglia** 31C2
GPS: n44,51667 e9,16000.➡.

10 ⛽free 🚿🚰 Ch free. **Surface:** grasstiles.
Distance: 🏖200m.
Remarks: Municipal parking.

Tuscany

🚐S **Alberese** 32B5
Parco Naturale della Maremma, Via del Bersagliere. **GPS:** n42,66944 e11,10416.
⬆.

50 ⛽€ 9/day, € 6/½day 🚿🚰 Ch free.
Surface: sand. ⏱ 01/04-30/09
Distance: 🏖100m 🏊7km ⊗on the spot.

🚐S **Anghiari** 32C4
Via Campo della Fiera. **GPS:** n43,53904 e12,05291.⬆.

8 ⛽free 🚿🚰 Ch free. **Surface:** asphalted.
Distance: 🏖on the spot ⊗on the spot 🛒on the spot.

🚐S **Anghiari** 32C4
Agriturismo Val della Pieve, Via della Fossa 8. **GPS:** n43,53657 e12,05131.⬆.
➡.

10 ⛽€ 12 🚿🚰 Ch ♨💧 3 WC 🗑📷🔊.
Surface: gravel. ⏱ 01/01-31/12

Distance: 🏖300m ⊗300m 🛒300m 🚋300m.
Remarks: Swimming pool € 3/pppd.

🍴S **Anghiari** 32C4
Agriturismo La Taverna dei Sorci, San Lorenzo. **GPS:** n43,51467 e12,07799.⬆.

20 ⛽free 🚿. **Surface:** metalled. ☐ 01/01-31/12
Distance: ⊗on the spot.

🚐S **Arcidosso** 32B5
Parco Faunistico Monte Amiata, Località Poderi. **GPS:** n42,83740 e11,52922.

15 ⛽free 🚰 Ch. **Location:** Rural, very simple, central, quit. **Surface:** grassy.
⏱ 01/01-31/12
Distance: 🏖10km.
Remarks: Nature reserve.

🚐S **Arezzo** 🍇 32C4
Via Da Palestrina/via Tarlati (centro-nord). **GPS:** n43,47213 e11,88773.

30 ⛽€ 8 🚿🚰 Ch 🔊free. **Surface:** asphalted.
Distance: 🏖centro storico 1km.

🚐 **Arezzo** 🍇 32C4
Parcheggio Pietri, Via Pietri. **GPS:** n43,47071 e11,88196.⬆.

50 ⛽free. **Surface:** asphalted. ☐ 01/01-31/12
Distance: 🏖centro storico 500m.

Tourist information Arezzo:
ℹ Informazioni Turistiche, Piazza della Repubblica, 28.
🎪 Week market.

IT

Barberino di Mugello 🏔🍴 32B3

SS65, Fraz. Monte di Fó. **GPS**: n44,07613 e11,28062.⬆.

30 🚐free ⛽🗑Chfree. **Surface**: metalled.
Distance: 🚶4km ⊗150m (camping) 🛒150m (camping).
Remarks: In front of campsite Il Sergente.

Barga 32A3

Area San Cristoforo, Via Hayange. **GPS**: n44,07234 e10,48131.⬆➡.
🚐€ 10/24h ⛽🗑Ch🧹(10x) WC🗑.
Distance: 🚶centro storico within walking distance.

Bibbiena 🍷🏔🍴 32C3

Agricola Casentinese, Loc. Casanova 63. **GPS**: n43,71669 e11,85173.

🚐€ 12, Apr, May, Oct € 15, Jun-Sep € 18, 2 pers.incl ⛽🗑
Ch🧹 WC🗑included 🚿€ 5, ironing services € 5. **Surface**: gravel. ⬛
15/03-01/11, Christmas
Distance: 🚶4km ⊗on the spot ➖on the spot.
Remarks: Swimming pool € 5/pp (free with a meal).

Borghetto 🌊 32C4

GPS: n43,18415 e12,02372.

4 🚐free ⛽🗑📥free. **Surface**: asphalted. ⬛ 01/01-31/12
Distance: ⛰150m ⊗100m.

Borgo a Mozzano 32A3

Via I° Maggio, SP2. **GPS**: n43,97612 e10,54113.⬆.

4 🚐free ⛽🗑Ch (4x)free. **Surface**: gravel.
Distance: 🚶200m ⚓Serchio river.
Remarks: At tourist office.

Buonconvento 🌿 32B5

Viale della Liberta. **GPS**: n43,13854 e11,48109.🛬.

🚐free. **Location**: Very simple. **Surface**: unpaved.
Distance: 🚶50m ⊗50m.
Remarks: SS2 exit centre, in opposite of the city walls.

Buonconvento 🌿 32B5

Viale Ferruccio Parri. **GPS**: n43,13065 e11,48349.⬆➡.

⛽€ 1 🗑Ch. ⬛ 01/01-31/12

Calci 32A4

Via Brogiotti. **GPS**: n43,72769 e10,51722.⬆.

6 🚐€ 8/24h ⛽🗑Ch🧹included. **Surface**: asphalted. ⬛ 01/01-31/12
Distance: 🚶100m 🛒200m.
Remarks: At sports park, payment only with coins.

Campiglia Marittima 32A5

Parcheggio La Pieve, Via di Venturina. **GPS**: n43,05672 e10,61439.⬆.

4 🚐free ⛽🗑Chfree. **Surface**: asphalted.
Distance: 🚶350m ⊗450m.
Remarks: Near gymnasium, in opposite of cemetery.

Capannoli 32A4

Campo Sportivo, Via Berlinguer. **GPS**: n43,59077 e10,67305.⬆➡.

IT

🛏free ⌐🔧Ch ✎free. **Surface:** metalled.
Distance: 🚶400m.

| 🅢 | Capraia e Limite | 32A3 |

Via delle Ginestre, zona industriale, loc. Capraia Fiorentina. **GPS:** n43,73660 e11,00442.⬆️.
🛏free ⌐🔧Ch free. **Surface:** metalled.

| 🅢 | Casola in Lunigiana | 31D3 |

GPS: n44,19916 e10,17333.⬆️➡️.

20 🛏€7 + €5/pp ⌐🔧Ch ✎ WC🗑 📶included. **Surface:** grassy. ⬛
01/01-31/12
Distance: 🏊on the spot.
Remarks: At little stream with swimming area.

| 🅢 | Castagneto Carducci | 32A5 |

Via del Seggio, Marina di Castagneto. **GPS:** n43,18401 e10,54841.⬆️.

30 🛏€10/24h ⌐🔧Ch. **Surface:** unpaved.
Distance: 🏖500m.

| 🅢 | Castagneto Carducci | 32A5 |

Viale delle Palme, Marina di Castagneto. **GPS:** n43,19323 e10,54152.⬆️.

30 🛏free ⌐🔧Chfree. **Location:** Rural. **Surface:** asphalted. ⬛ 01/01-31/12
Distance: 🚶500m.
Remarks: Follow 'P long stay'.

| 🅢 | Castelfiorentino | 32A4 |

Via Che Guevara, circonvallazione Ovest. **GPS:** n43,60885 e10,96365.⬆️.

5 🛏free ⌐🔧free. **Surface:** asphalted.

| 🅢 | Castellina in Chianti | 32B4 |

La Strada del Chianti, SR222. **GPS:** n43,47330 e11,28760.⬆️➡️.

15 🛏€10/24h, 01/11-31/03 free ⌐€ 0,20/10liter 🔧Ch ✎ (8x)included
WC€ 0,50. 🚐 **Location:** Rural, comfortable. **Surface:** asphalted. ⬛ 01/01-31/12
Distance: 🚶200m.

Tourist information Castellina in Chianti:
ℹ️ Uffici Informazione Turistica, Via Ferruccio 40.
🎪 Via IV Novembre. Week market. ⬛ Sa-morning.

| 🅢 | Castelnuovo di Garfagnana | 32A3 |

Via Valmaira. **GPS:** n44,11447 e10,40304.⬆️.

🛏free ⌐🔧Chfree. **Surface:** metalled. ⬛ 01/01-31/12
Distance: 🚶1km.
Remarks: At sports park.

20 🛏€10/24h ⌐🔧Ch. **Surface:** unpaved.
Distance: 🏖100m.
Remarks: Max. 48h, also dogs beach.

| 🅢 | Castel del Piano 🌿⛺🏔 | 32B5 |

Via Po. **GPS:** n42,88872 e11,53733.➡️.

| 🅢 | Castelnuovo di Val de Cecina | 32A5 |

Via della Fonte, Sasso Pisano. **GPS:** n43,16748 e10,86586.⬆️.

10 🛏free 🚰€ 2 🗑Ch 💧€ 3/12h. **Surface:** gravel.
Distance: 🚶100m.
Remarks: Next to football ground.

| 🅿️S | **Castiglion Fiorentino** | 32C4 |

Piazza Garibaldi, viale Marconi. **GPS:** n43,34465 e11,92278. ⬆️.

20 🛏free 🚰🗑Chfree WC. **Location:** Rural, very simple. **Surface:** asphalted. ⬛ 01/01-31/12 ⬤ Fri-morning market.
Distance: 🚶on the spot ⊗on the spot.

| 🅿️S | **Castiglione della Pescaia** 〰️⛵🌊 | 32A5 |

Rocchette Serignano, Via Rio Palma, Rocchette. **GPS:** n42,77970 e10,79955. ⬆️ ➡️.

± 50 🛏€ 20/day 🚰🗑Ch 💧(18x)included 🗑€ 1. **Surface:** unpaved. ⬛ 01/04-30/09
Distance: 🚶Castiglione della Pescaia 7km ⛱️200m ⊗200m.
Remarks: Beach parking, unguarded.

| 🅿️S | **Castiglione della Pescaia** 〰️⛵🌊 | 32A5 |

Viale Kennedy, SS158. **GPS:** n42,77447 e10,84395. ⬆️➡️.

40 🛏 Apr-Jun, Sep € 12, Jul/Aug € 15 🚰🗑Ch. **Surface:** asphalted. ⬛ 01/04-30/09
Distance: 🚶4km ⛱️500m ⊗4km 🍴4km.

| 🅿️S | **Castiglione d'Orcia** 〰️🏔️ | 32B5 |

Area Pro Loco, Viale Marconi. **GPS:** n43,00292 e11,61552. ⬆️.

5 🛏free 🚰🗑free. **Location:** Rural, very simple. **Surface:** gravel/sand. ⬛ 01/01-31/12
Distance: 🚶200m 🏃on the spot.

Tourist information Castiglione d'Orcia:
🏰 Rocco d'Orcia.Medieval citadel.

| 🅿️S | **Certaldo** | 32B4 |

Piazza dei Macelli. **GPS:** n43,54629 e11,04611. ⬆️➡️.

10 🛏free 🚰🗑Chfree. **Surface:** metalled. ⬛ 01/01-31/12
Distance: 🚶medieval centre 150m (elevator).

| 🅿️S | **Chiusdino** | 32B5 |

Abbazia San Galgano, SS441. **GPS:** n43,15283 e11,15137. ⬆️.

15 🛏€ 1,50/h, € 10/8-20h, overnight stay free 💧(9x)free. **Surface:** grasstiles. ⬛ 01/01-31/12
Distance: ⊗300m.
Remarks: Abbey of San Galgano 300m.

| 🅿️S | **Chiusi** | 32C5 |

Via Torri del Fornello. **GPS:** n43,01461 e11,94972. ⬆️.

5 🛏free 🚰🗑free. **Surface:** asphalted.
Distance: 🚶100m 🚲4,5km.
Remarks: Next to school.

| 🅿️S | **Cutigliano** | 32A3 |

Via di Risorgimento/Sp37. **GPS:** n44,09877 e10,75450.
14 🛏€ 1,50/h, € 15/24h 🚰🗑Ch💧.
Remarks: Max. 24h.

IT

Dicomano 32B3

Via Ciro Fabbroni. **GPS:** n43,88965 e11,52150.↑→.

16 🅣free ⌐🔌Chfree. **Surface:** asphalted. 🅞 01/01-31/12
Distance: 🚶500m ⊗500m 🛒500m.

Equi Terme 31D3

Via della Stazione. **GPS:** n44,17009 e10,15513.↑→.

40 🅣€ 10/night ⌐🔌Ch 🔌included. **Surface:** gravel.
Distance: ⊗100m.
Remarks: Near spa resort (100m), caves (500m) and marble quarry.

Firenze 32B3

FiPark, Viale Europa, Fraz. Bagno a Ripoli, Florence (Firenze). **GPS:** n43,75554 e11,30609.↑.

40 🅣7-19h € 1,50/h, 19-7h € 1/h, € 13,50/day ⌐🔌Ch. **Surface:** metalled.
🅞 01/01-31/12
Distance: 🚌bus 23/33 > centre.

Firenze 32B3

Area sociale 'Flog', Via M Mercati 24/b, zona Careggi, Florence (Firenze). **GPS:** n43,79491 e11,24835.

🅣€ 15/24h ⌐€ 3 🔌Ch. **Surface:** gravel. 🅞 01/01-31/12
Distance: 🚶city centre 2km ⊗Pizzeria 🚌centre : bus 4, 6-24h.

Firenze 32B3

Gelsomino SCAF, Via del Gelsomino 11, Florence (Firenze). **GPS:** n43,75173 e11,24388.
🅣€ 15/24h ⌐🔌Ch 🔌included. **Surface:** asphalted. 🅞 01/01-31/12
Distance: 🚶2km 🚌on the spot.

Firenze 32B3

Social Camper Firenze, Via di Scandicci 241, Florence (Firenze). **GPS:** n43,76267 e11,20875.↑.

25 🅣€ 20 ⌐🔌Ch 🔌WC 🚿included. 🐕 **Location:** Urban, comfortable, central. **Surface:** metalled. 🅞 01/01-31/12
Distance: 🚶4km 🚲5km 🚌150m.
Remarks: Terrain with video surveillance.
Tourist information Florence (Firenze):
ℹ️ U.I.A.T. (Ufficio Informazioni e di Accoglienza Turistica), Piazza Stazione, 4, www.firenze.turismo.toscana.it.Renaissance city with many curiosities.
👁 Ponte Vechio.Famous bridge with jeweller's shops.
✝ Cappella Brancacci, Santa Maria del Carmine.Renovated frescoes.
🛍 The Mall, le griffe, Via Europa 8, Leccio Reggello.Factory outlet.

Firenzuola 32B3

Area Picnic, Loc. Badia a Moscheta. **GPS:** n44,07586 e11,42064.🔝.

10 🅣free. **Surface:** gravel. 🅞 01/01-31/12
Distance: 🚶Firenzuola 8km ⊗500m agriturismo Badia di Moscheta.

Firenzuola 32B3

Loc. Pieve di Camaggiore. **GPS:** n44,14594 e11,45361.🔝.

20 🅣free. **Surface:** grasstiles. 🅞 01/01-31/12
Distance: 🚶Firenzuola 10km 🏊river 100m.
Remarks: Playground.

Fivizzano 31D3

Agriturismo Ristorante Al Vecchio Tino, Loc. Germalla 1, Monte dei Bianchi. **GPS:** n44,17155 e10,13325.
6 🅣€ 12 ⌐🔌Ch 🔌included. **Surface:** grassy. 🅞 01/01-31/12

Foiano della Chiana 32C4

Outlet Village Valdichiana, Via Enzo Ferrari 5, loc. Farniole. **GPS:** n43,22489 e11,80291.↑.

10 ⌇free. **Surface:** asphalted. ⬤ 01/01-31/12
Distance: ⊗on the spot ⬚on the spot.
Remarks: Motorhome parking at Outlet.

Follonica 32A5
Acquapark, Via Sanzio. **GPS:** n42,92804 e10,77569.
⌇€ 10, electricity incl ⟊€ 4 ⬚Ch ⚲.
Distance: ⚓beach 1,8km.

Gaiole in Chianti 32B4
Via Michelangelo Buonarroti. **GPS:** n43,46434 e11,43440.⬆➡.

⌇free ⟊⬚Chfree.
Location: Rural. **Surface:** metalled. ⬤ 01/01-31/12
Remarks: Nearby football ground.

Gallicano 32A3
Via dei Cipressi. **GPS:** n44,05827 e10,44565.⬆➡.

4 ⌇free ⟊⬚Ch ⚲(2x)free. **Surface:** metalled. ⬤ 01/01-31/12
Distance: ⚑500m.
Remarks: Grotta del Vento.

Greve in Chianti 32B4
Monte S. Michele, Via Montebeni. **GPS:** n43,59066 e11,31355.⬆➡.

17 ⌇free ⟊⬚free. **Location:** Rural, comfortable, quit. **Surface:** metalled.
⬤ 01/01-31/12
Distance: ⚑500m ⬚500m.
Tourist information Greve in Chianti:
🛈 Ufficio Informazioni, Via Luca Cini, 1.
⚘ ⬤ Sa-morning.

Isola dElba 32A5
San Bennato, Cavo. **GPS:** n42,85459 e10,42267.
50 ⌇€ 18/24h ⟊⬚Ch ⚲€ 2 ⌇€ 1.
Surface: gravel. ⬤ 01/06-30/09
Distance: ⚑600m ⚓400m.

Isola dElba 32A5
Loc. Bocchetto, Porto Azzurro. **GPS:** n42,77114 e10,39985.
60 ⌇€ 15/24h ⟊⬚.
Remarks: Nearby cemetery.

Isola dElba 32A5
Sighello, area La Pila, Marina di Campo. **GPS:** n42,75905 e10,23645.⬆.
20 ⌇€ 10/15 ⟊⬚Ch ⚲€ 3. **Surface:** unpaved. ⬤ 01/05-30/09
Distance: ⚓1,5km.
Remarks: At sports park.

Larciano 32A3
Residence Poggetto, Via Stradella 1489. **GPS:** n43,83319 e10,88042.⬆.

15 ⌇€ 10/24h, free with a meal ⟊⬚Ch ⚲. **Surface:** grassy/gravel. ⬤
01/01-31/12
Distance: ⚑1km ⊗1km.

Livorno 32A4
Il Cavalluccio, Via G. Pascoli 12, Fraz Quercianella. **GPS:** n43,45897 e10,36573.

44 ⌇€ 24/night ⟊⬚Ch ⚲ WC ⌇. **Surface:** unpaved.
Distance: ⚓50m.

Livorno 32A4
Piazza Ordoardo Borrani, Viale d'Antignano. **GPS:** n43,50465 e10,32144.⬆.

50 ⌇free. **Surface:** asphalted.
Distance: ⚓100m ⬚300m.

Tourist information Livorno:
🛈 Ufficio Informazioni, Piazza del Municipio.Medieval port city.

IT

Lucca 32A3

Il Serchio - Lucca

info@camperilserchio.it - www.camperilserchio.it

Excellent location for city visit
Ideal base for walking and cycling
Swimming pool

Il Serchio, Via del Tiro a Segno 704, loc. Sant'Anna. **GPS**: n43,85000 e10,48583. ⬆️.66 🚐 € 20/24h 🚿🔋Ch 💧 (66x), WC 🚻 💧 € 4,50 🔌included.
Surface: grasstiles. ☀️ 01/03-31/01
Distance: 🚶1km 🚲2km 🚏500m ⊗on the spot 🛒2km 🏧on the spot 🚂on the spot.
Remarks: Swimming pool € 5/pp.

Lucca 32A3

P-Caravana, Viale Gaetano Luporini. **GPS:** n43,84028 e10,48878. ⬆️➡️.

65 🚐 € 10/24h, € 3/h 🚿🔋Ch 💧 included. **Surface:** asphalted.
Distance: 🚶5 min walking 🚲2km.

Lucignano 32B4

SP19. **GPS:** n43,27664 e11,74512. ⬆️➡️.

20 🚐 free 🚿🔋Ch 💧 (9x)free. **Location:** Rural, very simple. **Surface:** grassy. ☀️ 01/01-31/12
Distance: 🚶500m.
Remarks: At the edge of village.

Marina di Cecina 32A4

Parcheggio Aqua Park, Marina di Cecina. **GPS:** n43,30070 e10,49948. ⬆️.

100 🚐 1/3-15/11 € 8 🚿🔋. **Surface:** metalled. ☀️ 01/01-31/12
Distance: 🚶1km.

Marina di Cecina 32A4

Via della Cecinella. **GPS:** n43,29278 e10,50785. ⬆️.

30 🚐 1/3-15/11 € 8/24h 🚿🔋Ch. **Surface:** asphalted. ☀️ 01/01-31/12
Distance: 🚶300m.

Marina di Grosseto 32B5

Oasi di Maremma, SP158 delle Collacchie Km 34,4. **GPS:** n42,72611 e10,99055. ⬆️➡️.

100 🚐 € 15, peak season € 18, 4 pers.incl 🚿🔋Ch 💧 (100x)€ 2 WC 🚻 € 1 💧 € 3. **Surface:** grassy. ☀️ 01/04-30/09
Distance: 🚶1km 🏊1km ⊗1km 🛒1km 🚂on the spot.
Remarks: Water at each pitch, shuttle € 1,50/pp.

Marina di Grosseto 32B5

Area di sosta l'Oasi, S332 > dir San Vincenzo d'Elba. **GPS:** n42,73466 e10,97483. ⬆️➡️.

50 🚐 Jun € 14, Jul/Aug € 18, Sep € 12, 4 pers.incl 🚿🔋Ch 💧 € 2 WC 🚻 € 2 🔌. **Surface:** grassy. ☀️ Easter-30/09
Distance: 🚶Marina 1,5km 🏊1,1km ⊗400m 🛒nearby.

Marina di Grosseto 32B5

Via Costiera, SP158. **GPS:** n42,73722 e10,96388. ⬆️➡️.

50 🚐 free. **Surface:** gravel. ☀️ 01/01-31/12 **Distance:** 🚶2km 🏊400m.
Tourist information Marina di Grosseto:
🌿 Parco Naturale della Maremma.Nature reserve. ☀️ Wed, Sa, Su 9h 01/06-30/09 guided walk 7h, 16h.

⊠S **Marina di Pisa** 31D4
Parcheggio Camper Pisamo, Viale Gabriela d'Annunzio. **GPS**: n43,67908 e10,27830.
130 ⛺ € 15/24h ⛽🚿Ch⚡. **Surface**: sand. ⬛ 01/01-31/12
Distance: 🏖sea 1km.

⊠S **Marradi** 🌻🏞🌳 32B3
Area Attrezzata, Via San Benedetto. **GPS**: n44,07347 e11,61166.⬆.

30 ⛺free ⛽🚿Ch➕€ 5. **Surface**: asphalted. ⬛ 01/01-31/12
Distance: 🚶50m.
Remarks: Caution key service € 7.

⊠S **Massa Marittima** 32A5
Viale del Risorgimento. **GPS**: n43,04530 e10,89050.⬆➡.

7 ⛺free ⛽🚿Chfree. **Surface**: asphalted. ⬛ 01/01-31/12
Distance: 🚶historical centre 650m 🚌on the spot.

⊠S **Minucciano** 31D3
Agriturismo Da Pasquino, Perdetola. **GPS**: n44,16644 e10,21514.
50 ⛺free with a meal ⛽🚿Ch⚡.

⊠S **Montalcino** 🌻🏔⛰ 32B5
Geen, Via Osticcio. **GPS**: n43,04913 e11,48749.⬆➡.

30 ⛺€ 5/24h ⛽🚿Chfree. 🏞 **Location**: Rural, comfortable, quit. **Surface**:
asphalted/metalled. ⬛ 01/01-31/12
Distance: 🚶700m ⊗700m 🛒700m.

⊠S **Monte San Savino** 32B4
Via del Casalino. **GPS**: n43,33177 e11,72204.⬆.

20 ⛺free ⛽🚿Chfree. **Location**: Rural, very simple. **Surface**: gravel. ⬛

01/01-31/12
Distance: 🚶on the spot 🚲4,2km ⊗200m.
Remarks: Steep path.

⊠ **Montecatini Terme** ⛲ 32A3
Piazza Pietro Leopoldo, SS 436. **GPS**: n43,88286 e10,76386.
40 ⛺free. **Surface**: asphalted. ⬛ 01/01-31/12 ⬤ Thu (market).
Distance: 🚲3km ⊗500m 🛒500m.
Remarks: In front of stadium.

⊠S **Montemignaio** 32B3
Via Molino. **GPS**: n43,73989 e11,62024.⬆➡.
⛺free ⛽🚿free. **Surface**: gravel. ⬛ 01/01-31/12
Distance: ⊗150m.

⊠S **Montepulciano** 🌻 32C5
P5, Piazza Pietro Nenni. **GPS**: n43,09577 e11,78684.⬆➡.

32 ⛺€ 10/24h ⛽🚿free. 🏞 **Location**: Rural. **Surface**: asphalted. ⬛ 01/01-
31/12 ⬤ Thu-morning closed because of market.
Distance: 🚶200m ⊗100m 🛒400m.

⊠S **Monteriggioni** 🌻 32B4
Strada di Monteriggioni. **GPS**: n43,38801 e11,22511.⬆.

12 ⛺€ 1/h 8-20h, max. € 5, overnight stay free. 🏞 **Location**: Rural,
comfortable. **Surface**: gravel. ⬛ 01/01-31/12
Distance: 🚶300m 🚲1,4km ⊗300m 🐾on the spot.

⊠S **Monteroni d'Arbia** 32B4
Via San Giusto. **GPS**: n43,23048 e11,42371.⬆➡.

⛺free ⛽🚿Chfree.
Location: Rural. **Surface**: sand. ⬛ 01/01-31/12
Distance: 🚶50m.
Remarks: P centre.

⊠S **Montespertoli** 32B4
Molino del Ponte, Via Volterrana Nord. **GPS**: n43,65606 e11,08445.
⛺free ⛽€ 1/100liter 🚿€ 2 Ch. **Surface**: asphalted. ⬛ 01/01-31/12
Distance: 🚶Montespertoli 2,3km.

⊠S **Montevarchi** 32B4
Via B. Latini. **GPS**: n43,53052 e11,56784.⬆.

🅿free 🚰🅿free. **Location:** Urban, very simple.
Surface: asphalted.
Distance: 🚲7km 🛒Coop.
Remarks: Nearby stadium.

6 🅿free. **Surface:** metalled. ☐ 01/01-31/12
Distance: 🚶on the spot.
Remarks: Next to cemetery, upper part of the parking.

🏕🆂 Montopoli in Val d'Arno 32A4
Piazza Amerigo Vespucci, Via di Masoria. **GPS:** n43,67333 e10,75222.⬆.

🏕🆂 Peccioli 32A4
Parco Preistorico, Via Cappuccini. **GPS:** n43,55694 e10,71889.⬆.

31 🅿free 🚰🔌Chfree. **Surface:** metalled. ☐ 01/01-31/12
Distance: 🛒within walking distance.

15 🅿free, after 2 days € 5/day 🚰WC. **Surface:** gravel. ☐ 01/01-31/12
Distance: 🚶500m ⊗500m.
Remarks: Playground, picknic area.

🏕🆂 Orbetello 🌊 32B6
Lanino Parco Sosta, Loc. Santa Liberata. **GPS:** n42,43346 e11,15959.⬆➡.

Tourist information Peccioli:
📍 Parco Preistorico, Via Cappuccini. ☐ 01/01-31/12.

🏕🆂 Pienza 🌿🎋 32B5
Via Mencattelli e Foro Boario. **GPS:** n43,07799 e11,68087.⬆➡.

50 🅿€ 10/motorhome, € 8/pp, € 5/child 🚰🔌Ch 🚿(40x)included WC🚽.
Surface: grassy/gravel. ☐ 01/01-31/12
Distance: 🚶Orbetello 5km ⛵50m ⊗200m 🛒alimentari.
Remarks: Max. 72h.

🅿8-20h: € 1,50/1h, € 5/4h, € 10/8h, overnight stay free 🚰🔌Ch 🚿
included WC. 🏪**Location:** Rural. **Surface:** asphalted. ☐ 01/01-31/12 ◼
Fri-morning market.
Distance: 🚶100m.

🏕🆂 Palazzuolo sul Senio 🌿🎋🍽🏞 32B3
Parcheggio Casone, Via Casone. **GPS:** n44,11073 e11,54968.⬆➡.

🏕🆂 Pieve Santo Stefano 32C3
Grey camper, Via della Verna. **GPS:** n43,67000 e12,03750.⬆.

100 🅿free 🚰🔌Chfree. **Surface:** asphalted. ☐ 01/01-31/12
Distance: 🚶100m ⊗100m 🛒100m.

🏕🆂 Palazzuolo sul Senio 🌿🎋🍽🏞 32B3
Via Francesco Pagliazzi. **GPS:** n44,11551 e11,54984.⬆.

15 🅿€ 10 🚰🔌Ch 🚿WC🚽included.
Surface: metalled. ☐ 01/01-31/12
Distance: 🚶on the spot 🚲1,7km.
Remarks: Nearby viaduct E45.

🏕🆂 Piombino 🌊 32A5
Camperoasi, Loc. Mortelliccio, Riotorto. **GPS:** n42,95416 e10,66638.⬆➡.

IT

93 ⌁ € 20, Apr-Jun, Sep € 26, Jul/Aug € 36 ⌁ Ch ⌁ WC included ⌁€ 0,50 ⌁. **Surface:** grasstiles/grassy. ⬛ 01/01-31/12
Distance: ⌁200m ⌁50m ⌁50m.
Remarks: Water/drainage at each pitch, reception open: 9.30-12.30 14-19.30, 10% discount on presentation of the guide 2012.

| ⌁ S | Piombino | 32A5 |

Carbonifera 1, Loc. Torre Mozza. **GPS:** n42,94750 e10,69277. ⬆➡.

± 75 ⌁ € 2/h, € 16/24h ⌁ Ch ⌁ included. **Surface:** grassy/gravel.
Distance: ⌁50m.
Remarks: Beach parking, no camping activity.

| ⌁ S | Piombino | 32A5 |

Parcheggio Caldanelle, Loc. Caldanelle. **GPS:** n43,00216 e10,52816. ⬆.

150 ⌁ € 2/h, € 17/8-20h, overnight stay free ⌁ Ch.
Surface: grassy.
Distance: ⌁Piombino 9km ⌁1,5km.
Remarks: Beach parking, shuttle, no camping activity.

| ⌁ S | Piombino | 32A5 |

Perelli 1-3, Loc. Perelli. **GPS:** n42,95527 e10,61944. ⬆.

15 ⌁ € 2/h, € 16/8-20h, overnight stay free ⌁ Ch included. **Surface:** grassy/sand. ⬛ 01/06-30/09
Distance: ⌁on the spot ⌁Perelli 1.
Remarks: Beach parking, no camping activity, dogs beach, service: Perelli 3.

Via della Pace. **GPS:** n42,93777 e10,52194⌁ | 32A5 |

15 ⌁free ⌁€ 0,10/10liter ⌁ Ch. **Surface:** metalled. ⬛ 01/01-31/12

| ⌁ | Pisa | 32A4 |

Parcheggio camper, Via Petrasantina. **GPS:** n43,72890 e10,38868. ⬆.

100 ⌁€ 12/night, € 1/h, € 5/6h ⌁€ 3 ⌁ Ch ⌁. **Surface:** asphalted.
Distance: ⌁800m ⌁7km ⌁on the spot.
Remarks: A12, exit 12 Pisa north.

Tourist information Pisa:
🛈 Agenzia per il turismo di Pisa, Via S. Pellico n° 6; Piazza Vittorio Emanuele; Piazza Arcivescovado, 8.

| ⌁ S | Pistoia | 32A3 |

Via Marino Marini/via della Quiete. **GPS:** n43,94389 e10,91556. ⬆➡.
50 ⌁free ⌁ ⌁. **Surface:** asphalted.
Distance: ⌁city centre 1km ⌁6km ⌁on the spot.
Remarks: At sports park.

| ⌁ S | Pistoia | 32A3 |

Agricamper Podere Campofossato. GPS: n43,99503 e10,89520.
8 ⌁€ 20 ⌁ Ch ⌁ included.
Distance: ⌁50m.
Remarks: Regional products.

| ⌁ S | Poggibonsi | 32B4 |

Via Fortezza Medicea, loc. Vallone. **GPS:** n43,46203 e11,14593. ⬆➡.

± 15 ⌁free ⌁€ 0,10/10liter ⌁ Ch ⌁ (6x)€ 1/12h. **Surface:** gravel. ⬛ 01/01-31/12
Distance: ⌁centre 500m.

Tourist information Poggibonsi:
🛈 Monteriggioni.Walled small town.

| ⌁ S | Pontassieve | 32B3 |

Viale Hanoi/viale Lisbona. **GPS:** n43,77370 e11,42764.
⌁free ⌁ Ch free. **Surface:** asphalted.

| ⌁ S | Porto Ercole | 32B6 |

Le Miniere, SP di Porto Ercole. **GPS:** n42,41749 e11,20386. ⬆➡.

130 ▥€ 23/24h, Aug € 25, Sep € 20 ⊶ ▭Ch ✎ WC included ▯€ 0,50 ▣€ 5))).
Surface: grassy. ⏹ Easter-30/09
Distance: ⛵Porto Ercole 2km ⛱800m ⊗800m.
Remarks: Free shuttle to beach, bread-service, borrow cycles for free.

5 ▥ free ⊶ ▭ Ch free. **Location:** Rural. **Surface:** grassy/gravel. ⏹ 01/01-31/12
Distance: ⛵400m.

▥S **Porto Ercole** ⛵ 32B6
Parking Da Renzo, SC della Feniglia. **GPS:** n42,41527 e11,20777. ⬆➡.

▥S **Radicondoli** 32B4
Il Pianetto. GPS: n43,25888 e11,04250. ⬆➡.

▥€ 1/1h, >1 hour € 0,50/h ⊶ ▭Ch ✎ (16x). **Surface:** unpaved. ⏹ 01/01-31/12
Distance: ⛵medieval centre 300m.

▥S **Rapolano Terme** ♨ 32B4
Villa dei Boschi, Loc. Villa dei Boschi 50, Fraz San Gimignanello, SP10. **GPS:** n43,22829 e11,65429. ⬆.

150 ▥€ 18 ⊶€ 7 ▭Ch ✎€ 3.
Surface: grassy. ⏹ Easter-01/10
Distance: ⛵Porto Ercole 3km ⛱beach 1km ⊗800m.
Remarks: Beach shuttle, no camping activity.

▥S **Pratovecchio** 32B3
Via Uffenheim. **GPS:** n43,78680 e11,71932. ⬆➡.

20 ▥€ 15, free with a meal ⊶ ✎ WC ▯included. **Location:** Rural. **Surface:** grassy. ⏹ 01/01-31/12
Distance: ⊗on the spot.

▥S **Rapolano Terme** ♨ 32B4
Area di sosta Le Terme, Via Trieste. **GPS:** n43,29243 e11,60752. ⬆.

12 ▥free ⊶ ▭ Ch ✎ free. **Surface:** asphalted. ⏹ 01/01-31/12
Distance: ⛵50m ⊗100m ☕100m.
Remarks: Along the river, follow signs instead of GPS.

▥S **Radda in Chianti** 🍇 32B4
Viale 20 Settembre. **GPS:** n43,48643 e11,37543. ⬆➡.

64 ▥€ 5/6h, € 8/12h, € 12/24h ⊶ ▭ Ch ✎ WC ▯included))) € 2. 🔌♻
Location: Rural, comfortable.
Surface: gravel/metalled. ⏹ 01/01-31/12
Distance: ⛵500m ⊗50m ☕200m.
Remarks: Terme Antica Querciolaia 50m.

▥S **Rosignano Marittimo** 32A4
Molino a Fuoco, Via dei Cavalleggeri Antica, Vada. **GPS:** n43,32816 e10,46005. ⬆➡.

6 ▥€ 12/24h ⊶ ▭ WC free. ▯⌂ **Location:** Rural. **Surface:** metalled. ⏹ 01/01-31/12
Distance: ⛵200m (stairs).

▥S **Radicofani** 32C5
Via della Mossa. **GPS:** n42,89427 e11,77598. ⬆.

70 ▥1/4-15/9 € 10 ⊶ ▭Ch. **Surface:** grassy/gravel.

IT

Distance: ⚓500m.
Remarks: Max. 72h.

🛏️ S   **Rosignano Marittimo**   32A4
Il Fortullino, Loc. Castiglioncello. **GPS**: n43,42889 e10,39750.

150 🚐 € 15/night, Jul-Aug € 20 🚰 Ch ⚡ 🚽 included. **Surface:** unpaved.
🏧 01/04-30/09
Distance: 🛒Castiglioncello 4km, Livorno 20km, Pisa 40km ⚓150m ⊗Pizzeria
100m 🚊5km.
Remarks: 4Km north from Castiglioncello.

🛏️ S   **Rosignano Marittimo**   32A4
SP39, Via Aurelia, Loc Caletta. **GPS**: n43,39900 e10,42807.

18 🚐 € 8 🚰 🚽. **Surface:** metalled.
Distance: 🛒on the spot ⚓300m 🚊100m.
Remarks: Along busy through road, max. 48h.

🛏️   **Rosignano Marittimo**   32A4
Parcheggio del Lillatro, Via Fratelli Gigli, loc Lillatro. **GPS**: n43,38380 e10,43206.

40 🚐 € 7,50. **Surface:** sand.
Distance: ⚓50m ⊗50m.

🛏️   **Rosignano Marittimo**   32A4
Sportiva Vada, Via Mare Mediterraneo, Vada. **GPS**: n43,35208 e10,45183. ⬆️➡️

75 🚐 € 10/day. **Surface:** unpaved.
Distance: ⚓200m.

🛏️   **San Casciano dei Bagni** 〰️⛲🏔♈   32C5
Via Della Pineta. **GPS**: n42,86530 e11,87383. ➡️

15 🚐free.
Location: Rural, very simple. **Surface:** gravel/sand. 🏧 01/01-31/12
Distance: 🛒500m.

🛏️ S   **San Casciano dei Bagni** 〰️⛲🏔♈   32C5
Piazzale del Ponte. **GPS**: n42,87024 e11,87742. ⬆️

15 🚐 € 5/12h, € 10/24h 🚰 Ch. **Surface:** asphalted. 🏧 01/01-31/12
Distance: 🛒100m.
Remarks: Near spa resort.

🛏️ S   **San Casciano in Val di Pesa**   32B4
Parco Il Poggione. **GPS**: n43,65395 e11,18768. ⬆️

5 🚐free 🚰 🚽free.

🛏️ S   **San Gimignano** 〰️⛲   32A4
Area di Sosta Santa Chiara, Via di Castel San Gimignano, Loc. Racciano. **GPS**:
n43,45572 e11,03476. ⬆️➡️

30 🚐 € 22/24h 🚰 Ch ⚡ WC 🚽included. **Surface:** gravel. 🏧 01/01-
31/12
Distance: 🛒3km ⊗osteria/bar 🚌shuttle.
Remarks: Free shuttle bus to San Gimignano, tennis.

🛏️ S   **San Gimignano** 〰️⛲   32A4
Park Santa Lucia, Loc. Santa Lucia. **GPS**: n43,45205 e11,05586. ⬆️➡️

IT

± 30 ⌁€ 1/h, € 15/24h 🚰 ⬛Ch 🛁(14x)included. **Surface:** gravel.
Distance: 🚶3km 🚌Citybus Linea 1.
Remarks: Next to swimming pool, 24/24 video surveillance.

🅂 San Miniato Basso — 32A4
Piazza G. Impastato, Via Pestalozzi/Via G. Pizzigoni, zona industriale. **GPS:** n43,69417 e10,83638.⬆

± 20 ⌁free. **Location:** Rural, very simple, quit. **Surface:** unpaved. ⬛ 01/01-31/12
Distance: ⊗350m.
Remarks: Nearby Adler Thermae.

🅂 San Romano in Garfagnana — 31D3
Via Campo Sportivo/via Prà di Lago. **GPS:** n44,17243 e10,34199.⬆➡

⌁free 🚰 ⬛free. **Surface:** asphalted.

🅂 San Miniato Basso — 32A4
Rimessaggio/Area Camper Il Salice, Via Pier delle Vigne 28/A, loc. La Catena. **GPS:** n43,68434 e10,82224.⬆

15 ⌁free 🚰 ⬛Chfree. **Surface:** grassy. ⬛ 01/01-31/12
Remarks: At sports park, Parco Avventura Selva del Buffardello 100m.

🅂 San Vincenzo — 32A5
Via Biserno. **GPS:** n43,08790 e10,54134.
100 ⌁€ 10/24h 🚰 ⬛Ch. **Surface:** sand. ⬛ 01/01-31/12
Distance: 🏖beach 200m 🛒50m.
Remarks: Beach parking, no camping activity.

🄸🅂 Sansepolcro 🌿 — 32C4
Via dei Molini. **GPS:** n43,56959 e12,14700.⬆➡

39 ⌁€ 15/24h 🚰 ⬛Ch 🛁 WC 🚿. **Surface:** gravel. ⬛ 01/01-31/12
Distance: 🚶1km 🚌on the spot.
Remarks: Shuttle to centre, max. 3 days.

🅂 San Piero a Sieve — 32B3
GPS: n43,96260 e11,32732.⬆
⌁free 🚰 € 2 ⬛Ch. **Surface:** metalled.
Distance: 🚶500m ⊗250m.

🅂 San Quirico d'Orcia 🌿 — 32B5
Via delle Scuole. **GPS:** n43,05607 e11,60682.⬆➡

20 ⌁free 🚰 ⬛Ch 🏪 🚿free. **Surface:** metalled. ⬛ 01/01-31/12
Distance: 🚶200m ⊗300m 🛒250m.

🄸🅂 Sansepolcro 🌿 — 32C4
Podere Violino, Loc. Gricigmano. **GPS:** n43,55539 e12,12312.⬆➡

30 ⌁€ 10/24h 🚰 ⬛free. 📷 **Location:** Rural. **Surface:** asphalted. ⬛
01/01-31/12
Distance: 🚶200m.
Remarks: Picnic area, children's play garden.

🅂 San Quirico d'Orcia 🌿 — 32B5
Strada di Bagno Vignoni, Bagno Vignoni. **GPS:** n43,02904 e11,62450.⬆

8 ⌁€ 6 + € 5/pp 🚰 ⬛Ch 🛁 WC 🚿included 🍽.
Surface: grassy.
Distance: 🚶2km ⟿river ⊗on the spot 🛒500m.
Remarks: Swimming pool available, restaurant closed on Sunday.

🅂 Santa Fiora — 32B5
Strada di San Rocco. **GPS:** n42,83531 e11,58397.⬆➡

20 ⛟free ⛽🍽Chfree 🚿(6x)€ 1/2h. **Location:** Rural. **Surface:** gravel/sand. ◻ 01/01-31/12
Distance: ⛁450m.

12 ⛟free ⛽🍽free. **Surface:** grasstiles.
Distance: ⛁2lkm.
Remarks: Nearby sports park.

🏕S | **Saturnia** ♨ | 32B5
L'Alveare dei Pinzi, Strada della Peschiera, Saturnia. **GPS:** n42,65597 e11,50368. ⬆➡.

🏕S | **Sesto Fiorentino** | 32B3
Area Antica Etruria, Via Ferruccio Parri. **GPS:** n43,84150 e11,17667.
50 ⛟€ 16/24h ⛽🍽Ch🚿⫿included. **Surface:** asphalted. ◻ 01/01-31/12
Distance: 🚲2,5km 🚌200m > Florence.

🏕S | **Sesto Fiorentino** | 32B3
Viale Ariosto. **GPS:** n43,83238 e11,18997.⬆.

400 ⛟€ 14/24h ⛽🍽Ch🚿(120x)€ 2 WC included ⫿€ 0,50 🔌€ 6🚿.
Surface: metalled. ◻ 01/01-31/12
Distance: ⛁Saturnia 3km 🏊1,5km ⊗on the spot.
Remarks: Panoramic view, free shuttle to spa resort and Saturnia, termen en Saturnia, Terme di Saturnia (sulfur baths) 1km, Cascate del Mulino (water fall, free entry) 1,5km, bread-service, bar/snack/fruit.

15 ⛟free ⛽🍽Chfree. **Surface:** asphalted. ◻ 01/01-31/12
Distance: 🚲3km 🔌on the spot 🚆train 100m.
Remarks: In front of Lidl supermarket, 20 mins to Florence by train.

🏕S | **Saturnia** ♨ | 32B5
La Quercia, Via Aurina 15. **GPS:** n42,66667 e11,50457.⬆➡.

🏕S | **Siena** 🌿🏛 | 32B4
P1, Palasport, Via Achille Sclavo. **GPS:** n43,33323 e11,31739.⬆.

30 ⛟€ 15/24h ⛽🍽Ch🚿WC ⫿€ 0,50 🔌. **Surface:** gravel. ◻ 01/01-31/12
Distance: ⛁200m ⊗100m 🚲100m.
Remarks: Shuttle bus, Terme di Saturnia (sulfur baths) 1,7km, Cascate del Mulino (water fall, free entry) 2,5km.

75 ⛟€ 20/motorhome (8.00-20.00h) ⛽🍽Ch WCfree. **Location:** Urban, very simple. **Surface:** metalled. ◻ 01/01-31/12
Distance: 🚌on the spot.

🍴S | **Scarperia** 🌿👥 | 32B3
Ranch Ricavo, Via di Galliano 21. **GPS:** n44,01189 e11,30681.⬆.

🏕S | **Siena** 🌿🏛 | 32B4
P2, Il Fagiolone, Via di Pescaia. **GPS:** n43,31456 e11,31760.⬆.

20 ⛟€ 10 ⛽🍽Ch🚿🔌included. **Surface:** grassy. ◻ 01/01-31/12
Distance: ⛁5km ⊗on the spot 🚲5km.

⛟€ 20/motorhome (8-20h), overnight stay free ⛽🍽 WCfree. **Location:** Urban, noisy. **Surface:** metalled. ◻ 01/01-31/12
Distance: 🚌on the spot.
Remarks: Along busy through road.

🏕S | **Sestino** | 32C3
Via Travicello. **GPS:** n43,71223 e12,30356.⬆➡.

IT

Siena 🌙⚓ 32B4

Acqua Calda, Via Fausto Coppi. **GPS:** n43,33627 e11,29695. ⬆.

🎞free.
Location: Urban, very simple. **Surface:** asphalted. ⬛ 01/01-31/12
Distance: ∕650m 🚌bus 10 centre Siena.

Siena 🌙⚓ 32B4

Via delle Province/via Napoli. **GPS:** n43,34168 e11,30512. ⬆.

🎞free.
Location: Urban, noisy. **Surface:** asphalted. ⬛ 01/01-31/12
Distance: ⊗200m McDonalds 🚌on the spot.

Tourist information Siena:
🛈 A.T. (Ufficio Informazioni e di Accoglienza Turistica), Piazza del Campo, 56, www.siena.turismo.toscana.it.Historical city.
👁 Palazzo Pubblico.Gothic town hall from 1342.
👁 Torre del Mangia.Bell tower. ⬛ daily.
✝ Duomo.Romanesque Gothic cathedral.
🎋 La Lizza.Week market. ⬛ Wed morning.
✸ Palio, Piazza del Campo.Famous historical horse race. ⬛ 02/07, 16/08.

Stia 32B3

Parco comunale del Canto della Rana, Via Londa, SP556. **GPS:** n43,80407 e11,70282. ⬆➡.

18 🎞free 🚰 🍽 Ch 🧹 free. **Surface:** gravel. ⬛ 01/01-31/12
Distance: 🏛500m.

Suvereto 32A5

Via dei Forni. **GPS:** n43,07572 e10,67802. ⬆.

12 🎞free 🚰 🍽free. **Surface:** grassy.
Distance: 🏛medieval centre 200m.

Torrita di Siena 🌙⚓ 32C4

Via di Ciliano. **GPS:** n43,16475 e11,77173. ⬆.

6 🎞free 🚰 🍽 Ch 🧹 free. **Location:** Rural, comfortable, quit. **Surface:** grasstiles/metalled. ⬛ 01/01-31/12
Distance: 🏛400m ⊗200m.

Venturina 32A5

Parco Termale Calidario, Via del Bottaccio. **GPS:** n43,03666 e10,60000. ➡.

20 🎞free 🚰€ 0,10/10liter 🍽 Ch. **Surface:** metalled.
Distance: ⊗50m 🚉800m.
Remarks: Thermal centre 50m.

Viareggio 31D3

Via Martiri di Belfiore. **GPS:** n43,88120 e10,25080. ⬆.

44 🎞€ 15/24h 🚰 🍽 Ch 🧹included.
Surface: asphalted. ⬛ 01/01-31/12
Distance: 🏛1km ∕2,5km.
Remarks: Check in at All Events Festival Puccini Viareggio, Viale Regina Margherita 1, 43,8673339 10,2431529, terrain with video surveillance.

Vinci 🌙 32A3

Via Girolamo Calvi. **GPS:** n43,78080 e10,92830. ⬆.
12 🎞free 🚰 🍽 Chfree. **Surface:** metalled. ⬛ 01/01-31/12
Distance: 🏛300m.
Remarks: At sports park.

Volterra 32A4

Parking P3, Fonti Docciola, Viale Dei Filosofi. **GPS:** n43,40306 e10,86417. ⬆.

15 �€ 8/24h 🚰🗑Ch. **Surface:** gravel.
Distance: 🚶historical center 100m.

San Marino

⌂S **San Marino** 32C3
P13, Baldasserona, Borgo Maggiore. **GPS:** n43,94054 e12,44289.

50 ⌃free 🚰🗑Ch. **Surface:** asphalted.

⌂S **San Marino** 32C3
Strada Genghe di Atto, Acquaviva. **GPS:** n43,94491 e12,42963.

5 ⌃free 🚰🗑Ch WC free. **Surface:** asphalted.

⌂S **San Marino** 32C3
P10, Via Napoleone Boneparte. **GPS:** n43,93567 e12,44362. ⬆.

20 ⌃€ 8/24h. **Surface:** asphalted.
Remarks: Elevator to centre 50m.

Tourist information San Marino:
ℹ Palazzo de Turismo, Contrada Omagnano, 20, www.visitsanmarino.com.
Tourist office.
⌂ Borgo Maggiore. Week market. 🗓 Thu.

Marche

⌂S **Abbadia di Fiastra** 32B3
Parcheggio, Via Ettore Pinzani. **GPS:** n43,89368 e11,53703. ⬆.

10 ⌃free 🚰🗑Ch WC free. **Surface:** asphalted. 🔵 01/01-31/12
Distance: 🚶500m ⊗500m 🚲500m 🚌10m.

⌂S **Acqualagna** 32D3
Parco Le Querce, Via Pianacce 1, Loc Furlo. **GPS:** n43,63681 e12,69968. ⬆➡.

90 ⌃€ 15/night 🚰🗑Ch. 🚿 WC included 🗑against payment. **Surface:** grassy. 🔵 26/03-30/09
Distance: 🚶Acqualagna 5km 🚲700m.

Tourist information Acqualagna:
⌂ Week market. 🗓 Thu.

⌃ **Acquasanta Terme** 33C2
Fra. Cagnano. **GPS:** n42,77096 e13,41388. ⬆.

15 ⌃free. **Surface:** asphalted.
Distance: ⊗200m Ristorante Laterna.
Remarks: At sports park.

⌂S **Amandola** 33B2
Piazzale Sandro Pertini. **GPS:** n42,97085 e13,35488.
⌃€ 8,50 🚰🗑Ch 🚿 WC 🗑included. **Surface:** asphalted. 🔵 01/01-31/12
Distance: ⊗850m.

⌃S **Ancona** 27A6
Via Sanzio Blasi, Loc. Posatora. **GPS:** n43,60061 e13,48562. ⬆➡.

30 ⌃€ 10 🚰🗑Ch 🚿included. **Surface:** grasstiles.
Distance: 🚶4,5km 🚌10m.
Remarks: Max. 72, entrance between 8-22h.

Ancona 27A6

Centro Commerciale Auchan, Via Scataglini, Zona Industriale Baraccola, SS16, Ancona-sud. **GPS:** n43,55133 e13,51506. ↑→.

25 free free.
Surface: asphalted. ◯ 01/01-31/12
Distance: 8km 3,6km.
Remarks: A14 exit Ancona south >Pesaro.

Tourist information Ancona:
ℹ Riviera del Conera.Touristic peninsula with beaches and several bathing resorts.
ℹ U.I.A.T. (Ufficio Informazioni e di Accoglienza Turistica), Stazione Maritiema. Old port city.

Apecchio 32C4

Via Isidoro Pazzaglia. **GPS:** n43,55938 e12,41969. ↑→.
10 free Ch (6x)free. **Surface:** metalled. ◯ 01/01-31/12
Distance: 100m 50m.

Tourist information Apecchio:
⛺ Week market. ◯ Fri-morning.

Ascoli Piceno 33C2

Ex Seminario, Viale Alcide Gasperi. **GPS:** n42,85222 e13,58222. ↑→.

20 € 4. **Surface:** asphalted.
Distance: city centre 100m 200m 200m.
Remarks: Guarded parking.

Ascoli Piceno 33C2

Bed & Breakfast Chartaria, Via Adriatico. **GPS:** n42,84792 e13,57306. ↑.
7 € 15 € 3. **Surface:** grassy.

Tourist information Ascoli Piceno:
ℹ City with many monumental bldg.
⛺ ◯ Wed, Sa.

Borgo Pace 32C3

Fraz. Lamoli, Loc Ripa, SS73bis km 25+500. **GPS:** n43,66284 e12,29509. ↑.

15 free. **Surface:** grassy. ◯ 01/01-31/12
Distance: 100m, Borgo Pace 5km 100m 100m.

Carpegna 32C3

Via Aldo Moro. **GPS:** n43,78083 e12,34040. ↑.

10 free € 1 Ch € 0,60/h.
Surface: concrete. ◯ 01/01-31/12
Distance: 300m 300m.

Castelfidardo 27A6

Croce Verde, Via Lumumba/via Donato Bramonte. **GPS:** n43,46603 e13,55584. ↑→.

4 free Chfree. **Surface:** asphalted. ◯ 01/01-31/12
Distance: 200m.

Colmurano 33B2

Via Piero della Francesca, Contrada Peschiera. **GPS:** n43,16260 e13,35828. ↑→.

8 free Ch WC free. **Surface:** asphalted. ◯ 01/01-31/12
Distance: 400m.
Remarks: Near sports park and historical centre.

Corinaldo 32D3

Ristorante Camping Colverde, Via per Montalboddo 52. **GPS:** n43,63458 e13,09665. ↑→.

€ 10,50 Ch WC included. **Surface:** grassy. ◯ 01/01-31/12
Distance: 5km on the spot.

Corinaldo 32D3

Viale Dante. **GPS:** n43,64703 e13,04910. ↑.

IT

12 🛏free 🚰 ♨Ch free.
Surface: asphalted. 🅿 01/01-31/12
Distance: 400m 🚉50m.
Tourist information Corinaldo:
ℹ️ I.A.T. (Ufficio Informazioni e di Accoglienza Turistica), Via del Corso ex Convento Agostiniani.Medieval mountain village in the wine area of Verdicchio.

| 🛏S | **Fabriano** | 33B1 |

Fraz. Poggio San Romualdo. **GPS:** n43,36473 e13,02534.⬆️

35 🛏free 🚰 ♨Ch free. **Surface:** grassy.

| 🛏S | **Fabriano** | 33B1 |

Via Bruno Buozzi. **GPS:** n43,34650 e12,91645.

18 🛏free 🚰€ 0,20/10liter ♨Ch ✂€ 3/12h. **Surface:** grassy. 🅿 01/01-31/12
Distance: 3km 🚉nearby.
Remarks: Next to sports centre.

| 🛏S | **Falerone** | 33C2 |

Ex-stazione FS di Piane di Falerone, Via Togliatti. **GPS:** n43,09944 e13,49944.⬆️

15 🛏free 🚰 ♨Ch ✂ free. **Surface:** metalled.
Distance: 100m ⊗200m.
Remarks: Nearby the old station and theatre Romano.

| 🛏S | **Fano** 🌷🚐 | 32D3 |

Lungomare Sassonia 3, Via Ruggeri. **GPS:** n43,84238 e13,03197.⬆️

100 🛏€ 7,50-8,50 🚰 2 ♨Ch ✂€ 2. 🅿 01/04-30/09
Distance: 600m 2km 🏖50m ⊗50m.

| 🛏S | **Fano** 🌷🚐 | 32D3 |

Area di Sosta Adriatico, SS16, Torrette di Fano. **GPS:** n43,80789 e13,08198.⬆️

30 🛏€ 13-20, Camperstop 18-9h€ 8-10 🚰 ♨Ch ✂ WC 🅿included. 🅿 24/04-12/09
Distance: 4km 9km 🏖on the spot ⊗on the spot 🚉on the spot.
Remarks: Service only € 5.

| 🛏S | **Fano** 🌷🚐 | 32D3 |

Via Kennedy. **GPS:** n43,84365 e13,01169.

50 🛏free 🚰 ♨Ch free. **Surface:** asphalted.
Distance: 200m 2,7km 🏖800m.
Remarks: Nearby cemetery.

| 🍴 | **Fano** 🌷🚐 | 32D3 |

BarRistorante La Tratta, Via Fratelli Zuccari 35. **GPS:** n43,83589 e13,04182.⬆️

10 🛏€ 6. **Surface:** unpaved.
Distance: 🏖50m.
Remarks: P camper.
Tourist information Fano:
ℹ️ U.I.A.T. (Ufficio Informazioni e di Accoglienza Turistica), Via Cesare Battisti, 10.Seaside resort with historical centre.
⛺ 🅿 Wed, Sa.

| 🛏S | **Fermo** | 33C1 |

Area Camper 2004, Via della Filosofia/Via delle Arti. **GPS:** n43,15085 e13,81382.⬆️

100 🛏️€ 9,with electricity € 11, weekend € 16, with electricity € 20 🚰🧹 Ch 🔌 (32x)included 🍴 hot shower against payment. **Surface:** grassy. ⬛ 01/04-15/09
Distance: 🚴2,5km 🏖️on the spot.

🛏️S Fermo 33C1
Baia dei Gabbiani, Viale A. de Gasperi, Lido S. Tomasso. **GPS:** n43,22158 e13,78113.⬆️➡️.

50 🛏️€ 13-15, Aug € 20 🚰🧹 Ch 🔌🍴€ 0,50 ▣. **Surface:** grassy/gravel. ⬛ 01/04-30/09
Distance: 🚴6,6km 🏖️Private beach.

🛏️S Fermo 33C1
Onda Verde, Via Usodimare, Lido di Fermo. **GPS:** n43,20289 e13,78825.⬆️➡️.

100 🛏️€ 10-€ 18 (Aug) 🚰🧹 Ch 🔌 2Amp WC 🍴included. **Surface:** grassy. ⬛ 01/04-30/09
Distance: 🚶Fermo 10km 🚴5,4km 🏖️10m ⊗10-500m 🛒200m.

🛏️S Fossombrone 32D3
Via Oberdan. **GPS:** n43,69301 e12,81835.

8 🛏️free 🚰🧹 Ch. **Surface:** asphalted. ⬛ 01/01-31/12
Distance: 🚶500m 🚴1,4km.

Tourist information Fossombrone:
🛈 I.A.T. (Ufficio Informazioni e di Accoglienza Turistica), Via Roma, 23.
🎪 Week market. ⬛ Mo.

🛏️S Gagliole 33B1
Loc. Fornaci. **GPS:** n43,22584 e13,06234.
🛏️🚰🧹 Ch 🔌 WC 🔥.

Remarks: Shuttle bus.

🔵S Genga 33B1
La Cuna, Fraz San Vittore. **GPS:** n43,40321 e12,97597.
50 🛏️€ 8/24h 🚰🧹 WC. **Surface:** gravel. ⬛ 01/01-31/12
Remarks: Nearby pay-desk Gole di Frasassi, free shuttle.

🛏️S Gradara 🌿 32D3
Piazza Paolo e Francesca. **GPS:** n43,94083 e12,77083.⬆️.

🛏️€ 10/24h 🚰🧹 Ch WC free.
Distance: 🚶historical center 100m 🚴7,3km ⊗on the spot 🛒400m.
Remarks: Parking in the centre.

🛏️S Grottammare 🏔️ 33C2
Via Carlo Alberto dalla Chiesa. **GPS:** n42,96673 e13,87694.⬆️.

30 🛏️free 🚰🧹 Ch free. **Surface:** gravel/sand.
Distance: 🚴2,7km 🏖️500m ⊗500m 🛒on the spot.
Remarks: Behind centro commerciale Cityper, along railwayline.

🍴S Grottammare 🏔️ 33C2
Briciola di Sole, Contr. Granaro 19. **GPS:** n42,98278 e13,84000.⬆️.

14 🛏️€ 15, guests free 🚰🧹 Ch 🔌 included. **Surface:** gravel/metalled. ⬛ 01/04-31/10
Distance: 🚴2,5km 🏖️sea 5km ⊗on the spot 🛒2km.
Remarks: Located on estate, restaurant with traditional kitchen.

🛏️S Jesi 33B1
Via delle Setaiole. **GPS:** n43,51882 e13,24168.⬆️.

10 🛏️free 🚰🧹 Ch free. **Surface:** asphalted.
Distance: 🚶500m centro storico.

IT

Tourist information Jesi:
🅘 Area with many vintages.
👁 Grotte di Frasassi.Caves.

🚐🅢 **Loreto** 〽 27A6
Area Camper Pro Loco, Via Maccari. **GPS**: n43,44125 e13,61491.

65 🚐€ 12/24h 🚽🧺 Ch 🔌€ 3/day WC 🗑 1. **Surface**: metalled.
Distance: 🚶150m 🏖15km.
Remarks: Max. 48h.

🚐🅢 **Loreto** 〽 27A6
Via Benedetto XXV. **GPS**: n43,44129 e13,60756.

15 🚐parking paid, free overnight stay 🚽🧺 WC.
Distance: 🚶300m 🏖50m.
Remarks: Parking at city wall.

🚐🅢 **Macerata** 33B1
Stadio Helvia Recina, Via dei Velini. **GPS**: n43,30701 e13,43722.⬆.

🚐free 🚽€ 1 🧺 Ch. **Surface**: asphalted. 🅾 01/01-31/12
Distance: 🚶1km.

🚐🅢 **Macerata Feltria** 32C3
Loc. San Gasparre. **GPS**: n43,80098 e12,42886.

4 🚐free 🚽🧺 Ch WC 🗑free. **Surface**: metalled. 🅾 01/01-31/12
Distance: 🚶1km 🔛on the spot ❌Pizzeria.
Remarks: Along Aspa river.
Tourist information Macerata Feltria:
🏕 Week market. 🅾 Tue.

🚐🅢 **Marina di Montemarciano** 27A6
Lungomare Alfredo Cappellini. **GPS**: n43,65280 e13,34380.
🚐€ 12 🚽🧺 Ch 🔌€ 2 🗑. 🅾 15/05-15/09
Distance: 🚶4km 🚴9km 🏖pebbled beach 60m.
Remarks: To coast road and railwayline.

🚐🅢 **Marotta** 32D3
Lungomare Colombo, Mondolfo. **GPS**: n43,76966 e13,13965.⬆.

80 🚐 7-11 🚽🧺 Ch 🔌(30x)€ 2 🗑. **Surface**: grassy. 🅾 01/04-30/09
Distance: 🚶500m 🚴1,5km 🏖50m.
Remarks: Between coast road and railwayline.

🚐🅢 **Matelica** 〽 33B1
Porte Capamante, Via Circonvallazione. **GPS**: n43,25917 e13,01083.⬆.

25 🚐free 🚽🧺 Chfree. **Surface**: asphalted.
Distance: 🚶200m ❌200m 🚰200m.

🛏🅢 **Matelica** 〽 33B1
Agriturismo Country House Salomone, Località Salomone, 437. **GPS**: n43,29635 e13,00031.⬆➡.

40 🚐€ 7, free with a meal 🚽🧺 Ch 🔌. **Surface**: gravel.
Distance: ❌on the spot.

🚐🅢 **Mercatello sul Metauro** 32C4
Agricampeggio Cá Montioni, Via Guinza 23. **GPS**: n43,62930 e12,30502.⬆.

11 🚐€ 15 🚽🧺 Ch 🔌 WC 🗑. **Surface**: metalled. 🅾 01/01-31/12
Distance: 🚶3km ❌200m.
Remarks: Farm products.

⬛S   Mergo   33B1

Via Colli. **GPS**: n43,47394 e13,03598.⬆️.

10 🛏️free 🚰🔌 Ch ⚡ WC ⬜. **Surface**: concrete. ⬤ 01/01-31/12
Distance: 🚶1km.
Remarks: Nearby sports park.

⬛S   Mondavio   32D3

Borgo Gramsci. **GPS**: n43,67450 e12,96700.⬆️.

2 🛏️free 🚰🔌 Ch WC free. **Surface**: metalled.
Distance: 🚶historical center 100m ⊗100m 🏛️200m.
Remarks: Nearby old town and medieval citadel Roveresca.

Tourist information Mondavio:
⛺ Week market. ⬤ Mo.

⬛S   Montalto delle Marche 🌿   33C2

Via Cuprense. **GPS**: n42,98726 e13,60870.⬆️.

6 🛏️free 🚰🔌 free. **Surface**: metalled. ⬤ 01/01-31/12
Distance: 🚶100m.

⬛S   Monte San Giusto   33C1

Campo Sportivo, Via Magellano, Villa San Filippo. **GPS**: n43,26343 e13,60070.
⬆️➡️.

20 🛏️free 🚰🔌 Ch free. **Surface**: asphalted.
Distance: 🚶1km.

⬛S   Monte Vidon Corrado   33C2

Viale Trento e Trieste. **GPS**: n43,12182 e13,48501.⬆️.

4 🛏️free 🚰 Ch free. **Surface**: metalled. ⬤ 01/01-31/12
Distance: 🚶200m ⊗200m.

⬛S   Montefiore dell'Aso 🌿🏞️   33C2

Piazza Pietro Nenni. **GPS**: n43,04992 e13,75021.

10 🛏️free 🚰🔌 Ch free. **Surface**: sand. ⬤ 01/01-31/12
Distance: 🚶200m.
Remarks: Follow parco communale.

📷S   Montefiore dell'Aso 🌿🏞️   33C2

Agricamper Il Poggio del Belvedere, Contrada Aso no. 11. **GPS**: n43,04611
e13,72500.⬆️.

6 🛏️€ 8/pp 🚰🔌 Ch ⚡ WC ⬜ included.
Surface: metalled. ⬤ 01/01-31/12

⬛S   Montelupone 🌿   33C1

Loc. San Firmano. **GPS**: n43,36383 e13,54950.

20 🛏️free 🚰🔌 free. **Surface**: asphalted.
Distance: 🚶500m.
Remarks: Parking sports park.

⬛S   Montelupone 🌿   33C1

Via Allesandro Manzoni. **GPS**: n43,34300 e13,57080.⬆️.

IT

10 🅿free 🚰🚽free. **Surface:** asphalted.
Remarks: Parking city park.

| 🏕🅂 | **Morro d'Alba** | 33B1 |

Via degli Orti. **GPS:** n43,60198 e13,21263. ⬆️➡️.

10 🅿free 🚰🚽free.
Surface: asphalted.
Distance: 🚶500m.
Remarks: Access with electronic card, Bar Pro Loco or town hall.

| 🏕🅂 | **Offida** 🌀 | 33C2 |

Via Tommaso Castelli. **GPS:** n42,93689 e13,69180. ⬆️.

10 🅿free 🚰🚽free. 🅾 01/01-31/12
Remarks: At the city walls.

| 🏕🅂 | **Pedaso** | 33C2 |

Via Martiri della Libertà. **GPS:** n43,09985 e13,84272.
🅿free. **Surface:** asphalted. 🅾 01/01-31/12
Distance: 🚶on the spot 🏖on the spot ⊗150m.
Remarks: Parking at the beach, access via northern side of the bay.

| 🏕🅂 | **Pergola** | 32D4 |

Via S. Biagio. **GPS:** n43,56522 e12,83575. ⬆️.

5 🅿free 🚰🚽 WCfree. **Surface:** asphalted. 🅾 01/01-31/12
Distance: 🚶50m ⊗100m 🚰50m.

| 🏕🅂 | **Pesaro** 🎣📡 | 32D3 |

Via dell Aquedotto. **GPS:** n43,90842 e12,90097. ⬆️.

12 🅿free 🚰🚽Chfree 🧹(12x)€ 1. **Surface:** asphalted.
Distance: 🚲7,5km.
Tourist information Pesaro:
ℹ️ I.A.T. (Ufficio Informazioni e di Accoglienza Turistica), Viale Trieste, 164.
🎪 Week market. 🅾 Tue.

| 🏕🅂 | **Petritoli** | 33C2 |

Impianti Sportivi. **GPS:** n43,07306 e13,65139. ⬆️.

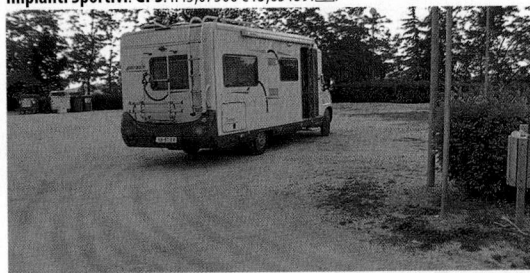

🅿free 🚰🚽Chfree. **Surface:** sand. 🅾 01/01-31/12
Distance: 🚶1km.
Remarks: Sports park.

| 🏕🅂 | **Piandimeleto** | 32C3 |

Via Giacomo Leopardi. **GPS:** n43,72541 e12,41328. ⬆️➡️.

9 🅿free 🚰🚽Chfree. **Surface:** grassy. 🅾 01/01-31/12
Distance: 🚶100m.

| 🏕🅂 | **Pietrarubbia** | 32C3 |

Vulcangas, Via Montefeltresca 107, Ponte Cappuccini. **GPS:** n43,80278 e12,36667. ⬆️.

2 🅿free 🚰🚽 WCfree. **Surface:** metalled. 🅾 01/01-31/12
Distance: 🚶200m.

| 🏕🅂 | **Pievebovigliana** | 33B2 |

Via Rancia. **GPS:** n43,06583 e13,08526. ⬆️.

10 ⌁free 🚰🔌Ch 💧. **Surface:** asphalted. ⬛ 01/01-31/12
Distance: 🚶300m.

🏕️S | Pioraco | 33B2
Loc. Buchetto, SS361 km77. **GPS:** n43,17997 e12,97449. ⬆️.

18 ⌁€ 10 🚰🔌Ch 💧 WC 🗑included. **Surface:** gravel. ⬛ 01/01-31/12
Distance: 🚶700m.

🏕️S | Pollenza | 33B1
Contrada Morazzano. **GPS:** n43,26482 e13,34614. ⬆️➡️.

8 ⌁free 🚰🔌Chfree. **Surface:** asphalted. ⬛ 01/01-31/12
Distance: 🚶500m.
Remarks: Max. 48h.

🏕️S | Porto Recanati | 27A6
Karting Club Pista del Conero, Viale Scarfiotti, loc. Scossicci. **GPS:** n43,47067 e13,64246.
30 ⌁€ 14/24h 🚰🔌Ch 💧 WC 🗑.
Surface: unpaved. ⬛ 01/01-31/12
Distance: 🏖️100m ⊗on the spot.

🏕️S | Porto Recanati | 27A6
Pro Loco, Viale Scarfiotti, loc. Scossicci. **GPS:** n43,44605 e13,65639. ⬆️.

40 ⌁€ 10/24h 🚰🔌Ch 💧€ 2 WC 🗑€ 1. **Surface:** grassy. ⬛ 01/04-30/09
Distance: 🚶500m 🚴3km 🏖️50m ⊗200m 🛒1km.
Remarks: Max. 72h. Along coast road in northern dir.

🏕️S | Porto San Giorgio | 33C1
La Perla Adriatico, Via San Martino 13. **GPS:** n43,16400 e13,80836.

---

75 ⌁€ 12/18 🚰🔌Ch 💧 WC 🗑📶.
Surface: unpaved. ⬛ 01/01-31/12
Distance: 🏖️beach 200m ⊗300m.
Remarks: Shuttle bus.

🏕️S | Potenza Picena | 27A6
Via Togliatti, Porto Potenza Picena. **GPS:** n43,36167 e13,69306. ⬆️.

⌁free 🚰🔌Ch 💧 (3x). **Surface:** asphalted. ⬛ 01/01-31/12
Distance: 🚶200m ⊗200m 🛒200m.

🏕️S | Recanati | 27A6
Via Campo Boario 4. **GPS:** n43,40398 e13,55096. ⬆️➡️.
12 ⌁free 🚰🔌Ch 💧 free. **Surface:** asphalted. ⬛ 01/01-31/12
Distance: 🚶500m.
Remarks: Max. 48h.

🏕️S | San Benedetto del Tronto ⬆️ | 33C2
Viale dello Sport. **GPS:** n42,92312 e13,89527. ⬆️.

20 ⌁free 🚰🔌Chfree. **Surface:** asphalted.
Distance: 🚴3km 🏖️500m.
Remarks: Along railwayline, under viaduct.

🏕️S | San Leo ⚜️ | 32C3
Via Michele Rosa. **GPS:** n43,89871 e12,34950. ⬆️➡️.

20 ⌁free 🚰🔌Ch 💧 free. **Surface:** asphalted. ⬛ 01/01-31/12
Distance: 🚶500m ⊗on the spot.

🏕️S | San Severino Marche | 33B1
Viale Mazzini. **GPS:** n43,22746 e13,18853. ⬆️➡️.

6 ⌁free 🚰🔌Chfree 💧 (6x)€ 0,50/kWh. **Surface:** asphalted. ⬛ 01/01-

31/12
Distance: 800m.
Remarks: Parking sports park.

🚐S **Sant'Agata Feltria** 🏔 **32C3**
Piazzale Europa. **GPS:** n43,86386 e12,20549. ↑ →

40 🚐€ 8/24h 🚰 🔌 (6x)free. **Surface:** asphalted.
Distance: 100m.

🚐S **Sarnano** **33B2**
Via Corridoni. **GPS:** n43,03444 e13,29972. ↑

15 🚐free 🚰 Ch WC free. **Surface:** asphalted.
Distance: 100m ⊗100m 🚰100m.

🚐S **Sassocorvaro** **32C3**
Via dell'Industria, loc. Marcatale. **GPS:** n43,79341 e12,49379.
🚐🚰Ch.
Remarks: In front of cemetery, overnight stay: 43.7911 12.4925.

🚐S **Sassoferrato** **33B1**
Via Raffaello Sanzio. **GPS:** n43,43139 e12,85468. ↑ →

7 🚐free 🚰 free 🔌(6x)€ 1. **Surface:** asphalted.
Distance: 500m.

🚐S **Senigallia** **32D3**
Via F. Podesti 234, SS16, Senigallia-sud. **GPS:** n43,70483 e13,23764.

14 🚐free 🚰free. **Surface:** asphalted. ⬛ 01/01-31/12
Distance: 2km 🚲3,3km ⚓150m.
Remarks: Max. 48h.

🚐S **Tolentino** **33B1**
GPS: n43,20773 e13,28784.

3 🚐free 🚰free. **Surface:** asphalted. ⬛ 01/01-31/12
Distance: 200m ⊗200m.

🚐 **Treia** **33B1**
Via Campo Sportivo. **GPS:** n43,31288 e13,30951. ↑ →

🚐free. **Surface:** metalled/sand. ⬛ 01/01-31/12
Distance: 100m ⊗100m 🚰100m.
Remarks: Nearby sports park.

🚐S **Treia** **33B1**
Loc. San Lorenzo, Fontelci. **GPS:** n43,31639 e13,24472. ↑

3 🚐free 🚰free. **Surface:** asphalted/gravel.
Distance: 7km ⊗3km 🚰7km.

🚐S **Treia** **33B1**
Viale C. Battisti. **GPS:** n43,31146 e13,31296.

4 🚐free 🚰. **Surface:** metalled.

🚐 **Treia** **33B1**
Viale A. Diaz. **GPS:** n43,31257 e13,31062.

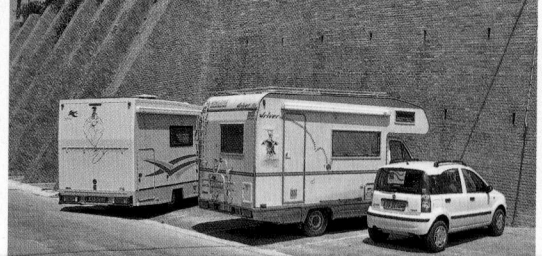

4 🛏free. **Surface:** asphalted.

🛏 S | Urbania � | 32C3
GPS: n43,67916 e12,51277. ⬆️➡️.
🛏free 🚰🔌Ch 🔑free.
Distance: 🚶1km.
Remarks: Behind former summer residence of dukes of Urbania, biking trail.

🛏 S | Urbania � | 32C3
Piazzale Fosso del Maltempo, Viale Michelangelo. **GPS:** n43,66482 e12,52191.
⬆️➡️.

7 🛏free 🚰🔌Ch 🔑free. **Surface:** asphalted. 🅾 01/01-31/12
Distance: 🚶500m.

Tourist information Urbania:
ℹ️ I.A.T. (Ufficio Informazioni e di Accoglienza Turistica), Corso Vittorio Emanuele, 21.Old city called after Pope Urbanus VII.
🛍 Week market. 🅾 Thu.

🛏 S | Urbino | 32D3
Via Pablo Neruda. **GPS:** n43,73333 e12,62722. ⬆️➡️.

10 🛏free 🚰🔌Chfree. **Surface:** metalled. 🅾 01/01-31/12
Distance: 🚶historical centre 2,5km.

Tourist information Urbino:
ℹ️ I.A.T. (Ufficio Informazioni e di Accoglienza Turistica), Piazza del Rinascimento, 1.Small medieval town with famous Palazzo Ducale. 🅾 01/06-31/10 9-19h, Su 9-13h, Mo 9-14h.
🛍 Week market. 🅾 Sa.

🛏 S | Urbisaglia �🔝 | 33B1
Abbadia di Fiastra, P4. **GPS:** n43,22111 e13,40722. ⬆️.

20 🛏free 🚰🔌Ch 🔑free.
Surface: metalled. 🅾 01/01-31/12
Distance: 🚶4km ⊗50m.
Remarks: Parking monastery, archaeological park Urbs Salvia 3km, hiking area.

🛏 S | Visso 🏔 | 33B2
Largo Gregorio XIII. **GPS:** n42,93139 e13,09141. ⬆️➡️.

15 🛏free 🚰🔌Chfree 🔑 € 0,80/h. **Surface:** asphalted.
Distance: 🚶800m.

Lazio

🛏 S | Acquapendente | 32C5
Agriturismo Buonomore, SS2 via Cassia km 130. **GPS:** n42,73367 e11,88361. ⬆️.

8 🛏 € 15, Aug € 30 🚰🔌Ch 🔑 WC 🛢included 🖼.
🅾 01/01-31/12
Distance: 🚶3km ⊗on the spot.

🛏 S | Acquapendente | 32C5
Via Campo Boario. **GPS:** n42,74130 e11,86280. ⬆️.

🛏free 🚰🔌Chfree. **Surface:** asphalted/metalled.
Distance: 🚶250m 🚏250m.

🛏 S | Albano Laziale | 33B4
Piazza Guerucci. **GPS:** n41,73206 e12,65213.
🛏🚰🔌Ch. **Surface:** asphalted.
Remarks: Next to post office and sports park.

🛏 S | Amatrice | 33B3
AgriCamper Amatrice, Località Retrosi. **GPS:** n42,62349 e13,31788.

IT

20 🛏€ 13 ⊞🗑Ch 🛠. **Surface:** gravel.
Remarks: Located in national nature reserve Gran Sasso.

🛏S	Bolsena 🐚🔼	32C5

Guadetto, Via della Chiusa. **GPS:** n42,63604 e11,98695. 🔼.

30 🛏€ 14/24h ⊞🗑Ch 🛠 included.
Surface: grassy/sand. 🔲 01/01-31/12
Distance: 🚶800m 🏊10m.

🛏	Bolsena 🐚🔼	32C5

Via Santa Maria. **GPS:** n42,63898 e11,98562. 🔼➡️.

50 🛏€ 5/12h, € 10/24h. **Surface:** asphalted. 🔲 01/01-31/12
Distance: 🚶800m 🏊100m ⛽on the spot ⊗400m 🍴400m 🚌100m.

Tourist information Bolsena:
ℹ️ Citadel and ramparts.

🛏S	Bracciano	33A4

Le Mimose, Via del Lago 25. **GPS:** n42,10856 e12,17893.
50 🛏€ 14/24h ⊞🗑Ch 🛠 € 3. **Surface:** gravel. 🔲 01/01-31/12
Distance: 🚶800m 🏊Lago di Bracciano 250m ⊗150m.

🛏S	Capodimonte 🏖️	32C6

Temporanea. **GPS:** n42,55979 e11,88714. 🔼.

50 🛏€ 10/24h ⊞🗑Ch. **Surface:** grassy. 🔲 01/01-31/12
Distance: 🚶2km 🏊on the spot.
Remarks: At lake Bolsena, check in at bar.

🛏S	Cassino	33C5

Parking Europa, Via Agnone 5. **GPS:** n41,48289 e13,83750.

🛏€ 13 ⊞🗑Ch 🛠 against payment.
Distance: 🚶800m.

Tourist information Cassino:
ℹ️ I.A.T. (Ufficio Informazioni e di Accoglienza Turistica), Via G. Di Biasio, 54.

🛏S	Castel di Tora	33B3

Via Turano, SP34. **GPS:** n42,21362 e12,96888.
15 🛏€ 5/24h ⊞🗑Ch 🛠. **Surface:** gravel. 🔲 01/01-31/12
Distance: 🚶1km 🏊on the spot.
Remarks: At Turano lake.

🛏S	Castel Gandolfo 🏖️	33B4

Parcheggio Bus Lago Albano, Via Spiaggia del Lago. **GPS:** n41,75797 e12,65359. 🔼.
🛏€ 10/24h. **Surface:** asphalted. 🔲 01/01-31/12
Distance: 🏊on the spot ⊗on the spot 🚌800m > Rome.
Remarks: At lake Albano.

🍴S	Castel Gandolfo 🏖️	33B4

Ristorante I Quadri 2000, Via dei Pescatori 21. **GPS:** n41,74930 e12,65384.
10 🛏€ 15/24h ⊞🗑Ch 🛠. **Surface:** sand. 🔲 01/01-31/12
Distance: 🏊on the spot ⊗on the spot.
Remarks: Private beach at Lago di Albano.

🛏S	Castro dei Volsci	33C5

Via Fosso 35. **GPS:** n41,51282 e13,39010.
🛏⛲
Remarks: Nearby restaurant Le Rocco.

🛏S	Civita Castellana 🏖️	33A3

Via Terni. **GPS:** n42,29905 e12,41520.

300 🛏free ⊞🗑free. **Surface:** asphalted. 🔲 01/01-31/12
Distance: 🚌50m.
Remarks: At cemetery.

Tourist information Civita Castellana:
👁️ Palazzo Farnese, Caprarola.Pentagonal country house, accessed by winding staircase.

🛏S	Colle di Tora	33B3

Via Maria Letizia Giuliani. **GPS:** n42,20898 e12,94915.
15 🛏€ 5/24h ⊞🗑Ch. **Surface:** gravel. 🔲 01/01-31/12
Distance: 🚶on the spot 🏊on the spot ⊗on the spot.
Remarks: At Turano lake.

🛏S	Colleferro 🌱	33B4

Viale Europa. **GPS:** n41,72540 e13,00989.
🛏⊞⛲
Distance: 🏊5km.
Remarks: Next to swimming pool.

Tourist information Colleferro:
ℹ️ Anagni.Region with number of old settlements.

🛏S	Farfa in Sabina	33B3

Abbazia di Santa Maria, SP41A. **GPS:** n42,22166 e12,71603.
🛏free ⊞🗑Chfree. **Surface:** gravel. 🔲 01/01-31/12
Distance: 🚶4,7km.

🛏S	Gaeta	33C5

Playa Colorada, Torre S.Agostino, SS 213, Sperlonga>Gaeta. **GPS:** n41,22583 e13,50502.

IT

30 ⌁ € 28-30, 2 pers.incl 🚿 🔌 Ch ⚡ WC included ⌁ € 1. **Surface:** grassy/gravel. 🅿 01/04-30/09
Distance: ⚓on the spot ⊗bar/restaurant 🍴on the spot.

⌁free. **Surface:** gravel.
Distance: ⚓on the spot ⊗on the spot.

🅂 Gradoli 32C6
Parcheggio camper San Magno, Strada di Gradoli, SP114 km 6+137. **GPS:** n42,59925 e11,86547.⬆️.

50 ⌁ € 10 🚿 🔌 Ch. **Surface:** grassy. 🅿 01/01-31/12
Distance: 🚲7km ⚓on the spot ⊗500m.
Remarks: At lake Bolsena.

🅂 Leonessa 33B3
GPS: n42,56436 e12,96172.⬆️.

50 ⌁free 🚿 🔌. **Surface:** asphalted.
Distance: 🚲500m ⊗500m 🍴500m 🚐300m.

🅂 Ladispoli 33A4
Area Sosta Torre Flavia, Via Roma. **GPS:** n41,95954 e12,05282.

🅂 Lubriano 32C5
Parco Paime, Piazza Palme. **GPS:** n42,63500 e12,10512.⬆️.

300 ⌁8-20h € 6, 20-8h € 6 🚿 € 3 🔌 Ch 🔄 € 3 WC ⌁ € 0,50. **Surface:** grassy/sand. 🅿 01/01-31/12
Distance: 🚲1,2km ⚓on the spot ⊗on the spot 🍴2km.
Remarks: At the beach.

17 ⌁ € 6/24h 🚿 🔌 ⚡ (36x).
Surface: grasstiles. 🅿 01/01-31/12
Distance: 🚲1km ⊗on the spot.

🅂 Ladispoli 33A4
Area Sosta Lady Beach, Via Roma. **GPS:** n41,95829 e12,05585.⬆️.
30 ⌁ € 10/24h 🚿 🔌 Ch WC ⌁ € 0,50. **Surface:** grassy/sand.
Distance: 🚲800m ⚓on the spot.

🅂 Lunghezza 33B4
Camper Club Mira Lago Roma Est, Via Lunghezzina 75. **GPS:** n41,93159 e12,67642.
⌁ € 18/24h 🚿 🔌 Ch ⚡ € 2 WC ⌁. **Surface:** grassy.
Distance: ⚓700m ⚓on the spot.
Remarks: At 2 small lakes.

🅂 Latina 33B5
Area Camper Alte Marea, Strada Lungomare 3253, SP39, Loc. Foce Verde. **GPS:** n41,41043 e12,86008.

🅂 Montalto di Castro 32B6
Via Arbea, Marina di Montalto di Castro. **GPS:** n42,32981 e11,57699.⬆️➡️.

100 ⌁ € 10-15 🚿 🔌 Ch ⚡ ⌁included. **Surface:** grassy. 🅿 Easter-30/09
Distance: ⚓on the spot ⚓50m ⊗on the spot.

50 ⌁ € 10/24h, € 5 01/10-31/12 🚿 🔌 Ch free. 🏠 **Location:** Rural. **Surface:** grassy/gravel. 🅿 01/01-31/12
Distance: 🚲250m ⚓200m ⊗200m 🍴200m.

🖼️S | **Montalto di Castro** | 32B6

Via Torre Marina, Marina di Montalto di Castro. **GPS**: n42,32137 e11,59015.⬆️➡️.

64 🏕️€ 5, 15/05-15/09 € 10 🚰🔌Ch ⚡ included.📳 **Surface**: sand. ⭕ 01/01-31/12

Distance: 🏖️500m 🏊200m ⊗400m 🚉300m.

🖼️S | **Montefiascone** | 32C6

Cantina di Montefiascone, Via Grilli 2. **GPS**: n42,53346 e12,04293.⬆️.

30 🏕️free 🚰🔌Ch ⚡. **Surface**: metalled. ⭕ 01/01-31/12

Distance: 🏖️1km.

🖼️S | **Montefiascone** | 32C6

Agricamper Bella Cima, Strada Limitone. **GPS**: n42,52241 e12,00767.⬆️➡️.

18 🏕️€ 15/24h 🚰🔌Ch ⚡ included.

Surface: gravel. ⭕ 01/01-31/12

Distance: 🏖️4km ⊗4km 🚉4km.

Remarks: Swimming pool.

🖼️S | **Nettuno** | 33B5

Area Sosta L'Ippocampo, Via Palestrina 9. **GPS**: n41,47354 e12,68916.

50 🏕️€ 10 🚰🔌Ch ⚡. **Surface**: gravel. ⭕ 01/01-31/12

Distance: 🏖️3km.

🖼️S | **Oriolo Romano** | 33A4

Via degli Artigiani. **GPS**: n42,16699 e12,13902.

🏕️free 🚰🔌free. **Surface**: asphalted. ⭕ 01/01-31/12

Distance: 🏖️850m 🚉on the spot 🚂station 600m Roma-Viterbo.

🖼️S | **Pescia Romana** | 32B6

Area La Pineta, Loc. Marina di Pescia Romana. **GPS**: n42,36367 e11,49738.⬆️.

50 🏕️€ 10-18 🚰🔌Ch ⚡€ 3 🏕️€ 1. **Surface**: grassy. ⭕ Easter-30/09

Distance: 🏖️Pescia Romana 7km 🏊100m ⊗100m.

🖼️S | **Pescia Romana** | 32B6

Campeggio Club degli Amici. GPS: n42,36717 e11,48828.⬆️.

20 🏕️€ 6/10 + € 6/10,50/pp 🚰🔌Ch ⚡ WC ⚡included ⚡€ 4. **Surface**: sand. ⭕ 01/05-3rd Su Sep

Distance: 🏖️lava beach 100m 🚉on the spot.

🖼️S | **Rieti** | 33B3

Via Fonte Cottorella. **GPS**: n42,39548 e12,86463.⬆️➡️.

10 🏕️free 🚰🔌. **Surface**: asphalted. ⭕ 01/01-31/12

Distance: 🏖️historical center 100m.

🖼️S | **Roma** 🌿⛽🛒 | 33B4

Area Attrezzata LGP Roma, Via Casilina 700, Rome (Roma). **GPS**: n41,87595 e12,55515.⬆️.

130 🏕️€ 15/<8m, € 22/8><10m, € 30/10><15m 🚰🔌Ch ⚡ included ⚡.

Surface: grassy. ⭕ 01/01-31/12

Distance: ⊗100m 🚉100m 🚌bus service to city centre day and night.

Remarks: Accessory shop, repairs, trailer/additonal car € 15 on separate parking € 7. Exit 18 ring road (G.R.A.), follow Roma centro, ± 4km dir centre, company is on the left side of the road, turning after 2nd lights.

🖼️S | **Roma** 🌿⛽🛒 | 33B4

Oasi del Camper, Via dell'Ippodromo di Tor di Valle 1, Rome (Roma). **GPS**: n41,82021 e12,43545.⬆️➡️.

🏕️€ 20 🚰🔌Ch ⚡ WC ⚡included.

Surface: gravel.

⭕ 01/01-31/12, 24/24h

Distance: 🏖️city centre 10km ⊗150m Arbino 🚇metro 150m.

Remarks: Terrain with video surveillance. Exit 28 ring road (G.R.A.), follow Roma centro, keep right Roma Ostiense, further indicated.

🖼️S | **Roma** 🌿⛽🛒 | 33B4

Prato Smeraldo, Via Ardeatina/Via di Tor Pagnotta 424, Rome (Roma). **GPS**: n41,80970 e12,52857.

🏕️€ 16 🚰🔌Ch ⚡ ⚡included. ⭕ 01/01-31/12, 24/24h

Distance: ⊗on the spot 🚉on the spot 🚇on the spot.

Remarks: Exit 25 ring road (G.R.A.), second light to the right, Via di Tor Pagnotta.

IT

🚿S　　　Roma　♨🏕🗑　　33B4

Le Terrazze, Via di Fioranello 170, Rome (Roma). **GPS**: n41,79250 e12,54083.
300 🚻€ 20, max. 4 pers.incl ⛽€ 2 🍳Ch♨(40x)included.
Surface: metalled.
📅 01/01-31/12
Remarks: Excursions. Exit 25 ring road (G.R.A.), dir Santuario Divino Amore.

🚿S　　　Roma　♨🏕🗑　　33B4

Parcheggio IAT, Air terminal Ostiense, Piazza G. da Verrazzano 9, Zone Mercati
Generali, Rome (Roma). **GPS**: n41,86931 e12,48944.
🚻€ 1,50, at least € 6 ⛽🍳Ch♨ included. **Surface**: asphalted.
Distance: 🚇metro 1km.

Tourist information Rome (Roma):
ℹ️ Città del Vaticano.Domicile of the pope. Independent state since 1929.
ℹ️ A.P.T. (Azienda di Promozione Turistica), Via Parigi, 11, www.romaturismo.
it.Capital of the country, a lot of curiosities in the old town centre. Roma
Archeologica Card: 7-days ticket € 20, free entrance to Roman National Museum,
Colosseum, Palatine, Baths of Caracalla, Tomb of Cecilia Metella and Villa of the
Quintili.
👁 Piazza del Campidoglio.
👁 Palatino, Via di S. Gregorio, 30.Archeological site. 📅 9h-sunset. 🎫 € 8, incl.
Colosseum.
👁 Subiaco.
Ⓜ Musei Vaticani, Città del Vaticano.Paintings and art objects.
✝ Basilica di San Pietro.Basilica with Sistine Chapel.
⛰ Colosseo, Piazza del Colosseo.Colosseum, anfiteatro, the most important
monument of ancient Rome. 📅 9h-sunset. 🎫 € 8.
⛰ Foro Romane, Via dei Fori Imperiali.Novel Forum, the political, economic, and
religious centre of ancient Rome. 📅 9h-sunset. 🎫 free.
⛰ Pantheon, Piazza della Rotonda.Church of Santa Maria ad Martyres. 🎫 8.30-
19.30h, Su 9-18h, Mass Sa 17, Su 10.30h, 16.30h. 🎫 free.
🎆 Città del Vaticano.Pope blesses the mob for the window of the library. 📅
Su 12h.
⚱ Piazza di Spagna.

IT

🚿S　　San Felice Circeo　　33B5

Circeo Camper Da Paolo, Viale Europa 1. **GPS**: n41,24095 e13,10426.

60 🚻€ 20-26 ⛽🍳Ch♨ WC 🗑included.
Surface: grassy. 📅 01/01-31/12
Distance: 🚶100m 🚲10m ⊗100m 🚉100m 🚌100m.

🚿S　　San Felice Circeo　　33B5

Area Camper La Rosa dei Venti, Viale Europa 9A. **GPS**: n41,24387 e13,10819.

50 🚻€ 24/12-12h ⛽€ 3 🍳Ch♨. **Surface**: gravel. 📅 01/01-31/12
Distance: 🚶500m 🚲10m ⊗on the spot 🚉600m 🚌600m.
Tourist information San Felice Circeo:
🎣 📅 Tue-morning.

🚿S　　　Sperlonga　　33C5

Aree di Sosta Oasi, SS 213, Sperlonga>Gaeta. **GPS**: n41,23596 e13,49069.

30 🚻€ 20 ⛽🍳Ch♨ WC included 🗑€ 1. **Surface**: gravel.
Distance: 🏖50m ⊗50m.
Remarks: Monitored parking.

🚿S　　　Sperlonga　　33C5

Sosta Camper Internationale, SS 213, Sperlonga>Gaeta. **GPS**: n41,23598
e13,49045.

30 🚻€ 20-25 ⛽🍳Ch♨ WC included 🗑€ 1. **Surface**: gravel.
Distance: 🏖on the spot ⊗on the spot.
Remarks: Monitored parking.

🚿　　　Tarquinia　　32C6

Largo Barriera San Giusto. **GPS**: n42,25307 e11,75410. 🆙.
5 🚻free. **Surface**: asphalted. 📅 01/01-31/12
Distance: 🚶100m ⊗100m 🚉100m.
Remarks: Archeological site 1km.

🚿S　　　Tarquinia　　32C6

Viale Andrea Doria/via Odisseo, Lido di Tarquinia. **GPS**: n42,22516 e11,70897.🆙.
🚻.
Distance: 🏖sandy beach 450m.

🚿S　　　Tivoli　　33B4

Via Aquaregna. **GPS**: n41,95841 e12,80465.
30 🚻free ⛽🍳Ch.
Surface: asphalted. 📅 01/01-31/12 🅿 Wed, market.
Distance: 🚶400m.
Remarks: Along the Aniene river.
Tourist information Tivoli:
👁 Villa d'Este.Country house with gardens and fountains, 16th century.
⛰ Villa Adriana.Roman villa.

🚿S　　　Tuscania　　32C6

Via Nazario Sauro. **GPS**: n42,42432 e11,87542.🆙.

12 🛏free ⊏–⛽free. **Surface:** asphalted. 🔲 01/01-31/12
Distance: 🚶250m ⊗250m ⛽250m.
Remarks: At cemetery.

| 🅂 | **Villa San Giovanni in Tuscia** | 32C6 |

Via P.M. Liberati. **GPS:** n42,28160 e12,05282.
🛏free ⊏–⛽Ch. **Surface:** asphalted. 🔲 01/01-31/12
Distance: 🚶200m.

| 🅂 | **Viterbo** | 32C6 |

Piazza Mariano Romiti, loc. Belcolle. **GPS:** n42,40897 e12,11049.⬆.
50 🛏free ⊏–⛽free. **Surface:** asphalted. 🔲 01/01-31/12
Distance: 🚶Lazise centre 300m 🚌on the spot.

| 🍴🅂 | **Viterbo** | 32C6 |

Bed&breakfast Axia, Strada Procoio 2/C. **GPS:** n42,41157 e12,05061.

30 🛏€ 12 ⊏–Ch ⚡€ 3. **Surface:** grassy. 🔲 01/01-31/12
Distance: 🚶Viterbo 4km.
Remarks: 10% discount at entrance Terme dei Papi (900m).

| 🍴 | **Viterbo** | 32C6 |

Agriturismo Monteparadiso, Loc. Monterazzano. **GPS:** n42,43192 e12,03004.
⬆.

5 🛏guests free. **Surface:** gravel.
Distance: 🚶7km.
Remarks: Near Termale Bullicame and Terme dei Papi.

| ♨ | **Viterbo** | 32C6 |

Terme dei Papi, Strada Montarone. **GPS:** n42,41487 e12,06351.

100 🛏free. **Surface:** grassy/gravel. 🔲 01/01-31/12

Distance: 🚶3km.
Remarks: At Terme dei Papi.

| 🅂 | **Vitorchiano** | 32C6 |

SP23 Via della Teverina. **GPS:** n42,47152 e12,17212.⬆➡.

10 🛏free. **Surface:** asphalted. 🔲 01/01-31/12
Distance: 🚶500m.

Umbria

| 🅂 | **Amelia** | 32D6 |

Piazzale del Mercato, Via Rimembranze. **GPS:** n42,55200 e12,41880.⬆.
10 🛏free ⊏–⛽Chfree. **Surface:** asphalted.
Distance: 🚶50m ⊗50m ⛽50m.

| 🅂 | **Assisi** 〰⛽🌳 | 33A2 |

Via Giosuè Borsi, loc. Santa Maria degli Angeli. **GPS:** n43,05972 e12,58747.⬆.

🛏€ 16/24h, € 1,60/h ⊏–⛽Ch ⚡.
Surface: asphalted. 🔲 01/01-31/12
Distance: 🚶2km 🚌bus >Assisi 20min (retour € 1,80).

| 🅂 | **Assisi** 〰⛽🌳 | 33A2 |

Area San Vetturino, SS147. **GPS:** n43,07710 e12,59957.⬆.

30 🛏€ 14/24h, € 2/h. **Surface:** asphalted. 🔲 01/01-31/12
Distance: 🚶500m.
Remarks: Convento di San Francesco 1km.

| 🅂 | **Assisi** 〰⛽🌳 | 33A2 |

Viale Vittorio Emanuele II/SS147. **GPS:** n43,06864 e12,61420.⬆.

10 🛏€ 20/24h. **Surface:** gravel. 🔲 01/01-31/12

IT

Distance: city centre 100m.

S Bevagna 33A2
Via Madonna del Cuore. **GPS**: n42,93417 e12,60639.

50 free Ch WC free. **Surface**: gravel.
Distance: 100m ⊗100m 100m.

S Cannara 33A2
Via Giaime Pintor, Loc. Casone. **GPS**: n42,99272 e12,57840.

20 free Ch free. **Surface**: asphalted.
Distance: 300m 300m.
Remarks: At sports park XXV Aprile, cycle routes.

Tourist information Cannara:
U.I.A.T. (Ufficio Informazioni e di Accoglienza Turistica), Piazza del Commune, Assisi.Medieval pilgrimage city.
Assisi Historical city.

Cascia 33B2
Piazzale Papa Leone XIII, Via della Molinella. **GPS**: n42,71968 e13,01605.

50 € 8/day, overnight stay free Ch free. **Surface**: asphalted. 01/01-31/12
Distance: 300m ⊗300m 300m 100m 100m.
Remarks: Escalator to city centre, service closed during wintertime.

S Cascia 33B2
Strada Statale Discascia. **GPS**: n42,72139 e13,01778.
20 € 7/24h included. **Surface**: gravel. 01/01-31/12
Distance: 1km.

Castelluccio di Norcia 33B2
Pian Grande. **GPS**: n42,80045 e13,18947.
free. **Surface**: grassy.
01/01-31/12
Distance: Castelluccio 5km.
Remarks: Parco Nazionale dei Monti Sibilini.

Castiglione del Lago 32C4
Viale Divisione Partigiani Garibaldi. **GPS**: n43,12389 e12,05054.

free. **Surface**: asphalted/sand.
Distance: 800m on the spot.
Remarks: At lake Trasimeno.

S Città di Castello 32C4
Piazzale E. Fermi. **GPS**: n43,45892 e12,23465.
free Ch free. **Surface**: gravel.
Distance: 300m 1,5km.

S Città di Castello 32C4
La Fontana del Boschetto, Via Aretina 38. **GPS**: n43,45737 e12,22882.
€ 12 Ch .
Distance: 2km ⊗on the spot.
Remarks: Free shuttle.

S Ferentillo 33B3
SS Valnerina, loc. Precetto. **GPS**: n42,61915 e12,78483.
10 free . **Surface**: asphalted.
Distance: 200m.

S Ficulle 32C5
Parco Cittadino, Via Orvieto SR 71. **GPS**: n42,83044 e12,06828.

25 free Ch free. **Surface**: gravel.
Distance: 500m 10km ⊗1km 500m.

S Gualdo Tadino 33B1
Piazza Federico II di Svevia. **GPS**: n43,23143 e12,78062.

⑊free 🚰🪣Ch free. **Surface:** asphalted.

🏕️S Gualdo Tadino 33B1
Via Perugia. **GPS:** n43,23756 e12,77235.
100 ⑊free 🚰🪣free.
Distance: ⊗400m 🚰20m.
Remarks: Nearby stadium.

🏕️S Gubbio 🌿 32D4
Camperclub Gubbio, Via del Bottegone. **GPS:** n43,35000 e12,56389.⬆️

80 ⑊free, 20-8h € 5 🚰🪣Ch free 🔌(8x)€ 1/2h.
Surface: asphalted.
Distance: 🚋historical centre, 10 min walking ⊗100m 🚰200m.

🏕️S Monte Castello di Vibio 🌿⚓🏠🍴 32C5
Via Bartolomeo Jacopo della Rovere. **GPS:** n42,84185 e12,35076.➡️

10 ⑊free 🚰🪣Ch free. **Surface:** gravel. ⬛ 01/01-31/12
Distance: 🚋350m ⊗50m.

🏕️S Montefalco 🌿⚓🍴 33A2
Viale delle Vittoria. **GPS:** n42,89230 e12,64791.⬆️

15 ⑊free 🚰🪣Ch⚡€ 1/1h WC 🪣. **Surface:** grasstiles.

🏕️S Montone 32C4
Via Aldo Bologni. **GPS:** n43,36346 e12,32499.
⑊€ 10/24h 🚰🪣Ch🔌. **Surface:** asphalted. ⬛ 01/01-31/12
Distance: 🚋200m ⊗250m.
Remarks: At sports park.

🏕️S Orvieto 🌿⚓🍽️🍴 32C5
Area Sosta Camper Orvieto, Strada della Direttissima, Piazza delle Pace. **GPS:** n42,72562 e12,12736.⬆️

36 ⑊€ 18/day 🚰🪣Ch 🔌 WC 🪣included ▣. **Surface:** metalled. ⬛
01/01-31/12
Distance: 🚋funicular (retour € 1,60) 5 min 🚶2,4km ⊗50m pizzeria.
Tourist information Orvieto:
 ℹ️ U.I.A.T. (Ufficio Informazioni e di Accoglienza Turistica), Piazza Duomo, 24.City on volcanic plateau.
 ⌂ Del Crocifisso del Tufo.Ruins of Etruscan city.

🏕️S Panicale 🌿⚓ 32C5
Area Camper, Viale della Repubblica. **GPS:** n43,02806 e12,10222.⬆️➡️

8 ⑊€ 8/24h 🚰€ 0,50 🪣Ch 🔌€ 0,50/kWh. **Surface:** grasstiles. ⬛
01/01-31/12
Distance: 🚋100m ⊗100m ▣50m.

🏕️S Passignano sul Trasimeno 32C4
Via Europa, SS75bis, km 35,8. **GPS:** n43,18509 e12,14348.⬆️

4 ⑊€ 12/24h 🚰€ 0,30/100liter 🪣Ch 🔌€ 0,30/h WC. **Surface:**
asphalted. ⬛ 01/01-31/12
Distance: 🚋400m ⚓100m.
Remarks: At lake Trasimeno.

🏕️S Perugia 🌿 32C4
Piazzale del Bove, Via Giovanni Ruggia. **GPS:** n43,09810 e12,38386.⬆️➡️

50 ⑊free 🚰🪣Ch free. **Surface:** asphalted.
Distance: 🚋1,5km 🚌on the spot.
Remarks: Parking police station.
Tourist information Perugia:

IT

ℹ️ A.T. (Ufficio Informazioni e di Accoglienza Turistica), Via Mazinni, 6, www. umbria.turismo.it.
✠ Palazzo dei Priori.
⚓ ⭕ Tue.

| 📷S | San Gemini | 33A3 |

Via della Libertà. **GPS**: n42,61200 e12,54372.
16 🚐 🚰 🍴 Ch 💧 WC 🔧 📶. **Surface**: metalled. ⭕ 01/01-31/12
Distance: 🚶300m ✖100m.

| 📷S | Scheggia e Pascelupo | 32D4 |

Camper Scheggia, Via Campo Sportivo. **GPS**: n43,40007 e12,66674.
🚐 €12/24h 🚰 🍴 Ch included. **Surface**: gravel. ⭕ 01/01-31/12
Distance: 🚶450m ✖500m.

| 📷S | Spello | 33B2 |

Via Centrale Umbra. **GPS**: n42,99371 e12,66730.⬆️

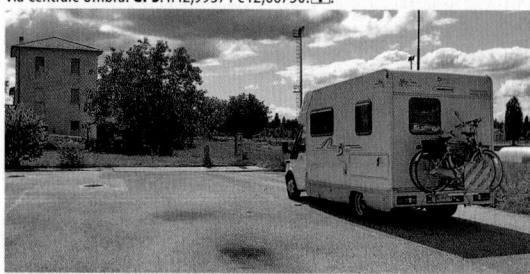

70 🚐 € 6/24h 🚰 🍴 Ch. **Surface**: asphalted.
Distance: 🚶500m 🚲1,1km ✖500m 🛒500m.
Remarks: Parking sports park.

| 📷 | Spoleto 🌿⛲🧺 | 33B2 |

Parcheggio Ponciano, Via del Tiro a Segno. **GPS**: n42,73687 e12,74212.➡️

20 🚐 € 5/24h. **Surface**: gravel. ⭕ 01/01-31/12
Distance: 🚶500m ✖500m 🛒500m.
Remarks: Escalator to city centre.

| 📷S | Spoleto 🌿⛲🧺 | 33B2 |

Via dei Filosofi. **GPS**: n42,74619 e12,73214.⬆️➡️

🚐free 🚰 🍴free. **Surface**: gravel.
Distance: 🚶800m.

Tourist information Spoleto:
ℹ️ U.I.A.T. (Ufficio Informazioni e di Accoglienza Turistica), Piazza del Liberta, 7.
👁 Montefalco.Village worth seeing, parking outside village, narrow streets.
👁 Ponte delle Torri.Aqueduct, 14th century.
⚓ ⭕ Tue, Fri.
🎆 Art festival. ⭕ 01/06-31/07.

| 📷S | Terni 🌿⛲🧺 | 33B3 |

Via Lombardo Radice. **GPS**: n42,56634 e12,63577.⬆️

🚐 €4/48h 🚰 € 0,50 🍴 Ch 🔧 included. **Surface**: asphalted
Distance: 🚶50m ✖50m.
Remarks: Exit Raccordo Roma-Perugia, near cemetery.

| 📷 | Terni 🌿⛲🧺 | 33B3 |

Piazzale Felice Fatati, SR209. **GPS**: n42,55690 e12,72006.

🚐free. **Surface**: unpaved.
Distance: 🚶Terni 7km ✖on the spot.
Remarks: Nearby waterfalls, along river.

| 📷S | Todi 🌿⛲🏕🍴 | 32C5 |

Area Porta Orvietana, Viale di Montesanto. **GPS**: n42,78120 e12,40168.⬆️

16 🚐 € 14/24h, € 3/h 🚰 🍴 Ch. **Surface**: asphalted.
Remarks: Elevator (free) to centre.

| 📷S | Torgiano | 32C5 |

Via Perugia. **GPS**: n43,02917 e12,43833.⬆️

10 🚐free 🚰 🍴 Chfree. **Surface**: asphalted. ⭕ 01/01-31/12
Distance: 🚶200m 🚲3,5km ✖200m 🛒300m.

| 📷S | Trevi | 33B2 |

Via Costa San Paolo. **GPS**: n42,87829 e12,75221.⬆️➡️

IT

50 🛏free 🚰🍴Chfree. **Surface:** grasstiles. ⬛ 01/01-31/12
Distance: 🏊500m 🚲5,1km.
Remarks: At the swimming pool.

Abruzzo

24 🛏€ 6,50 🚰🍴Ch 🧹 included.
Surface: gravel/sand. ⬛ 01/05-30/09
Distance: 🚲6,5km ⚓on the spot.
Remarks: Pebbled beach.

🏵🅂 Anversa degli Abruzzi 33C4

Bioagriturismo La Porta dei Parchi, Piazza Roma 3. **GPS:** n42,00014 e13,79899. ⬆➡.

4 🛏€ 10, free with a meal 🚰🍴Ch 🧹 WC 🛏 📶included. **Surface:** metalled. ⬛ 01/01-31/12
Distance: ⊗on the spot.

🏵🅂 Campotosto 33C3

Via Lago, SR557. **GPS:** n42,56208 e13,34805.
🛏€ 5 🚰. **Surface:** grassy. ⬛ 01/01-31/12
Distance: 🏊Campotosto 3km ⚓on the spot.
Remarks: At lake Campotosto.

🏵🅂 Cansano 33D4

Agriturismo Pietro Ruscitti, Via Vecchia Della Stazione. **GPS:** n42,00253 e14,01132.
10 🛏against payment 🚰🍴Chagainst payment.

🏵🅂 Casalbordino 33D3

Portobello, SS16, km 503, Lido di Casalbordino. **GPS:** n42,17070 e14,63928. ⬆.

8 🛏against payment 🚰🍴Ch 🧹(8x). **Surface:** asphalted. ⬛ 01/01-31/12
Distance: 🚲1,5km ⚓3km.
Remarks: Check in at bar.

🏵🅂 Fossacesia 33D3

Area Camper, Via Lungomare 16b. **GPS:** n42,24067 e14,52988. ⬆➡.

🏵🅂 Isola del Gran Sasso 33C3

S.Gabriele dell Addolorata. **GPS:** n42,51712 e13,65634. ⬆.

🛏free 🚰🍴Ch. **Surface:** gravel/sand.
Distance: 🏊on the spot 🚲4km ⊗on the spot 🎣on the spot.
Remarks: Nearby basilica.

🏵🅂 Lanciano 33D3

Area Attrezzata, Strada provinciale Lanciano-Frisa, Lancianovecchia. **GPS:** n42,23385 e14,39106. ⬆➡.

50 🛏free 🚰🍴Ch WCfree. **Surface:** asphalted.
Distance: 🏊300m (stairs and elevator).
Remarks: At city walls, upper part of the parking.

Tourist information Lanciano:
ℹ Historical city with medieval Jewish district, Ripa Sacca.

🏵🅂 L'Aquila ❄❄ 33C3

Via Strinella. **GPS:** n42,35323 e13,40708.
10 🛏free 🚰🍴Chfree. **Surface:** asphalted.
Distance: 🏊500m.
Remarks: In front of Hotel Federico II, adjacent Parco del Castello.

Tourist information L'Aquila:
ℹ U.I.A.T. (Ufficio Informazioni e di Accoglienza Turistica), Piazza S. Maria di Paganinca, 5.Capital of the province on the foot of the Gran Sasso.

🏵🅂 Notaresco 33C2

Via Martiri della Libertà. **GPS:** n42,65527 e13,89578. ⬆➡.
10 🛏free 🚰🍴Chfree 🧹against payment. **Surface:** asphalted.
Distance: 🏊on the spot.
Remarks: At tennis-courts.

🏵🅂 Penne 33C3

Agriturismo Il Portico, Contrada Colle Serangelo 26. **GPS:** n42,45592 e13,95165. ➡.

IT

15 🛏€ 10, free with a meal 🚰🔌Ch🔌 (7x)€ 3 WC⅃included 🗑.
Surface: grassy.

📷S | **Pescasseroli** 🏔❄ | 33C4
Area Camper S.Andrea, Loc. Sant'Andrea. **GPS:** n41,79888 e13,79222.⬆.

🛏€ 15, 2 pers.incl 🚰🔌Ch🔌 WC⅃included. ⬛ 8-13h, 14.30-20h
Remarks: Free shuttle to centre.

Tourist information Pescasseroli:
ℹ I.A.T. (Ufficio Informazioni e di Accoglienza Turistica), Viale Principe di Napoli.
🌿 Parco Nazionale d'Abruzzo.Nature reserve.

🍴 | **Pineto** | 33C2
Ristorante Aria e Sole, Borgo Santa Maria. **GPS:** n42,60891 e14,04341.
🛏.
Distance: 🚶200m.
Remarks: Nearby exit highway A14.

🍴📷S | **Roccaraso** 🏔❄ | 33D4
Hotel Park Il Poggio, SS17, C.da Poggio, 1 , Loc Il Poggio. **GPS:** n41,82638
e14,10111.⬆➡.

18 🛏€ 20 🚰🔌Ch🔌 (18x)included.
Distance: ⊗on the spot.
Remarks: Shuttle to piste.

📷S | **Roseto degli Abruzzi** | 33C2
Area di Sosta Camper Romeo, Via degli Orti 13, loc. Cologna Spiaggia. **GPS:**
n42,72287 e13,98076.⬆.

40 🛏€ 20/24h 🚰🔌Ch🔌 (40x) WC included ⅃€ 1. **Surface:** grassy. ⬛
01/01-31/12

Distance: 🚶200m 🏖750m ⊗on the spot 🛒100m.

📷S | **Roseto degli Abruzzi** | 33C2
Area di sosta Isola del Sole, Piana degli Ulivi. **GPS:** n42,66902 e14,01189.⬆➡.

11 🛏€ 20 🚰🔌Ch🔌 (11x)€ 2 WC⅃included. **Surface:** metalled. ⬛
01/01-31/12
Distance: 🚶3km 🏖3km.
Remarks: Swimming pool (summer).

📷S | **Roseto degli Abruzzi** | 33C2
Palazzo dello Sport. GPS: n42,66012 e14,02382.⬆➡.

🛏free 🚰🔌Chfree. **Surface:** asphalted.

📷 | **Roseto degli Abruzzi** | 33C2
Lungomare Trieste/via Danubio. **GPS:** n42,66187 e14,03059.⬆.
50 🛏free. **Surface:** unpaved.
Distance: 🏖on the spot.
Remarks: Max. 72h. 500m before campsite Arcobaleno.

📷S | **San Demetrio nei Vestini** | 33C3
La Grotta di Stiffe, Fraz. Stiffe. **GPS:** n42,25567 e13,54811.➡.

🛏free 🚰€ 2,50 🔌Ch🔌€ 2,50. **Surface:** metalled/sand.
Distance: 🚶l'Aquila 18km.

📷S | **San Salvo Marina** 🌊 | 27C4
Parking on the Beach, Via Amerigo Vespucci 20. **GPS:** n42,07233 e14,76945.⬆
➡.

35 🛏€ 15/30 🚰🔌Ch🔌 (30x)€ 3 WC⅃included ⬜€ 8. **Surface:**
asphalted. ⬛ 01/01-31/12
Distance: 🚶2km 🏖50m sandy beach ⊗50m 🛒Centro Commerciale 2km.

San Salvo Marina 27C4
Area Sosta Communale per Autocaravan. GPS: n42,07195 e14,76289.⬆.
30 🚿€ 15/24h, € 20/48h, € 30/72h ⚡ Ch WC included 🚿 cold shower.
Surface: grassy. 🅿 01/06-31/08
Distance: 🏖300m. 🚗2,2km ⚓300m.

Santo Stefano di Sessanio 33C3
GPS: n42,34706 e13,64545.
🚿free. 🅿 01/01-31/12

Santo Stefano di Sessanio 33C3
Ostello del Cavaliere, Piazza Della Giudea. GPS: n42,34429 e13,64314.⬆.
5 🚿guests free ⚡. **Surface:** metalled.
Distance: 🏖300m.

Sant'Egidio alla Vibrata 33C2
Zona industriale. GPS: n42,81937 e13,69915.⬆➡.

🚿free ⚡ Ch free. **Surface:** asphalted.

Torino di Sangro 33D3
Area camper Vitale, Lido le Morgie. GPS: n42,20403 e14,60349.⬆.
100 🚿€ 10 ⚡ Ch 🚿 € 2 WC 🚿€ 0,50. **Surface:** grassy/sand.
Distance: 🚗8km ⚓beach 70m.

Tortoreto Lido 33C2
Via Napoli. GPS: n42,78552 e13,95013.
30 🚿€ 12/24h ⚡ Ch 🚿 WC 🚿🚿.
Surface: asphalted. 🅿 01/01-31/12
Distance: ⚓beach 200m.

Villalago 33C4
SP82b. GPS: n41,92255 e13,85621.⬆.

13 🚿free ⚡ Ch free. **Surface:** asphalted.
Distance: ⚓on the spot.
Remarks: At lake Scanno.

Molise

Campobasso 34C5
Area di sosta Dominick Ferrante, Contrada Calvario 1. GPS: n41,56886
e14,65118.⬆➡.

20 🚿€ 10/24h, € 15/48h ⚡ Ch 🚿 included. **Surface:** gravel.
Distance: 🏖800m.

Monteroduni 33D4
Oasi San Nazzaro. GPS: n41,53448 e14,15924.

40 🚿€ 10, free with a meal ⚡ Ch 🚿 (6x)included. **Surface:** grassy. 🅿
01/01-31/12
Distance: 🎣Fish lake ⊗on the spot.

Petacciato Marina 34D4
SS16 Adriatica km535,5, Termoli ri Vasto. GPS: n42,02432 e14,88739.⬆.

60 🚿€ 15 ⚡ Ch 🚿 (50x)included WC 🚿. **Surface:** gravel/sand. 🅿
01/06-30/09
Distance: ⚓on the spot ⊗on the spot 🍴on the spot.
Remarks: Access via gate next to tower ruins.

Petacciato Marina 34D4
Parking spiaggia, Via del Mare, SS16. GPS: n42,03543 e14,85337.⬆.

40 🚿€ 6, 8-20h 🚿against payment. **Surface:** asphalted.
Distance: 🚗9,5km ⚓50m.
Remarks: Reserved place for motorhomes.

Termoli 34D4
Centro Commerciale Sannicola, SS 87 Sannitica, km216-256. GPS: n41,93880
e14,98754.⬆.

20 🚿free ⚡ Ch free. **Surface:** asphalted. 🅿 01/01-31/12

Puglia

Alberobello 34C1
Parcheggio Nel Verde, Via Cadore. GPS: n40,78266 e17,23418.⬆.

Remarks: Nearby SP41 dir Roccaspromonte.

IT

60 ⬛€ 15/24h, € 10/12h, € 8/6h ⛽🔌Ch included 🚿€ 3. **Surface:** grassy/gravel. ⭘ 01/01-31/12
Distance: 🚶Trulli-centre 50m ⊗50m 🚉100m.

Tourist information Alberobello:
ℹ️ Centre of the Trulli-region. Truilli houses are curious houses built without motar.
⛺ ⭘ Thu-morning.

⬛€ 5. **Surface:** grassy/gravel. ⭘ 01/01-31/12
Remarks: Parking at the caves of Castellana, overnight stay permitted.

⬛S Gallipoli — 34D2
GPS: n40,06000 e18,03939.
⬛€ 13 ⛽🔌Ch 🚿€ 5.
Distance: 🚶5 km.

🏞️S Bari — 34C1
Gran Parcheggio Alberotanza, Via Alberotaza, 43A. **GPS:** n41,09520 e16,87868.

🏞️S Lecce 🌿 — 34D1
Camperpark Fuori Le Mura, Via S.Oronzo Fuori Le Mura, 20. **GPS:** n40,39340 e18,16581.⬆️

250 ⬛€ 15 ⛽€ 0,50/30liter 🔌€ 2,50 Ch 🚿€ 0,50/kWh ♻️. **Surface:** asphalted. ⭘ 01/01-31/12
Distance: 🚗7,8km ⊗500m 🚉500m.
Remarks: Monitored parking.

Tourist information Bari:
ℹ️ A.P.T. (Azienda di Promozione Turistica), Piazza Moro, 33, www.regione.puglia.it.Important port city.

21 ⬛€ 15/24h ⛽🔌Ch 🚿 WC 🚻. ⭘ 01/01-31/12
Distance: 🚶city centre 3km ⊗300m.
Remarks: Shuttle to centre.

🏞️S Lesina 🌊 — 34A1
Oasi, Via Ludovica Ariosto. **GPS:** n41,86472 e15,35806.⬆️

🏞️S Brindisi 🌊 — 34D1
Area Attrezzata, Strada Minnuta 6. **GPS:** n40,63517 e17,91824.

⬛€ 10 ⛽🔌Ch 🚿 WC 🚻included. **Surface:** asphalted. ⭘ 01/01-31/12
Remarks: 24/24 surveillance.

Tourist information Brindisi:
ℹ️ A.P.T. (Azienda di Promozione Turistica), Via C. Colombo, 88, www.pugliaturismo.com.Important port city.

🏞️ Castellana Grotte 🌿 — 34C1
Le Grotte di Castellana. **GPS:** n40,87543 e17,14900.⬆️

15 ⬛€ 12, Sept-Mar-Apr € 15, May/Aug € 18 ⛽🔌Ch 🚿 WC 🚻included.
Surface: asphalted. ⭘ 01/01-31/12
Distance: 🚶300m ⊗on the spot 🚉500m.

🏞️S Lucera 🌿 — 34D5
Via Montello. **GPS:** n41,49987 e15,33223.⬆️

100 ⬛free ⛽🔌. **Surface:** asphalted. ⭘ 01/01-31/12
Remarks: At station.

Tourist information Lucera:
ℹ️ Art city with castle from 13th century and religious history.

IT

⊠S Margherita di Savoia 34B1
Lido Baywatch, Via Barletta. **GPS:** n41,36222 e16,17361.↑→.

12 ⊠€ 15, Aug € 20 ⚡⊟Ch⚡WC⊐included. **Surface:** gravel/sand. ⬤ 01/01-31/12
Distance: ⚡2km ⚡on the spot ⊗on the spot.

⊠S Massafra 34C1
Area di Sosta La Stella, SS7, SS Appia km 633, Le Forche. **GPS:** n40,59201 e17,09904.↑.

20 ⊠€ 10/16.00-12.00, € 20/24h ⚡⊟Ch⚡(18x)WCincluded ⊐€ 1.
Surface: grassy. ⬤ 01/01-31/12
Distance: ⚡1km ⊗500-700m ⚡1km.
Remarks: Beachshuttle € 2.

⊠S Mattinata ◁ 34B1
Punta Grugno, SS89dirB. **GPS:** n41,69797 e16,06236.↑→.

80 ⊠€ 11, Jun € 13, Jul € 16, Aug € 20 ⚡⊟Ch⚡€ 2,50 WC⊐€ 0,80.
Surface: grassy/sand. ⬤ 01/04-01/10
Distance: ⚡Mattinata 2km ⚡pebbled beach ⊗on the spot ⚡2km.

⊠S Mattinata ◁ 34B1
Eden Park, Porto di Mattinata, SP53. **GPS:** n41,70667 e16,06556.↑.

25 ⊠Jun € 10, Jul € 12, Aug € 15 ⚡⊟Ch WCincluded ⊐€ 0,50. **Surface:** grassy/sand. ⬤ 01/06-31/08
Distance: ⚡1km ⚡pebbled beach ⚡on the spot ⊗1km ⚡1km.

⊠S Melendugno 34D1
Area attrezzata SantAndrea - Salento, SP366 km 20.5, Sant'Andrea. **GPS:** n40,25550 e18,43748.

15 ⊠€ 25/24h ⚡⊟Ch⚡WC ⊐.
Distance: ⚡500m ⚡on the spot.
Remarks: Beachshuttle.

⊠S Melendugno 34D1
Camper club 'Campo Carleo', Az. Agr.la di De Pascalis Antonio S., Strada provinciale Lecce-Melendugno-San Foca, km.18. **GPS:** n40,27724 e18,40510.
40 ⊠€ 10-15, 20/07-31/08 € 30 ⚡⊟Ch⚡€ 5 WC⊐. **Surface:** unpaved.
⬤ 01/01-31/12
Distance: ⚡1,5km.
Remarks: Free shuttle.

⊠S Monopoli 34C1
Area du Sosta Camper Lido Millennium, SP90, Loc. Capitolo, SS16 km850 Uscita Capitolo. **GPS:** n40,90374 e17,35261.↑→.

100 ⊠€ 12-15-18 ⚡⊟Ch⚡ 6Amp WC⊐included. **Surface:** gravel. ⬤ Easter-30/09
Distance: ⚡500m ⚡50m ⊗50m ⚡50m.
Remarks: Private beach.

⊠S Otranto 34D1
Area Camper Fontanelle, Sp366, km28. **GPS:** n40,19159 e18,45494.

⊠€ 15/24h ⚡⊟Ch⚡WC⊐against payment.
Distance: ⚡Otranto 5km ⚡beach 200m.
Remarks: Shuttle bus to Otranto.

⊠S Otranto 34D1
Oasy Park, Via Renis. **GPS:** n40,14029 e18,48621.↑→.

50 ⊠€ 20 3 pers.incl ⚡⊟Ch⚡(70x), 16Amp WCincluded ⊐€ 1 ⊡€ 4.
Surface: grassy/gravel. ⬤ 01/01-31/12
Distance: ⚡400m ⚡700m ⊗400m ⚡400m.

Tourist information Otranto:
ℹ I.A.T. (Ufficio Informazioni e di Accoglienza Turistica), Piazza Castello, 8.

⊠S Peschici ⚜⛺◁ 34A1
Camper Marina Picola, Loc. Pantanello, Baia di Peschici. **GPS:** n41,94528 e16,00528.↑.

IT

45 🔲 Apr € 12, May € 13, Jun/Sep € 15, Jul € 20, Aug € 25 🔌 🔋
Ch 🔧 WC included 🔲 € 0,50. **Surface:** grassy/sand. ◯ 01/04-30/09
Distance: 🚶2,5km, walking 800m (stairs) ⛱ sandy beach 50m.

🔲 S Peschici 🌿 ✈ 🏖 34A1
AgriCamper Pane e Vino, SS89 km 2,6. **GPS:** n41,92372 e16,01534.
20 🔲 € 10 🔌 🔧 Ch 🔧 WC 🔲. **Surface:** sand.
Distance: 🚶3,5km ✗ on the spot.

🔲 S Peschici 🌿 ✈ 🏖 34A1
Area attrezzata per camper Dattoli, Via Spiaggia, SS89. **GPS:** n41,94522
e16,01138.
14 🔲 € 15 🔌 🔧 Ch 🔧 WC included 🔲 0,50. **Surface:** unpaved.
Distance: 🚶 Old city 300m (stairs) ⛱100m ✗100m.

Tourist information Peschici:
ℹ️ I.A.T. (Ufficio Informazioni e di Accoglienza Turistica), Via Magenta, 3.

🔲 Putignano 34C1
Grotte di Putignano, SS172. **GPS:** n40,85706 e17,10944.
🔲 free. ◯ 01/01-31/12

🔲 S Rodi Garganico 34A1
Area sosta camper Isola Bella, Via delle More. **GPS:** n41,92444 e15,84166. ⬆️
➡️.

30 🔲 € 15-20, Aug € 25 🔌 🔧 Ch 🔧 WC 🔲 included. **Surface:** grassy/sand.
◯ 01/06-15/09
Distance: 🚶 Lido del Sole 1,5km, Rodi Garganico 3,8km ⛱ sandy beach 10m
🚶 on the spot ✗100m 🛒1,5km.

🔲 S San Giovanni Rotondo 🌿 ✈ 🏔 34A1
Coppa Cicuta, Strada Comunale Pozzocavo-Tre Carrini. **GPS:** n41,69599 e15,70423.
⬆️➡️.

30 🔲 € 10, park € 5 🔌 🔧 Ch 🔧 (30x)€ 1,50/night WC 🔲 included 🔲 € 10.
Surface: gravel. ◯ 01/01-31/12
Distance: 🚶3km ✗ on the spot.
Remarks: Shuttle € 2/pp.

🔲 🍴 S San Giovanni Rotondo 🌿 ✈ 🏔 34A1
Di Cerbo, Circonvallazione Sud, SP45bis. **GPS:** n41,69725 e15,73097.
20 🔲 € 13 🔌 🔧 Ch 🔧 WC 🔲 € 0,50 🔲 € 1. **Surface:** asphalted. ◯
01/01-31/12
Distance: 🚶1km ✗ on the spot 🏊 on the spot 🚐 on the spot.

Remarks: Shuttle bus.

🅿️ San Giovanni Rotondo 🌿 ✈ 🏔 34A1
Viale Padre Pio. **GPS:** n41,70902 e15,70379.
150 🔲 € 2,50, overnight stay free. **Surface:** asphalted.
Remarks: Shrine Padre Pio 200m.

🔲 S Sannicola 🏖 34D2
Campo delle Bandiere, Loc. Padula Bianca. **GPS:** n40,09681 e18,01297.
🔲 € 20 🔌 🔧 Ch WC 🔲. **Surface:** sand. ◯ 01/06-01/09
Distance: ⛱ sandy beach.

🔲 S Santa Maria al Bagno 34D1
Area Camper Mondonuovo, Via Torre Mozza. **GPS:** n40,13494 e18,00166. ⬆️➡️.
30 🔲 € 15 🔌 🔧 Ch 🔧 🔲. **Surface:** grassy. ◯ 01/01-31/12
Distance: ⛱ beach 500m.

🔲 S Torre Canne di Fasano 34C1
Lido Tavernese, SS379, uscita Torre Canne Sud. **GPS:** n40,82023 e17,49875.

200 🔲 € 13, Aug € 15 🔌 🔧 Ch 🔧 (80x)€ 2 WC included 🔲 € 1. **Surface:**
grassy.
Distance: 🚶3,5km ⛱ on the spot ✗01/07-31/08.

🔲 S Torre Canne di Fasano 34C1
Il Privilegio Camper Service, Via Appia, SP90 > Savelletri. **GPS:** n40,84363
e17,46359.
🔲 🔌 🔧 Ch 🔧. **Surface:** gravel.
Remarks: Beach club.

🔲 S Troia 34D5
Via Sant'Antonio. **GPS:** n41,36158 e15,30616.

12 🔲 free 🔌 🔧 Ch 🔧. **Surface:** asphalted. ◯ 01/01-31/12
Distance: 🚶200m.
Remarks: Near the cathedral.

🔲 S Uggiano la Chiesa 34D1
Agriturismo Mulino a Vento, Via Badisco 59. **GPS:** n40,09694 e18,46006.
40 🔲 € 30, 2 pers.incl 🔌 🔧 Ch 🔧.
Distance: ⛱ beach 4km ✗ on the spot.
Remarks: Swimming pool.

🔲 S Vico del Gargano 34A1
Lido Azzurro. **GPS:** n41,94208 e15,98303. ⬆️.

80 🔲 Oct-Apr € 10, May-June € 15, Jul/Aug € 25 🔌 🔧 Ch 🔧 € 3, (Aug)

IT

WC included ⌐€ 1. **Surface:** sand. ◻ 01/01-31/12
Distance: ⬭Valazzo 4km ⬭sandy beach ⬭1km (camping).

🏕S　Vieste 🌿♨⚓⬛ 34B1
Fusilo Rosina, Contrada S.Lucia. **GPS:** n41,91028 e16,12944.⬆.

70 🏕Jun-Sep € 15, Jul € 20, Aug € 27,50 ⌐⬛ Ch ⬛ (70x)included WC ⌐€ 0,50. **Surface:** grassy. ◻ 01/06-15/09
Distance: ⬭4km ⬭300m ⊗50m ⬭100m ⬭50m.

🏕S　Vieste 🌿♨⚓⬛ 34B1
Residence Euro 92, Enrico Mattei 119. **GPS:** n41,85639 e16,17417.⬆.

50 🏕€ 15 (3p incl.), peak season € 20-27 (2p incl.) ⌐⬛ Ch ⬛ WC ⌐included ⬛⬛. **Surface:** grassy. ◻ 01/04-31/10
Distance: ⬭on the spot ⊗200m ⬭100m.

🏕S　Vieste 🌿♨⚓⬛ 34B1
Area Eden Blu, Lungomare Enrico Mattei. **GPS:** n41,85985 e16,17396.
40 🏕€ 20 ⌐⬛ Ch ⬛ WC ⌐. **Surface:** unpaved. ◻ 01/04-31/10
Distance: ⬭on the spot.

🏕　Vieste 🌿♨⚓⬛ 34B1
Bagno Lido Azzurro, Loc. Lido di Portonuovo. **GPS:** n41,84942 e16,17755.
🏕. **Surface:** sand. ◻ 01/01-31/12
Distance: ⬭on the spot ⊗on the spot.

Tourist information Vieste:
🛈 I.A.T. (Ufficio Informazioni e di Accoglienza Turistica), Piazza Kennedy.
⛪ ◻ Mo.

🏕S　Zapponeta 34B1
Zapponeta Beach, Via del Mare. **GPS:** n41,45694 e15,96083.⬆➡.

30 🏕€ 10, 1/7-15/7, 15/8-31/8 €12, 15/7-15/8 € 15/2 pers incl ⌐⬛ Ch ⬛€ 2 WC included ⌐€ 0,50. **Surface:** grassy/metalled. ◻ 01/04-30/09
Distance: ⬭250m ⬭on the spot ⬭on the spot ⊗500m ⬭500m.
Remarks: Narrow entrance.

Campania

🏕S　Bacoli 33D6
Sea Oasi Village, Via Strada Romana, loc. Fusaro. **GPS:** n40,82194 e14,04791.
± 100 🏕€ 15/20/24h, 4 pers.incl ⌐⬛ Ch ⬛€ 5 WC ⌐€ 1 ⬛. **Surface:** grassy/sand.
Distance: ⬭on the spot.

Remarks: At the beach.

⬛S　Bacoli 33D6
Parco Naturale Agriturismo Fondi di Baia, Via Fondi di Baia. **GPS:** n40,81132 e14,07518.

20 🏕€ 10 ⌐⬛ Ch ⬛included. **Surface:** asphalted. ◻ 01/01-31/12
Distance: ⬭3km ⊗Baia 700m ⬭100m.

🏕S　Benevento 🌿 34D6
Tennis Airola, Via Domenico Mustilli. **GPS:** n41,13141 e14,78960.
🏕€ 5 ⌐⬛ ⬛. ◻ 01/01-31/12
Distance: ⬭500m ⬭1,8km.

Tourist information Benevento:
🛈 U.I.A.T. (Ufficio Informazioni e di Accoglienza Turistica), Piazza Roma, 11, www.eptbenevento.it.City with historical monuments.
⛪ Piazza Risorgimento en Piazza Santa Maria. ◻ Wed, Sa 8-13h.

⬛　Casalbore 34D5
Agriturismo Le Mainarde. **GPS:** n41,24516 e15,00242.⬆.
30 🏕€ 15. ◻ 01/01-31/12
Distance: ⊗on the spot.

🏕S　Cava de' Tirreni 🌿⬛ 34D6
Via Ido Longo, loc. Sant'Arcangelo. **GPS:** n40,69984 e14,69553.
🏕free ⌐⬛ Ch free.
Distance: ⬭2,3km.

Tourist information Cava de' Tirreni:
🛈 Salerno.City with medieval centre.
🛈 A.A.C.S.T.(Azienda Autonoma di Cura Soggiorno e Turismo), Corso Roma, 19, Amalfi.Popular bathing resort.
Ⓜ Museo Civico, Amalfi.Museum with Tavole Amalfitane, the old Law of the Sea.
◻ 8-14h, Sa 8-12h ◻ holiday-Feiertag-jours de fête-giorni di festa.

⬛S　Contursi Terme ♨ 34D6
Agriturismo Il Giardino, Loc. Prato. **GPS:** n40,64891 e15,23002.
🏕€ 10 ⌐⬛ Ch ⬛.
Distance: ⬭4,4km ⊗on the spot.
Remarks: Le Terme Vulpacchio 50m.

🏕S　Marina di Camerota 34B3
Parcheggio Europa, Loc. Sirene. **GPS:** n40,00302 e15,36493.
🏕€ 18 ⌐⬛. ◻ Easter-30/09
Distance: ⬭on the spot.

🏕S　Napoli 🌿♨⚓⬛⬛ 33D6
Parking IPM, Via Colli Aminei 27, Naples (Napoli). **GPS:** n40,87038 e14,24616.

🏕7-21h € 10 21-8h €10 ⌐⬛ Ch included ⬛€ 2. **Surface:** asphalted. ◻ 01/01-31/12
Distance: ⬭1,2km ⬭bus R4 centre Napoli 30m.
Remarks: Monitored parking.

Tourist information Naples (Napoli):
🛈 A.A.C.S.T.(Azienda Autonoma di Cura Soggiorno e Turismo), Palazzo Reale, www.regione.campania.it.Capital of the province with many monuments and cultural treasures.

IT

👁 Vesuvio.Volcano, observatorium on western edge of the crater. Visit with guide possible.

👁 Mergellina.Smal peninsula with fishing-port and marina.

👁 Teatro San Carlo.Opera building.

Ⓜ Museo Nazionale Archeologico di Napoli, Piazza Museo Nazionale 19.Antique hellenic-roman civilisation. 🚪 Tue-Su 9-14h.

✖ Palazzo Reale.Royal palace. 🚪 9-13.30h ◉ Mo.

✝ Duomo San Gennaro.Cathedral with original interior.

∩ Ercolano/Herculaneum.Ancient city buried together with Pompeii. 🚪 9-14.45h, holidays 9-18.15h.

⚘ Mercato Corso Malta. 🚪 Mo, Fri.

🛏S	**Paestum** 🌿	34B3

Camper Village Maremirtilli, Via Linora di Paestum, SP278. **GPS**: n40,37607 e15,00119.

70 🍴€ 13-25 🚰🔌Ch🛁 WC🗑.

🛏🍴S	**Paestum** 🌿	34B3

Hotel Mandetta, Via Torre di Mare, 2. **GPS**: n40,41529 e14,99093.

20 🍴€ 15-20 🚰🔌Ch🗑.

Distance: 🚶500m 🏖on the spot ⊗on the spot.

Tourist information Paestum:

ℹ A.A.C.S.T.(Azienda Autonoma di Cura Soggiorno e Turismo), Via Magna Grecia, 151.Old city, founded by the Greeks. In the surroundings many vestiges from that time. 🚪 9h-sunset.

🛏S	**Palinuro**	34B3

Via Palorcio. **GPS**: n40,03722 e15,30944.

🍴€15 🚰🔌Ch WC🗑.

Distance: 🏖700m.

🛏S	**Pompei** 🌿	33D6

Parking Plinio, Via Plinio 98. **GPS**: n40,74710 e14,48756.

30 🍴8-20h € 10, 8-8h € 19, 20-8h € 12 🚰🔌Ch🛁 WC🗑included. **Surface:** asphalted. 🚪 01/01-31/12

Distance: 🚶Archeological site Pompei 250m 🍽300m.

Remarks: Monitored parking.

Tourist information Pompei:

ℹ Ancient city at the foot of Vesuvius. 🚪 9h-sunset ◉ holiday-Feiertag-jours de fête-giorni di festa.

🛏S	**Sala Consilina**	34B2

Via Santa Maria della Misericordia. **GPS**: n40,41376 e15,56397.⬆.

20 🍴€ 5/night 🚰🔌Ch🛁included.

Surface: metalled. 🚪 01/01-31/12

Distance: 🚶1,5km ⊗500m 🍽2,5km 🛒1,5km 🎿15km 🏊15km.

Remarks: Nearby hotel Vallis Dea, 300m>A3.

🛏S	**San Gregorio Matese**	33D5

Cooperative Falode, Loc. Acqua di Santa Maria Castello. **GPS**: n41,40547 e14,42756.

40 🍴 🚰🔌Ch🛁 against payment.

IT

🛏S	**Tramonti** 🏕🏞

Agriturismo Costiera Amalfitana - Tramonti

info@costieraamalfitana.it - www.costieraamalfitana.it

Open all year
Bar-restaurant
Picnic area

Agriturismo Costiera Amalfitana, Via Falcone, 12 - Frazione Pietre. **GPS**: n40,69929 e14,61811.⬆.

10 🍴01/09-14/06 € 22, 15/06-31/08 - 23/12-06/01 € 30 🚰🔌 Ch🛁 WC🗑included. **Location:** Rural, comfortable. **Surface:** grassy/gravel. 🚪 01/01-31/12

Distance: 🚶50m 🏊15km 🏖6km ⊗on the spot 🍽30m 🏪500m 🚌on the spot.

Remarks: Amalfi Coast.

Basilicata

🛏S	**Grumento Nova**	34B2

Agriturismo Al Parco Verde, Contrada Spineto, Moliterno-Grumento. **GPS**: n40,28110 e15,90563.⬆➡.

20 🍴€ 20 🚰🔌Ch🛁 WC🗑📶included 🛒. **Surface:** grassy. 🚪 01/06-01/10

Distance: 🚶8km 🛒2km 🍽5km 🚌on the spot 🎿2km 🏊1km.

Remarks: Archeological site 200m.

🛏🍴S	**Metaponto** 🌿	34C2

Camper parking Nettuno, Viale Magna Grecia, Metaponto Lido. **GPS**: n40,35693 e16,83221.⬆.

50 🍴€ 10/24h, € 15/01/07-31/08 🚰🔌Ch🛁 WC included 🗑€ 1. **Surface:** grassy/gravel. 🚪 01/01-31/12

Distance: 🏖50m ⊗on the spot 🍽300m.

Tourist information Metaponto:

ℹ Archeological site. 🚪 9h-sunset.

Calabria

🛏S	**Amantea**	34C3

Garden Park Caterina, SS. 18, loc Coreca. **GPS**: n39,09383 e16,08508.⬆.

10 🍴€ 8-12 🚰€ 3,50 🔌Ch🛁€ 1,50 🗑. **Surface:** grassy. 🚪 15/06-15/09

Distance: 🚶on the spot 🏖on the spot 🛒on the spot ⊗nearby.

🛏S	**Bova Marina**	34D5

Mafalda's Camper Park, Via Sotto Ferrovia, loc. San Pasquale. **GPS**: n37,92422 e15,94800.⬆.

20 🍴€ 10-20 🚰🔌Ch🛁included.

Surface: gravel/sand.

Distance: 🚶3km 🏖on the spot 🛒on the spot ⊗200m 🍽500m.

Remarks: Acces via unmetalled road along the beach.

🍴🅂 **Catanzaro Marina** ⚓

Il Chioschetto, Via Carlo Pisacane 24. **GPS**: n38,83321 e16,64862.

10 🅿free 🚰 🧹. **Surface**: sand.
Distance: ⛱sandy beach.

🅿🅂 **Cirella** 34C3

Area Camper Ulisse, SS 18 km 270, Diamante. **GPS**: n39,72500 e15,80930.

130 🅿€ 8-15 🚰 🍳 Ch 🧹 WC 🪥included. **Surface**: grassy/sand. 🌙 01/04-31/10
Distance: 🚶800m ⛱on the spot 🛒on the spot ⊗on the spot 🍴on the spot 🚍on the spot.

🅿🅂 **Cirella** 34C3

Lido Alexander, SS 18, Diamante. **GPS**: n39,72168 e15,81097.⬆

50 🅿€ 6 to € 20 peak season 🚰 🍳 Ch 🧹 € 3 WCincluded 🪥€ 1 📶€ 3.
Surface: grassy/gravel. 🌙 01/01-31/12
Distance: 🚶1,5km ⛱on the spot 🛒on the spot ⊗on the spot 🍴on the spot.

🅿🅂 **Cirella** 34C3

Lido delle Sirene, SS 18, Contr. Riviere. **GPS**: n39,71822 e15,81137.➡

100 🅿€ 11 🚰 🍳 Ch 🧹 WC 🪥. **Surface**: grassy. 🌙 01/06-20/09
Distance: 🚶1km ⛱on the spot 🛒on the spot ⊗on the spot 🍴1km.

🅿🅂 **Cirella** 34C3

Lido Tropical, Viale Glauco, 9, Diamante. **GPS**: n39,69222 e15,81556.⬆

200 🅿€ 8-18, Aug 25 🚰 🍳 Ch 🧹 WC 🪥 📶. **Surface**: grassy/sand. 🌙 01/01-31/12
Distance: 🚶1,5km ⛱on the spot 🛒on the spot ⊗200m 🍴200m 🚍shuttle to town.

🍴🅂 **Condofuri Marina** 34D5

Agriturismo Antonino Gemelli, Via Salinella 37. **GPS**: n37,92372 e15,85150.⬆
20 🅿€ 15-20 🚰 🍳 Ch 🧹 WC 🍽 📶. **Surface**: gravel/sand. 🌙 01/01-31/12
Distance: 🚶500m ⛱100m.

🍴🅂 **Corigliano Calabro** 34C3

B&B Club Tepee, Contrada Sant'Agata 42, SS106bis > Cantinella. **GPS**: n39,64140 e16,38617.
🅿€ 10 🚰 🍳 Ch 🧹 🪥.
Distance: 🚶Corigliano 14km.

🅿🅂 **Cropani Marina** ⚓ 34D3

Sena Park, Viale Venezia 34. **GPS**: n38,91143 e16,80963.⬆➡
25 🅿€ 15 🚰 🍳 Ch 🧹 WC 🪥€ 0,50 📶 🧺. **Surface**: grassy/sand. 🌙 01/01-31/12
Distance: 🚶500m ⛱400m 🛒400m ⊗ristorante/pizzeria 🍴500m.
Remarks: Washing motorhome € 20.

🅿🅂 **Crotone** 34D3

Coda Campione, Hera Lacinia Mare, Via Per Capo Colonna. **GPS**: n39,04193 e17,15297.⬆
10 🅿€ 25 🚰 🍳 Ch 🧹 🪥. **Surface**: gravel/metalled.
Distance: 🚶on the spot ⛱on the spot 🛒on the spot ⊗100m 🍴200m.
Remarks: Next to campsite.

🅿🅂 **Morano Calabro** 34C3

Via Gaetano Scorza. **GPS**: n39,84098 e16,13731.⬆➡

40 🅿free 🚰 🍳. **Surface**: asphalted. 🌙 01/01-31/12
Distance: 🚶200m 🛒7km ⊗200m 🍴200m.
Remarks: Next to church of San Bernardino, panoramic view.

🅿🅂 **Praia a Mare** 34B3

Nuova Playa, Contr. Fiucci. **GPS**: n39,86885 e15,78943.⬆

15 🅿€ 15, peak season € 25 🚰 🍳 Ch 🧹 included. **Surface**: grassy. 🌙 01/01-31/12
Distance: 🚶2km ⛱on the spot 🛒on the spot ⊗100m 🍴2km.

IT

Remarks: In front of Dino island, black sandy beach.

| 🏕️ S | **Praia a Mare** | 34B3 |

Punto Mare, Loc. Fiuzzi. **GPS:** n39,87633 e15,78727.

30 ⌁€ 6 🔌 🅗 Ch ⚡€ 5. **Surface:** grassy. ⬛ 01/06-30/09
Distance: 🏖️800m ⚓600m ⛽600m ⊗500m 🚏500m.

| 🏕️ S | **Scalea** 🏄 | 34B3 |

Dolce Vita, Via Fiume Lao 7. **GPS:** n39,79667 e15,79265. ⬆️

100 ⌁€ 7, Jul € 10, Aug € 13 🔌 🅗 Ch ⚡€ 5 WC 🚽 📶.
Surface: grassy.
⬛ 01/05-30/09
Distance: 🏖️on the spot ⚓on the spot ⛽on the spot ⊗on the spot 🚏800m.

| 🏕️ S | **Scalea** 🏄 | 34B3 |

Lido Zio Tom, Corso Mediterraneo km 261,7. **GPS:** n39,81306 e15,78917. ⬆️

140 ⌁€ 8, July € 11, Aug € 14 🅗 Ch ⚡€ 2, 4Amp WC 🚽 hot shower
against payment. **Surface:** grassy/gravel. ⬛ 15/04-15/10
Distance: ⚓on the spot ⊗300m 🚏1km 🚆1,5km.

Sardinia

| 🏕️ S | **Aglientu** | 31aC1 |

Oasi Gallura, Localita'Vignola Mare 19, SP 90 km 53. **GPS:** n41,12556 e9,06167.
70 ⌁€ 13-19 🔌 🅗 Ch ⚡€ 2,50 WC 🚽 hot shower € 1 📶€ 5.
Distance: ⚓50m ⊗on the spot 🚏on the spot.

| 🏕️ S | **Alghero** | 31aA2 |

Camperpark I Platani, Ss 291 Km 32,5 S.Maria la Palma - Fertilia. **GPS:** n40,60693 e8,27522.

⌁€ 16, Jul €18, Aug € 20 🔌 🅗 Ch ⚡WC 🚽included 📶€ 5.
Distance: 🏖️Alghero 7km ⚓1,5km.
Remarks: Monitored parking 24/24, shuttle bus to beach, swimming pool.

| 🏕️ S | **Alghero** | 31aA2 |

Paradise Park, Loc. Le Bombarde. **GPS:** n40,59180 e8,25610.

100 ⌁± € 18 🔌 🅗 Ch ⚡WC 🚽included.
Distance: 🏖️350m ⚓350m ⊗on the spot 🚏on the spot 🚆50m.

| 🏕️ S | **Bosa** | 31aB3 |

S'Abba Drucche Spiagge, SP49 Alghero-Bosa km 38+800. **GPS:** n40,31671 e8,47368.
⌁€ 15-20 🔌 🅗 Ch ⚡WC 🚽€ 1 📶€ 7. **Surface:** unpaved. ⬛ 01/06-30/09
Distance: ⚓on the spot ⊗on the spot.

| 🏕️ S | **Buggerru** | 31aB5 |

Area Terrazze. **GPS:** n39,40317 e8,40250.

50 ⌁€ 20/24h 🔌 🅗 Ch ⚡€ 5. **Surface:** sand.
Distance: 🏖️200m ⚓on the spot.
Remarks: Beach parking.

| 🏕️ S | **Buggerru** | 31aB5 |

Loc. Cala Domestica. **GPS:** n39,41757 e8,41147.
50 ⌁€ 10 🔌 🚽 cold shower. **Surface:** sand.
Distance: 🏖️4km ⊗on the spot.
Remarks: Beach parking.

Tourist information Buggerru:
ℹ️ I.A.T. (Ufficio Informazioni e di Accoglienza Turistica), Strada Provinciale.

| 🏕️ S | **Domus de Maria** | 31aB6 |

Loc. Spartivento, Chia. **GPS:** n38,88962 e8,86437.
⌁€ 15/24h 🔌 🅗 Ch ⚡ cold shower.
Surface: sand. ⬛ Easter-30/09
Distance: ⚓on the spot ⊗on the spot 🚏on the spot.
Remarks: In front of Hotel Su Giudeu.

| 🏕️ S | **Ghilarza** | 31aB3 |

SS131 km 6. **GPS:** n40,12604 e8,83942.
⌁free 🔌€ 0,50 🚽.

| 🏕️ S | **Nuoro** | 31aC3 |

P.le Anfiteatro cittadino, Piazza Veneto. **GPS:** n40,31652 e9,32587. ⬆️
30 ⌁free 🔌 Chfree.

| 🏕️ S | **Oristano** | 31aB4 |

Stadio Tharros, Via Dorando Petri. **GPS:** n39,89710 e8,58927. ⬆️
⌁free 🔌 🅗 Chfree.
Distance: ⊗500m 🚏Porta Nuova 650m.

| 🏕️ S | **Oristano** | 31aB4 |

Zona sportiva Sa Rodia, Viale Repubblica. **GPS:** n39,90605 e8,57878.
⌁free 🔌 Chfree.
Distance: ⛲historical centre.
Remarks: Parking in front of swimming pool.

| | San Teodoro | 31aC2 |

Via Donat Cattin. **GPS**: n40,76658 e9,66884.
30 ⌁ € 20.

| | San Teodoro | 31aC2 |

Via Marconi, Loc.La Cinta. **GPS**: n40,77243 e9,66990.
⌁ € 5.
Distance: ⌁on the spot.
Remarks: Beach parking.

| S | Santa Maria Navarrese | 31aD3 |

Area di sosta Costa Orientale, Loc.Tancau. **GPS**: n39,98770 e9,68750.
⌁ € 12-16 ⌁ Ch ⌁ WC ⌁.
Distance: ⌁15 min walking.

| S | Sorso | 31aB2 |

Camp Site, Via degli Oleandri, SP 81 km 13, Platamona Lido. **GPS**: n40,81565 e8,46462.
50 ⌁ € 12-18 ⌁ Ch ⌁ WC ⌁ ⌁. ⌁ 01/01-31/12
Distance: ⌁300m ⌁nearby ⌁on the spot.

| S | Stintino | 31aA2 |

La Pineta, Loc. Pozzo S.Nicola, SP34. **GPS**: n40,86843 e8,23610.⌁
⌁ € 19, Aug € 21 ⌁ Ch ⌁ WC included ⌁ hot shower € 1. **Surface:** grassy/sand.
Distance: ⌁3,5km ⌁on the spot.
Remarks: Free shuttle to beach.

| S | Tonara | 31aC3 |

Ostello delle Gioventù, Via Muggianeddu, 2. **GPS**: n40,02855 e9,17542.
⌁ € 10 ⌁ Ch ⌁. ⌁ 01/01-31/12
Distance: ⌁on the spot.

| S | Valledoria | 31aB2 |

Punto Maragnani, Via Cristoforo Colombo, Loc. Maragnani. **GPS**: n40,92470 e8,79548.
⌁ € 18/24h ⌁ Ch ⌁ WC ⌁included.
Distance: ⌁50m ⌁200m.

| S | Villaputzu | 31aC4 |

Area di sosta camper Torimar, via Nazionale 236, SS125. **GPS**: n39,46017 e9,60290.
⌁ € 8-16 ⌁ Ch ⌁ WC ⌁against payment.
Distance: ⌁Villaputzu 6km ⌁50m.

| S | Villasimius | 31aC5 |

Gli Aranci, Viale dei Carrubi, loc. Pranu Zinnigas. **GPS**: n39,14997 e9,51292.
100 ⌁ € 20 ⌁ Ch ⌁included. ⌁ 01/05-30/09
Distance: ⌁2km ⌁3km.
Remarks: Beachshuttle.

Sicily

| S | Augusta | 34C6 |

Area Attrezzata Camper Nelly, SS114 - Km 118,5, Contrada Agnone Bagni. **GPS**: n37,31148 e15,09260.
⌁ € 13, July € 14, Aug € 15/day ⌁ Ch ⌁ WC ⌁included. ⌁ 01/01-31/12
Distance: ⌁6km.

| | Caltagirone | 34C6 |

Loc. San Giovanni. **GPS**: n37,23808 e14,50781.

| S | Caltanissetta | 34B6 |

Via Guastaferro. **GPS**: n37,48959 e14,04515. ⌁⌁.
⌁ ⌁ Ch free.

| S | Castellammare del Golfo | 34A6 |

Playtime, Viale Leonardo da Vinci, SS187. **GPS**: n38,02494 e12,89086. ⌁⌁.
⌁ € 15/24h ⌁ Ch ⌁ WC ⌁ ⌁. **Surface:** grassy.
Distance: ⌁200m ⌁1km.

| S | Castelluzzo | 34A6 |

Parcheggio Trinacria, Via Calazza. **GPS**: n38,10694 e12,72861. ⌁⌁.

± 40 ⌁against payment ⌁ ⌁ ⌁. **Surface:** gravel. ⌁ summer
Distance: ⌁400m ⌁500m ⌁500m.
Remarks: Beach parking.

| | Castelluzzo | 34A6 |

Parking Macari, SP16. **GPS**: n38,13564 e12,73638.

⌁free. **Surface:** sand.

| | Castelluzzo | 34A6 |

SP16. **GPS**: n38,12166 e12,72666.

⌁free. **Surface:** gravel.
Distance: ⌁on the spot.
Remarks: Beach parking.

| S | Enna | 34C6 |

Ennacamper, C/da S.Giuseppe, Pergusa. **GPS**: n37,52277 e14,29000.
⌁ € 10/24h ⌁ Ch Service € 5 ⌁ € 2 ⌁. **Surface:** sand.
Remarks: Free shuttle, cleaning motorhome € 5.

| S | Enna | 34C6 |

Castello di Lombardia, Via Nino Savarrese. **GPS**: n37,56764 e14,28724.
⌁free.
Distance: ⌁on the spot.
Remarks: Parking at castle.

| S | Francavilla di Sicilia | 34C5 |

Maremonti, Via Cappuccini. **GPS**: n37,90855 e15,14347. ⌁⌁.

±50 ⌁gift ⌁. **Surface:** unpaved. ⌁ 01/01-31/12
Distance: ⌁400m ⌁Riverbed.
Remarks: Gole dell'Alcantara 6km.

IT

Furnari 34C5

Tonnarella, Corso Palermo 6. **GPS:** n38,13218 e15,12469. ⬆️.

44 🛏️ € 15, Jun € 16, Jul € 18, Aug € 20 🚐 🔌 Ch 💧 WC included 🚿 € 0,50.
Surface: gravel. 🅾️ 01/01-31/12
Distance: 🏖️on the spot 🏊on the spot ⊗150m ⚡250m.
Remarks: Excursion to the Eolie-islands.

Gela 34C6

Meridiana Park, Via Torre di Manfria, Contrada Piano Marina. **GPS:** n37,11166 e14,12444. ⬆️➡️.

80 🛏️ € 15/day 🚐 🔌 Ch 💧 WC 🚿. **Surface:** grassy.
Distance: 🏖️Gela 14km ⚡1,2km.
Remarks: Swimming pool, sandy beach.

Giardini Naxos 34C5

Parking Lagani, Via Stralcina 22, zona Recanati. **GPS:** n37,82092 e15,26753. ⬆️➡️.

30 🛏️ € 15-27 🚐 🔌 Ch 💧 WC 🚿 € 1(summer) 🔋€ 5 📶.
Surface: metalled.
🅾️ 01/01-31/12
Remarks: Special tariff for long stay during the winter, bar, view on Etna and Taormina.
Distance: 🏖️on the spot 🏊200m 🏊50m ⚡200m 🚌Bus to Taormina 300m.

Giardini Naxos 34C5

Holiday Sun, Viale Stracina 20. **GPS:** n37,82109 e15,26784.
🛏️ € 15-25 🚐 🔌 Ch 💧 WC 🚿 📶.
Distance: 🏊beach 500m ⊗on the spot.

Tourist information Giardini Naxos:
🏖️ 🅾️ Sa-morning.

Ispica 34D6

Associazione Camper Club Porto Ulisse. **GPS:** n36,69761 e14,98647. ⬆️.
🛏️ 🚐 🔌 Ch 💧 🚿. **Surface:** grassy. 🅾️ 01/01-31/12
Distance: 🏊100m.

Licata 34B6

Ristorante La Sorgente, Loc. Pisciotto. **GPS:** n37,12666 e13,85194. ⬆️➡️.

80 🛏️Jun € 15, Jul € 20, Aug € 25 🚐 🔌 Ch 💧 WC 🚿included. **Surface:** gravel.
Distance: 🏖️Licata 9km 🏊on the spot ⊗on the spot.

Remarks: Stairs to sandy beach.

Marina di Ragusa 34C6

Marina Caravan, Via Portovenere 57. **GPS:** n36,78472 e14,56486. ⬆️.

58 🛏️ € 10, 01/06-30/09 € 17,50 🚐 🔌 Ch 💧 WC 🚿included 🔋€ 4 📶.
Surface: grassy. 🅾️ 01/01-31/12
Distance: 🏖️500m 🏊300m ⊗100m ⚡100m 🏊200m.
Remarks: Water/drainage at each pitch.

Marina di Ragusa 34C6

Tanto per Camper, Via Donnalucata. **GPS:** n36,78944 e14,56666. ⬆️➡️.

40 🛏️15/9-14/6 € 10, 15/6-26/7 € 12, 27/7-30/8 € 15,, 2 pers.incl 🚐 🔌 Ch 💧 WC included 🚿 € 0,50 🔋€ 4. **Surface:** grassy/gravel. 🅾️ 01/01-31/12
Distance: 🏖️800m 🏊1,5km ⊗100m ⚡800m.
Remarks: Beachshuttle € 0,50.

Marsala 34A6

Beach Sibiliana, Contrada Fossarunza 205/z 14. **GPS:** n37,73520 e12,47497. ⬆️.
50 🛏️€ 17 🚐 🔌 Ch 💧 WC 🚿.
Distance: 🏊50m.

Marsala 34A6

Nautisub Club S. Teodoro, Contrada Birgi. **GPS:** n37,91046 e12,46178. ⬆️➡️.

± 50 🛏️€ 15/20 🚐 🔌 Ch 💧. **Surface:** grassy. 🅾️ 01/05-30/09
Distance: 🏖️5km 🏊on the spot ⊗on the spot.
Remarks: Sandy beach.

Marsala 34A6

Via Colonnello Maltese. **GPS:** n37,79621 e12,43164.
🛏️ 🔌 Ch.
Distance: 🏖️on the spot 🏊on the spot.

Tourist information Marsala:
ℹ️ 👁️ I.A.T. (Ufficio Informazioni e di Accoglienza Turistica), Via XI Maggio, 100. Cassaro Marsala, old city centre.

Messina 34C5

Via Catania 108. **GPS:** n38,17686 e15,54540.
🛏️ € 10/24h 🚐 🔌 Ch 💧.
Distance: 🏖️on the spot 🚲4,1km ⚡100m 🚋Tram.

Montallegro 34B6

Agriturismo Torre Salsa, Bove Marina. **GPS:** n37,37583 e13,32222. ⬆️➡️.

20 📷 € 15-22 🚰 4 🔌 Ch 🔧 consumption WC 🚿 1 📺 6 📶 € 1,50/h.
Surface: grassy. ⬛ 01/01-31/12
Distance: 🚶700m.
Remarks: Pitches on the beach without service, estate 300 acres, hiking and mountain bike trails.

| 🏕 S | Montevago | 34A6 |

Agricamper Mastragostino - Villa dei Pini. GPS: n37,70083 e12,98000.
📷 € 15 🚰 🔌 Ch 🔧 included. ⬛ 01/01-31/12
Distance: 🚶200m.

| 🏕 S | Montevago | 34A6 |

Centro Terme Acqua Pia, Loc. Acque Calde. **GPS:** n37,70602 e12,98092.
20 📷 🚰 🔧 against payment. ⬛ 01/04-31/10

| 🏕 S | Motta Camastra ✿ | 34C5 |

S185, fraz. Ficarazzi. **GPS:** n37,87876 e15,17615. ⬆.

10 📷 € 10, Jul/Aug € 15 🚰 🔌 Ch 🔧 WC 🚿 included. **Surface:** grassy/gravel.
Distance: ⊗300m 🍴1km.
Remarks: In front of entrance of Gole dell'Alcantara.

| 🏕 S | Mussomeli | 34B6 |

Piazzale Mongibello. GPS: n37,58343 e13,74956.
📷 free 🚰 🔌 Ch.
Distance: 🚶centro storico.

| 🏕 S | Noto | 34D6 |

Airone, Via San Corrado, Lido di Noto. **GPS:** n36,85916 e15,11555. ⬆➡.

55 📷 Jun € 12, Jul/Aug € 15 incl. 4 pers 🚰 🔌 Ch 🔧 € 2 WC 🚿. **Surface:** grassy/sand.
Distance: 🏖on the spot 🍴1,2km.
Remarks: Breat-service and meals, direct access to the beach.

| 🏕 S | Noto | 34D6 |

NotoParking, Contrada Faldino, Noto. **GPS:** n36,88353 e15,08595. ⬆➡.

40 📷 € 13-15 🚰 🔌 Ch 🔧 € 3 WC 🚿 € 1.
Surface: grassy/gravel.
⬛ 01/01-31/12
Distance: 🚶1km 🚲3km ⊗200m 🍴200m.
Remarks: Free shuttle bus to Noto, organised excursions in the surroundings.

| 🏕 S | Noto | 34D6 |

Parcheggio Calamosche, Oasi di Vendicari. **GPS:** n36,81611 e15,09888. ⬆➡.

40-50 📷 € 12 🚰 🔌 🔧 WC 🚿 included. **Surface:** grassy. ⬛ 01/01-31/12
Distance: 🚶Noto 10km 🚶20 min walking ⊗bar/restaurant.

| 🏕 S | Oliveri | 34C5 |

Azimut Sosta Camper, Corso Cristoforo Colombo. **GPS:** n38,12840 e15,05833. ⬆.
📷 € 12-15-20-22 🚰 🔌 Ch 🔧 WC 🚿 included. **Surface:** grassy/gravel.
Distance: 🚶500m, Tindari 1,2km 🏖beach 50m.

| 🏕 S | Pachino | 34D6 |

Dragomar, Strada Marzamemi Portopalo di Capo Passero, Marzamemi. **GPS:** n36,72732 e15,12083. ⬆➡.

50 📷 Jun/Sep € 10, Jul/Aug € 15 🚰 🔌 Ch 🔧 € 2 WC 🚿 hot shower € 0,50.
Surface: grassy/sand. ⬛ 01/06-15/09
Distance: 🏖100m ⊗100m 🍴750m 🚌Bus to Noto 100m.

| 🏕 S | Noto | 34D6 |

Il Canneto, Viale Lido di Noto, Lido di Noto. **GPS:** n36,86083 e15,11944. ⬆➡.

30 📷 € 10-15 🚰 🔌 Ch 🔧 WC 🚿. **Surface:** gravel. ⬛ 01/01-31/12
Distance: 🏖on the spot ⊗400m 🍴600m.
Remarks: Seaview, no beach.

IT

⌨S **Pachino** 34D6

La Cabana Service, Viale le Aloha, Contrada Granelli. **GPS:** n36,70562 e15,00689. ⬆️➡️.

200 🍴€ 15, Jul/Aug € 20 ⚡🔌 Ch 🚿 WCincluded 🚽 hot shower € 1.
Surface: grassy/sand. 🔲 01/01-31/12
Distance: 🚶Pachino 7km ⚓on the spot 🚂on the spot.
Remarks: Sandy beach, bar.

⌨S **Palermo** 〰️⚓🌊 34B6

Green Park, Via Quarto dei Mille 11b. **GPS:** n38,11016 e13,34307.
🍴€ 20/24h ⚡🔌 Ch 🚿 included. **Surface:** asphalted.
Distance: 🚶piazza Indipendenza 300m.

⌨S **Palermo** 〰️⚓🌊 34B6

Parking Ospedale Cervello, Via Trabucco. **GPS:** n38,15619 e13,31354.
🍴🔧🔌.
Remarks: Nearby hospital.

⌨S **Palermo** 〰️⚓🌊 34B6

Via Uditore 17. **GPS:** n38,13140 e13,32515.
🍴⚡🔌Ch🚿WC🚽. **Surface:** asphalted.
Remarks: Shuttle to centre.

⌨ **Palermo** 〰️⚓🌊 34B6

Piazza Alcide De Gasperi. **GPS:** n38,15170 e13,33944.
🍴free. **Surface:** asphalted.
Distance: 🚌on the spot.
Remarks: Nearby stadium.

⌨S **Palermo** 〰️⚓🌊 34B6

Freesbee Parking, Via Imperatore Federico 116. **GPS:** n38,14722 e13,35277.
100 🍴€ 20 ⚡🔌 Ch 🚿 WC 🚽 1. **Surface:** asphalted.
Distance: 🚶Cathedral Palermo 400m 🚌150m.
Remarks: Motorhome dealer Idea Vacanze, 24/24 surveillance.

Tourist information Palermo:
ℹ️ U.I.A.T. (Ufficio Informazioni e di Accoglienza Turistica), Piazza Castelnuovo, 34, www.regione.sicilia.it/turismo.Capital of Sicily, port and economical heart of the Island.
👁 San Giovanni degli Eremiti.
👁 Santa Catarina.
🏛 Vucciria, Via Cassari-Argenteria.Palermo's most famous, picturesque and historic market.

⌨S **Piazza Armerina** 34C6

Agriturismo Agricasale, Contrada Ciavarina. **GPS:** n37,34032 e14,38840.
🍴€ 15 ⚡🔌 Ch 🚿 included.
Distance: 🚶2km 🍽bar/restaurant.
Remarks: Swimming pool € 3/pppd.

⌨S **Piazza Armerina** 34C6

Agriturismo Gigliotto, SS 117bis km60. **GPS:** n37,37298 e14,35592.
4🍴🚿.
Remarks: Large swimming pool.

🍴S **Piazza Armerina** 34C6

SP90. **GPS:** n37,36674 e14,33426.
🍴against payment ⚡🔌 Ch 🚿against payment.
Distance: 🍽on the spot.
Remarks: Villa del Casale Romano 400m.

⌨S **Porto Empedocle** 34B6

Punta Piccola Park, Scala dei Turchi, SP68. **GPS:** n37,28916 e13,49250. ⬆️➡️.

99 🍴May € 18, Jun € 20, 1-15 Jul € 23 15 Jul-31 Aug € 23 ⚡🔌 Ch 🚿(65x) WC🚽€ 1. **Surface:** gravel. 🔲 25/04-30/09
Distance: 🚶2,5km ⚓on the spot ⊗200m 🚂1km.
Remarks: Direct access to sandy beach. SS115 km 178.70 SP68 dir Zona Lidi di Porto Empedocle.

Tourist information Porto Empedocle:
ℹ️ A.A.P.I.T.(Azienda Autonoma Provinciale per l'Incremento Turistico), Vialle della Vittoria, 255, Agrigento.
🏛 Valle dei Templi, Agrigento.The Valley of The Temples, archeology.

⌨S **Portopalo di Capo Passero** 🌊 34D6

Cicogna. **GPS:** n36,68333 e15,13638. ➡️.
20 🍴Jun/Sep € 10, Jul/Aug € 15 ⚡🔌 Ch 🚿(20x)included 🚽. **Surface:** gravel.
Distance: 🚶50m ⚓sandy beach 300m.

⌨S **Pozzallo** 34C6

Il Giardino di Epicuro, SP67. **GPS:** n36,73128 e14,86240. ⬆️➡️.

50 🍴€ 8, Jun € 10, Jul/Aug € 13 ⚡🔌 Ch 🚿(22x)€ 2 🚽 cold shower.
Surface: grassy/sand. 🔲 01/05-30/09
Distance: 🚶500m ⚓on the spot ⊗50m 🚂300m.
Remarks: Sandy beach.

⌨S **Pozzallo** 34C6

Salvamar, Zona Porto di Pozzallo. **GPS:** n36,71541 e14,82240. ⬆️.

30 🍴€ 10-€ 20 (Aug) ⚡🔌 Ch 🚿€ 3 🚽 1. **Surface:** grassy. 🔲 01/01-31/12
Distance: 🏊200m ⊗500m 🚂1km.

⌨S **Realmonte** 🌊 34B6

Sosta camper Zanzibar, C/o Capo Rossello. **GPS:** n37,29495 e13,45438. ⬆️➡️.

IT

100 �барcode€ 12-22, 01/10-30/03 € 10 🚰🔌Ch 🧹 WC included ☕ hot shower €
1. **Surface:** gravel. 🅿 01/01-31/12
Distance: 🏖sandy beach ⊗on the spot ⛲150m.
Remarks: Bus to Valle dei Templi (€ 7/pp, min. 4 pers).

📷S	Reitano 🌊	34B5

Via Lungomare Colonna. **GPS:** n38,01407 e14,33081.
📷€10 🚰🔌Ch 🧹☕ 0,50.
Distance: 🏖on the spot.

©S	Ribera	34B6

Kamemi, SS115, Secca Grande. **GPS:** n37,43840 e13,24469.
📷Camperstop € 8 🚰🔌Ch. 🅿 01/01-31/12 ⬤ 01/07-31/08 No
Camperstop.

📷S	Roccalumera	34C5

Park Jonio, Via Collegio, SS114 Roccalumera > Nizza di Sicilia. **GPS:** n37,97943
e15,39752. ⬆➡.

60 📷€ 13/24h, Jul/Aug € 15 🚰🔌Ch 🧹 (60x) ☕. **Surface:** gravel.
Distance: 🚶within walking distance 🏖250m ⊗Bar/snack 🍽on the spot.
Remarks: In front of Centro Sportivo.

🍴	San Giovanni La Punta	34C5

Entertainmentcity Isivillage, Via Fisichelli 63. **GPS:** n37,58929 e15,08612.
📷guests free. **Surface:** asphalted.

📷S	San Vito Lo Capo	34A6

Via Faro 36. **GPS:** n38,18472 e12,73277.

30 📷Jun € 15, Jul € 20, Aug € 25 🚰🔌Ch 🧹 included ☕ hot shower € 1.
Surface: asphalted/grassy.
Distance: 🚶1km 🏖on the spot ⊗300m ⛲1km.
Remarks: Terrace on the sea, no beach, sandy beach 400m.

📷S	San Vito Lo Capo	34A6

Via Savoia 13. **GPS:** n38,16222 e12,73666. ⬆.

---

90 📷€ 10, Jun € 12, Jul € 15, Aug € 18 🚰🔌Ch 🧹 (90x) WC ☕€ 0,50 ⬤€
5. **Surface:** gravel. 🅿 01/01-31/12
Distance: 🚶300m 🏖1,4km ⊗1km ⛲1km.
Remarks: Free shuttle to beach.

📷	San Vito Lo Capo	34A6

Via la Piana. **GPS:** n38,16886 e12,74307.

📷free. **Surface:** unpaved.
Distance: 🚶800m 🏖800m.
Remarks: Free shuttle to centre.

📷S	Sciacca	34B6

La Playa, C. da S. Giorgio 153. **GPS:** n37,49472 e13,16000. ⬆➡.

30 📷Jun/Sep € 18, Jul € 21, Aug € 25 🚰🔌Ch 🧹 WC ☕included. **Surface:**
gravel. 🅿 01/06-30/09
Distance: 🚶Sciacca 13km 🏖100m ⊗100m ⛲10km.
Remarks: Beach parking, bread service.

📷S	Scicli 🌊	

Club Piccadilly, Via Mare Adriatico, Donnalucata. **GPS:** n36,74750 e14,66306. ⬆.
📷€ 15-30 🚰🔌Ch 🧹 WC ☕ 🛁. 🅿 01/01-31/12
Distance: 🚶3km 🏖sandy beach 100m.

📷S	Scopello 🏔🌊	34A6

Azienda agricola Plaia Antonella, Fraz. Scopello. **GPS:** n38,06777 e12,81777.
⬆➡.

50 📷€ 17/24h 🚰🔌Ch 🧹☕included.
Surface: gravel.
🅿 01/05-30/09

IT

Distance: ⚓historical centre 200m ⛵1,5km ⊗100m 🛒400m.
Remarks: Shuttle to beach and Riserva dello Zingaro € 2,50/pp, farm products.

| 📷 S | Siracusa | 34D6 |

Parcheggio Von Platen, Via Augusto Von Platen 38. **GPS**: n37,07692 e15,28738.
🅿€ 15/day ⛽🗜Ch⚡WC🛢.
Remarks: Near archeological site and museum.

| 📷 S | Siracusa | 34D6 |

Via Procione 6, zona Golfetto, Fontane Bianche. **GPS**: n36,96361 e15,22027.
🅿€ 20 ⛽🗜Ch ⚡WC🛢. **Surface:** unpaved.
Distance: ⚓Siracusa 15km ⛵on the spot.
Remarks: Bus to Siracusa, natural swimming pool in sea.

| 📷 S | Sutera | 34B6 |

Piazza Rettore Carruba. **GPS**: n37,52450 e13,72960.
🅿free ⛽🗜Ch. **Surface:** asphalted.
Distance: ⚓on the spot ⊗on the spot.

| 📷 S | Terme Vigliatore 🏖 | 34C5 |

Area Trinacria, Via Lungomare Marchesana. **GPS**: n38,14018 e15,14596.⬆.

120 🅿€ 12, peak season € 18 ⛽🗜Ch ⚡🛢included. **Surface:** grassy. ◼
01/01-31/12
Distance: ⛵50m ⊗pizzeria 200m 🛒200m.
Remarks: Excursion to the Eolie-islands.

| 🍴 S | Trapani | 34A6 |

Hotel Le Saline, SP21 km4, contrada Nubia-Paceco. **GPS**: n37,98304 e12,53106.
20 🅿€ 15-20 ⛽🗜Ch ⚡🛢💿📶. **Surface:** metalled.

IT

SLOVENIA

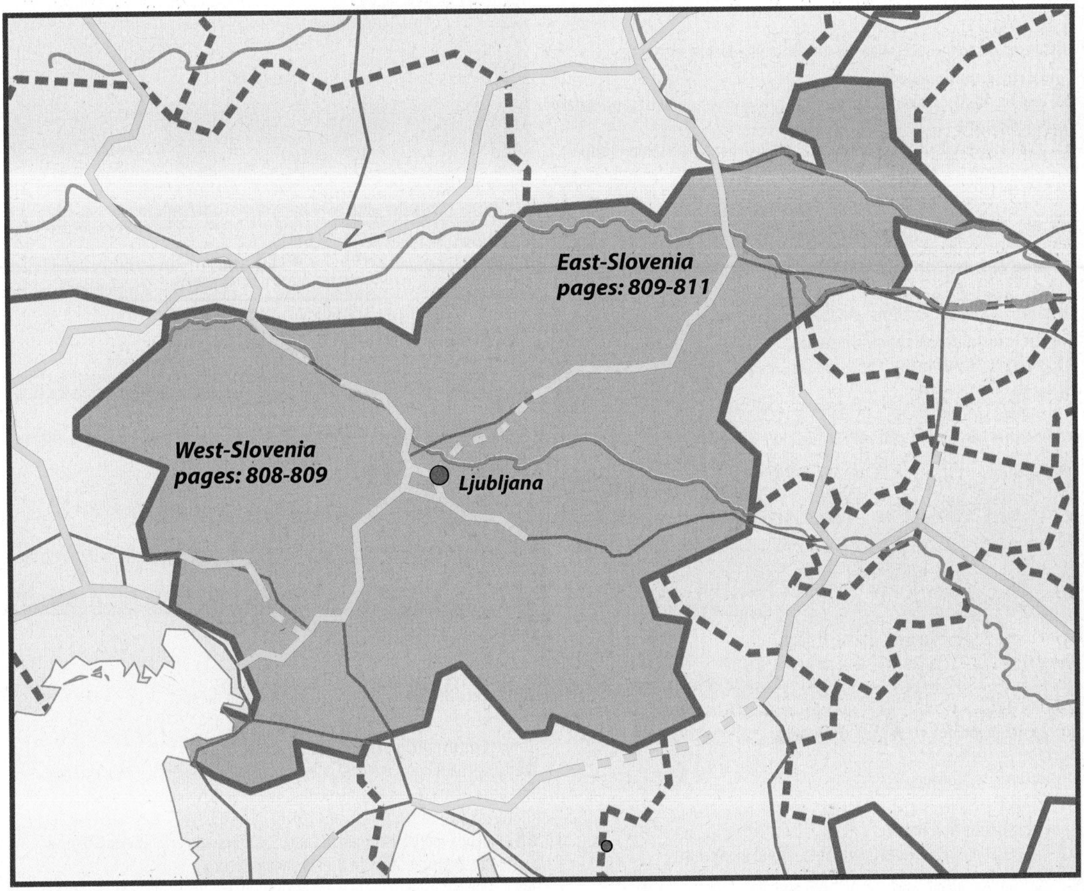

East-Slovenia
pages: 809-811

West-Slovenia
pages: 808-809

◉ *Ljubljana*

Capital: Ljubljana
Government: parliamentarian republic
Official Language: Slovenian
Population: 2.100,000 (2009)
Area: 20,273 km²

General information
Dialling code: 00386.
Currency: Euro
Credit card are accepted almost everywhere.

Regulations for overnight stays
There is no regulation against overnight camping, but it is not yet generally
accepted. In the National Park Triglav wild camping is forbidden.

Opening hours
Shops: Monday-Saturday 8am-7pm
Bank: Monday-Friday 9am-5pm.

Slovenia

Slovenia West

△S Bled 🌿⚓🏔️⚓ 26D3

Bled, Kidriceva 10c. **GPS**: n46,36162 e14,08221.

🚐 € 16-€ 25 🚰 ⚡Ch 🔌 ♻️.

🅾 01/04-15/10

Distance: ⚓on the spot ⚓on the spot ⚓on the spot ⚓on the spot.

Tourist information Bled:

ℹ️ Bled Tourist Association, Cesta svobode 15, www.bled.si.Tourist town on lake of the same name.

Ⓜ️ Bled Castle.Exhibition about the history of Bled, during the summer also open-air concerts. 🅾 8-17h.

⚓ Soteska Vintgar Gorge, TD Gorje, Podhom 0, Gorje.Trail over bridges and galleries along a river.

△S Bohinjsko jezero 🏔️⚓ 26C4

Zlatorog. GPS: n46,27917 e13,83611.

🚐 🚰⚡Ch 🔌 ♻️. 🅾 01/05-30/09

Distance: ⚓on the spot ⚓on the spot ⚓150m.

Tourist information Bohinjsko jezero:

ℹ️ Bohinj Tourist Information Center, Ribčev laz 48.

💧 Savica Falls.Water falls.

🚐S Bovec 🏔️🎯❄️ 26C4

Kanin Cable Car Station, Dvor. **GPS**: n46,33306 e13,53944. ⬆️➡️

15 🚐 € 6/24h, € 8/36h 🚰⚡Ch 🔌 included.
Surface: asphalted.
Distance: 🚲on the spot.
Remarks: Max. 36h.

Tourist information Bovec:

ℹ️ Triglav National Park, Dom Trenta, Soča.Information centre.

⚔️ Kluže Fortress, Trg golobarskih žrtev 8.Fort above gorge.

⚜️ Oltimers Gathering, Kanin.Gathering of skiers in traditional ski equipment.

🅾 Easter Mo.

⚓ Soča Trail, Soča.Hiking trail along the Soca river.

△S DovjeMojstrana 26D3

Kamne. GPS: n46,46444 e13,95778.

🚐🚰⚡Ch 🔌. 🅾 01/01-31/12

Distance: ⚓1km ⚓1km.

🚐S Izola ⚓ 26C6

Cankarjev Drevored. **GPS**: n45,53806 e13,66444. ⬆️

5 🚐 € 15 🚰⚡Ch 🔌 (4x)free. **Surface:** asphalted.
Distance: ⚓500m.

🚐S Jerzersko 26D3

Oranic tourist farm Makek, Zg. Jezersko 77. **GPS**: n46,38978 e14,50835.

🚐 € 8 🚰 WC.

△S Kamniška Bistrica 🏔️ 27A3

Kamp Alpe. GPS: n46,30510 e14,61110.

10 🚐 € 14, 2 pers.incl 🚰⚡Ch 🔌. 🅾 01/05-01/10

△S Kobarid 🏔️⚓ 26C4

Koren, Drezneske Ravne 333. **GPS**: n46,25083 e13,58667.

🚐 🚰⚡Ch 🔌 ♻️. 🅾 01/01-31/12

Distance: ⚓500m ⚓on the spot ⚓on the spot ⚓on the spot.

△S Kobarid 🏔️⚓ 26C4

Lazar, Gregorciceva 63. **GPS**: n46,25530 e13,58720.

🚐🚰⚡Ch 🔌. 🅾 01/04-31/10

Distance: ⚓on the spot ⚓on the spot.

Tourist information Kobarid:

Ⓜ️ Kobariski muzej, Gregorciceva 1.Museum about the first World War. 🅾 01/04-30/09 9-18h, 01/10-31/03 10-17h.

⚓ Tolmin Chutes, LTO Sotočje, Petra Skalarja 4, Tolmin.Touristic route along the rapid to the thermal source of the river.

△S Ljubljana 27A3

Ježica, Dunajska 270. **GPS**: n46,09778 e14,51889.

🚐🚰⚡Ch 🔌 ♻️.

🅾 01/01-31/12

Distance: ⚓on the spot ⚓on the spot ⚓on the spot.

Tourist information Ljubljana:

ℹ️ Ljubljana Tourist Card.Card offers among other things free public transport, free acces at museums and discount in restaurants, shops etc. Available at Tourist Office, railway station and several hotels. 🎫 € 35/72h.

ℹ️ Ljubljana Tourist Information Center, Stritarjeva, www.ljubljana-tourism.si.Capital, historical city with a lot of annual events.

Ⓜ️ National museum, Muzjeska 1.Archeological and historical museum. 🅾 10-18h, Thu 10-20h ⚫ Mo.

Ⓜ️ Plecnik museum, Kurunova 4.Architectonic museum in the house of Joze Plecnik. 🅾 Tue, Thu 10-14h.

Ⓜ️ Slovene Natural History Museum, Muzjeska 1.Zoological and botanic museum. 🅾 daily 10-18h, Thu 10-20h ⚫ Mo.

⚔️ Ljubljana Castle.Medieval fortress, tourist train at town centre. 🅾 01/10-30/04 10-21h, 01/05-30/09 9-22h.

🛖 Markt, Vodnikov trg. 🅾 daily, summer 6-18h, winter 6-16h.

🐾 Zoo Ljubljana.Zoo. 🅾 summer 9-19h, winter 9-16h.

🏔️S Locatec 26D4

A1. **GPS**: n45,89854 e14,25570.

6 🚐 free 🚰 WC free.
Distance: ⚓100m.
Remarks: Guarded parking petrol station LOM II, on both sides of the highway PO-LJ.

SL

Slovenia East

⚠S | Luče | 27A3
Camp Smica, Luče 4. **GPS**: n46,35644 e14,74290.
🚿🚰🔌Ch🛒♻️🚽 ☐ 01/05-30/10
Distance: ⚓on the spot ⊗on the spot 🚲900m.

Lukovica | 27A3
OMV Istrabenz. **GPS**: n46,16690 e14,69380.
2🚐free.
Remarks: Parking petrol station OMV Istrabenz.

⚠S | Portorož 🌊🏖️🍽️🍺 | 26C6
Strunjan, Strunjan 23. **GPS**: n45,52570 e13,61087.
🚿🚰🔌Ch🛒♻️ ☐ 01/01-31/12
Distance: ⚓on the spot 🚲100m.

Tourist information Portorož:
ℹ️ Tourist Information Portorož, Obala 16.Lively bathing resort.
ℹ️ Turistična organizacija Koper, Verdijeva 10, Koper.City with a Venetian past and a lot of curiosities.
Ⓜ️ Pomorski muzej Sergej Mašera, Cankarjevo nabrežje 3, Piran.Maritime museum. ☐ 9-12h, 15-18h, 01/07-31/08 9-12h, 18-21h 🔴 Mo.

S | Postojna | 26D5
Veliki Otok. GPS: n45,78028 e14,20333.⬆️

30🚐€18🚰🔌Ch🛒included.
Surface: concrete.
☐ 01/05-30/09
Distance: ⚓1km 🚤3km.
Remarks: Postojna caves 300m.

Tourist information Postojna:
👁️ Križna jama, Bloška polica 7, Grahovo.Largest water caves of Slovenia.
🏰 Perdjama Grad.Castle, 16th century and caves. ☐ 01/05-30/09 9-18, 01/10-30/04 10-16h.
⛰️ Postojnska Jama, Jamska cesta 30.Postojna caves. ☐ 01/05-30/09 9-18, 01/10-30/04 10-16h.

S | Smlednik | 26D4
Hotel Kanu, Valburga 7. **GPS**: n46,16785 e14,43046.⬆️
🚿🚰🔌Ch🛒 ☐ 01/01-31/12
Remarks: 5km from motorway.

S | Tolmin | 26C4
Kamp Siber, Klanec 8. **GPS**: n46,18082 e13,73792.

50🚐🚰🔌Ch🛒 WC⬜included. **Location:** Rural. **Surface:** grassy/gravel.
☐ 01/01-31/12
Distance: ⚓1km ⚓on the spot ⊗on the spot 🚲1km.

S | Zalošce | 26C5
Saksida Winery. GPS: n45,89039 e13,74732.⬆️
10🚐🚰🔌Ch🛒 WC⬜📶
Distance: 🚤4,6km.

🍽️S | Celje | 27B3
Parking Glazija, Ljubljanska cesta 20. **GPS**: n46,23059 e15,26010.
4🚐€10🚰🔌🛒included.
Surface: metalled.

Tourist information Celje:
ℹ️ Celje Tourist Information Center, Trg celjskih knezov 9.
👁️ Jama Pekel, Šempeter.Caves.
🏰 Stari Grad Castle.Reminders of castle.
⛰️ Rimska Nekropola, Šempeter.Roman Necropolis, archeological parc.

🍽️S | Dolenjske Toplice 🌿 | 27B4
Kamp Polje. GPS: n45,76739 e15,05151.⬆️

25🚐€8/24h🚰🔌Ch♿ **Location:** Rural, comfortable. **Surface:** unpaved.
☐ 01/03-15/11
Distance: ⚓800m ⚓on the spot ⚓on the spot ⊗800m 🚲800m 🚴on the spot 🏃on the spot.
Remarks: Along the Krka river, Terme Dolenjske Toplice 800m.

🍽️S | Ivanjkovci 🌿 | 27B3
Vinoteka Svetinjska Klet, Svetinje 5. **GPS**: n46,46220 e16,16990.⬆️

2🚐free 🛒. **Surface:** metalled.

🍴 | Kamnica 🌿 | 27B3
Gostilna Koblarjev Zaliv, Na otok 20. **GPS**: n46,56560 e15,61908.

20🚐free, use of a meal desired.
Surface: grassy. ☐ 01/01-31/12
Distance: ⚓Maribor 2km ⚓on the spot ⚓on the spot ⊗on the spot 🚲2km 🚌300m.
Remarks: Walking and bicycle area along the Drava river to Maribor centre.

🍴S | Laško 🌊🏖️🌿 | 27B3
Zdravilišče Laško, Zdraviliška 4. **GPS**: n46,15944 e15,23143.

SL

6 ⅀€ 10/day 🚐 💧 🗑️

Distance: 🚰on the spot ⊗on the spot 🛒on the spot 🛒on the spot.

Tourist information Laško:
ℹ️ Laško Tourist Information Center, Trg svobode 8.

Lendava ♈ 27B3
Terme Lendava. GPS: n46,55396 e16,45813.⬆️
⅀€ 24, 2 pers.incl 🚐🍽️Ch 💧€ 4. 🅾️ 01/01-31/12
Remarks: Including access spa resort.

Ljutomer 27B3
Grostilna Tmek. GPS: n46,55516 e16,21929.⬆️

25 ⅀free 💧. **Surface:** grassy. 🅾️ 01/01-31/12
Distance: ∠on the spot 🚐on the spot ⊗on the spot.

SL

Moravske Toplice 27B3
Kamp Moravske Toplice, Kranjčeva ulica 12 . **GPS**: n46,68298 e16,21953.
⅀€ 32, 2 pers.incl 🚐🍽️Ch 💧€ 4 🗑️. 🅾️ 01/01-31/12
Distance: ⊗100m 🛒200m.
Remarks: Including access spa resort 3000.

Tourist information Moravske Toplice:
🌿 Goričko Regional Park, Ulica ob igrišču 3, www.park-goricko.org.Information centre.

Obrežje Jug 27B3
OMV Istrabenz. GPS: n45,85517 e15,68513.
2 ⅀free.
Remarks: Parking petrol station OMV Istrabenz.

Podčetrtek 27B3
Terme Olimia Kamp Natura, Zdravillška cesta 24. **GPS**: n46,15619 e15,60792.
15 ⅀€ 16,60, 2 pers.incl 🚐🍽️Ch 💧€ 3,20 🗑️. 🅾️ 21/04-30/09
Distance: ⊗on the spot 🛒on the spot.
Remarks: Including access spa resort € 30,80.

Tourist information Podčetrtek:
👁️ Sedovška Homestead, Aškercev trg 24, Šmarje pri Jelšah.Traditional farmstead.
Ⓜ️ Rogatec Open-air Museum, Ptujska cesta 23, Rogatec.Open air museum, 18-20th century.
⛪ Božjepotna Marijina cerkev, Sladka Gora, Šmarje pri Jelšah.Pilgrimage church.
⛪ Olimje Monastery and Pharmacy, Olimje 82.Monastery and one of the oldest pharmacies in the world.

Podsmreka 27A3
A2. GPS: n45,94805 e14,77065.
5 ⅀free 🚰free.
Distance: 🚗100m.
Remarks: Guarded parking petrol station Petrol Podsmereka, highway Novo Mesto-Ljubljana.

Prebold 27B3
Dolina, Dolenja Vas 147. **GPS**: n46,24018 e15,09268.
⅀🚐🍽️Ch 💧. 🅾️ 01/01-31/12
Distance: ⊗200m 🛒200m.

Ptuj 🌿🏺🍲 27B3
Avtokamp Terme Ptuj, Pot v toplice 9. **GPS**: n46,42109 e15,85548.

⅀€ 28, 2 pers.incl, including access spa resort 🚐🍽️Ch 💧€ 4. 🅾️ 01/01-31/12
Remarks: Only overnight stays € 13 >18h <10h.

Tourist information Ptuj:
ℹ️ Maribor Tourist Board, Partizanska 47, Maribor, www.maribor-tourism.si.Old city with historical centre.
ℹ️ Tourist Information Center, Slovenski Trg 14, www.ptuj-turism.si.
Ⓜ️Ⓧ Mariborski Grad, Maribor.Castle, 15th century, regional museum. 🅾️ 01/04-31/12 Tue-Sa 9-17h, Su 9-14h ⭕ Mo.
Ⓜ️Ⓧ Ptujski Grad.Castle, 11th century with regional museum. 🅾️ 01/05-31/10 9-18h.

Rečica ob Savinji 27A3
Menina. GPS: n46,31167 e14,90917.
⅀🚐🍽️Ch 💧 🗑️. 🅾️ 01/01-31/12
Distance: ∠on the spot ⊗on the spot 🛒300m.

Tourist information Rečica ob Savinji:
🌿 Mozirski gaj, Hribernikova 1, Mozirje.Botanical garden. 🅾️ 01/04-31/10.
Ⓜ️ Musej Premogovništva, Stari jašek - Koroška cesta, Velenje.Coalmine museum.

Rogla 27B3
Climate Resort and Walking Centre. GPS: n46,45347 e15,33423.

4 ⅀€ 10/motorhome 🚐💧included.
Remarks: Altitude 1517m, tourist tax € 1 pp, 20% discount on swimming pool of the hotel.

Solcava 27A3
Park Logarska Dolina, Logarska Dolina 9. **GPS**: n46,39870 e14,63100.
⅀€ 10 🚐.

Tepanje 27B3
GPS: n46,34776 e15,48695.
5 ⅀free 🚰free.
Remarks: Guarded parking petrol station Petrol Tepanje I, on both sides of the highway Maribor-Ljubljana.

Visnja Gora 27A4
Kopaliska Ulica 25. **GPS**: n45,95258 e14,75210.

20 ⊠ ⊨⊟ Ch ⚓ WC ⊐. **Location:** Rural. **Surface:** grassy/sand. ☐
01/01-31/12

Distance: ⚲on the spot ⚑ 1,7km ⊗on the spot.

⌂S	Zrece	27B3

Thermal Spa. GPS: n46,37096 e15,39021.

4 ⊠ € 10/motorhome ⚡⚓ included.

Remarks: Tourist tax € 1 pp, 20% discount on swimming pool of the hotel.

SL

CROATIA

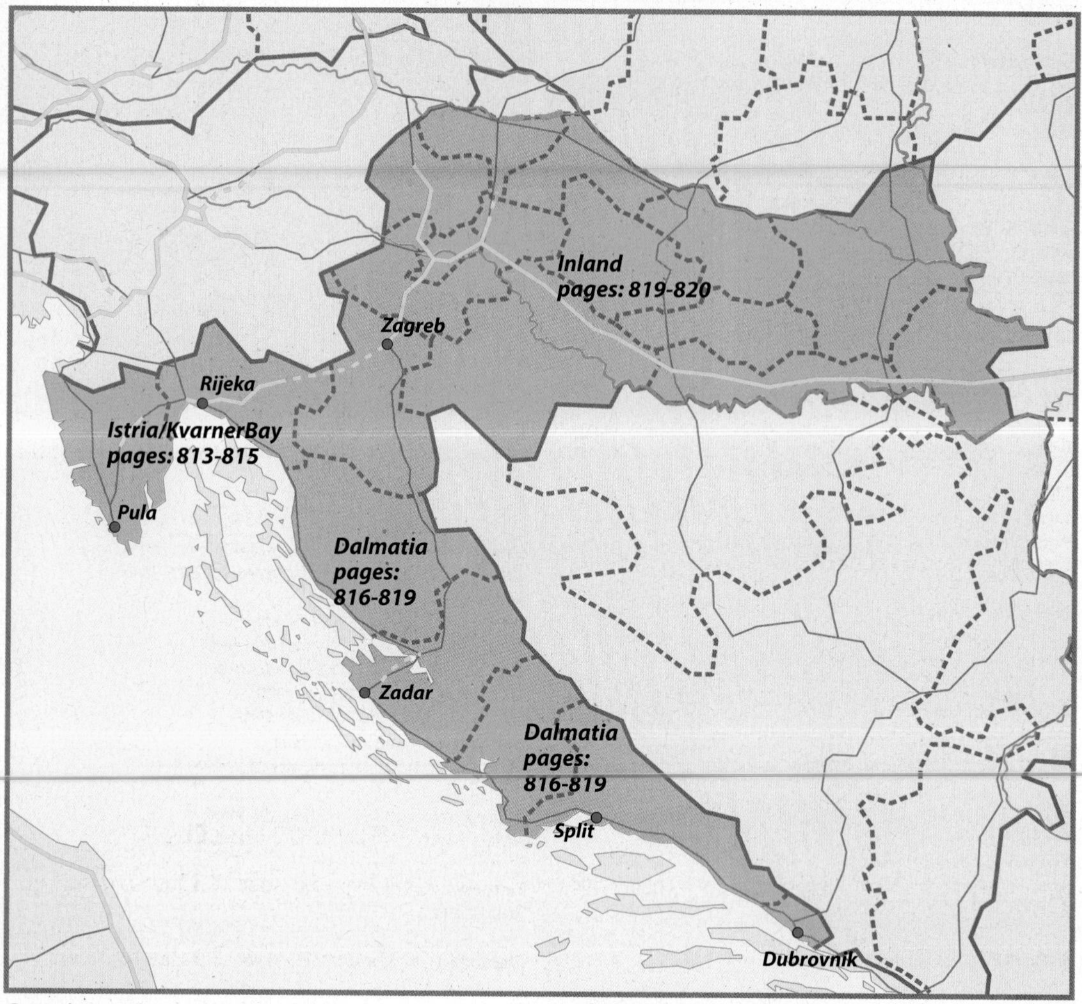

Inland
pages: 819-820

Zagreb

Rijeka

Istria/KvarnerBay
pages: 813-815

Pula

Dalmatia
pages:
816-819

Zadar

Dalmatia
pages:
816-819

Split

Dubrovnik

HR

Capital: Zagreb
Government: parliamentarian democracy
Official Language: Croatian
Population: 4,500,000 (2010)
Area: 56,594 km².

General information
Dialling code: 00385.
Currency: Kuna, kn, 1 kuna = 100 lipa, 1kn = € 0,13
(October 2012)
Credit card are accepted almost everywhere.

Regulations for overnight stays
Wild camping is forbidden.

Opening hours
Shops: Monday-Friday 8am-8pm, Saturday-Sunday
8am-2pm
Bank: Monday-Friday 8am-4pm.

Istria/Kvarner Bay

⚜S | Baderna | 26C6
Farm Pino, Olives & Oil, Katun 1. **GPS**: n45,21913 e13,72903.
24 🍴€ 10 + € 3/pp 🚿€ 4 🚽 Ch. **Surface**: metalled/sand.

🚻 | Bašanija 🏖 | 26C6
Svjetionicarska ulica. **GPS**: n45,49064 e13,49190.
15 🍴€ 8-16. 🚶 **Location**: Rural. **Surface**: grassy/gravel.
⚫ 01/01-31/12
Distance: ⚓on the spot ⛱on the spot ⊗500m.

⛺S | Cres/Cres | 27A4
Kovačine, Melin I, 20. **GPS**: n44,96278 e14,39694.
🍴from € 14,80 🚿🚻 Ch 🚽 WC 🚿included.
⚫ 15/04-15/10
Distance: ⚓on the spot.

Tourist information Cres/Cres:
ℹ️ Turisticka zajednica, Riva Creskih Kapetana, www.tzg-cres.hr.Island can be
reached with ferry service from Brestova, south of Rijeka and Valbiska, west Krk.

⛺S | Cres/Martinšćica | 27A5
Slatina. **GPS**: n44,82091 e14,34238.
🍴from € 15 🚿🚻 Ch 🚽 WC 🚿🏖 ⚫ 15/04-31/10

⛺S | Cres/Nerezine | 27A5
Baldarin, Punta Križa. **GPS**: n44,61680 e14,50834.
🍴from € 13,35 🚿🚻 Ch 🚽 WC 🚿included. ⚫ 15/04-01/10
Distance: ⛟3,5km ⚓on the spot.
Lopari, Nerezine. **GPS**: n44,68253 e13,39846. 🚻. ⚫ 15/04-30/09
Preko Mosta, Osor 76, Nerezine. 🚻. ⚫ 01/05-30/09
Rapoća, Rapoća, Nerezine. **GPS**: n44,66357 e13,39756. 🚻. ⚫ 01/05-30/09

⛺ | Cres/Osor | 27A5
Bijar. **GPS**: n44,69428 e14,39550. 🚻. ⚫ 01/05-30/09

⛺ | Cres/Valun | 27A5
Zdovice, Kastanija bb. **GPS**: n44,90598 e14,35900. 🚻. ⚫ 15/01-01/10

⛺ | Crikvenica 🏖 | 27A4
Kacjak, Kacjak BB. **GPS**: n45,16703 e14,70511. 🚻. ⚫ 15/05-15/09

Tourist information Crikvenica:
ℹ️ Turisticka zajednica, Trg Stepana Radica 1.

⛺ | Fažana | 27A5
Bi Village, Dragonja 115. **GPS**: n44,91750 e13,81111. 🚻.
⚫ 01/04-15/11

Tourist information Fažana:
🚶 Nationaal Park Brijuni, Brijuni.Nature reserve, boat connection from Fažana.
⚫ daily.

⛺ | Ičići | 26C6
Opatija. **GPS**: n45,31083 e14,28472. 🚻. ⚫ 01/04-01/10

⛺ | Klenovica | 27A4
Klenovica, Zidinice BB. **GPS**: n45,09667 e14,84556. 🚻. ⚫ 01/05-30/09
Distance: ⚓on the spot ⛱on the spot.

⛺S | Koromačno | 27A4
Tunarica. **GPS**: n44,96917 e14,09889.
🍴from € 16 🚿🚻 Ch 🚽 WC 🚿included. ⚫ 20/05-05/09

⛺ | Kraljevica | 27A4
Ostro. **GPS**: n45,27109 e14,56402. 🚻. ⚫ 01/05-30/09

⛺ | Krk/Baška ⛲🏖 | 27A4
Zablace, Emila Geitslicha 34, Baška. **GPS**: n44,96694 e14,74528. 🚻. ⚫ 01/05-01/10

Tourist information Krk/Baška:
ℹ️ Tourist Information, Kralja Zvonimira 114, www.tz-baska.hr.Largest bathing
resort on the island with beautiful beaches.

⛺ | Krk/Klimno | 27A4
Kampiralište, U. Soline, Klimno Br. 8. 🚻. **Remarks:** Mini-camp.
Klimno, Uvala Soline. **GPS**: n45,15036 e14,60886. 🚻.
Remarks: Mini-camp.

🏕S | Krk/Krk 🏖⛲🏖 | 27A4
Srecko Krajacic, Narodnog preporoda 51. **GPS**: n45,02900 e14,58100.⬆.

12 🍴€ 20, 1/6-30/9 € 25 🚿🚻 Ch 🚽 WC 🚿included. **Surface:** metalled.
⚫ 01/01-31/12
Distance: ⛟500m ⚓500m ⛱500m ⊗500m 🏪500m 🚌on the spot.

⛺S | Krk/Krk 🏖⛲🏖 | 27A4
Bor. **GPS**: n45,02250 e14,56194.
🍴from € 16,50 🚿🚻 Ch 🚽€ 4/day WC 🚿included ⊙🚿€ 3. ⚫ 01/01-31/12
Jezevac, Plavnička bb. **GPS**: n45,01877 e14,56684.
🍴from € 20,30 🚿🚻 Ch 🚽 WC 🚿included. ⚫ 01/05-30/09
Marta, Škrbcici 29. 🚻. **Remarks:** Mini-camp.

Tourist information Krk/Krk:
ℹ️ Tourist Information, Vela placa 1/1, www.krk.hr.Krk accessoe via toll-bridge
south-east from Rijeka.
☀ Jazz-festival, Kamplin. ⚫ Aug.

⛺S | Krk/Malinska ⛲🏖 | 27A4
Glavotok, Glavokok 4. **GPS**: n45,09472 e14,44111.
🍴from € 20 🚿🚻 Ch 🚽 WC 🚿included. ⚫ 01/05-30/09
Distance: ⚓on the spot.
Bogovic Ivan. 🚻. **Remarks:** Mini-camp.
Draga, Palih Boraca 4. 🚻. **Remarks:** Mini-camp.
K.-Stašic Nevenka. 🚻. **Remarks:** Mini-camp.
Košic Marica. 🚻. **Remarks:** Mini-camp.
Vila Iva, Portic 4. 🚻. **Remarks:** Mini-camp.

Tourist information Krk/Malinska:
ℹ️ Tourist Information, Obala 46, www.tz-malinska.hr.

⛺S | Krk/Njivice | 27A4
Njivice, Primorska bb. **GPS**: n45,17000 e14,54694.
🍴from € 19,40 🚿🚻 Ch 🚽 WC 🚿included. ⚫ 20/04-01/10

⛺ | Krk/Omišalj | 27A4
Pusca, Pušča bb. **GPS**: n45,23472 e14,54861. 🚻. ⚫ 01/06-30/09 **Remarks:**
Nearby bridge.

⛺ | Krk/Pinezici | 27A5
Amar, Njivine 8. **GPS**: n44,96484 e13,93448. 🚻. **Remarks:** Mini-camp.

⛺S | Krk/Punat ⛲🏖 | 27A4
Pila, Setalište Ivana Brusića. **GPS**: n45,01556 e14,62806.
250 🍴from € 20 🚿🚻 Ch 🚽 included. ⚫ 15/04-30/09
Škrila, Stara Baška. **GPS**: n44,96611 e14,67389.
350 🍴🚿🚻 Ch 🚽. ⚫ 01/05-30/09
Maslinik, Nikole Tesle 1. 🚻. **Remarks:** Mini-camp.

Tourist information Krk/Punat:
ℹ️ Tourist Information, Obala 72, www.tzpunat.hr.
✝ Otočić Košljun,Monastery.

⛺ | Krk/Šilo | 27A4
Kampiralište, Borca, 35. **GPS**: n45,14548 e14,66687. 🚻.
Remarks: Mini-camp.

⛺ | Labin 🏖 | 27A4
Marina. **GPS**: n45,03333 e14,15806. 🚻.
⚫ 15/04-30/09

Tourist information Labin:
ℹ️ Turisticka zajednica, Aldo Negri 20, www.istra.com/rabac.Old city with
several curiosities.
Ⓜ Narodni muzej, N. Katunara 6.Ethnological museum. ⚫ daily 10-13h,
17-19h.

⛺S | Lošinj/Mali Lošinj | 27A5
Kredo. **GPS**: n44,53444 e14,44751.

HR

🏕️± € 21,50 🚰🔌 Ch 💧 WC 🗑️. ◻ 01/01-31/12
Distance: 🚶2km 🌲on the spot.**Remarks:** Mini-camp.
Čikat. GPS: n44,53750 e14,45056.
940 🏕️from € 18,40 🚰🔌 Ch 💧 WCincluded. ◻ 15/04-15/10
Poljana. GPS: n44,55556 e14,44167.
🏕️from € 17,85 🚰🔌 Ch 💧 WC 🗑️included. ◻ 01/05-30/09

Tourist information Lošinj/Mali Lošinj:
ℹ️ Turisticka zajednica, Riva Losinjskih kapetana 29, www.tz-malilosinj.hr.
☀️ Dolphins day, action day with possibility for adoption of a dolphin. ◻ 1st
Sa Aug.

🔺Ｓ Medulin 🏖️ 27A5
Kazela. GPS: n44,80695 e13,95015.
🏕️from € 17,60 🚰🔌 Ch 💧 WC 🗑️included. ◻ 01/04-15/10
Medulin. GPS: n44,81417 e13,93194.
1500 🏕️from € 16,30 🚰🔌 Ch 💧 WC 🗑️included. ◻ 03/04-09/10
Brajdice, Indie Bd, Banjole. 🏕️. **Remarks:** Mini-camp.
Fuma, Indie 2. 🏕️. **Remarks:** Mini-camp.
Hrastovec, Gaia Commerce, Premantura-Munte Bb. 🏕️. **Remarks:** Mini-camp.
Indie, Banjole. 🏕️. ◻ 01/05-01/10
Karlo, Indie 18, Banjole. 🏕️. **Remarks:** Mini-camp.
Kranjski Kamp, Runke 52, Premantura. 🏕️. **Remarks:** Mini-camp.
Laguna, Indie 94. 🏕️. **Remarks:** Mini-camp.
Marina, Indie 52. 🏕️. **Remarks:** Mini-camp.
Milan Yachting, Pomer. 🏕️. **Remarks:** Mini-camp.
Mira, Indie 4, Banjole. 🏕️. **Remarks:** Mini-camp.
Oliva, Indie 94, Banjole. 🏕️. **Remarks:** Mini-camp.
Pineta, Rupice Bd. 🏕️. **Remarks:** Mini-camp.
Piškera, Indie 49, Banjole. 🏕️. **Remarks:** Mini-camp.
Pod Murvom, Indie Bd, Banjole. 🏕️. **Remarks:** Mini-camp.
Postolovic, Bumbište 10. 🏕️. **Remarks:** Mini-camp.
Runke, Premantura. 🏕️. ◻ 01/05-30/09
Sandra, Rupice 3. 🏕️. **Remarks:** Mini-camp.
Sidro, Banjole. 🏕️. **Remarks:** Mini-camp.
Širola, Rupice Bd. 🏕️.
Remarks: Mini-camp.
Stupice, Premantura. 🏕️. ◻ 01/05-25/09
Tasalera, Premantura. 🏕️. ◻ 01/04-30/09
Vega, Gaia Commerce, Premantura-Munte Bb. 🏕️.
Remarks: Mini-camp.

Tourist information Medulin:
ℹ️ Premantura.Most Southern place of Istria.
ℹ️ Tourist Information, Centrar 223, www.istra.com/medulin/eng/.Tourist
centre.
👁️ Banjole.Fisherman's village with natural harbour.

🔺Ｓ Moščenička Draga 🌿 26C6
I. GPS: n45,24000 e14,25028.
165 🏕️ 🚰🔌 Ch 💧. ◻ 15/04-15/10
Carl Dana, Aleja Slatina Bb. 🏕️. **Remarks:** Mini-camp.
Medveja. 🏕️. ◻ 01/04-15/10
Rudan Ivana, Aleja Slatina Bb. 🏕️. **Remarks:** Mini-camp.
Sencic Franko. 🏕️. **Remarks:** Mini-camp.

Tourist information Moščenička Draga:
ℹ️ Tourist Information, Aleja Slatina bb, www.tz-moscenicka-draga.hr.Forms
together with Opatija and Lovran the Opatija Riviera.

🏕️Ｓ Motovun 🌿 26C6
Motovun. GPS: n45,33507 e13,82498.

10 🏕️€ 23,40 🚰🔌 Ch 💧 WC 🗑️free. **Location:** Rural, comfortable. **Surface:**
gravel. ◻ 01/01-31/12
Distance: 🚶50m ✖️50m.

🔺Ｓ Novi Vinodolski 27B4
Autocamp Sibinje, Sibinj. **GPS:** n45,04403 e14,87816. 🏕️.
Distance: 🌲on the spot ✖️50m 🚶50m.
Remarks: Mini-camp.
Punta. GPS: n45,11587 e14,84725. 🏕️. ◻ 01/06-30/09
Distance: 🌲on the spot ⚓3km.
Remarks: Mini-camp..

🔺Ｓ Novigrad (Istria) 🏖️ 26C6
Mareda. GPS: n45,34306 e13,54833.
800 🏕️from € 17 🚰🔌 Ch 💧 WC 🗑️included. ◻ 15/04-30/09
Sirena. GPS: n45,31528 e13,57556.
🏕️from € 16,20 🚰🔌 Ch 💧 WCincluded. ◻ 01/04-30/09
Baia Bianca. 🏕️. ◻ 15/04-15/10

Tourist information Novigrad (Istria):
ℹ️ Turisticka zajednica, Porporella 6, www.istra.com/novigrad.
🎪 Boerenmarkt, Hoofdstraat van de oude stad. ◻ daily.
☀️ Feest van de beschermheilige Pelegrinus, Umag. ◻ 23/05.

🏕️Ｓ Poreč 🌿🏖️ 26C6
30. Travinja/Karla Huguesa. **GPS:** n45,22186 e13,60700.

🏕️120kn 💧. **Surface:** asphalted.
Distance: 🚶800m ✖️400m.

🔺Ｓ Poreč 🌿🏖️ 26C6
Bijela Uvala. GPS: n45,19139 e13,59667.
2000 🏕️from € 20 🚰🔌 Ch 💧 WC 🗑️included. ◻ 01/04-15/10
Laternacamp. GPS: n45,29639 e13,59444.
3000 🏕️from € 22,65 🚰🔌 Ch 💧 WC 🗑️included.
◻ 01/04-15/10
Puntica.
250 🏕️ 🚰🔌 Ch 💧. ◻ 11/04-13/10
Zelena Laguna. GPS: n45,19611 e13,58917.
1000 🏕️from € 20 🚰🔌 Ch 💧 WC 🗑️included.
◻ 01/04-15/10
Matesa, Materada. 🏕️. **Remarks:** Mini-camp.

Tourist information Poreč:
ℹ️ Turisticka zajednica, Zagrebacka 9, www.istra.com/porec.Old city, centre
tourist and cultural.
👁️ Decumanus.Roman main street with palazzi from the Venetian time.
Ⓜ️Ⓧ Zavicajnog muzeja poreštine.Native museum of Porec. ◻ daily 10-13h,
18-22h.
✝️ Eufrazijeva bazilika.Basilica, 6th century, in the centre. ◻ daily 7-19h.

🔺Ｓ Pula 🌿🏖️ 27A5
Puntižela. GPS: n44,89806 e13,80722.
🏕️from € 15,50 🚰🔌 Ch 💧 WC 🗑️included. ◻ 01/05-31/10
Stoja. GPS: n44,86000 e13,81472.

750 🛏 from € 17,40 ⚡🔌Ch 🚿 WC ⏞included. 🅾 03/04-02/11

Colona, Bale/Valle. 🛏. **Remarks:** Mini-camp.
Kažun, Family-Turist, Pavicini 5a, Marcana. 🛏. **Remarks:** Mini-camp.
Luka Krnica, Krnica. 🛏. **Remarks:** Mini-camp.
San Pol, Bale/Valle. 🛏. **Remarks:** Mini-camp.
Youth Hostel, Valsaline 4. 🛏.
Remarks: Mini-camp.

Tourist information Pula:
ℹ Turisticka zajednica, Forum 3, www.istra.com/pula.
Ⓜ Arheoloski Muzej Istre, Carrarina 3.Archeological museum. 🅾 winter Mo-Fri 9-14h, summer Mo-Sa 9-19h.
⌒ Amfiteatar.Large anfiteatro from Roman time. 🅾 daily 8-21h.
⚘ Ljetni klasicni Festival, Amfiteatar.Opera festival. 🅾 Aug.

| 🔺 | Rab 🌊⛱🍦🐚 | 27A5 |

Mel, Kampor 319. **GPS:** n44,79390 e14,70302. 🛏. **Remarks:** Mini-camp.
Planka, Kampor 326. **GPS:** **Remarks:** Mini-camp.

Tourist information Rab:
ℹ Tourist Information, Mali Palit bb.

| 🔺Ⓢ | Rabac ⛱🍦🐚 | 27A4 |

Oliva. GPS: n45,07960 e14,14777.
300 🛏 ⚡🔌Ch 🚿 WC 🔵. 🅾 15/03-30/09
Distance: ⚓on the spot.

Tourist information Rabac:
ℹ Tourist Information, Aldo Negri 20, Labin, www.rabac.hr.Former Fishing village now bathing resort.

| 🔺 | Rijeka | 26C6 |

Preluk Katalinic, Preluk 1. **GPS:** n45,35595 e14,32691. 🛏.
Remarks: Mini-camp.

Tourist information Rijeka:
ℹ Turisticka zajednica, Uzarska 14, www.grad-rijeka.hr/.
👁 Tourist Information, Kastav 47, Kastav.Walled city with rich history.
Ⓜ Pomorski i povijesni muzej, Muzejski trg 1.Navy museum. 🅾 Mo-Fri 10-13h, 18-21h.
⚘ Velika trznica.Market opposite to Modello palace.
⚘ Bella Nedeja, Kastav.Traditional wine celebration.
🅾 1st weekend Oct.
⚘ Carnaval van Rijeka. 🅾 Feb.

| ⒸⓈ | Rovinj 🌊⛱🍦🐚 | 27A4 |

Camping Polari. GPS: n45,06300 e13,67480.⬆

🛏87kn-174kn, Fr-Sa + 20% ⚡🔌Ch 🚿. **Surface:** grassy. 🅾 22/03-02/10
Distance: ⚓on the spot.
Remarks: Camperstop max. 48h.
Mon Paradiso, Uvala Veštar. **GPS:** n45,04947 e13,69000.
40 🛏 from € 17,20 ⚡🔌Ch 🚿. 🅾 01/06-30/09 **Remarks:** Mini-camp.
Polari. GPS: n45,06258 e13,67477.
2150 🛏 from € 22,50 ⚡🔌Ch 🚿 WC ⏞included. 🅾 01/04-30/09
Porton Biondi. GPS: n45,09410 e13,64232.
🛏 from € 16,95 ⚡🔌Ch 🚿 WC ⏞included. 🅾 01/04-30/09
Valdaliso. GPS: n45,10389 e13,62500.
400 🛏 from € 16 ⚡🔌Ch 🚿 WC ⏞included. 🅾 20/04-15/10
Vestar. GPS: n45,05389 e13,68639.
800 🛏 from € 17 ⚡🔌Ch 🚿 WC ⏞included. 🅾 15/04-30/09
Savinjska Dolina, Špandiga Bb. 🛏. **Remarks:** Mini-camp.
Špandiga, Špandiga Bb. 🛏. **Remarks:** Mini-camp.
Ulika, Polari Bd. **GPS:** n45,06528 e13,67583.
🛏€ 15-28 2 pers incl. 🅾 01/04-01/10 **Remarks:** Mini-camp.

| 🍴🛈Ⓢ | Rovinj 🌊⛱🍦🐚 | 27A4 |

Pizza-Grill Babilon.

20 🛏130kn ⚡🚿 WC ⏞included. 🅾 01/01-31/12 **Remarks:** 2,5km before Rovinj at the right-side of the road.

Tourist information Rovinj:
ℹ Turisticka zajednica, Budicin 12, www.istra.com/rovinj.City has been a cultural monument since 1963.
👁 Aquarium, Obala G. Paliage 5. 🅾 daily 9-21h.
⚘ Palazzo Califfi, Trg Marsala Tita 11. 🅾 Tue-Su 10.30-14h, summer 18-20h.
⚘ Market.
⚘ Grisia, Grisia.Art festival. 🅾 2nd week Aug.

| 🔺Ⓢ | Savudrija ⛱🐚 | 26C6 |

Pineta. GPS: n45,48667 e13,49250.
🛏from € 16,50 ⚡🔌Ch 🚿 WC included. 🅾 15/04-30/09
Veli Jože, Borozija. **GPS:** n45,49556 e13,50444.
🛏from € 14,70 ⚡🔌Ch 🚿 WC ⏞included. 🅾 01/04-30/09
Koncar. 🛏. **Remarks:** Mini-camp.
Koncar, Ravna Dolina. 🛏. 🅾 01/05-30/09

Tourist information Savudrija:
ℹ Tourist Information, Istarska 2.

| 🔺 | Selce | 27A4 |

Selce. GPS: n45,15175 e14,72267. 🛏. 🅾 01/04-31/10
Uvala Slana. GPS: n45,15250 e14,71972. 🛏. 🅾 01/05-30/09

Tourist information Selce:
ℹ Tourist Information, Setaliste Ivana Jelicica 1 .
Finida. GPS: n45,39278 e13,54194.
🛏from € 15,20 ⚡🔌Ch 🚿 WC ⏞included. 🅾 15/04-30/09

| 🔺Ⓢ | Umag ⛱🍦🐚 | 26C6 |

Ladin Gaj.
1800 🛏 ⚡🔌Ch 🚿. 🅾 15/04-30/09
Stella Maris. GPS: n45,45056 e13,52278.
400 🛏from € 17 ⚡🔌Ch 🚿 WC ⏞included. 🅾 15/04-15/10
Bencic. 🛏. **Remarks:** Mini-camp.

Tourist information Umag:
ℹ Tourist Information, Obala J.B.Tita 3/II.

| ⒸⓈ | Vrsar 🐚 | 27A4 |

Camping Valkanela. GPS: n45,16509 e13,60871.⬆

🛏€ 10, Jun € 14,50, Jul-Aug € 20 + tourist tax ⚡🔌Ch 🚿 included.
Surface: grassy. 🅾 23/04-23/09
Distance: ⚓on the spot.
Remarks: Camperstop max. 48h, use camp-site facilities incl.

| 🔺Ⓢ | Vrsar ⛱🐚 | 27A4 |

Porto Sole. GPS: n45,14139 e13,60222.
800 🛏from € 19 ⚡🔌Ch 🚿 WC ⏞included. 🅾 15/04-30/09

Tourist information Vrsar:
ℹ Tourist Information, Rade koncara 46, www.istra.com/vrsar/.

HR

Dalmatia

⛺ Babino Polje   27D6
Marina, Ropa 11. **GPS**: n42,73543 e17,54650. 🗑. **Remarks:** Mini-camp.
Mungos. 🗑. **Remarks:** Mini-camp.

⛺ Baška Voda ⚓🐚   27C6
Basko Polje. **GPS**: n43,34878 e16,96478. 🗑. ⬛ 15/05-30/09
Niko. 🗑. **Remarks:** Mini-camp.

Tourist information Baška Voda:
ℹ️ Turisticka zajednica, Obala Kralja Tomislava 16, Makarska, www.baskavoda.hr.
Ⓜ Gradski Muzej, Obala Kralja Tomislava 17/I, Makarska.City museum. ⬛ daily 7-15h.
Ⓜ Malakoloski Muzej, Franjevacki Put 1, Makarska.Mollusc museum. ⬛ daily 11-12h.

⛺ Bibinje ⚓🐚   27B5
Božidar. 🗑. **Remarks:** Mini-camp.
Dido, Punta. 🗑. **Remarks:** Mini-camp.
Ivan Sikiric, Bibinje 152. 🗑. **Remarks:** Mini-camp.
Maslina, Punta. 🗑. **Remarks:** Mini-camp.
Maslinovi Dvori, Punta. **GPS**: n44,06222 e15,29306. 🗑. **Remarks:** Mini-camp.
Mladen. 🗑. **Remarks:** Mini-camp.
Niko. 🗑. **Remarks:** Mini-camp.
Punta, Rajko Kero. 🗑. **Remarks:** Mini-camp.
Punta, Z.Sikirica 10. 🗑. **Remarks:** Mini-camp.
Puntica, Bibinje 41. 🗑. **Remarks:** Mini-camp.

Tourist information Bibinje:
ℹ️ Tourist Information, Bibinje bb.

⛺ Biograd na Moru 🌿⚓🐚   27B5
Bošana, Šetalište Bošana Bb. 🗑. **Remarks:** Mini-camp.
Crvena Luka. 🗑. ⬛ 01/06-30/09
Crvena Luka.
250 🗑. ⬛ 01/06-30/09
Dijana & Josip, Put Solina 26. **GPS**: n43,93422 e15,44828. 🗑. **Remarks:** Mini-camp.
Mia, Rajic Turizam. 🗑. **Remarks:** Mini-camp.
Soline. 🗑. ⬛ 01/05-30/09

Tourist information Biograd na Moru:
ℹ️ Tourist Information, Trg hrvatskih velikana 2, www.biograd.org.Old city with historical centre, lively bathing resort.

⛺ Bol   27C6
Kito. **GPS**: n43,26389 e16,64806. 🗑. ⬛ 01/05-31/10

⛺ Drace-Pelješac   27D6
Plaža, Janjina. **GPS**: n42,92477 e17,43079. 🗑. **Remarks:** Mini-camp.

⛺ Dubrovnik 🌿⚓🐚   27D6
Autokamp Kate, Tupina 1- Milini. **GPS**: n42,62472 e18,20806. 🗑.
⬛ 10/04-01/11
Porto, Srebreno. 🗑. ⬛ 01/05-01/10
Rudine, Orašac. 🗑.
⬛ 01/06-30/09

Tourist information Dubrovnik:
ℹ️ Turisticka zajednica, Cvijete Zuzoric 1/2, www.dubrovnik-online.hr.City with a rich cultural history.
👁 Aquarium, D. Jude 2. ⬛ Mo-Sa 9-13h.
👁 City Walls, Gunduličeva poljana 2.City wall surround the entire Old City. ⬛ 10-15h, 01/04-31/10 9-18.30h.
👁 Place Stradun.Main street with Onofrio-fountain and Sveti Frane monastery.
Ⓜ Dubrovacki Muzej, Pred Dvorom 3.History of the city. ⬛ Mo-Sa 9-14h.
Ⓜ Pomorski Muzej, Sveti Ivan.Shipping museum. ⬛ Tue-Sa 9-13h.
Ⓜ Rector's Palace, Pred dvorom 1.Bogisic-collection.
⬛ Mo-Sa 9.30-13h.
🎭 Zomerfestival. ⬛ 10/07-25/08.

⛺ Dugi Rat ⚓⛏🐚   27C6
Ante, Duce Rogac. 🗑. **Remarks:** Mini-camp.
B, Duce Rogac. 🗑. **Remarks:** Mini-camp.
Darko, Duce Rogac. 🗑. **Remarks:** Mini-camp.
Dijana, Duce Rogac. 🗑. **Remarks:** Mini-camp.
Duce, Duce Rogac. 🗑. **Remarks:** Mini-camp.
Ivan, Duce Rogac. 🗑. **Remarks:** Mini-camp.

Ivo. 🗑. **Remarks:** Mini-camp.
Ivo, Duce Rogac. **GPS**: n43,44111 e16,65778. 🗑. **Remarks:** Mini-camp.
Ljubica, Duce Rogac. 🗑. **Remarks:** Mini-camp.
Luka, Duce Rogac. 🗑. **Remarks:** Mini-camp.
Mira, Duce Rogac. 🗑. **Remarks:** Mini-camp.
Miroslav, Duce Rogac. 🗑. **Remarks:** Mini-camp.
More, Duce Rogac. 🗑. **Remarks:** Mini-camp.
Oru, Orij, Duce Rogac. 🗑. **Remarks:** Mini-camp.
Raj, Duce Rogac. 🗑. **Remarks:** Mini-camp.
Studenac, Duce Rogac. 🗑. **Remarks:** Mini-camp.

Tourist information Dugi Rat:
ℹ️ Tourist Information, Poljicka cesta 133.

⛺ Grebaštica 🐚   27B6
Ante&Toni, Brodarica. **GPS**: n43,63833 e15,95833. 🗑. ⬛ 01/05-01/10
Distance: 🚶100m ⚓on the spot.
Remarks: Mini-camp..
Tomas, D8. **GPS**: n43,62986 e15,95443. 🗑.
Distance: ⚓on the spot.
Remarks: Mini-camp..

⛺ Kaštel Kambelovac 🐚   27C6
U Dragama, A. Starcevica 39. **GPS**: n43,55045 e16,38269. 🗑. **Remarks:** Mini-camp.

⛺ Kaštel Štafilic   27C6
Koludrovac, Resnik Bb. **GPS**: n43,54985 e16,32873. 🗑. **Remarks:** Mini-camp.
Adria. **GPS**: n43,55143 e16,35349. 🗑. **Remarks:** Mini-camp.

⛺ Kaštel Stari   27C6
Kamp- Biluš Josip. 🗑.
Remarks: Mini-camp.

⛺ Kolan   27B5
Sveti Duh. **GPS**: n44,51654 e14,95175. 🗑. **Remarks:** Mini-camp.

⛺ Korčula 🌿⚓🐚   27C6
Kalac. **GPS**: n42,95056 e17,14500. 🗑.from € 11. ⬛ 01/06-01/10
Mala Glavica, Lumbarda. 🗑. **Remarks:** Mini-camp.
Mala Grščica, Mala Grščica, Korcula, Tonka Boglic, Blato. 🗑. **Remarks:** Mini-camp.
Mini Camp, Lumbarda Br. 8. 🗑. **Remarks:** Mini-camp.
Oskorušica, Oskorušica 27/VI, Racišce. 🗑. **Remarks:** Mini-camp.
Potirina, Ružica Šeparovic, Burcina, Blato. 🗑. **Remarks:** Mini-camp.
Ravno, Blato. 🗑. **Remarks:** Mini-camp.
Relax, Racišce. 🗑. **Remarks:** Mini-camp.
Solitudo, Sv. Anton, Lumbarajska Cesta. 🗑. **Remarks:** Mini-camp.
Uvala Racišce, Lumbarda 83. 🗑. **Remarks:** Mini-camp.
Vela Postrana, Lumbardra 142. 🗑. **Remarks:** Mini-camp.

Tourist information Korčula:
ℹ️ Turisticka zajednica, Obala Tudmana, www.korcula.net.City with historical centre, birth-place Marco Polo.
Ⓜ Gradski Muzej, Palaca Gabrielli.City museum. ⬛ 9-13h, 01/07-31/08 9-13h, 17-19h.
Ⓜ Zbirka Ikona, Trg Svih Sveti.Icon museum. ⬛ 01/07-31/08 10-12h, 17-19h.
🎭 Marco Polo fest. ⬛ 09/07-11/07.
🎭 Zwaarddansfestival. ⬛ daily 04/07-23/08.

🍴S Korenica   27B5
Bistro Marina. **GPS**: n44,74702 e15,70464.
10 🗑. **Location:** Urban. **Surface:** metalled.
Distance: 🚾100m.
Remarks: Free with a meal.

⛺S Kornati/Murter 🌿⚓🐚   27B5
Slanica. **GPS**: n43,82056 e15,57472.
🗑from € 14,30 ⚡🚐 🔌WC 🔌included. ⬛ 01/05-15/10
Jazina, Tisno. 🗑. ⬛ 01/05-30/09
Jezera-Lovišča, Jezera. 🗑. ⬛ 15/04-15/10
Kosirina, Betina. 🗑. ⬛ 01/05-30/09
Plitka Vala, Betina. 🗑. ⬛ 01/05-30/09

Tourist information Kornati/Murter:
ℹ️ Tourist Information, Rudina 3, www.tzo-murter.hr.Village where old crafts industry are carried out.

⛺S Kucište   27C6
Palme. **GPS**: n42,97639 e17,12917.
🗑€ 16,50-23 2 pers incl. ⬛ 01/06-01/10
Lovor, Viganj-Dol. 🗑. **Remarks:** Mini-camp.

HR

Mimoza, Viganj. ⛺. **Remarks:** Mini-camp.
Plaža, Viganj 4, Od Gaja. ⛺. **Remarks:** Mini-camp.
Ponta, Viganj 5. ⛺. **Remarks:** Mini-camp.
Vocnjak, Viganj 6. ⛺. **Remarks:** Mini-camp.

△	Lokva Rogoznica	27C6

Artina. ⛺. **Remarks:** Mini-camp.
Linda. **GPS:** n43,40934 e16,76415. ⛺. **Remarks:** Mini-camp.

△	Lovište	27C6

Lupiš. **GPS:** n43,02675 e17,03171. ⛺. **Remarks:** Mini-camp.

△	Lukoran	27B5

Novi Kamp, Punta 28. **GPS:** n44,10538 e15,15518. ⛺.
Remarks: Mini-camp.

△	Mlini	27D6

Kate, Tupina 1. **GPS:** n42,62472 e18,20806. ⛺. **Remarks:** Mini-camp.
Laguna, Za Gospom, Plat. ⛺. **Remarks:** Mini-camp.
Matkovica, Srebreno 8. ⛺. **Remarks:** Mini-camp.
Paradiso, Plat. ⛺. **Remarks:** Mini-camp.
Porto, Srebreno. ⛺. **Remarks:** Mini-camp.
Tigar, Kneza Branimira 41, 020-488-980. ⛺. **Remarks:** Mini-camp.

△	Mljet	27D6

Marina, Marina Matana,Ropa 11. **GPS:** n42,75260 e17,46000. ⛺. **Remarks:**
Mini-camp.

Tourist information Mljet:
ℹ Tourist Information, Zabrezje 2.

© S	Mokalo	27C6

Adriatic. **GPS:** n42,97694 e17,22500. ⛺. ◐ 01/04-31/10

△	Molunat	29D6

Adriatic II. ⛺. **Remarks:** Mini-camp.
Adriatic I, Višnjici 4, Đurinici. ⛺. **Remarks:** Mini-camp.
Marinero, Molunat 40. ⛺. **Remarks:** Mini-camp.

△	Nin	27B5

Dišpet, Ždrijac. ⛺. **Remarks:** Mini-camp.
Nick, Ždrijac. ⛺. **Remarks:** Mini-camp.
Nin, Nin 33. ⛺. **Remarks:** Mini-camp.
Ninska Laguna. **GPS:** n44,24639 e15,17389. ⛺. **Remarks:** Mini-camp.

Tourist information Nin:
ℹ Tourist Information, Trg Hrvatskih branitelja 1, www.nin.hr.
Ⓜ Arheološka zbirka Nin, Trg Kraljevac 8.Archeological museum. ◐ 01/10-
31/5 8-14h, 01/06-30/09 8-22h.

△	Novigrad (Dalmatia)	27B5

Adria-Sol Mulic. **GPS:** n44,18472 e15,54944. ⛺. **Remarks:** Mini-camp.

△	Omiš	27C6

Lisicina. **GPS:** n43,44407 e16,69216. ⛺. **Remarks:** Mini-camp.
Ribnjak. ⛺. ◐ 01/06-30/09

△	Opuzen	27D6

Rio, Put Zlatinovca 23. **GPS:** n43,01730 e17,56156. ⛺. ◐ 01/05-01/10

△ S	Orašac	27D6

Pod Maslinom, Put prema moru b.b.. **GPS:** n42,69907 e18,00592.
⛺€ 11,50-15, 2 pers.incl ⌐ᵁᶜ Ch ✦ WC ⅂. ◐ 01/05-30/09 **Remarks:**
Mini-camp.
Peca, Na Pržini 38. ⛺. **Remarks:** Mini-camp.

△	Pag	27B5

Dinjiška 1. ⛺. **Remarks:** Mini-camp.
Košljun. ⛺. **Remarks:** Mini-camp.
Košljun, Košljun B.B.. ⛺. **Remarks:** Mini-camp.
Milka, Dinjiška Bb, Dinjiška. ⛺. **Remarks:** Mini-camp.
Simuni. **GPS:** n44,43766 e15,05408. ⛺. ◐ 04/04-01/10

Tourist information Pag:
ℹ Tourist Information, Ulica od Spitala bb, www.pag-tourism.hr.

△ S	Pakoštane	27B5

Kozarica. **GPS:** n43,91833 e15,51028.
⛺from € 15,70 ⌐ᵁᶜ Ch ✦ WC ⅂included. ◐ 15/04-15/10
Adriatik. ⛺. **Remarks:** Mini-camp.
Blaž. ⛺. **Remarks:** Mini-camp.
Cuka, Brune Bušića 62. ⛺. **Remarks:** Mini-camp.
Dalmacija. ⛺. **Remarks:** Mini-camp.
Delfin, Uvala Dugovaca 13, Drage. ⛺. **Remarks:** Mini-camp.
Dugovaca, Drage. ⛺. **Remarks:** Mini-camp.
Dujo, Put Malenice, Drage. ⛺. **Remarks:** Mini-camp.

Karaba, B. Bušica Bb. ⛺. **Remarks:** Mini-camp.
Kico, Drage. ⛺. **Remarks:** Mini-camp.
Marela, Kralja Tomislava 26, Drage. ⛺. **Remarks:** Mini-camp.
Mario, Drage. ⛺. **Remarks:** Mini-camp.
Nirvana. **GPS:** n43,90989 e15,50767. ⛺. **Remarks:** Mini-camp.
Nordsee. ⛺. ◐ 01/04-03/10
Pakoštane. ⛺. **Remarks:** Mini-camp.
Srecko. ⛺. **Remarks:** Mini-camp.
Strana. ⛺. **Remarks:** Mini-camp.

Tourist information Pakoštane:
ℹ Tourist Information, Trg Kraljice Jelene 78, pakostane.tripod.com.Seaside
resort between the sea and the lake of Vrana, Vransko Jezero.

△ S	Pelješac/Orebić	27C6

Glavna Plaža. **GPS:** n42,97583 e17,18917.
⛺from € 15 ⌐ Ch ✦ WC ⅂included.
◐ 15/05-01/10
Trstenica, Šetalište Kneza Domagoja 50. **GPS:** n42,98095 e17,19435.
⛺from € 18,70 ⌐ᵁᶜ Ch ✦ WC ⅂included. **Remarks:** Mini-camp.
Bor. ⛺. **Remarks:** Mini-camp.
Cico, J.B. Jelacica 5. ⛺. **Remarks:** Mini-camp.
Orebic. ⛺. **Remarks:** Mini-camp.
Paradiso. **GPS:** n42,97475 e17,23497. ⛺. **Remarks:** Mini-camp.
Paradiso, Obala Pomoraca 30 A. ⛺. **Remarks:** Mini-camp.
Perna. ⛺. ◐ 01/05-30/09
Ponta. ⛺. **Remarks:** Mini-camp.
Radic. ⛺. **Remarks:** Mini-camp.
Videla, Put Ruskovica 25. ⛺. **Remarks:** Mini-camp.
Vocnjak. ⛺. **Remarks:** Mini-camp.

Tourist information Pelješac/Orebić:
ℹ Tourist Information, Trg Mimbeli bb, www.peljesac.info/orebic.Tourist town
on the island Pelješac.

△	Pelješac/Trpanj	27C6

Divna. **GPS:** n43,00944 e17,26806. ⛺. **Remarks:** Mini-camp.
Vrila. **GPS:** n43,00360 e17,28467. ⛺. ◐ 20/05-10/10

Tourist information Pelješac/Trpanj:
ℹ Tourist Information, Zalo 7, www.peljesac.info/trpanj.

△	Petrcane	27B5

Maestral, Put X. ⛺. **Remarks:** Mini-camp.
Pineta, Punta Radman 21. **GPS:** n44,18362 e15,16291. ⛺.
Remarks: Mini-camp.
Punta Radman. ⛺. **Remarks:** Mini-camp.
Šime, Petrcane 6. ⛺. **Remarks:** Mini-camp.

△	Podgora	27C6

Sutikla. **GPS:** n43,23451 e17,07741. ⛺. ◐ 01/05-30/09

△	Podstrana	27C6

Car, Sv. Martin 180. **GPS:** n43,48446 e16,55274. ⛺. **Remarks:** Mini-camp.
Tamaris, Sv.Martin 114. **GPS:** n43,47551 e16,56383.
50 ⛺from € 16,50. ◐ 01/01-31/12
Distance: ⚓on the spot. **Remarks:** Mini-camp..

Tourist information Podstrana:
⚜ Sinjska alka, Sinj.Knight celebration. ◐ 05/08.

△	Posedarje	27B5

Bristi. ⛺. **Remarks:** Mini-camp.
Kristina. **GPS:** n44,21239 e15,46858. ⛺. **Remarks:** Mini-camp.
Staro Selo, Brace Dežmalj. ⛺. **Remarks:** Mini-camp.

△	Povijana	27B5

Mali Dubrovnik, Kralja P. Svacica 1. ⛺. **Remarks:** Mini-camp.
Tomi, Ante Starcevica Bb. **GPS:** n44,34624 e15,11292. ⛺.
Remarks: Mini-camp.

△	Primošten	27B6

Adriatic. **GPS:** n43,60645 e15,92193.
⛺from € 24 ⌐ᵁᶜ Ch ✦ WC ⅂included ⚐. ◐ 01/05-15/10

△ S	Privlaka	27B5

Maritim. **GPS:** n44,27391 e15,13178.
⛺from € 15 ⌐ᵁᶜ Ch ✦included. ◐ 01/05-15/10
Darinka. ⛺. **Remarks:** Mini-camp.

△	Ražanac	27B5

Planik. **GPS:** n44,27778 e15,34472.
⛺€ 4,75-7,30 + € 2,95-4,50/pp. ◐ 15/05-30/09 **Remarks:** Mini-camp.
Puntica. **GPS:** n44,28389 e15,34306.

HR

€ 11 - € 19. **Remarks:** Mini-camp.

Rovanjska 27B5

Tamaris. **GPS**: n44,25003 e15,53806. . **Remarks:** Mini-camp.

Senj 27B4

Skver. **GPS**: n44,99389 e14,89978.
40 Ch WC . **Location:** Comfortable. **Surface:** gravel/metalled.
01/04-01/10
Distance: 500m on the spot on the spot 150m.
Bunica, Bunica 33. **GPS**: n45,02607 e14,88630. . **Remarks:** Mini-camp.
Ujca, M. Cihlar Nehajeva, 4. **GPS**: n44,96833 e14,92167.
from € 16,20. 01/05-01/10
Distance: on the spot. **Remarks:** Mini-camp.

Tourist information Senj:
Turistièka zajednica grada Senja i informativni centar, Stara cesta 2.

Šibenik 27B5

Krka. **GPS**: n43,79463 e15,68120.

free. 01/01-31/12
Remarks: 1km from Krka waterfalls.

Šibenik 27B5

Solaris.
Ch . 15/03-30/11
Solaris-Zablaće. . 01/05-30/09

Tourist information Šibenik:
Turisticka zajednica, Ulica Fausta Vrancica 18, www.summernet.hr.
Internationaal kinderfestival. 22/06-06/07.
Nacionalni Park Krka, Krka.Nature reserve.

Slano 27D6

Bambo. **GPS**: n42,78588 e17,89234.
10 from € 13 Ch WC included. **Remarks:** Mini-camp.
Auto Kamp, Osredina 5, Majkovi. . **Remarks:** Mini-camp.
Banici, Vedrana Limov, Banici. . **Remarks:** Mini-camp.
Banja, Put Od Banje. . **Remarks:** Mini-camp.
Budina, Banici. . **Remarks:** Mini-camp.
Maslina, Grguici. . **Remarks:** Mini-camp.
Milic, Sladenovici. .
Remarks: Mini-camp.
Rogac, Grgurici.
€ 4-5 + € 2-2,50/pp. 01/04-31/10 **Remarks:** Mini-camp.
Sladenovici, Sladenovici 9. .
Remarks: Mini-camp.

Slatine 27C6

Domic, Put Porta 71, Ciove. **GPS**: n43,50014 e16,32985. . **Remarks:** Mini-camp.

Split 27C6

Stobreč. **GPS**: n43,50401 e16,52644.

from € 20 Ch WC included € 0,30. **Location:** Urban. **Surface:**
. 01/01-31/12
Distance: centre ±7km on the spot.

Tourist information Split:
Turisticka zajednica, Trg Republike 2/1, www.visitsplit.com.
Arheoloski Muzej, Zrinjsko-Frankopanska 25.Findings from Roman time and Middle Ages. Tue-Fri 9-14h, Sa-Su 9-13h, 01/06-30/09 Tue-Fri 9-12, 13-20h, Sa-Su 9-13h.
Etnografski Muzej, Narodni Trg 1.Clothing and jewellery. Tue-Fri 10-13h, 18-21h, Sa-Su 10-13h.
Galerija Ivana Mestrovica, Setaliste I. Mestrovica 46.Gallery. Mo-Sa 10-18h, Su 10-14h.
Muzej Grada, Papaliveca 1.City museum. Mo-Sa 9-13h.
Muzej Hrvatskih Arheoloskih Spomenika, S. Gunjace bb.Archeological findings. Mo-Sa 9-20h.
Dioklecijanova palača.Roman palace.

Starigrad/Paklenica 27B5

Camp National Park, Paklenica.
30-38kn, 20-25kn/pp Ch . 01/04-31/10 **Remarks:** Mini-camp.
Adria, Punta Bb, Paklenica. . **Remarks:** Mini-camp.
Anica Kuk, Paklenickal7, Paklenica. . **Remarks:** Mini-camp.
Igor, Seline 124, Seline, Paklenica. . **Remarks:** Mini-camp.
Jaz, Seline, 17, Seline, Paklenica. . **Remarks:** Mini-camp.
Katic, Joze Dokoze 1, Paklenica. . **Remarks:** Mini-camp.
Marin, Put Stanova, 32, Paklenica. . **Remarks:** Mini-camp.
Marin, Seline, Joko, Paklenica. . **Remarks:** Mini-camp.
Marko, Paklenicka 7, Paklenica. . **Remarks:** Mini-camp.
Matija, Paklenica. . **Remarks:** Mini-camp.
Michael, Put Plantaže Bb, Paklenica. . **Remarks:** Mini-camp.
Palklenica. . 01/05-01/10
Paron Šime, Seline 12, Paklenica. . **Remarks:** Mini-camp.
Peko, Paklenica. . **Remarks:** Mini-camp.
Pinus, Ive Senjanina 5, Paklenica. . **Remarks:** Mini-camp.
Pisak, Paklenica. . **Remarks:** Mini-camp.
Plantaža, Put Plantaže 2, Paklenica. **GPS**: n44,29417 e15,44000. . **Remarks:** Mini-camp.
Popo, Kod Abulante, Paklinica. . **Remarks:** Mini-camp.
Senjski Porat, Joze Dokoza 17, Paklenica. . **Remarks:** Mini-camp.
Vesna, Paklenicka 103, Paklenica. . **Remarks:** Mini-camp.
Vrša, Seline, Jazic, Paklenica. . **Remarks:** Mini-camp.
Zrakoplovac, Selina, Paklenica. .
Remarks: Mini-camp.

Tourist information Starigrad/Paklenica:
Nacionalni park "Paklenica".Nature reserve, 150 km biking ad hiking trails, bird observation, tunnels and caves. T 30kn/day.

Ston 27D6

Ficovic, Hodilje. . **Remarks:** Mini-camp.
Prapratna. **GPS**: n42,81778 e17,67611. . 01/06-30/09
Vrela, Pelješac. . **Remarks:** Mini-camp.

Sukošan 27B5

Brajde. . **Remarks:** Mini-camp.
Brajde. . **Remarks:** Mini-camp.
Fontana. **GPS**: n44,04643 e15,31436. . **Remarks:** Mini-camp.
Ivana, Mala Makarska 120. . **Remarks:** Mini-camp.
Jadran. . **Remarks:** Mini-camp.
Jaz. . **Remarks:** Mini-camp.
Kaj. . **Remarks:** Mini-camp.
Malenica, Mala Makarska. . **Remarks:** Mini-camp.
Mira. . **Remarks:** Mini-camp.
Mrkva. . **Remarks:** Mini-camp.
Oliva. . **Remarks:** Mini-camp.
Podvare. . **Remarks:** Mini-camp.
Porto Dl Oro. . **Remarks:** Mini-camp.
Punta. . **Remarks:** Mini-camp.
Seka. . **Remarks:** Mini-camp.
Školjka. . **Remarks:** Mini-camp.
Stela. . **Remarks:** Mini-camp.
Zlošane. . **Remarks:** Mini-camp.

Supetar 27C6

Supetar. **GPS**: n43,38050 e16,56082. . 01/06-30/09

HR

| △ | Sutivan | 27C6 |

Mlin, Brac. **GPS**: n43,38316 e16,47795. ⌁. **Remarks:** Mini-camp.

| △ S | Sv. Filip I Jakov 🌿⛱🌳🍴 | 27B5 |

Djardin. **GPS**: n43,96139 e15,42750.
⌁from € 18 🚐🍴Ch 🏄 included. 🔲 01/05-30/09

Filip. **GPS**: n43,96055 **e15,42910**.
⌁from € 15,20 🚐🍴Ch 🏄 included. **Remarks:** Mini-camp.

Ante, Turanj. ⌁. **Remarks:** Mini-camp.

Barbarossa. ⌁. **Remarks:** Mini-camp.

Bepo, Turanj. ⌁. **Remarks:** Mini-camp.

Bozo 23207 Sv. Filip I Jakov, Sv. Petar, Bozo Colic, Sv. Petar. ⌁. **Remarks:** Mini-camp.

Frane Mladi, A. Starcevica 8 D, Turanj. ⌁. **Remarks:** Mini-camp.

Ivan, Medine, Turanj. ⌁. **Remarks:** Mini-camp.

Ivan, Sv. Petar 155. ⌁. **Remarks:** Mini-camp.

Ivan, Turanj 233. ⌁. **Remarks:** Mini-camp.

Ivo, Sv. Petar. ⌁. **Remarks:** Mini-camp.

J & A, Turanj. ⌁. **Remarks:** Mini-camp.

Jakov. ⌁. **Remarks:** Mini-camp.

Jugo, Turanj. ⌁. **Remarks:** Mini-camp.

Krca, Turanj. ⌁. **Remarks:** Mini-camp.

Livada. ⌁. **Remarks:** Mini-camp.

Lovre, Turanj. ⌁. **Remarks:** Mini-camp.

Maestral, Turanj 448. ⌁. **Remarks:** Mini-camp.

Maja, Vukovarska 54, Sv. Petar. ⌁. **Remarks:** Mini-camp.

Mara, Turanj. ⌁. **Remarks:** Mini-camp.

Marko, Sv. Petar. ⌁. **Remarks:** Mini-camp.

Martin, Sv. Petar 240. ⌁. **Remarks:** Mini-camp.

Medine. ⌁. **Remarks:** Mini-camp.

Mile, Sv. Petar. ⌁. **Remarks:** Mini-camp.

Mladen, Turanj 233. ⌁. **Remarks:** Mini-camp.

Moce. ⌁. **Remarks:** Mini-camp.

Njive, Turanj. ⌁. **Remarks:** Mini-camp.

Punta, Sv. Petar. ⌁. **Remarks:** Mini-camp.

Rio. **GPS**: n43,95583 e15,43500. ⌁. **Remarks:** Mini-camp.

Roko, Turanj. ⌁. **Remarks:** Mini-camp.

Šime. ⌁. **Remarks:** Mini-camp.

Tina. ⌁.
Remarks: Mini-camp.

Tourist information Sv. Filip I Jakov:
ℹ Tourist Information, Kuntrata bb, www.sv-filipjakov.hr/.

| △ | Tkon | 27B5 |

Adriana. **GPS**: n43,91753 e15,42601. ⌁. **Remarks:** Mini-camp.

Brist. ⌁. **Remarks:** Mini-camp.

Dužja. ⌁. **Remarks:** Mini-camp.

| △ | Tribanj | 27B5 |

Ante, Krušcica. ⌁. **Remarks:** Mini-camp.

C.T.T., Kopovine. ⌁. **Remarks:** Mini-camp.

Mate, Krušcica. **GPS**: n44,34983 e15,31575. ⌁. **Remarks:** Mini-camp.

Punta Šibuljina, Šibuljina. ⌁. **Remarks:** Mini-camp.

Venus, Šibuljina. ⌁. **Remarks:** Mini-camp.

| △ S | Trogir 🌿⛱🍴 | 27C6 |

Seget, Seget Donji. **GPS**: n43,51904 e16,22430.
50 ⌁from € 21. 🔲 01/03-31/10
Distance: 🏖800m ⛱on the spot.
Remarks: Mini-camp..

| △ S | Trogir 🌿⛱🍴 | 27C6 |

Vranjica Belvedere, Seget Vranjica. **GPS**: n43,51196 e16,19159.
⌁from € 20 🚐🍴Ch 🏄 WC🍴🧺. 🔲 15/04-15/10

Tourist information Trogir:
ℹ Tourist Information, Ivana Pavla II Square, www.trogir-online.com.City with rich culture from Greek, Roman and Venetian time.
Ⓜ Town Museum, Fanfogna palace, Garagnin.History of the city. 🔲 16/09-14/06 by request-14h, 15/06-15/09 9-21h.
Ⓜ Zbirka Kairos.Ecclesiastical art collection. 🔲 15/6-15/9 8-13, 15-19h.
✖ Fort Kamerlengo. 🔲 15/6-15/9 9-20h.
✝ Katedrala St. Lawrence.Bell-tower of Cathedral of St. Lawrence, 47m. 🔲 15/6-15/9 9-12, 16-19h. 🔲 5kn.

| △ | Vela Luka | 27C6 |

Mindel, Stani 193. **GPS**: n42,98389 e16,67083. ⌁. 🔲 01/01-31/12

| △ | Viganj | 27C6 |

Antony Boy. **GPS**: n42,97917 e17,10750. ⌁. 🔲 01/01-31/12

| △ | Vinjerac | 27B5 |

Niko, Stara Cesta 1. **GPS**: n44,25571 e15,46251. ⌁. **Remarks:** Mini-camp.

| △ | Vir | 27B5 |

Luka. ⌁. **Remarks:** Mini-camp.

Matea. ⌁. 🔲 01/06-01/10

Slatina. ⌁. **Remarks:** Mini-camp.

Vir. **GPS**: n44,29174 e15,11996. ⌁. **Remarks:** Mini-camp.

| △ S | Vodice | 27B6 |

Imperial. **GPS**: n43,75278 e15,79000.
⌁from € 22 🚐🍴Ch 🏄. 🔲 01/05-15/10

Rutke, Udovicic A. Kule, 13. ⌁. **Remarks:** Mini-camp.

| △ | Vransko Jezero | 27B5 |

Crkvine. **GPS**: n43,93035 e15,51012. ⌁. 🔲 15/04-15/10

| △ | Vrsi | 27B5 |

Bor, Mulo. ⌁. **Remarks:** Mini-camp.

Mulic, Mulo. **GPS**: n44,26085 e15,23323. ⌁. **Remarks:** Mini-camp.

Perkovic, Augusta Šenoe 7. ⌁. **Remarks:** Mini-camp.

Punta, Mulo. ⌁. **Remarks:** Mini-camp.

| △ S | Zaboric 🍴 | 27B6 |

Jasenovo. **GPS**: n43,65116 e15,95025.
50 ⌁from € 13 🚐🍴Ch 🏄 WC🍴. 🔲 01/05-01/10
Distance: ⛱on the spot.
Remarks: Mini-camp..

| △ S | Zadar 🌿⛱🍴 | 27B5 |

Rosmari, Emanuela Vidovica 2. **GPS**: n44,13250 e15,20861.
20 ⌁🚐🍴Ch 🏄 WC🍴.
Distance: 🏖on the spot ⛱on the spot.
Remarks: Mini-camp.

Borik. **GPS**: n44,13528 e15,21528. ⌁. 🔲 01/05-30/09

Tourist information Zadar:
ℹ Turisticka zajednica, I. Smiljanica bb, www.zadar.hr.
👁 Trg Pet Bunara.Square of the five fountains.
Ⓜ Arheoloski Muzej, Simuna Kozicica Benje bb.Archeological findings. 🔲 Mo-Sa 9-13h, 18-20h.
✖ Muziekavonden in de St. Donatius van Zadar. 🔲 01/07-15/08.

| △ | Zaostrog | 27C6 |

Uvala Borova. **GPS**: n43,13181 e17,28742. ⌁. 🔲 01/05-30/09

| △ | Zaton 🌳🍴 | 27B5 |

Zaton. **GPS**: n44,23385 e15,16671. ⌁. 🔲 01/05/30/09

Tourist information Zaton:
ℹ Tourist Information, Hrvatskih branitelja 2, www.zaton.hr.

| △ | Ždrelac | 27B5 |

Ruža. **GPS**: n44,00925 e15,28067. ⌁. **Remarks:** Mini-camp.

Ublog, Dobropoljana. ⌁. **Remarks:** Mini-camp.

| △ | Živogošče | 27C6 |

Dole. **GPS**: n43,18910 e17,15622. ⌁. 🔲 01/05-30/09

| △ | Žrnovo | 27C6 |

Palma. ⌁. **Remarks:** Mini-camp.

| △ | Žrnovo | 27C6 |

Tri Žala, Uvala Tri Žala 808. **GPS**: n42,95724 e17,11215. ⌁. **Remarks:** Mini-camp.

Vrbovica, Uvala Vrbovica. ⌁. **Remarks:** Mini-camp.

| △ | Žuljana | 27D6 |

Maslina, Brijezi 2. ⌁. **Remarks:** Mini-camp.

Sunce, Kraj 29. ⌁. **Remarks:** Mini-camp.

Vucina I. ⌁. **Remarks:** Mini-camp.

Vucina II, Kraj 93. ⌁. **Remarks:** Mini-camp.

Žuljana, Kraj 71. **GPS**: n42,89359 e17,45479. ⌁. **Remarks:** Mini-camp.

Inland

| △ | Lipovac | 27D4 |

Spacva. **GPS**: n45,04593 e18,99682. ⌁. 🔲 01/05-01/10

| ⌁ S | Plitviča | 27B4 |

Bear, Seliste Dreznicko 52. **GPS**: n44,94804 e15,63639.

HR

15 ⌇€ 20 ⌐▬&Ch ◢WC ▭included. **Surface:** grassy. ◑ 01/04-01/11
Remarks: Water falls Plitvica 5km, baker every morning.

⌇S	Plitviča	27B4

Cvetkovic, Jezerce 28. **GPS**: n44,86338 e15,63967.

20 ⌇€ 20 ⌐▬&Ch ◢WC ▭included ≋free. **Surface:** grassy/gravel.
Remarks: Water falls Plitvica 2km.

△	Plitviča	27B4

Korana. GPS: n44,99260 e15,64916.
⌇€ 6 + € 5/pp.

Tourist information Plitviča:
↯ Nacionalni Park Plitviča Jezera, www.np-plitvicka-jezera.hr.National park
Plitvice lakes. ◑ 9-17h.

△	Racovica	27B4

Turist. GPS: n44,97222 e15,64750. ⌇.

GREECE

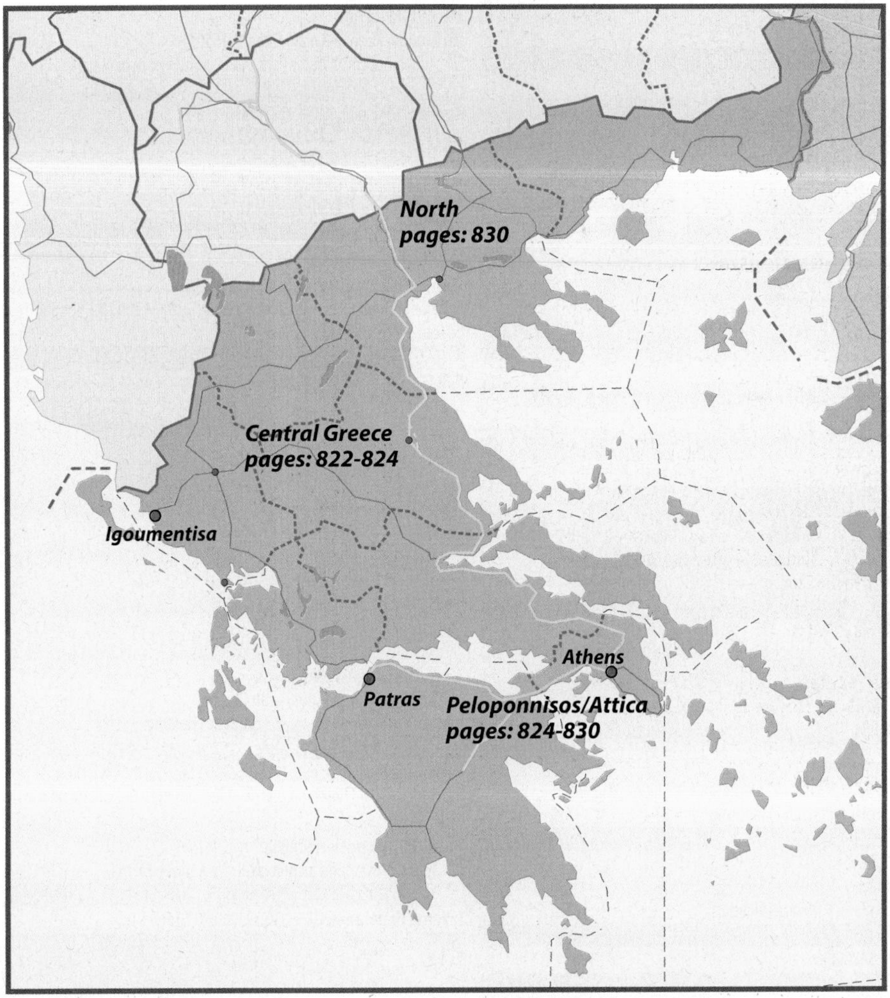

North
pages: 830

Central Greece
pages: 822-824

Igoumentisa

Athens

Patras

Peloponnisos/Attica
pages: 824-830

Capital: Athens
Government: Parliamentary democracy
Official Language: Greek
Population: 10,900,000 (2009)
Area: 131,990 km².

General information
Dialling code: 0030.
Currency: Euro

Regulations for overnight stays
Wild camping and overnight parking is not officially
allowed. Overnight parking places mentioned here
are not official motorhome stopovers but
tolerated areas.

Opening hours
Shops: Monday-Saturday 9am-1pm and 5pm-8.30pm,
Athens: Monday-Saturday 8am-8.30pm.
Banks: Monday-Thursday 8am-2pm, Friday
8am-1.30pm.

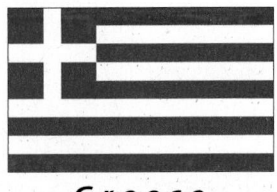

Central Greece

	Agios Nikolaos	35B4

GPS: n38,34959 e22,15661.
🏕. ⏻ 01/01-31/12
Remarks: Parking at harbour.

S	Ammoudia	35A4

GPS: n39,23989 e20,48116.

🏕 ⛽ 🍴. **Surface:** sand.
Distance: 🚶on the spot 🏊on the spot 🛒on the spot ⊗200m 🏖50m.
Remarks: Tolerated place. Beach parking.

S	Ammoudia	35A4

GPS: n39,23636 e20,48073.

🏕 ⛽. **Surface:** gravel/sand.
Distance: 🚶on the spot 🏊50m 🛒on the spot ⊗100m 🏖250m.
Remarks: Tolerated place. Parking in harbour.

	Arahova	35C4

GPS: n38,47948 e22,58164.
🏕. ⏻ 01/01-31/12
Remarks: Tolerated place. Parking in village.

S	Boukka	35B4

GPS: n38,93125 e21,14200.

🏕 🍴. **Surface:** sand.
Distance: 🏊on the spot.
Remarks: Tolerated place. Parking beach, next to sports fields.

△ S	Corfu	35A4

Dionysus, Dassia. **GPS**: n39,66472 e19,84440.
🏕⛽Ch.⚓. ⏻ 15/04-15/10

△ S	Corfu	35A4

Dolphin Camping, Sidari. **GPS**: n39,78890 e19,72354.
🏕⛽Ch. ⏻ 15/04-31/10
Remarks: Corfu-town dir Sidari/Roda, after that dir Sidari.

△ S	Corfu	35A4

Karda Beach, Dassia. **GPS**: n39,68611 e19,83861.
🏕⛽🍴Ch. ⏻ 01/04-15/10
Distance: 🏊on the spot.

Tourist information Corfu:
ℹ Kerkyra (Corfu).Capital of the island.
ℹ Esplanada, Kerkyra (Corfu).Meeting point for inhabitants and tourists.
✗ Kerkyra (Corfu).
✗ Frurion, Kerkyra (Corfu).Citadel, 1550.
⊙ Aqualand, Corfu Water Park, Ag.Ioannis.Leisure pool park.

△ S	Delphi	35C4

Apollon. GPS: n38,48388 e22,47550.
23 🏕 ⛽🍴Ch. ⏻ 01/01-31/12

△ S	Delphi	35C4

Delphi Camping. GPS: n38,47833 e22,47450.
🏕⛽Ch. ⏻ 20/03-30/11

△	Delphi	35C4

Chrissa. GPS: n38,47267 e22,46206. 🏕. ⏻ 01/01-31/12

Tourist information Delphi:
↷ Site of Delphi.Archeological site. ⏻ 7.30-17.30h ⊙ holiday-Feiertag-jours de fête-giorni di festa. 🎫 € 6.

	Eratini	35B4

N48/E65 km 47. **GPS**: n38,33838 e22,19385.

🏕. **Surface:** grassy/sand.
Distance: 🏊on the spot 🛒on the spot.
Remarks: Tolerated place, < 3,5t. Beach parking.

△ S	Erétria	35C4

Milos Camping. GPS: n38,39139 e23,77556. 🏕 ⛽ 🍴Ch.
Remarks: From Chalkis dir Eretria, 1 km in before the village on the right-hand of the road.

Tourist information Erétria:
↷ Seaside resort and archological site Antique Eretria.

S	Gliki	35A4

Taverne Panorama. GPS: n39,32726 e20,61568.

🏕guests free ⛽WC🍴. **Surface:** grassy.
Distance: 🚶500m 🏖500m.
Remarks: Along Acheron river.

S	Hiliadou	35B4

GPS: n38,39321 e21,92023.

⌇ ⟱ ⌐. **Surface:** gravel.
Distance: Nafpaktos 7km on the spot.
Remarks: Tolerated place. Beach parking.

| ▤ | Igoumenítsa ⚓⌇ | 35A4 |

GPS: n39,51278 e20,25741.

⌇.
Distance: on the spot ✎600m on the spot.
Remarks: Tolerated place. Parking supermarket at the ring-road 6, dir Ioánnina.

Tourist information Igoumenítsa:
🛈 Important port city.
⌒ Goumani (titani).Archeological site.

| ▤ | Ioánnina ⟱⌇ | 35A3 |

Sta Papagou 7. **GPS**: n39,67319 e20,85476.
30 ⌇ € 8. **Surface:** metalled. ◻ 01/01-31/12
Distance: 100m 100m ⊗100m.
Remarks: Monitored parking.

| △ | Ioánnina ⟱⌇ | 35A3 |

Limnopoula. **GPS**: n39,67770 e20,84280.
⌇.
◻ 01/04-15/10

Tourist information Ioánnina:
🛈 Capital of Epirus, important city in the Turkish time.
👁 Perama.Caves. ◻ daily.
Ⓜ Nisi.Island with museum (Turkish time).

| △ | Itea | 35C4 |

Ayannis, Kirra. **GPS**: n38,42440 e22,45880.
⌇.

| △ | Itea | 35C4 |

Kaparelis, Kirra. **GPS**: n38,43273 e22,45099.
⌇. ◻ 01/01-31/12

Tourist information Itea:
Ⓜ Nautical Museum, Mouseio, 4, Galaxídi.

| ▤ | Krioneri | 35B4 |

GPS: n38,34397 e21,58823.

⌇. **Surface:** gravel. ◻ 01/01-31/12
Distance: on the spot on the spot ⊗300m.
Remarks: Tolerated place. Parking at the beach.

| ▤ | Levkas | 35A4 |

Vlycho. **GPS**: n38,68318 e20,69819.
⌇.
Distance: on the spot.
Remarks: Tolerated place. Parking on the quay.

| △ | Levkas | 35A4 |

Dessimi Beach, Vlicho, Lefkada (Levkas). **GPS**: n38,67250 e20,71100.
⌇. ◻ 01/04-30/11

| △ | Levkas | 35A4 |

Poros Beach, Poros, Lefkada (Levkas). **GPS**: n39,64095 e20,69700.
⌇. ◻ 01/05-30/09

| ▤ | Mesolóngi ⌇ | 35B4 |

GPS: n38,36313 e21,41763.
⌇. ◻ 01/01-31/12
Remarks: Tolerated place. Parking harbour.

Tourist information Mesolóngi:
🛈 Tourist Information, Spyridonos Trikoupi 29.Fishing town.

| △S | Metéora ⟱⌇ | 35B4 |

Meteora Garden, Kalambaka. **GPS**: n39,70869 e21,60915.
⌇⟱Ch.
◻ 01/01-31/12
Remarks: 1 km after Kalambaka dir Ioannina at the right-hand of the way.

| △S | Metéora ⟱⌇ | 35B4 |

Rizos International, Kalambaka. **GPS**: n39,69010 e21,64564.
⌇⟱Ch.✎. ◻ 01/01-31/12

| △S | Metéora ⟱⌇ | 35B4 |

Vrachos Kastraki, Kastraki. **GPS**: n39,71338 e21,61588.
⌇⟱Ch. ◻ 01/01-31/12
Remarks: Kalambaka dir Kastraki after 1 km from beginning village on the left-hand of the road.

| ⍟S | Metéora ⟱⌇ | 35B4 |

Taverna Arsenis, East Street, Kalambaka. **GPS**: n38,69923 e21,64109.
8 ⌇guests free ⟱WC⌐. ◻ 01/01-31/12

Tourist information Metéora:
✝ Important cultural inheritance, 24 monasteries build on enourmous sandstone peaks, of which 6 can be visited. ◻ 9-13h, 15-17h. Ⓣ against payment.

| ▤ | Métsovo ⟱⛰❄ | 35A3 |

GPS: n39,76898 e21,17749.
⌇.
Remarks: Tolerated place. Parking dir village after leaving the main road, also parking in village.

Tourist information Métsovo:
🛈 Traditional mountain village.
Ⓜ Archotiko Tositsa.Restored 18th century mansion, museum or folk art. ◻ 8.30-13h, 16-18h. Ⓣ € 2.

| ▤ | Nafpaktos ⟱⌇ | 35B4 |

Xiliadou, N48/E65 km 80,5. **GPS**: n38,38139 e21,81661. ⌇.
Surface: gravel/sand.
Distance: on the spot on the spot ⊗nearby.
Remarks: Tolerated place. Parking at the beach.

| △S | Nafpaktos ⟱⌇ | 35B4 |

Platanitis Beach. **GPS**: n38,36824 e21,78007.
⌇⟱Ch. ◻ 15/05-31/10
Remarks: From Antirron dir Nafpaktos, ±5km before Nafpaktos on the right-hand of the road.

| △ | Nafpaktos ⟱⌇ | 35B4 |

Dounis Beach. **GPS**: n38,34288 e21,77013.
⌇.
◻ 01/05-31/10

Tourist information Nafpaktos:
🛈 Old city with Venetian Castle and circular walled harbor.

| △ | Paralia Agias Annas | 35C4 |

Agia Anna. **GPS**: n38,85976 e23,44418.
⌇. ◻ 01/05-30/09

| △S | Parga ⛰⌇ | 35A4 |

Enjoy Lichnos. **GPS**: n39,28358 e20,43340.
⌇⟱Ch. ◻ 01/05-15/10
Remarks: Igoumenitsa dir Parga ± 4 km before Parga.

| △ | Parga ⛰⌇ | 35A4 |

Valtos Camping. **GPS**: n39,28556 e20,38972.

◻ 01/05-30/09

Tourist information Parga:
🛈 Lively bathing resort.
⌒ Necromanteion of Ephyra.
Oracle of death.

| △S | Pilion ⟱⛰⌇ | 35C3 |

Hellas, Kato Gatzea. **GPS**: n39,31110 e23,10916.
⌇⟱Ch. ◻ 01/04-31/10
Remarks: Places directly at sandy beach. Volos dir Argalagti, 16 km after Volos.

GR

Pilion 35C3
Olizon, Milina. **GPS:** n39,16472 e23,21666.
Ch. 01/05-15/10
Remarks: Volos centre to Argalasti, then dir Horton-Milina.

Pilion 35C3
Sikia Fig Tree, Kato Gatzea. **GPS:** n39,30770 e2,11030.
Ch. 01/04-15/10
Remarks: Volos dir Agria-Tsangarada - 18 km from Volos.

Tourist information Pilion:
Mythological peninsula, beautiful nature, authentic mountain villages and fishing towns.
Tourist Information, Plateia Riga Feraiou, Vólos.The fastest growing industrial area of the country.
Makrinitsa.Village worth seeing, car-free.
Miliés.Folk museum. 01/04-31/10 Tue-Su, 01/11-31/03 Wed-Su.
Archeological Museum, Athanasáki 1, Vólos. Tue-Su holiday-Feiertag-jours de fête-giorni di festa.

Plataria 35A4
GPS: n39,44606 e20,27409.

. **Surface:** grassy/sand. 01/01-31/12
Distance: 500m on the spot on the spot 200m 250m.
Remarks: Tolerated place. Parking at the beach.

Plataria 35A4
Nautilos. **GPS:** n39,44389 e20,25806.
Ch. 01/04-20/10
Remarks: Igoumenitsa dir Parga, exit Sivota, 15 km after Plataria.

Plataria 35A4
Kalami Beach. **GPS:** n39,47361 e20,24083.
20/03-15/10

Préveza 35A4
Mitikas. **GPS:** n39,01719 e20,71555.

. **Surface:** asphalted/gravel.
Distance: Preveza 7km on the spot on the spot 500m.
Remarks: Tolerated place. Parking at the beach.

Préveza 35A4
GPS: n38,95008 e20,75498.

Remarks: Tolerated place. Parking on the quay.

Tourist information Préveza:
Port city with interesting districts.
Kassópi, Kassópi.Archeological site.
Nikopolis.Old Roman city.

Stilada 35C4
Interstation. **GPS:** n38,89701 e22,65573.
Ch. 01/01-31/12
Remarks: Highway Lamia-Thessaloniki, 3 km after Stylidia on the right-hand of the road.

GR

Vagia 35C4
Restaurant Ynaiopio, Palaia Ethniki Odos Athinon-Lamias. **GPS:** n38,34322 e23,19412.
free with a meal.

Vonitsa 35A4
Agio Sotiriou. **GPS:** n38,93188 e20,91802.

. **Surface:** grassy.
Distance: Vonitsa 3km lake on the spot taverne 3km.
Remarks: Tolerated place. N42, from Vonitsa exit left after km34, follow road 1km.

Peloponnisos/Attica

Agia Kyriaki 35C6
GPS: n36,71883 e23,02305.
Remarks: Tolerated place. At the beach.

Agios Andreas 35C5
GPS: n37,37120 e22,78262.

WC free. **Surface:** gravel.
Distance: 3km on the spot on the spot on the spot.
Remarks: Tolerated place. Parking in harbour.

Agios Andreas 35C5
Camping Agios Andreas. **GPS:** n36,86664 e21,92087.
20/04-30/09
Distance: on the spot.

Agios Fokas 35C6
GPS: n36,59722 e23,05917.

. **Surface:** sand.
Distance: Monemvasia 13km.
Remarks: Tolerated place, view on Monemvasia. Parking at pier.

Agios Kiriaki 35B5
GPS: n37,11963 e21,57611.
01/01-31/12
Remarks: Tolerated place. Road number 9 exit Filiatra, at the beach.

Alepochori 35B5
Poseidon. **GPS:** n37,98419 e21,79712.

🛒.

△	Assini	35C5

Ancient Assini Beach. **GPS**: n37,53139 e22,88306.
🛒. 🅾 01/04-31/10

△	Assini	35C5

Kastraki. **GPS**: n37,52861 e22,87556.
🛒. 🅾 01/04-01/10
Remarks: South of Nafplio.

🅿	Athens ♒🏕🛒	35C4

GPS: n37,96987 e23,72263.
🛒. 🅾 01/01-31/12
Remarks: Tolerated place. Parking of the Acropolis, guarding after authorization Probably only outside the main season.

△S	Athens ♒🏕🛒	35C4

Athens camping, Leoforis Athinon. **GPS**: n38,00889 e23,67222.
🛒 € 25, 2 pers.incl 🚰🍽 Ch 🔌 included.
🅾 01/01-31/12

Tourist information Athens:
ℹ Capital of the country, city with a lot of curiosities, new city is a modern one.
👁🏕🛒 Monasteraki.Old district with Athenian flea market.
🅾 Su 8-14h.
👁 Panathenaic Stadium.Stadium of the first Olympic Games in 1896.
👁🛒 Plaka.Old district around the Acropolis.
👁 Tomb of the Unknown Soldier, Plateía Syntágmatos.Sunday 11h changing of the guard.
⌒ Acropolis.Archeological site. 🅾 01/05-31/10 Mo-Fri 8-18.30h, Sa-Su 8.30-14.30h, 01/11-30/04 8.30-16.30h 🅾 01/05, 28/10, holiday.

🅿	Diakofto	35B4

GPS: n38,19747 e22,20167.

🛒. **Surface:** asphalted.
🅾 01/01-31/12
Distance: 🏖on the spot 🛒on the spot 🅾on the spot 🍴500m.
Remarks: Tolerated place. A8/E65 Patras/Korinthos, 50km south east of Patras, at harbour.

Tourist information Diakofto:
👁 Rack railway, Kalavryta.Train journey with rack-railway.

🅿	Dimitsána	35B5

Kefalari tou Ai-Yanni. **GPS**: n37,59058 e22,04286.
4🛒.
Remarks: Tolerated place. Parking watermuseum, 2km south of Dimitsána.

Tourist information Dimitsána:
♨ Loúsios-kloof.5km long and 300m deep, marked trails.

🅿	Elefsina	35C4

GPS: n38,04235 e23,53942.
🛒. 🅾 01/01-31/12
Remarks: Tolerated place. Athens dir Korinthos, parking in front of the ruins in the city center.

△	Eleonas Diakofto Achaia	35B4

Eleon Beach. **GPS**: n38,19938 e22,17201.
🛒.

🅿S	Epidaurus	35C5

GPS: n37,59675 e23,07444.

🛒 🚰WCfree. **Surface:** gravel.
Remarks: Tolerated place. Overnight stay on parking at the Ancient theater is generally tolerated.

△	Epidaurus	35C5

Bekas, Palea Epidavros Argolida. **GPS**: n37,61877 e23,15561.
🛒. 🅾 01/04-20/10

Tourist information Epidaurus:
⌒ Ancient Epidaurus.Archeological site. 🅾 8-19h.

△	Ermioni	35C5

Hydras Wave. **GPS**: n37,40583 e23,31556.
🛒. 🅾 01/01-31/12

🅿	Galatas	35C5

GPS: n37,49591 e23,45101.
🛒.
Remarks: Tolerated place. Exit south, at the quay.

🅿	Gerolimenas	35C6

GPS: n36,48230 e22,39969.

🛒. **Surface:** asphalted/grassy.
Distance: 🏖on the spot 🛒on the spot 🅾50m 🏕on the spot.
Remarks: Parking at the beach.

△S	Gialova Pylou	35B6

Navarino Beach. **GPS**: n36,94770 e21,70620.
🛒🚰🍽Ch🛒🛒. 🅾 01/04-31/10

△S	Glifa Kyllini	35B5

Ionion. **GPS**: n37,83640 e21,13340.
🛒🚰🍽Ch🛒🛒🛒. 🅾 01/01-31/12

🅿	Gythion	35C6

GPS: n36,78883 e22,58225.
🛒.
Remarks: Tolerated place. At the beach, ± 5km from Gythion dir Skala.

△S	Gythion	35C6

Gythion Bay. **GPS**: n36,72920 e22,55243.
🛒🚰🍽Ch🛒. 🅾 01/01-31/12

🅿	Kakovatos 🛒	35B5

GPS: n37,45721 e21,63869.
🛒. **Surface:** asphalted.
Remarks: Tolerated place. Parking areas along the beach.

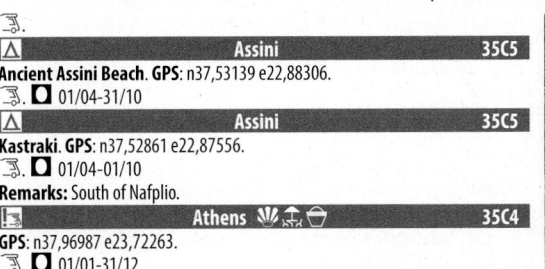

.GR

Kalogria 35B5

Kalogria Camper Stop - Kalogria

info@camperclub.gr - www.facebook.com/CamperStop

**Located in nature reserve
nearby the beach
BBQ area**

Kalogria Camper Stop, Kalogria Peloponnes. **GPS**: n38,15986 e21,37162.
40 €10, 16/07-31/08 €12 ⏚Ch (20x)€ 3/day WC included.
Surface: unpaved. 01/05-31/10
Distance: 5km 11km 250m 300m 50m on the spot on the spot on the spot.

Tourist information Kalogria:
Kotychi, Lapas. Visitors centre, swamp area.

Kamares 35C6
GPS: n36,68253 e22,52187.

Surface: sand.
Distance: on the spot on the spot 350m.
Remarks: Tolerated place. At the beach.

Kameras Irion 35C6
Poseidon. GPS: n36,68826 e22,51753.

Kastro 35B5
Loutra Kilinis. GPS: n37,86533 e21,10903.
WC free.
Remarks: Tolerated place. Parking at the beach.

Kastro 35B5
Killinis Beach. **GPS**: n37,87413 e21,10748.

Surface: grassy/sand.
Distance: 2km on the spot on the spot Beach taverne.
Remarks: Tolerated place.

Tourist information Kastro:
Chlemoutsi. Medieval castle.

Kato Alissos 35B5
Kato Allissos. **GPS**: n38,14986 e21,57740.

€ 19 Ch 01/04-20/10
Remarks: Plenty of shade from olive trees, lemon trees and poplars. Patras dir Pyrgos, take the Old National Road at first occasion, after 20 km to the right, dir campsite.

Kifisiá 35C4
Dionissiotis. GPS: n38,10535 e23,81355.
ChWC. 01/01-31/12
Remarks: 18km north of Athens, route Athens dir Lamia.

Tourist information Kifisiá:
Holiday resort of the Athenian since the Roman time.
Goulándris, Levidou 13. History of nature.

Kilada Ermionidos 35C5
Relax. GPS: n37,40974 e23,12691.
01/04-15/10

Killini 35B5
GPS: n37,93460 e21,14664.

Surface: asphalted/sand.
Distance: on the spot on the spot on the spot 200m on the spot.
Remarks: Tolerated place. Parking in harbour.

Korfos 35C5
GPS: n37,76361 e23,13302.

Surface: gravel.
Remarks: Tolerated place. At fishing port.

Korinthos 35C5
Afrodites Waters, Ancient Corinth. **GPS**: n37,91139 e22,87861.

30 € 10 Ch WC 01/01-31/12
Distance: 350m 350m 350m.

Korinthos 35C5
GPS: n37,88983 e22,86761.

Remarks: Tolerated place. Parking Akrokorinth.

Korinthos 35C5
Ancient Korinthos. **GPS**: n37,90750 e22,87806.

GR

🛏.
Remarks: Tolerated place.

| △S | Korinthos 🌿⚓📶 | 35C5 |

Blue Dolphin, Lecheon. **GPS:** n37,93460 e22,86490.
🛏.⚓📶Ch. ◘ 01/04-15/10
Remarks: Some kilometres west of Korinthos.

| △ | Korinthos 🌿⚓📶 | 35C5 |

Isthmia Beach, Isthmia. **GPS:** n37,88950 e23,00530.

◘ 15/04-15/10

Tourist information Korinthos:
ℹ️ Important trade centre.
👁 Korinth Canal.Canal, 23m wide.
⌒ Acrocorinth.Fortress. ◘ 8-19h. 🅣 free.
⌒ Ancient Korinthos.Archeological site.
◘ 01/04-31/10 8-19h, 01/11-31/03 8-17h ⬤ 25/12-26/12, 01/01, 25/03, Easter, 01/05.

| 🅿 | Koroni 🌿📶 | 35B6 |

GPS: n36,79729 e21,96002.

🛏.
Remarks: Tolerated place. Parking at harbour.

| △ | Koroni 🌿📶 | 35B6 |

Camping Koroni. **GPS:** n36,81168 e21,93303.
🛏.
Distance: ⛱600m 🏊on the spot.

| △ | Koroni 🌿📶 | 35B6 |

Memi Beach. **GPS:** n36,99270 e21,50200.
🛏. ◘ 01/05-30/09
Remarks: At harbour, narrow access.

Tourist information Koroni:
ℹ️ Port city with Venetian castle, 1206.

| 🅿S | Kotronas | 35C6 |

GPS: n36,61899 e22,49367.

🛏.⚓free. **Surface:** concrete.
Distance: 🏊on the spot 🛶on the spot ⊗50m.
Remarks: Tolerated place. Parking at pier.

| △ | Kyparissia | 35B5 |

Kyparissia. **GPS:** n37,25830 e21,67170.
🛏. ◘ 04/04-30/09

| △ | Lambiri | 35B4 |

Tsolis, Old National Road. **GPS:** n38,32083 e21,97194.
🛏. ◘ 15/04-30/09

| 🅿 | Legrena | 35D5 |

GPS: n37,66206 e23,99772.
🛏. ◘ 01/01-31/12
Remarks: Tolerated place. The most southern point, south of Athens, at sandy beach.

| △ | Marathon 🌿 | 35D4 |

Ramnous. **GPS:** n38,13139 e24,00722.
🛏.
◘ 01/04-31/10

Tourist information Marathon:
ℹ️ www.marathon.gr.The name marathon, course of 41 km, comes from this town.

| △ | Mayroyouni/Gythion | 35C6 |

Meltemi. **GPS:** n36,72986 e22,55360.
🛏.

Tourist information Mayroyouni/Gythion:
ℹ️ Tourist Information Areópoli,
Vasiléos Pávlou 21, Máni.Peninsula.
👁 Pýrgos Diroú, Máni.Caves.

| 🅿 | Monemvasía 🌿📶 | 35C6 |

GPS: n36,68240 e23,03821.
🛏.
Remarks: Tolerated place. Parking in harbour.

| 🅿 | Monemvasía 🌿📶 | 35C6 |

GPS: n36,68875 e23,05076.
🛏.
Surface: asphalted.
Distance: ⊗on the spot ⛱on the spot 🚌shuttle to old town.
Remarks: Tolerated place, may cause problems during peak season. Parking on both sides before the bridge to the island.

Tourist information Monemvasía:
ℹ️ Fortified city, lower town have been restored.
✝ Agía Sofia.Church 13th century.

| △ | Mycenae | 35C5 |

Atreus. **GPS:** n37,71911 e22,74114.

◘ 01/01-31/12

Tourist information Mycenae:
Ⓜ Archeological Museum, Argos.
⌒ Archeological site. ◘ 1/4-31/10 8-19h, 1/11-31/3 8-17h ⬤ holiday-Feiertag-jours de fête-giorni di di festa.
⌒ Agora Argos, Argos.Archeological site. ◘ summer 8.30-15h.

| 🅿 | Nafplio 🌿⚓📶 | 35C5 |

GPS: n37,76860 e22,99850.
2🛏.
Remarks: Tolerated place. Parking new train station.

| 🅿 | Nafplio 🌿⚓📶 | 35C5 |

GPS: n37,56823 e22,80170.

GR

🛏. **Surface:** asphalted.
Distance: ⚓500m ⊗300m.
Remarks: Tolerated place. Parking marina.

Tourist information Nafplio:
ℹ️ Tourist information, Ikostispémtis Martiou 2.First Greek capital.
Ⓜ Archeological Museum.
◻ Tue-Su 8.30-15h ◼ Mo.
✖ Palamídi.Citadel 18th century.

⚠	Nea Makri	35D4

Nea Makri, Marathonos Ave 156. **GPS**: n38,09285 e23,97379.
🛏. ◻ 01/01-31/12

🅱	Neo Itylo	35C6

GPS: n36,69246 e22,38969.

🛏. **Surface:** asphalted.
Distance: ⚓on the spot ⚓on the spot ⊗50m.
Remarks: Tolerated place, not in front of hotel. At the beach.

⚠	Olympia	35B5

Alphios. GPS: n37,64360 e21,61930.
🛏. ◻ 01/04-31/10

⚠	Olympia	35B5

Olympia. GPS: n37,65090 e21,62460.
🛏. ◻ 01/01-31/12
Remarks: 500m before Olympia.

Tourist information Olympia:
Ⓜ Archeological Museum.Important Greek archeological museum. ◻ Mo 11-19h, Tue-Su 8-19h.

🅱	Paralia Astros	35C5

GPS: n37,44475 e22,74800.

🛏. **Surface:** gravel.
Distance: ⚓on the spot ⚓on the spot ⊗200m.
Remarks: Tolerated place. At the beach, 12km north from Paralia Astros.

🅱 S	Paralia Platanou	35B4

GPS: n38,17104 e22,26828.

🛏 ⅃. **Surface:** gravel.
Distance: ⚓on the spot.
Remarks: Tolerated place. At the beach.

🅱 S	Paralia Rizomilos	35B4

GPS: n38,21898 e22,14745.

🛏 ⌐🍽 free. **Surface:** gravel.
Distance: ⚓on the spot ⚓on the spot ⊗on the spot 🛒mini market (summer).
Remarks: Tolerated place, not in front of hotel. At the beach.

⚠	Pátra	35B5

Golden Sunset, Old national Road km 19. **GPS**: n38,14389 e21,58778.
🛏. ◻ 01/04-15/10

Tourist information Pátra:
ℹ️ Tourist Information, Filepimonos 26.Big city and important harbour.
👁 Archaïa Klauss.First commercial producer of wine of Greece.

🅱	Perahóra	35C4

GPS: n38,01520 e22,91564.
🛏.
Distance: ⊗on the spot.
Remarks: Tolerated place. Parking at the beach.

🅱 S	Petalidi	35B6

GPS: n36,95850 e21,93450.
🛏 ⌐. **Surface:** asphalted.
Remarks: Tolerated place. Nearby marina and football ground.

	Petalidi	35B6

GPS: n36,95915 e21,92870.

🛏. **Surface:** asphalted.
Distance: ⊗on the spot.
Remarks: Tolerated place. Parking in village, near the sea.

🅱 S	Plaka	35C5

GPS: n37,14824 e22,89222.

20 🛏€ 5/24h ⌐ 🍽 ⅃ WC ⅃included. **Surface:** asphalted.
Distance: ⚓on the spot ⚓on the spot ⊗50m 🛒50m ⚓on the spot.
Remarks: Motorhome parking at the beach, can be reached by narrow road.

🍴	Porto Kagio	35C6

Taverna Porto. GPS: n36,42811 e22,48697. ⬆.
max. 3 🛏guests free. **Surface:** grassy.
Distance: ⚓on the spot ⚓on the spot ⊗on the spot 🛒mini market.

GR

| Pylos | 35B6 |

GPS: n36,91633 e21,69524.

⛭. **Surface**: concrete.
Distance: 🚶100m ⊗100m.
Remarks: Tolerated place. Parking at pier.

| Rafina | 35D4 |

GPS: n38,01835 e24,01227.

⛭.

🚻 01/01-31/12
Remarks: Tolerated place. Exit harbour.

Tourist information Rafina:
ℹ️ Lively fishing port, Mati: trendy holiday village.

| Salandi | 35C5 |

GPS: n37,44748 e23,12474.

⛭. **Surface**: gravel.
Distance: 🚶Didyma 5km ⊘on the spot 🛟on the spot.
Remarks: Tolerated place. At the beach.

| Savalia | 35B5 |

Savalia Beach. **GPS**: n37,79685 e21,25578.

⛭. **Surface**: asphalted.
Distance: ⊘on the spot 🛟on the spot.
Remarks: Tolerated place.

| Skoutari | 35C6 |

GPS: n36,65984 e22,49762.

max. 3 ⛭. **Surface**: concrete.

Distance: ⊘on the spot 🛟on the spot ⊗within walking distance.
Remarks: Tolerated place. At fishing port.

| Sounion | 35D5 |

Camping Bacchus. **GPS**: n37,67694 e24,04750.

⛭.

🚻 01/01-31/12
Remarks: 60km S of Athens.

Tourist information Sounion:
Ⓜ Mineralogical Museum, Lavrió.Old mine shaft of the silvermines. 🚻 Wed, Sa-Su.
⌒ Archeological site.

| Tolo | 35C5 |

GPS: n37,51469 e22,85662.

⛭ 🚰 WC. **Surface**: asphalted.
Distance: 🚶500m ⊘100m 🛟on the spot ⊗200m.
Remarks: Tolerated place. At fishing port.

| Tyrchu | 35C5 |

Taverne Ostria. **GPS**: n37,31414 e22,82054.

3 ⛭guests free. **Surface**: gravel. 🚻 15/05-30/09
Distance: 🚶Tyros 10km ⊘on the spot 🛟on the spot ⊗on the spot.
Remarks: At the beach, via steep path.

| Zacharo | 35B5 |

Wohnmobil-Stellplatz. **GPS**: n37,47994 e21,62237.⬆️

50 ⛭ € 12 🚰 🗑 Ch 🚿 WC 🗑included 📷€ 2. **Surface**: grassy/gravel. 🚻 01/01-31/12
Distance: 🚶2km ⊘on the spot 🛟on the spot ⊗300m 🛒2km.
Remarks: Motorhome parking at the beach.

| Zacharo | 35B5 |

GPS: n37,51917 e21,60248.

GR

GPS: n41,00633 e25,12028.

🦶.

Distance: ⚓on the spot.

Remarks: Tolerated place. North of lake, follow Thermal Springs of Kaifa.

△	Zacharo	35B5

Tholo Beach. GPS: n37,41160 e21,66830.

🦶. ❑ 01/04-31/10

Greece North

△	Ag.Mamas Moudania	35C3

Ouzoni Beach. GPS: n40,21611 e23,31833.

🦶. ❑ 01/05-30/09

△	Akt Armenistis Sithonia	35C3

Armenistis. GPS: n40,15222 e23,91361.

🦶. ❑ 01/05-15/09

🏖	Alexandroúpoli ⛱🌊	35D2

GPS: n40,84364 e25,87693.

🦶.

Remarks: Tolerated place. Parking harbour.

🏖	Alexandroúpoli ⛱🌊	35D2

Apollonias. GPS: n40,84342 e25,86477.

🦶.

Remarks: Tolerated place. Parking near stadium.

Tourist information Alexandroúpoli:

ℹ️ Tourist Information, Mákris.Large holiday resort, beautiful beach.

△	Gerakani	35C2

Kouyoni. GPS: n40,26464 e23,46347.

🦶. ❑ 01/05-30/09

🏖S	Kastoriá �	35A3

GPS: n40,50441 e21,27992.

🦶against payment ╦.

Remarks: Voluntary contribution. Parking near monastery.

△	Lithóchoro 🌿	35B3

Olympios Zeus. GPS: n40,09333 e22,56472.

🦶.

Tourist information Lithóchoro:

ℹ️ Tourist Information, Evangelou Karavákou 20.Hiking cards for sale detailing excursions in the National Park of Mount Olympus.

⌒ Ancient Díon.Archeological findings. ❑ daily ⬤ holiday-Feiertag-jours de fête-giorni di festa.

△	Metamorphosi	35C3

Sunny Bay. GPS: n40,22694 e23,58944.

🦶. ❑ 01/05-31/10

🏖S	Moustheni	35C2

Moystheni Station. GPS: n40,84085 e24,11623.

🦶free ╦🍴Ch🔥.

Surface: asphalted.

Distance: 📏10m ⊗on the spot 🛒mini market.

Remarks: Special part for motor homes, shop, restaurant, station 24/24.

△S	Neos Marmaras	35C3

Areti. GPS: n40,02389 e23,81722.

🦶╦🍴Ch🔧. ❑ 01/05-15/10

△	Nikiti Akti Koytloumousi	35C3

Lacara. GPS: n40,17229 e23,85272.

🦶. ❑ 01/05-30/09

△	Ouranoupoli	35C2

Ouranoupoli. GPS: n40,33944 e23,97056.

🦶.

🏖S	Porto Lagos	35D2

5 🦶free ╦. **Surface:** asphalted.

Distance: ⊗on the spot.

Remarks: Tolerated place. Parking at pier.

△	Sithonia	35C3

Kalamitsi. GPS: n39,98750 e23,98694.

🦶.

△	Sithonia	35C3

Sithon. GPS: n40,23472 e23,56472.

🦶. ❑ 01/05-30/09

GR

INDEX

INDEX

INDEX